BIOLOGY
A Guide to the Natural World

David Krogh

Custom Edition Community College of Philadelphia

Biology 106–107

Taken from:
Biology: A Guide to the Natural World, Third Edition
by David Krogh

PEARSON
Custom
Publishing

PEARSON
Prentice
Hall

Taken from:

Biology: A Guide to the Natural World, Third Edition
by David Krogh
Copyright © 2005, 2002, 2000 by Prentice-Hall, Inc.
A Pearson Education Company
Upper Saddle River, New Jersey 07458

This special edition published in cooperation with Pearson Custom Publishing.

Printed in the United States of America

10 9 8 7 6 5 4 3 2

ISBN 0-536-27239-5

2006140093

JD

Please visit our web site at *www.pearsoncustom.com*

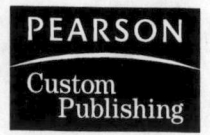

PEARSON CUSTOM PUBLISHING
75 Arlington Street, Suite 300, Boston, MA 02116
A Pearson Education Company

Community College of Philadelphia

Department of Biology

General Biology 1
Biology 106

Course Syllabus, Objectives
and
Laboratory Schedule

Main Campus: Department of Biology Office
Room W2-5A
Department Head: Dr. Linda Powell
Spring Semester Hours: 9-5, M-F
Phone: 215-751-8432   Fax: 215-751-8937
Email: lpowell@ccp.cc.pa.us
Departmental Website: http://faculty.ccp.cc.pa.us/dept/biol/

Name _____

Class Section: _____

Instructor's Name _____

Office Number _____   Office Phone _____

Office Hours _____   Email _____

CATALOG DESCRIPTION

Biology 106 (3-2-4) General Biology I   Introduction to the general principles of biology using the human as the model for study. Topics include structural organization, metabolism and energy, reproduction and inheritance, evolution and ecology. This course is designed for non-biology majors and allied health students.

LEARNING OUTCOMES

Biology 106 Provides students with a firm knowledge of biology, and prepares students to explore and critically evaluate the social and ethical implications of biological research. Upon completion of biology 106, students will have learned concepts that are included in the following content areas:

1. Thought processes of scientists
2. Characteristics of living organisms
3. Reproduction and inheritance
4. Biodiversity – structural organization of living systems
5. Natural selection
6. Ecology

Each of the major units of the course will be introduced with a "discovery question," which will provide a focus for the ensuing learning activity. Classroom and laboratory learning activities will center on this question. At the end of the semester, the student will develop and discuss meaningful and scientifically sound answers to the meta-question – **"How can humans become more fully integrated into the biosphere"?**

The list of objectives included with each discovery question describes the minimum subject material that the student is expected to master. Individual instructors may choose to elaborate on selected topics. They determine grading and evaluation policies as well. Your instructor is required to provide you with a written copy of her/his policy.

RESOURCE MATERIALS

Textbook
> Krogh, Biology A Guide to the Natural World, 3rd Ed. Prentice Hall Publishing
> *A copy of the textbook is on reserve in learning lab – W3-26*

Laboratory Manual and Equipment
> Community College of Philadelphia Biology Department Customized Laboratory Manual for General Biology I   (Biology 106) 11th Edition

Students are required to provide their own Safety Glasses and Gloves for the laboratory.

ACADEMIC SUPPORT SERVICES

Library: First floor Mint building, Main Campus
................8:00 AM to 10:00 PM Monday through Friday
................8:30 AM to 5:00 PM Saturday
West learning lab (W3-26): tutoring and study groups (for appointment call 751-8482)
Northeast Regional Center Learning Lab (Room 123): tutoring available

ATTENDANCE AND WITHDRAWAL POLICY

Students are expected to fulfill their academic obligation by attending all class and lab sessions, unless prevented from doing so by illness or other emergency. College policy stipulates that an instructor may file an administrative withdraw to remove a student from class if s/he has missed the equivalent of two (2) weeks work without an acceptable excuse. It is incumbent upon the student to drop a course they no longer attend. Individual faculty members also have the right to establish attendance regulations, which may include reduced grades for students who miss class and/or lab. Your instructor must provide their attendance policy in writing at the beginning of the semester.

A student may withdraw from class without penalty up to the eleventh week of the semester. It is advised that a student first discuss with their teacher any plans regarding withdraw. Failure to attend classes does not constitute a withdrawl and will result in the assignment of a failing grade. Students who withdraw due to illness or some other emergency should petition the Vice President of Student Affairs for an Excused Withdraw.

POLICY OF ACADEMIC DISHONESTY

All members of the College community are expected to obey public law and abide by College regulations. Students are expected to be well motivated and constructive in their pursuit of learning. Attendance of the College is a privilege, not a right; and students, through the act of registration, concede to the College the right to dismiss any student at any time when it is deemed necessary in order to safeguard the College's ideals of scholarship and character, and to secure compliance with its regulations.

Plagiarism

Students are expected to maintain the highest standards of integrity in all their academic work. It is further expected that any written assignment presented by students in fulfillment of course requirements will reflect their own work unless credit is properly given to others. Therefore, students must identify any part of an assignment which uses the words or materials of other people and give credit for the source. Failure to do so is a form of stealing known as plagiarism and is a very serious offense.

Plagiarism is defined as the act of appropriating all or part of a literary composition of another person or language of another person and passing them off as one's own. (Black's Law Dictionary, 6th Edition, West Publishing Co., St. Paul, MN, 1990). It may consist of quoting from a source without using quotation marks, transcribing or paraphrasing published material without attribution, or submitting work which has been reproduced or bought from another person. Anyone who assists another in such academic dishonesty is equally responsible. The faculty are encouraged to inform their students of the College's policy on plagiarism at the beginning of each semester

In Class Cheating
Unless directed to do the contrary, students are expected to present their original work in the classroom. In some instances, students might be allowed to use texts, books, notes, and/or magazines during an in-class writing assignment or test-taking and are expected to identify or give credit to their sources. Cheating is understood to consist of student actions including, but not limited to, the following: posing as another student (or having another student pose as oneself); copying from extraneous materials such as notebooks, textbooks, or other kinds of written materials (including the work of other students) or recorded materials; or borrowing non-print materials, such as drawings or other visual aids, in the context of an in-class writing assignment or test-taking and identifying these materials as one's own original work. Any student actions such as these would be construed as "cheating" and would open the student to disciplinary action. Anyone who assists another in such in-class cheating will be held equally responsible. CHEATING

Outside the Classroom
There are three major areas of concern in regard to cheating outside the classroom.
1. Leaving during classroom examinations.
In most cases, it is not appropriate to leave the classroom during examinations. In the instances that a student must leave, it is recommended that the instructor have already established guidelines to advise the students about their responsibilities during such interruptions in their exam-taking.
2. Take-home exams, term papers, essays and other out of class projects.
For take-home exams, project, term papers, essays and the like, the instructor must provide specific guidelines as part of the written instructions for such out-of-class assignments, including the intellectual norms regarding integrity defined by the discipline. It is incumbent on the instructor to make students aware in as many ways as possible of the ethical considerations regarding academic work and the discipline they are studying
3. Collaborative preparation.
It is important that the instructor make sure that each student in a collaborative effort makes his/her own contribution to the project, even as some students are learning from others or seeing other students as mentors. It is necessary when the instructor assigns collaborative projects that the separate contributions of the individual students be easily evaluated (unless otherwise stipulated). The point of creating an awareness of this kind of cheating is to prevent a student from benefiting inappropriately from a group effort in which the student made little contribution.

Faculty rights: sanctions available to faculty include, but are not limited to:
1. Requiring the student retake test or rewrite report
2. Drop the item in the calculation of the final grade or provide a substitute item in grading
3. Give the student a zero on the item
4. Drop the student's final grade by one letter
5. Administratively withdraw the student from the course (if before the eleventh week)
6. Give the student a failing grade in the course

Student's rights: Students may appeal decisions regarding final grades as per college policy. A copy of student's rights and obligations are available in the student handbook. It is recommended that you obtain a copy from the Office of Student Life (M2-37). Please note that the Biology department's committee of academic review of evaluation will NOT hear cases of alleged academic dishonesty.

General Course Outline

Unit 1: The Facts of Life

Unit 1, Session 1
Chapter 1

Discovery Questions: What characteristics do all living things have in common? What variables must be considered when designing an experiment and what ethical principles should a scientist be held to when performing research?

At the end of this unit students should be able to:

- describe the characteristics of living organisms
- describe the scientific method
- compare science as a way of knowing and thinking about the natural world with other ways of knowing and thinking

Unit 1, Session 2
Chapters 2 and 3

Discovery Question: How do collections of inanimate molecules function in concert to bring about the living state?

At the end of this unit students should be able to:

- define the organic and inorganic molecules that are important for life
- discuss the importance of enzymes to the maintenance of the living state and the factors that can influence enzyme activity
- describe the formation of life on the planet

Unit 1, Session 3
Chapters 4 and 5

Discovery Question: What are the parts of the cell? What are the functions of the cell membrane and the cellular organelles?

At the end of this unit students should be able to:

- differentiate between prokaryotic and eukaryotic cells
- define the structures that cells have and the function of those structures that enable cells to perform various functions
- discuss the mechanisms that cells have that enable them to exchange materials with their environment

Unit 1, Session 4 (optional – at your instructors discretion)
Chapters 6, 7 and 8

Discovery Question: What is energy and where does it come from?

At the end of this unit students should be able to:

- compare and contrast autotrophic and heterotrophic nutrition
- summarize the process of photosynthesis
- describe how food is converted to energy
- compare and contrast the processes that take place in the chloroplast versus the mitochondria

Unit 2 Designer Genes

Unit 2, Session 1
Chapters 9 and 10

Discovery Question: How do cells divide?

At the end of this unit students should be able to:

- compare and contrast mitosis and meiosis as far as what cells it occurs in, number of chromosomes involved, number of divisions, number of daughter cells, and why the process is important

Unit 2, Session 2
Chapters 11, 12 and 13

Discovery Question: What are the patterns of inheritance?
  At the end of this unit students should be able to:

- analyze patterns of inheritance when given examples of: chromosome abnormalities, dominance, recessive, incomplete dominance, sex-linked, multiple alleles, polygenic and multifactorial traits

Unit 2, Session 3
Chapter 14

Discovery Question: How do genes work?

At the end of this unit students should be able to

- explain the importance of the role of DNA and RNA
- discuss the structure and importance of DNA and how organisms are affected by mutations in the DNA

Unit 2, Session 4
Chapter 15

Discovery Question: What are the implications of genetically engineering biological systems and the influence of industrial growth and biotechnology on the environment?

At the end of this unit students should be able to:

- explain and discuss the strengths and limitations of biotechnology including the work of the Human Genome Project

Unit 3:   Evolution and Diversity of Life

Unit 3, Session 1
Chapters 16, 17 and 18

Discovery Question: What is Evolution?

At the end of this unit students should be able to:

- describe the evidence for evolution.
- explain the terms adaptation and fitness when discussing specific examples of natural selection
- explain the mechanisms involved in the change of allele frequencies in populations over time.

Unit 3. Session 2
Chapter 19

Discovery Question: How did humans evolve from primate ancestors?

At the end of this unit student should be able to:

- Describe the evolution of humans

Unit 3. Session 3
Chapter 20, 21, 23 and 24 (overview / selected readings)

Discovery Question: What are the characteristics of living systems?

At the end of this unit students should be able to:

- explain what characteristics set living things apart from non-living things
- compare and contrast the characteristics of living things found in the three domains.
- compare and contrast the characteristics of living things found in the four kingdoms within the Domain Eukarya.
- describe the adaptive structures and functions of the prokaryotes.

Unit 3, Session 4
Chapter 22   (overview / selected readings)

Discovery Question: What are the characteristics of animals?

At the end of this unit students should be able to:

- differentiate between the major phyla of animals

Unit 4 Ecology

Unit 4, Session 1
Chapter 32

Discovery Question: What are ecosystems and how do they function?

At the end of this unit students should be able to:

- Describe the flow of energy through ecosystems
- Explain how nutrients and water cycle through ecosystems
- Explain climate and the effects it has on the distribution of life
- Describe and compare the major biomes of the planet and the non-living factors found within them that determine the life found there

Unit 4, Session 2
Chapter 31

Discovery Question: How do organisms interact with one another, and how do humans affect the stability and diversity of the global environment?

- Explain how environmental resistance and biotic potential affect population size
- Describe the factors that affect the size of a human population
- Identify, when given examples, the following types of interactions: predator/prey, symbiosis (parasitism, commensalism, mutualism)
- Explain why a grassland (or pond) could become a forest and what factors would affect the rate of change
- Discuss the natural and human-made factors that affect the biodiversity of the planet citing specific examples

VIII. Meta-question: How can humans become more fully integrated into the biosphere?

Laboratory Schedule

Lab #	Topic
1	Orientation and Safety The Nature of Scientific Research
2	Solubility, Detection of Proteins and Carbohydrates *Safety glasses and gloves required*
3	Introduction to Cells and the Microscope
4	Osmosis and Diffusion *Safety glasses and gloves required*
5	Acids, Bases, and Cells *Safety glasses and gloves required*
6	Photosynthesis *Safety glasses and gloves required*
7	Epidemiology and Hand Washing
8	Population Genetics
9	Classification of Animals
10	The Animal Kingdom – Hydra and Invertebrate Worms
11	Ecology and Predator-Prey Relationships
12	Acid Rain and Global Warming *Safety Glasses and Gloves Required*

-

Students are expected to prepare for the laboratory by reading the laboratory activity in Community College of Philadelphia Customized Laboratory Manual for General Biology I (Biology 106) and textbook references, and completing the pre-lab exercise.

During the laboratories specified above, students are required to wear approved eye protection and gloves. Any student who does not wear safety glasses and gloves will not be permitted in the lab room. Please note that students are required to sign a departmental agreement to follow the policies and procedures as outlined in the laboratory manual.

Contents

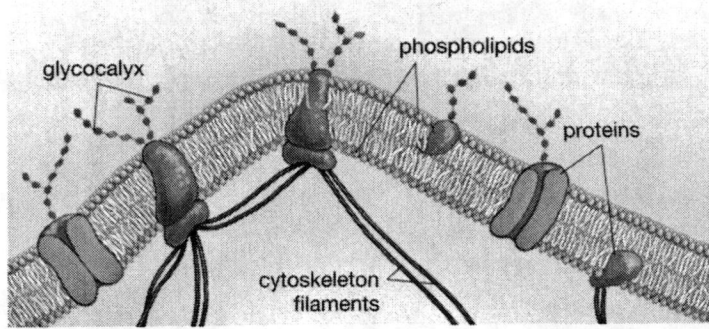

Unit 2   Energy and Its Transformations

Unit 3 How Life Goes On: Genetics

Unit 5 A Bounty That Feeds Us All: Plants

Unit 6 What Makes the Organism Tick? Animal Anatomy and Physiology

Chapter 27 Defending the Body: The Immune System   **590**

Chapter 28 Transport and Exchange: Blood, Breath, Digestion, and Elimination   **608**

0.5 inch

0.7 inch

6 weeks   7 weeks   8 weeks

Unit 7   The Living World as a Whole: Ecology and Animal Behavior

High biodiversity   Low biodiversity

BIOLOGY
A Guide to the Natural World

1

A Guide to the Natural World

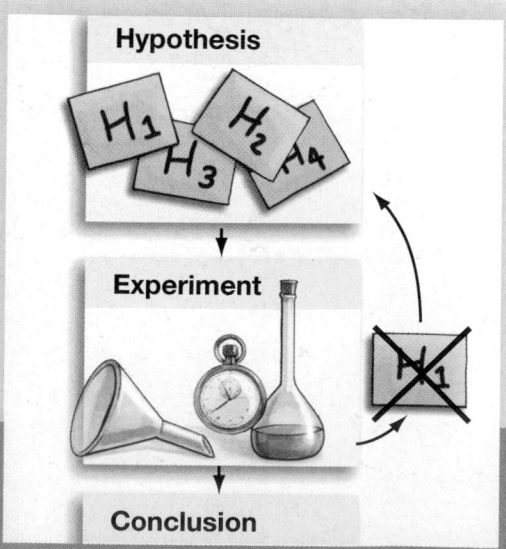

How scientists think about the world—the scientific method.
(Section 1.2, page 7)

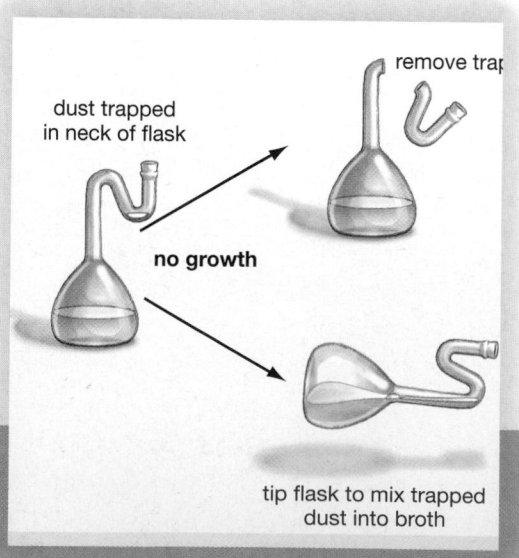

A famous experiment by a famous scientist.
(Section 1.2, page 8)

From atom to rain forest, the hierarchy of life.
(Section 1.3, page 13)

Science has great impact on our lives now and stands to have greater impact on them in the future. Science is both a body of knowledge and a means of acquiring knowledge. Biology, a branch of science, is the study of life.

1.1 How Does Science Impact the Everyday World?

Late in 2002, a Canadian chemist created quite a stir when, at a press conference, she announced that her company had cloned a human being. Now, set aside for the moment the fact that no evidence was ever offered for this claim, and just consider the announcement. Average citizens may not have understood exactly how the company carried off its supposed feat, but they had a rough idea of what the company was claiming: that it had produced one human being who was a genetic copy of another. Moreover they understood that this person was conceived not through sex, but through genetic manipulation in the laboratory.

Though this announcement may have been surprising, it was not startling, for by the time it was made people had some context in which to place cloning. It would not have been unusual in 2002 for a couple of office workers to note, at the watercooler, that it would be great if a particularly bright employee could be "cloned." Likewise, neighbors might observe, across the backyard fence, that one child seemed like a "clone" of another. The remarkable thing is how far the concept of cloning had to come to reach this common-knowledge status. Five years before the Canadian chemist made her announcement, the word clone was a technical term known to a handful of molecular biologists and a few science-fiction enthusiasts. What made the difference was, first, the cloning of Dolly the sheep in 1997 and then a steady tick of announcements: cloned pigs, cloned mice, and the fight over the possibility of a cloned human being. In a sense, however, the transition that cloning made is par for the course in the modern world. Here at the start of the twenty-first century, scientific innovations are moving with breathtaking speed from the laboratory to everyday life.

To appreciate this swift pace of change, consider electronic technology. The fundamental breakthrough that brought about modern electronics, including the computer, was the invention of the transistor at Bell Labs in 1947. Average American

Nature's finery—it's evolutionary.
(Section 1.4, page 14)

Poison dart frog—also evolutionary.
(Section 1.4, page 14)

You don't know what this insect is, but it scares you. Why?
(Section 1.4, page 15)

3

workers then *heard* about computers for 30 years, but not until the mid-1980s were they *using* computers right on their desktops, at home and at work. Once this revolution in circuits got going, however, things came in a torrent. VCRs and CD players were newfangled devices in the mid-1980s; now people are "burning" their own CDs and throwing out their VCRs as antiquated relics of the era before DVDs (**see Figure 1.1**).

In a similar vein, the breakthrough that brought about the biotechnology industry was the description of the DNA molecule in 1953 by James Watson and Francis Crick. People heard more about genes in

(a)

(b)

Figure 1.1
Then and Now

(a) A technician enters data into the world's first programmable computer, run initially in 1948. Called "Baby," the computer was more than 2 meters (6 feet) tall and almost 5 meters (15.5 feet) wide, but had a total memory of only 128 bytes—less than one-ten-thousandth the amount of data that can be put on a common floppy disk today.

(b) An employee of Japan's Fujifilm corporation holds a tiny, mobile printer that can receive wireless signals from cell phones, like the one on the right, and print on card-sized, instant color film.

subsequent years, but it took another 25 years for the first genetically engineered medicine (human insulin) to appear. Now one-quarter of the corn grown in the United States is genetically modified; criminals are regularly convicted (and innocent people freed) through use of DNA "fingerprints," salmon are grown to eating weight in half the normal time thanks to gene splicing; and the announcement that a human being has been cloned is a claim that has to be taken seriously.

It may go without saying that these various innovations and discoveries entail value judgments on the part of society. Before the online music service Napster was shut down in 2001, it was an operation that facilitated large-scale music sharing or large-scale music theft, depending on your point of view. President Bush had to think long and hard in 2001 about whether to allow federal funding for embryonic "stem cell" research—a research avenue that holds out great promise, but entails the destruction of human embryos. For nearly a decade, people have argued passionately for and against the use of genetically modified foods.

Note that all these issues have been brought to society by science, we might say. But things also work the other way around. Scarcely a week goes by without society calling on scientists to provide advice on issues of the day. Think of such charged environmental questions as global warming or the logging of public lands. Is global warming being caused by human activity? Does thinning out forests reduce the risk of catastrophic forest fires? Then there is health. Does a high-fat diet lead to heart disease? Should women undergoing menopause undertake hormone replacement therapy? In all these instances, average citizens look to science to provide answers.

If we take a step back from all this, the message is that society is being driven by science and technology to a greater extent than ever before. Accordingly, to fully participate in the workforce, to make informed choices at the ballot box, or simply to make routine decisions, the average person must now be more scientifically literate than at any time in the past. To get a sense of how this plays out over the course of everyday life, let's look at some biology-related news that came to Americans through one magazine (*Time*) during one short period (January through May 2003). More than a score of biology-related stories were featured in *Time* during this period. Six are noted here.

Cracking the Ice said the headline in the February 3 issue of *Time*, in a story about why portions of enormous ice shelves that jut out from the Antarctic continent have started "calving" or breaking off into the sea with greater frequency. "Within the past year, scientists watched in awe as a giant ice shelf disintegrated in the Antarctic Peninsula in just over one month's time, and in a remote region of West Antarctica, satellites have detected an expanse where glaciers are worrisomely speeding up their transport of ice to the sea," wrote correspondent J. Madeleine Nash. One suspected cause of this series of events is global warming. But what is global warming? *Time* didn't have the space to delve into this question, but readers of this textbook who want to know can turn to page 725 for an explanation.

The Secret of Life was the cover story for *Time's* February 17 issue, which celebrated the fiftieth anniversary of Watson and Crick's discovery of the structure of DNA (see **Figure 1.2**). Some human genes, *Time* said, "trace back to a time when we were fish; more than 200 come directly from bacteria. Our DNA provides a history book of where we come from and how we evolved. It is a family Bible that connects us all; every human being on the planet is 99.9% the same." But what are the lengths of DNA called genes? And how is DNA something that connects people not only with each other but with all living things? To find out, see Chapter 9, beginning on page 170.

Botox without the Needle was a March 3 story regarding new variants on the Botox injections people get as a means of getting rid of those pesky, middle-aged forehead lines. But did you know that Botox works by paralyzing muscles and that the substance it is purified from is a deadly bacterial toxin? How could a bacterial toxin paralyze muscles? And why should something that is a toxin in one context work as a cosmetic in another? For an account, see "The Muscular System" in Chapter 25 on page 551.

AIDS Vaccine: A Successful Failure was a March 10 story on the results of an AIDS vaccine trial that showed once again why AIDS is such a formidable enemy. AIDS is, of course, caused by HIV—the human immune deficiency virus—which is devastating because it attacks the very immune system that is meant to kill microbial invaders. How does HIV operate? To find out, see "Viruses: Making a Living by Hijacking Cells," in Chapter 20 on page 403. For an account of what AIDS does to the immune system, see "AIDS: Attacking the Defenders" in Chapter 27 on page 600.

The No. 1 Killer of Women was the title of an April 28 *Time* cover story. "No, it's not breast cancer," said

Time. "More women die of heart disease than of all cancers combined." The magazine also noted that "the common belief that premenopausal women are immune to heart problems is just plain wrong. Heart attacks strike 9,000 women younger than 45 each year." But what is a heart attack? What leads to one, and what does it do to the heart? You can find out in Chapter 28 on page 613.

Healthy Junk Food was a story that appeared in the May 12 issue. *Time* said such food is increasingly available, as evidenced by Frito-Lay's new "natural" varieties of such long-time favorites as Tostitos and Cheetos. What's the difference between the old and new varieties? For one thing, the natural versions are cooked in oil that has no trans fats in it. But what's a trans fat, and what does it have to do with health? You'll find an answer in "From Trans Fats to Omega 3's" in Chapter 3 on page 54.

What Do Americans Know about Science?

If you knew the scientific background to most of the *Time* stories, that probably puts you in a pretty select group of Americans. As you can see in

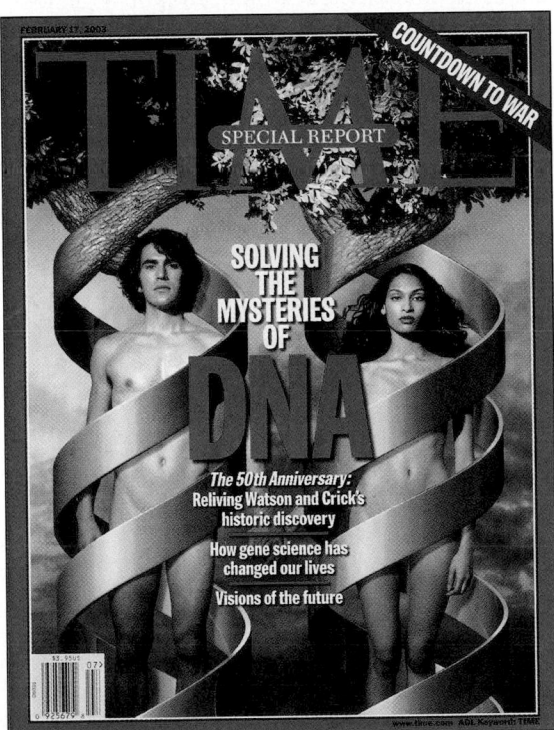

Figure 1.2
Science in the News
The importance of science to everyday life is reflected in the large number of news stories that focus on science. Pictured is a cover story on DNA that *Time* magazine ran in February 2003.

Figure 1.3, the average American has what might be called an uneven knowledge of science and the scientific process. Eighty-seven percent of a sample of American adults questioned in 2001 knew that the oxygen we breathe comes from plants. Yet one-quarter of this same group said that the sun goes around the Earth, rather than Earth around the sun. Almost 80 percent understood that "the continents on which we live have been moving their location for millions of years." Yet more than 50 percent believed that "the earliest human beings lived at the same time as the dinosaurs." (In fact, dinosaurs died out more than 60 million years before the first human beings appeared.) What factors go into making people scientifically literate? An important one is the number of science courses they have had in high school or college: as the number of courses goes up, so does the degree to which people feel well informed about scientific issues.

1.2 What Is Science?

Having looked a little at the impact that science has, it might be helpful to consider the question of what science *is*. The point here is to give you some sense of the underpinnings of science—to review something about the how and why of it before you begin looking at the nature of one of its disciplines, biology.

Science as a Body of Knowledge

Science is in one sense a process—a *way* of learning. In this respect, it is an activity carried out under certain loosely agreed-to rules, which you'll get to shortly. **Science** is also a body of knowledge about the natural world. It is a collection of unified insights about nature, the evidence for which is an array of facts. The unified insights of science are commonly referred to as *theories*.

It's unfortunate but true that *theory* means one thing in everyday speech and something almost completely different in scientific communication. In everyday speech, a theory can be little more than a hunch. It is an unproven idea that may or may not have any evidence to support it. In science, meanwhile, a **theory** is a general set of principles, supported by evidence, that explains some aspect of nature. There is, for example, a Big Bang theory of the universe. It is a general set of principles that explains how our universe came to be and how it developed. Among its principles are that a cataclysmic explosion occurred 13–14 billion years ago; and that, after it, matter first developed in the form of gases that then coalesced into the stars we can see all around us. There are numerous facts supporting these principles, such as the current size of the universe and its average temperature.

As you might imagine, with any theory this grand some *pieces* of it are in dispute; some facts don't fit with the theory, and scientists disagree about how to interpret this piece of information or that. On the whole, though, these general insights have withstood the questioning of critics, and together they stand as a scientific theory.

The Importance of Theories

Far from being a hunch, a scientific theory actually is a much more valued entity than is a scientific fact, for the theory has an *explanatory* power, while a fact is generally an isolated piece of information. That the universe is at least 13 billion years old is a wonderfully interesting fact, but it explains very little in comparison with the Big Bang theory. Facts are important; theories could not be supported or refuted without them. But science is first and foremost in the theory-building business, not the fact-finding business.

Figure 1.3
What Do Americans Know about Science?
Some results published by the National Science Foundation (*Science & Engineering Indicators—2002*).

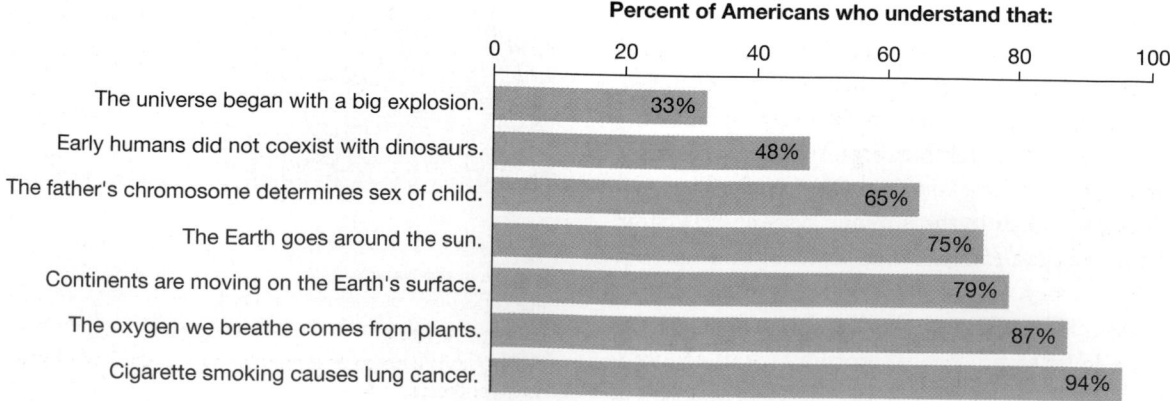

Percent of Americans who understand that:

The universe began with a big explosion.	33%
Early humans did not coexist with dinosaurs.	48%
The father's chromosome determines sex of child.	65%
The Earth goes around the sun.	75%
Continents are moving on the Earth's surface.	79%
The oxygen we breathe comes from plants.	87%
Cigarette smoking causes lung cancer.	94%

Science as a Process: Arriving at Scientific Insights

So how does a body of facts and theories come about? What is the process of scientific investigation, in other words? When **science** is viewed as a process, it could be defined as a means of coming to understand the natural world through observation and the testing of hypotheses. This process is referred to as the **scientific method**. The starting state for scientific inquiry is always *observation*: A piece of the natural world is observed to work in a certain way. Then follows the *question*, which broadly speaking is one of three types: a "what" question, a "why" question, or a "how" question. Biologists have asked, for example, What are genes made of? Why does the number of species decrease as we move from the equator to the poles? How does the brain make sense of visual images?

Formulating Hypotheses, Performing Experiments

Following the formulation of the question, various hypotheses are proposed that might answer it. A **hypothesis** is a tentative, testable explanation for an observed phenomenon. In almost any scientific question, several hypotheses are proposed to account for the same observation. Which one is correct? Most frequently in science, the answer is provided by a series of *experiments*, meaning controlled tests of the question at hand (**see Figure 1.4**). It may go without saying that scientists don't regard all hypotheses as being equally worthy of undergoing experimental test. By the time scientists arrive at the experimental stage, they usually have an idea of which is the most promising hypothesis among the contenders, and they then proceed to put that hypothesis to the test. Let's see how this worked in an example from history.

The Test of Experiment: Pasteur and Spontaneous Generation

Does life regularly arise from anything *but* life, or can it be created "spontaneously," through the coming together of basic chemicals? The latter idea had a wide acceptance from the time of the ancient Romans forward, and as late as the nineteenth century it was championed by some of the leading scientists of the day. So how could the issue be decided? The famous French chemist and medical researcher Louis Pasteur formulated a hypothesis to address this question (**see Figure 1.5**). He believed that many purported examples of life arising spontaneously were simply instances of airborne microscopic organisms landing on a suitable substance

and then multiplying in such profusion that they could be seen. Life came from life, in other words, not from spontaneous generation. But how could this be demonstrated? In 1860, Pasteur sterilized a meat broth in glass flasks by heating it, while at the same time heating the glass *necks* of the flasks, after which he bent the necks into a "swan" or S-shape. The ends of the flasks remained open to the air, but inside the flasks there was not a sign of life. Why? The broth remained sterile because microbe-bearing dust particles got trapped in the bend of the flask's neck. If Pasteur broke the neck off before the bend, however, the flask soon had a riot of bacterial life growing within it. In another test, Pasteur tilted the flask so that the broth *touched* the bend in the neck, a change that likewise got the microbes growing.

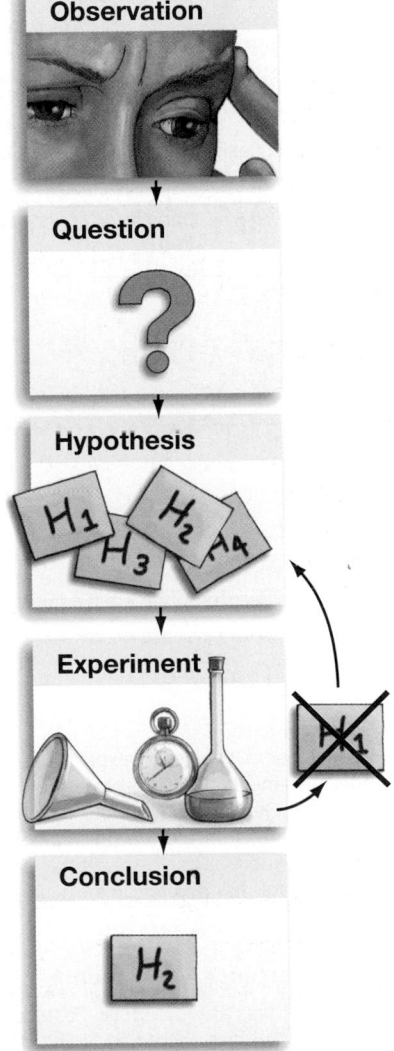

Figure 1.4
Scientific Method
The scientific method enables us to answer questions by testing hypotheses.

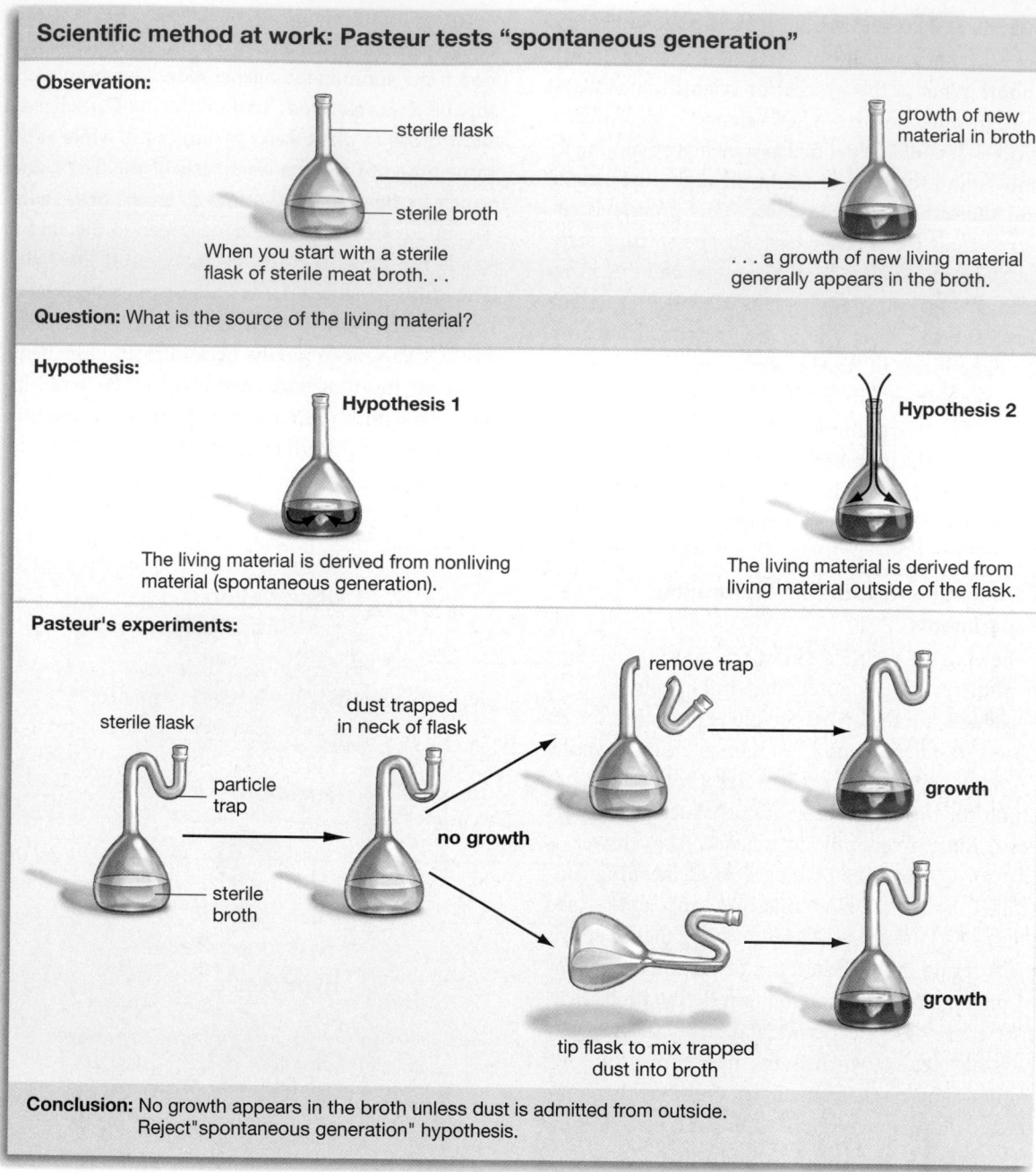

Scientific method at work: Pasteur tests "spontaneous generation"

Observation:

sterile flask

sterile broth

When you start with a sterile
flask of sterile meat broth. . .

growth of new
material in broth

. . . a growth of new living material
generally appears in the broth.

Question: What is the source of the living material?

Hypothesis:

Hypothesis 1

The living material is derived from nonliving
material (spontaneous generation).

Hypothesis 2

The living material is derived from
living material outside of the flask.

Pasteur's experiments:

sterile flask

particle
trap

sterile
broth

dust trapped
in neck of flask

no growth

remove trap

growth

tip flask to mix trapped
dust into broth

growth

Conclusion: No growth appears in the broth unless dust is admitted from outside.
Reject "spontaneous generation" hypothesis.

Figure 1.5
Pasteur's Experiments
Pasteur's spontaneous generation experiments and the scientific method. Nineteenth-century observation made clear that life
would appear in a medium, such as broth, that had been sterilized. But what was the source of this life? One hypothesis was that it
arose through "spontaneous generation," meaning it formed from the simple chemicals in the broth. Conversely, Pasteur hypothesized that it originated from airborne microorganisms. He was able to design an experiment that offered evidence for this hypothesis. The device he used was an S-shaped flask, which enabled air to enter the flask freely while trapping all particles (including
invisible microorganisms) in a bend in the neck.

Web Tutorial 1.1
Scientific Method

Elements in Pasteur's Experiments

Now, note what was at work here. Pasteur had a preconceived notion of what the truth was, and designed experiments to test his hypothesis. Critically,
he performed the same set of steps several times in
the experiments, keeping all the elements the same
each time—except for one. The nutrient broth was

the same in each test; it was heated the same
amount of time and in the same kind of flask. What
changed each time was one critical **variable**, meaning
an adjustable condition in an experiment. In this
case, the variable was either the shape of the flask
neck, or the tilt of the flask. Given that all other elements of the experiments were kept the same, the

experiments had rigorous controls: All conditions were held constant over several trials, except for a single variable. A **control** can be defined as a comparative condition in an experiment in which no variables are introduced. Pasteur's finding that no life grew in the bent-necked flask is interesting, but tells us very little by itself. We learn something only by comparing this finding to the result in the control condition: that life did grow when the flask neck was straight.

Note also that the idea of spontaneous generation was not banished with this one set of experiments—nor should it have been. Pasteur's experiments provided one of the *facts* mentioned earlier, in this case the fact that flasks of liquid will remain sterile under certain conditions. The idea that life arises only from life is, however, one of the scientific *theories* noted earlier, meaning that it requires the accumulation of many facts pointing in the same direction.

Other Kinds of Support for Hypotheses

Some scientific questions are difficult or impossible to test purely through experiment. For example, there currently is a controversy over whether birds are the direct descendants of dinosaurs. What kind of experiment could be run to test this hypothesis? Certain modern-day evidence is available to us—the DNA of living birds, for example—but examining DNA does not amount to an experiment. Instead it is observation, which is another valid way to test a hypothesis. Evidence from the past can also be observed, of course, which in this case means the observation of dinosaur and bird fossils. Indeed, fossils have been the key evidence in convincing most experts that birds are the descendants of dinosaurs. Experiment and observation are enhanced with the tool of statistics, which frequently is used in science, as you can see in "Lung Cancer, Smoking, and Statistics in Science" on page 10.

From Hypothesis to Theory

When does an idea move from hypothesis to theory? One of the ironies of the orderly undertaking called science is that there's nothing orderly about the change from hypothesis to theory. No scientific supreme court exists to make a decision. Scientists aren't polled for their views on such questions, and even if they were, at what point would we say something had been "proven"? When more than 50 percent of the experts in the field assent to it? When there are no dissenters left?

Provisional Assent to Findings: Legitimate Evidence and Hypotheses

This lack of finality in science fits in, however, with one of its central tenets, which is that nothing is ever finally proven. Instead, every finding is given only *provisional* assent, meaning it is believed to be true for now, pending the addition of new evidence. This principle is so deeply embedded in science that scientists rarely have reason to think about it (just as drivers would seldom contemplate why they are driving on the right-hand side of the road). Yet it is profoundly important because it is the thing that most starkly separates science from belief systems, such as those that operate in culture, politics, or religion. Every principle and "fact" in science is subject to modification, based solely on the best evidence available. There are no immutable laws and no unquestioned authority figures. This means there is a paradox in science: its only bedrock is that there is no bedrock; everything scientists "know" is subject to change.

In practice, this is a difficult ideal to live up to. Even when a body of evidence starts to point in a new direction, scientists—like anybody else—may be reluctant to give up old ways of thinking. Recognizing this tendency in human nature, Charles Darwin's friend Thomas Henry Huxley, writing in 1860, gave a beautiful description of the attitude scientists should have when investigating nature:

> Sit down before fact as a little child, be prepared to give up every preconceived notion, follow humbly wherever and whatever abysses nature leads, or you will learn nothing.

This principle of science's openness to revision is one of three important scientific principles having to do with hypotheses and evidence. Here are all three, stated briefly:

- Every assertion regarding the natural world is subject to challenge and revision, based on evidence.

- Results obtained in experiments must be *reproducible*. Different investigators must be able to obtain the same results from the same sets of procedures and materials.

- Any scientific hypothesis or claim must be *falsifiable*, meaning open to negation through means of scientific inquiry. The assertion that "UFOs are visiting the Earth" does not rise to the level of a scientific claim, because there is no way to prove that this is *not* so.

Lung Cancer, Smoking, and Statistics in Science

Valuable as they are, experimental and observational tests often are not enough to provide answers to scientific questions. In countless instances, scientists employ an additional tool in coming to comprehend reality—a mathematical tool—as you'll see in the following example.

The evidence that cigarette smoking causes lung cancer (and heart disease and emphysema and on and on) has been around for so long that most people have no idea why smoking was looked into as a health hazard in the first place. You might think that scientists were suspicious of tobacco decades ago and thus began experimenting with it in the laboratory, but this wasn't the case. Instead, the trail that led to tobacco as a health hazard started with a mystery about disease.

When the lung-cancer pioneer Alton Ochsner was in medical school in 1919, his surgery professor brought both the junior and senior classes in to see an autopsy of a man who had died of lung cancer. The disease was then so rare that the professor thought the young medical students might never see another case during their professional lifetimes. Prior to the 1920s, lung cancer was among the rarest forms of cancer, because cigarette smoking itself was rare before the twentieth century. It did not become the dominant form of tobacco use in the United States until the 1920s. This made a difference in lung-cancer rates because cigarette smoke is inhaled, while pipe and cigar smoke generally are not.

If you look at **Figure 1**, you can see the rise in lung-cancer mortality in U.S. males and females from 1930 forward. Note that women show a later rise in lung-cancer deaths; this is because women started smoking en masse later. (Also note that in the 1990s, lung-cancer rates finally began to level off—or drop in the case of men. This was a direct result of a decline in smoking that began in the 1970s.)

Given the lung-cancer trends that were apparent in males by the 1930s, the task before scientists was to explain the alarming increase in this disease. What could the cause of this scourge be, the medical detectives wondered? The effects of men being gassed in World War I? Increased road tar? Pollution from power plants? Through the 1940s, cigarette smoking was only one suspect among many.

Laboratory experiment eventually would play a part in fingering tobacco as the lung-cancer culprit, but the original indictment of smoking was written in numbers—in statistical tables showing that smokers were contracting lung cancer at much higher rates than nonsmokers.

It has sometimes been said that "science is measurement," and the phrase is a marvel of compact truth. For centuries, people had an idea that smoking might be causing serious harm, but this information fell into the realm of guessing or of *anecdote*, meaning personal stories. The problem with anecdote is that there is no measurement in it; there is no way of judging the validity of one story as opposed to the next. Related to anecdote is the notion of "common sense," which is valuable in many instances, but which also had us believing for centuries that the sun moved around the Earth. In the case of smoking, it took the extremely careful measurement provided by a discipline called *epidemiology*—the study of disease distributions—to separate truth from fiction.

1.3 The Nature of Biology

Let us shift now from an overview of science to a more narrow focus on **biology**, which can be defined as the study of life. But what is life? It may surprise you to learn that there is no standard short answer to this question. Indeed, the only agreement among scholars seems to be that there is not, and perhaps cannot be, a short answer to this question. The main impediment to such a definition is that any one quality common to all living things is likely to exist in some nonliving things as well. Some living things may "move under their own power," but so does the wind. Living things may grow, but crystals and fire do the same thing. Therefore, biologists generally define life in terms of a group of characteristics possessed by living things. Looked at together, these characteristics are sufficient to separate the living world from the nonliving. We can say that living things:

- Can assimilate and use energy
- Can respond to their environment
- Can maintain a relatively constant internal environment
- Possess an inherited information base, encoded in DNA, that allows them to function
- Can reproduce, through use of the information encoded in DNA
- Are composed of one or more cells
- Evolved from other living things
- Are highly organized compared to inanimate objects

Probability in Science

Note that "measurement" in this instance was a matter of calculating *probability*, which is often the case in science. Epidemiologists found a linkage between smoking and lung cancer, in the sense that those who smoked were more likely to get the disease. But having seen this, scientists then had to ask: Could this result be a matter of pure chance? A person tossing a coin might get heads five times in a row, and it might be written off to chance. But would it be the same if the person came up with heads *fifty* times in a row? No; at that point there would be justification for assuming that some force other than chance was in operation (such as a rigged coin). When the epidemiologists looked at their statistical tables and saw so many more smokers than nonsmokers getting lung cancer, they had to ask whether this result fell into the realm of five heads in a row, or fifty. Even in the earliest studies they concluded that more than chance was at work in the results. After many studies, they concluded that smoking was *causing* lung cancer. But how did they judge what was probable and what was not in an issue as complicated as this one? The researchers relied on techniques developed in the branch of mathematics called *statistics*.

The importance of probability and statistics to science can hardly be overstated. These tools are used frequently in nearly every scientific discipline. Imagine that 10 experimental plots of land are being compared, five with fertilizer added to them, the other five without. The plots with the added fertilizer end up with more growth but fewer kinds of plants. Could the differences between the two kinds of plots be a matter of chance? Here, as in so many other tests, scientists would use the tools of statistics to get at the truth.

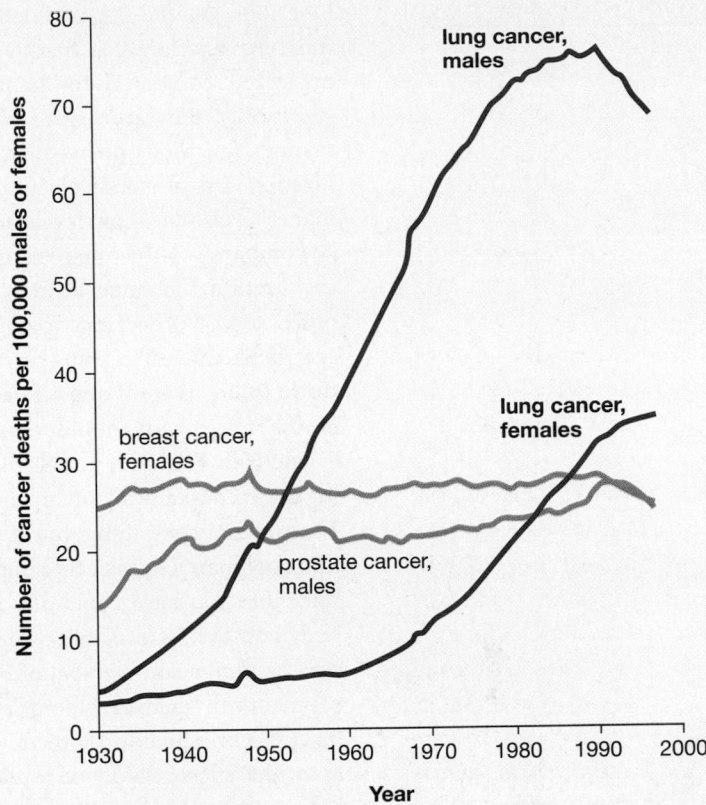

Figure 1
Rise in Lung-Cancer Mortality in U.S. Males and Females from 1930 Forward

Every one of these qualities exists in all the varieties of Earth's living things. The simplest bacterium needs an energy source no less than any human being. Our energy source is the food that's familiar to us; the bacterium's might be the remains of vegetation in the soil. The bacterium responds to its environment, just as we do. You would take action if you smelled gas in your house; the bacterium would move away if it encountered something it regarded as noxious. Humans maintain **homeostasis** or a relatively stable internal environment by, for example, sweating when they get hot. When the bacterium's external environment gets too hot, it has certain genes that will switch on to keep it functioning. Both humans and bacteria use the molecule DNA as a repository of the information necessary to allow them to live. Bacteria and human beings both reproduce—bacteria by simple cell division, human beings through the use of two kinds of reproductive cells (egg and sperm). A bacterium is a single-celled life-form, while humans are a 100-trillion-celled life-form. Bacteria and humans both evolved from complex living things and ultimately share a single common ancestor.

There are some exceptions to these "universals." For example, the overwhelming majority of honeybees and ants are sterile females; they can't reproduce, but no one would doubt that they're alive. In the main, however, if something is living, it has all these qualities.

Life Is Highly Organized, in a Hierarchical Manner

One item on the list of qualities requires a little more explanation. It is that living things are highly organized compared to inanimate matter. More specifically, they are organized in a "hierarchical" manner, meaning one in which lower levels of organization are progressively integrated to make up higher levels. The main levels in this hierarchy could be compared to the organization of a business. In a corporation, there may be individuals making up an office, several offices making up a department, several departments making up a division, and so forth. In life, there is one set of organized "building blocks" making up another (**see Figure 1.6**).

Actually life is not just "highly" organized. Nothing else comes *close* to it in organizational complexity. The sun is a large thing, but it is an uncomplicated thing compared to even the simplest organism. Consider that you have about 100 trillion cells in your body and that, with some exceptions, each of these cells has in it a complement of DNA that is made up of chemical building blocks. How many building blocks? Three billion of them. Now, you probably know that most cells divide regularly, one cell becoming two, the two becoming four, and so on. Each time this happens, each of the 3 billion DNA building blocks must be faithfully *copied*, so that both of the cells resulting from cell division will have their own complete copy of DNA. And this copying of the molecule—before anything is actually done with it—is carried out in almost all the varieties of the 100 trillion cells we have. Complex indeed. Let's see what life's levels of organization are.

Levels of Organization in Living Things

The building blocks of matter, called *atoms*, lie at the base of life's organizational structure. (See Chapter 2 for an account of them.) Atoms come together to form *molecules*, meaning entities consisting of a defined number of atoms that exist in a defined spatial relationship to one another. A molecule of water is one atom of oxygen bonded to two atoms of hydrogen, with these atoms arranged in a very precise way. Molecules in turn form what are called *organelles*, meaning "tiny organs" in a cell. Each of your cells has, for example, hundreds of organelles in it called *mitochondria* that transform the energy from food into an energy form your body can use. Such an organelle is not just a collection of molecules that exist close to one another. It is a highly organized structure, as you can tell just from looking at the rendering of it in Figure 1.6.

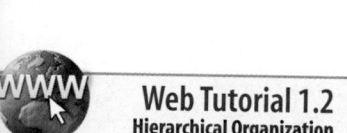

Figure 1.6
Levels of Organization in Living Things

| atom | molecule | organelle | cell | tissue | organ |
| (hydrogen) | (water) | (mitochondrion) | (muscle) | (muscle) | (heart) |

At the next step up the organizational chain are entities that are actually *living*, as opposed to entities that are components of life. *Cells* are units that can do all of the things listed earlier: assimilate energy, reproduce, react to their environment, and so forth. Indeed, most experts would agree that cells are the only place that life exists. You may say: But isn't there a lot of material in between my cells? The answer is yes; it's mostly water with a good number of other molecules in the mix. But if all the cells were removed from this watery milieu, there would be nothing resembling life left in it.

The next step up is to a *tissue*, meaning a collection of cells that serve a common function. Your body contains collections of muscle cells that serve the same function (contraction). Each concentration of these cells constitutes muscle tissue. Several kinds of tissues can come together to form a functioning unit known as an *organ*. Your heart, for example, is a collection of muscle tissue and connective tissue, among other types. An assemblage of cells, tissues, and organs can then form a multicelled *organism*. (Of course, back down at the cell level, a one-celled bacterium is also an organism; it's just not one with organs and so forth.)

From here on out, life's levels of organization all involve *many* organisms. Members of a single type of living thing (a species), living together in a defined area, make up what is known as a *population*. When you look at *all* the kinds of living things in a given area, you are looking at a *community*. Finally, all the communities of the Earth—and the physical environment with which they interact—make up the *biosphere*.

1.4   **Special Qualities of Biology**

Biology traces its origins to the ancient Greeks. In the work of such Greeks as Hippocrates and Galen, we can find the origins of modern medical science. In the work of Aristotle and others, we can find the origins of "natural history," which led to what we think of today as mainstream biology and the larger category of the **life sciences**: a set of disciplines that focus on varying aspects of the living world. Apart from biology, the life sciences include such areas of study as veterinary medicine and forestry.

Despite its ancient origins, biology is, in a sense, a much younger science than, say, physics, which is one of the **physical sciences**, meaning the natural sciences not concerned with life. Western Europe's revolution in the physical sciences probably can be dated from the sixteenth century, when Nicholas Copernicus published his work *On the Revolution of Heavenly*

organism
(human)

population
(Yanomamö tribe)

community
(Amazon rain forest)

biosphere
(Earth)

Spheres, which demonstrated that Earth moves around the sun. Meanwhile, biology did not come into its own as a science until the *nineteenth* century. Prior to the 1800s, biology was almost purely "descriptive," meaning that the naturalists who we would today call biologists largely confined themselves to describing living things—what kinds there were, where they lived, what features they had, and so forth. Beginning in about the 1820s, however, biologists began to formulate biological theories as that term was defined earlier. They began to postulate that all life exists within cells, that life comes only from life, that life is passed on through small packets of information that we now call genes, and so forth. To put this another way, biologists in the nineteenth century began describing the *rules* of the living world, whereas before they were largely describing *forms* in the living world.

This change moved biology closer to the same scientific footing as physics. But biology was then, and remains now, a very different kind of science from any of the physical sciences, with physics being a clear case in point. One reason for this difference is that the constituent parts of physics are very uniform and far fewer in number than is the case in biology. Physics deals with only 92 stable elements, such as hydrogen and gold, and to a first approximation, if you've seen one electron, you've seen them all.

Meanwhile, in biology, if you've seen one species you've seen just that—one species. Each species is at least marginally different from another, and many are greatly dissimilar. Moreover, there are thought to be at least 4 million species on Earth. And each of these species has all the organizational levels of elements in physics *and more*. (They not only have electrons and atoms, they have organelles, cells, tissues, and so on.) Biology is concerned with the rules that govern all species, and you've seen that there are some biological "universals." But when cancer researchers are looking for the principles that underlie cell division, they are likely to be looking at only one of two main kinds of cells; when ecologists are looking at what causes dry grassland to turn into desert, their findings are likely to have little relevance to the rain forest. Put simply, the living world is tremendously diverse compared to the nonliving world, and such diversity means that universal rules in biology are likely to be few and far between. Biology is concerned with the *particular* to a greater degree than is the case in the physical sciences. Note also that "universals" in biology may not apply beyond Earth; we don't know if life even exists anywhere else, much less what its rules are. Meanwhile, the rules of physics truly are universal in that they are equally applicable on Earth or in the farthest reaches of the cosmos.

Biology's Chief Unifying Principle

Almost all biologists would agree that the most important thread that runs through biology is **evolution**, meaning the gradual modification of populations of living things over time, with this modification sometimes resulting in the develop-

**Figure 1.7
Evolution Has Shaped the
Living World**

(a) A peacock displaying his plumage

(b) A poison dart frog in Colombia

(c) Pine trees in the South Pacific

ment of new species. Evolution is central to biology, because every living thing has been shaped by evolution. (There are no known exceptions to this universal.) Given this, the explanatory power of evolution is immense. Why do peacocks have their finery, or frogs their coloration, or trees their height (**see Figure 1.7**)? All these things stand as wonders of nature's diversity, but with knowledge of evolution they are wonders of diversity that *make sense*. For example, why do so many unrelated stinging insects look alike? Evolutionary principles suggest they *evolved* to look alike because of the general protection this provides from predators. Think of yourself for a moment as a bee predator. Having once gotten stung, would you annoy *any* roundish insect that had a black-and-yellow-striped coloration? You probably learned your lesson about this in connection with one species, but many species of insects are now protected from you simply by virtue of the coloration they share with the others (**see Figure 1.8**). Thus, there were reproductive benefits to individuals who, through genetic chance, happened to get a slightly more striped coloration: They left more offspring, because they were bothered less by predators. Over time, entire populations moved in this direction. They evolved, in other words.

The means by which living things can evolve is a topic this book takes up beginning in Chapter 16. Suffice it to say for now that a consideration of evolution is never far from most biological obser-

vations. So strong is evolution's explanatory power that, in uncovering something new about, say, a sequence of DNA or the life cycle of a given organism, one of the first things a biologist will ask is: Why would evolution shape things in this way?

1.5   The Organization of This Book

This book has something in common with the levels of organization you looked at earlier, in that it too goes from constituent parts to the larger whole. It begins with atoms, moves on to the biological molecules that atoms make up, and then goes to cells. The end of the book covers the highest levels of biological organization, which is to say natural communities and Earth's biosphere. In between, however, are tours of such facets of life as energy, DNA-encoded information, and reproduction. Even in these sections, however, you'll be moving in a general way from the small to the large, because much of the first part of the book is given over to **molecular biology**—meaning the study of individual molecules (such as DNA) as they affect living things. Then you'll move into evolution, which touches on **organismal biology**, meaning the study of whole organisms within biology. Next is the **physiology** or physical functioning of plants and animals, which largely concerns tissues and organs. Finally there is **ecology**, which is the study of the interactions of organisms with each other and with their physical environment. And so, let's begin to look at biology—as a body of knowledge and a way of learning.

**Figure 1.8
Similar Enough to Yield a Benefit**
These are two of the many stinging insects that have the black-and-yellow-striped coloration that warns away predators.

(a) Golden northern bumblebee

(b) Sandhills hornet

Chapter Review

Summary

1.1 How Does Science Impact the Everyday World?

- Science is playing an increasingly important role in the everyday lives of Americans. Scientific advances regularly confront society with choices that have an ethical dimension to them. Society frequently turns to scientists to answer questions about health, the environment, and other domains of life.

- Americans have an uneven knowledge about science. Almost 80 percent of adult Americans know that the continents are moving about the face of the Earth, for example, but one-quarter think the sun goes around the Earth.

1.2 What Is Science?

- In one of its facets, science is a body of knowledge, a collection of unified insights about nature, the evidence for which is an array of facts.

- The unified insights of science are known as theories. A theory is a general set of principles, supported by evidence, that explains some aspect of nature.

- Science can also be defined as a way of learning: a process of coming to understand the natural world through observation and the testing of hypotheses.

- Science works through the scientific method, in which an observation leads to the formulation of a question about the natural world. Then comes a hypothesis—a tentative, testable explanation that has not been proven to be true. The hypothesis may be tested through observation or through a series of experiments, as aided by statistical procedures. An example of hypothesis testing is Louis Pasteur's experiment on the spontaneous generation of life.
Web Tutorial 1.1: Scientific Method

- In science, every assertion regarding the natural world is subject to challenge and revision; results obtained in experiments must be reproducible by other experimenters; and scientific claims must be falsifiable, meaning open to negation through means of scientific inquiry.

1.3 The Nature of Biology

- Biology is the study of life. Life is defined by a group of characteristics possessed by living things. These are that living things can assimilate energy, respond to their environment, maintain a relatively constant internal environment, and possess an inherited information base, encoded in DNA, that allows them to function. Living things can also reproduce, are composed of one or more cells, are evolved from other living things, and are highly organized compared to inanimate objects.

- Life is organized in a hierarchical manner, running in increasing complexity from atoms to molecules and then in sequence to organelles, cells, tissues, organs, organisms, populations, communities, and the biosphere.
Web Tutorial 1.2: Hierarchical Organization of Life

1.4 Special Qualities of Biology

- Until the early nineteenth century, biology was largely a descriptive science, meaning it largely catalogued and described the Earth's living things. Beginning about the 1820s, however, life science researchers began to formulate biological theories, such as that life comes only from life and exists only within cells.

- Biology's subject matter—the living world—is notable for its complexity and diversity compared to other aspects of the natural world (such as stars and atoms). Because of this, biology does not deal in universal rules to the extent that a discipline such as physics does; instead, biological research may focus on particular species, processes, or portions of the living world.

- Biology's chief unifying principle is evolution, which can be defined as the gradual modification of populations of living things over time, with this modification sometimes resulting in the development of new species. Evolution provides the means for making sense of the forms and processes seen in living things on Earth today.

Key Terms

biology 10	**organismal biology** 15
control 9	**physical sciences** 13
ecology 15	**physiology** 15
evolution 14	**science** 6
homeostasis 11	**scientific method** 7
hypothesis 7	**theory** 6
life sciences 13	**variable** 8
molecular biology 15	

Understanding the Basics

Multiple-Choice Questions (answers in the back of the book)

1. Which of the following statements best describes the nature of a scientific hypothesis?
   a. A hypothesis is an idea that is widely accepted as a description of objective reality by a majority of scientists.
   b. A hypothesis must stand alone, and not be based on prior knowledge.
   c. A hypothesis must be testable through experimentation, observation, or mathematical demonstration.
   d. A hypothesis must deal with an aspect of the natural world never dealt with before.
   e. A hypothesis when accepted becomes a scientific law.

2. A *theory*, as used in scientific discourse, is
   a. An established fact, such as the distance from the Earth to the sun
   b. A long-accepted belief about the natural world
   c. A concept that is in doubt among most scientists
   d. A set of principles, supported by evidence, that explains some aspect of nature
   e. An initial guess about how some aspect of nature works

3. Pasteur's experiments on spontaneous generation made correct use of a variable in that Pasteur
   a. varied the bacteria he employed with each experiment
   b. used statistics to prove his hypothesis
   c. observed the bacteria as they were growing in the flasks
   d. held all conditions constant in each test except one
   e. was willing to vary to the extent necessary from the standard hypotheses of his day

4. Evolution is a central, unifying theme in biology because
   a. It is not a falsifiable hypothesis.
   b. Humans have evolved from ancestors we share with present-day monkeys.
   c. It has occurred in the past, even though it no longer operates today.
   d. The enormously diverse forms of life on Earth have all been shaped by it.
   e. Almost all biologists believe in it.

5. Biologists generally define life in terms of a group of characteristics possessed by living things. Which of the following is *not* a characteristic of living things?
   a. All living things possess an inherited information base, encoded in DNA, that allows them to function.
   b. All living things can respond to their environment.
   c. All living things can maintain a relatively constant internal environment.
   d. All living things evolved from other living things.
   e. All living things are composed of two or more cells.

Brief Review

1. What is science? In what ways is science different from a belief system such as religious faith?

2. What is a controlled experiment? Why is it important to keep all variables but one constant in a scientific experiment?

3. How did Louis Pasteur cast doubt on the idea of spontaneous generation?

4. Describe the defining features of life as we know it on the Earth.

5. Living things are organized in a hierarchical manner. List all the levels of the biological hierarchy that you can think of.

Applying Your Knowledge

1. Would you agree that it is valuable for a nation to have a citizenry that is reasonably well versed in science? Give reasons for your answer. Would you say this need has become especially urgent in the last two decades? If so, why?

2. Is it harder to prove a hypothesis than to disprove it? Imagine you wanted to establish that cheetahs are the fastest land animals, and assume you have the ability to clock any animal moving at its top speed. Now, what would it take to disprove the idea that cheetahs are the fastest land animals? What would it take to prove that cheetahs are the fastest land mammals, meaning no other land mammal could run faster than they?

3. If you were sent on an interplanetary mission to investigate the presence of life on Mars, what would you look for? Would you explore the land and the atmosphere? Imagine you discover an entity you suspect is a living being. Realizing that life elsewhere in the universe may not be organized by the same rules as on Earth, which of the features of life on Earth, if any, would you insist that the entity display before you would declare it living?

2 *Chemistry and Life*

Pure gold. It's elementary.
(Section 2.1, page 22)

neon (Ne)

argon (Ar)

Filled shells mean stability.
(Section 2.2, page 24)

electron transfer

Na

C

ionic compound
(Na+Cl−)

You put it on popcorn.
(Section 2.2, page 28)

Life is carried on through chains of chemical reactions.

Cities are made of buildings and buildings are made of bricks; bricks are made of earth and earth is made of . . . ? To answer this question, in this chapter we will look at what the material world is made of. Biology is our subject, but to fully understand it, you need to learn a little about what underlies biology. You need to learn a little about what *biology* is made of, in a sense. And to do this, you need to understand some of the basics in two other fields: chemistry and physics.

How are these disciplines relevant to biology? Well, consider chemistry. The average person probably is aware that living things are made up of individual units called cells. But beyond this bit of knowledge, reality fades and a kind of fantasy takes over. In it, the cells that populate people or plants or birds carry on their activities under the direction of their own low-level consciousness. A cell *decides* to move, it *decides* to divide, and so on. Not so. By the time our story is finished, many chapters from now, it will be clear to you that the cells that make up

complex living things do what they do as the result of a chain of chemical reactions. Repulsion and bonding, latching on and reforming, depositing and breaking down; what makes people and plants and birds function at this cellular level is *chemistry*.

What is chemistry concerned with? Look around you. Do you see a table, light from a lamp, a patch of night or daytime sky? Everything that exists can be viewed as falling into one of two categories: matter or energy. You will learn something about energy in this chapter, but we are most concerned here with *matter and its transformations*, which is the subject of chemistry. Matter can be defined as anything that takes up space and has **mass**. This latter term is a measure of the *quantity* of matter in any given object. How much space does an object occupy—how much "volume," to put it another way—and how *dense* is the matter within that space? These are the things that define mass. For our purposes, we may think of mass as being equivalent to weight, though in physics they make a distinction between these two things.

The ties that bond water molecules together.
(Section 2.2, page 29)

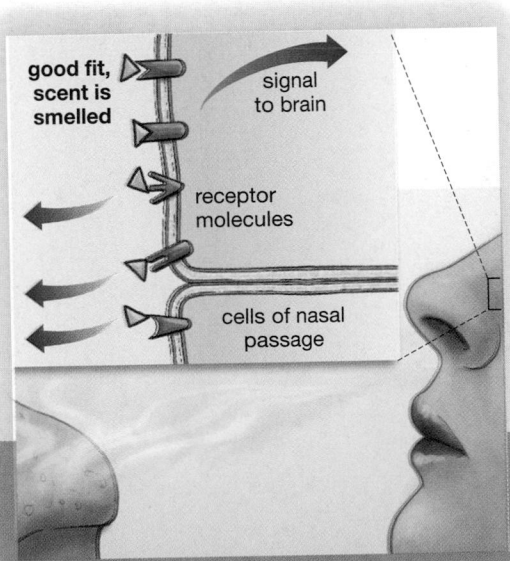

Do I smell bread in the oven?
(Section 2.3, page 30)

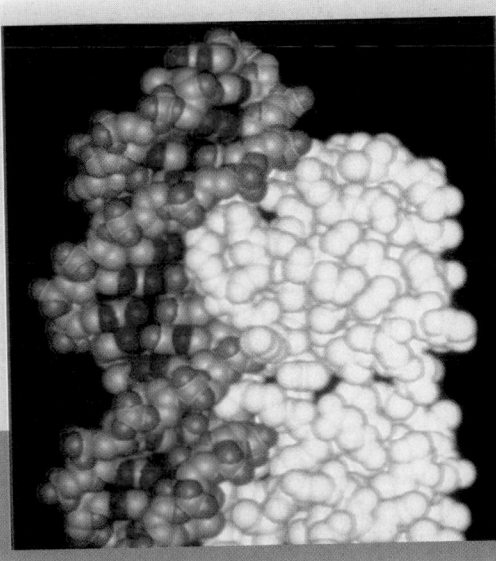

Many molecules are large and complex.
(Section 2.3, page 31)

2.1 The Nature of Matter: The Atom

Beholding matter all around us, it is natural to ask, what is its nature? A child sees a grain of sand, pounds it with a rock, sees the smaller bits that result and wonders: What is this stuff like at the end of these divisions? Not surprisingly, adults too have wondered about this question—for centuries. About 2,400 years ago, the Greek philosopher Plato accepted the notion that all matter is made up of four primary substances: earth, air, fire, and water. A near-contemporary of his, Democritus, believed that these substances were in turn made up of smaller units that were both invisible and in*div*isible—they could not be broken down further. He called these units atoms (**see Figure 2.1**).

Well, at least one cheer for Democritus, because he had it partly right. Centuries of painstaking work lying between his time and ours has confirmed that matter is indeed composed of tiny pieces of matter, which we still call atoms. But these atoms are not indivisible, as Democritus thought. Rather, they are themselves composed of constituent parts. A superficial account of *all* the parts scientists have discovered to date would go on for pages and still be incomplete. Physicists are continually slamming together parts of atoms with ever-greater force in an effort to determine what *else* there may be at the heart of matter. This is what the machines called "atom smashers" do. The physicists who run them could be compared to people who, in trying to find out what parts a watch has, throw it on the ground and record the way its various mechanisms fly out upon impact (**see Figure 2.2**).

Web Tutorial 2.1
Structure of Atoms, Elements, Isotopes

Interesting stuff, but it is purely the business of physics, with little relation to biology. We are not concerned here with what's at the very end of these divisions. We do care a good deal, however, about what's *nearly* at the end of them.

Protons, Neutrons, and Electrons

For our purposes there are three important constituent parts of an atom: **protons**, **neutrons**, and **electrons**. These three parts exist in a spatial arrangement that is uniform in all matter. Protons and neutrons are packed tightly together in a core (the atom's **nucleus**), and electrons move around this core some distance away (**see Figure 2.3**). The one variation on this theme is the substance hydrogen, the lightest of all the kinds of matter we will run into. Hydrogen has no neutrons, but rather only one proton in its nucleus and one electron in motion around it.

These three "subatomic" particles have mind-bending sizes and proportions. As P. W. Atkins has pointed out, an atom is so small that 100 million carbon atoms would lie end to end in a line of carbon about this long: ———————
(3 centimeters). Things are just as disorienting when we consider the size of the atom as a whole, relative to the nucleus. The whole atom, with electrons at its edge, is 100,000 times bigger than the nucleus. If you were to draw a model of an atom *to scale* and began by sketching a nucleus of, say, half an inch, you'd have to draw some of its electrons more than three-quarters of a mile away.

Although the nucleus accounts for very little of the *space* an atom takes up, it accounts for almost all

Figure 2.1
The Building Blocks of Life
Viewing this idealized feather at different levels of magnification, we eventually arrive at the building block of all matter, the atom. The atom selected here, from among a multitude that make up the feather, is a single hydrogen atom, composed of one proton and one electron.

of the *mass* an atom has. So negligible are electrons in this regard, in fact, that all of the mass (or weight) of an atom is considered to reside with the nucleus' protons and neutrons.

The components of atoms have another quality that interests us: electrical charge. Protons are positively charged and electrons are negatively charged. Meanwhile, neutrons—as their name implies—have no charge, but are electrically neutral. Because all these particles do not exist separately, but *combine* to form an atom, as a whole the atom may be electrically neutral as well. The negative charge of the electrons balances out the positive charge of the protons. Why? Because in this state the number of protons an atom has is exactly equal to the number of electrons it has (though we'll see a different, "ionic" state later in this chapter). In contrast, the number of *neutrons* an atom has can vary in relation to the other two particles.

With this picture of atoms in mind, we can begin to answer the question that has been handed down to us through history: What is matter? We certainly have a commonsense answer to this question. Matter is any substance that exists in our everyday experience. For example, the iron that goes into cars is matter. But what is it that differentiates this iron from, say, gold? The answer is that an iron atom has 26 protons in its nucleus, while a gold atom has 79.

Fundamental Forms of Matter: The Element

Gold is an **element**—a substance that is "pure" because it cannot be reduced to any simpler set of component substances through chemical processes.

Figure 2.2
Getting to the Heart of Matter
Understanding what the tiny objects called atoms are made of requires the use of extremely large particle accelerators or "atom smashers," such as this one at Fermilab in Batavia, Illinois. Subatomic particles are accelerated around Fermilab's magnetic ring, some 6.3 kilometers or 3.8 miles in circumference, and then slammed into each other or into a fixed target. How big is this operation? The detectors that record the collisions weigh 5,000 tons apiece and are three stories high.

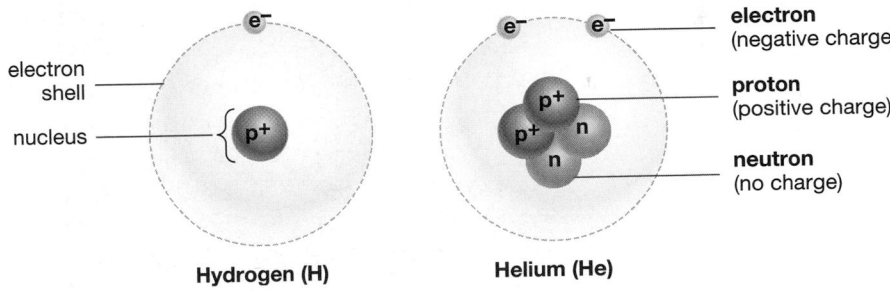

Figure 2.3
Representations of Atoms
One conceptualization of two separate atoms, hydrogen and helium. The model is not drawn to scale; if it were, the electrons would be perhaps a third of a mile away from the nuclei. The model also is simplified, giving the appearance that electrons exist in track-like orbits around an atom's nucleus. In fact, electrons spend time in volumes of space that have several different shapes.

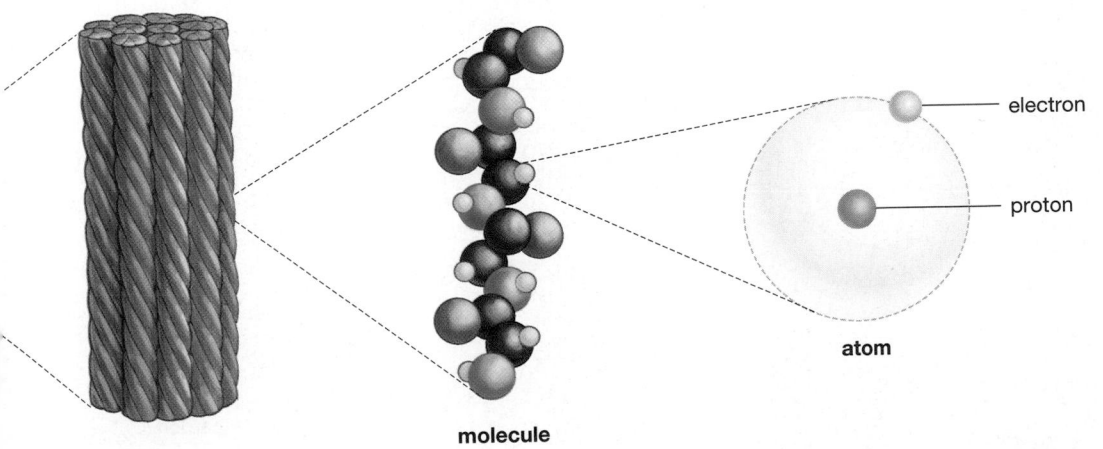

And the thing that defines each element is the number of protons it has in its nucleus. A solid-gold bar, then, represents a huge collection of identical atoms, each of which has 79 protons in its nucleus (**Figure 2.4**). In making gold jewelry, an artist may combine gold with another metal such as silver or copper to form an alloy that is stronger than pure gold, but the gold atoms are still present, all of them retaining their 79-proton nuclei.

Given what you've just read about protons, neutrons, and electrons, you may wonder why gold—or any other element—cannot be reduced to any "sim-

pler set of component substances." Aren't protons and neutrons components of atoms? Yes, but they are not component *substances,* because they cannot exist by themselves as matter. Rather, protons and neutrons must *combine* with each other to make up atoms.

Assigning Numbers to the Elements

In the same way that buildings can be defined by a location, and thus have a street number assigned to them, these elements, which are defined by protons in their nuclei, have an **atomic number** assigned to them. We have observed that hydrogen has but one proton in its nucleus, and it turns out that scientists have constructed the atomic numbering system so that it goes from smallest number of protons to largest. Thus, hydrogen has the atomic number 1. The next element, helium, has two protons, so it is assigned the atomic number 2. Continuing on this scale all the way up through the elements found in nature, we would end with uranium, which has an atomic number of 92.

Given this view of the nature of matter, we are now in a position to answer the question posed at the beginning of the chapter: What is a handful of earth—or anything else—made of? The answer is one or more elements. If you look at **Figure 2.5**, you can see the most important elements that go into making up both the earth's crust and human beings.

Isotopes

All this seems like a nice, tidy way to identify elements—one element, one atomic number, based on number of protons—except that we're leaving out

Figure 2.4
Pure Gold
Gold is an element because it cannot be reduced to any simpler set of substances through chemical means. Each gold bar and nugget is made up of a vast collection of identical atoms—those with 79 protons in their nuclei.

Figure 2.5
Constituent Elements
The major chemical elements found in Earth's crust (including the oceans and the atmosphere) and in the human body.

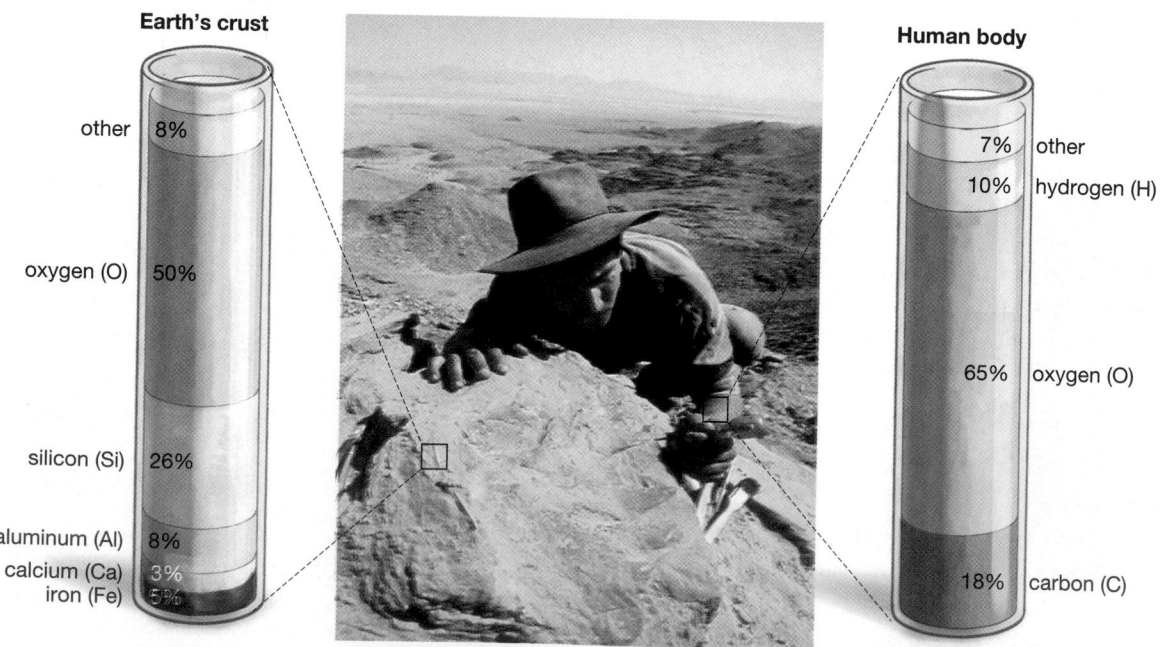

Earth's crust

other | 8%
oxygen (O) | 50%
silicon (Si) | 26%
aluminum (Al) | 8%
calcium (Ca) | 3%
iron (Fe) | 5%

Human body

7% | other
10% | hydrogen (H)
65% | oxygen (O)
18% | carbon (C)

something. Recall that atoms also have neutrons in their nuclei, that these neutrons add weight to the atom, and that the number of neutrons can vary independently of the number of protons. What this means is that in thinking about an element in terms of its weight, we have to take neutrons into account. Furthermore, because the number of neutrons in an element's nucleus may vary, we can have various *forms* of elements, called **isotopes**. Most people have heard of one example of an isotope, whether or not they recognize it as such. The element carbon has six protons, giving it an atomic number of 6. In its most common form, it also has six neutrons. However, a relatively small amount of carbon exists in a form that has *eight* neutrons. Well, the element is still carbon, and in this form the number of its protons and neutrons equals 14, so the *isotope* is carbon-14, which is used in determining the ages of fossils and geologic samples.

Most elements have several isotopes. Hydrogen, for example, which usually has one proton and one electron, also exists in two other forms: deuterium, which has the proton, electron, and one neutron; and tritium, which has one proton, one electron, and two neutrons (**see Figure 2.6**). **Figure 2.7** shows you how isotopes are used in medicine.

The Importance of Electrons

In our account so far of the subatomic trio, we have had much to say about protons and neutrons, but little to say about electrons. This was necessary because we needed to go over the nature of matter, but in a sense you can regard what has been set forth to this point as so much stage-setting, because what's most important in biology is the way elements *combine* with other elements. And in this combining, it is the outermost electrons that play a critical role. Just as you come into contact with the world through what lies at your surface—your eyes, your ears, your hands—so atoms link up with one another through what lies at their outer edges. The interior of an atom is very quiet in a sense, while the atom's outer electrons exist in a world that can be one of continual forming and breaking of alliances.

2.2 Matter Is Transformed through Chemical Bonding

The process of chemical combination and rearrangement is called **chemical bonding**, and for us it represents the heart of the story in chemistry. When the outermost electrons of two atoms come into contact, it becomes possible for these electrons to

reshuffle themselves in a way that allows the atoms to become attached to one another. This can take place in two ways: One atom can *give up* one or more electrons to another, or one atom can *share* one or more electrons with another atom. Giving up electrons is called ionic bonding; sharing electrons is called covalent bonding. A third type of bond, which we'll get to shortly, also is important for our purposes: the hydrogen bond.

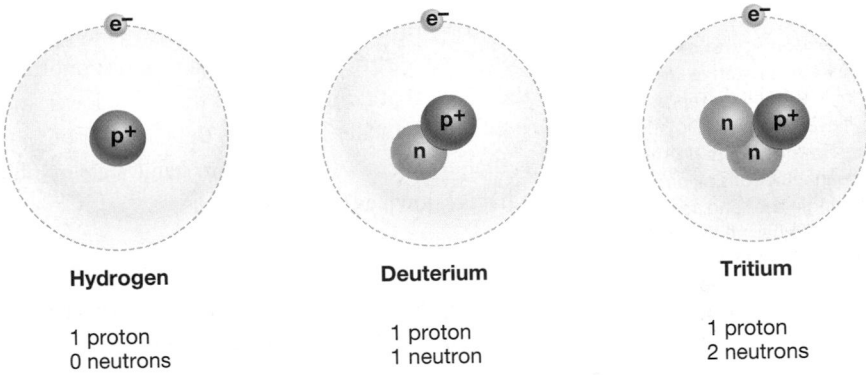

Hydrogen	Deuterium	Tritium
1 proton 0 neutrons	1 proton 1 neutron	1 proton 2 neutrons

Figure 2.6
Same Element, Different Forms
Pictured are three isotopes of hydrogen. Like all isotopes, they differ in the number of neutrons they have.

Figure 2.7
Imaging the Body with Isotopes
The radioactive isotopes technetium 99 was used in a nuclear medicine scan to provide these images of skeletal portions of the human body.

Figure 2.8
Electron Configurations in Some Representative Elements
The concentric rings represent energy levels or "shells" of the elements, and the dots on the rings represent electrons. Hydrogen has but a single shell and a single electron within it, while carbon has two shells with a total of six electrons in them. Helium, neon, and argon have filled outer shells and are thus unreactive. Hydrogen, carbon, and sodium do not have filled outer shells and are thus reactive—they readily combine with other elements.

Energy Always Seeks Its Lowest State

Atoms that undertake bonding with one another do so because they are in a more *stable* state after the bonding than before it. A frequently used phrase is helpful in understanding this kind of stability: Energy always seeks its lowest state. Imagine a boulder perched precariously on a hill. A mere shove might send it rolling toward its lower energy state—at the bottom of the hill. It would not then roll *up* the hill, either spontaneously or with a light shove, because it is now existing in a lower energy state than it did before—one that is clearly more stable than its former precarious perch. When we turn to electrons, the energy is not gravitational, but electrical. Atoms bond with one another to the extent that doing so moves them to a lower, more stable energy state. The critical thing for our purposes is that atoms move to this more stable state by filling what is known as their outer shells.

Seeking a Full Outer Shell: Covalent Bonding

What are these "outer shells"? As it happens, electrons reside in certain well-defined "energy levels" outside the nuclei of atoms. The number of these energy levels varies depending on the element in question. Here we need only note the practical effect of these levels

on bonding: *Two* electrons are required to fill the first energy level (or shell) of any given atom, but *eight* usually are required to fill all the levels thereafter. If you look at the electron configurations pictured in **Figure 2.8**, you can see that two elements—hydrogen and helium—have so few electrons in orbit around them that they have nothing *but* a first energy level, while the other elements pictured have two or three energy levels. This means that hydrogen and helium require only two electrons in orbit around their nuclei to have filled outer shells, but that the other elements pictured require eight electrons to have this kind of complete outer electron complement.

How Chemical Bonding Works in One Instance: Water

To see how chemical bonding works in connection with this concept of filled outer shells, take a look at the bonding that occurs with the constituent parts of one of the most simple (and important) substances on Earth, water. In so doing, you'll see one of the kinds of bonding we talked about—covalent bonding.

The familiar chemical symbol for water is H_2O. This means that two atoms of hydrogen (H) have combined with one atom of oxygen (O) to form water. (See "Notating Chemistry" on page 26 for an explanation of symbols in chemistry.) Recall that hydrogen has but one electron running around in its single energy level. Also recall, however, that this first level is not completed until it has *two* electrons in it. Hydrogen could fill this shell in any number of ways. It might, for example, come into contact with another hydrogen atom. These two atoms can then form a **covalent bond** by sharing a *pair* of electrons with each other—one electron from each atom. These electrons can now be found orbiting the nuclei of both atoms. As a result, both have two electrons in their outer energy levels, which makes them filled.

Our hydrogen atom might also, however, come into contact with an oxygen atom, which has eight electrons. Looking at **Figure 2.9**, you can see what this means: Two electrons fill oxygen's first energy level, which leaves six left over for its second. But remember that the second shells of most atoms are not completed until they hold *eight* electrons. Thus oxygen, like hydrogen, would welcome a partner. Only it needs *two* electrons to fill its outer shell, which means that two atoms of hydrogen would do. Once again, pairs of electrons are shared. The oxygen atom and first hydrogen atom donate one electron each for the first pair; and the oxygen and second hydrogen atom each donate one electron for the second pair. The result? H_2O: Two atoms of hydrogen and one atom of oxygen, covalently bonded together and all of them

Unstable, very reactive atoms

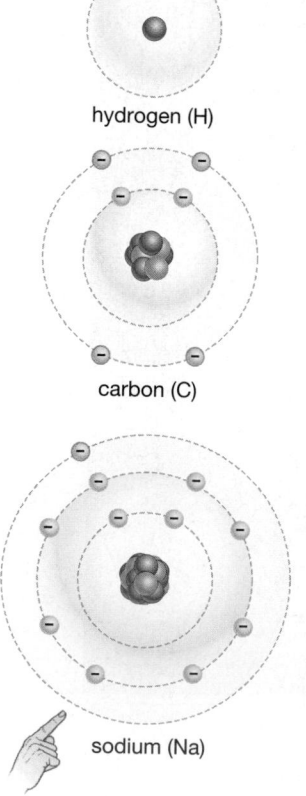

hydrogen (H)

carbon (C)

sodium (Na)

Outermost electron shells unfilled

Stable, unreactive atoms

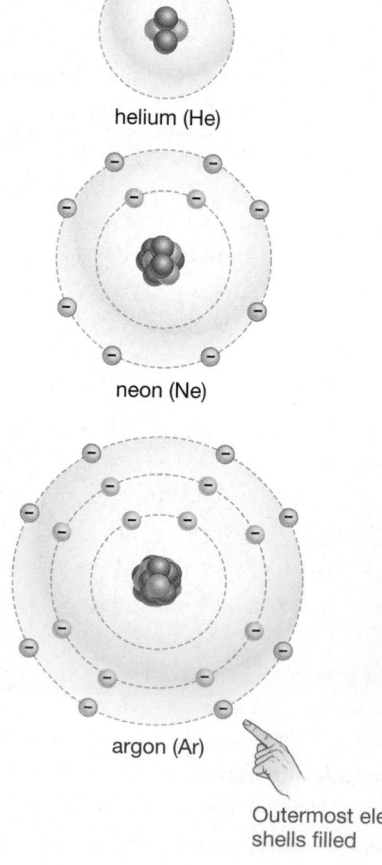

helium (He)

neon (Ne)

argon (Ar)

Outermost electron shells filled

"satisfied" to be in that condition. (Occasionally in nature, covalent bonding will take place in a way that leaves one atom with an unpaired electron, a potentially harmful phenomenon you can read about in "Free Radicals" on page 30.)

Matter Is Not Gained or Lost in Chemical Reactions

Note that when this pairing up of electrons happens, no matter has been gained or lost. We started with two atoms of hydrogen and one atom of oxygen, and we finish that way. The difference is that these atoms are now bonded. This points up an important principle, known as the **law of conservation of mass**, which states that matter is neither created nor destroyed in a chemical reaction.

What Is a Molecule?

When two or more atoms combine in this kind of covalent reaction, the result is a **molecule**: a compound of a defined number of atoms in a defined spatial relationship. Here, one atom of oxygen has combined with two atoms of hydrogen to create *one water molecule*. (What we commonly think of as water, then, is an enormous, linked collection of these individual water molecules.) A molecule need not be made of two different elements, however. Two hydrogen atoms can covalently bond to form one hydrogen molecule. On the other side of the coin, a molecule could contain many different elements bonded together. Consider sucrose, or regular table sugar, which is $C_{12}H_{22}O_{11}$ (12 carbon atoms bonded to 22 hydrogen atoms and 11 oxygen atoms).

Reactive and Unreactive Elements

The elements considered so far all welcome bonding partners, because all of them have incomplete outer shells. This is not true of all elements, however. There is, for example, the helium atom, which has two electrons. It thus *comes equipped*, we might say, with a filled outer shell. As such, it is extremely stable—it is unreactive with other elements. It is so unreactive that it is part of a family of elements that at one time were known as the inert gases, because it was thought that these elements never combined with anything. (In more recent times, however, all but two have been coaxed into such combining.) At the opposite end of the spectrum are elements that are extremely reactive. Look again at the representation of the sodium atoms in Figure 2.8. It has 11 electrons, two in the first shell and eight in the second, which leaves but one electron in the third shell—a very unstable state. Between the extremes of sodium and helium are elements with a range of outer (or *valence*) electrons.

(a) Hydrogen molecule

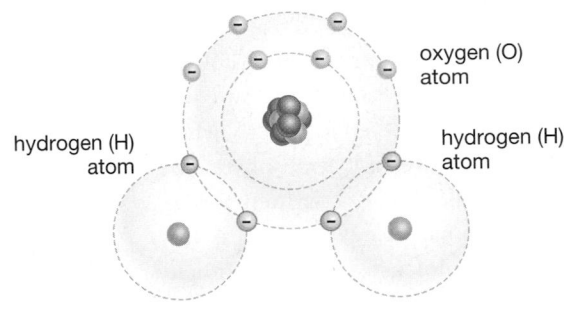

(b) Water molecule

Figure 2.9
Covalent Bonding
A covalent bond is formed when two atoms share one or more pairs of electrons.

(a) Two atoms of hydrogen have come together, and each shares its lone electron with the other. This gives both atoms a filled outer shell—and stability.

(b) Two hydrogen atoms have linked with one oxygen atom; in this case, two pairs of electrons are shared, one pair between each of the hydrogen atoms and the oxygen atom.

Thus, there is a spectrum of stability in the chemical elements, based on the number of outer-shell electrons each element has—from 1 to 8, with 1 being the most reactive and 8 being the least reactive.

Polar and Nonpolar Bonding

Not all covalent bonds are created alike. When two hydrogen atoms come together, the result is a hydrogen molecule (H_2). Now, in the hydrogen molecule, the electrons are shared *equally*. That is, the two electrons the hydrogen atoms are sharing are equally attracted to each hydrogen atom. This is not the case, however, with the water molecule.

Look at the representation of the water molecule in **Figure 2.10a**. As it turns out, the oxygen atom has a greater power to attract electrons to itself than do the hydrogen atoms. The term for measuring this kind of pull is **electronegativity**. Because the oxygen atom has more electronegativity than do the hydrogen atoms, it tends to pull the shared electrons away from the hydrogen and toward itself. When this happens, the molecule takes on a **polarity** or a difference in electrical charge at one end as opposed to the other. Because electrons are negatively charged, and because they can be found closer to the oxygen nucleus, the oxygen end of the molecule becomes slightly negatively charged, while the hydrogen regions become slightly positively charged. We still have a covalent bond, but it is a specific type: a **polar covalent bond**. Conversely, with the hydrogen molecule—where electrons are being shared equally—we have a **nonpolar covalent bond**.

structural formula

ball-and-stick model

space-filling model

Notating Chemistry

One of the "languages of science" is the system of symbols that chemistry uses. Somewhat forbidding at first viewing, this system soon comes to serve its intended purpose of conveying a lot of information very quickly. Our starting place is that each chemical element has its own symbol, so that hydrogen becomes H, carbon C, and platinum Pt.

When we begin to combine these elements into molecules, it is necessary to specify how *many* atoms of each element are part of the molecule. If we have two atoms of oxygen together—which is the way oxygen is usually packaged in our atmosphere—we have the molecule O_2. Three molecules of O_2 is written as $3O_2$. This kind of notation is known as a **molecular formula**. It is very helpful in stipulating the makeup of molecules, from the simple, such as oxygen, to the complex, such as chlorophyll, which is notated $C_{55}H_{72}MgN_4O_5$.

To see a molecular formula is to learn a lot about what atoms are in a molecule, but nothing about the way the atoms are *arranged* in relation to one another. (Look at chlorophyll's formula. Is there a line of 55 carbon atoms followed by 72 hydrogen atoms? From the molecular formula, how could you tell?) To convey this ordering information, chemists and biologists use

what are known as **structural formulas**—two-dimensional representations of a given molecule. Methane (CH_4) is a very simple molecule composed, as the molecular formula shows, of one atom of carbon and four of hydrogen. In a structural formula, these constituent parts are conceptualized like this:

$$\begin{array}{c} \text{H} \\ | \\ \text{H} - \text{C} - \text{H} \\ | \\ \text{H} \end{array}$$

methane

Note that there is a single line between each hydrogen atom and the central carbon atom. This has not been done just because a single line is easy to draw. The bond between any of the hydrogen atoms and carbon is a **single bond**: Each line represents *one* pair of electrons being shared. Thus:

There can also be **double bonds** and **triple bonds**. When carbon dioxide forms, there are two oxygen atoms. Each shares two

(a) Polar water molecule

δ−

slight negative charge

polar

slight positive charge

δ+   δ+

(b) Nonpolar methane molecule

δ+   δ+

nonpolar because charges are symmetric

δ+   δ+

Figure 2.10
Polar and Nonpolar Covalent Bonding

(a) In the water molecule, the oxygen atom exerts a greater attraction on the shared electrons than do the hydrogen atoms. Thus the electrons are shifted toward the oxygen atom, giving the oxygen atom a partial negative charge (because electrons are negatively charged) and the hydrogen atoms a partial positive charge. ("Partial" here is indicated by the Greek delta symbol δ.) The molecule as a whole is polar, meaning it has a difference in charge at one end, as opposed to the other.

(b) In the methane molecule, the carbon atom is more electronegative than the hydrogen atoms, but the methane molecule as a whole is nonpolar because its hydrogen atoms are arranged symmetrically around the central carbon atom, meaning the partial charges that exist balance each other out. Thus, methane has no difference in charge at one end, as opposed to the other.

pairs of electrons with a lone carbon atom. Here's how we would notate the double bond in a carbon dioxide (CO_2) molecule:

$$O = C = O$$
carbon dioxide

Though structural (or "skeletal") formulas can tell us a good deal about the ordering of atoms in a molecule, they tell us very little about the *three-dimensional* arrangements of atoms. For this, we rely on two other kinds of representations, the **ball-and-stick model** and the **space-filling model**. An ammonia molecule (NH_3) is pictured next in both forms, with the molecular and structural formulas added to show the progression:

molecular formula	structural formula	ball-and-stick model	space-filling model

Note that the ball-and-stick model gives us a better idea of molecular angles of the atoms, but that the space-filling model gives us a better idea of the relative size of these atoms and how one actually hugs the other.

Finally, it is useful to have a way to notate the "before" and "after" stages of a chemical reaction. This is done by employing a simple arrow, as when carbon reacts with hydrogen to form methane: $C + 4H \rightarrow CH_4$. The carbon and hydrogen atoms on the left are **reactants**, the arrow means "yields," and the methane molecule on the right is the **product** of the reaction. Here's a graphic representation of what is happening:

An important thing to keep in mind about notation goes back to the law of conservation of mass (page 25): Matter is neither created nor destroyed in a chemical reaction. It follows that reactions such as the one above must be *balanced*: We must have the same number of atoms when the reaction is finished (on the right) as when it started (on the left). Thus, we could not have $C_2 + 4H \rightarrow CH_4$. This is an unbalanced reaction. We started out with two atoms of carbon on the left, but somehow ended up with one atom of carbon on the right. Nature doesn't play that way.

To grasp the importance of this, consider the water molecule, with its positive and negative regions. What's going to happen when it comes into contact with *other* polar molecules? The oppositely charged parts of the molecules will attract and the similarly charged parts will repel. It's like having a bar magnet and trying to bring its positive end into contact with the positive end of another magnet: Left on its own, the second magnet just flips around, so that positive is now linked to negative. In the same way, molecules flip around in relation to their polarity.

It is possible for atoms with different electronegativity to link together and still have the resulting molecule be nonpolar. Water is polar because the atom with more electronegativity (the oxygen) lies to one *side* of the two hydrogen atoms. Meanwhile, in a molecule such as methane, four hydrogen atoms are arranged in a symmetrical way around a central, and more electronegative, carbon atom (**see Figure 2.10b**). In this arrangement the differing charges balance each other out, leaving methane with no positive or negative end—meaning it is nonpolar. In sum, some molecules are polar while others are nonpolar, and this difference has significant consequences for chemical bonding.

Ionic Bonding: When Electrons Are Lost or Gained

So we've gone from nonpolar covalent bonding, where electrons are shared equally, to polar covalent bonding, where electrons are pulled to one side of the resulting molecule. What if we carried this just one step further and had instances in which the electronegativity differences between two atoms were so extreme that electrons were pulled *off* of one atom altogether, only to latch onto the atom that was attracting them? This is what happens in our second type of bonding, **ionic bonding**. The classic illustration of this type of bonding involves the sodium we looked at earlier and the element chlorine. Recall that sodium has 11 electrons, meaning that there's a lone electron flying around in its third electron shell. Chlorine, meanwhile, has 17 electrons, meaning it has 7 electrons in the third shell. Remember that 8 is a magic number for outer-shell stability. Sodium could get to this number by *losing* one electron, while chlorine could get to it by *gaining* one electron. That's just how this encounter goes: Sodium does in fact lose its one electron, chlorine gains it, and both parties become stable in the process (**see Figure 2.11**).

What Is an Ion?

But this story has a postscript. Having lost an electron (with its negative charge), sodium (Na) then takes on an overall *positive* charge. Having gained an electron, chlorine (Cl) takes on a negative charge. Each is then said to be an **ion**—a charged atom—or, to put it another way, an atom whose number of electrons differs from its number of protons. We denote the ionized forms of these atoms like this: Na^+, Cl^-. Were an atom to gain or lose more electrons than this, we would put a number in front of the charge sign. For example, to show that the magnesium atom has lost two electrons and thus become a positively charged magnesium ion, we would write Mg^{2+}.

Note that we now have two ions, Na^+ and Cl^-, with differing charges in proximity to one another. They are thus attracted to one another through an *electrostatic attraction,* and have an ionic bond between them. This hardly ever happens with just *two* atoms, of course. Many billions of atoms are bonded together in this way, up, down, and sideways from each other. This whole collection is, likewise, called an ion; or, if two or more elements are mixed together this way, an **ionic compound**. The particular ionic compound just described actually is very familiar. Sodium and chlorine combine to create sodium chloride, which is better known as table salt. The notation should properly be written Na^+Cl^-, but it is usually denoted as just plain NaCl.

Figure 2.11
Ionic Bonding

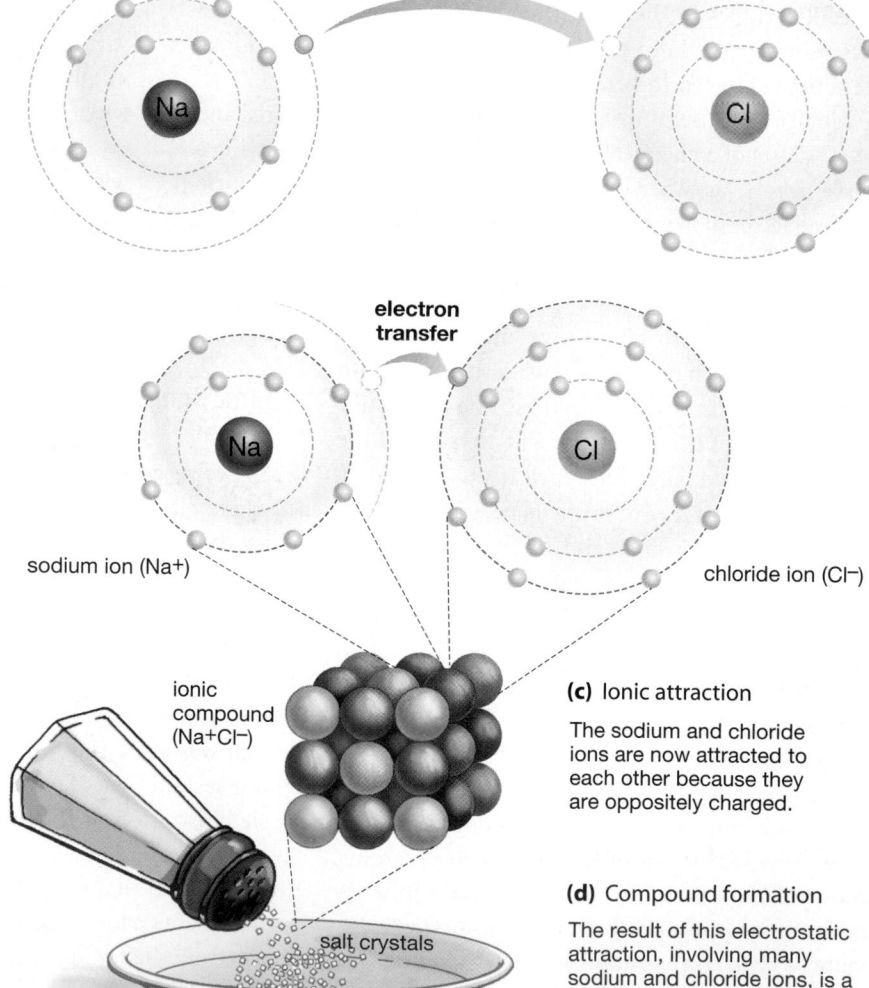

(a) Initial instability

Sodium has but a single electron in its outer shell, while chlorine has seven, meaning it lacks only a single electron to have a completed outer shell.

sodium atom (Na)

chlorine atom (Cl)

electron transfer

(b) Electron transfer

When these two atoms come together, sodium loses its third-shell electron to chlorine, in the process becoming a sodium ion with a net positive charge (because it now has more protons than electrons.) Having gained an electron, the chlorine atom becomes a chloride ion, with a net negative charge (because it has more electrons than protons).

sodium ion (Na+)

chloride ion (Cl−)

ionic compound (Na+Cl−)

salt crystals

(c) Ionic attraction

The sodium and chloride ions are now attracted to each other because they are oppositely charged.

(d) Compound formation

The result of this electrostatic attraction, involving many sodium and chloride ions, is a sodium chloride crystal (NaCl), better known as table salt.

Is it apparent how an ionic compound differs from a molecule? In an ionic compound, there is no fixed number of atoms linked up in a defined spatial relationship, as in H_2O. Rather, an undefined number of charged atoms are bonded together, as in NaCl.

To take a step back for a second, recall that bonding runs a gamut from the nonpolar covalent bonding (where electrons are shared equally) to the slightly charged polar covalent bonding (where they are shared somewhat unequally) to the charged ionic bonding (where electrons are gained or lost altogether). It's important to recognize that there is a *spectrum of polarity,* and that within it, some bonds are almost completely ionic (as with sodium chloride) while others are completely nonpolar (as with the hydrogen molecule).

A Third Form of Bonding: Hydrogen Bonding

We need to look at one more variant on bonding, called hydrogen bonding. Recall that in any water molecule, the stronger electronegativity of the oxygen atom pulls the electrons shared with the hydrogen atoms toward the oxygen nucleus, giving the oxygen end of the molecule a partial negative charge and the hydrogen end of the molecule a partial positive charge. So what happens when you place several water molecules together? A positive hydrogen atom of one molecule is weakly attracted to the negative, *unshared* electrons of its oxygen neighbor. Thus is created the **hydrogen bond**, which links an already covalently bonded hydrogen atom with an electronegative atom (in this case with oxygen; **see Figure 2.12**). Hydrogen bonding is a linkage that, for our purposes, nearly always pairs hydrogen with either oxygen or nitrogen. These relatively weak bonds are important in linking the atoms of a single molecule to one another, but they are just as important in creating bonds *between* molecules, as in the example. The hydrogen bond, indicated by a dotted line, exists in many of the molecules of life—in DNA, proteins, and elsewhere.

2.3 Some Qualities of Chemical Compounds

Molecules Have a Three-Dimensional Shape

We now need to make more explicit what has been noted only by implication in our diagrams of water molecules: that molecules and ionic compounds have a three-dimensional shape. It is useful to depict them as two-dimensional chains and rings and such, but in real life a molecule is as three-dimensional as a sculpture. A fair number of shapes are

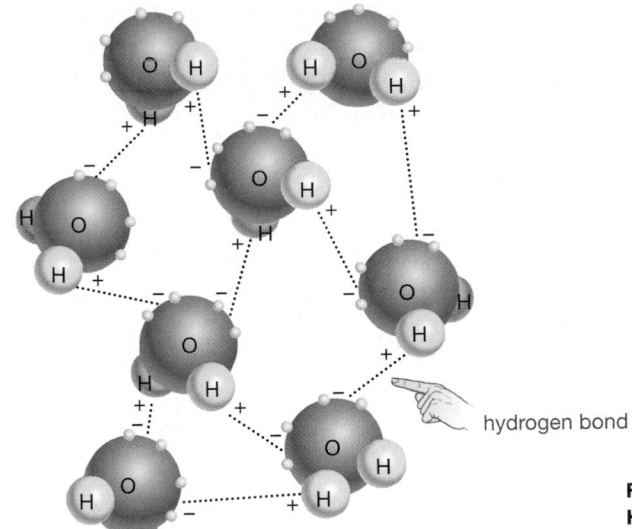

hydrogen bond

possible, even in simpler molecules. Atoms may be lined up in a row, or in triangles or pyramid shapes. As an example, look at another representation of the water and methane molecules (**see Figure 2.13**). You can see that in water there is a very definite spatial configuration: Its hydrogen atoms are splayed out from its oxygen atom at an angle of 104.5°.

Molecular Shape Is Very Important in Biology

Why does molecular shape matter? It is critical in enabling biological molecules to carry out the activities they do. This is so because molecular shape determines the capacity of molecules to latch onto or "bind" with one another. When, for example, you smell the aroma of fresh-baked bread, gas molecules wafting off the bread bind with receptor molecules in your nasal passages, thus sending a message to the brain about the presence of bread. It is the precise shape of the gas

**Figure 2.12
Hydrogen Bonding**
The hydrogen bond, in this case between water molecules, is indicated by the dotted line. It exists because of the attraction between hydrogen atoms, with their partial positive charge, and the unshared electrons of the oxygen atom, with their partial negative charge.

Web Tutorial 2.3
Geometry, Chemistry and Biology

**Figure 2.13
Three-Dimensional Representations of Molecules**

(a) In the case of water there is an angle of 104.5° between hydrogen atoms.

(b) Methane is a molecule with an angle of 109.5° between hydrogen atoms.

(a) Water (H_2O)

(b) Methane (CH_4)

109.5°

104.5°

$$\cdot\ddot{N}: \;+\; :\ddot{O}: \longrightarrow \; \cdot\ddot{N}::\ddot{O}:$$

nitrogen oxygen   nitric oxide

unpaired electron

free radical

Free Radicals

Their name makes them sound like a group of sixties activists set loose after years in jail, but **free radicals** aren't people at all; they are atoms or molecules. They *have* been set loose, however—to damage human bodies in illnesses that may range from cancer to coronary heart disease.

The way the public normally hears about these culprits is through the recommended means of limiting their harm: a diet rich in vitamins C, E, and the substance beta carotene. Looking at free radicals from another angle, however, we can see how they represent a damaging exception to the rules of chemical bonding.

You know that atoms "seek" to have a full outer energy shell, which in most cases means eight electrons. In covalent bonding, atoms achieve this state by sharing *pairs* of electrons with one another, one electron of each pair coming from each of the atoms

involved. Occasionally in nature, however, atoms come together to create a molecule in which one of the component atoms has an *unpaired electron* in its outer shell. Nitrogen can come together with oxygen, for example, to form nitric oxide (NO). Recall that oxygen has six outer electrons (and thus needs two for stability), while nitrogen has five outer electrons (and thus needs three). When oxygen and nitrogen hook up, they can share only two electrons with one another before oxygen's outer shell is filled. This, however, leaves nitrogen with an unpaired electron.

unpaired electron

$$\cdot\ddot{N}: \;+\; :\ddot{O}: \longrightarrow \; \cdot\ddot{N}::\ddot{O}:$$

nitrogen oxygen   nitric oxide

free radical

Figure 2.14
The Importance of Shape
Gas molecules wafting off from bread (the triangles) bind with specific receptors on the surface of the cell, thus acting as signaling molecules that set a cellular process in motion. For this binding to take place, the gas and nasal receptor molecules must fit together; this fit is governed by the shape of each molecule.

molecules and nasal receptor molecules that allows them to bind with one another. Look at **Figure 2.14** to see how this works. If you look at **Figure 2.15**, you can get an idea of how large some biological molecules are, relative to the simple molecules considered so far.

Having learned a little about atoms and molecules, we now need to review a few final concepts that will aid us in understanding chemistry on a slightly larger scale.

signal molecules (aroma from bread)

good fit, scent is smelled

signal to brain

bad fit, scent is not smelled

receptor molecules

cells of nasal passage

Solutes, Solvents, and Solutions

Take a glass of water and pour a little salt in it. When you stir that up, the salt quickly disappears. It has not actually gone anywhere, of course. It has simply mixed with the water. Now, if it has mixed uniformly, so that there are no lumps of salt here or there, you have created a **solution**—a homogeneous mixture of two or more kinds of molecules, atoms, or ions. The salt is what's being dissolved here, so it is the **solute**. The water is doing the dissolving, so it is the **solvent** (**see Figure 2.16**).

Molecules vary greatly in the degree to which they are *soluble*—are able to be dissolved—in different solvents. This is because, for something to act as a solvent, it must be able to form chemical bonds with the solute. The more bonding a solvent can do with a solute, the greater capacity that solvent will have to break down the solute.

A general rule is that like dissolves like. Substances that are nonpolar dissolve best in nonpolar solvents; substances that are polar dissolve best in polar solvents. Salt and water are both polar, and the one dissolves in the other. Conversely, the ingredient in soap that actually breaks up nonpolar greases and dirt is a long, nonpolar molecular chain composed of hydrogen and carbon atoms.

On to Some Detail Regarding Water

In biology, you will often see casual references to a molecule being *soluble* in a certain way. And you

Unstable molecules like this usually exist only briefly, as intermediate molecules in chemical reactions. And in people, that's just the problem. Human beings are among the many species that use a terrific amount of oxygen to extract energy from food. In this process, oxygen is constantly picking up electrons. Through the many steps in metabolism, oxygen may come together with other substances to create a type of free radical called reactive oxygen. Though any one reactive oxygen molecule is short-lived, the damage comes by way of a destructive chain reaction: Seeking partners, one free radical begets more, which beget more.

Where's the harm? Well, for one thing, free radicals may irritate or scar artery walls, which invites artery-clogging fatty deposits around the damage. They also may have a mutation-causing or "mutagenic" effect on human DNA, which can be a factor leading to cancer. Some primary sites of free-radical generation and damage are the "powerhouses" in cells—structures called mitochondria—which are primary sites at which energy is extracted from food. Indeed, a growing body of evidence supports a long-standing theory of human aging, which holds that many of the things we associate with getting older—memory loss, hearing impairment—can be traced to the cumulative effects of free radicals damaging DNA in the mitochondria, thus diminishing the body's energy supply.

Free radicals are the natural product of metabolism in human beings; they are the price we pay for being alive. However, they can be created in us in *greater* numbers in accordance with our behavior. Some of the usual suspects seem to be involved here—cigarette smoking, alcohol consumption, and sunlight exposure. Radiation provides a good example of how free radicals can be produced in us. Medical workers guard against getting excessive exposure to X-rays, because, like other forms of "ionizing" radiation, X-rays cause water molecules in living tissue to break down in such a way that they yield free radicals.

Against this production of free radicals, however, nature has also provided its own set of free-radical scavengers, among them the aforementioned beta carotene and vitamins C and E. We can control these, in the sense of making sure we have plenty of them in our diets. We can buy them in pill form, of course, but the jury is still out on the effect of very large doses of these substances. The best bet is to eat the right kinds of foods—meaning a lot of citrus fruits, whole grains, and vegetables of the green leafy, orange, and yellow variety.

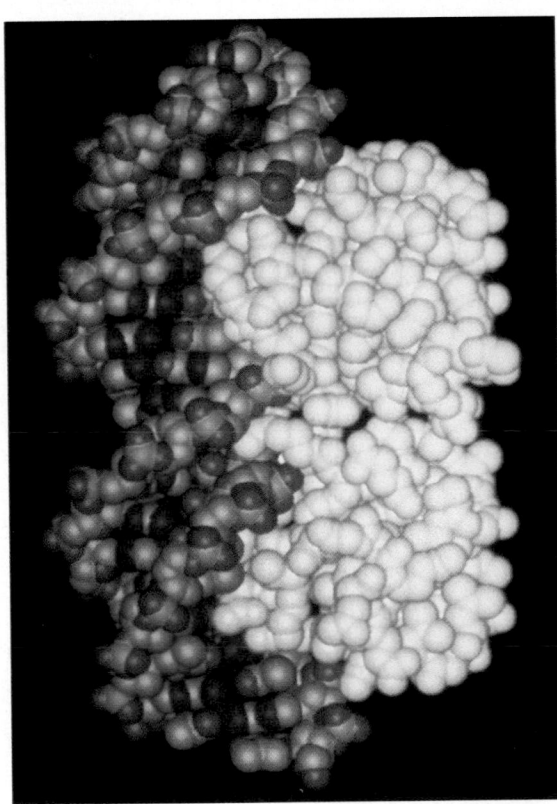

Figure 2.15
Complex Binding
A computer model of some real-life molecular binding. In this case a protein (the yellow atoms) binds to a length of DNA. (The protein is a "repressor" that turns off the activity of this section of DNA.) This space-filling model provides some idea of the enormous number of atoms and the complicated shapes that make up some of the molecules employed by living things.

will see this most commonly mentioned in two ways: as something being fat-soluble or water-soluble. Does it dissolve in fat or does it dissolve in water? Both things are important to life, but the importance of water as a solvent cannot be overstated. Water accounts for about 75–85 percent of a cell's weight, and most cells are surrounded by it. It is not difficult to see why water should be so prominent in this way. Living things existed solely in water for billions of years, much life lives in it today, and our own ancestors made the transition from sea to land essentially by carrying their wet environment with them—inside themselves. So important to life is this simple, common molecule that we end with it here, only to take it up again in our next chapter in a more detailed way.

Figure 2.16
A Solute Dissolved by a Solvent Makes a Solution
When we pour a small amount of table salt (a solute) into water (a solvent), the salt crystals dissolve into the water, yielding a solution.

Chapter Review

Summary

2.1 The Nature of Matter: The Atom

- The fundamental unit of matter is the atom. The three most important constituent parts of an atom are protons, neutrons, and electrons. Protons and neutrons exist in the atom's nucleus, while electrons move around the nucleus, at some distance from it. Protons are positively charged, electrons are negatively charged, but neutrons carry no charge.

- An element is any substance that cannot be reduced to any simpler set of constituent substances through chemical means. Each element is defined by the number of protons in its nucleus.

- The number of neutrons in an atom can vary independently of the number of protons. Thus a single element can exist in various forms, called isotopes, depending on the number of neutrons it possesses.
  Web Tutorial 2.1: Structure of Atoms, Elements, Isotopes

2.2 Matter Is Transformed through Chemical Bonding

- Atoms can link to one another in the process of chemical bonding. Among the forms this bonding can take are covalent bonding, in which atoms share one or more electrons, and ionic bonding, in which atoms lose and accept electrons from each other.

- Chemical bonding comes about as atoms "seek" their lowest energy state. An atom achieves this state when it has a filled outer electron shell. Hydrogen and helium require two electrons in orbit around their nuclei to have filled outer shells, while most other elements require eight electrons to have filled outer shells.

- A molecule is a compound of a defined number of atoms in a defined spatial relationship. For example, two hydrogen atoms can link with one oxygen atom to form one water molecule.

- Atoms of different elements differ in their power to attract electrons. The term for measuring this power is electronegativity. Through electronegativity, a molecule can take on a polarity, meaning a difference in electrical charge at one end compared to the other. Covalent chemical bonds can be polar or nonpolar. A polar covalent bond exists when shared electrons are not being shared equally among atoms in a molecule, due to electronegativity differences.

- Two atoms will undergo a process of ionization when the electronegativity differences between them are great enough that one atom loses one or more electrons to the other. This process creates ions, meaning atoms whose number of electrons differs from their number of protons. The charge differences that result from ionization can produce an electrostatic attraction between ions. This attraction is an ionic bond. When atoms of two or more elements bond together ionically, the result is an ionic compound.

- Hydrogen bonding links a covalently bonded hydrogen atom with an electronegative atom. In water, a hydrogen atom of one water molecule will form a hydrogen bond with an unshared oxygen electron of a neighboring water molecule.
  Web Tutorial 2.2: Chemical Bonding

2.3 Some Qualities of Chemical Compounds

- Three-dimensional molecular shape is important in biology because this shape determines the capacity molecules have to bind with one another.
  Web Tutorial 2.3: Geometry, Chemistry and Biology

- A solution is a homogeneous mixture of two or more kinds of molecules, atoms, or ions. The compound being dissolved in solution is the solute; the compound doing the dissolving is the solvent.

- A general rule in chemistry is that like dissolves like: Substances that are nonpolar dissolve best in nonpolar solvents, while substances that are polar dissolve best in polar solvents.

Key Terms

atomic number 22	molecular formula 26
ball-and-stick model 27	molecule 25
chemical bonding 23	neutron 20
covalent bond 24	nonpolar covalent bond 25
double bond 26	nucleus 20
electron 20	polar covalent bond 25
electronegativity 25	polarity 25
element 21	product 27
free radical 30	proton 20
hydrogen bond 29	reactant 27
ion 28	single bond 26
ionic bonding 27	solute 30
ionic compound 28	solution 30
isotope 23	solvent 30
law of conservation of mass 25	space-filling model 27
	structural formula 26
mass 19	triple bond 26

Understanding the Basics

Multiple-Choice Questions (answers in the back of the book)

1. Carbon is an element with an atomic number of 6. Based on this information, which of the following statements is true? (More than one may be true.)
   a. Carbon can be broken down into simpler component substances.

b. Carbon cannot be broken down into simpler component substances.

c. Each carbon atom will always have 6 neutrons.

d. Each carbon atom will always have 6 protons.

e. Protons + electrons = 6.

2. Suppose that you are reviewing for a test, and some fellow students say that the equation for photosynthesis is $6CO_2 + H_2O \rightarrow C_6H_{12}O_6 + 6O_2$. How would you reply?

a. They are right.

b. The way this equation is written violates the law of the conservation of matter.

c. The CO_2 is held together by ionic bonds.

d. A hydrogen bond holds the two hydrogens to the oxygen in the water molecule.

e. There are 12 carbons in sugar.

3. Neon used to be called an inert gas. Thus it

a. easily forms perfect covalent bonds

b. easily forms ionic bonds

c. has a filled outer shell

d. is polar

e. all of these

4. Oxygen and hydrogen differ in their electronegativity. Thus

a. They can share electrons, but unequally.

b. Sometimes oxygen takes electrons completely away from hydrogen.

c. They can share electrons equally.

d. Hydrogen is attracted to oxygen, but does not bond with it.

e. They have the same number of protons.

5. A molecule that does not have a net electrical charge at one end as opposed to the other is:

a. an isotope

b. a polar molecule

c. a reactant

d. a nonpolar molecule

e. a solvent

6. You add sugar to black coffee, and the sugar dissolves. Thus the coffee is the _____ and the sugar is the _____.

a. solute . . . solvent

b. solvent . . . solute

c. polar covalent bond . . . nonpolar covalent bond

d. nonpolar covalent bond . . . polar covalent bond

e. ionic bond . . . hydrogen bond

7. The two strands of a DNA molecule are held together because large numbers of hydrogens that are covalently bonded to oxygen or nitrogen in one strand are weakly attracted to oxygens or nitrogens in the opposite strand. Therefore the two strands of DNA are held together by

a. polar covalent bonds

b. nonpolar covalent bonds

c. ionic bonds

d. inert bonds

e. hydrogen bonds

8. While baking cookies for a friend, you're having a hard time keeping your roommate from eating them because the smell is driving her wild. She is able to smell the cookies because the molecules wafting from them

a. have a shape that allows them to bind to receptors in her nose

b. form permanent attractions to nerves in her nose by ionic bonding

c. form temporary attractions to nerves in her nose by covalent bonding

d. dissolve in her blood and travel to her brain

e. travel along her nerves—causing changes as they go—until they reach the brain, where they are recognized

Brief Review

1. As with most elements, carbon comes in several forms, one of which is carbon-14. What are these forms called, and how does one differ from the other?

2. Draw a line and label one end "complete + or − charge" and the other end "no charge" to indicate the charges on the molecules or ions after bonding has occurred. Along the line, indicate where polar covalent bonds, nonpolar covalent bonds, and ionic bonds should be placed.

3. Why are free radicals so dangerous when they are produced in our bodies?

4. Compare the size of an atom with the size of its nucleus. Where are the electrons? In light of this, what occupies most of an atom?

5. Why are atoms unlikely to react when they have their outer shell filled with electrons?

Applying Your Knowledge

1. In the Middle Ages alchemists labored to turn common materials such as iron into precious metals such as gold. If you could journey back in time, how could you convince an alchemist that iron cannot be changed into gold?

2. Why does a balloon filled with helium float? Hydrogen can make balloons float, but it is not used for this purpose today, because it is flammable. Based on chemical principles reviewed in the chapter, can you see why helium is not flammable? (*Hint:* Think what you are adding to a fire when you blow on it.)

Life's Components

3 Water, pH, and Biological Molecules

Water's cohesive power.
(Section 3.1, page 37)

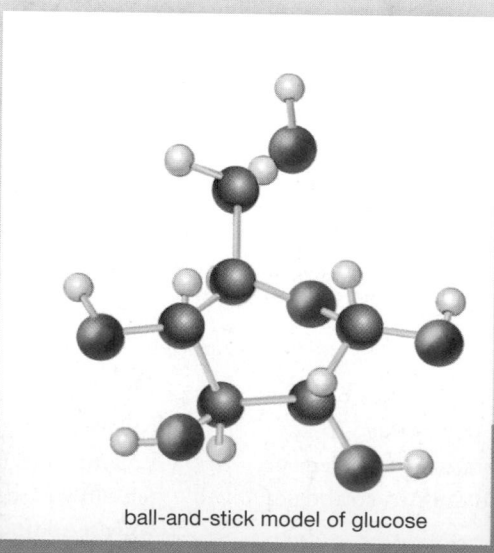

ball-and-stick model of glucose

The most important energy source for our bodies.
(Section 3.3, page 45)

A dual-natured molecule with head and tails.
(Section 3.6, page 55)

The qualities of water have shaped life. The degree to which solutions are acidic or basic has strong effects on living things. Four kinds of biological molecules form the living world.

Imagine that it's raining outside as you read this, the rhythm of individual drops combining to create a sound that is like no other. It's a sound that most people find comforting. And isn't that the way with other sounds water makes when it's in motion? With ocean waves or a running stream? It may be that these things are soothing purely *as sounds*—something about their tone, or their steady pace. But isn't it possible that we are calmed by the sounds of rain or streams because they are the sounds *of water*? Rain has fallen on leaves for millennia, sending our ancestors—and now us—a timeless message: Water's here; you and your family will have enough to drink; food will be abundant; all is well.

3.1 The Importance of Water to Life

Human societies tend to come together precisely where water exists, of course. In places where it's plentiful, water seems less like a substance than an environment: People drink it, cook in it, bathe in it, wash wastes away in it, harness it for power, swim in it. Some 71 percent of Earth's surface is ocean water, and human bodies are about 66 percent water by weight, so that if we have, say, a 128-pound person, about 85 pounds of him or her will be water. If Earth amounts to a watery environment flecked by the landmasses we call continents, the human body amounts to a watery mass with significant proportions of other materials immersed in it.

Water Is a Major Player in Many of Life's Processes

This preponderance of water in living things gives rise to an important point. Recall that you learned, in Chapter 2, what a solution is. Well, a specific kind of solution—a so-called aqueous solution—is one in which water is the solvent, acting to break down the materials or *solutes* that have been put into it. If

A protein found over almost all of your body.
(Section 3.7, page 58)

The building blocks of DNA.
(Section 3.8, page 61)

A portrait of the most famous molecule in all of biology.
(Section 3.8, page 61)

Figure 3.1
Water's Power as a Solvent

(a) Attraction

water
(solvent)

H

O

H

Na⁺ Cl⁻

sodium
chloride
(solute)

Sodium chloride's
positively charged
sodium ions (Na⁺) are
attracted to water's
negatively charged
oxygen atoms, while its
negatively charged
chloride ions (Cl⁻) are
attracted to water's
positively charged
hydrogen atoms.

(b) Separation

Pulled from the crystal,
and separated from each
other by this attraction,
sodium and chloride ions
become surrounded by
water molecules.

(c) Dispersion

Sodium and
chloride ions
dissolved
in water

This process of separating
sodium and chloride ions
repeats until both ions are
evenly dispersed, making
this an aqueous solution.

you look at **Figure 3.1**, you can get a detailed view of water's solvent power in connection with sodium and chloride ions. Attracted by the polar nature of the water molecule, these ions separate from a crystal—and from each other. Each ion is then surrounded by several water molecules (Figure 3.1b). These units keep the sodium and chloride ions from getting back together. In other words, they keep the ions evenly dispersed throughout the water, which is what makes this a solution (Figure 3.1c). Water works as a solvent here because the ionic compound sodium chloride carries an electrical charge. What *generally* makes water work as a solvent, however, is its ability to form hydrogen bonds with other molecules.

Water's Structure Gives It Many Unusual Properties

When we note water's ability to act as a solvent, we're actually not giving water its due. Water is not just *a* solvent: Over the range of substances, nothing can match it as a solvent. It can dissolve more compounds in greater amounts than can any other liquid.

Ice Floats Because It Is Less Dense than Water

But solvency power is merely the beginning of water's abilities. It is a multitalented performer. And it achieves this status because it is ... odd. Compared to other molecules, water is like some zany eccentric whose powers stem precisely from its eccentricity. Consider the fact that ice floats on water. This is so because the solid form of H_2O is less dense than the liquid form—a strange reversal of nature's normal pattern. Things work this way with H_2O because, when water molecules slow their motion in cooling,

they are able to form the maximum number of hydrogen bonds with each other. The result is that water molecules are spaced *farther apart* when frozen. Thus, ice is less dense than water. This may seem like some minor, quirky quality but it actually has the effect of making possible life as we know it. Ice on the surface of water acts to insulate the water beneath it from the freezing surface temperatures and wind above, creating a warmer environment for organisms such as fish (**see Figure 3.2**). If ice *sank*, on the other hand, the entire body of water would freeze solid at colder latitudes, creating an environment in which few living things could survive for long.

Water Has a Great Capacity to Absorb and Store Heat

Water serves as an insulator not only when it is frozen, but also when it is liquid or gas. This has to do with a quality called **specific heat**: the amount of energy required to raise the temperature of a substance by 1 degree Celsius. As it turns out, water has a high specific heat. Put a gram container of drinking alcohol (ethyl alcohol) side by side with one of water, heat them both, and it will take almost twice as much energy to raise the temperature of the water one degree as it will the alcohol. Having absorbed this much heat, however, water then has the capacity to *release* it when the environment around it is colder than the water itself. The result? Water acts as a great heat buffer for Earth. The oceans absorb tremendous amounts of radiant energy from the Sun, only to release this heat when the temperature of the air above the ocean gets colder. Without this buffering, temperature on Earth would be less stable. People who have spent a day and a night in a

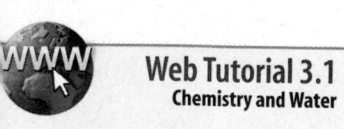

Web Tutorial 3.1
Chemistry and Water

In ice, the maximum number of hydrogen bonds form, causing the molecules to be spread far apart.

In liquid water, hydrogen bonds constantly break and reform, enabling a more dense spacing than in ice.

Figure 3.2
Life Under the Ice
Water is unusual in that its solid form (ice) is less dense than its liquid form. This means that ice floats, and this in turn means that life can flourish in cold-weather aquatic environments. Pictured are some shrimp-like krill, feeding on algae that grow on the underside of ice in the waters off Antarctica.

desert can attest to this effect. The searing heat of the desert day radiates off the desert floor; but at night, with little water vapor in the air to capture this heat, the desert cools off dramatically. In the same way, our *internal* temperature can remain much more stable because the water that makes up so much of us is first able to absorb and then to release great amounts of heat. The sweat that we throw off in exercise has considerable cooling power because each drop of perspiration carries with it a great deal of heat.

Water derives these powers from its chemical structure, in particular from the hydrogen bonding described earlier. Weak and shifting though individual hydrogen bonds may be, collectively they have a great strength. Heat is the motion of molecules. To get molecules moving, though, chemical bonds must first be broken. Because water has a formidable set of hydrogen bonds, it takes a lot of energy to break them and get its molecules moving. This very same set of bonds gives water molecules another notable characteristic: cohesion, meaning a tendency to stay together. With this quality, a chain of water molecules can be drawn (by evaporation) in one continuous column from a plant's roots all the way up to its leaves and out into the air as water vapor.

Water's Cohesion Gives It Surface Tension

Water's cohesion imparts a special quality, called *surface tension,* in places where water meets air. Water molecules below the surface are equally attracted in all directions to other water molecules. *At* the surface, however, water molecules have no such attraction to the air above them—they are pulled

down and to the side, but not up. This causes the "beading" that water droplets do on surfaces. More important for our purposes, surface water molecules pack together more closely than do interior molecules, allowing all kinds of small animals to move across the surface of water rather than sinking into it. Note the familiar water strider in **Figure 3.3**.

(a) Walking on water

(b) Beading up

Figure 3.3
Walking on Water

(a) Water's high surface tension enables small animals, such as this pond skater, to walk on it.

(b) This same surface tension also causes water to bead up on waxy or oily surfaces, such as this goose feather.

Having looked at the qualities of water, you may be tempted to think how *uncanny* it is that water has all these qualities that are conducive to life. But there actually is nothing surprising about this. Life went on solely in water for billions of years before living things ever came onto land. Thus, water has fundamentally conditioned life as we know it. Being surprised about water's life-enhancing qualities is like being surprised that a stage is a good place to put on a play.

What Water Cannot Do

With its great complexity, life requires molecules that *can't* be dissolved by water. Such is the case with non-polar covalent molecules. Compounds made of hydrogen and carbon (**hydrocarbons**) are good examples of nonpolar molecules. Recall that Chapter 2 presented methane (CH_4) as an example of a nonpolar molecule. Petroleum products are more complex hydrocarbons than is methane, and you can see a vivid demonstration of their water-insolubility in oil spills (**see Figure 3.4**). Oil doesn't dissolve in water because the oil carries almost no electrical charge that water can bond with; thus water has no way to separate one oil molecule from another.

Two Important Terms: Hydrophobic and Hydrophilic

The ability of molecules to form bonds with water has a couple of important names attached to it. Compounds that will interact with water—such as the sodium chloride considered earlier—are known as **hydrophilic** ("water-loving"), while compounds that do not interact with water are known as **hydrophobic** ("water-fearing"). Both terms are mislead-

ing, in that no substance has any emotional relationship with water. *Hydrophobic* is particularly off the mark, because water does not repel hydrophobic molecules; instead, the strong bonding that water molecules do with each other causes them to form circles around concentrations of hydrophobic molecules, as if they had lassoed them.

The importance of hydrophobic molecules can be illustrated in part by the common milk carton. Why is the milk carton important? Because it can keep milk separate from everything else. We living organisms need some kind of "carton" that can separate the world outside of us from ourselves. Likewise, organisms have great use *within* themselves for compartments that can be sealed off to one degree or another. If water broke down every molecule of life it came in contact with, then it would break down all these divisions of living systems. Molecules do not have to be completely hydrophilic or hydrophobic. Indeed, as you'll see, a number of important molecules have both hydrophilic and hydrophobic portions.

3.2 Acids and Bases Are Important to Life

When considering the question of aqueous solutions, an important concept is that of acids, bases, and the pH scale used to measure their levels.

We've all had experience with acids and bases, whether we've called them by these names or not. Acidic substances tend to be a little more familiar: lemon juice, vinegar, tomatoes. Substances that are strongly acidic have a well-deserved reputation for being dangerous: The word *acid* is often used to mean something that can sear human flesh. It might seem to follow that bases are benign, but ammonia is a strong base, as are many oven cleaners. The safe zone for living tissue in general lies with substances that are neither strongly acidic nor strongly basic. Science has developed a way of measuring the degree to which something is acidic or basic—the pH scale. So widespread is pH usage that it pops up from time to time in television advertising ("It's pH-balanced!").

Acids Yield Hydrogen Ions in Solution; Bases Accept Them

The "H" in pH stands for hydrogen, while the "p" can be thought of as standing for power. Thus we get "hydrogen power," which describes what lies at the root of pH. An **acid** is any substance that *yields hydrogen ions* when put in aqueous solution. A **base** is any substance that *accepts* hydrogen ions in solution.

How might this yielding or accepting come about? Recall first that an ion is a charged atom, and that atoms become charged through the gain or loss

Figure 3.4
Oil and Water Do Not Mix
When there is an oil spill in the ocean, the oil stays concentrated even as it spreads out, because oil and water do not form chemical bonds with each other. Here trawlers are using a boom to clean up after an oil spill in Great Britain.

of one or more electrons. Because electrons carry a negative charge, the loss of an electron leaves an atom with a net *positive* charge. Also recall that the hydrogen atom amounts to one central proton and one electron that circles around it. A hydrogen ion, then, is a lone proton that has lost its electron—a positively charged ion whose symbol is H^+.

Now, suppose you put an acid—hydrochloric acid (HCl)—into some water. What happens is that HCl *dissociates* or breaks apart into its ionic components, H^+ and Cl^-. The HCl has therefore yielded a hydrogen ion (H^+). Now, with a greater concentration of hydrogen ions in it, the water is more acidic than it was (**see Figure 3.5**).

Figure 3.5
Hydrogen Ions and pH

pure water
(H_2O)

(a) Starting with pure water

Pure water is a "neutral" substance in terms of its pH levels.

HCl

acid

(b) Making water more acidic

Hydrochloric acid (HCl), poured into the water, dissociates into H^+ and Cl^- ions. With a higher concentration of H^+ ions in it, the water moves towards the acidic end of the pH scale.

NaOH

base

(c) Making water more basic

An equal concentration of sodium hydroxide, poured into water, dissociates into Na^+ and OH^- ions, moving the water toward the basic end of the scale.

$HCl \rightarrow H^+ + Cl^-$ $NaOH \rightarrow Na^+ + OH^-$

(d) Combining acidic and basic solutions

When the acid and base solutions are poured together, the OH^- ions from **(c)** accept the H^+ ions from **(b)**, forming water and keeping the solution at a neutral pH.

$$H_2O + H^+ + OH^- \longrightarrow 2H_2O$$

acid   base   neutralized
solution

What about bases? There is a compound called sodium hydroxide (NaOH)—better known as lye—that, when poured into water, dissociates into Na^+ (sodium) and OH^- (hydroxide) ions. The place to look here is the OH^- ions. Negatively charged as they are, they would readily bond with positively charged H^+ ions. In other words, they would *accept* H^+ ions in solution, which is the definition of a base. This accepting of the H^+ ions makes the solution more basic—or, to look at it another way, *less acidic.* Thus, acids and bases are something like a teeter-totter: When one goes up, the other comes down. As you might have guessed, in the right proportions they can balance each other out perfectly. Look at Figure 3.5 to see how this would play out with the solutions you've looked at so far. Should H^+ and OH^- ions be poured together into water, for each pair of ions that interacts, the result is:

$$H^+ + OH^- \longrightarrow H_2O$$

Water, which is neutral on the pH scale. The acid and the base have perfectly balanced one another out. The OH^- ion, generally referred to as the **hydroxide ion**, is important because compounds that yield them in quantity are strongly basic and can be used to move solutions from the acidic toward the basic.

Many Common Substances Can Be Ranked According to How Acidic or Basic They Are

Look at **Figure 3.6** to get an idea of how acidic or basic some common substances are. Following from the notion of what pH amounts to, it's clear that battery acid, for example, is strongly acidic because, when it dissociates in solution, it yields a large number of hydrogen ions. As you move on to lemon juice and then tomatoes, however, you run into weaker acids, which is to say substances that yield fewer H^+ ions in solution. By the time you get to seawater, you've arrived at substances that *accept* hydrogen ions.

The pH Scale Allows Us to Quantify How Acidic or Basic Compounds Are

The net effect of all this yielding and accepting of hydrogen ions is the concentration of H^+ ions in solution. Through this concentration, the notion of pH can be *quantified*—can have numbers attached to it. What is employed here is the **pH scale**: a scale utilized in measuring the relative acidity of a substance. Look at Figure 3.6 again, this time in connection with the numbers that mark it off. You can see that zero on the scale is the most acidic while 14 is the most basic. It's important to note that the pH scale is *logarithmic:* A substance with a pH of 9 is 10 times as basic as a substance with a pH of 8 and 100 times as basic as a substance with a pH of 7.

Some Terms Used When Dealing with pH

Here are some notes on pH terminology:

- As a solution becomes more basic, its pH *rises.* Thus the higher the pH, the more basic the solution; and the lower the pH, the more acidic the solution. Oven cleaner is said to have a high pH, while lemon juice has a low pH.

- Given that a hydrogen ion amounts to a single proton, it is also correct to say that an acid is something that yields *protons* in solution, while a base is something that accepts protons. This is how you will often hear hydrogen ions talked about in biology.

- A solution that is basic is also referred to as an **alkaline** solution.

Why Does pH Matter?

So, why do we care about pH? The brief answer is: because living things are sensitive to its levels in many ways. There is, for example, a class of proteins called enzymes that you'll be reading about later in this chapter. Enzymes are chemical tools that must retain a very specific shape to function. However, if you put an enzyme in a solution whose pH is too acidic, the enzyme loses it shape. Why? Because the charged nature of the acidic solution starts breaking down the enzyme's chemical bonds. (Remember, lots of positively charged protons are floating around in an acidic solution.) Likewise, cell membranes—which serve the milk carton function noted earlier—can start to break down if pH levels start to go outside normal limits. Membranes and enzymes are so fundamental to life that when they are interfered with, death can result. It is not surprising, then, that many organisms have developed so-called acid-base **buffering systems**, meaning physiological systems that function to keep pH within normal limits. What are these limits? The usual range for living things is about 6–8, with the pH of the human cell being about 7 and that of the blood in our arteries being about 7.4. To break down food, our stomachs receive a digestive acid that gives the interior of the stomach a pH that lies below 2, and tiny digestive structures within cells called lysosomes have a low pH. But lysosomes and the stomach are sealed containers, in a sense, in that their contents don't mix with bodily fluids in general.

The molecules that function in buffering systems generally are weak acids or bases that work to neutralize any sudden infusion of acid or base. The challenge for human pH buffering systems usually is to keep our fluids from becoming too acidic, since the food we eat tends to pull our fluids toward the acidic side of the pH scale. Because the consequences of pH imbalance are so extreme, however, the body also has what might

Figure 3.6
Common Substances and the pH Scale
Chemists use units called moles per liter to measure the concentration of substances in solution. The pH scale, derived from this framework, measures the concentration of hydrogen ions per liter of solution. The most acidic substances on the scale have the greatest concentration of hydrogen ions, while the most basic (or alkaline) substances have the least concentration of hydrogen ions. The scale is logarithmic, so that wine, for example, is 10 times as acidic as tomatoes, and 100 times as acidic as black coffee.

Acid Rain: When Water Is Trouble

I f the concept of pH seems remote from the real world, consider that in parts of New England, more than 70 percent of red spruce forests have been damaged not by natural processes, but by civilization's impact on how acidic the rain is. Likewise, numerous lakes in New England and in New York's Adirondacks region have become so acidic that populations of fish and other wildlife have become reduced or have died off altogether.

What is at work here is a phenomenon commonly called acid rain, but which more properly is known as acid deposition, since acid *snow* and a dry form of acid discharge are problems as well. In acid deposition you can see an application of pH principles, only played out this time on an enormous scale. You've learned something about acids and bases and the importance of *internal* pH to living things. It makes sense, then, that when rainwater itself has a skewed pH, there is going to be widespread trouble. And this is indeed what has happened, not only in the United States, but in Canada, in Eastern Europe and England, in China—in short, worldwide, though industrialized nations are the most affected.

Acid precipitation comes primarily from two sources: the sulfur dioxide (SO_2) emissions of coal- and oil-burning factories (in particular power plants), and the nitric oxide (NO) and nitrogen dioxide (NO_2) emissions that come mostly from cars, with an assist from factories (**Figure 1**). When these compounds rise into the air, they come together with a culprit you've seen before: an oxygen radical, specifically the hydroxyl radical (OH). In so doing, they are converted to sulfuric acid and nitric acid. *These* compounds then combine with the rainwater in clouds, and the result is acidic rain or snow.

Acid deposition can do its damage directly or indirectly. By simply making a lake more acidic, it begins to interfere with the metabolic processes of the animals who live there. Acid rain also has the effect, however, of leaching metals from the soil it passes through. Aluminum brought into lakes in this way damages the gills of fish, destroying their ability to absorb oxygen from the water. This same effect takes place in connection with land vegetation, where leached metals can kill plant roots outright or keep them from absorbing nutrients.

Acid deposition will have different effects on different environments, and here again you can see the basics of pH at work. Soils are not neutral in their pH; should acid rain fall on soil that is significantly basic (or "alkaline"), the buffering process you've read about will take place: Basic compounds in the soil will combine with the water and accept hydrogen ions from the rain, thus resulting in water that is less acidic. Likewise, aquatic environments may contain basic ions that can neutralize incoming water.

The extent to which such environments possess basic ions is known as their *acid-neutralizing capacity*. Given what you've read about pH, it might be apparent that this capacity is not limitless but instead can dwindle as more acidic compounds are added. Indeed, soils can suffer from a long-term depletion of basic compounds, and this has happened in some eastern U.S. forests. A 1990 amendment to the federal Clean Air Act resulted in a reduction in

be termed emergency processes for dealing with sudden, sharp pH fluctuations. Indeed, you may have experienced one of these processes if you have ever hyperventilated. Breathing excessively raises blood pH (by getting rid of too much carbon dioxide), and this rise initially brings on a light-headedness and a slight numbness in the hands and feet. If a person were, say, extremely anxious and continued hyperventilating long enough, the resulting pH imbalance would cause him or her to pass out, after which the breathing rate would return to normal, and pH levels would follow. If you look at the "Acid Rain" essay, you can see how pH is important not only to individual organisms, but to life on very large scales.

Web Tutorial 3.2
Chemistry of Carbon

3.3 Carbon Is a Central Element in Life

You're crossing a bridge of sorts here. To this point, the discussion has largely been about water and hydrogen and various ions. From time to time, mention was made of the element *carbon* (**see Figure 3.7**), although only as one substance among many. But carbon is not that at all.

Carbon as a Starting Ingredient

Life is based on carbon, or if you will, on carbon compounds immersed in water. You could think of carbon in life in the same way as you do flour in baking. How many times does a baking recipe begin: "Start with two cups of flour"? With the molecules of life, the recipe often begins: "Start with a carbon ring," or "start with a chain of carbon atoms." But just as cinnamon or fruit will be folded into flour, thus imparting special qualities to the basic ingredient, so will other elements join carbon: A little addition of this here, a little of that on the end, and, presto! A complex molecule that serves a very specific purpose.

U.S. sulfur emissions, but left some nitrogen emissions unchanged through the middle of the decade. This meant there was an overall decline in acid *deposition* in the Adirondacks in the period 1992–1999. Despite this, however, many Adirondack lakes continued to get more acidic through end of the 1990s. Why would lakes get more acidic if acid deposition has been reduced? Because the acid-neutralizing capacity of the lakes and the soil around them had been so depleted by years of acid rain. More recent measurements have found a welcome decline in the acidity of some lakes in the Northeast, but ecologists remain concerned about the health of both lakes and soils in the region. A return to real health for them would require continued reductions in acid deposition over a long period of time, which is far from a sure thing.

(a) How acid rain forms

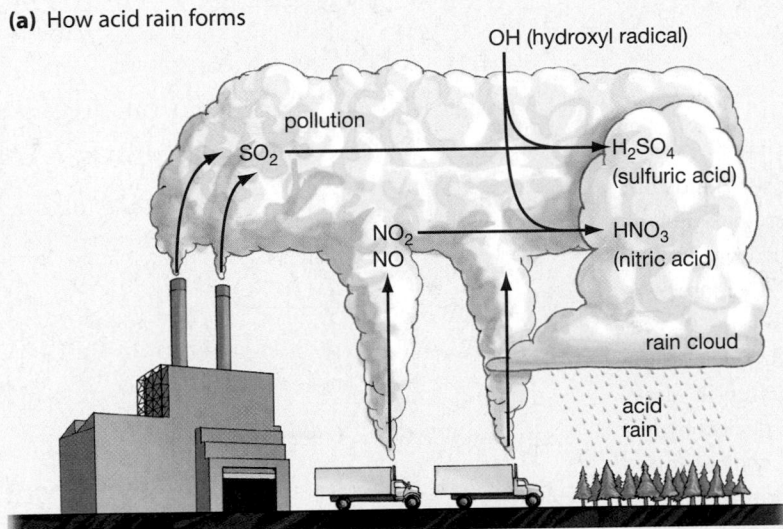

(b) Damage from acid rain

Figure 1
How Acid Rain Forms

(a) Sulfur dioxide (SO_2) from coal- and oil-burning power plants rises into the air along with nitric oxide (NO) and nitrogen dioxide (NO_2), which come mostly from cars. These compounds combine with hydroxyl radicals (OH) in the atmosphere to produce sulfuric acid (H_2SO_4) and nitric acid (HNO_3), which combine with atmospheric water, making it acidic.

(b) Trees affected by acid rain in New York State's Harriman State Park.

How does carbon come by its great powers? Linkage. Recall from Chapter 2 that carbon has four outer-shell, or "valence," electrons, but that most elements (except hydrogen and helium) need *eight* outer-shell electrons for maximum stability. This means that carbon achieves maximum stability by linking up with four more electrons, which in turn means that carbon's bonding capacity is great. Moreover, the bonds that carbon creates are covalent—it is *sharing* electrons with other atoms—which means its linkages are more stable than those formed by elements that bond ionically. Given the natural forces that can buffet life about, such as ultraviolet radiation and heat, this stability is an important quality in first getting life going and then keeping it going. So important is carbon that it forms one whole area of chemistry—**organic chemistry**, a branch of chemistry devoted to the study of compounds that have carbon as their central element.

Figure 3.7
Pure Carbon, Mostly Carbon
A diamond is pure carbon and the hardest natural material known. Surrounding the diamond is a lump of coal, which has a high carbon content because it is made up mostly of the remains of carbon-rich, ancient vegetation.

How does carbon link up with itself or other atoms? You've already had a look at a model of a very simple carbon compound, methane (CH_4). Look at it again:

Note that the only elements present are hydrogen and carbon atoms. Now observe a slightly more complex hydrocarbon, the familiar gas propane (C_3H_8):

You can see that instead of being surrounded by four hydrogen atoms, the carbons here link up with other carbons, as well as with the hydrogens. This process of extension keeps going with still more complex hydrocarbons. For obvious reasons, the preceding configuration is known as a *straight-chain* carbon molecule. But carbon has more tricks up its sleeve than simple straight-line extensions. The next hydrocarbon up the line is butane (C_4H_{10}), the fuel found in cigarette lighters. It can be just another straight-chain extension, looking like this:

But it can also look like this:

These two forms of butane are known as **isomers**—molecules that are the same in their chemical formulas, but differ in the spatial arrangement of their elements.

Carbon can also form rings. Here is the structure of benzene (C_6H_6), which is found in petroleum products:

Note the three sets of double lines in the molecule. Recall that this means there are double *bonds* between these atoms; the atoms involved are sharing *two* pairs of electrons.

It just so happens that all the carbon molecules introduced so far are made of nothing but carbon and hydrogen. But this is the exception rather than the rule. Here are two representations of a molecule mentioned already—glucose, better known as blood sugar:

So here are some added oxygen atoms. Notice how the second model, below the first, with its heavy line down at the bottom, looks a little different than the benzene ring? Such a model is meant to give you a slightly more realistic picture of the actual arrangement of atoms when a carbon ring is present. Think of the ring as lying at an angle to the paper, with the heavy line closer to you than the line in the back; the H and OH groups then lie above and below the plane of the ring, as shown. You may also notice that when things get this complicated, space starts getting a little tight for writing in the letters that stand for the various atoms that are a part of the molecule. Because most rings are formed predominately of carbon, it is common to dispense with the Cs when a structural formula is presented. Here is a third representation of the glucose model, written in this stripped-down form:

You can see that carbon is *assumed* to exist at each bond juncture in the ring; if some other element occupies one of these points, it is explicitly noted. Often the solitary Hs that are attached to carbons are left out as well.

ball-and-stick model of glucose

space-filling model of glucose

Figure 3.8
Ball-and-Stick and Space-Filling Models of Glucose
The simple sugar glucose is the single most important energy source for our bodies. Because it has several OH groups, it is highly hydrophilic and thus readily breaks down in water. Note how the carbon atoms (in red) form the core of the molecule, with oxygen (in blue) and hydrogen (in white) at the periphery.

Such models as these, as you'll recall from the last chapter, don't show the actual three-dimensional form of a molecule. To do so, ball-and-stick or space-filling models will do. Shown in **Figure 3.8** are examples of these models.

3.4 Functional Groups

Having seen how carbon compounds start to become specialized through the addition of other kinds of atoms, it's worth noting that such atoms often are affixed to carbon compounds in *groups*. Each of these units is a **functional group**: a group of atoms that confers a special property on a carbon-based molecule. Just as an attachment on a wrench might make the difference between an Allen wrench and a socket wrench, so a functional group can make the difference between one molecule and another. Look here at the formula for the hydrocarbon ethane, which is a flammable gas:

$$H-\overset{\overset{\displaystyle H}{|}}{\underset{\underset{\displaystyle H}{|}}{C}}-\overset{\overset{\displaystyle H}{|}}{\underset{\underset{\displaystyle H}{|}}{C}}-H$$

Now let's substitute a functional group, called the hydroxyl or −OH group, for the rightmost hydrogen atom in ethane and thus get:

$$H-\overset{\overset{\displaystyle H}{|}}{\underset{\underset{\displaystyle H}{|}}{C}}-\overset{\overset{\displaystyle H}{|}}{\underset{\underset{\displaystyle H}{|}}{C}}-OH$$

With this, we no longer have a gas; we have a liquid—the drinkable liquid ethyl alcohol. Anytime an −OH group is added to a hydrocarbon chain, some sort of alcohol is formed, be it the isopropyl alcohol used to disinfect cuts, the methanol used to power turbine engines, or some other variety. Thus, the −OH group has a generalized function in connec-

tion with hydrocarbons and is therefore referred to as a functional group. Now note another effect of this group. The ethane we started with was nonpolar—there was no difference in charge at one end of the ethane molecule as opposed to the other. But the addition of the −OH group changed this; the oxygen atom it contains has such strong electronegativity that ethyl alcohol does have a polarity, meaning it can bond with other charged or polar molecules, including water. This exemplifies a general characteristic of functional groups, which is that they often impart an electrical charge, or at least a polarity, onto molecules, which makes a big difference in their bonding capacity. The −OH group serves this polarizing function not only when it is added to hydrocarbons, but when it is part of other molecules as well. If you look at **Table 3.1**, you can see some of the functional groups that are most important in living things.

Table 3.1 Functional groups

Group:	Structural formula:	Found in:
Carboxyl (—COOH)	$-C\overset{\displaystyle O}{\underset{\displaystyle OH}{\big\langle}}$	fatty acids, amino acids
Hydroxyl (—OH)	—OH	alcohols, carbohydrates
Amino (—NH$_2$)	$-N\overset{\displaystyle H}{\underset{\displaystyle H}{\big\langle}}$	amino acids
Phosphate (—PO$_4$)	$-O-\overset{\overset{\displaystyle O}{\|}}{\underset{\underset{\displaystyle O^-}{\|}}{P}}-O^-$	DNA, ATP

3.5 Carbohydrates

With this review of carbon structures under your belt, you're ready to begin looking at some of the classes of carbon-based molecules—the molecules of living things. You'll explore four groupings of these organic compounds: carbohydrates, lipids, proteins, and nucleic acids.

As you get into this section, it will be a great help to keep in mind that *complex* organic molecules often are made from *simpler* molecules. Many of the molecules you'll be reading about have a building-blocks quality to them: Take a simple sugar, or monosaccharide, such as glucose, put it together with another monosaccharide (fructose), and you have a larger *dis*accharide called sucrose (better known as table sugar). Put *many* monosaccharide units together and you have a polysaccharide, such as starch. The starch is an example of a **polymer**—a large molecule made up of many similar or identical subunits. Meanwhile, the glucose is an example of a **monomer**—a small molecule that can be combined with other similar or identical molecules to make a polymer. Look at **Table 3.2** for examples of both.

Carbohydrates: From Simple Sugars to Cellulose

Happily, for purposes of memory, the elements in the first molecules we'll look at, carbohydrates, are all hinted at in the name: **Carbohydrates** are organic molecules that always contain carbon, oxygen, and

Web Tutorial 3.3
Monomers and Polymers

Web Tutorial 3.4
Carbohydrates

hydrogen and that in many instances contain nothing *but* carbon, oxygen, and hydrogen. Furthermore, they usually contain exactly twice as many hydrogen atoms as oxygen atoms. For example, the carbohydrate glucose ($C_6H_{12}O_6$) contains 12 atoms of hydrogen and 6 of oxygen. Most people think of carbohydrates purely in terms of foods such as breads and pasta (**see Figure 3.9**); but as you'll see, carbohydrates have more roles than this in nature.

The building blocks of the carbohydrates are the **monosaccharides** mentioned earlier, which also are known as **simple sugars**. You've already seen several views of one of these molecules—glucose. Glucose has a use in and of itself: Much of the food we eat is broken down into it, at which point it becomes our most important energy source. Glucose can also bond with other monosaccharides, however, to form more complex carbohydrates. Let's take a look at how this happens. If you look at **Figure 3.10**, you can see an example of two glucose molecules bonding to create the disaccharide called maltose.

Several things are worth noting here. In maltose, as you can see, the link that joins the two glucose monomers is a single oxygen atom linked to carbons of each of the glucose units. To get this, two atoms of hydrogen and one atom of oxygen are split off (on the left side of the equation) from the original glucose molecules. What becomes of these three atoms? Look at the far right-hand side of the reaction and see the $+H_2O$. The product of this reaction is a molecule of maltose and a molecule of water.

Now note the arrows in the middle of the reaction. You've been used to seeing a single, rightward-pointing arrow, but here the arrows go both ways. What this means is that this is a reversible reaction—it can proceed in either of the two directions. When maltose is placed in water, it can be split apart to yield two *glucose* molecules. Finally, note the existence of the $-OH$ functional group in both the glucose and maltose molecules.

Kinds of Simple Carbohydrates

You have thus far seen examples of one of the simplest carbohydrates, the monosaccharide glucose, and one slightly more complex carbohydrate, a disaccharide called maltose. There are many kinds of mono- and disaccharides, however. Among the monosaccharides are, for example, fructose and deoxyribose. Among disaccharides, there are sucrose and lactose. At the risk of pointing out the obvious, note that all these sugars have *-ose* at the end of their name: If it's an *-ose*, it's a sugar (**see Figure 3.11**).

Table 3.2 Monomers, Polymers

If the monomer is...	The polymer is...
A **monosaccharide** (for example, glucose, fructose)	A **polysaccharide** (for example, starch, glycogen, cellulose)
An **amino acid** (for example, arginine, leucine)	A **polypeptide** or **protein** (A- and B-chains of insulin are polypeptides and insulin is a protein)
A **nucleotide** (sugar, phosphate, base in combination)	A **nucleic acid** (for example, DNA, RNA)

Figure 3.9
Carbohydrates in Foods
Breads, cereals, and pasta make up a significant proportion of our diets. These foods are all rich in carbohydrates, one of the four main types of biological molecules.

glucose   +   glucose   =   maltose   +   water

$$CH_2OH \quad\quad\quad CH_2OH \quad\quad\quad\quad\quad CH_2OH \quad\quad CH_2OH$$

$$+ \quad H_2O$$

Figure 3.10
Carbohydrates Follow a Building-Blocks Model
In this example, two units of the monosaccharide (or simple sugar) glucose link to form the disaccharide maltose. In addition to maltose, the reaction yields water. The double arrows indicate that this reaction is reversible; a single maltose molecule can yield two glucose molecules.

Figure 3.11
Sugars Come in Many Forms
Sucrose or table sugar comes to us from sugarcane or sugar beets, and glucose is found in corn syrup. Fructose comes to us in sweet fruits and in high-fructose corn syrup, which often is used to sweeten soft drinks.

Complex Carbohydrates Are Made of Chains of Simple Carbohydrates

If you go another couple of bumps up from disaccharides, you get to the polymers of carbohydrates, the **polysaccharides**. The *poly* in polysaccharide means "many," while *saccharide* means "sugars," and the term is apt. In the polysaccharide molecule cellulose, for example, there may be 10,000 glucose units linked up with one another. The basic unit here is the six-carbon monosaccharide glucose, $C_6H_{12}O_6$, from which chains of glucose units are built up. The complexity of these molecules gives them their alternate name of complex carbohydrates. Four different types of complex carbohydrates interest us: starch, glycogen, cellulose, and chitin (**see Figure 3.12**).

Starch is a complex carbohydrate found in plants that exists in the form of such foods as potatoes, rice, carrots, and corn. In plants, these starches serve as the main form of carbohydrate *storage*, sometimes as seeds (rice and wheat grains), or sometimes as roots (carrots or beets); **see Figure 3.12a**.

Another complex carbohydrate, **glycogen**, serves as the primary form of carbohydrate storage in animals. Thus, glycogen does for animals what starch does for plants. For this reason, glycogen is sometimes called animal starch. The starches or sugars we eat are broken down, eventually into glucose, at which point some of the glucose may be used immediately. Some may not be needed right away, however, in which case it is moved into the muscle cells and liver to be stored as the more complex carbohydrate glycogen. The "carbohydrate loading" that swimmers and runners do before races (by eating lots of pasta, for example) could just as easily be called glycogen loading (**see Figure 3.12b**).

Cellulose is a rigid, complex carbohydrate contained in the cell walls of many organisms. Despite this innocuous-sounding function, cellulose is important because it makes up so much of the natural

Figure 3.12
Four Examples of Complex Carbohydrates

All complex carbohydrates are composed of chains of glucose, but they differ in the details of their chemical structure.

(a) Starch serves as a form of carbohydrate storage in many plants. Here starch granules can be seen within the cells of a slice of raw potato.

(b) Glycogen serves as a form of carbohydrate storage, as shown in this photo of glycogen globules in the liver.

(c) Cellulose, running as fibers through cell walls, provides structural support for plants. The photo is of sets of cellulose fibers running at right angles to one another in the cell wall of marine algae.

(d) Chitin provides structural support for some animals. The outer "skin" or cuticle of insects is composed mostly of chitin. The photo shows the exoskeleton of a tick.

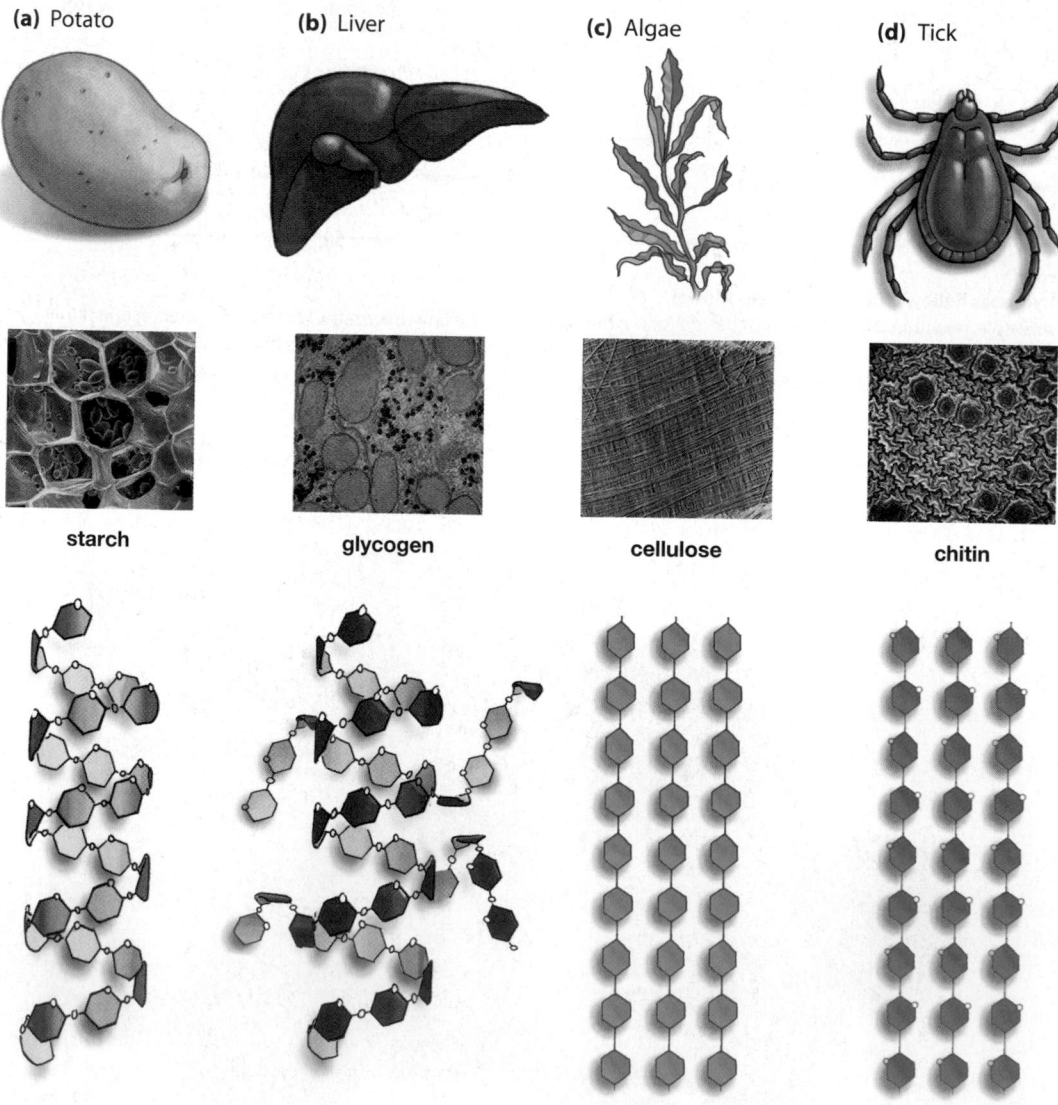

(a) Potato   **(b)** Liver   **(c)** Algae   **(d)** Tick

starch   glycogen   cellulose   chitin

world. It is easily the most abundant carbohydrate on Earth: Trees, cotton, leaves, and grasses are largely made of it. When cellulose is enmeshed with a hardening compound called *lignin*, the result is a set of cell walls that can hold up giant redwood trees. Because cellulose is so dense and rigid, it is not surprising that human beings and other mammals cannot digest it. This statement may make you wonder about grasseating *cows*, but in fact cows have cellulose digested for them by special bacteria that reside in their digestive tract. Cellulose is important to humans in that it is our major source of insoluble fiber, which helps move foods through the digestive tract. Because cellulose exists in the cell walls of plants, we can get our fiber from such foods as whole grains and fresh fruits (**see Figure 3.12c**).

Chitin is a complex carbohydrate that forms the external skeleton of the arthropods—all insects, spiders, and "crustaceans," such as crabs. In all these animals, chitin plays a "structural" role similar to that of cellulose in plants: It gives shape and strength to the structure of the organism (**see Figure 3.12d**).

3.6 Lipids

We turn now to the **lipids**, a class of biological molecules whose defining characteristic is their relative insolubility in water. It turns out that lipids are made of the same elements as carbohydrates—carbon, hydrogen, and oxygen. But lipids have much more hydrogen, relative to oxygen, than do the carbohydrates. We're all familiar with some lipids; they exist as fats, as oils, as cholesterol, and as hormones such as testosterone and estrogen. Unlike the other biological molecules you'll be studying, a lipid is not a polymer composed of component-part monomers; no single structural unit is common to all lipids. Thus, the one characteristic shared by pure lipids is that they do not readily break down in water. Remember an earlier discussion about the need life has to create internal containers? Well, thanks to their insolubility, lipids are able to serve this function. In addition, lipids have considerable powers to store energy and to provide insulation.

One Class of Lipids Is the Glycerides

The glyceride, the most common kind of lipid, can be thought of as a molecule in two parts. The first is a "head" composed of a particular kind of alcohol, usually glycerol. Attached to the glycerol head is the second part of the glyceride, a series of fatty acids, each one consisting of a long chain of carbon and hydrogen atoms (see Figure 3.15 on page 50).

The structural formula for stearic acid, one of the fatty acids found in animal fat, is shown in

Figure 3.13. This monotonous chain of hydrogen and carbon is, as you might have guessed, the hydrocarbon portion of the stearic fatty-acid molecule. Fatty acids can have from 4 to 22 carbons linked up like this. On the left side, you can see that the chain terminates with one of the functional groups we talked about earlier, a COOH chemical group (indicated in red), properly known as a *carboxyl group*.

**Figure 3.13
Structural Formula for Stearic Acid**

Now look at the other part of the fat molecule we discussed, the alcohol known as glycerol:

As you know, the hallmark of alcohols is that they have an −OH group, which you can see here. Bringing the −OH portion of glycerol together with the carboxyl part of the fatty-acid chain is what makes a *glyceride*. But you can see that the glycerol has *three* −OH groups on the right. Thus there is, you might say, docking space on glycerol for three fatty acids, and in the synthesis of many glycerides, this linkage takes place: Three fatty acids link up with glycerol to form a triglyceride, which is an important form of lipid. **Figure 3.14** shows how it works schematically.

Web Tutorial 3.5
Lipids

glycerol + 3 fatty acids = triglyceride + water

**Figure 3.14
Formation of a Triglyceride**

The Rs on the right end of the COOH group stand for whatever the hydrocarbon chain is of that particular fatty acid. To get a better idea of the shape of a completed triglyceride, look at the space-filling model in **Figure 3.15**. This particular triglyceride, called tristearin, has three stearic fatty acids stemming like tines on a fork from the glycerol. But this is only one possibility among many, and is exceptional, rather than usual, in that all three fatty acids are the same. Among the dozens of fatty acids that exist, several *different* kinds of fatty acids generally will hook up in glycerol's three "slots" to form a triglyceride. Actual fat products, such as butter, are composed of different proportions of various fatty acids.

We've seen three fatty acids linking with glycerol to form *tri*glycerides, but monoglycerides (one fatty acid joined to glycerol) and diglycerides (two fatty acids joined with glycerol) can be formed as well. Triglycerides are the most important of the glycerides, however, because they constitute about 90 percent of the lipid weight in foods. In short, the substances we call fats usually are composed mostly of triglycerides.

With all this under your belt, you're ready for a couple of definitions. A **triglyceride** is a lipid molecule formed from three fatty acids bonded to glycerol. A **fatty acid** is a molecule found in many lipids that is composed of a hydrocarbon chain bonded to a carboxyl group.

Saturated and Unsaturated Fatty Acids: A Linkage with Solids and Liquids and with Health

If you now look at **Figure 3.16**, you can see three different fatty acids: palmitic, oleic, and linoleic. There is an obvious difference among them, in that the oleic and linoleic hydrocarbon chains are "bent"

compared to the straight-line palmitic chain. Upon closer inspection, you can see that the palmitic acid has an unbroken line of single bonds linking its carbon atoms. Meanwhile, the oleic acid has one double bond between the carbons in its chain and the linoleic acid has two. Furthermore, note that these double bonds exist precisely where the "kinks" appear in these molecules.

Fatty Acids: From Solid to Liquid

What these variations describe are the differences between three *kinds* of fatty acids. First, there is a **saturated fatty acid**—a fatty acid with no double bonds between the carbon atoms of its hydrocarbon chain. Then there is a **monounsaturated fatty acid** (a fatty acid with one double bond between carbon atoms), and a **polyunsaturated fatty acid** (a fatty acid with two or more double bonds between carbon atoms). What a saturated fatty acid is saturated *with* is hydrogen atoms. A given monounsaturated fatty acid could theoretically have its lone carbon-carbon double bond replaced with a *single* bond between the carbons. This change would entail the addition of two more hydrogen atoms at the bond sites. Once this happened, this fatty acid would contain the maximum number of hydrogen atoms possible, meaning it would be a saturated fatty acid.

This may not sound like much of a difference, but it has several important consequences. First, at room temperature, as you move from saturated to unsaturated, you also move in general from fats in their solid form to fats in their liquid form, which we call **oils**. For decades, food producers have turned naturally occurring oils *into* fats by saturating them—by bubbling hydrogen through the oils in a process called hydrogenation. Why would this turn a liquid into a solid? The reason is a familiar one: molecular shape. Saturated fatty acids have a straight-line form that allows them to pack together tightly, like so many boards in a lumber yard. In contrast, unsaturated fatty acids stick out at varying angles to one another in a triglyceride, a disorder that generally makes them liquid at room temperature. The "kinks" in unsaturated fatty acids have consequences.

Saturated Fatty Acids and Health

The distinction between saturated and unsaturated fatty acids also has another important effect, this one related to human health. Think of it this way: To the degree that *fatty acids* are saturated, the *fats* they make up will be saturated—and consumption of saturated fats has been linked with heart disease.

glycerol

fatty acids

Figure 3.15
The Triglyceride Tristearin
This lipid molecule is composed of three stearic fatty acids, stemming rightward from the glycerol OH "heads." Tristearin is found both in beef fat and in the cocoa butter that helps make up chocolate.

(a) Palmitic acid

saturated (no double bonds)

(b) Oleic acid

The "kinks" imparted by double carbon-bonds make unsaturated fatty acids more likely to be liquid oils, rather than solid fats, at room temperature.

monounsaturated (one double bond)

(c) Linoleic acid

polyunsaturated (more than one double bond)

The linkage here is that saturated fats increase the amount of cholesterol in circulation in the body. When this cholesterol lodges in the arteries of the heart in excessive amounts, heart disease can begin. The picture on fats in general and heart disease is a complicated one, however. The industrial hydrogenation process just noted plays a part in creating a particularly harmful sort of fat you may have heard of, called trans fat, but it turns out there are other fats that are actually good for your heart. You can read more about this in "From Trans Fats to Omega 3's" on page 54.

Energy Use and Energy Storage via Lipids and Carbohydrates

Lipids have something in common with carbohydrates in connection with energy *storage* on the one hand and energy *use* on the other. To be stored, lipids must be in their triglyceride form; to be used to provide energy, they must first be broken down into glycerol and fatty acids. Carbohydrates, meanwhile, are stored as the complex carbohydrate glycogen; to be used for energy expenditure, they must be broken down to simple carbohydrates, often glucose. This process of alternately building up molecules for energy storage, or breaking them down for energy expenditure, is a major task of living things. If you look at **Figure 3.17**, you can see how carbohydrates and lipids are alternately stored and used by plants and animals.

A Second Class of Lipids Is the Steroids

Steroids are a class of lipid molecules that have, as a central element in their structure, four carbon rings. What separates one steroid from another are the various side chains that can be attached to these rings (**see Figure 3.18**). When you see how different steroids are structurally from the triglycerides, you can understand why the monomers-to-polymers framework doesn't apply to lipids.

Among the most well known steroids are cholesterol and two of the steroid hormones, testos-

terone and estrogen. Like fats in general, cholesterol has a bad reputation; but also like fats in general, it serves good purposes too. **Cholesterol** is a steroid molecule that forms part of the outer membrane of all animal cells, and that acts as a precursor for many other steroids. One of the steroids formed from it is the principal "male" hormone testosterone; another is the principal "female" hormone estrogen. (Both hormones actually are produced in both sexes, though in differing amounts.) The term *steroids* by itself undoubtedly rings a bell, because the phrase "on steroids" has come to mean artificially bulked up or supercharged. In this common usage, steroids refers to manufactured drugs that are close chemical cousins of the muscle-building "male" steroid hormones (**see Figure 3.19**).

Figure 3.17
Storage and Use of Carbohydrates and Lipids
Carbohydrates and lipids generally are stored in one form, but used in another.

(a) In plants, carbohydrates commonly are stored as starch, a complex carbohydrate that is a major component of such vegetables as carrots. Human beings can consume such a starch, after which it may be broken down into the smaller, simple carbohydrate glucose and used immediately—for exercise or other purposes—or stored in the liver and muscles as the larger, more complex carbohydrate glycogen.

(b) Cows use their fat for energy storage and insulation. The fat portion of the meat that humans consume may be used for energy, but only after being broken down into its glycerol and fatty-acid components. Conversely, humans may convert the components back into triglycerides to be stored in fat cells, providing energy reserves for later.

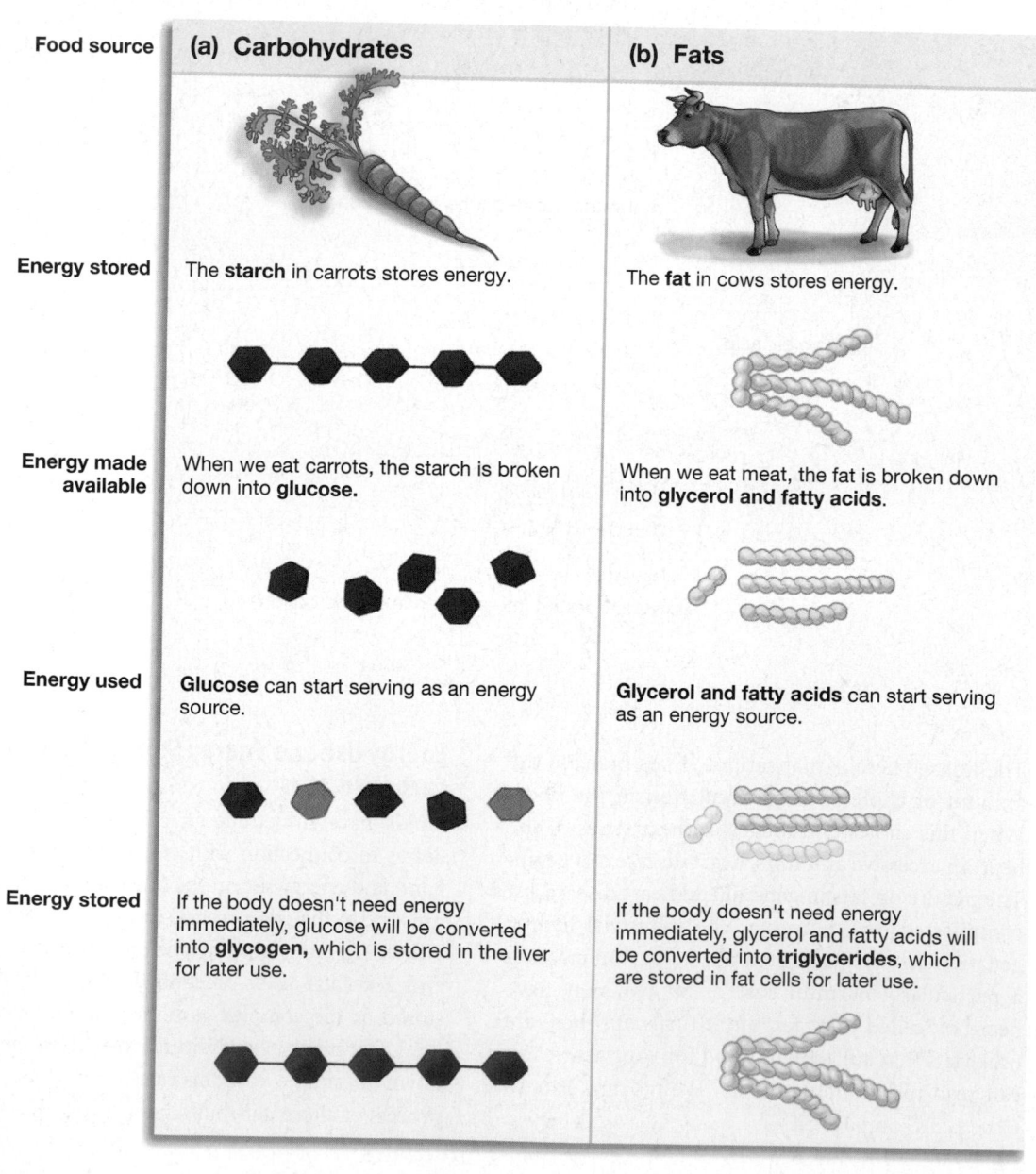

Food source	(a) Carbohydrates	(b) Fats
Energy stored	The **starch** in carrots stores energy.	The **fat** in cows stores energy.
Energy made available	When we eat carrots, the starch is broken down into **glucose.**	When we eat meat, the fat is broken down into **glycerol and fatty acids**.
Energy used	**Glucose** can start serving as an energy source.	**Glycerol and fatty acids** can start serving as an energy source.
Energy stored	If the body doesn't need energy immediately, glucose will be converted into **glycogen,** which is stored in the liver for later use.	If the body doesn't need energy immediately, glycerol and fatty acids will be converted into **triglycerides,** which are stored in fat cells for later use.

(a) Four-ring steroid structure

(b) Side chains make each steroid unique

OH
CH_3
CH_3
testosterone
O

OH
CH_3
estrogen
HO

CH_3
HC—CH_3
CH_2
CH_2
CH_2
HC—CH_3
CH_3
CH_3
cholesterol
HO

Figure 3.18
Structure of Steroids

(a) The basic unit of steroids, four interlocked carbon rings.

(b) Types of steroids, each differentiated from the other by the side chains that extend from the four-ring skeleton. Testosterone is a principal "male" hormone, while estrogen is a principal "female" hormone. Both of these steroid hormones actually are found in both men and women, though in differing amounts. Cholesterol is also a prevalent and important steroid in both men and women. Although cholesterol has a bad reputation, it has several important functions—for example, breaking down fats.

(a) Natural steroids

(b) Pharmaceutical steroids

Figure 3.19
Steroids, in Uses Natural and Unnatural

(a) Some steroid hormones, such as estrogen and testosterone are important in natural processes, such as reproduction.

(b) Pharmaceutical steroids can be used in potentially harmful ways—for example, to build muscle mass. Pictured is British sprinter Linford Christie, who in 1999 tested positive for substances produced by a banned steroid called nandrolone.

From Trans Fats to Omega-3's: Fats and Health

Saturated and unsaturated fats, trans fats, omega-3's. What a confusing situation. Average Americans might understandably throw up their hands, assume that all fats are unhealthy, and try to reduce their intake of every variety. But a closer look at the various kinds of fats reveals that, while some are indeed bad for the heart when consumed in too great an amount, others actually are healthy. Thus it's possible to rate various kinds of lipids based on their health effects. Here is a hierarchy of dietary fats, starting with the most healthful and going to the most harmful:

- Fats containing omega-3 fatty acids
- Monounsaturated and polyunsaturated fats
- Saturated fats
- Trans fats

It is the last two of these—saturated fats and trans fats—that can be harmful. Meanwhile, the poly- and monounsaturated fats have no negative impact on the heart, and the omega-3-containing fats actually are beneficial. What makes the difference? All authorities are agreed that a critical factor in getting heart disease going is the proportion of low-density lipoproteins or LDLs you have in your bloodstream relative to the proportion of high-density lipoproteins or HDLs you have. Think of LDLs as capsules of protein that carry cholesterol *from* the liver and small intestines to various places in the body, including the heart. Meanwhile, HDLs are protein capsules that carry cholesterol *to* the liver from the heart and other tissues, thus clearing this cholesterol from the system. It is the lodging of LDL-cholesterol molecules in the arteries of the heart that gets the most prevalent form of heart disease going. Therefore, anything that raises LDL-cholesterol levels ought to be avoided, while anything that raises HDL-cholesterol levels ought to be sought out.

When we look at the various kinds of fats within this framework, we find that it is *only* the saturated fats and trans fats that raise LDL-cholesterol levels. None of the other varieties of fat stand to affect LDL-cholesterol levels any more than, say, carbohydrates do. Authoritative U.S. dietary guidelines have for years recommended limiting the proportion of calories Americans get from fats, but this has been done primarily to limit the consumption of *saturated* fats. Why? Because nothing raises LDL-cholesterol levels more than saturated fats. Each 1 percent increase in these fats in the diet leads to a 2 percent increase in LDL-cholesterol levels. This is not to say that people should eat no saturated fats; but average Americans need to reduce their consumption of them (down to less than 7 percent of total calo-

ries). The usual source for saturated fats is animal fat—primarily fatty meat and dairy products—but they can also be found in a few plant products, such as coconut oil and cocoa butter.

In contrast to the saturated fats, the polyunsaturated fats leave LDL levels unchanged, though they do slightly lower the "good" HDL-cholesterol levels. Should you *substitute* polyunsaturated fats for saturated fats, however, the net result would be a lowering of your LDL levels. Polyunsaturated fats can be found in safflower and corn oil.

Healthier yet are the monounsaturated fats, which leave both LDL and HDL levels unchanged. It may be, however, that these fats are not just "neutral" with respect to heart disease, but may actually work to prevent it. Several studies have shown that residents of Mediterranean countries have significantly lower levels of heart disease than people in other parts of the developed world. What these residents have in common, in terms of diet, is consumption of large amounts of the monounsaturated fats that come in olive oil. Other sources of monounsaturated fats are canola and peanut oils, and avocados.

When we look at one particular variety of polyunsaturated fat—those that contain omega-3 fatty acids—we find the healthiest lipid of all. As you saw in the main text, a polyunsaturated fatty acid is one that has two or more carbon-carbon double bonds somewhere in its hydrocarbon chain. Now, the far end of the hydrocarbon chain (away from the glycerol head) is called the omega end. When a carbon double bond is located three carbons up from the omega end, the result is an omega-3 fatty acid. Polyunsaturated fats containing these fatty acids guard against blood-clot formation, they reduce fat levels generally in the bloodstream, and they reduce the growth of the fatty deposits that clog up heart arteries. Omega-3 fatty acids are found in certain kinds of fatty fish, including salmon, albacore tuna, mackerel, lake trout, and sardines; and in lesser amounts in plant-based foods such as walnuts and the soybean-based product tofu.

Now, what about the worst of the fats noted earlier, the trans fats? Recall from the main text that there is an industrial process, called hydrogenation, in which hydrogen is bubbled into mono- or polyunsaturated oils. Food manufacturers do this for several reasons: it turns these oils into fats at room-temperature, it often gives them a creamy texture that consumers like, and it increases the shelf life of the foods that result. Thus, if you want packaged cookies that stay fresh for a long time, hydrogenate the fatty acids in them. The problem is that hydrogenation changes the chemical structure of fatty acids in ways that make them unhealthful. In some instances, hydrogenation has the effect of replacing carbon atoms in fatty-acid chains with hydrogen atoms, thus turning unsaturated fatty acids into *saturated* fatty acids. In other instances, however, it has the effect not of putting more hydrogen atoms in a fatty acid, but of changing the *orientation* of the hydrogen atoms that already exist at carbon-carbon double bonds. Whereas normally these pairs of hydrogens are on the same side, like this:

cis form (hydrogen atoms on same side of chain)

With hydrogenation they can end up on the opposite or *trans* sides, like this:

trans form (hydrogen atoms on opposite sides of chain)

Thus do we get the term *trans* fatty acids. The trans fats that result from this change are found in lots of packaged and fast foods: not only cookies, but french fries, cakes, crackers, doughnuts, popcorn, and candy, to name a few. These fats raise LDL levels while lowering HDL levels—a twin set of unhealthy effects that not even saturated fats can manage. In addition, they appear to boost fat levels in general in the blood while impairing the ability of blood vessels to open or "dilate."

How can you know how much trans fat you are consuming? At present, you can't. The federal Food and Drug Administration has announced that it will require food producers to list trans fats separately in the ubiquitous "Nutrition Facts" labels on food packages, but this requirement won't go into effect until 2006. The best you can do until then is look for the phrase "partially hydrogenated oil" on the list of product ingredients. When present, it means that the product probably contains some trans fat, though it's impossible to tell how much.

Web Tutorial 3.6
Nutrition Labels

A Third Class of Lipids Is the Phospholipids

The final class of lipids, phospholipids, has something of the same makeup as triglycerides, in that a phospholipid has a glycerol head with fatty acids attached to it. But where triglycerides have three fatty acids stemming from the glycerol, phospholipids have only two (**see Figure 3.20**). Linking up with glycerol's third —OH group is a **phosphate group**, meaning a phosphorus atom surrounded by four oxygen atoms. Thus, we can define a **phospholipid** as a charged lipid molecule composed of two fatty acids, glycerol, and a phosphate group.

The combination of a phosphate group and fatty-acid tails is extremely important because it gives phospholipids a dual nature: Being hydrocarbons, the fatty-acid tails are hydrophobic; but the phosphate head is hydro*philic* because it is *charged*. In Figure 3.20, you can see the effect of this structure in solution. Imagine a phospholipid as a marker buoy in deep water. No matter how you push the hydrocarbon tail around, it's going to end up waving free *out* of the water, while the head is going to be submerged in it. You will learn more about these molecules later, when you get to cells; for now, just note that the material on the periphery of cells—the outer membrane of a cell—is largely made of phospholipids. Living things need the kind of partitions described earlier, and these partitions are composed to a significant extent of phospholipids.

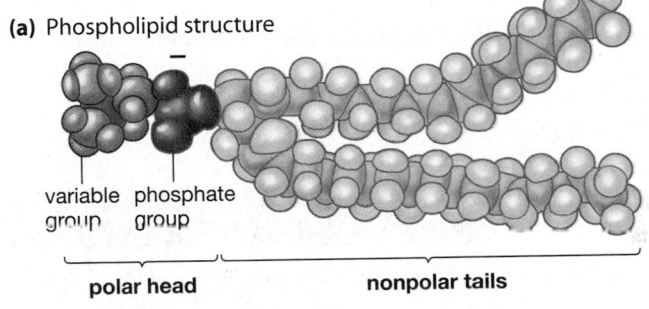

(a) Phospholipid structure

variable group phosphate group

polar head   nonpolar tails

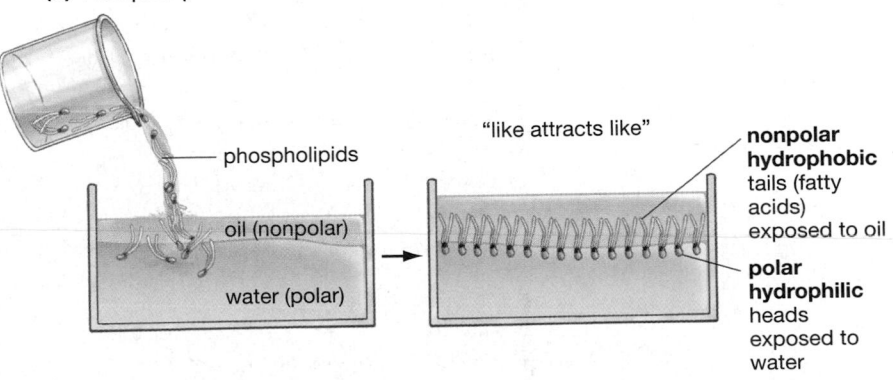

(b) Phospholipid orientation

phospholipids

oil (nonpolar)

water (polar)

"like attracts like"

nonpolar hydrophobic tails (fatty acids) exposed to oil

polar hydrophilic heads exposed to water

Figure 3.20
A Dual-Natured Molecule

(a) Phospholipids are composed of two long fatty-acid "tails" attached to a "head" containing a phosphate group (which carries a negative charge) and another variable group (which often carries a charge).

(b) Because the head is polarized, it can bond with water and thus will remain submerged in it; the tails, on the other hand, have no such bonding capability.

55

3.7 Proteins

Living things must accomplish a great number of tasks just to get through a day, and the diverse biological molecules you've been looking at allow this to happen. You've seen carbohydrates do some things, and you've seen lipids do some more. But in the range of tasks that molecules accomplish, proteins reign supreme. Witness the fact that almost every chemical reaction that takes place in living things is hastened—or, in practical terms, *enabled*—by a particular kind of protein called an enzyme. These molecules function in nature like some vast group of tools, each one taking on a specific chemical task. Accordingly, an animal cell might contain up to 4,000 different types of enzymes.

We might marvel at proteins solely because of what enzymes can do, but the amazing thing is that enzymes are only *one class* of proteins. Proteins also form the scaffolding, or structure, of a good deal of tissue; they're active in transporting molecules from one site to another; they allow muscles to contract and cells to move; some hormones are made from them. If you factor out water, they account for about half the weight of the average cell. In short, it's hard to overestimate the importance of these molecules. **Table 3.3** lists some of the different kinds of proteins.

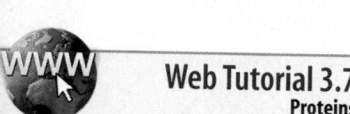

Web Tutorial 3.7
Proteins

Proteins Are Made from Chains of Amino Acids

Proteins are prime examples of the building-block type of molecule described earlier. The monomers in this case are called amino acids. String a minimum number of them together in a chain—some say 10, some say 30—and you have a **polypeptide**, defined as a series of amino acids linked in linear fashion. When the polypeptide chain *folds up* in a specific three-dimensional manner, you have a **protein**, defined as a large, folded chain of amino acids. As a practical matter, proteins are likely to be made of hundreds of amino acids strung together and folded up. As you'll see, it's not unusual for two or more polypeptide chains to be part of a single protein.

Figure 3.21a gives the fundamental structural unit for amino acids, followed by a couple of examples. You can see carbon at the center of this unit, an amino group off to its left, and a carboxyl group to its right. (The name *amino acid* comes from the fact that there is both an *amino* group and a carboxyl group, which is an *acid* group.) What differentiates one amino acid from another is the group of atoms that occupies the R or "side-chain" position. In **Figure 3.21b** you can see examples of actual amino acids, tyrosine and glutamine, with their different occupants of the R position.

Table 3.3 Types of Proteins

Type	Role	Examples
Enzymes	Quicken chemical reactions	Sucrase: Positions sucrose (table sugar) in such a way that it can be broken down into component parts of glucose and fructose
Hormones	Chemical messengers	Growth hormone: Stimulates growth of bones
Transport	Move other molecules	Hemoglobin: Transports oxygen through blood
Contractile	Movement	Myosin and actin: Allow muscles to contract
Protective	Healing; defense against invader	Fibrinogen: Stops bleeding Antibodies: Kill bacterial invaders
Structural	Mechanical support	Keratin: Hair Collagen: Cartilage
Storage	Stores nutrients	Ovalbumin: Egg white, used as nutrient for embryos
Toxins	Defense, predation	Bacterial diphtheria toxin
Communication	Cell signaling	Glycoprotein: Receptors on cell surface

A Group of Only 20 Amino Acids Is the Basis for All Proteins in Living Things

Although only two examples are shown here, it is a group of 20 amino acids that is the basis for all the proteins that occur in living organisms. The thousands of proteins that exist can be made from a mere 20 amino acids, because these amino acids can be strung together in different *order*. Substitute an alanine here for a glutamine there, and you've got a different protein. In this, amino acids commonly are compared to letters of the alphabet. In English, substituting one letter can take us from *bat* to *hat*. In the natural world, 20 amino acids can be put together in different order to create a multitude of proteins, each with a different function.

The stringing together of amino acids happens in a regular way: The carboxyl group of one amino acid joins to the amino group of another, with the loss of a water molecule resulting. Look at **Figure 3.22** to see how three amino acids come together.

(a) What all amino acids have in common is an amino group and a carboxyl group attached to a central carbon.

amino group   carboxyl group

side chain

(b) What makes the 20 amino acids unique are side-chains attached to the central carbon.

tyrosine

glutamine

Figure 3.21
Structure of Amino Acids

(a) The structural element that is common to all amino acids is an amino group and a carboxyl group (on the left and right), linked by a central carbon with a hydrogen attached to it. What makes one amino acid different from another is the side-chain of atoms that occupies the R position.

(b) Two examples of actual amino acids; the differing occupants of the R position give us the amino acids tyrosine and glutamine.

The linkage of several amino acids...

...produces a polypeptide chain like this:

A typical protein would consist of hundreds of amino acids

Figure 3.22
Beginnings of a Protein
Amino acids join together to form polypeptide chains, which fold up to become proteins. The linking of amino acids yields water as a by-product. In this figure, alanine (ala) first joins with glutamine (gln), which then is linked to isoleucine (ile). (A list of all 20 primary amino acids can be found on page 265.)

Shape Is Critical to the Functioning of All Proteins

Now, recall that a protein is a chain of amino acids that has become *folded up* in a specific way. As the amino acids are being strung together in sequence, all the kinds of chemical forces discussed in Chapter 2 begin to work on the chain; as a result, it begins to twist and turn and fold into a unique three-dimensional shape. And it turns out that in the functioning of proteins, this shape, or *protein conformation*, is utterly crucial. Here's an example of why. The hormone insulin, which is a protein, is released from a person's pancreas; it moves through the bloodstream and latches onto muscle cells; its presence then allows blood sugar to get into the muscles and provide energy. Now, how does insulin "latch onto" muscle cells? By *linking* itself with a molecule, called an insulin receptor, that lies on the surface of the muscle cell. But protein and receptor must be precisely shaped for such linkage or "binding" to occur.

This binding of a protein hormone to surface receptor sounds important enough; but recall that in addition to being hormones, proteins are the chemical enablers called enzymes, and they're transport molecules, and so forth. In *all* these functions, shape is critical. The American architect Frank Lloyd Wright had a famous dictum about his designs: "Form follows function." With proteins, we can turn this around and say that function follows form (**see Figure 3.23**).

Figure 3.23
Made of Protein
A human hair, shown here emerging from a follicle in the skin, is composed mostly of the protein keratin. Each hair is composed of many groups of keratin strands that wrap around each other in alpha helices, giving hair its structure, which is flexible and much longer than it is wide.

There Are Four Levels of Protein Structure

So, what forms do proteins take? Well, the answer to this depends on what vantage point you adopt in looking at them. There are four levels of structure in proteins that determine their final shape. You can see all four levels in **Figure 3.24**. The first of these levels, the **primary structure** of a protein, is simply its sequence of amino acids. Everything about the final shape of a protein is dictated by this sequence. Electrochemical bonding and repulsion forces act on this structure, and the result is the folded-up protein.

As it turns out, when these forces begin to operate on the amino acid sequence, a couple of common shapes begin to emerge in the **secondary structure** of proteins, defined as structure proteins assume after having folded up. The **alpha helix**, a common secondary structure of proteins, has a shape much like a corkscrew. Another common secondary structure in proteins, the **beta pleated sheet**, takes a form like the folds of an accordion. Proteins can be made almost entirely of alpha helices. This is the case with hair, nails, horns, and the like. Likewise, proteins can be made entirely of beta pleated sheets. The most familiar example of this is silk, in which the beta sheets lie pancake-style on one another. Often, however, alpha helices and beta pleated sheets form what we might think of as design motifs within a larger protein structure; they periodically give way to the less regular segments called random coils. The larger-scale three-dimensional shape that a protein takes is its **tertiary structure**. The way in which *two or more* polypeptide chains come together to form a protein results in that protein's **quaternary structure**.

Proteins Can Come Undone

As noted, proteins fold up into a precise conformation in order to function. However, proteins can *lose* their shape, and thus their functionality. You saw an example of this earlier in connection with pH and enzymes. In the wrong pH environment, an enzyme can unfold, losing its tertiary structure and thus losing its ability to hasten a chemical process. Alcohol works as a disinfectant on skin because it *denatures* or alters the shape of the proteins of bacteria.

Lipoproteins and Glycoproteins

Some molecules in living things are hybrids, or combinations of the various types of molecules you've been looking at. **Lipoproteins**, as their name implies, are molecules that are a combination of lipids and proteins. Active in transporting fats throughout the body, lipoproteins are transport molecules that amount to a capsule of protein surrounding a globule of fat.

Two kinds of lipoproteins have managed to enter public consciousness despite the handicap of having long names. These are high-density lipoproteins and low-density lipoproteins, also known as HDLs and LDLs. What makes them more or less dense is the ratio of protein to lipid in them; lipid is less dense than protein, so a low-density lipoprotein has a relatively large amount of lipid, in comparison to protein. LDLs have acquired a reputation as villains, because they carry cholesterol *to* outlying tissues including the coronary arteries of the heart, where this cholesterol may come to reside, thickening eventually into "plaques" that can block coro-

nary arteries and bring about a heart attack. HDLs, meanwhile, are regarded as the cavalry; they carry cholesterol *away* from outlying cells to the liver. A high proportion of HDLs in relation to cholesterol is predictive of keeping a healthy heart.

Glycoproteins are combinations of proteins and *carbohydrates*. Remember the discussion about insulin traveling through the bloodstream and latching onto a receptor on the surface of a muscle cell? Well, such receptors are usually glycoproteins, meaning mostly protein with a side-chain made of carbohydrate. A profusion of these receptors sits on cell surfaces like so many antennae, ready for a partner

Figure 3.24
Four Levels of Structure in Proteins

Four Levels of Structure In Proteins

(a) Primary structure

The primary structure of any protein is simply its sequence of amino acids. This sequence determines everything else about the protein's final shape.

(b) Secondary structure

Structural motifs, such as the corkscrew-like alpha helix, beta pleated sheets, and the less organized "random coils" are parts of many polypeptide chains, forming their secondary structure.

(c) Tertiary structure

These motifs may persist through a set of larger-scale turns that make up the tertiary structure of the molecule.

(d) Quaternary structure

Several polypeptide chains may be linked together in a given protein, in this case hemoglobin, with their configuration forming its quaternary structure.

amino acid sequence

beta pleated sheet

alpha helix

random coil

folded polypeptide chain

two or more polypeptide chains

with just the right shape to come by and latch on. Some hormones themselves are glycoproteins, along with many other proteins released from cells.

3.8 Nucleotides and Nucleic Acids

Nucleotides are the last major type of biological molecule we'll study. They are important molecules in and of themselves and as building blocks for a couple of very important molecules.

As molecules in their own right, some nucleotides, called adenosine phosphates, serve as chemical energy carriers. When you study energy within cells, you'll find many references to a molecule called adenosine triphosphate, or ATP. As money is to shopping, so ATP is to getting things done in living organisms. In this text, the most detailed discussion of nucleotides, however, comes in connection with their role as monomers in building two very large and important polymers—the nucleic acids DNA and RNA, which are considered next.

DNA Provides Information for the Structure of Proteins

You've learned that proteins perform a large number of biological functions, and that one class of proteins, the enzymes, may be represented with up to 4,000 types in a single animal cell. If you had a factory that turned out four thousand different kinds of tools, you would obviously need some direction on how each of these tools was to be manufactured: This part of the tool goes here first, and then that goes there, and so on. There is a molecule that in essence provides this kind of information for the construction of proteins. It is **DNA**, or **deoxyribonucleic acid**: the primary information-bearing molecule of life, composed of two linked chains of nucleotides. How many nucleotides? In human beings, about 3 billion of them are strung together to form our main molecule of DNA, and one copy of this molecule exists in each of our cells.

Web Tutorial 3.8
Nucleic Acids

The information contained in the DNA molecule is much like the information contained in a cookbook, only what the DNA "recipes" are calling for are precisely ordered chains of amino acids, the building blocks of proteins. "Start with an alanine, then add a cysteine, then a tyrosine . . . " and so on for hundreds of steps, the DNA-encoded instructions will say, after which—through a series of steps—a protein becomes synthesized and then gets busy on some task. A player in this series of steps is another nucleic acid, **ribonucleic acid** or **RNA**, a molecule composed of nucleotides that is active in the synthesis of proteins. RNA's functions include ferrying the DNA-encoded instructions to the sites in the cell where proteins are put together. It also helps make up a protein-synthesizing workbench you'll look at later, called a ribosome.

The Structural Unit of DNA Is the Nucleotide

Look at **Figure 3.25a** and you'll see the structure of the building blocks that make up DNA. Each nucleic acid **nucleotide** is a molecule in three parts: A *phosphate* group, a *sugar* (deoxyribose), and a nitrogen-containing *base*. One nucleotide then attaches to another, forming a chain. Two of these chains then link together—as if a ladder, split down the middle, were coming together—forming the most famous molecule in all of biology, the DNA double helix.

On to Cells

Before getting to the story of this elegant DNA molecule, you need to learn a little bit about the territory in which it does its work. What you'll be looking at is a profusion of jostling, roiling, ceaselessly working chemical factories that make up all living things. These factories are called cells. Look at **Table 3.4** on page 62, and you'll find a summary of all the types of molecules that were reviewed in this chapter.

(a) Nucleotides are the building blocks of DNA.

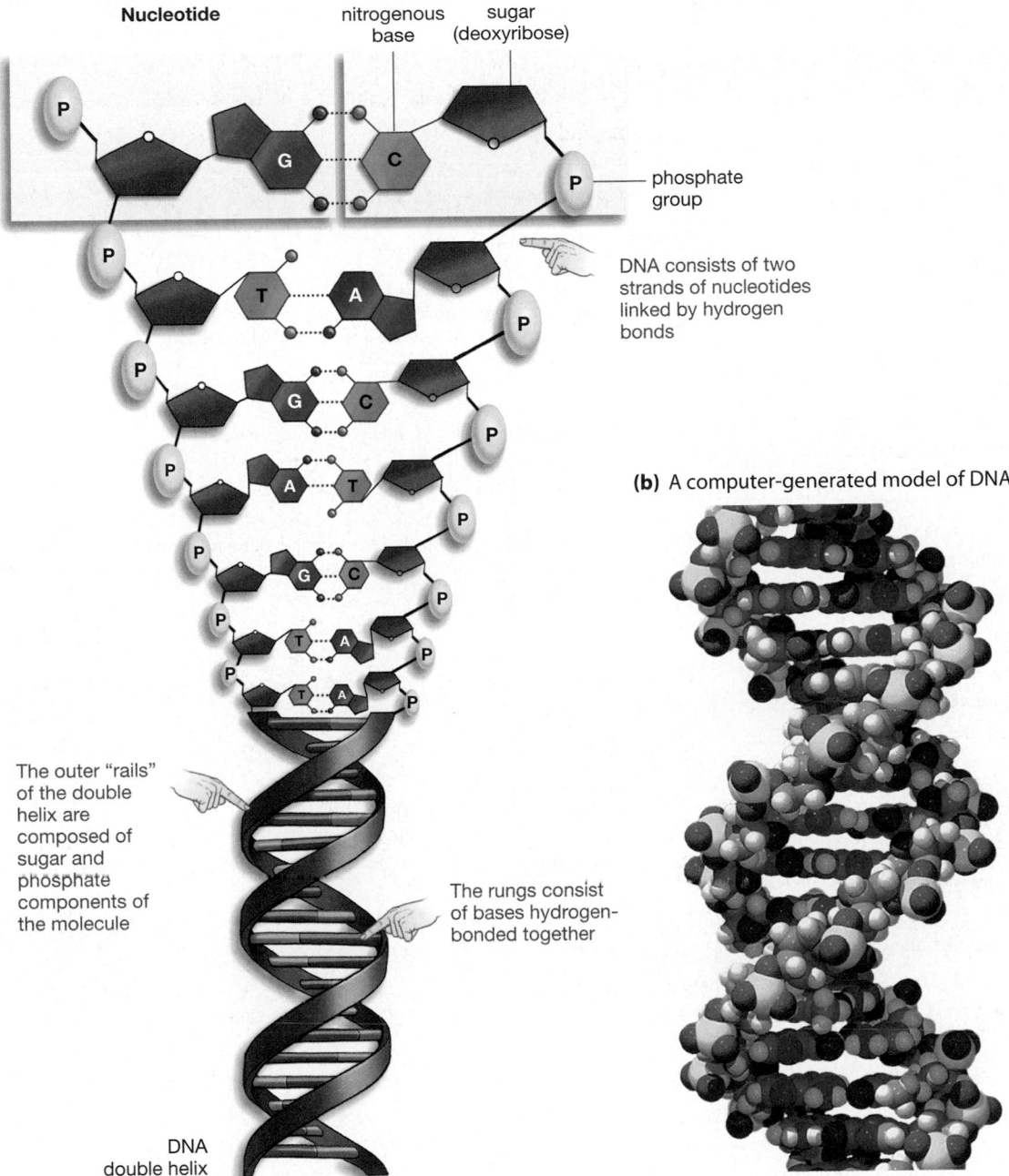

Nucleotide   nitrogenous base   sugar (deoxyribose)

phosphate group

DNA consists of two strands of nucleotides linked by hydrogen bonds

(b) A computer-generated model of DNA

The outer "rails" of the double helix are composed of sugar and phosphate components of the molecule

The rungs consist of bases hydrogen-bonded together

DNA double helix

Figure 3.25
Nucleotides Are the Building Blocks of DNA

(a) The basic unit of the DNA molecule is the nucleotide, a molecule in three parts: a sugar, (deoxyribose), a phosphate group, and a nitrogen-containing base. A given nucleotide might contain any of four bases: Adenine (A), Guanine (G), Cytosine (C), or Thymine (T). The sugar and phosphate components of the nucleotides link up to form the outer "rails" of the DNA molecule, while the bases point toward the molecule's interior. Two chains of nucleotides are linked, via hydrogen bonds, to form DNA's double helix. Note that the hydrogen bond is between one base and another.

(b) A computer-generated space-filling model of DNA.

Table 3.4 Summary Table of Biological Molecules

Type of Molecule	Subgroups	Examples and Roles
Carbohydrates	Monosaccharides	Glucose: Energy source
	Disaccharides	Sucrose: Energy source
	Polysaccharides	Glycogen: Storage form of glucose Starch: Carbohydrate storage in plants; used by animals in nutrition Cellulose: Plant cell walls, structure; fiber in animal digestion Chitin: External skeleton of arthropods
Lipids	Triglycerides 3 Fatty acids and glycerol	Fats, Oils (butter, corn oil): Food, energy, storage, insulation
	Fatty acids Components of Triglycerides	Stearic Acid: Food, energy sources
	Steroids Four-ring structure	Cholesterol: Fat digestion, hormone precursor, cell membrane component
	Phospholipids Polar head, nonpolar tails	Cell membrane structure
Proteins	Enzymes Chemically active	Sucrase: Breaks down sugar
	Structural	Keratin: Hair
	Lipoproteins Protein-lipid molecule	HDLs, LDLs: Transport of lipids
	Glycoproteins Protein-sugar molecule	Cell surface receptors
Nucleotides	Adenosine phosphates	Adenosine triphosphate (ATP): Energy transfer
	Nucleic acids Sugar, phosphate group, base	DNA, RNAs: Contain information for and facilitate synthesis of proteins

Chapter Review

Summary

3.1   The Importance of Water to Life

- Water has several qualities that have strongly affected life on Earth. It is a powerful solvent, being able to dissolve more compounds in greater amounts than any other liquid. Because water's solid form (ice) is less dense than its liquid form, bodies of water in colder climates do not freeze solid in winter, which allows life to flourish under the ice.

- Water has a great capacity to absorb and retain heat. Because of this, the oceans act as heat buffers for the Earth, thus stabilizing Earth's temperature. Water has a high degree of cohesion, which allows water to be drawn up through plants, via evaporation, in one continuous column, from roots through leaves.

- Some compounds do not interact with water. Hydrocarbons such as petroleum are examples of such hydrophobic compounds. Water cannot break down hydrophobic compounds, which is why oil and water don't mix. Compounds that do interact with water are polar or carry an electric charge and are called hydrophilic compounds.
  Web Tutorial 3.1: Chemistry and Water

3.2   Acids and Bases Are Important to Life

- An acid is any substance that yields hydrogen ions when put in solution. A base is any substance that accepts hydrogen ions in solution. A base added to an acidic solution makes that solution less acidic, while an acid added to a basic solution makes that solution less basic.

- The concentration of hydrogen ions that a given solution has determines how basic or acidic that solution is, as measured on the pH scale. This scale runs from 0 to 14, with 0 being most acidic, 14 being most basic, and 7 being neutral. The pH scale is logarithmic; a substance with a pH of 9 is 10 times as basic as a substance with a pH of 8. Living things function best in a near-neutral pH, though some systems in living things have different pH requirements.

3.3   Carbon Is a Central Element in Life

- Carbon is a central element to life, because most biological molecules are built on a carbon framework. Carbon plays this central role because its outer shell has only four of the eight electrons necessary for maximum stability. Carbon atoms are thus able to form stable, covalent bonds with a wide variety of atoms, including other carbon atoms. The complexity of living things is facilitated by carbon's linkage capacity.
  Web Tutorial 3.2: Chemistry of Carbon

3.4   Functional Groups

- Groups of atoms known as functional groups can confer special properties on carbon-based molecules. For example, the addition of an – OH group to a hydrocarbon molecule always results in the formation of an alcohol. Functional groups often impart an electrical charge or polarity onto molecules, thus affecting their bonding capacity.

3.5   The Molecules of Life: Carbohydrates

- Carbohydrates are formed from the building blocks or monomers of simple sugars, such as glucose. These can be linked to form the larger carbohydrate polymers such as starch, glycogen, cellulose, and chitin. Carbohydrates generally are stored in polymer form in living things (glycogen in animals, for example) but broken down into monomers to be used (glucose in animals).
  Web Tutorial 3.3: Monomers and Polymers
  Web Tutorial 3.4: Carbohydrates

3.6   Lipids

- There are several different varieties of lipids. Among the most important are the triglycerides, composed of a glyceride and three fatty acids. Most of the fats we consume are triglycerides. Another important variety of lipids is the steroids, which include cholesterol, and such hormones as testosterone and estrogen.
  Web Tutorial 3.5: Lipids
  Web Tutorial 3.6: Nutrition Labels

3.7   Proteins

- Proteins are a diverse group of biological molecules composed of the monomers called amino acids. Important groups of proteins include enzymes, which hasten chemical reactions, and structural proteins, which make up such structures as hair. The primary structure of a protein is its amino acid sequence; this sequence determines how a protein folds up. The activities of proteins are determined by their final, folded shapes.
  Web Tutorial 3.7: Proteins

3.8   Nucleotides and Nucleic Acids

- Nucleic acids are polymers composed of nucleotides. The nucleic acid DNA is composed of nucleotides that contain a phosphate group, a sugar (deoxyribose), and one of four nitrogen-containing bases. DNA is a repository of genetic information. The sequence of its bases encodes the information for the production of the huge array of proteins produced by living things.
  Web Tutorial 3.8: Nucleic Acids

Key Terms

acid 38
alkaline 40
alpha helix 58
base 38
beta pleated sheet 58
buffering system 40
carbohydrate 46
cellulose 48
chitin 49
cholesterol 52
deoxyribonucleic acid (DNA) 60
fatty acid 50
functional group 45
glycogen 48
glycoprotein 59
hydrocarbon 38
hydrophilic 38
hydrophobic 38
hydroxide ion 40
isomer 44
lipid 49
lipoprotein 58
monomer 46
monosaccharide 46

monounsaturated
fatty acid 50
nucleotide 60
oil 50
organic chemistry 43
pH scale 40
phosphate group 55
phospholipid 55
polymer 46
polypeptide 56
polysaccharide 48
polyunsaturated fatty acid 50
primary structure 58
protein 56
quaternary structure 58
ribonucleic acid (RNA) 60
saturated fatty acid 50
secondary structure 58
simple sugar 46
specific heat 36
starch 48
steroid 52
tertiary structure 58
triglyceride 50

Understanding the Basics

Multiple-Choice Questions (answers in the back of the book)

1. Near an ocean or other large body of water, air temperatures do not vary as much with the seasons as they do in the middle of a continent. This tendency of water to resist changes in temperature is the result of water's
   a. high density
   b. low density
   c. being a good solvent
   d. low specific heat
   e. high specific heat

2. A frog survives a freezing-cold winter on the bottom of a pond because
   a. Ice, which floats on water, insulates the water beneath it.
   b. The cells of a frog's body cannot freeze.
   c. Water has a low specific heat.
   d. The surface tension of water protects the frog's body.
   e. All of these are factors.

3. Janine has dry skin, so she uses body oil every morning. The oil seals in some of the water on her skin, so that it doesn't get as dry. This is possible because oils:
   a. are hydrophilic
   b. are rare in nature

   c. have a high specific heat
   d. are more dense than water
   e. are hydrophobic

4. Detergent added to water disrupts the network of hydrogen bonds between water molecules. One way entomologists (biologists who study insects) trap bees for population surveys is to place a tray of sugar water in the field to which they add a few drops of detergent. The bees are attracted to the sugar water and they land on its surface. Why do these investigators bother adding detergent when they know it's sugar that bees are attracted to?
   a. The detergent works with sugar to make the trays more attractive.
   b. They want to wash off any bee that's gathered.
   c. Water without hydrogen bonds is toxic to bees and therefore makes an effective trap.
   d. Water without hydrogen bonds is a much more effective bee attractant.
   e. Bees will sink into water with fewer hydrogen bonds, and so cannot escape.

5. When you eat starch such as spaghetti, an enzyme in your mouth breaks it down to maltose. Eventually, the maltose enters your small intestine, where it is broken down to glucose, which you can absorb into your bloodstream. The starch is a _____, the maltose is a _____, and the glucose is a(n) _____.
   a. protein   dipeptide   amino acid
   b. monosaccharide   disaccharide   polysaccharide
   c. triglyceride   fatty acid   glycerol
   d. amino acid   dipeptide   protein
   e. polysaccharide   disaccharide   monosaccharide

6. In some vintage science fiction movies space travelers find themselves on a planet orbiting a distant star in which there are curious forms of life based on silicon instead of carbon. Although the story clearly is sci-fi, there is an aura of plausibility in the choice of silicon, an atom with 14 protons, in place of carbon as this alien lifeform's central atom. This is because silicon:
   a. is lighter than carbon.
   b. is heavier than carbon.
   c. has one more proton than carbon, so is very similar to it.
   d. has 4 electrons in its outer-most shell.
   e. is an isotope of carbon.

7. The myoglobin protein, which carries oxygen in muscle cells, has only the first three levels of protein structure. In other words, it lacks a quaternary level. From this you can conclude that myoglobin
   a. is made of nucleic acids
   b. is made of only one polypeptide chain
   c. lacks hydrogen bonds
   d. is not helical or pleated
   e. is a fiber

8. You received your genetic information from your parents in the form of DNA. This DNA carried the instructions for making
   a. carbohydrates such as glycogen
   b. fatty acids

c. phospholipids for making the membranes of your cells

d. proteins

e. all of the above

9. John is lactose intolerant. The *-ose* ending indicates that John cannot digest a certain

a. sugar

b. polysaccharide

c. protein

d. steroid

e. enzyme

Brief Review

1. Describe two ways that water serves as a heat buffer.

2. Both low-density lipoproteins (LDLs) and high-density lipoproteins (HDLs) are involved with carrying fats through the bloodstream. If your LDL count is unusually high, should you be concerned? What if your HDL count is high? Why are they different?

3. List as many functions of proteins as possible. Why are proteins able to do so many different types of jobs? How does this affect the world we live in?

4. How does cohesion allow water to move through plants?

5. What effects does hydrogen bonding have on the properties of water?

Applying Your Knowledge

1. Would you buy a pH-balanced shampoo, or one that is not? Explain your answer.

2. Suppose that you are designing clothing to be worn at a space station on a very cold planet. Should you consider designing clothing that has a layer of water between two layers of plastic? Why or why not? What else might you need to consider?

3. Many species of beans produce a poisonous group of glycoproteins called lectins, which cause red blood cells to clump together (agglutinate) and cease to function. (Fortunately, cooking destroys most of them.) Using what you learned about the structure and function of glycoproteins, suggest how they might do this. What benefit do you think plants might get just by causing red blood cells to clump together?

MediaLab

You Are What You Eat: Food and the Molecules of Life

Not only do we obtain all of the matter that makes up our body from the food and water we take in, but the quality of the foods we consume is critical to our overall health. To learn more, enter the *Web Tutorial* and learn to analyze food labels so you can interpret the energy sources and classes of macromolecules found in your diet. Using the *Web Investigation*, you can determine your specific daily Calorie requirements, and recommended dietary allowances (RDAs) for macromolecules, minerals, and vitamins. In the *Communicate Your Results* section, you will develop strategies for designing a healthy diet.

The online version of this *MediaLab* can be found in Chapter 3 on your Companion Website (www.prenhall.com/krogh3).

WEB TUTORIAL

Obtaining enough Calories to perform our daily tasks is not hard for most Americans (although there is hunger in America). Indeed, many of us struggle with the problem of consuming too many Calories. Diets high in lipids (fats and oils) contribute to many health problems, including heart disease and cancer. How can you tell if your diet is healthy? In this *Web Tutorial*, you'll learn how to evaluate your diet using food labels.

Activity

1. *First you will learn to determine the Calories (energy content) in fats, carbohydrates, and protein molecules, and learn to find Calorie content on a nutrition label.*

2. *Then you will use this knowledge in calculating serving sizes and determining what percentage of Calories come from fats, carbohydrates, and proteins so that you can compare your results with the dietary levels suggested for a healthy diet.*

After learning to read a nutrition label, you'll be ready to tailor your diet to your specific energy requirements in the *Web Investigation*.

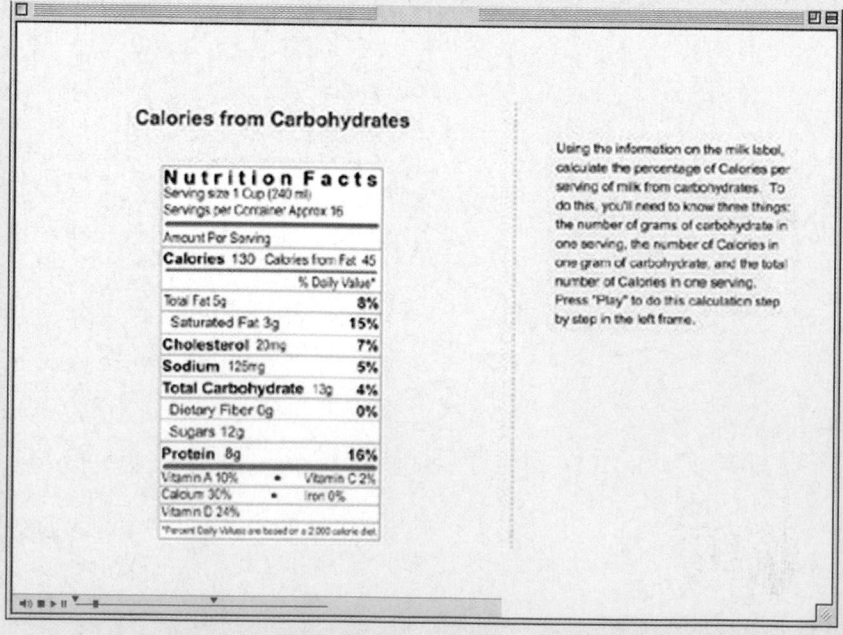

Investigation 1

Estimated time for completion = 5 minutes

Now that you have learned to read a food label and understand what you are eating, wouldn't it be nice to have a personal nutritionist determine the ideal diet for you? Select the keyword **HEALTHY BODY CALCULATOR** on the Website for this *MediaLab*. Then enter your personal description and submit it. You'll receive an analysis of your health status, including whether you are at a healthy weight and body fat percentage. You'll also receive a personalized daily guide for your food consumption.

Investigation 2

Estimated time for completion = 15 minutes, after keeping a 24-hour diet diary

Dieters often consider Calories when analyzing their diet, but forget to include healthy amounts of all food groups. To compare your recommended diet (from *Web Investigation 1*) with your actual diet, keep a 24-hour record of what you eat. When you are ready to analyze that diet, select the keyword **DIET ANALYSIS TOOL** on the Website for

this *MediaLab*, and enter your personal demographic and diet information. The site will calculate the total Calories consumed (for fats, proteins, and carbohydrates) and compare the result to your specific requirements.

Investigation 3

Time for completion = 5 minutes

The United States has one of the fattest populations on Earth. Over 20 percent of U.S. adults can be classified as clinically obese (due largely to our inability to resist a barrage of good-tasting, inexpensive, high-fat foods). By adding low-calorie fat substitutes, food manufacturers have responded to public pressure for foods with reduced fat content. How can you recognize a fat substitute, and are they good for you? Clip an ingredients label from a package of reduced or low-fat food, and make a list of any fat substitutes. To help you identify them, select the keyword **FAT SUBSTITUTES** on the Website for this *MediaLab*.

Now that you have analyzed your own diet, discuss with your peers what you have learned about creating a healthy diet.

Exercise 1

Estimated time for completion = 25 minutes

In the United States, many states now impose taxes on tobacco to discourage smoking and to help offset the health costs associated with smoking. However, heart disease, which has been linked to a high-fat diet, is the country's number one killer. In addition, more cancer cases in the United States are related to diet than to smoking. Compose a 250-word argument supporting or refuting the following plan: Taxing high-fat foods would be a great way to reduce the incidence of heart disease and help offset the cost of its treatment. The taxes could also be used to educate the public to the dangers of a high-fat diet, in the same way that taxes on cigarettes are used for antismoking ads.

Exercise 2

Estimated time for completion = 15 minutes

Compare the diet analysis that you did in *Web Investigation 2* with the diet of another student to determine ways you might help each other create a more healthy diet. How are your diets related? What nutrients or food groups are you eating too much of, or too little of? Revise your day's diet to match RDA guidelines, especially with less than 30 percent of total Calories from fat.

Exercise 3

Estimated time for completion = 5 minutes

Make a list of all the fat substitutes that you found on your ingredients label from *Web Investigation 3*. Indicate what type of fat substitute you found (like the synthetic fat Olestra). Can you determine how many Calories you would save by eating this reduced-fat product instead of the high-fat one?

4 *The Cell*

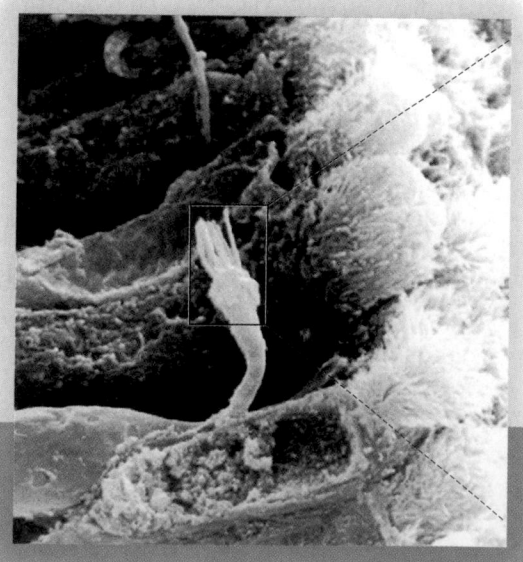

Are those muffins I smell?
(Section 4.1, page 70)

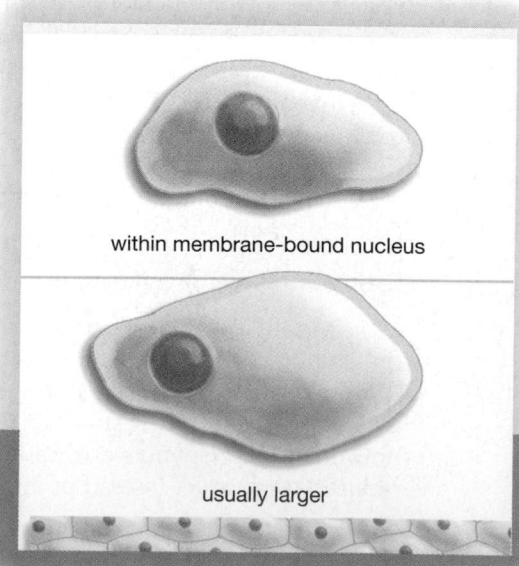

within membrane-bound nucleus

usually larger

Some cells need oxygen.
(Section 4.2, page 71)

Inside the cell.
(Section 4.3, page 74)

> **All life exists within cells. These tiny entities can be compared to factories whose products maintain life.**

The United States Senate has 100 members in it, and all of them do occasionally gather together to consider given issues. But if you want to know how the Senate actually gets something *done*, you must look elsewhere. The business of the nation is simply too complex for all Senate members to deal with all issues. Instead, issues are dealt with one at a time within the specialized working units of the Senate known as committees.

Something similar to this goes on in the natural world. If we look at birds or trees or people and ask how any of these living things actually gets something done, the answer once again is through working units—in this case the working units known as cells.

4.1 Cells Are the Working Units of Life

Muffins are in the oven and you are in the living room. Gas molecules from the baking muffins waft into the living room, and some of them happen to make their way to your nose, there to travel a short distance to your upper nasal cavity and land on a set

Nature's Fundamental Unit

(a) Human red and white blood cells inside a blood vessel. The large, dark ovals that can be seen in the background are flat cells that form the interior lining of the blood vessel.

(b) Cells of the fungus brewer's yeast, which is used to make wine, beer, and bread.

(c) Cells of a spinach leaf, with the leaf seen in cross-section. Two layers of outer or "epidermal" cells can be seen at top and bottom; many of the cells in between perform photosynthesis.

(a)

(b)

(c)

The protein production pathway.
(Section 4.4, page 75)

The center of attention.
(Section 4.4, page 76)

mRNA   ribosome

amino
acid chain

Where proteins take shape.
(Section 4.4, page 77)

69

of ceaselessly waving hair-like projections called cilia. These actually are the extensions of some specialized nerve cells (see **Figure 4.1**). If enough muffin molecules bind with enough of the cilia, an impulse is passed along (through other nerve cells) to trigger not only the *sensation* of smell, but the *association* of this smell with muffins you have smelled in the past. How do we know muffins are in the oven? Through cells. How do we move our hands or read this page? Through cells. Life's working units are cells, and in our amazingly complex natural world, there is a great specialization in them. The nerve cells in human beings are specialists in transmitting nerve signals, red blood cells are specialists in transporting oxygen, and muscle cells are specialists in contracting.

Running like a thread through this diversity, however, is the unity of cellular life. Every form of life either is a cell, or is composed of cells. The one possible exception to this is viruses, but even they must use the machinery of cells in order to reproduce. There is unity, too, in the way cells come about: Every cell comes *from* a cell. Human beings are incapable of producing cells from scratch in the laboratory, and so far as we can tell, nature has fashioned cells from simple molecules only once—back when life on Earth got started. The fact that all cells come from cells means that each cell in your body is a link in a cellular chain that stretches back more than 3.5 billion years.

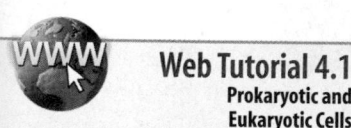

Web Tutorial 4.1
Prokaryotic and
Eukaryotic Cells

4.2 All Cells Are Either Prokaryotic or Eukaryotic

So, what are these tiny, working units we call cells? It follows, from the variety of cells that exist, there is no such thing as a "typical" cell. There are, however, certain *categories* of cells that are important, and the two most important of these are prokaryotic and eukaryotic cells. Every cell that exists is one or the other, and this simple either-or quality extends to the organisms that fall into these camps. All prokaryotic cells either are bacteria or another microscopic form of life known as archaea. Setting bacteria and archaea aside, *all other cells* are eukaryotic. This means all the cells in plants, in animals, in fungi—all the cells in every living thing except in the bacteria and the archaea.

Prokaryotic and Eukaryotic Differences

The name *eukaryote* comes from the Greek *eu*, meaning "true," and *karyon*, meaning "nucleus," while *prokaryote* means "before nucleus." These terms describe the most critical distinction between the two cell types. **Eukaryotic cells** are cells whose primary complement of DNA is enclosed within a nucleus. **Prokaryotic cells** are cells whose DNA is not enclosed within a nucleus. To complete this circle, a **nucleus** is a membrane-lined compartment that encloses the primary complement of DNA in eukaryotic cells.

While having a nucleus is the most important difference between eukaryotic and prokaryotic cells, it is not the only difference. It may seem sensible to think of two single-celled creatures—one a prokaryote, the other a eukaryote—as being very similar, but the distance between them as life-forms is immense. Human beings and chimpanzees are nearly identical in comparison. Eukaryotic cells tend to be much larger than their prokaryotic counterparts; indeed, thousands of bacteria could easily fit into an average eukaryotic cell (see "The Size of Cells" on page 72). Eukaryotes are quite often multicelled organisms, while prokaryotes are always single-celled. And al-

Figure 4.1
Cells Can Specialize
In more complex organisms, different cells carry out different functions. In the picture at left, you can see one type of cell,—a nerve cell, in this case located in the lining of the nose and surrounded by gray accessory cells. A closer look at one of these nerve cells, in the picture at right, shows a number of hair-like extensions, called cilia, protruding from it. When we smell muffins in the oven, gas molecules that waft off the muffins bind with the cilia, which sets in motion a nerve impulse to the brain about the muffins.

cilia

nasal
nerve
cell

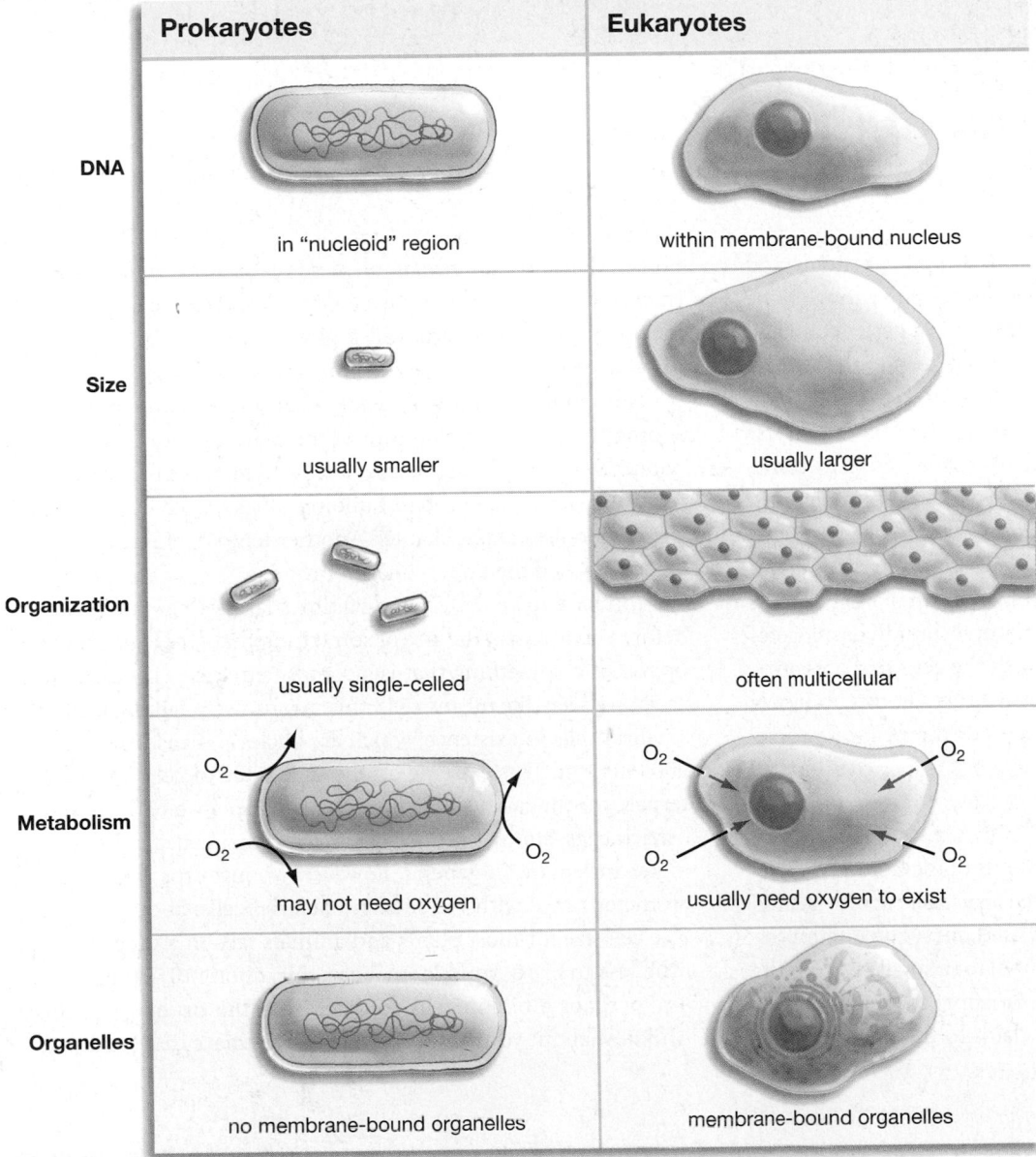

Prokaryotes	Eukaryotes
DNA in "nucleoid" region	within membrane-bound nucleus
Size usually smaller	usually larger
Organization usually single-celled	often multicellular
Metabolism may not need oxygen	usually need oxygen to exist
Organelles no membrane-bound organelles	membrane-bound organelles

**Figure 4.2
Prokaryotic and Eukaryotic
Cells Compared**
A prokaryotic cell is a self-contained organism, since the prokaryotes—bacteria and archaea—are all single-celled. Eukaryotic organisms, which may be single- or multicelled, include plants, animals, fungi, and another group called protists.

most all eukaryotes are aerobic—they need oxygen to exist—whereas many prokaryotes can get along with or without oxygen, while others actually are poisoned by it (**see Figure 4.2**).

Perhaps the most notable distinction between prokaryotic and eukaryotic cells, though, is that eukaryotic cells are *compartmentalized* to a far greater degree than is the case with prokaryotes. The nucleus in eukaryotic cells turns out to be only one variety of **organelle**: a highly organized structure, internal to a cell, that serves some specialized function. Eukaryotic cells contain several different kinds of these "tiny organs." There are organelles called mitochondria, for example, that transform energy from food, and organelles called lysosomes that recycle the raw materials of the cell. In prokaryotic cells, meanwhile, there is only a single type of organelle—a kind of workbench for producing proteins we'll look at later.

If we look at eukaryotes that are familiar to us, such as trees, and mushrooms, and horses, it's easy to see that there is a fantastic diversity in the *forms* of eukaryotes, compared to the strictly single-celled prokaryotes. It does not follow from this, however, that prokaryotes are uniform, nor that they are unsuccessful. On the contrary, prokaryotes differ greatly from one another in, say, the way they obtain nutrients, and they are extremely successful, if success is defined as living in a lot of places in huge numbers. As Lynn Margulis and Karlene Schwartz have observed, more bacteria are living in your mouth right now than the number of people who have ever existed. But for the range of biological structures and processes we want to look at, eukaryotic cells are more diverse, and hence are the initial focus of our study.

The Size of Cells

For several chapters, you've been going over atoms and ions and molecules and such—things small enough to be invisible to the unaided eye. For the most part, you've had to imagine what these things look like, simply because most of them are so small that we either have no pictures of them at all (as with electrons) or few clear pictures (as with atoms). If you flip through the pages of this chapter and those to come, however, you begin to see a fair number of actual photographs. They don't have the same quality as summer vacation snapshots, but they are recognizable as pictures, or more properly as **micrographs** (pictures taken with the aid of a microscope). Micrographs enable us to see surprising things; for example, hundreds of bacteria on the tip of a pin (**Figure 1**). So, with the cells that are introduced in this chapter, there has obviously been a bump up in size into a world that is more easily visible with the help of various kinds of technology.

How Small Are They?

In taking stock of the micro-world, two units of measure are particularly valuable. The smaller of them is the **nanometer**, abbreviated as nm; the larger is the **micrometer**, abbreviated μm. (The unfamiliar-looking first letter there is the Greek symbol for a small *m*. Scientists are not trying to be purposely obscure in using it; another unit of the metric system, the millimeter, lays claim to the mm abbrevia-tion.) What these abbreviations stand for is a billionth of a meter (nm) and a millionth of a meter (μm). A meter equals about 39.6 inches, or just over a yard, which gives you some starting sense of physical reality in understanding the rest of these sizes.

Now look at **Figure 2** to see what size various objects are. Atoms are down at the bottom of the scale, at about a tenth of a nanometer. Something less than a tenfold increase from there gets us to the size of the protein building blocks, called amino acids, that you looked at last chapter. Another tenfold-plus increase and you've reached the upper limit on proteins.

You have to go better than 10 times larger than this, however, before you arrive at the size of something that is actually *living*, as opposed to something that is a component part of life. Because, as you've seen, life means cells, this means we're talking about the smallest cells in existence, which are bacteria measuring perhaps 200–300 nm. This extreme on the small side of cells has a counterpart on the large side with the single cells we call chicken or ostrich eggs, and with certain nerve cells that can stretch out to a meter in length. In general, however, we just cross into the micrometer range with the smaller bacterial cells: about 1–10 μm. The cell size for most plants and animals falls in a range that is a little less than 10 times larger than this, about 10–30 μm. At 10 μm, perhaps a billion cells could fit into the tip of your finger. And how about your whole body? One estimate is 100 trillion.

(a) Bacteria on a pin, magnified x 85

(b) Magnified x 425

(c) Magnified x 2100

Figure 1
Hidden Life
Microscope enlargements of the tip of this pin show an abundance of life—in this case bacteria—thriving on an object that we normally think of as being devoid of living organisms.

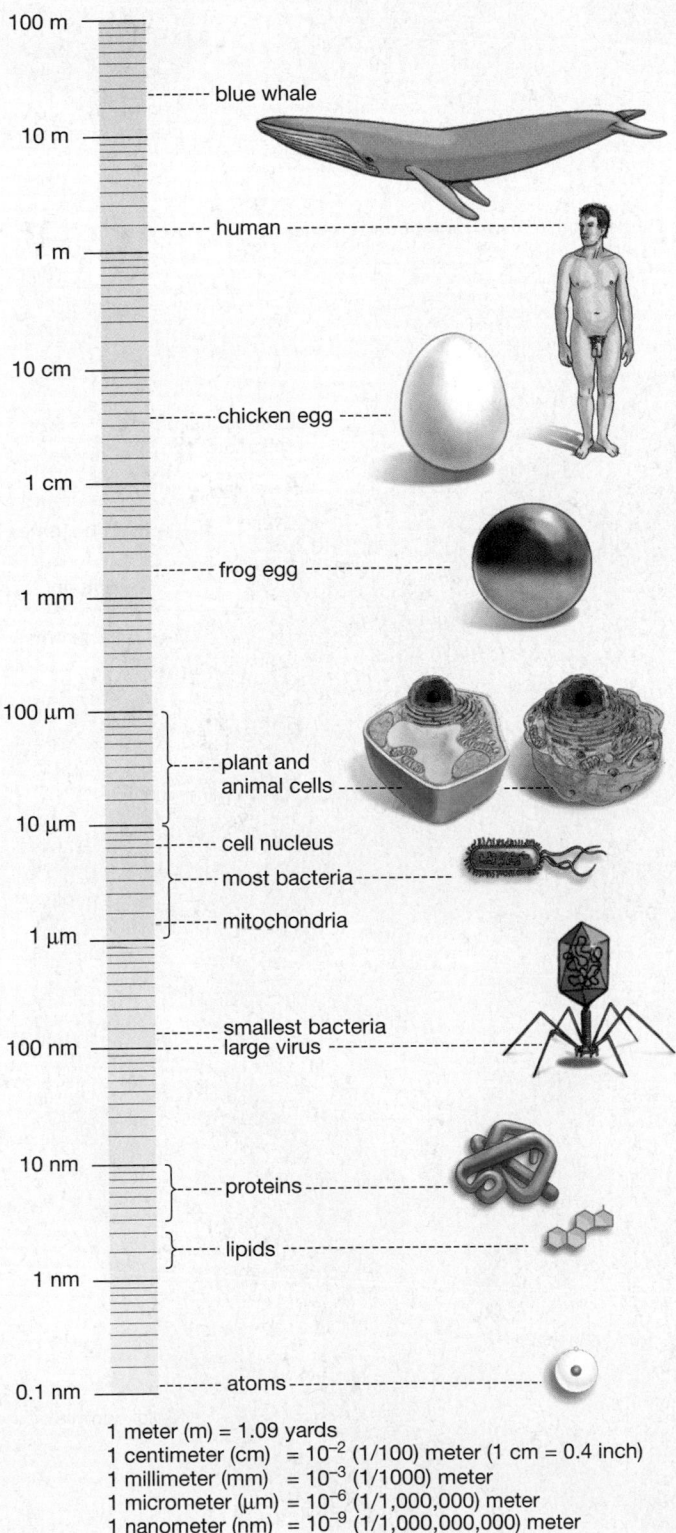

100 m — blue whale

10 m —

1 m — human

10 cm — chicken egg

1 cm —

frog egg

1 mm —

100 μm —

plant and
animal cells

10 μm — cell nucleus

most bacteria

mitochondria

1 μm —

smallest bacteria

100 nm — large virus

10 nm — proteins

lipids

1 nm —

0.1 nm — atoms

1 meter (m) = 1.09 yards
1 centimeter (cm) = 10^{-2} (1/100) meter (1 cm = 0.4 inch)
1 millimeter (mm) = 10^{-3} (1/1000) meter
1 micrometer (μm) = 10^{-6} (1/1,000,000) meter
1 nanometer (nm) = 10^{-9} (1/1,000,000,000) meter

Figure 2
Little and Big
The sizes of some selected objects in the natural world.

So, Why So Small?

Having learned how small cells are, you might then well ask: *Why* are they so small? As noted, cells are small chemical factories, and just like any factory, they are constantly shipping things in and out. A primary size-limiting factor for cells is having enough surface area to export and import all that they need.

This constraint comes about because of a fundamental mathematical principle: As the surface area of an object increases, its *volume* increases even more. Say you have a cube, 1 inch long on each of its sides. Its surface area is 6 square inches (length × width × number of sides), while its volume is one cubic inch (length × width × height). Now say you increase the side dimension to 8 inches. The surface area goes from 6 to 384 square inches, but the *volume* goes from 1 to 512 cubic inches. Where, at a 1-inch dimension, there were *six* square inches of surface area for every cubic inch of volume, now there are only *three-quarters* of an inch of surface for every cubic inch of volume. Beyond a certain volume, then, a cell simply would not have enough surface area to import and export all the materials it needs. This effectively sets an upper limit on how big cells can be and helps explain why most of the cells in an elephant are no bigger than those in an ant, though the elephant does have more cells than the ant. **Figure 3** shows you some size comparisons in the micro-world.

poliovirus

section
of DNA
molecule

ribosome

glucose
(blood sugar)
molecule

carbon
atom

5 nm

Figure 3
Small Is a Relative Thing
The sizes and shapes of five natural-world entities, each magnified a million times.

Components of eukaryotic cells

nucleus

other organelles

cytosol

cytoskeleton

plasma membrane

Figure 4.3
Eukaryotic Cell
This cutaway view of a eukaryotic cell displays the elements that nearly all such cells possess: a nucleus, other membrane-bound organelles, a jelly-like cytosol, a cytoskeleton, and an outer plasma membrane.

nuclear pores

DNA

nucleus

nuclear envelope

nucleolus

smooth endoplasmic reticulum

free ribosomes

cytoskeleton

cytosol

lysosomes

rough endoplasmic reticulum

plasma membrane

transport vesicle

mitochondria

Golgi complex

Figure 4.4
The Animal Cell

4.3 The Eukaryotic Cell

What are the constituent parts of eukaryotic cells? Here are five larger structures that in turn have smaller structures within them. The first two have been mentioned already (**see Figure 4.3**).

- The cell's nucleus
- Other organelles (which lie outside the nucleus)
- The **cytosol**, a protein-rich, jelly-like fluid in which the cell's organelles are immersed
- The *cytoskeleton*, a kind of internal scaffolding consisting of three sorts of protein fibers; some of these can be likened to tent poles, others to monorails
- The **plasma membrane**, the outer lining of the cell

In any discussion of a cell, you are likely to hear the term **cytoplasm**, which simply means the *region* of the cell inside the plasma membrane but outside the nucleus. The cytoplasm is different from the cyto*sol*. If you removed all the structures of the cytoplasm—meaning the organelles and the cytoskeleton—what would be left is the cytosol, which is mostly water. This does not mean that the cytosol is simply a passive medium for the other structures. But it is not an organized structure in the way the organelles are. Almost all the organelles you'll see are encased in their own membranes, just as the whole cell is encased in its plasma membrane. What are membranes? Until you get the formal definition next chapter, think of a membrane as the flexible, chemically active outer lining of a cell or of its compartments. In the balance of this chapter, we'll explore all of the constituent parts listed above except for the plasma membrane, which is so special it gets its own chapter.

The Animal Cell

Scientists sometimes make a convenient division of eukaryotic cells into two types: animal cells and plant cells. These cell types have more similarities than they do differences, but they are different *enough* that it will be helpful to look at them separately. We'll start by examining animal cells and then look at how plant cells differ from them.

Insofar as we can characterize that elusive creature, the "typical" animal cell (**see Figure 4.4**), it is roughly spherical, surrounded by, and linked to, cells of similar type, immersed in water; and about 25 micrometers (μm) in diameter, meaning that about 30 of them could fit side by side within the period at the end of this sentence.

4.4 A Tour of the Animal Cell: Along the Protein Production Path

You are now going to take an extended tour of the animal cell, which can be thought of as a living factory. Much of the first part of your trip will be spent tracing the way this factory puts together a product—a protein—for export outside itself. Just as a new employee might tour an assembly line as a means of learning about factory equipment, so you are going to follow the path of protein production as a means of learning about cell equipment.

Figure 4.5 shows the path you'll be taking, from nucleus to the outer edge of the cell. Don't be bothered by the unfamiliar terms in Figure 4.5, because they'll all be explained in the text. The important thing is that, before we begin our tour, you have some sense of the path that protein production takes.

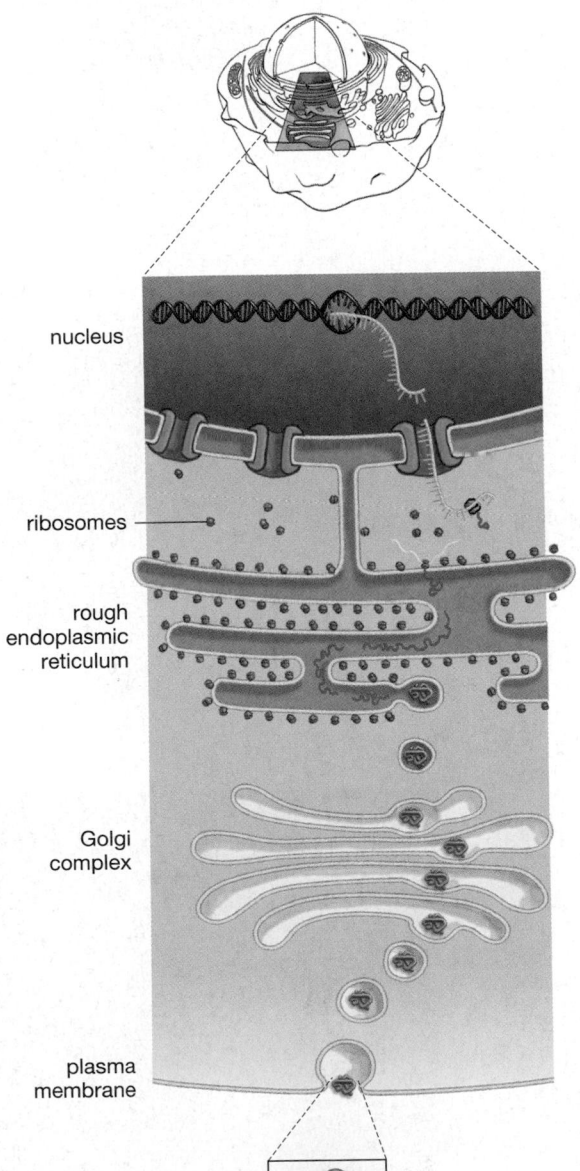

nucleus

ribosomes

rough endoplasmic reticulum

Golgi complex

plasma membrane

1. Instructions from DNA are copied onto mRNA.

2. mRNA moves to ribosome.

3. Ribosome moves to endoplasmic reticulum and "reads" mRNA instructions.

4. Amino acid chain growing from ribosome is dropped inside endoplasmic reticulum membrane. Chain folds into protein.

5. Protein moves to Golgi complex for additional processing and for sorting.

6. Protein moves to plasma membrane for export.

Figure 4.5
Path of Protein Production in Cells

Beginning in the Control Center: The Nucleus

As noted in Chapter 3, proteins are critical working molecules in living things, and DNA contains the information for producing these proteins. Our entire complement of DNA is like a cookbook that contains individual recipes, which we call genes. Each gene's chemical building blocks in effect say, "Now give me some of this, now some of this, then some of this," the final result being the specifications for a protein. (See Chapter 3, p. 60.) In the eukaryotic cell, as you've seen, DNA is largely confined within a nucleus bound by a membrane. If you look at **Figure 4.6**, you can see the nature of this membrane. It is the **nuclear envelope**: the double membrane that lines the nucleus in eukaryotic cells.

There comes a point in the life of most cells when they divide, one cell becoming two. Because (with a few exceptions) all cells must possess the set of instructions that are contained in DNA, it follows that when a cell divides, its original complement of DNA must *duplicate*, so that both cells that result from the cell division can have their own DNA. The nucleus, then, is not just the site where DNA exists; it is the site where new DNA is put together, or "synthesized," for this duplication.

Messenger RNA

At the end of Chapter 3, you saw that the process of protein synthesis requires that DNA's instructions first get copied onto another long-chain molecule, RNA.

Figure 4.6
The Cell's Nucleus
The DNA of eukaryotic cells is sequestered inside a compartment, the nucleus, which is lined by a double membrane known as the nuclear envelope. Compounds pass into and out of the nucleus through a series of microscopic channels called nuclear pores. The prominent spherical structure within the nucleus is the nucleolus, an area that specializes in the production of ribosomal RNA—the material that helps make up ribosomes. Protein production is dependent upon the information encoded in DNA's sequence of chemical building blocks. This information is copied onto a length of messenger RNA (mRNA), which then exits from the nucleus through a nuclear pore. (Micrograph: ×4400)

Nucleus

nucleolus

nuclear envelope

DNA

DNA

mRNA

inner membrane

outer membrane

nuclear pore

Nuclear envelope

This step is akin to having a cassette tape (of DNA) and then making a copy of it (onto RNA). Our RNA "tape" then moves out to the cell's cytoplasm to continue the process of protein synthesis. As it turns out, RNA comes in several forms. The one that the DNA instructions are copied onto is called *messenger RNA* (mRNA). Given that mRNA goes to the cytoplasm, it must, of course, have some way of getting out of the nucleus; its exit points turn out to be thousands of channels that stud the surface of the nuclear envelope—the *nuclear pores*. Materials can go the other way through the nuclear pores as well: Proteins and other materials pass from the cytoplasm into the nucleus by way of them.

mRNA Moves Out of the Nucleus

Imagine shrinking down in size so that the nucleus seems about as big as a house, with you standing outside it. What you would see in protein synthesis is lengths of mRNA, rapidly moving out through nuclear pores and dropping off into the cytoplasm. Several varieties of RNA actually come out like this, but for now, let's just follow the trail of the mRNA. You're about ready to leave the nucleus to continue your cell tour, but before you do, note two things. First, DNA contains information for making proteins, and the mRNA coming out of the nuclear pores amounts to a means of disseminating this information. Thus, it's not hard to conceptualize the nucleus as a control center for the cell. Beyond this, in looking at Figure 4.6, you've probably noticed that there is a rather imposing structure *within* the nucleus, called the nucleolus. For now, just *hold that thought*; the mRNA tapes have come out of the nuclear pores and are making a short trip to another part of the cell.

Ribosomes

Small structures called ribosomes are the destination for our mRNA tapes. For now, we can define the **ribosome** as an organelle that serves as the site of protein synthesis in the cell. In line with this, ribosomes are commonly described as the "workbenches" of protein synthesis, which is a fine metaphor. But following the notion of mRNA as a cassette tape, you might look at a ribosome as a kind of *playback head* on a cassette deck. What does such a head do in an actual deck? As a tape is run through it, it reads signals that have been laid down on it (as magnetic bits) and turns these into sound. Likewise, each ribosome acts as a site that an mRNA tape runs through, only the information on this tape results in the production of an *object* that grows from the ribosome: A chain of amino acids that folds up into the molecule we call a protein (**see Figure 4.7**).

Rough endoplasmic reticulum

nuclear envelope

ribosomes

cisternae

cisternal spaces

mRNA   ribosome

amino acid chain

1. mRNA docks on ribosome. Amino acid chain production begins.

2. Ribosome docks on ER. Amino acid chain moves into cisternal space as it is completed.

3. Amino acid chain folds up making a protein.

4. Side chains added to protein.

5. Vesicle formed to house protein while in transport.

Figure 4.7
Proteins Taking Shape: Ribosomes and the Rough Endoplasmic Reticulum
The steps of the lower figure begin with a messenger RNA "tape," which has migrated from the nucleus of a cell. (**1**) The tape binds with a ribosome that is free-standing in the cytoplasm. The ribosome then starts to "read" the length of the mRNA, which bears instructions for producing a protein. The result is an amino acid (or polypeptide) chain that begins to grow from one part of the ribosome. The ribosome soon halts this activity, however, and moves toward the rough endoplasmic reticulum (rough ER). (**2**) The ribosome docks on the outside face of the rough ER and resumes reading the mRNA tape. When it is completed, the resulting amino acid chain drops into the cisternal space of the rough ER. (**3**) The amino acid chain folds up, thus becoming a protein. (**4**) The protein undergoes processing (in this example, by having a side-chain added). (**5**) The protein is then encased in a membrane-lined vesicle, which will bud off from the rough ER and be transported to the Golgi complex. (Micrograph: ×90,500)

You may remember that the kind of protein we are tracking will eventually be exported out of the cell altogether. The synthesis of this kind of protein actually stops when only a very short sequence of the amino acid (or "polypeptide") chain has grown from the ribosome. Why? "Export" polypeptide chains need to be processed within other structures in the cell before they can become fully functional proteins. The first step in this process is for the ribosome, and its associated cargo, to migrate a short distance in the cell and then attach to another cell structure.

The Rough Endoplasmic Reticulum

If you look again at Figure 4.4, you can see that, though the nucleus cuts a roughly spherical figure out of the cell, there is, in essence, a folded-up continuation of the nuclear envelope on one side. This mass of membrane has a name that is a mouthful: the **rough endoplasmic reticulum**. This structure can be defined as a network of membranes that aids in the processing of proteins in eukaryotic cells. The rough endoplasmic reticulum is rough because it is studded with ribosomes; it is endoplasmic because it lies within (endo) the cyto*plasm*; and it is a reticulum because it is a network, which is what *reticulum* means in Latin. Understandably, it is generally referred to as the rough ER or the RER.

Our ribosome, bound up with its mRNA and polypeptide chains, will migrate to the rough ER and dock on its outside face, thus joining a multitude of other ribosomes that have done the same thing. As noted, the polypeptide chain that is being output from the ribosome is, in essence, an unfinished protein that needs to go through more processing before it can be exported. The first step in this processing leads only to the other side of the ER wall the ribosome is embedded in. As the ribosome goes on with its work, the polypeptide chain it is producing drops into chambers inside the rough ER.

If you look at Figure 4.7, you can see that the whole of the rough ER takes the shape of a set of flattened sacs (called *cisternae*). The membrane that the rough ER is composed of forms the periphery of these sacs. Inside are the *cisternal spaces* of the rough ER (sometimes referred to as rough ER's *lumen*). As polypeptide chains enter the cisternal spaces, they first fold up into their protein shapes, as you saw in Chapter 3. Beyond this, most proteins that are exported from cells have sugar side-chains added to them here. Quality control of the production line is in operation in the RER as well. Polypeptide chains that have faulty sequences are detected in the RER cisternal space and ejected out of the protein production line altogether, after which they are degrad-ed into their component parts. Other proteins will pass the quality control tests, however, and will then move out of the RER for more processing.

Several Locations for Ribosomes

All of the mRNA that comes out of the nuclear pores goes to ribosomes, but only some of these ribosomes end up migrating to the rough ER. A multitude of ribosomes will remain "free ribosomes," which is to say ribosomes that remain free-standing in the cytosol. What makes the difference? Remember how, in the ribosome we looked at, only a small stretch of the polypeptide chain it was producing emerged before the ribosome first halted its work and then migrated to the RER? That small stretch of the chain contained a chemical signal that said, in effect, "RER processing needed." The result was the ribosome's move to the RER. In general, these RER-linked ribosomes produce proteins that will reside in the cell's membranes or that will be exported out of the cell altogether (making them **secretory proteins**). Meanwhile, free ribosomes tend to produce proteins that will be used within the cell's cytoplasm or nucleus.

A Pause for the Nucleolus

Before you continue on the path of protein processing, think back a bit to the discussion about the nucleus, when you were asked to hold the thought about the large structure *inside* the nucleus, called the nucleolus. This is the point where its story can be told, because now you know what ribosomes are.

It turns out that *ribosomes* are mostly made of RNA. (They are made of a mixture of proteins and *ribo*nucleic acid.) But so great is the cell's need for ribosomes that a special section of the nucleus is devoted to the synthesis of RNA. This is the nucleolus. The *type* of RNA that's part of the ribosomes is, fittingly enough, called ribosomal RNA or rRNA, and it's one of the multiple varieties of RNA mentioned before. With this in mind, we can define the **nucleolus** as the area within the nucleus of a cell devoted to the production of ribosomal RNA.

Ribosomes are brought only to an unfinished state within the nucleolus, after which they pass through the nuclear pores and into the cytoplasm; when put together in final form there, they begin receiving mRNA tapes. They are the one variety of organelle that is not lined by a membrane. (They are also the one variety of organelle that prokaryotic cells have.) The cell's traffic in ribosomes is considerable; with millions of them in existence, lots are going to be wearing out all the time. Perhaps a thousand need to be replaced every minute.

Elegant Transportation: Transport Vesicles

The proteins that have been processed within the rough ER need to move out of it and to their "downstream" destinations before being exported. But how do proteins move from one location to another within the cell? Recall that the rough ER and the nuclear membrane amount to one long, convoluted membrane. And, as just noted, all the organelles in the cell except ribosomes are "membrane-bound," meaning they have membranes at their periphery. Each of these membranes has its own chemical structure, but collectively they have an amazing ability to work together: A piece of one membrane can *bud off*, as the term goes, carrying inside it some of our proteins-in-process. Moving through the cytosol, this tiny sphere of membrane can then *fuse* with another membrane-bound organelle, releasing its protein cargo in the process. The membrane-lined spheres that move within this network, carrying proteins and other molecules, are called **transport vesicles**. The network itself is known as the **endomembrane system**: an interactive group of membrane-lined organelles and transport vesicles within eukaryotic cells.

This system gives cells a remarkable capability. One minute a piece of membrane may be an integral part of, say, the rough ER; the next it is separating off as a spheroid and moving through the cytosol, carrying proteins within. It is this system that makes it possible for our proteins-in-process to move out of the rough ER. Note, though, that many different *kinds* of proteins are being processed at any one time in the rough ER cisternae. It is as if the cellular factory has a lot of different assembly lines working at once. Most of the proteins under construction are, however, initially bound for the same place—the Golgi complex.

Downstream from the Rough ER: The Golgi Complex

Once a transport vesicle, bearing proteins, has budded off from the rough ER, it then moves through the cytosol to fuse with the membrane of another organelle, one first noticed by Italian biologist Camillo Golgi at the beginning of the twentieth century. The **Golgi complex** is a network of membranes that processes and distributes proteins that come to it from the rough endoplasmic reticulum. Some side-chains of sugar may be trimmed from proteins here, or phosphate groups may be added. But the Golgi complex does something else as well. Recall that some proteins in this production line are bound for export outside the cell, while others will end up being used within various membranes in the cell. It follows that proteins have to be *sorted and shipped* appropriately, and the Golgi does just this, acting as a kind of distribution center. Chemical "tags" that are part of the proteins often allow for this routing. Remember how, in the rough ER, carbohydrate side-chains might be attached to a newly formed protein? Oftentimes these side-chains serve as the routing tags; other times a section of the protein's amino acid sequence will serve this function.

The Golgi is similar to the ER in that it amounts to a series of cisternae, or connected membranous sacs with internal spaces (**see Figure 4.8**). Proteins

Figure 4.8
Processing and Routing: The Golgi Complex
Transport vesicles from the rough endoplasmic reticulum (RER) move to the Golgi complex, where they unload their protein contents by fusing with the Golgi membrane. The protein is then passed, within other vesicles, through the layers of disk-shaped Golgi cisternae, where editing of the protein may occur. At the part of the Golgi furthest from the rough ER, the proteins are sorted, packed in vesicles, and shipped to sites mostly in cell membranes or outside the cell altogether. The vesicles in the micrograph are the pink and purple spheres.

Golgi complex

1. Transport vesicle from RER fuses with Golgi

2. Protein undergoes more processing in Golgi

Side chains are edited (sugars may be trimmed, phosphate groups added).

3. Proteins are sorted and shipped...

for export out of cell

to plasma membrane

to cytosol

cisternae

cisternal space

vesicle

arrive at the Golgi housed in transport vesicles that fuse with the Golgi "face" nearest the RER, at which point the vesicles release their protein cargo into the Golgi cisternal sacs for processing. Once processed, proteins of the sort we are following eventually bud off from the outside face of the Golgi, now housed in their final transport vesicles.

From the Golgi to the Surface

For secretory proteins, the journey that began with the copying of DNA information onto messenger RNA is almost over. Once a vesicle buds off from the Golgi, all that remains is for it to make its way through the cytosol to the plasma membrane at the outer reaches of the cell. There, the vesicle fuses with the plasma membrane and the protein is ejected into the extracellular world. This last step, called exocytosis, is a process you'll be looking at next chapter. With it, one finished product of the cellular factory has rolled out the door.

4.5 Outside the Protein Production Path: Other Cell Structures

A functioning cell engages in more activities than the protein synthesis and shipment just reviewed, for the simple reason that cells do a lot more than produce proteins.

The Smooth Endoplasmic Reticulum

If you look back to Figure 4.4, you can see that there actually are *two* kinds of endoplasmic reticuli. The part of the ER membrane, farther out from the nucleus, that has no ribosomes is called the smooth endoplasmic reticulum or smooth ER. It's "smooth" because it is not peppered with ribosomes, and this very quality means it is not a site of protein synthesis. Instead, the **smooth endoplasmic reticulum** is a network of membranes that is the site of the synthesis of various lipids, and a site at which potentially harmful substances are detoxified within the cell. The tasks the smooth ER undertakes, however, will vary in accordance with cell type. The lipids we normally think of as "fats" are synthesized and stored in the smooth ER of liver and fat cells, while the "steroid" lipids reviewed last chapter—testosterone and estrogen—are synthesized in the smooth ER of the ovaries and testes. The detoxification of potentially harmful substances, such as alcohol, takes place largely in the smooth ER of liver cells.

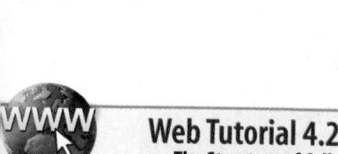

Web Tutorial 4.2
The Structure of Cells

Tiny Acid Vats: Lysosomes and Cellular Recycling

Any factory must be able to get rid of some old materials, while recycling others. A factory also needs new materials, brought in from the outside, that probably will have to undergo some processing before being used. A single organelle in the animal cell aids in doing all these things. It is the **lysosome**: an organelle found in animal cells that digests worn-out cellular materials and foreign materials that enter the cell. Several hundred of these membrane-bound organelles may exist in any given cell. You could think of them as sealed-off acid vats that take in large molecules, break them down, and then return the resulting smaller molecules to the cytosol. What they cannot return, they retain inside themselves or expel outside the cell. They carry out this work not only on molecules entering the cell from the outside (say, invading bacteria) but on materials that exist inside the cell—on worn-out organelle parts, for example (**see Figure 4.9**).

A given lysosome may be filled with as many as 40 different enzymes that can break larger molecules into their component parts—an enzymatic array that allows each lysosome to break down most of what comes its way. A lysosome gets ahold of its macromolecule prey through the endomembrane system. A lysosome will fuse with the membrane surrounding a worn-out organelle part; proceeding to engulf it, the lysosome then goes to work breaking the organelle down. The small molecules that result then pass freely out of the lysosome and into the cytosol for reuse elsewhere. Thus, there is recycling at the cellular level. Cells carry out this kind of self-renewal at an amazing rate. Christian de Duve, who with his colleagues discovered lysosomes in the 1950s, has noted the effect of this activity on human brain cells. In an elderly person, he notes, such cells

> have been there for decades. Yet most of their mitochondria, ribosomes, membranes, and other organelles are less than a month old. Over the years, the cells have destroyed and remade most of their constituent molecules from hundreds to thousands of times, some even more than 100,000 times.

There are certain things, however, that even lysosomes cannot digest, and over time these substances can cause lysosomes to leak their acidic contents into the cell, causing great harm. You may have heard of an affliction called black lung disease that miners are prey to. One form of this disease, called silicosis, is caused by the inability of lysosomes to digest the silica fibers that miners inhale. Because these fibers have a needle-like shape, they can cause the lysosomes to leak. The result is an acid spill that can kill cells and produce scar tissue in the lungs, thus reducing the miners' ability to breathe.

Extracting Energy from Food: Mitochondria

Just as there is no such thing as a free lunch, there is no such thing as free lysosome activity, or ribosomal action, or protein export. There is a price to be paid for all these things, and it is called energy expenditure. The fuel for this energy is contained in the food that cells ingest. But the energy in this food has to be converted into a molecular *form* that the cell can easily use, just as the energy in, say, coal needs to be converted by a power plant into a form that home appliances can easily use—electricity. The place to look for most of this conversion is inside

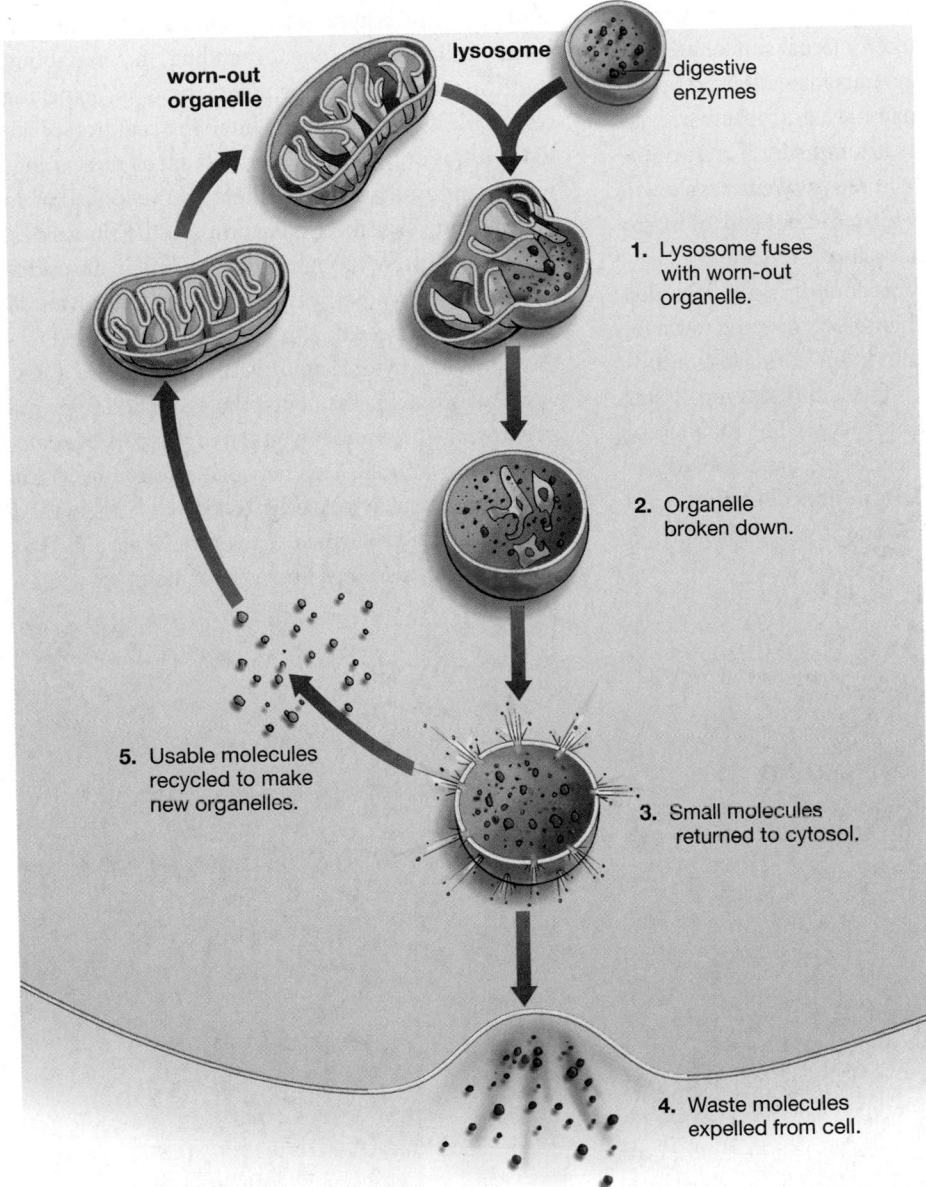

worn-out organelle

lysosome

digestive enzymes

1. Lysosome fuses with worn-out organelle.

2. Organelle broken down.

3. Small molecules returned to cytosol.

5. Usable molecules recycled to make new organelles.

4. Waste molecules expelled from cell.

Figure 4.9
Cellular Recycling: Lysosomes
Lysosomes are membrane-bound organelles that contain potent enzymes capable of digesting large molecules, such as worn-out organelles. The useful parts of such organelles will be returned to the cytosol and used elsewhere—a form of cellular recycling. If a lysosome cannot digest a given material, it may expel it outside the cell, though, in multicelled organisms, lysosomes generally will hold on to such materials, so as not to harm structures outside the cell. Lysosomes also digest small particles, such as food, that come from outside the cell, along with invading organisms, such as bacteria.

the **mitochondria**, which can be defined as organelles that are the primary sites of energy conversion in eukaryotic cells. While cells that don't use much energy might have one or two mitochondria within them, an energy-ravenous liver cell might have one thousand. Most of the heat in our bodies is generated within mitochondria, and almost all the food we eat is ultimately consumed in them.

Figure 4.10 shows a classical view of a mitochondrion. Note that there is a continuous outer membrane enclosing an inner membrane that has a series of convolutions in it. The effect of these infoldings is to give mitochondria a larger internal surface area for carrying out their energy transformation activities. This nice, tidy picture may have a problem with it, however, in that scientists are not sure if mitochondria really are the kind of discrete, oval entities shown, or if they actually take the form of a network of membranes—more like the endoplasmic reticulum.

Few details about mitochondria are included here, because much of Chapter 7 is devoted to them. Suffice it to say that to carry out their work, mitochondria need not only food, but oxygen. (Ever wonder why you need to breathe?) The *products* of mitochondrial activity, meanwhile, are carbon dioxide, water, and the energy molecule that cells "spend" on their activities, adenosine triphosphate, or ATP.

Another thing to note about mitochondria is that they are probably the descendants of resident aliens. It is likely that they are the end products of bacterial cells that invaded eukaryotic cells more than a billion years ago, only to end up living within them (see "The Stranger within," on page 84).

4.6 The Cytoskeleton: Internal Scaffolding

When you see a set of cells in action, the word that comes to mind is hyperactive. Cells are not passive entities. Jostling, narrowing, expanding, moving about, capturing objects and bringing them in, expelling other objects: This is life as a bubbling cauldron of activity. It was once thought that cells did all these things with pretty much the equipment you've looked at so far, meaning that the Golgi complex, the ribosomes, and so forth were thought to be floating in an undifferentiated soup that was the cytosol. But advanced microscopy showed that there is, in fact, a tangled forest within the cytoplasm. It is the **cytoskeleton**: a network of protein filaments that functions in cell structure, cell movement, and the transport of materials within the cell. This network is found in its full form only in eukaryotic cells, but in the last few years scientists have confirmed that bacteria have at least one type of cytoskeletal fiber within them.

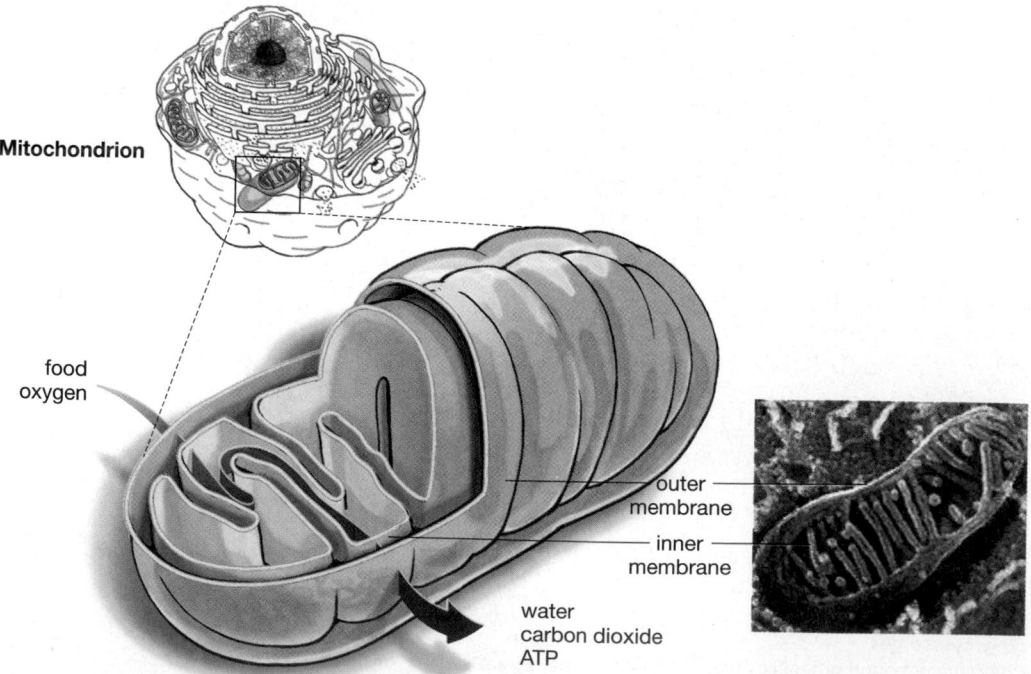

Mitochondrion

food
oxygen

outer membrane

inner membrane

water
carbon dioxide
ATP

Figure 4.10
Energy Transformers: Mitochondria
Just as a power plant converts the energy contained in coal into useful electrical energy, mitochondria convert the energy contained in food into a useful molecular form of energy for the cell—the molecule ATP. Cells can contain anywhere from a single mitochondrion to several thousand.

(a) Microfilaments

(b) Intermediate filaments

(c) Microtubules

Figure 4.11
Structure and Movement: The Cytoskeleton
Three types of fibers form the inner scaffolding or cytoskeleton of the eukaryotic cell: microfilaments, intermediate filaments, and microtubules.

7 nm

Main function: changes in cell shape

10 nm

Main function: maintenance of cell shape

25 nm

Main functions: maintenance of cell shape, movement of organelles, cell mobility (cilia and flagella)

Some of the cytoskeleton's fibers are permanent and relatively static, but many are moving and some are assembled or disassembled very rapidly. The cytoskeleton usually is divided into three component parts. Ordered by size, going from smallest to largest in diameter, they are microfilaments, intermediate filaments, and microtubules (**see Figure 4.11**). Let's take a look at some of the characteristics of each.

Microfilaments

The most slender of the cytoskeletal fibers, **microfilaments** are made of the protein *actin* and serve as a support or "structural" filament in almost all eukaryotic cells. Microfilaments can also help cells move or capture prey, essentially by growing very rapidly at one end—in the direction of the movement or extension—while decomposing rapidly at the other end. You can see a vivid example of microfilament-aided cell extension in **Figure 4.12**. Some bacteria have been shown to have an actin-like set of cytoskeleton fibers that helps give them their shape.

Figure 4.12
Microfilaments in Action
Certain cells can move or capture prey by sending out extensions of themselves called pseudopodia ("false feet"). It is the rapid construction of actin microfilaments—in the direction of the extension—that makes this possible. Here a type of blood-borne guard cell called a macrophage is about to use a pseudopodium it is constructing to capture a green bacterium.

The Stranger within: Endosymbiosis

If pressed to think about it, most people would probably agree that there's something slightly creepy about being made up of cells. Jostling and slithering as they are, dividing, working and dying within us without so much as asking permission, they give us the feeling that the unitary *self* that we so cherish actually amounts to an unruly collection of creatures within.

How sobering it is, then, to realize that we may be composite beings in more ways than one. Each of our *cells* may have within it the vestiges of yet other living things: the descendants of bacteria that long ago invaded our ancestors' cells, only to take up residence there. In plant and animal cells, the mitochondria that serve as cellular "powerhouses" appear to be the descendants of bacteria. Plant and algae cells appear to have an additional set of bacterial descendants in them, the plastids, which include the chloroplasts that carry out photosynthesis.

The idea that these structures are descended from free-standing bacteria is called the endosymbiotic theory—*endo* for "within" the cell, and *symbiotic* for "symbiosis," meaning a situation in which two organisms not of the same species live in close association. Endosymbiosis is not a new idea; it was proposed as far back as the nineteenth century. It has, however, made quite a journey in recent years. Regarded as a crackpot notion as late as the 1960s, it came to be given some grudging credibility over time. By the mid-1980s it had made the transition from interesting hypothesis to generally accepted theory. The person primarily responsible for this change was Lynn Margulis, a professor of botany at the University of Massachusetts, Amherst. Resurrecting endosymbiosis in her 1965 Ph.D. thesis, Margulis went on to be its champion, at first taking it through derision and skepticism, and then seeing it through to vindication.

What makes us think that endosymbiosis really happened? First of all, mitochondria and plastids—which, remember, are *organelles* within eukaryotic cells—have many of the characteristics of free-standing *cells*, specifically free-standing bacterial cells. They have their own ribosomes and their own DNA, both of a bacterial type, and they reproduce through a bacteria-like division, partly under their own genetic control. All of this makes mitochondria look suspiciously like once-independent cells that now find themselves living inside other cells. Moreover, sequencing of the chemical building blocks of mitochondrial DNA has allowed researchers to trace the evolutionary origins of these organelles to a single, ancient bacterial species. Fittingly, this species is a close relative of a group of modern bacteria that make their living as parasites inside other cells.

Margulis believes that mitochondria completed the transition to endosymbiotic living about 1.4 billion years ago. Prior to this, they existed as an aggressive form of oxygen-using bacteria. Critically, they were living in a period in which oxygen was making up more and more of Earth's atmosphere. In this situation, they seized an opportunity: they invaded a form of bacteria that was fairly intolerant of oxygen. The arrangement the two species eventually came to was simple. The host provided food to the invader; and the oxygen-using invader, now domesticated, allowed the host to survive in an oxygenated world.

Intermediate Filaments

Intermediate filaments are filaments of the cytoskeleton intermediate in diameter between microfilaments and microtubules. These in-between-sized proteins are the most permanent of the cytoskeletal elements, perhaps coming closest to our everyday notion of what a skeleton is like. They stabilize the positions of the nucleus and other organelles within the cell.

Microtubules

Microtubules are the largest of the cytoskeletal filaments, taking the form of tubes composed of the protein tubulin. Microtubules play a structural role in the cell; in fact, theirs seems to be the preeminent structural role in the sense of determining the shape of the cell. But they take on several other tasks in addition. They serve, for example, as the monorails discussed earlier. Recall that protein-laden vesicles move from one organelle to another in the cell. These spheres are moving along the "rails" of microtubules, while sitting atop the "engine" of one of the so-called motor proteins (**see Figure 4.13**).

Cell Extensions Made of Microtubules: Cilia and Flagella

Microtubules also form the underlying structure for two kinds of cell extensions, cilia and flagella (see Figure 4.13). **Cilia** are microtubular extensions of cells that take the form of a large number of active, hair-like growths stemming from them. The function of cilia is simple: Move back and forth very rapidly, perhaps 10

(a) Transport monorails

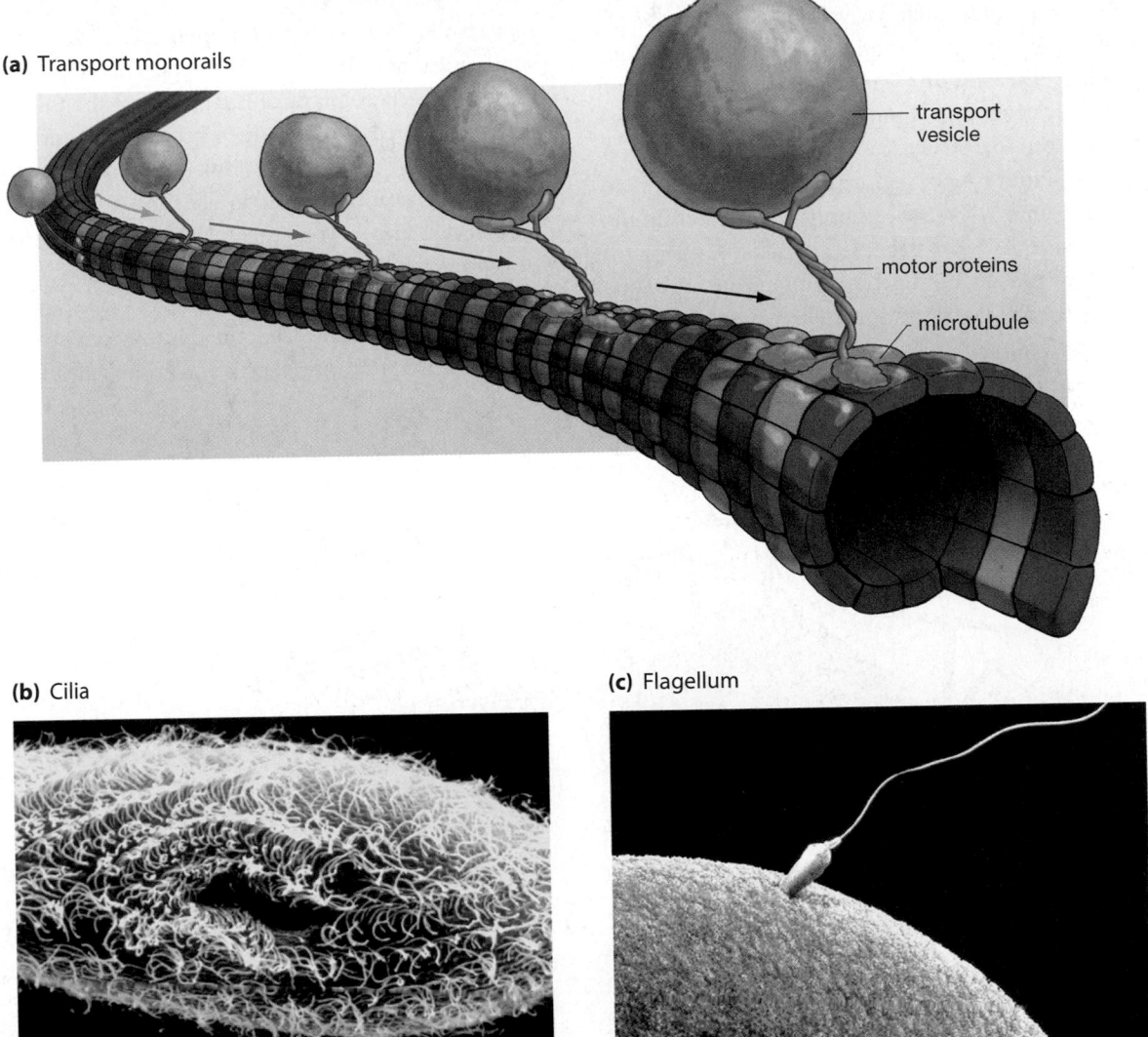

transport
vesicle

motor proteins

microtubule

(b) Cilia

(c) Flagellum

Figure 4.13
Several Functions for Microtubules

(a) They are the "rails" on which vesicles move through the cell, carried along by "motor proteins."

(b) They exist outside the cell in the form of cilia, which are profuse collections of hair-like projections that beat rapidly, forming currents that can propel a cell or move material around it.

(c) They are also found outside cells in the form of flagella. The flagellum on this sperm cell is enabling it to seek entry into an egg.

to 40 times per second. The effect of this movement can be either to propel a cell or to move material *around* a cell. Cilia are extremely common among single-celled organisms and in some of the cells of simple animals (sponges, jellyfish). You saw an example of cilia in humans earlier in connection with our sense of smell. Our lungs also are lined with cilia, whose job it is to sweep the lungs clean of whatever foreign matter has been inhaled. These cilia, like most others, all beat at once in the same direction, acting like rowers in a crew.

Cilia grow from eukaryotic cells in great profusion, but it is a different story with **flagella**—the relatively long, tail-like extensions of some cells that function in cell movement. It is sometimes the case

that several flagella will sprout from a given cell, but often there is but a single flagellum. Only one kind of animal cell is flagellated, and it scarcely needs an introduction: A sperm is a single cell that whips its flagellum in a corkscrew motion in order to get to an unfertilized egg.

In Summary: Structures in the Animal Cell

In your tour of the cell so far, you've pictured a cell as a factory, one that synthesizes proteins in a "production line" that starts with DNA in the nucleus and then goes to the ribosomes (via mRNA), to the rough ER, to the Golgi complex, and finally to the protein's destination (the plasma membrane, export, and so on). You've also seen that cells have other structures such as lysosomes for digestion and recycling, mitochondria for energy transformation, the smooth endoplasmic reticulum for detoxification and lipid synthesis, and the cytoskeleton for structure and movement. If you look at **Figure 4.14**, you can see, in metaphorical form, a "map" of these component parts within the cell. Table 4.1 (on page 88 in the discussion of plant cells) lists cellular elements found in plants and animals, as well as some elements found only in plant cells.

4.7 The Plant Cell

As noted earlier, plant and animal cells have more similarities than they do differences. This is understandable because plant cells do most of the things that animal cells do (produce proteins, transform energy, and so on). A quick look at **Figure 4.15** will confirm for you how structurally similar plant and animal cells are. As you see, a plant cell has a nucleus (with a nucleolus), the smooth and rough ERs, a cytoskeleton—most of the things you've just gone over in animal cells. Indeed, there is only one structure present in the animal cells you've looked at that

Figure 4.14
The Cell as a Factory
This comparison may help you to remember some roles of the different parts of the cell.

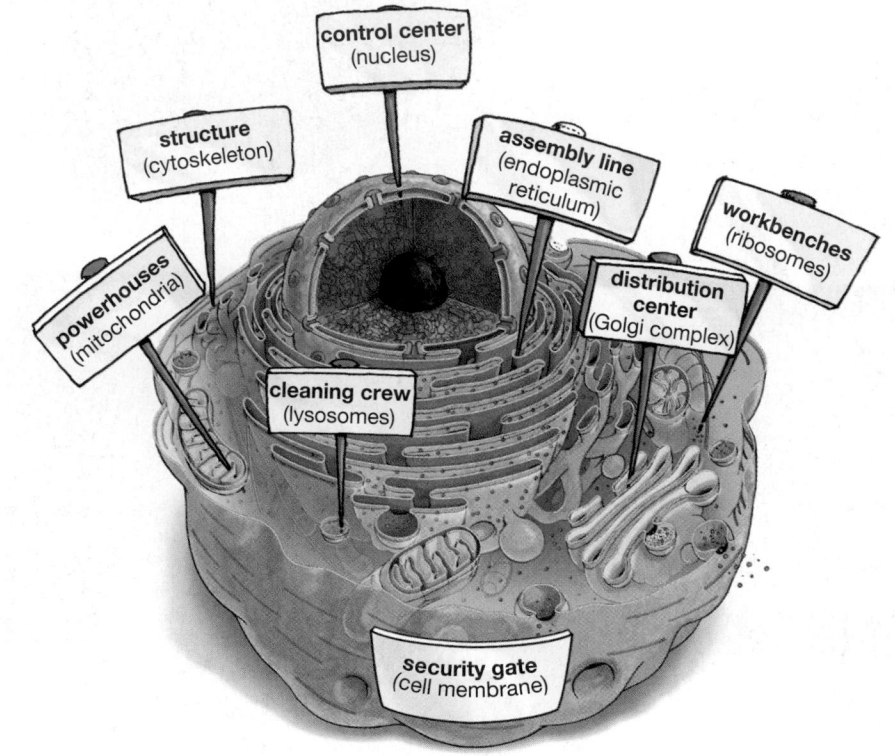

Figure 4.15
Common Structures in Animal and Plant Cells

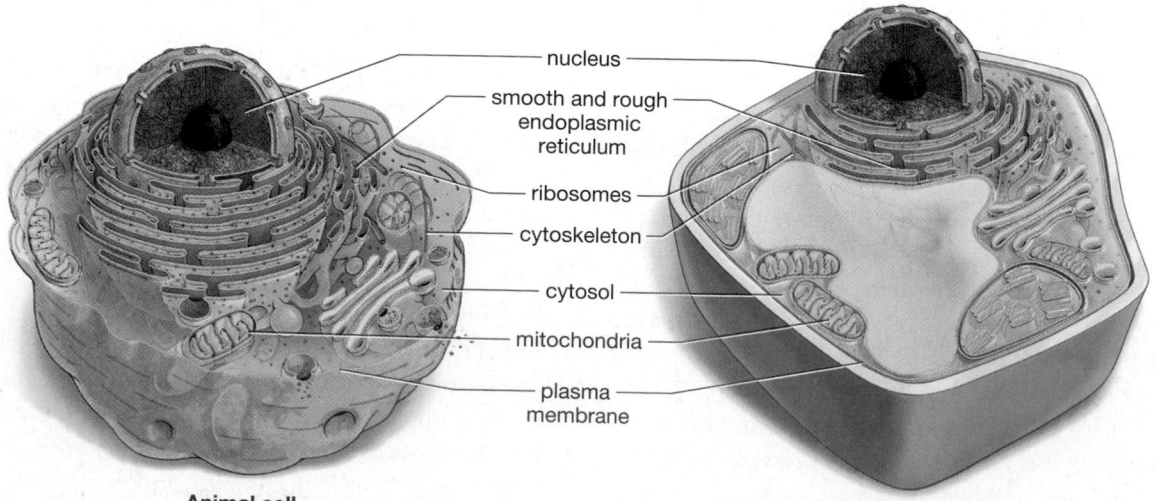

Animal cell

Plant cell

plant cells don't have: the lysosome. What jumps out at you when you look at plant cells is not what they lack compared to animal cells, but what they *have* that animal cells do not. As you can see in **Figure 4.16**, these additions are

- A thick cell wall
- A large structure called a central vacuole
- Structures called plastids, one important variety of which is the chloroplast

The Cell Wall

Plant cells have an outer protective lining, called a **cell wall**, that makes their plasma membrane, just inside it, look rather thin and frail by comparison. This is because it is thin and frail by comparison; the plasma membrane of a plant cell may be 0.01 μm thick, while the combined units of a cell wall may be 700 times this width—7 μm or more. Cell walls are nearly always present in plant cells. They also exist in many organisms that are neither plant nor animal—bacteria, protists, and fungi—though their cell walls differ in chemical composition from those of plants.

What do cell walls do for plant cells? They provide them with structural strength, put a limit on their absorption of water (as you'll see next chapter), and generally protect plants from harmful outside influences. So, if they're so useful, why don't *animal* cells have them? Cell walls make for a rather rigid, inflexible organism—like plants, which are stationary. Animals, meanwhile, are mobile and thus must remain flexible.

Cell walls in plants can come in several forms, but all such forms will be composed chiefly of a molecule you were introduced to last chapter:

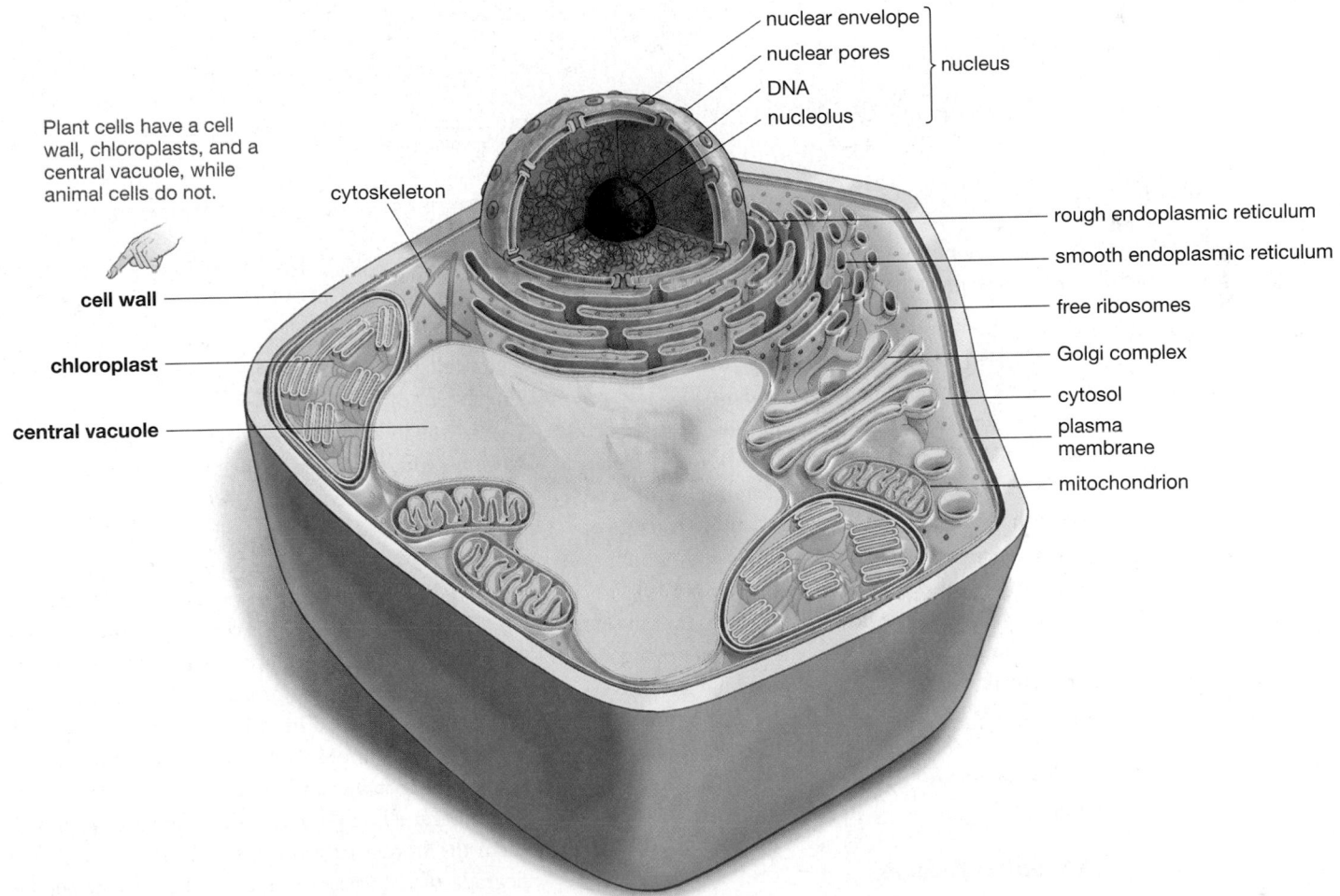

Plant cells have a cell wall, chloroplasts, and a central vacuole, while animal cells do not.

cytoskeleton

cell wall

chloroplast

central vacuole

nuclear envelope
nuclear pores   } nucleus
DNA
nucleolus

rough endoplasmic reticulum
smooth endoplasmic reticulum
free ribosomes
Golgi complex
cytosol
plasma membrane
mitochondrion

Figure 4.16
The Plant Cell
The cell wall, central vacuole, and chloroplasts do not exist in animal cells, but all other components are common to both plant and animal cells.

Table 4.1 Structures in Plant and Animal Cells

Name	Location	Function
Cytoskeleton	Cytoplasm	Maintains cell shape, facilitates cell movement and movement of materials within cell
Cytosol	Cytoplasm	Protein-rich fluid in which organelles and cytoskeleton are immersed
Golgi complex	Cytoplasm	Processing, sorting of proteins
Lysosomes (in animal cells only)	Cytoplasm	Digestion of imported materials and cell's own used materials
Mitochondria	Cytoplasm	Transform energy from food
Nucleolus	Nucleus	Synthesis of ribosomal RNA
Nucleus	Inside nuclear envelope	Site of most of the cell's DNA
Ribosomes	Rough ER, Free-standing in cytoplasm	Sites of protein synthesis
Rough endoplasmic reticulum	Cytoplasm	Protein processing
Smooth endoplasmic reticulum	Cytoplasm	Lipid synthesis, storage; detoxification of harmful substances
Vesicles	Cytoplasm	Transport of proteins and other cellular materials
Cell walls (in plant cells only)	Outside plasma membrane	Limit water uptake; maintain cell membrane shape, protect from outside influences
Central vacuole (in plant cells only)	Cytoplasm	Cell metabolism, pH balance, digestion, water maintenance
Plastids (in plant cells only)	Cytoplasm	Nutrient storage, pigmentation, photosynthesis (chloroplasts)

cellulose, a complex sugar or "polysaccharide" that is embedded within cell walls in the way reinforcing bars run through concrete. In some cell walls, cellulose is joined by a compound called lignin, which imparts considerable structural strength. You can see a vivid demonstration of this in the material we know as wood, which is largely made of cell walls (**see Figure 4.17a).**

Cell walls can serve different functions over the life of an organism. Generally, they are the site of a good deal of metabolic activity, and thus should not be considered mere barriers. On the other hand, the outer portion of tree bark consists mostly of *dead* cell walls, which clearly are serving a barrier function (**see Figure 4.17b**).

The Central Vacuole

In looking at the diagram of the plant cell, you'll see one structure, the central vacuole, that is so prominent it appears to be a kind of organelle continent surrounded by a mere moat of cytosol. In a mature plant cell, one or two central vacuoles may comprise 90 percent of cell volume.

Although animal cells can have vacuoles, the imposing central vacuole in plants is different. For a start, it is composed mostly of water, which demonstrates just how watery plant cells are. A typical animal cell may be 70 to 85 percent water, but for plant cells the water proportion is likely to be 90 to 98 percent.

The watery milieu of the central vacuole contains hundreds of other substances. Many of these are nutrients, others are waste products. There are also hydrogen ions, pumped in to keep the cell's cytoplasm at a near-neutral pH. Given these diverse materials, the **central vacuole** can be defined as a large, watery plant organelle that has many functions, among them the storage of nutrients and the retention and degradation of waste products. In this latter role, the central vacuole uses digestive enzymes, much like the lysosomes in animal cells. There is even an aesthetic side to the central vacuole: Many red and blue flowers owe their colors to the pigments it contains.

Plastids

Plastids are a diverse group of organelles that are found only in plants and algae. Some gather and store nutrients for plant cells; others are pigment-containing organelles that give us, for example, the red color of the tomato skin. The best known of the plastids, however, are the chloroplasts.

Human beings are indebted, in a sense, to chloroplast-containing organisms, because most of the food we eat and the oxygen we breathe comes from them. This is so because these organisms carry out photosynthesis, the process by which organisms produce their own food (a sugar), using nothing but the energy contained in sunlight and the starting materials of carbon dioxide, water, and a few minerals. As it turns out, the **chloroplast** is the organelle that is the site of photosynthesis in plant and

(a) Wood is mostly cell walls

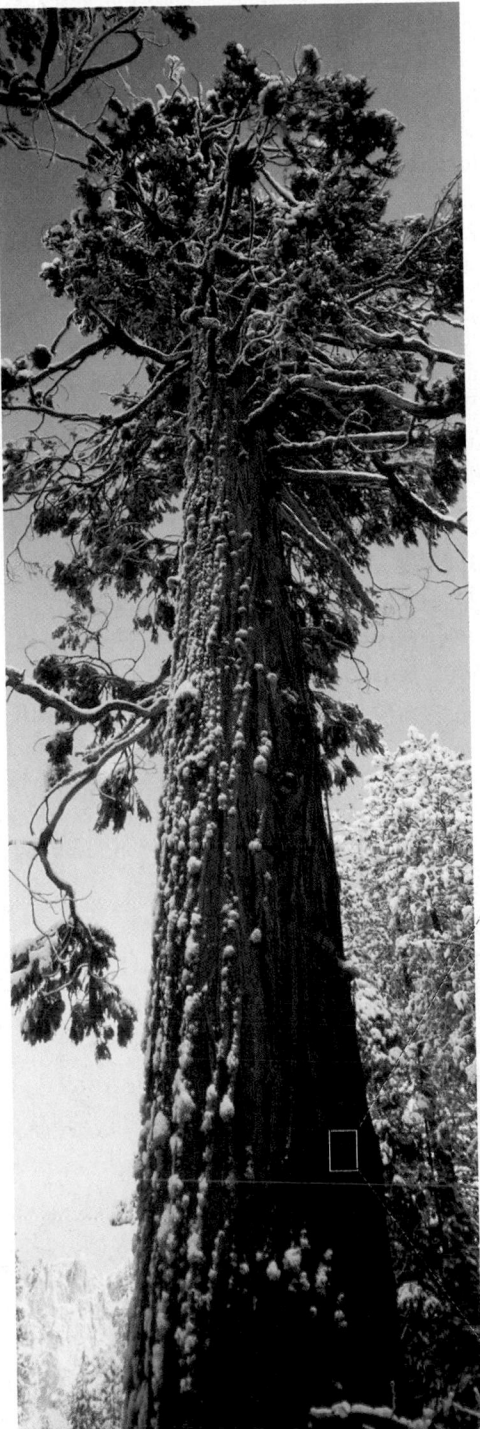

(b) A magnified view of bark

Figure 4.17
Great Strength from Small Things

(a) Redwoods such as this one can reach enormous heights because of the strength of their wood, which is largely made of cell walls.

(b) Cell walls play important roles in living cells, but they also are valuable as the strong, remaining components of dead cells; here they help make up this redwood bark. ($\times 240$)

algae cells (**see Figure 4.18**). This may not seem like such a big deal until you try to name a food you eat that is not a plant or does not itself eat plants. A by-product of photosynthesis is oxygen, whose significance to us can scarcely be overstated.

4.8 Cell-to-Cell Communication

Most of what you've seen so far has made the cell seem like an isolated entity, but this is not the case. Single-celled organisms can exist as separate entities, along with certain plant or animal cells (red blood cells, for example), but most plant and animal cells are linked together in organized collections referred to as tissues. Not surprisingly, these assemblages of cells—be they plant or animal—have the ability to communicate with one another.

Communication among Plant Cells

Having noted the thickness of something like the cell walls in plants, you might wonder how one plant cell could interact with another. Communication between plant cells takes place quite readily, however, through a series of tiny channels in the plant cell wall called **plasmodesmata** (singular, plasmodesma). The structure of these channels is such that the cytoplasm of one plant cell is continuous with that of another—so much so that the cytoplasm of an entire plant can be properly looked at as one continuous whole (**see Figure 4.19a**). The structure of plasmodesmata is more complex than that of a simple opening, but the basic idea is of a channel-like linkage between two plant cells.

Communication among Animal Cells

There are no plasmodesmata in animal cells, but there are three other kinds of *cell junctions*, or linkages, one of which serves to facilitate cell communication. It is called a gap junction, and it consists of clusters of protein structures that shoot through the plasma membrane of a cell from one side to the other, forming a kind of tube. When these tubes line up in adjacent cells, the result is a channel for passage of small molecules and electrical signals (see Figure 4.19b). Thus, we can define a **gap junction** as a protein assemblage that forms a communication channel between adjacent animal cells. Note that animal gap junctions and plant plasmodesmata are very different kinds of channels. Plasmodesmata can be thought of as permanent channels between plant cells, whereas gap junctions open only as necessary.

How Did We Learn?

The cellular world you have been reading about was completely unknown to human beings before the seventeenth century. It came as quite a shock back then to learn that the human body had, living within it, a multitude of creatures who were so small they could not be perceived with the naked eye. In "First Sightings: Anton van Leeuwenhoek" on page 92, you can read about the Dutchman who was one of the first visitors to the micro-world.

Figure 4.18
Food Source for the World
Chloroplasts, the tiny organelles that exist in plant and algae cells, are sites of photosynthesis—the process that provides food for most of the living world. Using the starting materials of water, carbon dioxide, and a few minerals, these organisms use energy from sunlight to produce their own food. A double membrane lines the chloroplasts.
(Micrograph: ×13,000)

water
carbon dioxide
minerals

outer membrane
inner membrane

sugar (food)
oxygen

(a) Plant tissues

plasma
membrane

cell walls

cytoplasm

plasmodesmata

Figure 4.19
Cell Communication

(a) Plasmodesmata

In plants, a series of tiny pores between plant cells, the plasmodesmata, allow for the movement of materials among cells. Thanks to the plasmodesmata channels, the cytoplasm of one cell is continuous with the cytoplasm of the next; the plant as a whole can be thought of as having a single complement of continuous cytoplasm.

(b) Animal tissues

gap junction

plasma
membranes

cytoplasm

(b) Gap junctions

In animals, protein assemblies come into alignment with one another, forming communication channels between cells. A cluster of many such assemblies—perhaps several hundred—is called a gap junction.

On to the Periphery

Having looked at what is inside the cell, you've arrived at the cell's periphery, the plasma membrane, which is where you'll be staying for awhile. It may at first seem strange to devote a whole chapter to an outer boundary. How much attention would you pay, after all, to a factory's wall as opposed to its contents? The answer: A lot, if that wall could facilitate communication with the outer world, continually renew itself, and let some things in while keeping others out. Such is the case with the plasma membrane, a slender lining that manages to make one of the most fundamental distinctions on Earth: Inside, life goes on; outside it does not.

How Did We Learn?
First Sightings: Anton van Leeuwenhoek

To the list of explorers that includes Columbus and Balboa we could add the name Anton van Leeuwenhoek. This unassuming Dutchman was the great early voyager into another world, the micro-world.

It was not until the seventeenth century that human beings realized that things as small as cells existed. Leeuwenhoek began to report in the 1670s on what he saw with the aid of a device that had been invented at the end of the 1500s—the microscope (**Figure 1**). One of Leeuwenhoek's contemporaries, Englishman Robert Hooke, coined the term *cell* after viewing a slice of cork under a simple microscope, but Hooke's purpose was to reveal the detailed structure of familiar, small objects, such as the flea. Leeuwenhoek, by contrast, revealed the *existence* of creatures unimagined until his time. Moreover, he carried out this work in the most extraordinary fashion: Laboring alone in the small town of Delft with palm-sized magnifiers he himself had created, looking at anything that struck his fancy. (And many things struck his fancy; he once looked at exploding gunpowder under a microscope, nearly blinding himself in the process.) For 50 years, while working as shopkeeper and minor city official, this untrained amateur of boundless curiosity examined the micro-world and reported on it in letters he posted to the Royal Society in London.

Who could believe what he uncovered? How was it possible that there was a buzzing, blooming universe of "animalcules" (little animals) whose existence had been completely unsuspected? Prior to his work, no one thought that any creature smaller than a worm could exist within the human body. Yet, examining scrapings from his own mouth, Leeuwenhoek tells us:

> I saw, with as great a wonderment as ever before, an inconceivably great number of little animalcules, and in so unbelievably small a quantity of the foresaid stuff, that those who didn't see it with their own eyes could scarce credit it.

The animalcules that Leeuwenhoek beheld over his career were single-celled organisms that today are known as bacteria and protists. It would be two hundred years before Leeuwenhoek's findings were fully integrated into a modern theory of cells. Yet the man from Delft had shown that only a small portion of the world's living things are visible things.

(a) What Leeuwenhoek could see

(b) Leeuwenhoek with two of his microscopes

Figure 1

(a) What Leeuwenhoek Could See
Biologist Brian Ford used an actual 300-year-old Leeuwenhoek microscope to capture this image of spiny spores from a truffle. ($\times$600)

(b) Leeuwenhoek's Microscopes Were Hand-Held and Paddle-Shaped
Leeuwenhoek revealing the micro-world to Queen Catherine of England, wife of King Charles II (1630–1685).

Chapter Review

Summary

4.1 Cells Are the Working Units of Life

- With the possible exception of viruses, every form of life on Earth either is a cell or is composed of cells. Cells come into existence only through the activity of other cells.

4.2 All Cells Are Either Prokaryotic or Eukaryotic

- All cells can be classified as prokaryotic or eukaryotic. Prokaryotic cells either are bacteria or another single-celled life-form called archaea. Setting bacteria and archaea aside, all other cells are eukaryotic.

- Eukaryotic cells have most of their DNA contained in a membrane-lined compartment, called the cell nucleus, whereas prokaryotic cells do not have a nucleus. Eukaryotic cells also tend to be much larger than prokaryotic cells, and they have more of the specialized internal structures called organelles than do prokaryotic cells. Many eukaryotes are multicelled organisms, whereas all prokaryotes are single-celled.
Web Tutorial 4.1: Prokaryotic and Eukaryotic Cells

4.3 The Eukaryotic Cell

- There are five principal components to the eukaryotic cell: the nucleus, other organelles, the cytosol, the cytoskeleton, and the plasma membrane. Organelles are "tiny organs" within the cell that carry out specialized functions, such as energy transfer and material recycling. The cytosol is the fluid outside the nucleus in which these organelles are immersed. (The cytosol should not be confused with the cytoplasm, which is the region of the cell inside the plasma membrane but outside the nucleus.) The cytoskeleton is a network of protein filaments that function in cell structure, cell movement, and the transport of materials within the cell. The plasma membrane is the outer lining of the cell. A membrane can be defined as the flexible, chemically active outer lining of a cell or of its compartments.

4.4 A Tour of the Animal Cell: Along the Protein Production Path

- Information for the construction of proteins is contained in the DNA located in the cell nucleus. This information is copied onto an informational "tape" of messenger RNA (mRNA) that departs the cell nucleus through its nuclear pores and goes to the sites of protein synthesis, structures called ribosomes, which lie in the cytoplasm. Many ribosomes that receive mRNA tapes process only a short stretch of them before migrating to, and then embedding in, one of a series of sacs in a membrane network called the rough endoplasmic reticulum (RER). The polypeptide chains produced by the ribosomal "reading" of the mRNA tapes are dropped from ribosomes into the internal spaces of the RER; there, the polypeptide chains fold up, thus becoming proteins, and undergo editing.

Some ribosomes are not embedded in rough endoplasmic reticulum but instead remain free-standing in the cytosol.

- Materials move from one structure to another in the cell via the endomembrane system, in which a piece of membrane, with proteins or other materials inside, can bud off from one organelle, move through the cell, and then fuse with another membrane-lined structure. Membrane-lined structures that carry cellular materials are called transport vesicles.

- Once protein processing is finished in the rough endoplasmic reticulum, proteins undergoing processing move, via transport vesicles, to the Golgi complex, where they are processed further and marked for shipment to appropriate cellular locations.

4.5 Outside the Protein Production Path: Other Cell Structures

- The smooth endoplasmic reticulum is a network of membranes that functions to synthesize lipids and to detoxify potentially harmful substances. Lysosomes are organelles that break down worn-out cellular structures or foreign material that comes into the cell. Once this digestion is completed, the lysosomes return the molecular components of these materials to the cytoplasm for further use. Mitochondria are organelles that function to extract energy from food and to transform this energy into a chemical form the cell can use.
Web Tutorial 4.2: The Structure of Cells

4.6 The Cytoskeleton: Internal Scaffolding

- Cells have within them a web of protein strands, called a cytoskeleton, that provide the cell with structure, facilitate the movement of materials inside the cell, and facilitate cell movement.

- There are three principal types of cytoskeleton elements. Ordered by size, going from smallest to largest in diameter, they are microfilaments, intermediate filaments, and microtubules. Microfilaments are made of the protein actin. They help the cell move and capture prey by forming rapidly in the direction of movement and decomposing rapidly at their other end. Intermediate filaments provide support and structure to the cell. Microtubules play a structural role in cells and facilitate the movement of materials inside the cell by serving as transport "rails."

- Cilia and flagella are extensions of cells composed of microtubules. Cilia extend from cells in great numbers, serving to move the cell or to move material around the cell. By contrast, one—or at most a few—flagella extend from cells that have them. The function of flagella is cell movement.

4.7 The Plant Cell

- Plant cells have almost all the structures found in animal cells. In addition, plant cells have a cell wall, a large central vacuole, and organelles called plastids, one variety of which is the chloroplasts that are the sites of photosynthesis. The cell wall gives the plant structural strength and helps regulate the intake and retention of water.

4.8 Cell-to-Cell Communication

- Cells are able to communicate with each other through special structures. Plant cells have channels, called plasmodesmata, that are always open and hence have the effect of making the cytoplasm of one plant cell continuous with that of another. Adjacent animal cells have channels, called gap junctions, that are composed of protein assemblages that open only as necessary, allowing the movement of small molecules and electrical signals between cells.

Key Terms

cell wall 87	microtubule 84
central vacuole 88	mitochondria 82
chloroplast 89	nanometer 72
cilia 84	nuclear envelope 76
cytoplasm 75	nucleolus 78
cytoskeleton 82	nucleus 70
cytosol 75	organelle 71
endomembrane system 79	plasma membrane 75
eukaryotic cell 70	plasmodesmata 90
flagella 85	prokaryotic cell 70
gap junction 90	ribosome 77
Golgi complex 79	rough endoplasmic reticulum 78
intermediate filament 84	secretory protein 78
lysosome 80	smooth endoplasmic reticulum 80
microfilament 83	transport vesicle 79
micrograph 72	
micrometer 72	

Understanding the Basics

Multiple-Choice Questions (answers in the back of the book)

1. Jerome has strep throat, a bacterial infection. The cause of the infection is
   a) the growth of a virus
   b) the presence of archaea
   c) eukaryotic cells dividing in his throat
   d) organelles that take control of his organs—in this case, his throat
   e) prokaryotic cells

2. Where would you expect to find a cytoskeleton?
   a) primarily inside the nucleus
   b) as the internal structure of a mitochondrion
   c) between bacterial cells
   d) throughout the cytosol
   e) as an outer coat on an insect

3. Suppose Dr. Hyde found a cell that had many mitochondria, a nucleus, a cell wall made of cellulose, and an endoplasmic reticulum, as well as many other parts. He might assume that he has found
   a) a plant cell
   b) an animal cell
   c) a bacterial cell
   d) one of these three types, but he will not know which type without further investigation
   e) either a plant cell or an animal cell, but not a bacterial cell

4. Cells in the pancreas manufacture large amounts of protein. Which of these would you expect to find a large amount of, or number of, in pancreatic cells?
   a) lysosomes
   b) rough endoplasmic reticulum
   c) smooth endoplasmic reticulum
   d) chloroplasts
   e) plasma membrane

5. Suppose that a cell could be seen to lack intermediate filaments. Which of these would be the most likely effect of this condition?
   a) an inability to get energy out of food
   b) an inability to manufacture proteins
   c) a tendency for the nucleus and organelles in the cell to drift around inside the cell
   d) an inability of the skeletal muscles to contract
   e) an inability to move proteins from one part of the cell to another

6. Heart muscle cells have a number of gap junctions connecting them to their adjoining cells. From this you can conclude that heart muscle cells
   a) exchange nuclei very frequently
   b) have plasmodesmata
   c) move vacuoles from cell to cell
   d) communicate frequently
   e) lack the ability to divide

7. Which is the correct ranking of these "small" things, from smallest to largest? (Use typical sizes.)
   a) animal cells < atoms < bacteria < proteins < amino acids
   b) atoms < amino acids < proteins < bacteria < animal cells
   c) atoms < proteins < amino acids < animal cells < bacteria
   d) bacteria < atoms < amino acids < proteins < animal cells
   e) bacteria < animal cells < atoms < amino acids < proteins

8. Cells need large amounts of ribosomal RNA to make proteins. The ribosomal RNA is made in a specialized structure known as _____, which is found in _____.
   a) a chloroplast ... the cytosol
   b) a ribosome ... the cytosol
   c) the endoplasmic reticulum ... the nucleus
   d) the nuclear envelope ... the nucleus
   e) the nucleolus ... the nucleus

9. Many antibiotics work by blocking the function of ribosomes. Therefore, these antibiotics will:
   a) block DNA synthesis
   b) block RNA synthesis
   c) block protein synthesis
   d) prevent the movement of proteins through nuclear pores
   e) make the two nuclear membranes fuse into one

Brief Review

1. Suppose your entire body were just one gigantic cell with one central nucleus and lots of organelles outside it to perform the various functions. What problems can you envision with this system?

2. What are some of the differences between eukaryotic cells and prokaryotic cells?

3. Insulin, the hormone that controls sugar levels in the body, is a protein that is exported from special cells in the pancreas. Trace the path from a length of DNA in the nucleus that carries the code for insulin to the release of the hormone in the bloodstream.

4. What are cilia and flagella? What are some of the roles they play in the human body?

5. Consider what plants would be like if they had no plasmodesmata. Explain why this would be a problem.

6. What is a gap junction, and what is its function?

Applying Your Knowledge

1. The earliest organisms in the fossil record are all single-celled. Why do you think life had to "start small" like this?

2. Why do membranes figure so prominently in eukaryotic cells? What essential function do they serve?

MediaLab

Would We Miss Them if They Were Gone? Organelles

Catastrophic damage to your liver, lung, heart, or even kidneys can lead to complete organ failure. Under these circumstances, the only cure is finding a new, healthy organ to replace the old one. An organ is irreplaceable because each performs a unique function for our bodies. Similarly, each organelle performs a unique function within our cells and cannot substitute for another kind of organelle if it is damaged or defective. Most of us are familiar with the consequence of organ failure, but can you imagine what might occur in organelle failure? In the *Web Tutorial* you will review some of the functions performed by organelles, and in the *Web Investigations* you can read about new studies linking many genetic illnesses and some of the decline seen with aging to malfunctioning organelles.

The online version of this *MediaLab* can be found in Chapter 4 on your Companion Website (www.prenhall.com/krogh3).

WEB TUTORIAL

Eukaryotic cells sequester cellular activities in discrete (often membrane-enclosed) structures within their cytoplasm, called organelles. This *Web Tutorial* will lead you through the major differences between eukaryotic and prokaryotic cells, and review the activities performed by organelles in eukaryotic cells.

Activity

1. *You will learn the defining difference between the two major cell categories, prokaryotic and eukaryotic.*

2. *Then you will extend your knowledge of the function of organelles in plant and animal cells.*

Now that you have reviewed the functions of the different eukaryotic organelles, in the following section you can investigate a few of the medical consequences of interfering with the activity of just one of those organelles, the lysosome.

WEB INVESTIGATION

Investigation 1
Estimated time for completion = 5 minutes

You know that lysosomes digest food and defective organelles, but did you know that our cells also use lysosomes to dispose of harmful bacteria? Click on the keyword **BIOANIMATIONS** on the Website then click the link Animations, and scroll through the list on the bottom of the page to reach the link to the Intracellular infection by salmonella to see what happens inside a cell fighting off a salmonella bacterium, a common cause of food poisoning.

Investigation 2
Estimated time of completion = 5 minutes

Just how important are lysosomes to our cells? Well, at least 30 different human genetic diseases, many lethal, are caused by a defect in production of lysosomal enzymes. These defective enzymes often accumulate inside the cell as well as in the bloodstream and urine, and commonly result in developmental defects, defects in the neural and immune systems, skeletal abnormalities, and death at an early age. Click on the keyword **LYSOSOMES** on your Website click on the table of diseases, and then select one of these disorders. Read as much information as you can about the disorder. What is the exact problem with the lysosomes? What symptoms are observed? Is there a genetic test available for the disease? Have they identified the gene responsible, and will this lead to a treatment?

Investigation 3
Estimated time of completion = 10 minutes

Plaques in our arteries and brains, osteoporosis, sagging skin, age spots—all are symptoms of aging.

Why do they occur? One of the hot theories to explain why our tissues age is called accumulated cellular damage. One sign of damage is the brown pigment lipofuscin—"the aging pigment"—that accumulates in older cells, especially liver and heart cells. The pigment results from oxidative degradation of mitochondria and/or lysosomes. You say you don't want to have liver spots. Hasn't somebody come up with a cure? Many are trying; read one article from the Life Extension Foundation by clicking on the keyword **EAT LESS** on your Website for this *MediaLab* to learn what they have found.

COMMUNICATE YOUR RESULTS

Exercise 1
Estimated time for completion = 5 minutes

The salmonella bacterium plays right into the hands of its host cell during invasion, by actually causing itself to be engulfed into a vacuole destined for destruction in the lysosome. What goes wrong? In 20 words, can you describe why the lysosome does not digest the bacterium inside the food vacuole?

Exercise 2
Estimated time for completion = 15 minutes

Prepare a 50-word description of the lysosomal storage disorder you investigated in *Web Investigation 2* to inform your classmates about these devastating diseases.

Exercise 3
Estimated time for completion = 15 minutes

Freeze your head? Exercise more? Vitamins? You want to live a long, full life; but according to the article you read in *Web Investigation 3*, what is currently the only demonstrated mechanism for extending maximum life span? Why should this work? Compose a 50-word description of one of the observed physical changes resulting from eating less, and explain why this should help you live longer.

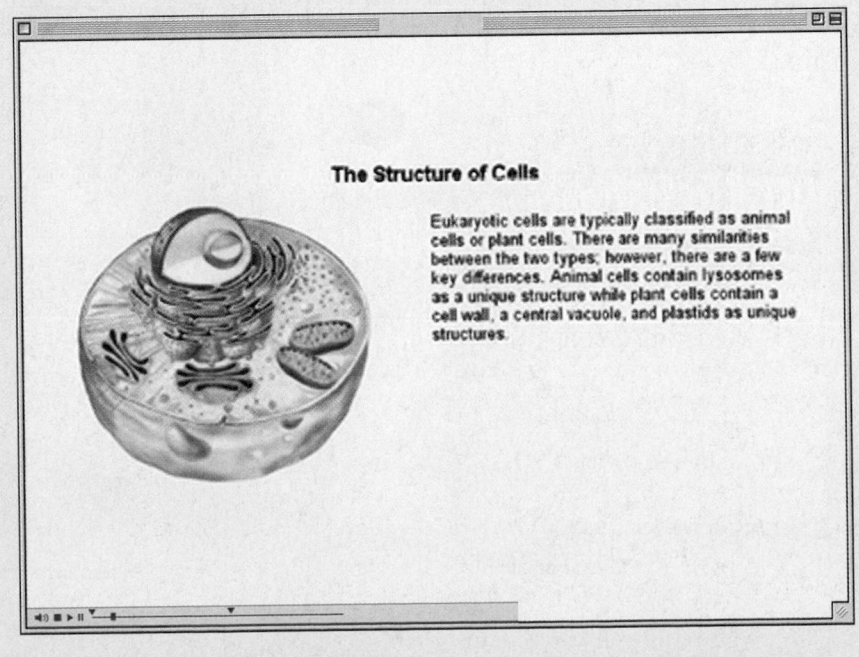

The Structure of Cells

Eukaryotic cells are typically classified as animal cells or plant cells. There are many similarities between the two types; however, there are a few key differences. Animal cells contain lysosomes as a unique structure while plant cells contain a cell wall, a central vacuole, and plastids as unique structures.

5 *The Plasma Membrane*

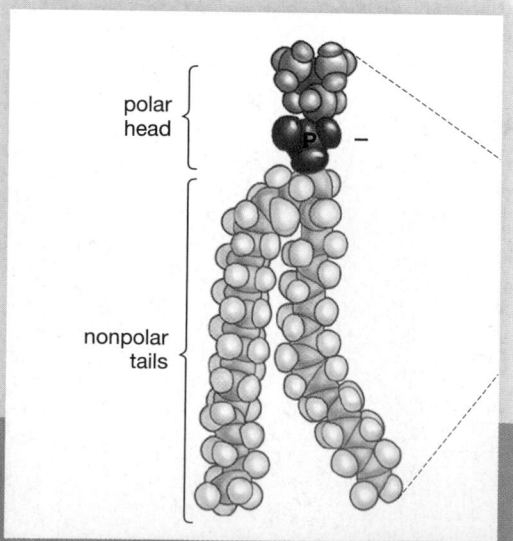

Membrane molecule.
(Section 5.1, page 101)

A cellular sandwich.
(Section 5.1, page 101)

Picturing the membrane.
(Essay, page 112)

> **The outer lining of cells is in a sense the outer border of life. In its roles as protector, gatekeeper, and message carrier, this lining is indispensable to life.**

During his 14 years with the Cincinnati Bengals, New York Jets, and Arizona Cardinals, quarterback Boomer Esiason made it once to the Super Bowl and twice to the Pro Bowl. His toughest challenge, however, has come not on the field but at home, where he and his wife have struggled to care for their son Gunnar, who was born with the disease cystic fibrosis.

Like other children who have cystic fibrosis, Gunnar is plagued by a mucus that accumulates in his lungs. The lungs of healthy children are lined by mucus too, but in a layer that is thin and wet enough to be regularly swept away by the hair-like cilia that extend into lung passages like so many tiny brooms. In cystic fibrosis patients, the mucous layer is thicker and drier and becomes a site for repeated bacterial infections. In time, these infections can result in the lung passages being destroyed. The average life expectancy for a cystic fibrosis patient is 30 years.

The difference between a healthy child and Gunnar Esiason comes down to this: Because of a faulty gene, the substance chloride cannot be transported in sufficient quantity from the inside of Gunnar's cells to the outside of them. Healthy individuals have a protein that acts as a channel for chloride—a kind of passageway that spans the cell's outer membrane. In contrast, the cells of cystic fibrosis patients have either defective chloride channels or none at all. The result is a lack of chloride outside their cells, which gets the mucus buildup going.

As noted last chapter, life goes on only inside cells. The fact that the cell's outer, or "plasma," membrane is out on life's edge may prompt the thought that it's *merely* at the edge, as if the real action is taking place deep within the cell. But consider, as in cystic fibrosis, the effect of having a *defective* plasma membrane. The focus in this chapter is to learn more about this important cell lining.

Transport across the membrane.
(Section 5.3, page 106)

protein

cytosol

Moving out of the cell.
(Section 5.4, page 108)

Moving out of the cell.
(Section 5.4, page 108)

5.1 The Nature of the Plasma Membrane

So, what is the nature of the plasma membrane? First, it's worth noting that it's very much like the membranes described in Chapter 4. Much of what follows about the plasma membrane could also be said of the various membranes that are internal to the cell—those that line lysosomes or that make up the Golgi apparatus, for example. There are some important differences between the plasma and other membranes, however, because the plasma membrane is constantly interacting with the world outside the cell, whereas internal membranes are not.

When we start to consider the qualities of the plasma membrane, we find that, even in the micro-world of cells, it is an extremely *thin* entity. If you stacked 10,000 of them on top of one another, their combined width would be about that of a sheet of paper. Next, the plasma membrane has a fluid and somewhat fatty makeup. If we looked for a counterpart to it in our everyday world, a soap bubble might come close, meaning this membrane is very flexible. Yet it is stable enough to stay together despite being constantly re-formed, due to the endless movement of materials in and out of it. If you imagine half the surface of your skin remaking itself every 30 minutes or so, you begin to get the picture about how dynamic this membrane is. Let's look now at the most important component parts of it. All of these components are illustrated in **Figure 5.1**. They are:

Web Tutorial 5.1
Plasma Membranes and Diffusion

- The phospholipid bilayer. Just as bread is made mostly from flour, the plasma membrane is made mostly from two layers of phospholipid molecules, whose "tails" mingle together, but whose "heads" point in opposite directions—to the interior of the cell in one direction, and to the world outside the cell in the other.

- Cholesterol. Like mortar between bricks, cholesterol acts as a "patching" material for the membrane; it also keeps the membrane at an optimal level of fluidity.

- Proteins. These molecules shoot through the membrane and lie on either side of it, serving as support structures, signaling antennas, identification markers, and cellular passageways.

- Glycocalyx. This is the collective term for a set of carbohydrate chains that layer the outside of the membrane.

Now let's look at each of these components in greater detail.

First Component: The Phospholipid Bilayer

You may recall the discussion in Chapter 3 of phospholipids—molecules that have two long fatty-acid chains linked to a phosphate-bearing group (**see Figure 5.2**). You may also recall that, because fatty-acid chains are lipids, they are hydrophobic or "water-fearing," meaning they will not bond with water. Conversely, phosphate groups are charged, hydro*philic* molecules, meaning they are "water-loving" and will *readily* bond with water. When such phosphate and lipid components are put together, the resulting phospholipid is a molecule with a dual nature. Its phosphate "head" will seek water, but its fatty-acid "tail" will avoid it. Drop a group of phospholipids in water, and they will arrange themselves into the form you see in Figure 5.2: two *layers* of phospholipids sandwiched together, the tails of each layer pointing inward (thus avoiding water) and the heads pointing outward (thus bonding with the watery environment that lies both inside and outside the cell). With this in mind, the **phospholipid bilayer** can be defined as a chief component of the plasma membrane, composed of two layers of phospholipids, arranged with their fatty-acid chains pointing toward each other.

This phospholipid structure has a couple of important consequences for the plasma membrane. First, it helps give the membrane its fluid nature: the bilayer's fatty-acid tails have a chemical makeup that is more like that of oil than shortening. Second, because these are two hydrophobic layers of tails, the only substances that can pass through them with ease are *other* hydrophobic substances or a few very small molecules. This stems from the rule of thumb about solvents noted in Chapter 3: Like dissolves like. Fats dissolve in fats, charged molecules dissolve in charged molecules. Thus, various steroid hormones (which, remember, are lipids) gain fairly easy entry into the cell, as do fatty acids, because these substances will dissolve in the lipid bilayer. Conversely, hydro*philic* substances—ions, amino acids, all kinds of polar molecules—will not dissolve in the membrane and thus cannot make it past the fatty-acid chains without help. What kind of help? Stay tuned.

Second Component: Cholesterol

Molecules of the lipid material cholesterol nestle between phospholipid molecules throughout the plasma membrane, performing two functions. First, they act as a kind of patching substance on the bilayer, keeping some small molecules from getting through. Second, they help keep the membrane at an optimum level of fluidity. Without cholesterol,

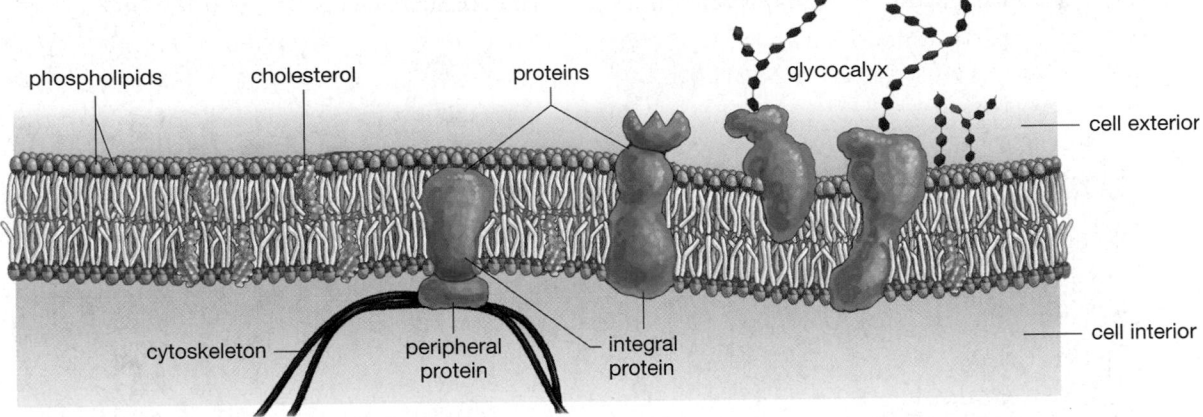

phospholipids   cholesterol   proteins   glycocalyx

cell exterior

cytoskeleton   peripheral protein   integral protein   cell interior

- **Phospholipid bilayer:** a double layer of phospholipid molecules whose hydrophilic "heads" face outward, and whose hydrophobic "tails" point inward, toward each other.

- **Cholesterol** molecules that act as a patching substance and that help the cell maintain an optimal level of fluidity.

- **Proteins,** which are integral, meaning bound to the hydrophobic interior of the membrane, or peripheral, meaning not bound in this way.

- **Glycocalyx:** sugar chains that attach to proteins and phospholipids, serving as protein binding sites and as cell lubrication and adhesion molecules.

Figure 5.1
The Plasma Membrane
The cell's outer lining or plasma membrane is composed of four main structural elements, as shown in the figure.

(a) Phospholipid molecule   **(b)** Phospholipid bilayer

polar head

nonpolar tails

watery extracellular fluid

hydro*philic*

hydro*phobic*

hydro*philic*

watery cytosol

hydrophobic molecules pass through freely

hydrophilic molecules do not pass through freely

Figure 5.2
Dual-Natured Lining
(a) The essential building block of the cell's plasma membrane is the phospholipid molecule, which has two elements: a hydrophilic "head," containing a charged phosphate group that bonds with water; and hydrophobic "tails," composed of fatty acids that do not bond with water.

(b) Two layers of phospholipids sandwich together to form the plasma membrane. The phospholipids' hydrophobic tails form the interior of the membrane, while their hydrophilic heads jut toward the watery environments that exist on both sides of the membrane. Though the bilayer forms a barrier to all but the smallest hydrophilic molecules, hydrophobic molecules can pass through it fairly easily.

the plasma membrane would react to low temperatures the same way cooking oil does: it would change from a flexible substance to a hardened one—a dysfunctional condition for a cell. The cholesterol molecules nestled between the phospholipid's fatty-acid tails keep this from happening by keeping these chains from packing too closely together. Likewise, they keep the membrane from becoming too fluid when temperatures rise.

Third Component: Proteins

Embedded within, or lying on, the phospholipid bilayer is a third major group of membrane components, membrane proteins, of which there are two principal types, integral and peripheral. **Integral proteins** are plasma membrane proteins that are bound to the membrane's hydrophobic interior. In some cases, these proteins span the entire membrane—popping out on either side of it—while in other cases, they extend only partway in. **Peripheral proteins** are plasma membrane proteins that lie on either side of the membrane, but that are not bound to its hydrophobic interior. They are usually attached to integral proteins at the surface of the membrane.

It is hard to overstate the importance of proteins to the plasma membrane. By itself, the lipid bilayer has a handful of capabilities. With the addition of proteins, it is turned into a structure with a huge

(a) Structural support **(b)** Recognition **(c)** Communication **(d)** Transport

Figure 5.3
Roles of Membrane Proteins
Plasma membrane proteins serve
four principal functions, as shown
in the figure.

Membrane proteins can
provide structural
support, often when
attached to parts of the
cell's scaffolding or
"cytoskeleton."

Binding sites on some
proteins can serve to
identify the cell to other
cells, such as those of
the immune system.

Receptor proteins,
protruding out from the
plasma membrane, can
be the point of contact for
signals sent to the cell via
traveling molecules, such
as hormones.

Proteins can serve as
channels through
which materials can
pass in and out of
the cell.

array of capabilities. Here is a selected set of the roles
that membrane proteins play (**see Figure 5.3**).

Structural Support

Peripheral proteins that lie on the interior or "cytoplasmic" side of the membrane often are attached to
elements of the cell's cytoskeleton. Thus anchored,
they help to stabilize various parts of the cell and
play a part in giving animal cells their characteristic
shape. (Why not plant cells? Because their shape is
determined by the cell wall.)

Recognition

Much like military sentries, some cells need to know
the answer to a critical question: Who goes there,
friend or foe? The sentries are immune-system cells,
moving through the body and interacting with proteins that extend from cell surfaces. These proteins
have "binding sites" on them whose shape can convey a message to immune cells: "Self here, pass on
by." Conversely, a cell with a *foreign* set of binding
sites on its proteins can convey the message: "Invader here, begin an immune-system attack." Have you
ever wondered what it means for people to have, say,
type A blood? It means that they have type A recognition proteins extending from the plasma membranes of their red blood cells. These proteins have
binding sites on them that allow the body's immune
system to recognize "self" and pass on by.

Communication

Cells communicate with one another in various ways.
Signals can be sent from one cell to a neighboring
cell, and communication over longer distances is possible through the chemical messengers known as hor-

mones. These signals are likely to be channeled
through a **receptor protein**—a plasma membrane protein that binds with a signaling molecule.

Receptor proteins—usually just called receptors—
have binding sites on them whose shape is so specific
that they generally will bind only to a single type of signaling molecule. To take one example of this, the hormone insulin is a signaling molecule. The message it
conveys to cells is: "Glucose levels are rising in the
bloodstream; please construct some protein channels
in your plasma membranes so that you can take some
of this glucose in." Now, how does insulin transmit this
message? It binds with an insulin receptor protein that
spans a given cell's plasma membrane. This binding
causes a chemical change on the portion of the protein
that lies *inside* the cell. The result is a cascade of cellular
reactions that puts in motion the construction of the
protein channels. Note that, through this means, a signaling molecule need not come into the cell to have an
effect; it merely needs to bind with a receptor protein
that spans the plasma membrane.

Transport

You have seen that most materials cannot simply
pass through the cell's plasma membrane. Yet cells
need many of these very materials. How do they get
in? Different kinds of integral proteins take on a
transport task—they act as channels through which
materials pass both into cells and out of them. In
some cases these proteins form what might be called
passive passageways—microtunnels that simply
provide a hydrophilic opening through a hydrophobic environment. In other cases, however, these protein channels are actively involved in moving

materials through. We'll review all the forms of protein-aided transport shortly. For now, just note the existence of **transport proteins** proteins that facilitate the movement of molecules or ions from one side of the plasma membrane to the other.

Fourth Component: The Glycocalyx

If you look at Figure 5.1 and focus on the extracellular face of the plasma membrane, you can see, protruding from proteins and phospholipids alike, a number of short, branched extensions. These are simple carbohydrate chains, meaning sugar chains. It turns out that these chains serve as the actual binding sites for many signaling molecules, including insulin. (Remember in Chapter 4 how many of the proteins that were constructed had sugar side-chains added to them? Well, now you can see what some of these chains do.) Sugar chains also serve to lubricate cells, and allow them to stick to other cells by acting as an adhesion layer. Collectively, all these chains form the **glycocalyx:** an outer layer of the plasma membrane, composed of short carbohydrate chains that attach to membrane proteins and phospholipid molecules.

The Fluid-Mosaic Membrane Model

With this review of component parts under your belt, you're ready for a definition of the **plasma membrane.** It is a membrane, forming the outer boundary of many cells, composed of a phospholipid bilayer that is interspersed with proteins and cholesterol and coated on its exterior face with carbohydrate chains.

Taking a step back, the general message here is that the plasma membrane is a loose, lipid structure peppered with proteins and coated with sugars. A better image, however, might be of a *sea* of lipids that has proteins floating on it, because as it turns out, the plasma membrane is fluid enough that most of its elements are able to move sideways or "laterally" through it fairly freely. Indeed, membrane proteins frequently are compared to icebergs drifting through an ocean. (The proteins are numerous enough, however, that it's tempting to liken the cell surface to the Arctic Ocean at about the time the ice pack starts to break up.) When we overlay this quality of movement on the basic membrane structure just reviewed, the result is the contemporary view of the plasma membrane, the **fluid-mosaic model:** A conceptualization of the plasma membrane as a fluid, phospholipid bilayer that has, moving laterally within it, a mosaic of proteins.

5.2   Diffusion, Gradients, and Osmosis

It may be obvious that one of the main roles of the plasma membrane is to let in whatever's needed and to keep out whatever's not. Having learned something about the membrane's makeup, you will now see how it carries out this task of passage and blockage.

It is necessary to begin this story, however, not with the cell, but with the more general notion of how substances go from places where they are more concentrated to places where they are less concentrated. Anyone who has put some food dye in water has a sense of how this works: A few drops of, say, red dye will tumble into the liquid, start dispersing, and eventually the result is a solution that is uniformly more reddish than plain water (**see Figure 5.4**). The question that will be addressed here is why this takes place.

(a) Dye is dropped in   **(b)** Diffusion begins   **(c)** Dye is evenly distributed

water molecules

dye molecules

Figure 5.4
From Concentrated to Dispersed
Diffusion is the movement of molecules or ions from areas of their greater concentration to areas of their lesser concentration. In this sequence of photos and diagrams, a few drops of red dye, added to a beaker of water, are at first heavily concentrated in one area but then begin to diffuse, eventually becoming evenly distributed throughout the solution.

Random Movement and Even Distribution

All molecules or ions are constantly in motion, and this motion is random. (The *degree* to which molecules are in motion defines their temperature; absolute zero is the point at which all molecular motion has ceased.) The laws of thermodynamics dictate that, because the motion of molecules is random, they will naturally move from any initial *ordered* state—in our example, their concentrated state when first dropped in the container—to their most disordered state, meaning evenly distributed throughout a given volume.

What is at work here is **diffusion**: the movement of molecules or ions from a region of their higher concentration to a region of their lower concentration. This notion carries with it the concept of a gradient. A **concentration gradient** is defined as the difference between the highest and lowest concentration of a solute within a given medium. In our example, the solute is the dye and the medium is water. As with bicycles coasting down a grade, the natural tendency for any solute is to move *down* its concentration gradient, from higher concentration to lower. Our dye did just that. Bikes and solutes can move up a grade or gradient; but there is a price to be paid, and that price is the expenditure of energy. (On its own, would red dye ever spontaneously come *back* to its concentrated state in the container? Not without some work being performed, which is to say not without some energy being expended.)

Diffusion through Membranes

So far, you have looked at molecules diffusing in an undivided container. But the subject here is divisions—those provided by the plasma membrane. Let us consider, therefore, what happens to a solution in a container that is divided by a membrane. If that membrane is *permeable* to both water and the solute—that is, if both water and the solute can freely pass through it—and the solute lies only on one side of the membrane, then the predictable happens: The solute moves down its concentration gradient, diffusing right through the membrane, eventually becoming evenly distributed on both sides of it.

Now let's imagine a *semi*permeable membrane, one that water can freely move through but that solutes cannot. **Figure 5.5** shows you what happens if more solute is put on the right side of the membrane than the left. Water flows through the membrane both ways, but *more* water flows into the right chamber, which has a greater concentration of solutes in it. The result is that the solution on the right side rises to a higher level than the one on the left.

This seems strange on first viewing, as if gravity were taking a vacation on the right side of the container. But what has been demonstrated here is **osmosis**: the net movement of water across a semipermeable membrane from an area of lower solute concentration to an area of higher solute concentration. Why should this occur? In the case of a solute like salt, water molecules will surround and bond with the sodium and chloride ions that salt separates into in solution. Because these solutes are not free to pass through the membrane, the water molecules bound to them will likewise remain confined to the right side. This means that more "free" water will exist on the left side, and the result is a net movement of water into the right side (see Figure 5.5).

The Plasma Membrane as a Semipermeable Membrane

So what does movement of water have to do with the cell's outer lining? The cell's phospholipid bilayer is itself a semipermeable membrane. It is somewhat permeable to water and lipid substances but not permeable to larger charged substances. Thus, osmosis can take place across the plasma membrane—indeed, it does all the time. It is the primary means by which plants get water, and it is a player in all sorts of routine metabolic processes in animals.

**Figure 5.5
Osmosis in Action**

(a) An aqueous solution divided by a semipermeable membrane has a solute—in this case, salt—poured into its right chamber.

salt

solute

solvent

semipermeable membrane

(b) As a result, though water continues to flow in both directions through the membrane, there is a net movement of water toward the side with the greater concentration of solutes in it.

osmosis

(c) Why does this occur? Water molecules that are bonded to the sodium (Na⁺) and chloride (Cl⁻) ions that make up salt are not free to pass through the membrane to the left chamber of the container.

pure water

water bound to salt ions

In humans, the fluid portion of blood is at one point driven out of the blood vessels called capillaries by the force of blood pressure. How does this fluid get back in? Osmosis. The proteins that remain in the capillaries are like the salt in the container: they bring about an osmosis that pulls the fluid back into the blood vessels.

It is possible, however, for cells to experience an "osmotic imbalance," meaning a situation in which osmotic pressure is either flooding cells or drying them out. In some of these situations, plant cells have a great advantage over animal cells—their cell walls. Remember from Chapter 4 that one function of the cell wall is to regulate water uptake. Well, now we can see why this is so valuable. Animal cells, which do not have a cell wall, can expand until they burst when water comes in (**see Figure 5.6**). Plant cells, conversely, will expand only until their membranes push up against the cell wall with some force, setting up a pressure, or turgor, that keeps more water from coming in. Such tight quarters actually are an optimal condition for plants. A nice, crisp celery stick is one that has achieved this kind of *turgid* state, while a droopy stick that has lost this quality has cells that are *flaccid*; flowers in the latter condition are *wilted*.

Osmosis and Cell Environments

Is a given cell likely to lose water to its surroundings, gain water from them, or have a balanced flow back and forth with them? Any of these things are possible, depending on what the solute concentration is outside the cell as opposed to inside. Three terms are helpful in describing the various conditions that can exist. A fluid that has a higher concentration of solutes than another is said to be a **hypertonic solution**. If a cell's surroundings are hypertonic to the cell's cytoplasm, water will flow out of the cell. Two solutions that have equal concentrations of solutes are said to be **isotonic**. If one of these solutions is the cell's cytoplasm and the other the fluid surrounding the cell, fluid flow will be balanced between cell and surroundings. Finally, a fluid that has a lower concentration of solutes than another is a **hypotonic solution**. If a cell's surroundings are hypotonic to the cell's cytoplasm, water will flow into the cell. Figure 5.6 gives examples of what can happen to cells in all three types of environments.

5.3   Moving Smaller Substances In and Out

This excursion into the land of diffusion and osmosis has prepared us to start looking at the ways materials actually move into and out of the cell,

(a) Hypertonic surroundings   **(b)** Isotonic surroundings   **(c)** Hypotonic surroundings

Animal cell:

plasma membrane

Plant cell:

plasma membrane

cell wall

H_2O

H_2O

H_2O

H_2O

H_2O

H_2O

wilted ◄─────────────────────────► turgid

Net movement of   Balanced water   Net movement of
water out of cell   movement   water into cell

**Figure 5.6
Osmosis in Cells**

(a) When solutes (such as salt) exist in greater concentration outside the cell than inside, water moves out of the cell by osmosis and the cell shrinks. Here, the fluid surrounding the cell is hypertonic to the cell's cytoplasm.

(b) When solute concentrations inside and outside the cell are balanced, there is a balance of water movement into and out of the cell. Here, the fluid surrounding the cell is isotonic to the cell's cytoplasm.

(c) When solutes exist in greater concentration inside the cell than outside, water moves into the cell by osmosis. This influx may cause animal cells to burst, but plant cells are reinforced with cell walls and thus remain turgid—generally a healthy state for them. Here, the fluid surrounding the cell is hypotonic to the cell's cytoplasm.

across the plasma membrane. The big picture here is that some molecules are able to cross with no more assistance than is provided by diffusion or osmosis. Other molecules require these forces and the protein channels we talked about, and still others require channels and the expenditure of energy to get across. Different terms are applied to these different kinds of transport. **Active transport** is any movement of molecules or ions across a cell membrane that requires the expenditure of energy. **Passive transport** is any movement of molecules or ions across a cell membrane that does not require the expenditure of energy (**see Figure 5.7**). Our review of transport begins with two varieties of passive transport.

Passive Transport
Simple Diffusion

Web Tutorial 5.2
Passive and Active Transport

Gases such as oxygen and carbon dioxide are such small molecules that they need only move down their concentration gradients to pass into or out of the cell. Having been delivered by blood capillaries to an area just outside the cell, oxygen exists there in greater concentration than it does inside the cell. Moving down its concentration gradient, it diffuses through the plasma membrane and emerges on the other side. This is an example of **simple diffusion**, meaning diffusion through a cell membrane that does not require a special protein channel. Molecules that are larger than oxygen, but that are fat soluble, such as the steroid hormones

Figure 5.7
Transport through the Plasma Membrane

mentioned before, also move into the cell in this manner. Carbon dioxide, which is formed *in* the cell as a result of cellular respiration, has a net movement *out* of the cell through simple diffusion.

Facilitated Diffusion: Help from Proteins

Water can traverse the lipid bilayer through simple diffusion, moving through *despite* its hydrophilic nature primarily because it's such a small molecule. Yet with water itself—and certainly with polar molecules larger than water—protein channels begin to be required for passage in and out of the cell. With this, the method of passage is no longer *simple* diffusion; it is **facilitated diffusion**, meaning passage of materials through the plasma membrane that is aided by a concentration gradient and a transport protein.

Here you can begin to see the protein specificity referred to earlier. Each transport protein acts as a conduit for only one substance, or at most a small group of associated substances. The process of transport begins with the kind of binding explained earlier. A circulating molecule of glucose, for example, latches onto the binding site of a glucose transport protein. This binding causes the protein to change its shape, thus allowing the glucose molecule to pass through. In addition to glucose, other hydrophilic molecules, such as amino acids, move through the plasma membrane in this way. In some cases, a protein channel might not need to change shape. It simply remains open all the time, and is thus one of the passive passageways we talked about, though it will only let specific molecules pass through.

Note that this facilitated diffusion does not require the expenditure of energy, because it has a concentration gradient working in its favor. Glucose exists in greater concentration outside most cells than inside them. It is moving *down* its concentration gradient, then, by passing into the cell through a protein channel. So facilitated diffusion has something in common with simple diffusion. *Both* processes are driven by concentration gradients, meaning that neither requires metabolic energy. Thus, both are specific examples of passive transport.

Though the glucose in our example moved only one way in facilitated diffusion (into the cell), in general transport proteins are a channel for movement *either* way through the membrane. All that's required is a concentration gradient and a binding of the material with the transport protein.

Active Transport

If passive transport—either in simple or facilitated diffusion—were the only means of membrane passage available, cells would be totally dependent

Passive transport

simple diffusion

Materials move down their concentration gradient through the phospholipid bilayer.

facilitated diffusion

The passage of materials is aided both by a concentration gradient and by a transport protein.

Active transport

Molecules again move through a transport protein, but now energy must be expended to move them against their concentration gradient.

on concentration gradients. If, for example, molecules of a given amino acid come to exist in the same concentration on both sides of the plasma membrane, these amino acid travelers will continue to be transported, but they will be flowing out of the cell at the same rate they are flowing in. For cells, the problem is that some solutes are *needed* in greater concentration, say, inside the cell as opposed to outside. For example, the liver needs to take in large amounts of glucose because it is a prime storage site for glucose. Left alone, however, the glucose molecules that are so abundant in the liver would follow their concentration gradient and diffuse *out* of liver cells and back into the bloodstream. How do cells deal with such a situation? The cell's solution is pumps: it expends energy and pumps molecules against their concentration gradients. This is active transport at work. Many kinds of pumps are in operation in a cell, each of them being specific to one or perhaps two substances. The energy source for this transport often is ATP (adenosine triphosphate), though the cell also harnesses the power of oppositely charged ions to move substances across the membrane. One of the most important and best studied of the active transport mechanisms is known as the sodium-potassium pump.

The Sodium-Potassium Pump

The sodium-potassium pump allows the cell to maintain an environment of high potassium (K^+) *inside* the cell, and high sodium (Na^+) *outside* the cell. Imagine that we could take a snapshot of a cell at a given moment in time that would allow us to see these ion concentrations. With lots of Na^+ ions outside the cell, the result is predictable: A slow "leakage" of them into the cell as they follow their concentration gradient down and move in through transport proteins. K^+ ions, meanwhile, are moving out.

But our fantasy snapshot would also reveal something else. An abundance of protruding proteins that are busy pumping these molecules the *other way*, acting like so many bilge pumps moving seawater that has leaked into a ship back out into the ocean. If you look at **Figure 5.8**, you can see how the sodium-potassium pump works. The point here is not to count the movement of so many molecules in and out, but just to observe the process. One critical aspect of this is the shape-changing noted before with transport proteins.

You may wonder, though: Why would a cell spend so much energy to maintain this imbalance in sodium and potassium ions? Well, to take one example, nerve cells undertake this task for the same reason you undertake the task of charging your cell

1. Three sodium ions (Na^+) located within the cell's cytoplasm bind with a transport protein.

2. The energy molecule ATP gives up an energetic phosphate group to the transport protein.

3. This binding causes the protein to open its channel to the extracellular fluid; to lose its Na^+ binding sites, thus releasing the ions into the fluid; and to create binding sites for potassium ions (K^+).

4. Two K^+ move into the protein's K^+ binding sites, which brings about the release of the phosphate group.

5. This loss returns the protein to its original shape, releasing the K^+ into the cytoplasm and readying the protein for binding with another set of Na^+.

Figure 5.8
Active Transport in the Sodium-Potassium Pump

phone batteries: to have ready access to a capability. In your case, the capability is talking on the phone. In the nerve cell's case, the capability is being able to instantly take in large numbers of Na⁺ ions. This capability is crucial in getting a nerve signal under way—something you can read about in Chapter 26.

5.4 Getting the Big Stuff In and Out

Pumps and channels, diffusion and osmosis—these mechanisms move substances in and out of the cell, but as it turns out they only move relatively *small* substances. Remember an earlier discussion about the immune system cells that check to see if a given cell is friend or foe? Well, if an immune sentry finds a bacterial foe, it may have to ingest this *whole cell*. As you might guess, a cell cannot do this by employing little channels or pumps. You learned a bit in Chapter 4 about what does happen in these cases; now you'll be looking at it in somewhat greater detail.

The methods in question here are endocytosis, which brings materials into the cell; and exocytosis, which sends them out. What these mechanisms have in common is their use of vesicles, the membrane-lined enclosures that alternately bud off from membranes or fuse with them.

Movement Out: Exocytosis

Exocytosis is defined as the movement of materials out of the cell through a fusion of a vesicle with the plasma membrane. As **Figure 5.9** shows, exocytosis involves a transport vesicle making its way to the plasma membrane and fusing with it, whereupon the vesicle's contents are released into the extracellular fluid. You observed in Chapter 4 that cells use exocytosis when they are exporting proteins. For single-celled creatures, waste products may be released into the extracellular fluid through this process.

Movement In: Endocytosis

Endocytosis is the movement of relatively large materials into the cell by infolding of the plasma membrane. It can take any of three forms: pinocytosis, receptor-mediated endocytosis, and phagocytosis.

Pinocytosis

Pinocytosis means "cell drinking," and if you look at **Figure 5.10**, you can see why this term is fairly accurate. The cell invaginates, creating a kind of harbor on its exterior. Whatever material happens to be enclosed in the harbor when it pinches off to become a vesicle is brought into the cell. What is brought in, of course, is mostly water, with some solutes in it. **Pinocytosis** can be defined as a form of endocytosis that brings into the cell a small volume of extracellular fluid and the materials suspended in it. Remember how it was noted earlier that the plasma membrane is constantly being "remade," due to the movement of materials in and out of it? With pinocytosis you can get some sense of this. Through this form of endocytosis, whole sections of the plasma membrane are continually budding off and moving to the interior of the cell. These sections have to be replaced, of course, with membrane brought up from the cell's interior. The result is a membrane in a constant state of flux.

Receptor-Mediated Endocytosis (RME)

As its name implies, the second form of endocytosis, **receptor-mediated endocytosis** (RME), depends on receptors, whose role is to bind to specific molecules and then hold onto them. Groups of receptors bearing these molecules then make a lateral migration through the cell membrane and congregate in a place that is literally a pit; it is a depression in the cell, referred to as a *coated pit*. (What it is coated with is a layer of a protein, called clathrin, on the cytoplasmic

Web Tutorial 5.3
Exocytosis and Endocytosis

Figure 5.9
Movement Out of the Cell

(a) In exocytosis, a transport vesicle—perhaps loaded with proteins or waste products—moves to the plasma membrane and fuses with it. This section of the membrane then opens, and the contents of the former vesicle are released to the extracellular fluid.

(b) Micrograph of material being expelled from the cell through exocytosis.

(a) Exocytosis

(b) Micrograph of exocytosis

(a) Pinocytosis

In pinocytosis, the plasma membrane invaginates to create a kind of harbor. The harbor then encloses completely, pinches off as a vesicle, and moves into the cell's cytoplasm, carrying with it whatever material was enclosed.

Micrograph of pinocytosis in a capillary cell.

(b) Receptor-mediated endocytosis

In receptor-mediated endocytosis, many receptors bind to molecules. Then, while holding on to the molecules, the receptors migrate laterally through the cell membrane, arriving at a depression called a coated pit. The coated pit pinches off, delivering its receptor-held molecules into the cytoplasm.

Formation of an RME vesicle.

(c) Phagocytosis

In phagocytosis, food particles—or perhaps whole organisms—are taken in by means of "false feet" or pseudopodia that surround the material. Pseudopodia then fuse together, forming a vesicle that moves into the cell's interior with its catch enclosed.

A human macrophage (colored blue) uses phagocytosis to ingest an invading yeast cell.

Figure 5.10
Three Ways to Get Relatively Large Materials into the Cell

side.) Eventually, the pit deepens and pinches off, creating the familiar vesicle moving into the cell. RME is very important in getting nutrients and other substances into cells. (It is the way cholesterol gets into your cells, for example.) The scale of the RME operation can be judged from the fact that, in mammalian cells, coated pits might take up 20 percent of a plasma membrane's surface area. RME is also a clear example of the kind of icebergs-on-the-ocean migration that proteins are capable of within the plasma membrane.

How Did We Learn?
The Fluid-Mosaic Model of the Plasma Membrane

The richly detailed illustrations found in science textbooks do a great job of presenting information, but they also can be a little misleading. Given their clarity, such illustrations might leave students with the impression that many of the discoveries that scientists make would be apparent to anyone who simply looked in the right place with the right microscope.

Figure 1a presents an example of the kind of pictures (or "micrographs") we have of the plasma membrane, while **Figure 1b** presents an example of the kind of artist's rendering you've been seeing of it.

> *Our view of the cell membrane was constructed piece by piece in an intellectual chain that stretched out for decades.*

You'll probably agree that no one could have discerned the detail in 1b just by looking at 1a. How, then, do we know that the plasma membrane actually is structured as you see it in 1a? How do we know that it is largely lipid, and that proteins move about on the surface of it like so many icebergs? As it turns out, our view of the cell membrane was constructed piece by piece in an intellectual chain that stretched out for decades.

The idea that the surface of the cell is largely made of lipid material was set forth as early as 1855 by investigator Carl Nägeli. In 1899, Charles E. Overton came to the same conclusion by working with some cellular extensions of plant roots. What Overton found was that lipid-soluble substances moved quite easily into these "root hairs," while water-soluble substances did not. Remember now the adage about like dissolving like: Lipid substances would dissolve within *lipid materials.* Overton's conclusion was that the outside lining of the root cells was made of just such materials. From our vantage point—knowing about the phospholipid bilayer that makes up much of the membrane—we can see that he was right.

In 1925, two Dutch scientists, E. G. Gorter and F. Grendel, decided to take red blood cells and measure their lipid content. They knew from the work of another scientist that a given volume of phospholipids would cover a certain *area* when arrayed in a layer. What they found, however, was that the lipids they extracted from the blood cells spread out into an area *twice* as large as would be expected from this benchmark. This doubling, they concluded, came about because the cell membrane was doubled; it existed as the *bi*layer you've been reading about.

Following this advance, however, it was apparent that the plasma membrane had to be composed of more than just two layers of lipids pressed together. For one thing, it was clear that closely related types of hydrophilic molecules passed through the membrane at different rates. This was difficult to reconcile with a uniform phospholipid membrane, which would have let all such substances pass through at nearly the same rate. Given such evidence, James Danielli, writing with Hugh Davson, proposed a view of the plasma membrane that ended up having a long run in science. With modifications over time, the Davson-Danielli model, as it was called, wore the mantle of being "generally accepted" by scientists from the time it was set forth in 1935 until the early 1970s. It proposed that a *layer of proteins* coated each side of the phospholipid bilayer.

Phagocytosis

The third form of endocytosis is a means of bringing even larger materials into the cell. It is phagocytosis (literally, "cell eating"). This is the mechanism mentioned earlier, by which a human immune-system cell might ingest a whole bacterium (see Figure 5.10c). This is also the way that many one-celled creatures eat, so it's probably apparent that relatively large materials are being ingested here. How large? Vesicles of perhaps 1–2 μm are created in this process, as opposed to pinocytosis and RME, where the vesicles might be a tenth this size. Not all the materials brought into the cell by phagocytosis are whole cells; parts of cells and large nutrients are fair game as well.

As you can see in Figure 5.10, phagocytosis begins when the cell sends out extensions of its plasma membrane called pseudopodia ("false feet"). These surround the food and fuse their ends together. What was once outside is now inside, encased in a vesicle and moving toward the cell's interior. Once this happens, lysosomes in the cell move to the vesicle, fuse with it, and begin breaking down the material in it. **Phagocytosis** can be defined as a process of bringing relatively large materials into a cell by means of wrapping extensions of the plasma membrane around the materials and fusing the extensions together.

(a) Micrograph of the plasma membrane

0.1μm

(b) Artist's rendering of it

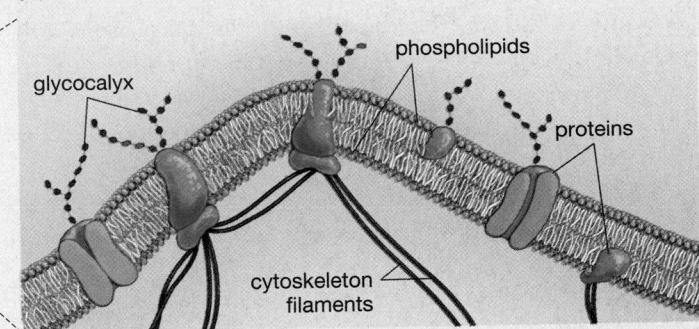

glycocalyx
phospholipids
proteins
cytoskeleton filaments

Figure 1
How Much Can a Picture Tell Us?

By the 1950s, electron microscopes had become refined enough that they yielded a "railroad track" picture of the plasma membrane: two dark bands separated by a space in the middle (the view you see in **Figure 2** on the next page). Seduced, perhaps, by the comforts of what was "known" to be true, scientists took such pictures to be visual proof of Davson-Danielli. The two dark lines were protein bands, it was thought, and the space in the middle was the phospholipid bilayer. We now know, however, that the "tracks" actually were electrons that bound with both membrane proteins and the charged portions of the phospholipid bilayer, thus creating the impression of a continuous track. In reality, there were no protein bands.

Through these years, it was also becoming apparent that there wasn't just one membrane in the cell, there were many: membranes encasing the mitochondria, membranes making up the Golgi complex, and so forth. In 1960, J. David Robertson set forth a proposal that saw *all* the cell's membranes as existing within the framework of Davson-Danielli. By that time the venerable model had been modified to include the notion of some proteins *spanning* the bilayer, from cytoplasm to outside face. This, then, was the generally accepted view of cell membranes in the early 1960s: Davson-Danielli-Robertson which posited a phospholipid bilayer coated on each side with a protein layer, and shot through here and there with other proteins.

Into this situation came a chemist, then at Yale, named Jonathan Singer. In 1962, Singer got to thinking about cell membranes and realized that Davson-Danielli-Robertson had a real problem: It would require hydro*phobic* parts of the supposed protein coat to be in contact with *water*. This was like assuming you could set one marble on top of another and expect it to stay there. By 1964, Singer was convinced not only that Davson-Danielli-Robertson had some shortcomings, but that he had a model that improved on it. It's one thing, however, to believe you're right, based on general chemical principles, and quite another to prove it.

"What happened was that I wasn't going to propose a model without some kind of experiments to go with it," Singer said in an interview. Working with a postdoctoral student of his, John Lenard, Singer published a scientific paper in 1966 that made the basic break with Davson-Danielli-Robertson. The view that emerged from this paper was that the membrane had a series of *individual* proteins that either were embedded in the bilayer or lay on it. By 1971, Singer was able to set forth a case for his model in great detail in a book chapter. The problem was that nobody paid much attention to it. So he set out to write a review of the same subject in *Science* magazine. In the interval between the book chapter and the magazine article, however, one last piece of the membrane puzzle fell into place.

(continued)

How Did We Learn?

How do we know that the plasma membrane has the structure you've just been reading about—the phospholipid bilayer, the proteins moving about like icebergs on the ocean, and so forth? This knowledge was gained through a series of investigations that lasted from the nineteenth century to the 1970s. You can read about this chain of discovery in "The Fluid-Mosaic Model of the Plasma Membrane" above.

On to Energy

Your tour of the cell and its plasma membrane is now complete. What's coming up next is something called bioenergetics. In our story of biology so far, there have been continuing vague references to proteins that are called enzymes and to a molecule called ATP and to energy expenditures. This has been rather like a description of an elephant that avoids the subject of its trunk. We will now embark on the subject of bioenergetics, however, which describes forces that are so basic they condition all of biology.

(continued)

Recall that the modern view of the cell membrane is the fluid-mosaic model. It is *mosaic* because it posits discrete proteins within the phospholipid bilayer; but it is *fluid* because these proteins (and the phospholipids themselves) can *move* laterally through the membrane. In 1971, Singer had the mosaic part; by 1972, he had the fluid as well.

"I came to Dr. Singer's lab in 1967," said Garth Nicolson, who was a graduate student with Singer in those days and is now pres-

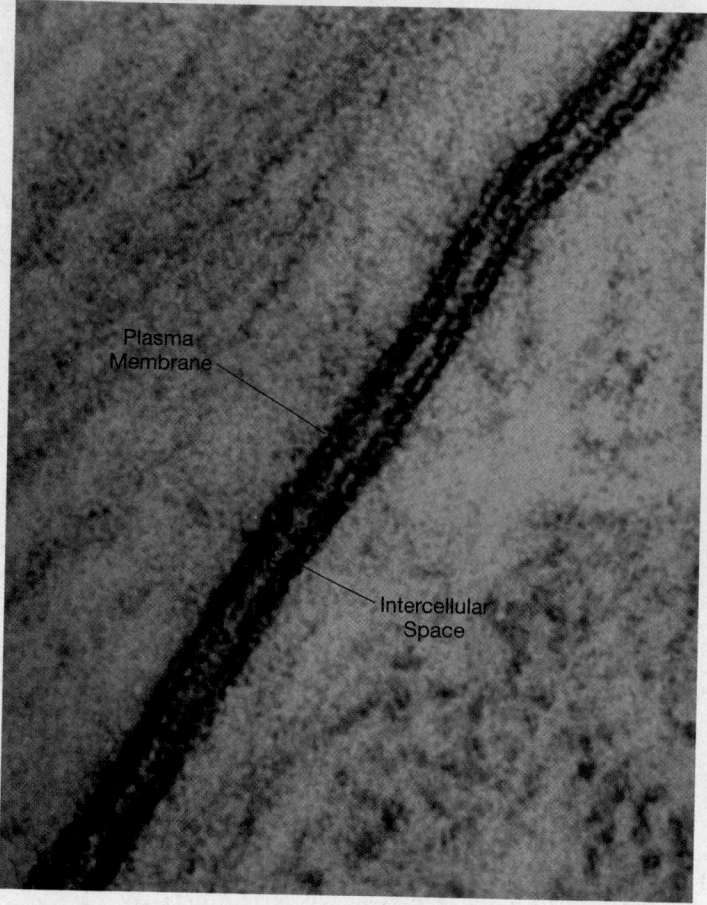

ident of the Institute for Molecular Medicine in Huntington Beach, California. "I became very interested in the polarity of membranes . . . what I found when doing this work was that the distribution of components [on the surface of the cell] seemed to change dynamically." What Nicolson saw, in other words, was that the constituent parts of the membrane were shifting around on it.

Singer and Nicolson are agreed that a paper by L. D. Frye and Michael Edidin made Singer a believer in the rapid movement of materials across the cell surface. The upshot was a paper called "The Fluid Mosaic Model of the Structure of Cell Membranes," which appeared in *Science* magazine in February of 1972, with Singer and Nicolson as authors. It turned out to have great impact. Read any biology textbook today, and the account of the cell's plasma membrane is essentially the view set forth in this paper. The illustrations contained in textbooks likewise all look like a drawing in the *Science* article. Such was its effect that the fluid-mosaic model is just as likely to be referred to as the "Singer-Nicolson" model, even though, as Garth Nicolson is the first to say, "this is really [Singer's] model . . . he should get the credit for the membrane as far as I'm concerned."

Does this mean that the fluid-mosaic model has at last given us an accurate picture of the membrane? We might wonder about this because, after all, Davson-Danielli was generally accepted for more than 30 years. Singer believes, however, that fluid-mosaic does describe reality. "It's not going to change," he says. "Things rattle around for awhile, but then you get settled in on the right picture."

Figure 2
A Close-up of the Plasma Membrane
Electron micrograph of two adjoining cells, each of which has a plasma membrane with a "railroad track" appearance. The intercellular space is the space between the two cells. (×470,000)

Chapter Review

Summary

5.1   The Nature of the Plasma Membrane

- The plasma membrane is a thin, fluid, lipid entity that manages to be very flexible and yet stable enough to stay together despite being continually remade, due to the constant movement of materials in and out of it. The plasma membrane has four principal components: (1) A phospholipid bilayer, (2) molecules of cholesterol interspersed within the bilayer, (3) proteins that are embedded in or that lie on the bilayer, and (4) short carbohydrate chains on the cell surface, collectively called the glycocalyx, that function in cell adhesion and as binding sites on proteins.

- Phospholipids are molecules composed of two fatty-acid chains linked to a charged phosphate group. The fatty-acid chains are hydrophobic, meaning they avoid water, while the phosphate group is hydrophilic, meaning it readily bonds with water. Such phospholipids arrange themselves into "bilayers"—two layers of phospholipids in which the fatty-acid "tails" of each layer point inward (avoiding water) while the phosphate "heads" point outward (bonding with it). Phospholipids take on this configuration in the plasma membrane because a watery environment lies on either side of the membrane.

- The cholesterol molecules that are interspersed between phospholipid molecules in the plasma perform two functions: they act as a patching material that helps keep some small molecules from moving through the membrane; and they keep the membrane at an optimal level of fluidity.

- Some plasma membrane proteins are integral, meaning they are bound to the hydrophobic interior of the phospholipid bilayer. Others are peripheral, meaning they lie on either side of the membrane but are not bound to its hydrophobic interior.

- The functions that membrane proteins serve include (1) structural support; (2) cell identification, by serving as external recognition proteins that interact with immune system cells; (3) communication, by serving as external receptors for signaling molecules; and (4) transport, by providing channels and associated structures for the movement of compounds into and out of the cell.

- The plasma membrane today is described by a conceptualization called the fluid-mosaic model, which views the membrane as a fluid, phospholipid bilayer that has moving laterally within it a mosaic of proteins.
Web Tutorial 5.1: Plasma Membranes and Diffusion

5.2   Diffusion, Gradients, and Osmosis

- Diffusion is the movement of molecules or ions from a region of their higher concentration to a region of their lower concentration. A concentration gradient defines the difference between the highest and lowest concentrations of a solute within a given medium. Through diffusion, compounds naturally move from higher to lower concentrations—meaning down their concentration gradients. Energy must be expended, however, to move compounds against their concentration gradients.

- A semipermeable membrane is one that allows some compounds to pass through freely while blocking the passage of other compounds. Osmosis is the net movement of water across a semipermeable membrane from an area of lower solute concentration to an area of higher solute concentration. Because the plasma membrane is a semipermeable membrane, osmosis operates in connection with it. Osmosis is a major force in living things; it is responsible for much of the movement of fluids into and out of cells. Osmotic imbalances can cause cells either to dry out from losing too much water or (in the case of animal cells) to break from taking too much in. Plant cells generally do not have this latter problem, because their cell walls limit their uptake of water.

- Cells will gain or lose water relative to their surroundings in accordance with what the solute concentration is inside the cell as opposed to outside. A cell will lose water to a surrounding solution that is hypertonic—a solution that has a greater concentration of solutes in it than does the cell's cytoplasm. A cell will gain water when the surrounding solution is hypotonic to the cytoplasmic fluid. Water flow will be balanced between the cell and its surroundings when the surrounding fluid and the cytoplasmic fluid are isotonic to each other—when they have the same concentration of solutes.

5.3   Moving Smaller Substances In and Out

- Some compounds are able to cross the plasma membrane strictly through diffusion and osmosis; others require these forces and special protein channels; still others require protein channels and the expenditure of cellular energy. Active transport is any movement of molecules or ions across a cell membrane that requires the expenditure of energy. Passive transport is any movement of molecules or ions across a cell membrane that does not require the expenditure of energy.

- Two forms of passive transport are simple diffusion and facilitated diffusion. Simple diffusion is diffusion that does not require a protein channel. Facilitated diffusion is diffusion that requires a protein channel. In facilitated diffusion, transport proteins function as channels for larger hydrophilic substances—substances that, because of their size and electrical charge, cannot diffuse through the hydrophobic portion of the plasma membrane.

- Cells cannot rely solely on passive transport to move substances across the plasma membrane. It may be that a given cell needs to have, on one side of its membrane a greater concentration of a given substance than exists on the other side. Yet passive transport serves to equalize concentrations of substances on both sides of the plasma membrane. To deal with such needs, cells employ chemical pumps to move compounds across the plasma membrane against their concentration gradients. One prime example of such a transport mechanism is the sodium-potassium pump.
Web Tutorial 5.2: Passive and Active Transport

5.4   Getting the Big Stuff In and Out

- Larger materials are brought into the cell through endocytosis and moved out through exocytosis. Both mechanisms employ vesicles, the membrane-lined enclosures that alternately bud off from membranes or fuse with them.

- There are three principal forms of endocytosis: (1) pinocytosis, in which the plasma membrane invaginates, creating an enclosure that pinches off to become a vesicle that moves into the cell, carrying with it extracellular fluid and the materials suspended in it; (2) receptor-mediated endocytosis, in which cell-surface receptors bind with materials to be brought into the cell and then migrate laterally through the cell membrane, congregating in a "coated pit," where vesicle-budding will bring them into the cell; and (3) phagocytosis, in which certain cells engulf whole cells, fragments of them, or other large organic materials, and bring these materials into the cell inside vesicles that bud off from the plasma membrane.
Web Tutorial 5.3: Exocytosis and Endocytosis

Key Terms

active transport   106

concentration gradient   104

diffusion   104

endocytosis   108

exocytosis   108

facilitated diffusion   106

fluid-mosaic model   103

glycocalyx   103

hypertonic solution   105

hypotonic solution   105

integral protein   101

isotonic solution   105

osmosis   104

passive transport   106

peripheral protein   101

phagocytosis   110

phospholipid bilayer   100

pinocytosis   108

plasma membrane   103

receptor-mediated
endocytosis (RME)   108

receptor protein   102

simple diffusion   106

transport protein   103

Understanding the Basics

Multiple-Choice Questions (answers in the back of the book)

1. If the plasma membrane lacked a glycocalyx, the cell would have difficulty
   a. keeping its fluid state
   b. transporting materials across the membrane
   c. adhering to other cells
   d. binding to the cytoskeleton on the inside of the membrane
   e. keeping small particles from passing easily across the membrane

2. You eat spaghetti for dinner and digest the starch in it to glucose. The glucose is now in high concentration in the cells of your small intestine, relative to its concentration in your bloodstream. Predictably, the glucose diffuses across the plasma membrane of your intestinal cells, into your bloodstream.
   a. True.
   b. False, because molecules cannot move across membranes by diffusion.
   c. False, because diffusion moves materials from low concentration to high concentration.
   d. False, because molecules are too large to move across membranes.
   e. False, because energy is required for diffusion.

3. When a human cell is placed into water, it swells. This is said to be due to osmosis. What's happening to make the cell swell?
   a. Solutes are growing larger inside the cell
   b. Solutes are being drawn into the cell across the plasma membrane.
   c. Water is diffusing across the plasma membrane from a region of lower solute concentration (outside the cell) to a region of higher solute concentration (inside the cell).
   d. Water is diffusing across the plasma membrane from a region of higher solute concentration (outside the cell) to a region of lower solute concentration (inside the cell).
   e. The cell synthesizes new biological macromolecules as a protective response against a watery environment.

4. Tyrone gave Lakeisha a rose for the anniversary of their first date. Now the rose has wilted, because
   a. The cells have taken too much water in and burst.
   b. The cell walls have broken down.
   c. The plasma membrane has lost the proteins that keep water in.
   d. The phospholipid bilayer has broken down.
   e. The plant's cells have insufficient water in them to push against their cell walls.

5. The protein that functions in the sodium-potassium pump is an *integral* protein. The word *integral* tells you that this protein
   a. functions on only one side of the membrane
   b. is connected to a cholesterol molecule
   c. is essential to the cell
   d. is connected to the hydrophobic interior of the plasma membrane
   e. is connected to the glycocalyx

6. You get a cut on your finger and some bacteria enter. Your immune-system cells kill off the invaders by ingesting them. This is an example of
   a. pinocytosis
   b. phagocytosis
   c. receptor-mediated endocytosis
   d. exocytosis
   e. active transport

7. According to the fluid-mosaic model of membrane structure, the membrane is made up of a
   a. continuous base of proteins with phospholipids in it that have fairly free lateral movement
   b. bilayer of phospholipids with proteins interspersed in it that have fairly free lateral movement
   c. bilayer of protein with layers of phospholipids on the outside and inside
   d. bilayer of phospholipid with layers of proteins on the outside and inside
   e. bilayer of phospholipids sandwiched between two bilayers of proteins

8. Calcium ions (Ca^{++}) are present in the endoplasmic reticulum at 1000-fold higher concentrations than in the cytosol (the gel-like material of the cell outside of organelles). One protein on the endoplasmic reticulum membrane is devoted to allowing Ca^{++} to move from the endoplasmic reticulum to the cytosol and another protein moves Ca^{++} from the cytosol to the endoplasmic reticulum. These processes are not trivial, as Ca^{++} released into the cytosol allows such things as muscle contraction and communication between nerve cells. In this pair of Ca^{++} transport proteins, you would predict that the protein moving Ca^{++} from the endoplasmic reticulum to the cytosol _____ and the protein that moves Ca^{++} from cytosol to the endoplasmic reticulum _____.
   a. is large; is small
   b. is small; is large
   c. requires ATP; works without ATP
   d. works without ATP; requires ATP
   e. transports calcium slowly; transports calcium rapidly

9. Endocytosis and exocytosis are similar in that both involve the use of
   a. vesicles that carry materials into and out of the cell
   b. the Golgi apparatus to package materials
   c. diffusion to carry food and wastes across the plasma membrane
   d. starch to supply large amounts of energy
   e. the rough ER to manufacture proteins

10. Osmosis refers to the net movement of _____ across a _____
    a. energy . . . medium
    b. solutes . . . semipermeable membrane
    c. solutes . . . permeable membrane
    d. glucose . . . protein channel
    e. water . . . semipermeable membrane

Brief Review

1. Imagine a receptor on the surface of one of your muscle cells that responds only to glucose. Plenty of insulin molecules are passing by this receptor, but it does not respond to them. Why not?

2. You often hear how dangerous it is for athletes to take steroids to "bulk up" and how many problems steroids cause in various parts of the body. Why do these drugs affect all parts of the body—not just the muscles?

3. Explain why the phospholipid "heads" of the plasma membrane are always pointed toward the cytosol and extracellular fluid, whereas the "tails" are always oriented toward the middle of the membrane.

4. Describe the process of receptor-mediated endocytosis.

5. As you saw in this chapter, all cellular membranes are similar in structure. However, what differences are likely to exist between the plasma membrane and membranes in the interior of the cell?

Applying Your Knowledge

1. All life-forms on Earth exist either as single cells or as collections of cells that have a plasma membrane at their periphery (though some cells have cell walls outside their plasma membrane). Why do you think the plasma membrane exists in all living things? Why aren't there living things that don't have a membrane at their periphery?

2. Because materials move from high concentration to low concentration by simple diffusion, and they move the same way by facilitated diffusion, why do cells make proteins to carry out facilitated diffusion? Isn't this just a waste of energy?

3. Place a number of marbles on one end of a cafeteria tray. Shake the tray gently a few times, keeping it level. What happens to the marbles? Start over and shake faster the next time. What happens now? Explain how this is like diffusion.

MediaLab

Balancing Your Imports and Exports: Membrane Transport

In this chapter, you read that without the efficient, rapid movement of substances across your membranes, you would not be able to move, absorb nutrients, or even see this page. The *Web Tutorial* illustrates the different types of membrane transport involved in all these processes. In the following *Web Investigation*, you will examine the importance of membranes in organisms ranging from bacteria to humans, so that in the *Communicate Your Results* section you can analyze how membrane transport has been manipulated to treat wounds, cystic fibrosis, or drug addiction.

The online version of this *MediaLab* can be found in Chapter 5 on your Companion Website (www.prenhall.com/krogh3).

WEB TUTORIAL

In order to live, a cell must import some substances and export others. There are four different ways of transporting substances across membranes; each is illustrated through graphic animations in this *Web Tutorial*.

Activity

1. First, you will discover how small molecules, including water, may be able to move across the lipid portion of the membrane using **diffusion** in a process called **passive transport**.

2. You will then compare this to the process of **active transport**, where the energy of ATP must be used to pump molecules across protein channels in the membrane.

3. Finally, you will learn how other substances—critical in nerve transmission—are moved in bulk within membrane "bubbles," a process called **endocytosis** or **exocytosis**.

After completing this activity, you should be familiar enough with these transport mechanisms to begin the *Web Investigation* into how they work together in cells.

WEB INVESTIGATION

Investigation 1
Estimated time for completion = 10 minutes

Cigarettes, chocolate, and cocaine: Have you ever wondered how they make us feel so good? Our brain contains millions of neurons that help us respond to the environment, coordinating sight, smell, hearing, touch, and even pleasure. All these neurons must communicate with each other using membrane transport. Most addictive drugs are able to elevate the natural neuron communication that occurs after pleasant sensations like a hug, or a bite of candy. Select the keyword **ADDICTION** on your Website for this *MediaLab* to read more about nerve-cell communication. Once you have read about nerve cells, click on the next link, "drugs," at the bottom of the page to view how cocaine acts. After reading the article, select the keyword **NERVES** to view an animation of one nerve cell communicating with another.

Investigation 2

Estimated time for completion = 15 minutes

Why do we wash our hands with soap, or cleanse a wound with alcohol or iodine? They are all antiseptics—substances that kill cells. What is it in soap or alcohol that would harm bacteria but not our own cells? Select the keyword **ANTISEPTICS** on your Website, and read Table 2 in the linked article to find out how these antiseptics harm bacteria. Antiseptics are commonly found in many different household products, including cleaning supplies and mouthwashes. Select the keyword **MOUTHWASH** to read an article listing the active ingredients in mouthwash. Then, clip a label from an antiseptic product and use these two websites to determine its active ingredients.

Investigation 3

Estimated time for completion = 15 minutes

At the opening of this chapter you read about cystic fibrosis, a debilitating disease caused by a genetic disorder. The disease is caused by a defect in the gene that produces the protein CFTR, which forms channels in the cell membranes involved in the active transport of chloride ions. Because this disease greatly reduces life expectancy, you would expect few of these defective genes to be passed on to future generations. Yet, cystic fibrosis has been around for centuries. Could there possibly be a benefit to having a defective gene like this? Select the keyword **ADVANTAGE**, and read about evolution and the selective advantage of the cystic fibrosis gene.

COMMUNICATE YOUR RESULTS

Exercise 1

Estimated time for completion = 20 minutes

In *Web Investigation 1*, you saw how membrane transport operates to conduct nerve impulses. In 50 words, identify the types of membrane transport involved in passing nervous impulses, and describe their roles. These nerve impulses may be sending messages of pain (or pleasure in the case of addictive drugs) to your central nervous system. How does cocaine cause pleasurable sensations? Can you propose a way to interrupt neuron communications such as pain signals? Does this knowledge help to explain how painkillers and other drugs like cocaine or morphine work?

Exercise 2

Estimated time for completion = 15 minutes

What's the best way to cleanse your mouth, hands, or wounds of harmful bacteria? In *Web Investigation 2*, you read a list of antiseptics and saw that many of them kill bacteria by disrupting cell membranes. Create a list of all the active ingredients from the labels of your common household antiseptics that act by disrupting cell membranes.

Exercise 3

Estimated time for completion = 15 minutes

The article in *Web Investigation 3* explores the idea that if detrimental alleles, like the one for cystic fibrosis, remain in the population, they must have some selective advantage. In 50 words, describe the selective advantage provided by the cystic fibrosis allele. Propose a hypothesis to explain this advantage, given what you know about the cause of cystic fibrosis.

6 An Introduction to Energy

Freeing energy from chemical bonds.
(Section 6.2, page 121)

A downhill reaction releases energy.
(Section 6.3, page 122)

Activation energy.
(Section 6.6, page 126)

Energy flows through life in a never-ending pattern of acquisition, storage, and use.

When my daughter Tessa was young, she had a teddy bear with a music box in it that let us listen to "Brahms's Lullaby." All I had to do was wind up the key that attached to the music box. After a few turns of the wrist, the melody would cycle through several times, then slow for a last few bars, then stop. This process could be repeated as many times as I wound the music box. However—no surprise here—the music box never seemed to wind itself. As we listened, a mechanism in the music box kept the melody coming out at an even tempo. Even the slowing at the end seemed just right for a lullaby, since the audience was a sleepy child.

6.1 Energy Is Central to Life

The forces that determined how Tessa's teddy bear worked also turn out to condition life, since, in order to function, both the music box and life must be supplied with the same thing: energy. Just as the music from the box depended on energy from an "outside hand" (mine) to continue, so almost all life on Earth depends on energy from an outside source: the sun, whose daily showering of energetic rays lets the green world of plants and algae flour-

ish. These organisms then pass their bounty along to animals and other living things in the form of food to eat and oxygen to breathe.

Beyond this, the sun and the music box have something else in common: their energy always runs downhill, from more concentrated to less. The spring in the music box spontaneously unwinds, but it does not rewind itself. The sun sends out light and heat, but this energy does not spontaneously come together to form another sun. The music from the music box eventually must come to a stop, and in a similar way, even the sun will not shine forever. With all its grandeur, its energy is winding down, its brilliance dispersing. The difference is that once the sun's showering of energy comes to a stop, nothing will restart it.

While the sun's gift lasts, however, living things can transform its energy and use it to do things like sprout leaves and swim through oceans. Such complex activities make it imperative, though, that living things be able to *control* the energy they capture. The spring within the music box unwinds at a measured rate, spinning out the melody at just the right pace; similarly, living things have elaborate mechanisms in place that allow them to make the most out of the energy they receive.

The site of action in an enzyme.
(Section 6.6, page 127)

How an enzyme does its job.
(Section 6.6, page 127)

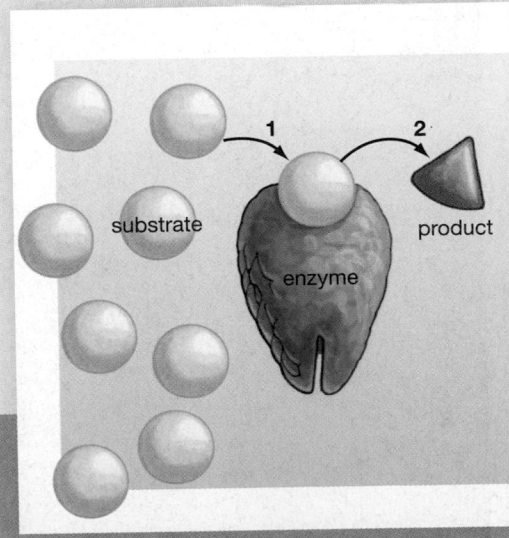

Regulating enzymatic activity.
(Section 6.7, page 128)

119

Principles such as these are important enough to biology that this chapter and the two that follow are devoted to the subject of energy and life. In this chapter you'll learn some basics about energy and some energy-saving molecules called enzymes. Then, in Chapter 7, you'll see how living things "harvest" energy, meaning how they extract energy from food. Finally, in Chapter 8, you'll look at the ways that plants, algae, and some bacteria capture the sun's energy in the process called photosynthesis. We'll start now by looking at the energy basics.

6.2 What Is Energy?

Energy is commonly defined as the capacity to do work, but this definition merely passes the question mark along, to the word *work*. Given this, here's one possible definition of **energy**: the capacity to bring about movement against an opposing force. The thing that makes energy so tricky as a concept is that although we can measure it with great precision, and we can experience its effects, we cannot grasp it or see it. We can see the water that drives a waterwheel, but who has seen the energy the water contains? (**See Figure 6.1.**)

The Forms of Energy

Energy can be thought of as coming in different forms, many of them familiar. Mechanical energy is captured in the wound-up spring of the musical teddy bear. Chemical energy is the energy held in the chemical bonds of a lump of coal. One other way to conceptualize energy is as potential and kinetic. **Potential energy** is stored energy: the rock perched precariously at the top of the hill; the charged ions kept on one side of a cell membrane. Conversely, **kinetic energy** is energy in motion, as with the rock tumbling down the hill or water driving a waterwheel. If we define energy as the capacity to bring about movement against an opposing force, we can see how kinetic energy fits into this scheme. A rock that tumbles off a cliff and into a lake would cause the water in the lake to splash upward—against the force of gravity.

The Study of Energy: Thermodynamics

Given how important energy is to life, it makes sense that there is a branch of biology, called *bioenergetics*, that links biology with a scientific discipline known as **thermodynamics**, the study of energy. Though thermodynamics is a mathematical and rather abstract discipline, research into it was prompted originally by a very down-to-earth goal: the desire to build a better steam engine. British inventors had harnessed steam power in the eighteenth century, and this discovery had the awesome impact of sparking the Industrial Revolution. The word *revolution* is fitting here because, before the advent of steam power, people used the stored energy in, say, wood or coal solely to produce *heat*. The steam engine was a device that allowed them to use heat to perform *work* on a scale that was previously impossible. Heat could be channeled, it was discovered, to drive an engine, which in turn could power any number of industrial processes.

With this development, new questions confronted scientists: How exactly did heat drive a steam engine? Was there a finite quantity of energy, such that it could all be used up? Research carried out in England, Germany, and France during the nineteenth century yielded the answers to these questions, and the result was the development of some insights known as the laws of thermodynamics.

The First Law of Thermodynamics: The Transformation of Energy

The **first law of thermodynamics** states that energy is never created or destroyed, but is only transformed. The sun's energy is not used up by green plants; rather, some of it is *converted* by the plants into chemical form. Plants use the sun's energy to put together carbohydrates, whose chemical bonds contain some of the energy that previously existed in the sun's rays.

A critical point here is the qualification that plants turn *some* of the sun's energy into chemical form. As it turns out, a plant cannot convert *all* of

Figure 6.1

Figure 6.1
Where's the Energy?
Part of the water moving over these falls is channeled to a water wheel, which turns as a result. Though the fall of the water is plainly visible, the energy released is not.

the solar energy it receives into carbohydrates. Likewise, a steam engine actually converts only a fraction of the energy contained in coal into the movement of a piston. What happens to the energy that is not stored in carbohydrates or transformed into motion? It can't be destroyed; that's clear from the first law. What happens is that it is converted into the form of energy known as *heat*. For every energy "transaction" that takes place, at least some of the original energy is converted into heat. This is true for every transaction in every energy system: cars burning gasoline, electric utilities burning coal, and your brain decoding this sentence.

The way this concept is usually phrased, however, is that some of the original energy is *lost* to heat. At first glance, this may seem like an unfair knock on heat, which after all has intrinsic value. Why, then, is energy "lost" to heat?

Well, consider what might be called the before-and-after of this energy transaction. In the "before," a lump of coal is a very ordered object, containing carbon atoms that exist in a precise spatial relationship to one another. Thus bonded, these atoms are not free to move. However, bringing a flame to the lump of coal causes the coal's carbon atoms to react with oxygen. Chemical bonds are broken through this process, and the energy stored in these bonds is released as heat. But heat is the random motion of molecules, and these molecules have no tendency to stay concentrated. Thus, it's clear that we have gone from the *ordered, concentrated* chemical bonds of coal to the *disordered, dispersed* energy of heat.

The Second Law of Thermodynamics: The Natural Tendency toward Disorder

And this gets us to the critical thing. Energy transformations will spontaneously run *only* from greater order to lesser order. Some of the heat produced in a steam engine is useful; it's driving a piston. Some of it is not, however—it's simply dissipated. But *all* of it amounts to a form of energy that is more dispersed than coal and that will quickly disperse further. Once this happens, there is no chance that it will spontaneously convert into anything *but* heat. We expect to see a lump of coal burn to ashes, and to feel the hot air that results disperse. But we do not expect to see the ashes re-form into a lump of coal, nor to feel the hot air concentrate itself again.

In yielding energy, matter goes from a more-ordered state to a less-ordered state. The scientific principle that speaks to this is the **second law of thermodynamics**: Energy transfer always results in a greater amount of disorder in the universe. In con-

nection with this law there is a term you will hear—*entropy*, which is a measure of the amount of disorder in a system. The greater the entropy, the greater the disorder. **Figure 6.2** summarizes the thermodynamic principles of the first and second laws of thermodynamics. **Figure 6.3** shows you how much energy is lost to heat in several energy systems.

The Consequences of Thermodynamics

All of this may seem like just so much … *hot air*. But it turns out that few things so profoundly condition the universe we live in as these thermodynamic rules. Indeed, the relentless increase in entropy that the second law entails may dictate nothing less than the fate of the universe.

3. Mechanical energy

piston-driven flywheel

2. Heat energy

heat   heat

coal → **steam** → **motion**

Total energy is constant.

Entropy Increases.

1. Chemical bond energy

Figure 6.2
The Transformations of Energy
In a steam engine, energy locked up in the chemical bonds of coal is transformed into heat energy and mechanical energy. There is no loss of energy in this process, but energy is transformed from a more-ordered, concentrated form (the chemical bonds of coal) to a less-ordered, more dispersed form (heat). Thus, the amount of disorder—or entropy—increases in the transaction.

34% conventional power plant

System

human respiration of glucose

25% automobile engine

0   20   40   60

Efficiency

Figure 6.3
Energy Efficiency
The efficiency of several energy systems, as measured by the proportion of energy they receive relative to what they then make available to perform work. In measuring the efficiency of the car engine, the question is, how much of the energy contained in the chemical bonds of gasoline is converted by the car into the kinetic energy of wheel movement? In each system, most of the energy not available for work is lost to heat.

Allow yourself, for a second, to think of the universe as consisting solely of the sun, the Earth, and the space between them. The sun is a concentration of hydrogen that is undergoing a nuclear reaction, thus releasing light and heat. Living things on Earth manage to capture buckets of this energy, through the activities of plants and the other photosynthesizers. But every time one of these buckets is poured into another—every time light energy from the sun is transformed into energy stored in plants, for example—there is some spillage into heat. And once heat is generated, there is no spontaneous way it can make its way back into the orderly form of sunlight or carbohydrates. With every firing of a car's cylinder or contraction of a muscle, then, some amount of energy is transformed into heat.

Against this, life as we know it is made possible by ordered concentrations of energy. The sun can sustain life, but dispersed heat will not. One day, our sun will have wound down like the spring in a music box, bringing to an end the energy source for life on Earth. One possible scenario for the universe as a whole is that *all* its stars eventually will darken, leaving a cold universe with little potential for life—indeed, with little activity of any sort. The laws of thermodynamics are powerful indeed.

6.3 How Is Energy Used by Living Things?

A sprouting plant is constantly building itself up; it is making larger, more complex molecules (proteins, starches) from smaller, simpler ones (amino acids, simple sugars). This increasing organization stands in contrast to the spontaneous course of things—breakdown and disorder—and thus may seem to be a violation of the second law. But it is

not. In the context of the universe as a whole, living things are contributors to its entropy. Any given biological activity, such as building a leaf, generates heat and thus increases the disorder in the universe as a whole. But living things can bring about *local* increases in order (in themselves) by using the energy that comes ultimately from the sun.

Up and Down the Great Energy Hill

The building of complex molecules from simpler ones is an example of so-called synthetic work, and in it, we begin to see how living things use energy. A starchy carbohydrate is a more complex thing than the simple sugars it is made of. It is a more *ordered* arrangement of atoms than is a group of individual simple sugars. As such, the second law tells us, it should *take* energy to make a starch from simple sugars, and this is indeed the case. Going in the opposite direction, the breakdown of a starchy carbohydrate into simple sugars is an action favored by the second law, because it brings about *less* order. Such a process therefore should not take energy—no more than it takes energy for a boulder to roll down a hill. Indeed, this process should *release* energy, and this too is the case.

Breakdown operations, such as starches breaking down into sugars, are examples of **exergonic reactions**: reactions in which the starting set of molecules (the reactants) contains more energy than the final set of molecules (the products). Meanwhile, buildup operations are examples of **endergonic reactions**: reactions in which the products contain more energy than the reactants. This is what happens when, for example, simple glucose molecules are brought together to form glycogen, which is a storage form of carbohydrates (**see Figure 6.4**).

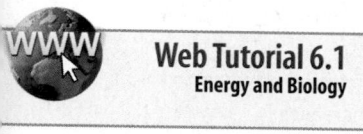

Web Tutorial 6.1
Energy and Biology

Figure 6.4
Energy Stored and Released
It takes energy to build up a more complex molecule (in this case glycogen) from simpler molecules (in this case glucose). Such a buildup is thus an endergonic or uphill reaction. Conversely, energy is released in reactions in which more complex molecules are broken down into simpler ones. Such reactions are exergonic or downhill reactions.

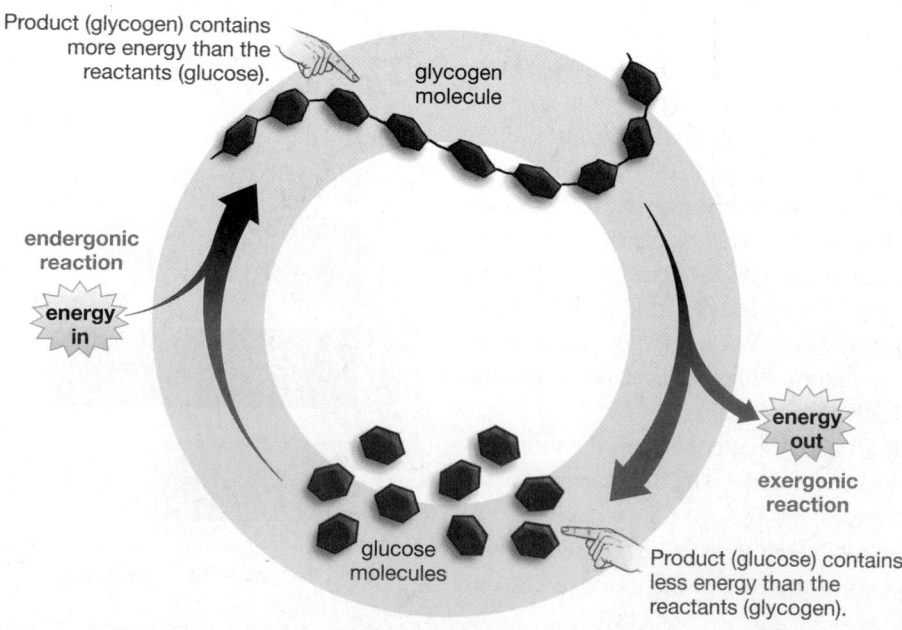

Product (glycogen) contains more energy than the reactants (glucose).

glycogen molecule

endergonic reaction

energy in

glucose molecules

energy out

exergonic reaction

Product (glucose) contains less energy than the reactants (glycogen).

Coupled Reactions

With this as background, we arrive at a critical insight: endergonic and exergonic reactions are constantly linked in living things. Why should this be so? If you want to get something uphill—into a higher energy state—you have to power that process. And that means *using* some energy. Just as it takes energy to get a bicycle uphill, so it takes energy to power the endergonic reaction that results in glycogen. Now, where is this energy going to come from? It must come from an energy-releasing *exergonic* reaction. The result is a **coupled reaction**: a chemical reaction in which an exergonic reaction powers an endergonic reaction. You actually observed some coupled reactions in Chapter 5, though they weren't labeled as such then. Remember how the sodium-potassium pump moved sodium ions out of the cell against their concentration gradient? (See page 107.) For the sodium ions, this was an uphill reaction: They finished the reaction in a higher energy state than they started, because they were moved up their electrical and concentration gradients.

And how was this movement powered? Through a downhill reaction. All you observed in Chapter 5 was that a molecule in the cell furnished the energy that powered the sodium pump. What this really meant was that a complex, energy-rich molecule was broken down to yield the energy for the pump. And what was this molecule? ATP.

6.4 The Energy Currency Molecule: ATP

Adenosine triphosphate. If you look at **Figure 6.5**, you can see that ATP is one of the nucleotides discussed in Chapter 3—a three-part molecule containing a sugar (ribose in this case), a nitrogen-containing base (adenine) and one or more phosphate groups. Actually, it is ATP's *three* phosphate groups that are of most interest to us. Notice that they all are negatively charged. This is the key to understanding why ATP serves as such an effective energy transfer molecule. Remember that like charges repel each other, and in this case three phosphate groups are doing just that. Energy was required to put these phosphate groups together as they are, in this relatively unstable state. This linkage represents a move *up* the energy hill. With ATP, it is as though someone squeezed a jack-in-the-box back into the box and shut the lid. It should be no surprise that when the lid is opened, a good deal of energy will be released.

**Figure 6.5
Energy Release from
Breakdown of ATP**
ATP (adenosine triphosphate) is life's most important energy transfer molecule. It stores energy in the form of chemical bonds between its phosphate groups. When the bond between the second and outermost phosphate group is broken, the outermost phosphate separates from ATP and energy is released. This separation transforms ATP into adenosine diphosphate or ADP, which then goes on to pick up another phosphate group, becoming ATP again.

How ATP Functions

Now, how is the energy from ATP used? As a starting point, consider an action that ATP molecules carry out within muscle cells (**see Figure 6.6**). Under the right conditions, ATP will bind to a type of protein, called an enzyme, that spans the membrane of this cell. The ATP molecule is then split, with the outermost of its phosphate groups breaking off from the rest of the molecule. This is a downhill reaction: It took energy to get the third of ATP's phosphate groups onto it (in an uphill push), and this stored energy is now being released. The subsequent attachment of this phosphate group to the protein causes the protein to change its shape. This shape change happens to drive the transport of calcium ions across the protein. For our purposes,

however, what's important is that something that would not have happened on its own took place because of the energy provided by the ATP molecule.

The ATP/ADP Cycle

There is another side to this ATP-driven reaction, however. Once the outermost phosphate group has split off, ATP has become a molecule containing only *two* phosphate groups, adenosine *di*phosphate or ADP. It is now free to have a third phosphate group added to it again (in an uphill reaction). This is just what happens: ADP returns to being ATP, which is capable of providing energy for yet another reaction. This shuttling from ATP to ADP and back takes place constantly in cells.

ATP as Money

It is often said that ATP is the cell's "energy currency" molecule. Now you're in a position to see why: It really does function like money. Imagine working at a typical job, in which you're called upon to do dozens of different things. You do this and you do that, but in the end what you get for all this activity is *money*. You can then take this cash and pay the rent, buy some CDs, or go bowling. Now think of animals and their breakdown of food. They have to obtain food in the first place and then digest the resulting fats and carbohydrates and proteins; but what they get in the end from all this work is ATP. It is the final outcome of the energy-harvesting process. And, like money, ATP then can be *used* to do any number of things, such as transport calcium ions across a cell membrane. Summing up, **ATP** can be defined as a nucleotide that functions as the most important energy transfer molecule in living things.

Between Food and ATP

The essence of our story so far is that, in animals, energy harvesting starts with the ingestion of food and ends with the synthesis of ATP. This is, however, such a bare-bones description that it is rather like a synopsis of *Cinderella* that goes: There was a young girl who was mistreated by her stepmother; then she married a prince. What's missing is everything that happened in between to make things come out this way. In the case of energy in ourselves, the end of the story is getting that third phosphate molecule attached to ADP, making it ATP. The beginning is that we have energy contained in food. Now, how do we *channel* that energy from food, and thus drive the attachment of the phosphate group onto ADP? It is almost time to answer this question—it will be in Chapter 7—but first, you need to know something about a group of proteins that living things use to control energy.

Figure 6.6
How ATP Functions
By transferring a phosphate group to the enzyme shown in this figure, ATP causes the enzyme to change shape in a manner that transports calcium ions across the cell membrane.

6.5   Efficient Energy Use in Living Things: Enzymes

Lactose—better known as milk sugar—is composed of two simple sugars, glucose and galactose, that are linked together by a single atom of oxygen. It follows from what you've seen so far that lactose will *split* into its glucose and galactose parts without any energy being required. Indeed, a little energy will be released in this process, because chemical bonds have been broken and two smaller molecules have been produced. Such a splitting is therefore a downhill reaction.

If we actually took a small amount of lactose, however, and put it in some plain water, it would certainly be hours—it might be days—before *any* of the lactose molecules would break down into glucose and galactose. How can this be? Most of us drink milk and it doesn't seem to pile up in us.

Accelerating Reactions

The secret is that when lactose is metabolized in living things, it isn't being split up in plain water. Something else is present that speeds up this process immensely, accelerating it perhaps a billionfold. That something is an **enzyme**, a type of protein that accelerates a chemical reaction. This particular enzyme is called lactase, but it is merely one of thousands of enzymes known to exist. Each of these compounds is working on some chemical process, but not all are involved in splitting molecules. Some enzymes combine molecules, some rearrange them.

Given their numbers, it may be apparent that enzymes are involved in a lot of different activities; but this doesn't begin to give them the recognition they deserve. Enzymes facilitate nearly every chemical process that takes place in living things. No organism could survive without them. Technically, these compounds are only *accelerating* chemical reactions that would happen anyway, as with lactase splitting lactose. But in practical terms, they are *enabling* these reactions, because no living thing could wait days or months for the milk sugar it ingests to be broken down, or for hormones to be put together, or for bleeding to stop.

To get an idea of the importance of enzymes, consider the millions of Americans who are known as lactose intolerant because, after childhood, their bodies reduced their production of lactase. When these people consume milk, the lactose in it *does* simply stay in their intestines. It is eventually digested not by them, but by the bacteria that live in the human digestive tract (something that causes bloat and gas).

Specific Tasks and Metabolic Pathways

From the sheer number of enzymes that exist, you can probably get a sense of how specifically they are matched to given tasks. Although some enzymes can work on *groups* of similar substances, a specific enzyme usually facilitates a specific reaction: It works on one or perhaps two molecules and no others. Thus, lactase breaks down lactose—and *only* lactose—and the products of its activity are always glucose and galactose. The substance that is being worked on by an enzyme is known as its **substrate**. Thus, lactose is the substrate for lactase. The *-ase* ending you see in *lactase* is common to most enzymes. As you can see, the substrate (lactose) is identified in the enzyme's name (lactase).

Certain activities in living things, such as blood clotting, are much more complex than the breakdown of lactose. They are multistep processes, *each step of which* requires its own enzyme. Most large-scale activities in living things work this way: leaf growth, digestion, hormonal balance. The result is a **metabolic pathway**: a set of enzymatically controlled steps that results in the completion of a product or process in an organism. In such a sequence, each enzyme does a particular job and then leaves the succeeding task to the next enzyme, with the product of one reaction becoming the substrate for the next (**see Figure 6.7**). The sum of all the chemical reactions that a cell or larger organism carries out is known as its **metabolism**. To put things simply, enzymes are active in all facets of the metabolism of all living things.

Web Tutorial 6.2
Enzymes

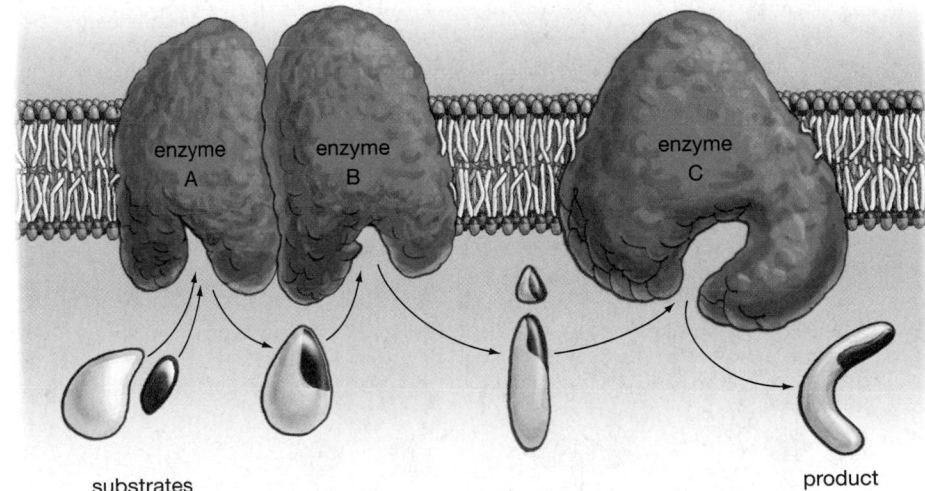

substrates

product

Figure 6.7
Metabolic Pathway: Sequence of Enzyme Action
Most processes in living organisms are carried out through a metabolic pathway—a sequential set of enzymatically controlled reactions in which the product of one reaction serves as the substrate for the next. Enzymes perform specific tasks on specific substrates. In this example, enzyme A combines two substrates, enzyme B removes part of its substrate, and enzyme C changes the shape of its substrate.

6.6 Lowering the Activation Barrier through Enzymes

All this information about enzymes is well and good, you may be saying at this point, but what does it have to do with energy? The answer is that in carrying out their tasks, enzymes are in the business of lowering the amount of energy needed to get chemical reactions going. And this means that the reactions can get going faster.

An analogy may be helpful here. Consider the now-familiar rock perched at the top of a hill. Situated in this way, it has a good deal of potential energy. If it rolled down the hill, it would release this potential energy as kinetic energy. But here is the critical question: What would be required to get this rock going? It is perched at the top of the hill because it is *stable* at the top of the hill. To get it going would require *additional* energy in the form of, say, a push.

Now consider the lactose molecule. It is "perched" like the rock, in a sense, because it lies "uphill" from the glucose and galactose it can break into. But just as the rock is stable because of its position in the ground, so the lactose is stable because it has a strong set of chemical bonds holding its atoms in a fixed position.

Figure 6.8
Enzymes Accelerate Chemical Reactions

How is lactose split into glucose and galactose? Without an enzyme, the amount of energy necessary to activate this reaction is high. In the presence of the enzyme lactase, however, a low activation energy is sufficient to get the process started. The energy released from the splitting of lactose is the same in both cases.

The question thus becomes: Is there anything that can lower the amount of energy required to break these bonds? The answer is yes—an enzyme. If you look at **Figure 6.8**, you can see this in schematic terms. Imagine that you had to push a boulder up the hill in (a) to get it to roll down the other side. Now imagine that you only had to push a boulder up the hill in (b) to get the same result. In which situation would you be able to get your desired result *faster*? What is at work here is a lowering of **activation energy**: the energy required to initiate a chemical reaction.

How Do Enzymes Work?

How do enzymes carry out this task of lowering activation energy? As you'll see shortly, they bind to their substrates, and in so doing make these substances more vulnerable to chemical alteration. The amazing thing is that they do this without being permanently altered themselves. Enzymes are **catalysts**—substances that retain their original chemical composition while bringing about a change in a substrate. At the end of its cleaving of the lactose molecule, lactase has exactly the same chemical structure as it did before. It is thus free to pick up another lactose molecule and split *it*. All this takes place in a flash: The fastest-working enzymes can carry out 100,000 chemical transformations per second.

Enzymes generally take the form of globular or ball-like proteins whose shape includes a kind of pocket into which the substrate fits. If you look at **Figure 6.9**, you can see a space-filling model of one enzyme, called hexokinase. You can also see, buried there in the middle, its substrate—glucose, which is better known as blood sugar. As with all proteins, enzymes are made up of amino acids, but only a few of the hundreds of amino acids in an enzyme are typically involved in actually binding with the substrate. Five or six would be common. These amino acids help form the substrate pocket, known as the **active site**: the portion of an enzyme that binds with and transforms a substrate.

In some cases, the participants at the active site include, along with amino acids, one or more accessory molecules. One variety of these molecules is the **coenzymes**: molecules other than amino acids that facilitate the work of enzymes by binding with them. If you've ever wondered what vitamins do, participation in enzyme binding is a big part of it. Once we have ingested them, many vitamins are transformed into coenzymes that sit in the active site of an enzyme and provide an added chemical attraction or repulsion that allows the enzyme to do its job.

(a) Without enzyme

lactose

glucose + galactose

activation energy without enzyme

net energy released from splitting of lactose

(b) With enzyme

lactase

lactose

glucose + galactose

activation energy with enzyme

net energy released

An Enzyme in Action: Chymotrypsin

The details of how enzymes carry out their work are complex, and they vary according to enzyme. Let's consider in a general way, however, the activity of a much-studied enzyme called chymotrypsin.

Chymotrypsin is delivered from the human pancreas to the small intestine, where it works with water to break down proteins we have ingested. Its function is to clip protein chains in between their building-block amino acids. It does this by breaking the single bond that binds one amino acid to the next (**see Figure 6.10**). How does it work? After having bound to part of a protein chain, chymotrypsin then interacts with it to create a transition-state molecule. In effect, it distorts the shape of the protein—and holds it in this new shape briefly—in such a way that the protein becomes vulnerable to bonding with ionized water molecules. This allows carbon and nitrogen atoms to latch onto new partners, and the protein chain is clipped. Chymotrypsin then returns to its original form and proceeds to a new reaction.

6.7   Regulating Enzymatic Activity

The activity of enzymes is regulated in several ways. The question here is: What factors influence the amount of "product" an enzyme turns out? One of these factors, quite logically, is the amount of substrate in the enzyme's vicinity. If there's no substrate to work on, no product can be turned out.

The work of enzymes can, however, be reduced in several other ways. For example, some molecules that are not the normal substrate for an enzyme can still bind to the enzyme at its active site. An enzyme that is "occupied" in this way is not free to bind with its normal substrate and thus is not able to carry out its usual catalytic activity.

This happens all the time in minor ways in our bodies, but to sharpen the point, consider an extreme example of it. There is a nerve gas, called sarin, that was developed in the 1930s to kill people. In 1995 it did just that, when it was maliciously released in a Tokyo subway. Sarin works by binding very strongly to the active site of an enzyme called acetylcholinesterase. Under normal circumstances, acetylcholinesterase's substrate is acetylcholine—a compound that travels, ferryboat-like, out of one nerve cell and binds to the next. The effect of this binding is to cause the second nerve cell to fire. Each binding is, however, supposed to bring about *one* nerve-signal firing, after which acetylcholine is broken down by acetylcholinesterase. But if acetylcholinesterase is occupied by sarin, it cannot do its job. The result is that there is no end to the nerve-signal firing. This means a breakdown of

Figure 6.9
Shape Is Important in Enzymes
Substrates generally fit into small grooves or pockets in enzymes. The location at which the enzyme binds the substrate is known as the enzyme's active site. Pictured is a computer-generated model of a glucose molecule (in red) binding to the active site of an enzyme called hexokinase (in blue).

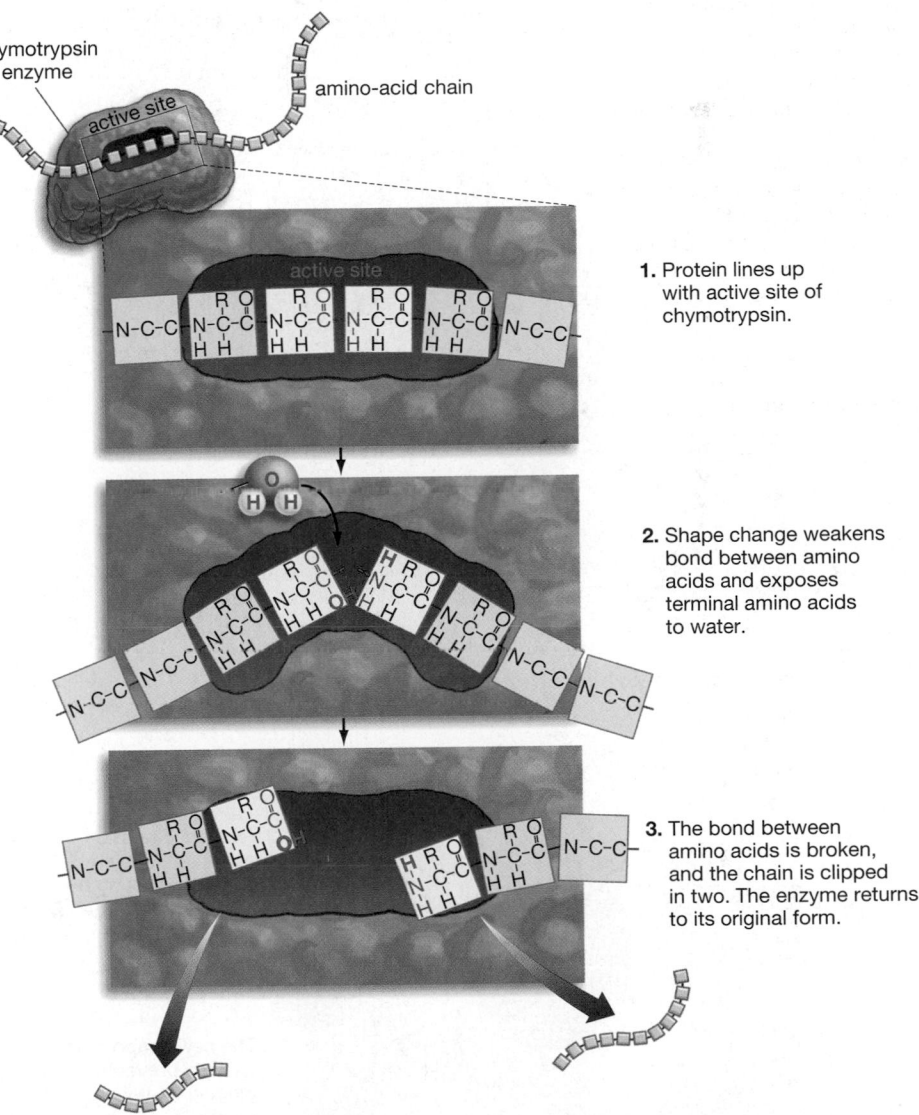

1. Protein lines up with active site of chymotrypsin.

2. Shape change weakens bond between amino acids and exposes terminal amino acids to water.

3. The bond between amino acids is broken, and the chain is clipped in two. The enzyme returns to its original form.

Figure 6.10
How the Enzyme Chymotrypsin Works
In this example, the enzyme chymotrypsin is facilitating the breakdown of a protein by changing the protein's shape. In the absence of chymotrypsin, this process would take a billion times longer.

the nervous system and, in some cases, death from a paralysis of the breathing muscles. A number of toxins work by carrying out this kind of enzyme occupation, which is known as *competitive inhibition*.

Allosteric Regulation of Enzymes

Living things routinely regulate enzyme activity by another means. Earlier, you saw a model of an enzyme called hexokinase, which works on the substrate glucose. The product of this reaction is something called glucose-6-phosphate. Though this is an enzymatic product, it can bind to hexokinase at a site other than its active site, and in so doing change hexokinase's shape. This change renders hexokinase less able to bind with its substrate, glucose, meaning hexokinase's work is temporarily reduced. If you look at **Figure 6.11**, you can see how this process works schematically.

This is but one example of the process known as **allosteric regulation**—the regulation of an enzyme's activity by means of a molecule binding to a site on the enzyme other than its active site. Many variations on this theme are possible. In the case of hexokinase, its own product (glucose-6-phosphate) bound with it and cut down on its activity, but molecules other than the enzymatic product can bind with an enzyme at one of its additional binding sites. Furthermore, the effect of such binding need not be negative; allosteric binding can increase the activity of enzymes as well as reducing it.

The importance of such regulation is that enzymes are not simply fated to turn out product as long as there is substrate to work on. If a cell has too much of a product, allosteric control can cut down on it; if there is too little, its concentration can be increased.

On to Energy Harvesting

So, to review for a second, you've seen that, for animals, the energy that comes bound in food can be extracted from it. The result of this energy "harvesting" is the production of the energy currency molecule, ATP, which is used to power various processes. The question we will tackle next is: How does the body actually do its energy harvesting— what are the steps by which it extracts energy from food and then channels this energy into pushing phosphate groups onto ADP? That is the subject of Chapter 7.

**Figure 6.11
Allosteric Regulation of Enzymes**
The frequency of chemical reactions can be controlled by the binding of a molecule to an enzyme at a site other than its active site. In this instance, the enzyme's own product binds with the enzyme in this way, thereby reducing the enzyme's activity.

(a) Substrate becomes product

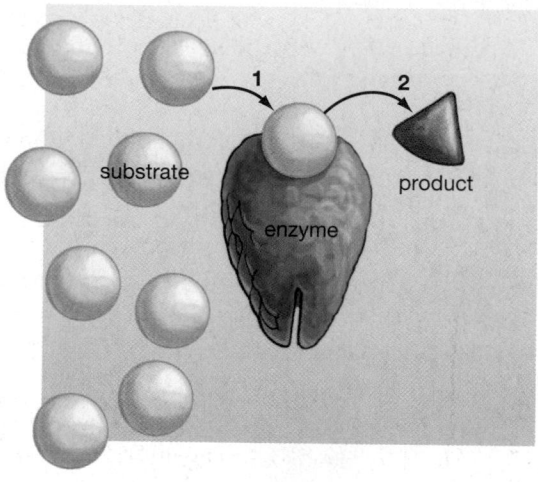

substrate

product

enzyme

1. Substrate binds to enzyme.

2. Enzyme transforms substrate to product.

(b) Product feeds back on enzyme

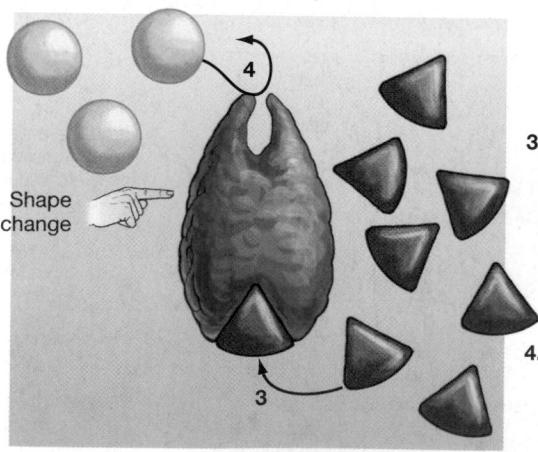

Shape change

3. Product binds to a *different* site on the enzyme, causing the enzyme to change shape.

4. The new shape of the enzyme prevents it from binding to any more substrate.

Chapter Review

Summary

6.1 Energy Is Central to Life

- All living things require a source of energy. The sun is the ultimate source of energy for most living things. The sun's energy is captured on Earth by photosynthesizing organisms (such as plants), which then pass on this energy to other life-forms.

6.2 What Is Energy?

- Energy can be defined as the capacity to bring about movement against an opposing force. Energy can be conceptualized as being either potential energy, meaning stored energy; or kinetic energy, meaning energy in motion. The study of energy is known as thermodynamics.

- Two fundamental principles of energy are the first law of thermodynamics, which states that energy is never created or destroyed, but is only transformed; and the second law of thermodynamics, which states that energy transfer will always result in a greater amount of disorder in the universe.

- In line with the second law of thermodynamics, in every energy transaction, some energy will be lost to the disordered form of heat. Entropy is a measure of the amount of disorder in a system; the greater the entropy, the greater the disorder.

6.3 How Is Energy Used by Living Things?

- Living things can bring about local increases in order (in themselves), through their metabolic processes. They can, for example, build up more-ordered molecules (starches, proteins) from less-ordered molecules (simple sugars, amino acids). However, it takes energy to do this.

- Energy in living things is stored away in endergonic (uphill) reactions, in which the products of the reaction contain more energy than the starting substances (or "reactants"). Conversely, energy is released in exergonic (downhill) reactions, in which the reactants contain more energy than the products. The linkage of simple sugars to form a complex carbohydrate is an endergonic reaction. Such reactions will not occur without an input of energy. Conversely, the breakdown of a complex carbohydrate into simple sugars is an exergonic reaction. Such reactions release energy. Endergonic and exergonic reactions are linked in coupled reactions—reactions in which an energy-yielding exergonic reaction powers an energy-using endergonic reaction. The molecule most often used in living things to power coupled reactions is ATP.

Web Tutorial 6.1: Energy and Biology

6.4 The Energy Currency Molecule: ATP

- Adenosine triphosphate (ATP) is the most important energy transfer molecule in living things. It is the final product of the energy-harvesting process, in which energy is extracted from food. ATP's energy transfer powers stem from the fact that it contains three phosphate groups, each of which is negatively charged, meaning these groups repel each other. ATP drives chemical reactions by donating its third phosphate group to them. In the process, it becomes the two-phosphate molecule adenosine diphosphate (ADP). To once again become ATP, it must have a third phosphate group attached to it. In animals, the energy supplied by food powers the process by which third phosphate groups are attached to ADP.

6.5 Efficient Energy Use in Living Things: Enzymes

- An enzyme is a type of protein that increases the rate at which a chemical reaction takes place in an organism. Nearly every chemical process that takes place in living things is facilitated by an enzyme. For example, the enzyme lactase facilitates the splitting of the sugar lactose into its component sugars, glucose and galactose.

- Many activities in living things are controlled by metabolic pathways, in which a series of interrelated reactions is undertaken in sequence, each one of them facilitated by an enzyme. The substance that an enzyme helps transform through chemical reaction is called its substrate. Lactose is the substrate of the enzyme lactase. The sum of all the chemical reactions that a cell or larger living thing carries out is its metabolism.

Web Tutorial 6.2: Enzymes

6.6 Lowering the Activation Barrier through Enzymes

- Enzymes work by lowering activation energy, meaning the energy required to initiate a chemical reaction. Enzymes are catalysts: They bring about a change in their substrates without being chemically altered themselves.

- Enzymes generally take the form of globular or ball-like proteins whose shape includes a pocket into which the enzyme's substrate fits. This pocket is the active site—that portion of an enzyme that binds with and transforms a substrate.

6.7 Regulating Enzymatic Activity

- Enzyme activity can be controlled in several ways. One of these is allosteric regulation: A molecule binds with the enzyme at a site other than its active site, thus changing the enzyme's shape, and thereby decreases or increases the enzyme's ability to bind with its substrate.

Key Terms

Understanding the Basics

Multiple-Choice Questions (answers in the back of the book)

1. According to the first law of thermodynamics, energy
   a. is never lost or gained, but is only transformed
   b. always requires an ultimate source such as the sun
   c. can never be gained, but can be lost
   d. can never really be harnessed
   e. can never be transformed

2. Each time there is a chemical reaction, some energy is exchanged. According to the second law of thermodynamics, with each exchange
   a. Some energy is lost, but other energy is created.
   b. Some energy must come from the sun.
   c. Some energy is transformed into heat.
   d. Energy is gained for future use.
   e. Some energy is permanently and completely destroyed.

3. Your car uses gasoline to fuel the engine. Can you explain why you need a coolant system for your car?
   a. it helps the car move through the air easier
   b. it is needed to absorb the heat energy that results from fuel combustion
   c. it is required to help move the heat to the drive shaft
   d. it is required to move the fuel to the correct location
   e. it is required to assist in making the fuel the correct temperature

4. ATP stores energy in the form of
   a. mechanical energy
   b. heat
   c. complex carbohydrates
   d. chemical bond energy
   e. amino acids

5. People who are lactose intolerant lack a compound called lactase in their digestive tract. You know that this compound, lactase, is probably a(n)

a. hormone, because it causes a change in the person
b. coenzyme, because it helps the enzyme, lactose, do its job
c. vitamin, because it is essential to health
d. substrate, because it is involved with food
e. enzyme, because its name ends in -ase

6. Glycolysis is a metabolic pathway that helps living things extract energy from food. From this we know that glycolysis
   a. consists of a series of chemical reactions
   b. uses a number of enzymes
   c. involves the modification of a series of substrates
   d. proceeds by means of each enzyme leaving a succeeding reaction to a different enzyme
   e. all of the above

7. Each molecule of ATP stores a good deal of energy because
   a. ATP is such a large protein
   b. ATP captures energy directly from the sun
   c. ATP's third phosphate group exists in a highly energetic state
   d. a long metabolic pathway is required for the production of ATP

8. Which of the following will lower the activation energy of a reaction in a cell?
   a. lowering the temperature
   b. lowering the pressure
   c. using an enzyme
   d. changing the amount of the reactants
   e. supplying ATP

9. The active site of enzyme A is occupied by a molecule other than its substrate. Enzyme B has had its activity reduced by means of a molecule binding to it at a site other than its active site. What is taking place in connection with enzyme A and then enzyme B?
   a. a reaction acceleration, a coupled reaction
   b. a lowering of activation energy, ATP use
   c. allosteric regulation, competitive inhibition
   d. allosteric regulation, coenzyme participation
   e. competitive inhibition, allosteric regulation

10. Enzymes
    a. accelerate specific chemical reactions
    b. are not permanently altered by binding with a substrate
    c. lower the activation energy of specific chemical reactions
    d. all of the above
    e. a and c only

Brief Review

1. A plant leaf is more ordered and complex than are carbon dioxide and water. In photosynthesis, plants take small, relatively disordered carbon dioxide and water molecules and make complex, ordered sugars out of them. How is it possible for this to happen without violating the second law of thermodynamics?

2. The text notes that in the sodium-potassium pump, sodium ions are moved out of the cell against their concentration gradient and that ATP plays a part in this. Explain how this is a coupled reaction.

3. Where does the energy come from that is stored and released by ATP? In what way is ATP an energy currency molecule?

4. The average person thinks of enzymes only as substances in their digestive tract that break down food. How would you explain the role of enzymes to your little sister, who has heard about digestion in grade school biology?

5. What is meant by allosteric regulation of an enzyme?

Applying Your Knowledge

1. In light of the laws of thermodynamics, explain why you get so much hotter when you run than when you are sitting still.

2. Which is easier to have: a messy, disordered room or a neat, ordered room? Is the second law of thermodynamics at work in this situation? What is the price of bringing order to a room?

3. Physicists say that it is impossible to create a perpetual motion machine—a machine whose own activity keeps it running perpetually. What energy principle precludes the possibility of a perpetual motion machine?

7 Deriving Energy from Food

One effect of oxidation: rust.
(Section 7.2, page 135)

The stages of energy harvesting.
(Section 7.3, page 137)

A transition step in respiration.
(Section 7.5, page 141)

To remain alive, living things must put the energy they acquire into a form they can use—ATP.

In May of 1996, the world's attention was riveted on news coming out of Nepal, in Southeast Asia. Disaster had struck several groups of mountain climbers who had been attempting to scale the world's highest peak, Mt. Everest. A vicious storm had taken the members of two Everest expeditions by surprise as they were moving down from Everest's summit, toward the safety of lower altitudes. Within 36 hours, five climbers had lost their lives and another was so badly frostbitten that one of his hands had to be amputated.

One of the expeditions was led by a highly respected guide from New Zealand, Rob Hall. Courageously remaining near the summit in an effort to bring down one of his clients (who had collapsed), Hall ended up spending a night in a howling storm on Everest without a tent. When the sun rose the next day, the factors working against him included cold and wind, which he might have encountered in lots of inhospitable places on Earth. Also bedeviling him, however, was something that human beings rarely encounter: a lack of oxygen. At his altitude—sitting in the snow at 8,700 meters (or about 28,500 feet)—the oxygen he took in with each breath was little more than a third of the amount he would have inhaled with each breath at sea level. Technology might have come to his aid, as he had two oxygen bottles with him, but his intake valve for them had become clogged with ice.

Down at Everest's lower altitudes, other climbers—some of them Hall's friends—had to endure the agony of talking to him by two-way radio while not being able to reach him physically. All of them knew that a lack of oxygen was draining not only his muscles but his mind. Here is Hall in one of his radio transmissions asking about another guide on the ill-fated expedition: "Harold was with me last night, but he doesn't seem to be with me now. Was Harold with me? Can you tell me that?" In the end, the mountain without mercy claimed Rob Hall. He never got up from the place where he spent his night on Everest.

Exhausted Near the Everest Summit
Two members of the ill-fated expeditions that climbed Mount Everest in May 1996 approach the mountain's summit. At this altitude, each breath brings with it only about one-third the amount of oxygen available at sea level.

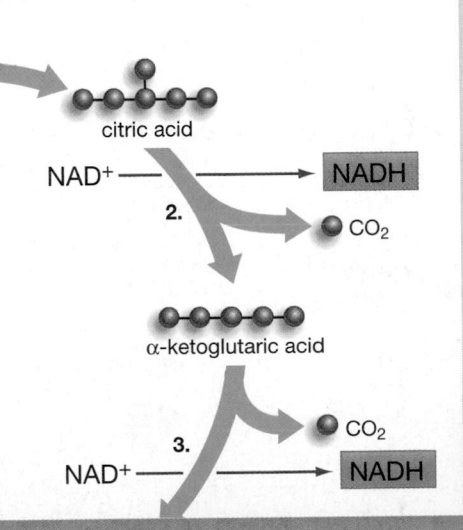

A closer look at energy harvesting.
(Section 7.5, page 142)

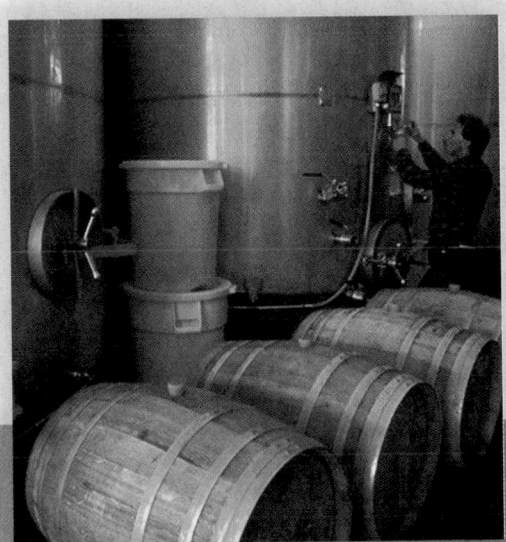

Fruit of the vine.
(Essay, page 140)

Big ATP harvest.
(Section 7.6, page 143)

The tragedy of the 1996 Everest expeditions drives home a point and raises a paradox: No one needs to be reminded that we need to breathe in order to live, and most people are aware that oxygen is the most important thing that comes in with breath. That said, of the next 100 people you meet, how many could tell you what oxygen is *doing* to sustain life? Put another way, why do we need to breathe?

The short answer is that breathing and oxygen are in the energy transfer business. They are part of a system that allows us to extract, from food, energy that is then used to put together the "energy currency" molecule, ATP. As you'll recall from Chapter 6, the body uses ATP (adenosine triphosphate) to power activities that range from muscle contraction to thinking to cell repair. Living things need large amounts of ATP to live, and organisms such as ourselves use oxygen to produce much of our ATP. If we don't get enough oxygen to keep making ATP, our bodies and minds start failing.

Oxygen is not required for all the "harvesting" we do of the energy contained in food. When you lift a box, the short burst of energy that is required comes largely from a different sort of energy harvesting, which you'll learn more about shortly. But even here, the essential *product* of energy harvesting is ATP. Keep that in mind and you won't get lost in the byways of energy transfer. How does the body produce enough ATP to allow us to read a book or climb a mountain? In this chapter, you'll find out.

7.1 Energizing ATP

Given the importance of ATP to this story, let us begin with a brief review of how this molecule works. Recall from Chapter 6 that each ATP molecule has three phosphate groups attached to it, and that ATP powers a given reaction by losing the outermost of these phosphate groups. In this process ATP is transformed into a molecule with *two* phosphate groups, adenosine diphosphate or ADP. To return to its more "energized" ATP state, it must have a third phosphate group attached again. This is, however, a trip *up* the energy hill, because the product (ATP) contains more energy than the reactant (ADP). Thus, getting that third phosphate group onto ADP requires energy. It is like preparing a spring-loaded mousetrap for action. It takes energy to pull a mousetrap bar back, and the same is true of putting a third phosphate group onto ATP (**see Figure 7.1**). Where does the energy come from? For animals such as ourselves, it comes from food; energy that is extracted from food powers the phosphate group up the energy hill—and literally onto ADP.

7.2 Electrons Fall Down the Energy Hill to Drive the Uphill Production of ATP

In tracking the extraction of energy from food, we will use as an example one particular food molecule, glucose, to see how energy is harvested from it. Though the details here are complex, the essential

1. Energy from food is required to push a third phosphate group onto ADP.

2. Energy from food is then stored as a phosphate bond in ATP.

3. Energy is then released when the phosphate bond is broken, and can be used to fuel our everyday activities.

energy in

ATP

energy out

energy hill

P + ADP

P + ADP

Figure 7.1
Storing and Releasing Energy
Adenosine triphosphate (ATP) is the most important energy-releasing molecule in our bodies. The energy it contains is used to power everything from muscle contraction to thinking.

story is simple. *Electrons* derived from glucose, which is high in energy, will be running downhill; they will be channeled off, a few at a time, and their downhill drop will power the *uphill* push needed to attach a phosphate group onto ADP. The glucose-derived electrons will be transferred to several intermediate molecules in their downhill journey, but the *final* molecule that will receive them at the bottom of the energy hill is oxygen. We need to breathe because we need oxygen to serve as this final electron acceptor.

As you are following this process, you may well wonder why so many steps are required to transfer energy from food to ATP. Why isn't there just *one* step in energy transfer—food to ATP? It turns out that the gradual transfer of energy, through many steps, allows the body to make the most of the energy it receives. Think of it this way. You could have water drop 1,000 feet straight off a cliff onto a waterwheel below. In this case, the wheel would simply be pulverized by the water crashing onto it. In the process, the potential energy that had been contained in the water at the top of the cliff would be transformed almost entirely into useless heat. Conversely, you could have a stream that ran briskly downhill for 1,000 vertical feet with waterwheels spaced periodically to channel the energy off a little at a time, thereby conserving the energy for work. The steps you are going to read about amount to this kind of controlled channeling off of energy—the energy that's contained in food.

The Great Energy Conveyors: Redox Reactions

The basis for electron transfers down the energy hill is straightforward: Some substances more strongly attract electrons than do others. A substance that loses one or more electrons to another is said to have undergone **oxidation**. We hear the related word "oxidized" all the time—when paint on an outdoor surface has become dulled, for example, or when metal rusts (**see Figure 7.2**). Meanwhile, the substance that *gains* electrons in this reaction is said to have undergone **reduction**. (This seems about as logical as saying a country lost a war by winning. One way to think about it is that, because electrons carry a negative charge, any substance that gains electrons has had a reduction in its *positive charge*.)

In cells, oxidation and reduction never occur independently. If one substance is oxidized, another must be reduced. It's like a teeter-totter; if one side goes down, the other must come up. The combined operation is known as a reduction-oxidation reaction, or simply a **redox reaction**: the process by which electrons are transferred from one molecule

Figure 7.2
An Effect of Oxidation
Rust has formed on a hook atop a corroded steel sheet.

to another. Critically, the substance being oxidized in a redox reaction has its electrons traveling energetically *downhill*.

Many Molecules Can Oxidize Other Molecules

The term *oxidation* might give you the idea that oxygen must be involved in any redox reaction, but this is not the case. Any compound that serves to pull electrons from another is a so-called oxidizing agent. In living things, a large number of molecules are involved in energy transfer, and each has a certain tendency to gain or lose electrons relative to the others.

This is how electrons can be passed down the energy hill: The starting "energetic" molecule of glucose is oxidized by another molecule, which in turn is oxidized by the *next* molecule down the hill. The whole thing might be thought of as a kind of downhill electron bucket brigade. Molecules that serve to transfer electrons from one molecule to another in ATP formation are known as **electron carriers**. The thing that makes their role a little complicated is that many of the electrons they accept are bound up originally in hydrogen atoms. You may remember from Chapter 3 that a hydrogen atom amounts to one proton and one electron. In transferring a hydrogen atom, then, a molecule is transferring a single electron (bound to a proton), which means a redox reaction has taken place.

Redox through Intermediates: NAD

The most important electron carrier in energy transfer is a molecule known as **nicotinamide adenine dinucleotide**, or **NAD**, which can be thought of as a city cab. It can exist in two states: loaded with passengers or empty. And like a cab, it can switch very easily between those two states. The passengers that NAD picks up and drops off are electrons (**see Figure 7.3**).

The "empty" state that NAD comes in is ionic: NAD^+. Remembering back to the discussion about ions, you can see that NAD^+ is positively charged, meaning that it has fewer electrons than protons. In a redox reaction, what NAD^+ does is pick up, in effect, one hydrogen atom (an electron and a proton) and one solo electron (from a second hydrogen atom). The isolated electron that NAD^+ picks up turns it from positively charged to neutral $(NAD^+ \rightarrow NAD)$; the whole hydrogen atom takes it from NAD to NADH. Keeping an eye on redox reactions here, NAD^+ has become NADH by oxidizing a substance—by accepting electrons from it.

So much for half of NAD's role: picking up passengers. *Now*, as NADH, it is loaded with these passengers. It can proceed down the energy hill to donate them to molecules that have a greater potential to *accept* electrons than it does. Having dropped its passengers off with such a molecule, it returns to being the empty NAD^+ and is ready for another pickup. Through this process, NADH transfers energy from one molecule to another.

How Does NAD Do Its Job?

The molecule that NAD^+ is oxidizing is the starting glucose molecule (or actually derivatives of it). To carry out its oxidizing role, NAD^+ obviously needs to be brought together with the glucose derivatives. What have you been looking at that brings substances together in this way? Enzymes! One of the things you'll be seeing, therefore, is NAD^+ and glucose derivatives being brought together by enzymes, at which point NAD^+ accepts electrons from these derivatives, later to hand them off to another molecule.

Electron transfer through intermediate molecules such as NAD^+ provides the energy for most of the ATP produced. Thus, when looking at the diagrams in this chapter that outline respiration, you'll see:

or:

What these drawings indicate is the electron carrier shifting between its empty state (NAD^+) and its loaded state (NADH), or vice versa.

7.3 The Three Stages of Cellular Respiration: Glycolysis, the Krebs Cycle, and the Electron Transport Chain

All the energy players are finally in place: glucose, redox reactions, electron carriers, enzymes, and the rest. In terms of a molecular formula, the big picture on respiration looks like this:

$$C_6H_{12}O_6 + 6O_2 + 36ADP + 36P \rightarrow$$
$$6CO_2 + 6H_2O + 36ATP$$

The starting molecule on the first row $(C_6H_{12}O_6)$ is glucose, which is food, storing chemical energy. You can also see, next to it, the oxygen $(6O_2)$ that is needed as the final electron acceptor. Then there is ADP, the two-phosphate molecule; and inorganic phosphate molecules (the 36P), which are pushed on ADP to make it ATP. The *products* of this reaction, on the second row, are carbon dioxide $(6CO_2)$ and water $(6H_2O)$ as by-products, and energy in the form of ATP. How *much* ATP does the breakdown of one molecule of glucose yield? The answer is contained in the formula: a maximum of 36 molecules.

Figure 7.3
The Electron Carrier NAD^+
In its unloaded form (NAD^+) and its loaded form (NADH), this molecule is a critical player in energy transfer, picking up energetic electrons from food and transferring them to later stages of respiration.

1. NAD^+ within a cell, along with two hydrogen atoms that are part of the food that is supplying energy for the body.

2. NAD^+ is reduced to NAD by accepting an electron from a hydrogen atom. It also picks up another hydrogen atom to become NADH.

3. NADH carries the electrons to a later stage of respiration then drops them off, becoming oxidized to its original form, NAD^+.

Though many separate steps are involved in actually getting energy from glucose to ATP, respiration can be divided into three main phases. These are known as *glycolysis*, the *Krebs cycle*, and the *electron transport chain*.

In overview, energy harvesting through these three phases goes like this: We get some ATP yield in glycolysis and the Krebs cycle, and glycolysis is useful in providing small amounts of ATP in quick bursts. But for most organisms, the main function of glycolysis and the Krebs cycle is the transfer of electrons to the electron carriers such as NAD^+. Bearing their electron cargo, these carriers then move to the third phase of energy harvesting, the electron transport chain (ETC). Here the electron carriers are themselves oxidized and the resulting movement of their electrons through ETC provides the main harvest of ATP. Indeed, about 32 of the approximately 36 molecules of ATP that are netted per glucose molecule are obtained in the ETC. If you look at **Figure 7.4**, you can see two representations of the three stages of energy extraction.

Web Tutorial 7.2
Stages of Cellular Respiration

Figure 7.4
Overview of Energy Harvesting

(a) In metaphorical terms

(b) In schematic terms

36 ATP maximum per glucose molecule

Just as the video games in some arcades can use only tokens (rather than money) to make them function, so our bodies can use only ATP (rather than food) as a direct source of energy. The energy contained in food—glucose in the example—is transferred to ATP in three major steps: glycolysis, the Krebs cycle, and the electron transport chain. Though glycolysis and the Krebs cycle contribute only small amounts of ATP directly, they also contribute electrons (on the left of the token machine) that help bring about the large yield of ATP in the electron transport chain. Our energy-transfer mechanisms are not quite as efficient as the arcade machine makes them appear. At each stage of the conversion process, some of the original energy contained in the glucose is lost to heat.

As with the arcade machine, the starting point in this example is a single molecule of glucose, which again yields ATP in three major sets of steps: glycolysis, the Krebs cycle, and the electron transport chain (ETC). These steps can yield a maximum of about 36 molecules of ATP: 2 in glycolysis, 2 in the Krebs cycle, and 32 in the ETC. As noted, however, glycolysis and the Krebs cycle also yield electrons that move to the ETC, aiding in its ATP production. These electrons get to the ETC via the electron carriers NADH and $FADH_2$, shown on the left. Oxygen is consumed in energy harvesting, while water and carbon dioxide are produced in it. Glycolysis takes place in the cytosol of the cell, but the Krebs cycle and the ETC take place in cellular organelles, called mitochondria, that lie within the cytosol.

Glycolysis: First to Evolve, Less Efficient

The division among the three energy-harvesting phases is, in one sense, a division of evolutionary history. For most organisms, energy harvesting's first phase, glycolysis, could be likened to a nineteenth-century steam engine working side by side with a state-of-the art electric turbine. By itself, glycolysis produces only two ATP molecules per glucose molecule, which is pretty small in comparison to the 36 ATP molecules likely to come from all three phases. And glycolysis doesn't even yield many electrons compared to energy harvesting's second phase, the Krebs cycle. Yet glycolysis takes place in all living things—at the very least, as the first phase in energy harvesting—and for certain primitive one-celled organisms it can be the *only* phase in energy harvesting.

All of this points to glycolysis being a more ancient form of energy harvesting than the other two phases. It existed first, and then at some time in the evolutionary past, most organisms added to it the processes we now call the Krebs cycle and the ETC. The critical factor in this change was the use of oxygen in energy harvesting—specifically the use of oxygen in the ETC. Because the products of glycolysis feed ultimately into the ETC, the entire three-stage energy-harvesting process is referred to as oxygen-dependent or *aerobic* energy transfer. Taken as a whole, the aerobic harvesting of energy is known as **cellular respiration**.

The separation between glycolysis and the other two phases is also a physical separation. In eukaryotic cells, glycolysis takes place in the watery material that lies outside the cell's nucleus—the cytosol—while the Krebs cycle and the ETC take place within tiny organelles, called mitochondria, that are immersed in the cytosol. Let's start now to look at all three phases of cellular respiration.

7.4 First Stage of Respiration: Glycolysis

Glycolysis, the first stage of energy harvesting, means "sugar splitting," which is appropriate because our starting molecule is the simple sugar glucose. Briefly, here is what happens during glycolysis. First, this one molecule of glucose has to be prepared, in a sense, for energy release. ATP actually has to be *used*, rather than synthesized, in two of the first steps of glycolysis, so that the relatively stable glucose can be put into the form of a less-stable sugar. This sugar is then split in half. The two molecules formed have three carbons each (whereas the starting glucose has six). Once this split is accomplished, the steps of glycolysis take place in *duplicate:* It is like taking one long piece of cloth, dividing it in two, and then proceeding to do the same things to both of the resulting pieces. If you look at **Figure 7.5**, you can see the individual steps of glycolysis. (If your class is studying glycolysis in detail, you will need to look carefully at Figure 7.5, as it is the only place in the text where the individual steps of glycolysis are reviewed.)

Now, what are the results of these steps? Glycolysis accomplishes three valuable things in energy harvesting: It yields two ATP molecules, it yields two energized molecules of NADH, and it results in two molecules of pyruvic acid. These pyruvic acid molecules are the derivatives of the original glucose molecule. Now *they* are the molecules that will be oxidized—that will have electrons removed from them—in the next stage of energy harvesting. Keeping our eye on the ball here, we have some net ATP through glycolysis, some traveling electrons that will help make more ATP in the electron transport chain, and a derivative of the original glucose molecule (pyruvic acid) that will now move to the next stage of energy harvesting, where more energy will be extracted from it.

Before continuing on to this next stage, you may wish to read more about what might be called the consequences of glycolysis. Even oxygen-using organisms such as ourselves rely on glycolysis when short bursts of energy are needed. And, as noted, for some organisms, glycolysis is the end of the line in energy harvesting. You can read about this in "When Energy Harvesting Ends at Glycolysis" on page 140. Glycolysis fits into a special place in providing energy for human exercise; you can read about this in "Energy and Exercise" on page 144.

7.5 Second Stage of Respiration: The Krebs Cycle

Since glycolysis yielded only two of the 36 molecules of ATP that eventually are harvested, the glucose derivative that resulted from glycolysis, pyruvic acid, still clearly has a lot of energy left in it. Some of this energy will be harvested in the second stage of cellular respiration, the **Krebs cycle**. This stage is named for the German and English biochemist Hans Krebs, who in the 1930s used the flight muscles of pigeons to find out how aerobic respiration works. Because the first product of the Krebs cycle is citric acid, the cycle is sometimes referred to as the **citric acid cycle**. The ATP yield in this cycle is once again a paltry two molecules. But the Krebs cycle serves to set the stage for the big harvest of ATP in the electron transport chain by supplying energy-bearing electron carriers, as you will see.

Steps in glycolysis

1. Delivered by the bloodstream, glucose enters a cell and immediately has a phosphate group from ATP attached to it. Because this process, called phosphorylation, attaches the phosphate to the sixth carbon of glucose, it now goes under the name glucose-6-phosphate. Note that one molecule of ATP has been *used* in this step.

    ATP ledger now reads: -1 ATP

2. Glucose 6-phosphate is rearranged to become a molecule called fructose-6-phosphate.

3. Another molecule of ATP is used to add a second phosphate to fructose-6-phosphate, which now becomes fructose-1,6-diphosphate.

    ATP ledger now reads: -2 ATP

4. The single, six-carbon sugar fructose-1,6-diphosphate now becomes two molecules of a 3-carbon sugar, glyceraldehyde-3-phosphate, each with a phosphate group attached. From here on out, glycolysis happens in duplicate: What happens to one of the glyceraldehyde molecules happens to the other.

5. An enzyme brings together glyceraldehyde-3-phosphate, the electron carrier NAD+, and a phosphate group. The glyceraldehyde-3-phosphate molecule is oxidized by NAD+, which in its new form, NADH, moves to the electron transport chain bearing its electron cargo. The oxidation of NAD+ is energetic enough that it allows the phosphate group to become attached to the main molecule, now called 1,3-diphosphoglyceric acid. Because everything is happening in duplicate, two NADH molecules are produced.

6. 1,3-diphosphoglyceric acid loses one of its phosphate groups, thus becoming 3-phosphoglyceric acid. The reaction is energetic enough to push this phosphate group onto an ADP molecule, yielding ATP. Because of duplication, two ATP are produced.

    ATP ledger now reads: 0 ATP

7. In two reactions, 3-phosphoglyceric acid becomes phosphoenolpyruvic acid, which generates more ATP as it transfers its phosphate group to ADP. Two more ATP molecules are produced. The phosphate transfer turns phosphoenolpyruvic acid into pyruvic acid—the derivative of the original glucose that now will enter the Krebs cycle.

    ATP ledger now reads: +2 ATP

molecules in

molecules out

Red balls are carbons and gold ovals are phosphate groups

ATP   glucose   ADP

1. glucose-6-phosphate

2. fructose-6-phosphate

ATP   fructose-6-phosphate   ADP

3. fructose-1,6-diphosphate

4. glyceraldehyde-3-phosphate

$2 NAD^+ + 2 P \longrightarrow$ **2 NADH** $+ 2 H^+$

5. 1,3-diphosphoglyceric acid

2 ADP $\longrightarrow$ **2 ATP**

6. 3-phosphoglyceric acid

2 ADP $\longrightarrow$ **2 ATP**

7. pyruvic acid

Figure 7.5
Glycolysis
In glycolysis, the single glucose molecule is transformed in a series of steps into two molecules of a substance called pyruvic acid. These two molecules then move on to the next stage of cellular respiration (the Krebs cycle). Glycolysis also produces two molecules of electron-carrying NADH, which move to the electron transport chain. Although two molecules of ATP are used in the early stages of glycolysis, four are produced in the later stages, for a net production of two ATP.

glycolysis

2 ATP

2 NADH

When Energy Harvesting Ends at Glycolysis, Beer Can Be the Result

For many bacteria—and even sometimes for people—energy harvesting ends with the set of steps called glycolysis, rather than proceeding on through the Krebs cycle and electron transport chain. When this happens, organisms need a way to recycle their energy transfer molecules in a way that doesn't depend on oxygen. (The NADH they produced in glycolysis needs to lose its added electrons and become NAD^+ again, so it can be reused in glycolysis.) The solution to this dilemma is a kind of electron dumping, the *products* of which turn out to be some of the most familiar substances in the world.

Fermentation in Yeast

Yeast is a good example of how this works, because it is a busy single-celled fungus. Yeasts can live by glycolysis alone, or they can go through aerobic respiration. Say, then, that yeasts are working away on sugar, going through glycolysis, but doing so in an oxygenless environment. Recall that the final "substrate" product of glycolysis is two molecules of a substance called pyruvic acid. In yeasts, the pyruvic acid they end up with is converted to a molecule called acetaldehyde, and *it* takes on the electrons from NADH, meaning the recycling problem is now solved. Having taken on NADH's electrons, though, acetaldehyde now is converted to something very familiar: ethanol, better known as drinking alcohol.

For yeasts, alcohol is simply a by-product of the fermentation they carry out.

Human beings *put* yeasts in environments in which this will happen, of course, because this is how we make wine and beer. Imagine yeast cells inside a dark, airless wine cask, working away on burgundy grape juice, harvesting energy from the grape-juice sugars, but in so doing turning out pyruvic acid, which is turned into alcohol. Things are going along fine for these yeast cells, until the alcohol content of the wine reaches a level (about 14 percent) at which they can no longer survive in it. This whole process is known as **alcoholic fermentation**, the process by which yeasts produce alcohol, as a by-product of glycolysis they perform in an oxygenless environment.

For yeasts, alcohol is simply a waste by-product of the glycolysis they utilize in *anaerobic* energy conversion, meaning conversion in an oxygenless environment. The same is true of the carbon dioxide that also results from their conversion of pyruvic acid. Here again, humans have found great use for the refuse of nature. Put the right yeast into dough, and its continuing fermentation produces the CO_2 that causes bread to rise and become "light," because of the air holes now in it. (And the alcohol? It evaporates.)

Fermentation in Animals

Alcoholic fermentation is the solution that fungi (and occasionally plants) employ to sustain glycolysis in the absence of oxygen. But animals take a different tack, because in them the product of glycolysis, pyruvic acid, accepts the electrons from NADH. In this process, pyruvic acid is turned into another substance: **lactic acid**. Thus, the kind of fermentation that animals (and certain bacteria) carry out is called **lactate fermentation**. Have you ever experienced the muscle "burn" that comes with, for example, climbing several flights of stairs? If so, you have experienced a buildup of lactic acid in your muscles. Human beings cannot function in oxygenless environments, of course, but we do rely on glycolysis and lactate fermentation when we need a quick burst of energy. In such a situation, our relatively slow oxygen-using system—glycolysis, the Krebs cycle, and electron transport chain—just doesn't have time to respond.

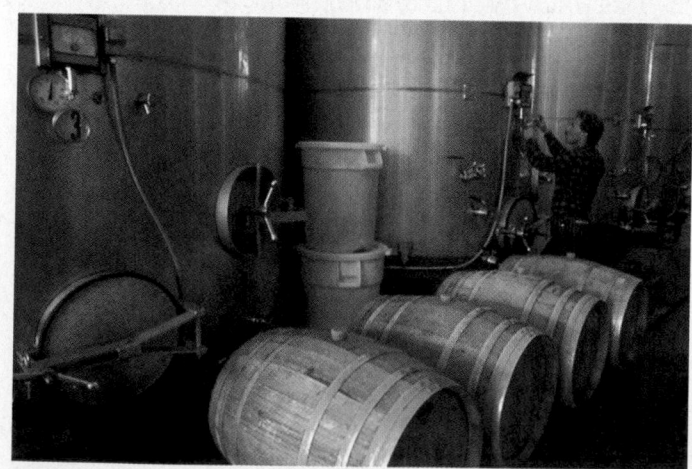

Yeast Inside, Performing Fermentation
This man is inspecting a gauge on a huge metal tank of fermenting wine. The alcohol in the wine is a by-product of the glycolysis carried out by yeast in an oxygenless environment.

Site of Action Moves from the Cytosol to the Mitochondria

Glycolysis yielded its two molecules of pyruvic acid in the cytosol, but the site of energy harvesting quickly shifts, with the pyruvic acid, to the new site of energy transfer, the mitochondria. These organelles are where all the action takes place from here on out, so now would be a good time to look at **Figure 7.6** and examine their structure. You can see that mitochondria have both an inner and an outer membrane. The Krebs cycle reactions take place to the interior of the inner membrane—in an area known as the inner compartment—while the reactions of the ETC take place *within* the inner membrane.

Between Glycolysis and the Krebs Cycle, an Intermediate Step

There actually is a transition step in respiration between glycolysis and the Krebs cycle. In it, the 3-carbon pyruvic acid molecule combines with a substance called coenzyme A, thus forming acetyl coenzyme A (acetyl CoA). One outcome of this reaction is that acetyl CoA enters the Krebs cycle as the derivative of the original glucose molecule. There are, however, two other products of this reaction. One is a carbon dioxide molecule that, like others you'll be seeing, eventually diffuses out of the cell and into the bloodstream. (This is a major source of the CO_2 that we exhale when we breathe.) The other product is one more molecule of NADH, which finds its way to the ETC. This reaction takes place twice for each glucose molecule (**see Figure 7.7**).

Figure 7.7
Transition between Glycolysis and the Krebs Cycle
The pyruvic acid product of glycolysis does not enter directly into the Krebs cycle. Rather, it must first be transformed into acetyl coenzyme A. The consequences of this reaction are the production of CO_2, which diffuses into the bloodstream, and the production of an NADH molecule, which continues onto the electron transport chain. Because one molecule of glucose produces two molecules of pyruvic acid, two molecules of NADH are produced in this step.

Figure 7.6
Energy Transfer in the Mitochondria
Mitochondria are organelles, or "tiny organs," that exist within cells. They are the location for the second and third sets of steps in cellular respiration, the Krebs cycle and the electron transport chain. Following a transitional step (see Figure 7.7), the products of glycolysis—the downstream products of the original glucose molecule—pass into the inner compartment of a mitochondrion, where the Krebs cycle takes place. Electrons derived from the Krebs cycle then migrate, via electron carriers, from the Krebs cycle site into the highly folded inner membrane of the mitochondrion, where the bulk of ATP is produced in the electron transport chain.

Into the Krebs Cycle: Why Is It a Cycle?

Acetyl CoA now enters the Krebs cycle. The reason this is a *cycle* becomes clear when you look at **Figure 7.8**. You can see that, in the first step of the cycle, acetyl CoA combines with a substance called oxaloacetic acid to produce citric acid. If you look over at about 11 o'clock on the circle, however, you can see that the *last* step in the cycle is the *synthesis* of oxaloacetic acid. Thus, a substance that's necessary for this chain of events to take place is itself a product of the chain.

Stroll around the circle now to see how the Krebs cycle functions in a little more detail. In essence, what's happening is that, as the entering acetyl CoA molecule is transformed into these various molecules, it is being oxidized by electron carriers, with the resulting electrons moving on to the ETC. ATP is also derived, and CO_2 is a product. The only major player that's unfamiliar here is the FAD–$FADH_2$ that can be seen taking part in a redox reaction at about 8 o'clock. It is simply another electron carrier, similar to NAD^+/NADH.

In counting up the Krebs cycle's yield of both ATP and electron carriers (NADHs and so on), recall that *two turns* around this cycle result from the original glucose molecule (because it provided two molecules of the starting acetyl CoA). This means a total yield of 6 NADH, 2 $FADH_2$, and 2 ATP from Krebs for each glucose molecule. Figure 7.8 reviews the Krebs cycle step by step. (If your class is studying the Krebs cycle in detail, you should look carefully at Figure 7.8, as it is the only place in the text where the individual steps of the cycle are reviewed.)

Figure 7.8
The Krebs Cycle
The Krebs cycle is the major source of electrons that are transported to the electron transport chain by the carriers NADH and $FADH_2$. For each molecule of acetyl coenzyme A that enters the cycle, 3 NADH molecules, 1 $FADH_2$, and 1 ATP are produced. Because two acetyl CoA molecules enter per molecule of glucose, the yield per glucose is 6 NADH, 2 $FADH_2$, and 2 ATP.

Steps in the Krebs cycle

1. Acetyl CoA combines with the four-carbon oxaloacetic acid and the CoA fragment separates from this compound. The result is the energetic six-carbon molecule citric acid, which will now be oxidized.

2. A citric acid derivative is oxidized by NAD^+; the resulting NADH carries electrons to the ETC. An intermediate molecule then loses a CO_2 molecule. Citric acid is now alpha-ketoglutaric acid.

3. Alpha-ketoglutaric acid loses a CO_2 molecule and the resulting four-carbon molecule is oxidized by NAD^+.

4. An alpha-ketoglutaric acid derivative is split, releasing enough energy to attach a phosphate to ADP, making it ATP. Alpha-ketoglutaric acid has become succinic acid.

5. Succinic acid is oxidized by FAD, losing two complete hydrogen atoms to it. The resulting $FADH_2$ then moves to the ETC. In a series of steps, succinic acid is transformed into malic acid.

6. Malic acid is oxidized by NAD^+. This step transforms malic acid to oxaloacetic acid—the molecule that enters the first step of the Krebs cycle.

7.6 Third Stage of Respiration: The Electron Transport Chain

Having moved through the Krebs cycle, you've reached the main event in cellular respiration: the production of 32 more ATP molecules through the work of the **electron transport chain**, the third stage of aerobic energy harvesting. Glycolysis took place in the cytosol, and the Krebs cycle took place in the inner compartment of the mitochondria. Now, however, the action shifts to the mitochondrial inner membrane, the site of the ETC (**see Figure 7.9**). The "links" in this chain are a series of molecules. You've been looking for some time now at how NADH and FADH$_2$ carry off the electrons derived from glycolysis and the Krebs cycle. This is the destination of these electron carriers and their cargo.

Upon reaching the mitochondrial inner membrane, the electron carriers donate electrons and hydrogen ions to the ETC. Once again, this is a trip down the energy hill, only *NADH* is now the molecule whose electrons exist at a higher energy level. Thus, when NADH runs into the appropriate enzyme in the ETC, NADH is oxidized, donating its electrons and proton to the ETC. This process then is simply repeated down the whole ETC, each carrier donating electrons to the next electron carrier in line. A carrier is reduced by receiving these electrons; donating them to the next carrier, it then returns to an oxidized state. Each carrier thus alternates between oxidized and reduced states.

Looking at Figure 7.9, you can see the carriers in the ETC: there are three large enzyme complexes with

Figure 7.9
The Electron Transport Chain (ETC)
The movement of electrons through the ETC powers the process that provides the bulk of the ATP yield in respiration. The electrons carried by NADH and FADH$_2$ are released into the ETC and transported along its chain of molecules. The movement of electrons along the chain releases enough energy to power the pumping of hydrogen ions (H$^+$) across the membrane into the outer compartment of the mitochondrion. It is the subsequent energetic "fall" of the H$^+$ ions back into the inner compartment that drives the synthesis of ATP molecules by the enzyme ATP synthase.

Energy and Exercise

One minute we're sleeping, the next we're looking for our running shoes, and 10 minutes after that we're bounding down the road trying to cover three miles at a faster pace than yesterday. Coming to the steep hill at the end of our run, we go all out—charging up to the top of it, slowing down only after we start going downhill, breathless and spent. How can the human body cope with a range of energy demands that runs from sleeping to sprinting? Its secret is having a kind of energy trio at its service, with each member of the group specializing in delivering energy in particular situations.

The essence of any kind of exercise is the contraction of muscles, and the only energy molecule that can power the contraction of skeletal muscle is ATP. You have seen that the human body uses a three-stage process to produce ATP: glycolysis, the Krebs cycle, and the electron transport chain. As a whole, this system is dependent on oxygen, but glycolysis is not directly dependent on it. For brief periods of time we can produce a good deal of the ATP we need through a glycolysis that is de-coupled from the Krebs cycle and the electron transport chain, though there is a price to be paid for this, which is the buildup of lactic acid in our muscles (see "When Energy Harvesting Ends at Glycolysis" on page 140). Oxygen-independent glycolysis can thus be thought of as the first member of the body's energy trio, while *aerobic* or oxygen-using energy transfer can be thought of as the second member. Our cells also have a capacity to *store* small amounts of ATP, however, and they can also stockpile another molecule,

phosphocreatine (PCr), that acts as a reservoir of phosphate groups that can be used to produce ATP. This stored ATP/PCr is the third member of the energy ensemble. Let's now see how all three players would work together in the course of a bike ride, starting out at a fairly brisk pace.

With the first turns of the pedals, bike riders bump up their body's energy demands tremendously. In their cycling, they could easily burn up 10 times the calories they would while in a resting state. (As a point of comparison, in doing housework a person typically burns up about three times the calories he or she does while at rest.)

So, how do muscle cells accommodate such large increases in their need for ATP? In the first few seconds, the small reservoirs of ATP/PCr take the lead role, with a proportionately smaller contribution from glycolysis and a smaller contribution yet from aerobic metabolism. These differences reflect the time it takes for each of these systems to get going. You've seen how many steps there are in glycolysis, and how many *more* steps there are in the Krebs cycle and electron transport chain. By comparison, the output of ATP from stored ATP/PCr is instantaneous. Remember, though, that the ATP/PCr reservoir is small. A person who had to depend solely on it for a full-ahead sprint would have only enough energy to last about six seconds. On a longer bike ride, glycolysis and ATP/PCr are contributing roughly equal amounts of ATP within 10 seconds. Within 30 seconds, glycolysis has greatly eclipsed PCr as an energy provider.

two smaller mobile molecules that link them. When NADH arrives at the inner membrane, it bumps into the ETC's first carrier and donates electrons to it; this carrier then donates these electrons to the next carrier, and so on down the line to the last electron acceptor, which is oxygen in the inner compartment (note the O_2).

Where's the ATP?

At this point you may be tapping your foot, waiting for this promised harvest of ATP to appear. So far, all that's taken place is a transfer of electrons in the ETC. Well, note what happens in the first ETC enzyme complex. The movement of electrons through it releases enough energy to power the movement of *hydrogen ions* (H^+ ions) through the complex,

pushing them from the inner compartment into the outer compartment. (The fall of the electrons causes the enzyme complex to change its shape in a way that facilitates the passage of H^+ ions through it and into the outer compartment.) By the time the electrons have completed their movement through the ETC, this pumping of H^+ ions will occur with the two other large enzyme complexes. Critically, these H^+ ions are being pumped *against* their concentration and electrical gradients (reviewed in Chapter 5). Put another way, the ions are being pumped up the energy hill with energy supplied by the *downhill* fall of electrons through the ETC.

Here's where the ATP is produced at last. The H^+ ions that have been pumped into the outer compartment now move *back down* their concentration and

Duration of maximal exercise

	Seconds			Minutes					
	10	30	60	2	4	10	30	60	120
Percent anaerobic	90	80	70	50	35	15	5	2	1
Percent aerobic	10	20	30	50	65	85	95	98	99

Figure 1
Different Contributions over Time
Relative contributions of anaerobic and aerobic respiration to exercise during the duration of a workout. "Anaerobic" here means a combination of glycolysis and stored ATP/PCr release. At the 1-minute mark, aerobic respiration is supplying only 30 percent of the body's energy needs; at the 10-minute mark, it is supplying 85 percent. (Adapted from P. O. Astrand and K. Rodahl, *Textbook of Work Physiology*. New York: McGraw Hill Book Company, © 1977.)

At about this same 30-second mark, the third player, aerobic respiration, is supplying only about 20 percent of the ATP, but its contribution is growing fast. In **Figure 1**, you can see how the aerobic contribution to ATP yield grows over the course of a long, strenuous workout. At the start, oxygen-dependent respiration is supplying less than 10 percent of our ATP, but 10 minutes into the workout it is delivering 85 percent.

You might think that this would be the final division of ATP contributions among the three players, but the amounts they supply can vary over time depending on the intensity of the activity. **Figure 2** shows how this would work in an actual professional-level bicycle race. Going along at a steady state in "pack" riding, you can see the overriding contribution of aerobic metabolism. In the final sprint, however, stores of

ATP/PCr—replenished during the pack riding—are fully utilized, with the contribution of glycolysis increasing as well. In stretches of difficult hill climbing, meanwhile, glycolysis is fully utilized.

Of course, lots of sports have no aerobic component to them at all. The energy for a sport like football is supplied almost entirely by stored ATP/PCr. Even in a competition as long as a 400-meter sprint—about once around a regulation track—about 70 percent of the energy comes from a combination of ATP/PCr and glycolysis.

Figure 2
Different Activities, Different Energy Stores
Energy-harvesting processes used at different stages in a bicycle race. (Adapted from J. T. Kearney, "Training the Olympic Athletes." *Scientific American*, June 1996, p. 54.)

energy gradients, into the inner compartment, through a special enzyme called ATP synthase. This remarkable enzyme is driven by the H$^+$ ions flowing through it, which cause part of the enzyme to rotate (as fast as 100 revolutions per second). We could think of it as being something like a waterwheel, except that its movement is driven not by water, but by the movement of H$^+$ ions that are passing through it, on their way back into the inner compartment. It is this energetic spinning that puts a third phosphate group (P) onto ADP, thus making ATP. **ATP synthase** can thus be defined as an enzyme that functions in cellular respiration by bringing together ADP and inorganic phosphate molecules to produce ATP.

The basic mechanism here—the pumping of hydrogen ions powering the synthesis of ATP—was first proposed in 1961 by British biochemist Peter Mitchell, who won the Nobel Prize in 1978 for his contribution to bioenergetics. Lest it pass by too quickly, *this* is the essence of aerobic respiration. The downhill drop of electrons derived from food has powered the uphill synthesis of the molecule that powers the vast majority of our activities.

Bountiful Harvest: ATP Accounting

In the ETC, each NADH molecule will be responsible for the production of three molecules of ATP. And, of course, every molecule of NADH that comes to the chain will result in this amount of ATP. And how many are coming? Ten: two produced in glycolysis, two from pyruvic acid conversion, and six from the Krebs cycle. The FADH$_2$ carrier that came from the Krebs cycle joins the ETC a little later than does NADH and as such produces only about two ATP molecules, compared to NADH's three. The upshot of all this is summarized in **Table 7.1** which presents the final count on our energy harvest.

What's apparent from looking at this table is that the ETC is a mighty energizer. Think about how efficient this process is compared to glycolysis (34 ATP compared to 2). Imagine one car that got 34 miles to the gallon compared to another that got 2. The 36 total ATP yield actually is the amount that can be derived under optimal conditions. (The "loss, due to active transport" in the table refers to the expenditure of ATP required to move the NADH produced in glycolysis into the mitochondria.)

Table 7.1 Energy Harvesting Accounting			
Stage	**NADH**	**FADH$_2$**	**ATP yield**
Glycolysis	2		2
Pyruvic acid conversion	2		
Krebs cycle	6	2	2
Electron transport chain	10		30
		2	4
Loss, due to active transport:			–2
Total ATP:			**36**

Finally, Oxygen Is Reduced, Producing Water

The story of the breakdown of glucose—the saga of *one molecule's* transformation—is nearly complete. The only unfinished business lies at the end of the ETC. As noted earlier, oxygen is the final acceptor of the working electrons. In the mitochondrial inner compartment, a single oxygen atom $\left(\frac{1}{2} O_2\right)$ accepts two electrons from the ETC and two H^+ ions. The result is H_2O: water. That's why the formula for respiration is written as:

$$C_6H_{12}O_6 + 6O_2 + 36ADP + 36P \rightarrow$$
$$6CO_2 + 36\ ATP + 6H_2O$$

Glucose, plus oxygen, plus ADP and phosphate yield carbon dioxide, plus ATP, plus water: That's the short story of aerobic respiration.

7.7 Other Foods, Other Respiratory Pathways

By looking at aerobic respiration as it applies to glucose, which was used as the starting molecule, you've been able to go through the whole respiratory chain. But it goes without saying that there are many kinds of nutrients besides glucose—for example, fats, proteins, and other sugars. All these can provide energy by being oxidized within the chain of reactions you've just gone over. However, none of them proceeds through the chain in exactly the same way as glucose. In addition, the body has more uses for foods than breaking them down to produce ATP. At any given moment, an organism may need to go the other way: toward the *buildup* of proteins from amino acids or the synthesis of the fats we call triglycerides. Organisms are able to handle this variability because nutrients and their derivatives can be *channeled* through pathways in different directions in the respiratory chain in accordance with cell needs. The alternation of the breakdown of food molecules and the buildup of food storage molecules is one of the central functions that living things carry out.

Alternate Respiratory Pathways: Fats as an Example

To give one example of how this channeling of nutrients works, consider the possible fates of triglycerides. As you learned in Chapter 4, triglycerides are fats made of a 3-carbon glycerol "head" and three long hydrocarbon chains that look like tines on a fork. Imagine that a given cell needs energy from fat. The question is, how do *triglycerides* go through aerobic respiration, as opposed to glucose?

The first thing that happens is that a triglyceride molecule is split by enzymes into its constituent parts of fatty acids and glycerol. Glycerol is then converted into glyceraldehyde phosphate. This formidable name may not ring a bell, but if you look back to step 4 in Figure 7.5, you'll see that it is one of the *downstream* derivatives of glucose in glycolysis. To put this another way, glycerol does not first get converted to glucose and then march through *all* of the steps of glycolysis. Instead, it joins the glycolytic pathway several steps down from glucose and is then converted to pyruvic acid. Then, as pyruvic acid, it goes through the Krebs cycle and ETC, producing ATP. And the fatty acids? They are converted to acetyl CoA, which you may remember is the substrate that enters the Krebs cycle, yielding energy by becoming oxidized there.

What Happens When Less Energy Is Needed?

So much for what happens when an organism needs a good deal of energy from fats. But what happens to the triglyceride components when this need is reduced? Glycerol, which had been converted to glyceraldehyde phosphate and begun marching through glycolysis, can be converted to *glucose* in a process that, in its main steps, is glycolysis in reverse. The resulting glucose molecules can then be used to do any number of things. They might, for example, be put together to create the storage form of glucose, glycogen.

You may be getting a sense that the metabolism is rather like a traffic circle: Molecules can enter at different points and leave at different points for varying destinations, depending on the needs of the organism. In **Figure 7.10**, you can see a summary of the way foods are broken down through various respiratory pathways.

On to Photosynthesis

This long walk through cellular respiration has illustrated how living things harvest energy from food. Recall, however, that almost all living things have one source to thank for this food: the sun's energy, which is trapped by plants in the chemical bonds of carbohydrates. This capture of energy takes place through a process that has a beautiful symmetry with the respiration you have just looked at. That process is called photosynthesis.

Figure 7.10
Many Respiratory Pathways
Glucose is not the only starting material for cellular respiration. Other carbohydrates, proteins, and fats can also be used as fuel for cellular respiration. These reactants enter the process at different stages.

Chapter Review

Summary

7.1 Energizing ATP: Adding a Phosphate Group to ADP

- The molecule adenosine triphosphate (ATP) supplies the energy for most of the activities of living things. For ATP to be produced, a third phosphate group must be added to adenosine diphosphate (ADP), a process that requires energy.

7.2 Electrons Fall Down the Energy Hill to Drive the Uphill Production of ATP

- In animals, the energetic fall of electrons derived from food powers the process by which the third phosphate group is attached to ADP, making it ATP.

- Electron transfer in the production of ATP works through redox reactions, meaning reactions in which one substance loses electrons to another substance. The substance that loses electrons in a redox reaction is said to have been oxidized, while the substance that gains electrons is said to have been reduced. In energy transfer in living things, starting food molecules are oxidized, and the electrons they lose ultimately power the process by which ATP is produced.

- Electrons are carried between one part of the energy-harvesting process and another by electron carriers, the most important of

which is nicotinamide adenine dinucleotide or NAD. In its "empty" state, this molecule exists as NAD^+. Through a redox reaction, it picks up one hydrogen atom and another single electron from food, thus becoming NADH, a form it will retain until it drops off its energetic electrons (and a proton) in a later stage of the energy-harvesting process.
Web Tutorial 7.1: Oxidation and Reduction

7.3 The Three Stages of Cellular Respiration: Glycolysis, the Krebs Cycle, and the Electron Transport Chain

- In most organisms, the harvesting of energy from food takes place in three principal stages, glycolysis, the Krebs cycle, and the electron transport chain (ETC). Taken as a whole, this oxygen-dependent three-stage harvesting of energy is known as cellular respiration.

- Some organisms rely solely on glycolysis for energy harvesting. For most organisms, glycolysis is a primary process of energy extraction only in certain situations—when quick bursts of energy are required, for example—but it is a necessary first stage to the Krebs cycle and the ETC.

- Glycolysis takes place in the cell's cytosol, while the Krebs cycle and the ETC take place in cellular organelles, called mitochondria, that lie within the cytosol. Glycolysis yields two net molecules of ATP per molecule of glucose, as does the Krebs cycle. The net yield in the electron transport chain is a maximum of about 32 ATP molecules per molecule of glucose. Glycolysis and the Krebs cycle are critical, however, in that they yield electrons that are carried to the ETC (via electron carriers such as NAD^+) for the final high-yield stage of energy harvesting.

Web Tutorial 7.2: Stages of Cellular Respiration

7.4 First Stage of Respiration: Glycolysis

- When glycolysis begins with a single molecule of glucose, the ultimate products are two molecules of NADH (which move to the ETC, bearing their energetic electrons) and two molecules of ATP (which are ready to be used). Glycolysis also produces two molecules of pyruvic acid—the derivatives of the original glucose molecule—which move on to the Krebs cycle.

7.5 Second Stage of Respiration: The Krebs Cycle

- There is a transition step in respiration between glycolysis and the Krebs cycle. In it, each pyruvic acid molecule that was produced in glycolysis combines with coenzyme A, thus forming acetyl coenzyme A (acetyl CoA), which enters the Krebs cycle. There are also two other products of this reaction. One is a molecule of carbon dioxide, which diffuses to the bloodstream; the other is one more molecule of NADH, which moves to the ETC. For each starting molecule of glucose, two molecules of pyruvic acid go through this step; thus its product per molecule of glucose is two molecules each of carbon dioxide, NADH, and acetyl CoA.

- In the Krebs (or citric acid) cycle, the derivatives of the original glucose molecule are oxidized, with the result that more energetic electrons are transported by the electron carriers NADH and $FADH_2$ to the ETC. The net energy yield of the Krebs cycle is six molecules of NADH, two molecules of $FADH_2$, and two molecules of ATP per molecule of glucose.

7.6 Third Stage of Respiration: The Electron Transport Chain

- The ETC is a series of molecules that are located within the mitochondrial inner membrane. Upon reaching the ETC, the electron carriers NADH and $FADH_2$ are oxidized by molecules in the chain. Each carrier in the chain is then reduced by accepting electrons from the carrier that came before it. The last electron acceptor in the ETC is oxygen.

- The movement of electrons through the ETC releases enough energy to power the movement of hydrogen ions (H^+ ions) through the three ETC protein complexes, moving them from the mitochondrion's inner compartment to its outer compartment. The movement of these ions down their concentration and charge gradients, back into the inner compartment through an enzyme called ATP synthase, drives the synthesis of ATP from ADP and inorganic phosphate. In the inner compartment, oxygen accepts the electrons from the ETC and hydrogen ions, thus forming water.

7.7 Other Foods, Other Respiratory Pathways

- Nutrients and their derivatives can be channeled through different pathways in cellular metabolism, in accordance with the needs of the organism. At any given moment, a cell may need to work more on synthesizing organic molecules than on breaking them down. Proteins and lipids enter the metabolic pathway for ATP production at different points than does the glucose reviewed in detail in the chapter.

Key Terms

alcoholic fermentation 140	Krebs cycle 138
ATP synthase 145	lactate fermentation 140
cellular respiration 138	lactic acid 140
citric acid cycle 138	nicotinamide adenine
electron carrier 135	dinucleotide (NAD) 135
electron transport	oxidation 135
chain (ETC) 143	redox reaction 135
glycolysis 138	reduction 135

Understanding the Basics

Multiple-Choice Questions (answers in the back of the book)

1. You need energy to think, to keep your heart beating, to play a sport, and to study this book. This energy is directly supplied by _____, which is (are) produced in the process of cellular respiration.
   a. enzymes
   b. ATP
   c. NAD^+
   d. vitamins
   e. proteins

2. Energy transfer in living things works through redox reactions, in which one substance is _____ by another substance, thereby _____.
   a. transported … becoming more energetic
   b. digested … becoming more energetic
   c. reduced … losing electrons to it
   d. oxidized … losing electrons to it
   e. oxidized … gaining electrons from it

3. _____ and _____ are important not so much for the ATP produced in them, but for their _____.
   a. Glycolysis … the Krebs cycle … yield of electrons transported to the ETC
   b. Glycolysis … the ETC … yield of electrons transported to the cytosol
   c. Redox reactions … fatty acid breakdown … yield of calories
   d. The Krebs cycle … the ETC … numerous redox reactions
   e. The Krebs cycle … the ETC … fatty-acid breakdown

4. What happens when a cell in your body momentarily has an abundance of ATP?
   a. It stops oxidizing food and starts building up storage food molecules from smaller food molecules.
   b. It continues to produce ATP at the same rate so that it is ready for the next emergency.
   c. It starts harvesting energy solely through glycolysis.
   d. It forms glucose out of extra ATP.
   e. It dies.

5. At most, how many molecules of ATP can be produced per glucose molecule in cellular respiration?
   a. 2
   b. 8
   c. 24
   d. 36
   e. 75

6. Where does the Krebs cycle occur in this model of a mitochondrion?
   a. A
   b. B
   c. C
   d. D
   e. none of these

7. When NADH passes its electrons to the ETC, it is
   a. electrolyzed
   b. polarized
   c. reduced
   d. oxidized
   e. deformed

8. We need to breathe because we need
   a. both atmospheric nitrogen and the oxygen for energy transformation
   b. oxygen to donate electrons to NAD^+
   c. nitrogen to donate phosphate groups to oxygen
   d. oxygen to act as the final acceptor of electrons in the ETC
   e. oxygen to donate phosphate groups to ADP, making it ATP

9. Why is the Kreb's Cycle so important for cells?
   a. it is where most ATP molecules are made
   b. it serves to assist in protein synthesis
   c. it is where many of the NADH molecules are made that will be used later
   d. it is where glucose is first broken down
   e. it is not that important.

Brief Review

1. Living things need ATP to power most of the processes that go on within them. In essence, how does cellular respiration yield this ATP?

2. Where do you expect people would have more mitochondria: their skin cells or their muscle cells? Why?

3. In the ETC, what is physically moved across the inner membrane—and energetically moved to a higher state—in order to drive the attachment of phosphate groups to ADP?

4. Where does the energy come from that powers this movement across the inner membrane in the ETC?

5. Most of the ATP we use is produced in the ETC. So when we have to run across the street to avoid traffic, does the ATP we are using come primarily from the ETC?

Applying Your Knowledge

1. In Madeleine L'Engle's children's novel *A Wrinkle in Time*, the mitochondria in one of the characters start to die. Describe what would happen to people who lost their mitochondria, and explain why it would happen.

2. Most of the heat in the human body is generated within mitochondria. Why should this be?

3. The food we eat is broken down in our digestive tract, but where are most of the calories in this food actually "burned"?

MediaLab

Dietary Fad or Miracle Drug? Using Science to Understand Metabolism

You've heard the claims: "Burns fat while you sleep!" "Energy fuel capsules!" and even "Magic weight-loss pills!" Companies entice us to try some new product by exploiting our ignorance about the actual process of cellular metabolism—how cells extract energy from food. This *MediaLab* covers the basic concepts needed to understand how cells really use the energy from food. To learn more, enter the *Web Tutorial* for an animated review of metabolism. Once you have completed the *Web Tutorial*, try the *Web Investigation* to uncover how metabolism may be misrepresented in diet claims on the Internet. Finally, *Communicate Your Results* will help you practice the skills you'll need to critically appraise the material you read.

The online version of this *MediaLab* can be found in Chapter 7 on your Companion Website (www.prenhall.com/krogh3).

WEB TUTORIAL

Americans are presented with such an abundance of food that they tend to equate the word *diet* with limiting the consumption of Calories, not as a necessary source of energy and nutrients. However, if you can see how your body uses the molecules in food, then you can begin to see why you need to consume certain foods. This *Web Tutorial* is designed to review metabolism.

Activity

1. First, you will examine the role of the cellular energy currency, ATP, and the energy conveyors, redox reactions.

2. Then you will investigate why we eat, by following the series of steps needed to convert the energy from food (carbohydrates, proteins, and fats) into ATP.

After reviewing the concepts of metabolism in these processes, you'll be ready to test your knowledge in the *Web Investigation* section by uncovering unfounded, impossible diet and exercise claims on the Internet.

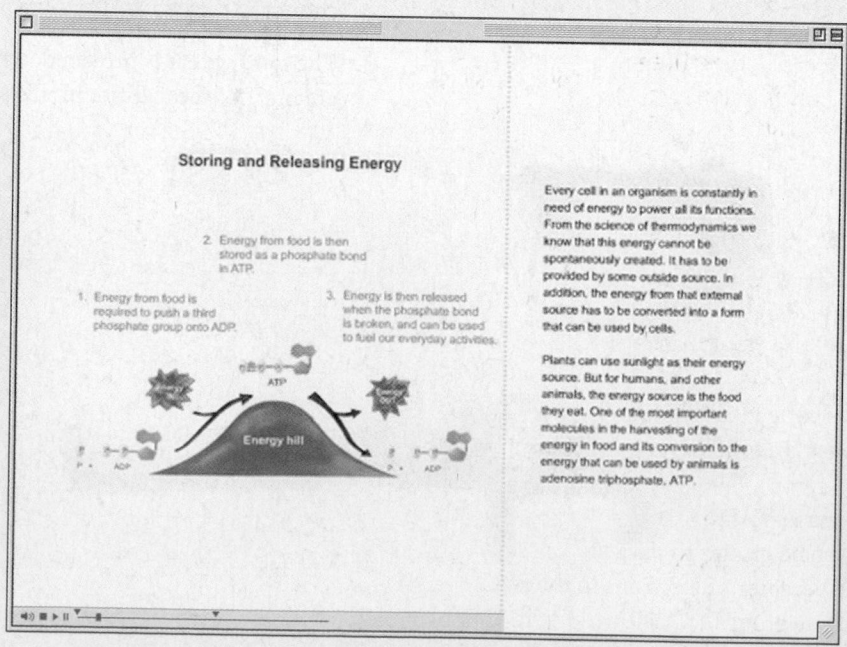

Investigation 1

Estimated time for completion = 10 minutes

How do we know this diet stuff won't live up to its promises? There is an excellent Web page devoted to disseminating information on how to recognize fraudulent weight-loss products and programs. Select the keyword **WEIGHT-LOSS FRAUD** on your Website for this *MediaLab*. After you've read the criteria, perform a search of the Internet to locate examples of weight-loss websites that make one of the promises described in the fraud article, like magic weight loss without dieting or exercise.

Investigation 2

Estimated time for completion = 5 minutes

Chromium picolinate is a common weight-loss supplement found in diet pills like Metabolife. What is it?

Does it work? How can you tell? Select the keyword **CHROMIUM SUPPLEMENTS 1** or **2** on your Website for this *MediaLab* to read two contradictory articles about chromium. Which one do you believe?

Investigation 3

Estimated time for completion = 5 minutes

Over 70 percent of adult Americans purchase dietary supplements to improve their health, but who tests the accuracy of the health claims made by supplement manufacturers? The responsibility for checking the safety of products and the truthfulness of label claims lies in the hands of consumers and manufacturers, not in an impartial government agency like the FDA. Select the keyword **FDA GUIDE TO SUPPLEMENTS** on your Website for this *MediaLab* to read the FDA's guide to dietary supplements.

Determine the integrity of the websites from the *Web Investigation* section by applying rigorous questions in the following examples.

Exercise 1

Estimated time for completion = 5 minutes

How can you determine what to believe on the Internet, when websites include scientific terminology and definitions that may not be based on tested, controlled experiments? Consumers can be embarrassingly gullible when they believe incredible diet claims. Search for one of these too-good-to-be-true sites and describe in two or three sentences why you think the product falls under the examples listed in the diet fraud article.

Exercise 2

Estimated time for completion = 20 minutes

Many diet-supplement companies promote the idea that human health problems can be remedied through ingesting supplements. How would a scientist determine the credibility of these claims? Here is a list of guidelines:

- *Do the websites refer to studies published in reputable science journals with rigorous standards, or do they refer to testimonials and stories?*

- *Do the author's credentials lend credibility, or are they unrelated?*

- *Does the author stand to benefit financially by the sales of the product?*

Compose a 250-word argument describing the claims made at the two websites listed in *Web Investigation 2*. Using the scientific criteria just listed, explain which claim is most credible.

Exercise 3

Estimated time for completion = 15 minutes

After reading the FDA report on supplements in *Web Investigation 3*, compose a letter to the FDA expressing whether you think the current system provides adequate protection to Internet consumers. Include your opinion on whether supplements should be subjected to the same rigorous clinical studies as drugs to determine their effectiveness, safety, possible interactions with other substances, and appropriate dosages. Should the FDA take more responsibility for removing potentially unsafe dietary supplements? Should the FDA take a greater role in enforcing prosecution of companies making false or erroneous health claims for its supplements?

Applying rigorous questions like these helps prepare you to critically analyze future material that you may find on the Internet. Internet material is not always filtered or checked for accuracy, so you'll need the skills practiced in this section to assess it on your own.

8 *Photosynthesis*

The electromagnetic spectrum.
(Section 8.2, page 154)

Capturing the sun's energy.
(Section 8.2, page 157)

Electrons in transit.
(Section 8.3, page 159)

On a summer's evening, out by a pond as the sun is going down, nature tunes up her symphony. The crickets bring their chirping to the fore, while frogs chime in with their own countermelody. Silently, something else is changing as the last light fades: The green world is shutting down. Microscopic pores that dot the undersides of leaves are closing up, ceasing to be openings for the carbon dioxide that flows in and the water vapor that flows out during the day. The green world is alive at night, but the activities it carries out are not much different from those a human listener might be undertaking while relaxing at water's edge. The green world has a special talent, but sunlight must be falling for it to be put into place.

8.1 Photosynthesis and Energy

The green world's special talent is called photosynthesis, and the wonder of it can perhaps best be appreciated by imagining what life would be like if we humans possessed it. The bone and muscle within us—and the energy to make them work—come from the foods we eat: carbohydrates and fats and proteins. Imagine, though, being able to flourish simply by spending time in the sun and having access to three things: water, small amounts of minerals, and carbon dioxide. In this condition we would not *eat* carbohydrates in the usual forms (bread, sugar, potatoes).

Rather, we would transform the simple gas carbon dioxide *into* carbohydrates using nothing more than water, minerals, and sunlight. Carbohydrates produced in this way are as useful as any food; they can be stored away as starches, used to provide ATP for energy needs, or transformed to make proteins. This, then, is what plants do: They *make their own food*. They use the energy provided by the sun to take a simple gas, carbon dioxide, join it to a carbohydrate (a sugar) and then *energize* that sugar, thus transforming it into food. In this activity, they are joined by a variety of other photosynthesizing organisms (**see Figure 8.1**).

Figure 8.1
Three Types of Photosynthesizers
Photosynthesis is carried out not only by familiar plants, such as these sunflowers **(a)**, but by algae, such as this giant kelp **(b)**, and by some bacteria, such as these cyanobacteria **(c)**. (magnified × 1025)

(a) Sunflowers (plants) **(b)** Giant kelp (algae) **(c)** Cyanobacteria (bacteria)

The Calvin cycle begins.
(Section 8.5, page 160)

3 molecules

carbon fixation

6 molecules of 3-PGA

6 ATP

6 ADP

Warm-weather photosynthesis.
(Section 8.6, page 161)

CO₂

Calvin cycle

sugar

A different path for photosynthesis.
(Section 8.7, page 162)

From Plants, a Great Bounty for Animals

The process of photosynthesis is not only good for plants; it's good for other living things, including animals, since most of the living world ultimately depends upon photosynthesis for food. Try naming something you eat that isn't a plant or doesn't itself eat plants to survive, and you will come up with a very short list indeed.

Food, however, is only half the bounty that plants provide. A by-product of photosynthesis—a kind of castoff from the work of plants—is oxygen. As part of photosynthesis, plants break water molecules apart. In doing so, they *use* electrons and protons from H_2O, but they *leave behind* oxygen molecules (O_2). This is the oxygen that exists in our atmosphere; it is the oxygen that we breathe in every minute of every day, or suffer the mortal consequences.

With this, you can step back and view the largest picture of them all with respect to energy flow in living things. It is a great pathway in which energy comes from the sun and then, in photosynthesis, is stored in plants in the complex molecules we call carbohydrates. Thus stored—in such forms as wheat grains or grass leaves—these carbohydrates can be broken down and used, either by the plants themselves or by the organisms that eat them. The breakdown of this food ends with the "cellular respiration," covered last chapter, that provides ATP.

Up and Down the Energy Hill Again

Looked at another way, photosynthesis and cellular respiration are trips up and down the energy hill that became so familiar in Chapter 7. In respiration, the trip was down the hill, meaning from more stored

energy (in food) to less, as the food was being broken down to produce ATP. Photosynthesis is a trip up the energy hill. Here electrons are being removed from water, boosted to a more energetic state by the power of sunlight, and then brought together with a sugar and carbon dioxide, resulting in an *energy-rich* sugar—food in the form of a carbohydrate. The story of how this carbohydrate creation is accomplished is the subject of this chapter. To encapsulate this story in a definition, **photosynthesis** is the process by which certain groups of organisms capture energy from sunlight and convert this solar energy into chemical energy that is initially stored in a carbohydrate.

8.2 The Components of Photosynthesis

We can think of photosynthesis as starting with the absorption of sunlight by leaves. *Absorption* here means just what it sounds like: Light is taken in by the leaves. Actually, leaves capture only a *portion* of the light that falls on them. The sunlight that makes it to the Earth's surface is composed of a spectrum of energetic rays (measured by their "wavelengths") that range from very short, ultraviolet rays, through visible light rays, to the longer and less-energetic infrared rays. (In **Figure 8.2** you can see that these wavelengths are, in turn, part of a larger range of electromagnetic radiation.) Photosynthesis is driven by part of the *visible light* spectrum—mainly by blue and red light of certain wavelengths. Tune a laser to emit blue light of a certain wavelength, shine this beam on a plant, and the plant will absorb a great deal of this light. On the other hand, tune the laser to emit *green* light, and the plant will scatter most of this light. This is why plants are green: They strongly scatter the green portion of the visible light spectrum.

Where in the Plant Does Photosynthesis Occur?

So, where is this light absorption occurring within plants? To answer this question, you need to know something about the playing fields of photosynthesis, leaves.

The broad, flat leaves that are so common in nature have in essence a two-part structure: A *blade* (which we usually think of as the leaf itself) and a *petiole*, more commonly referred to as the leaf stem. If you look at the idealized leaf in **Figure 8.3**, you can see that the blade can be likened to a kind of cellular sandwich, with one layer of outer (or epidermal) cells at the top, another layer at the bottom, and layers of mesophyll cells in between. Take time now to read through Figure 8.3's drawings and captions; as you do, you'll go from the leaf's layers of cells, then into the cells themselves, and

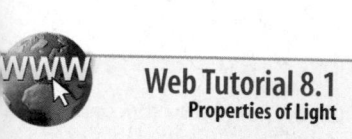

Web Tutorial 8.1
Properties of Light

Figure 8.2
The Electromagnetic Spectrum
Sunlight is composed of rays of many different wavelengths, but we can see only those in the visible light range (represented by the color spectrum). When the light of the sun shines on a green leaf, it is primarily the sun's green rays that are scattered, while frequencies in other ranges are absorbed; frequencies in the red and blue ranges drive photosynthesis most strongly.

1. Leaf

The primary site of photosynthesis in plants, leaves have a two-part structure: a petiole (or stem) and a blade (normally thought of as the leaf).

petiole

blade

2. Leaf cross-section

In cross section, leaves have a sandwich-like structure, with epidermal layers at top and bottom and mesophyll cells in between. Most photosynthesis is performed within mesophyll cells. Leaf epidermis is pocked with a large number of microscopic openings, called stomata, that allow carbon dioxide to pass in and water vapor to pass out.

epidermis

mesophyll cells

epidermis

stomata

3. Mesophyll cell

A single mesophyll cell within a leaf contains all the component parts of plant cells in general, including the organelles—called chloroplasts—that are the actual sites of photosynthesis.

nucleus

chloroplast

cell wall

vacuole

4. Chloroplast

Each chloroplast has an outer membrane at its periphery; then an inner membrane; then a liquid material, called the stroma, that has immersed within it a network of membranes, the thylakoids. These thylakoids sometimes stack on one another to create. . .

thylakoids

stroma

granum

inner membrane

outer membrane

5. A Granum

Electrons used in photosynthesis will come from water contained in the thylakoid compartment, and all the steps of photosynthesis will take place either within the thylakoid membrane, or in the stroma that surrounds the thylakoids.

Energy from sunlight is absorbed by pigments in the thylakoid membrane.

thylakoid

thylakoid membrane

thylakoid compartment

Figure 8.3
Site of Photosynthesis

then into the tiny structures *within* the cells—the chloroplasts—that are the primary sites of photosynthesis.

Here is some detail on the structures seen in Figure 8.3. The **stomata** seen in the figure are the microscopic pores, mentioned at the start of the chapter, that let carbon dioxide pass into leaves and water vapor pass out of them. There is no shortage of stomata for this work; a given square centimeter of plant leaf may contain from a thousand to a hundred thousand of them.

Going down a couple of levels, **chloroplasts** can be defined as the organelles within plant and algae cells that are the sites of photosynthesis. Anywhere from one to several hundred of these oblong structures might exist within a given leaf cell, each capable of carrying out photosynthesis on its own. As Figure 8.3 shows, chloroplasts present another example of something you've seen before—membranes within membranes. The chloroplast has outer and inner membranes at its periphery. Moving inside them, to the interior of the chloroplast, there is a network of chloroplast membranes, active in photosynthesis, called **thylakoids**. These thylakoids often stack on top of one another like so many pancakes, creating structures called *grana*. Thylakoids are immersed in the liquid material of the chloroplast, the **stroma**, and have an interior fluid space called the **thylakoid compartment**. All the steps of photosynthesis take place in the thylakoid membrane or the stroma of the chloroplast.

Embedded in the thylakoid membranes are the molecules that actually absorb the sunlight—pigments. Anything that strongly absorbs certain visible wavelengths of sunlight is called a pigment. Thylakoid membranes contain a pigment, called **chlorophyll *a***, that can be defined as the primary pigment active in plant photosynthesis. Chlorophyll *a* is then aided by several substances known as *accessory pigments*, which do just what their name implies: they aid chlorophyll *a* in absorbing energetic rays from the sun, after which they pass the absorbed energy along.

There Are Two Essential Stages in Photosynthesis

Keeping these structures and concepts in mind, you can now begin tracing the steps of photosynthesis. It is helpful to divide photosynthesis into two main stages. In the first stage (the *photo* of photosynthesis), the power of sunlight will do two things—strip water of electrons and then boost these electrons to a higher energy level. Thus boosted, the electrons are passed along through a series of the electron *carriers* you were introduced to in Chapter 7. All of this takes place in the thylakoid membranes. This first stage of photosynthesis ends when the original, energized electrons get attached to a mobile electron carrier, called $NADP^+$, that transports them to the second set of reactions. In this second stage (the *synthesis* of photosynthesis), the electrons come together with carbon dioxide and a sugar. The attachment of the electrons and CO_2 to this sugar produces a high-energy sugar—meaning food. This second stage takes place in the stroma of the chloroplast.

The steps in the first stage of photosynthesis obviously depend directly on sunlight. Thus, these steps are sometimes referred to as the *light reactions*. Meanwhile, the second set of steps are referred to as the *Calvin cycle*, in honor of Melvin Calvin, the scientist who first revealed their details. You will be following both sets of steps as they occur in time—from the collection of sunlight to the synthesis of carbohydrates.

The Working Units of the Light Reactions

Looking first at the light reactions, we see that they take place within a set of working units. Each of these units is a **photosystem**—an organized complex of molecules within a thylakoid membrane that, in photosynthesis, collects solar energy and transforms it into chemical energy. If you look at **Figure 8.4**, you can see the components that make up a photosystem. First, there is a group of a few hundred pigment molecules that serve to absorb the sunlight. The majority of these molecules—most of the chlorophyll *a* and all of the accessory pigments—serve only as "antennae" that absorb energy from the sun and pass it on. At the center of the antennae system, however, there is a **reaction center**—a pair of special chlorophyll *a* molecules and associated compounds that first receive the solar energy from photosystem pigments and then transform this solar energy into chemical energy. As you can see in Figure 8.4, the reaction center includes a molecule that could be thought of as the first recipient of the absorbed solar energy, the "primary electron acceptor."

You could conceptualize photosynthesis as beginning when sunlight is absorbed by any of the hundreds of antennae pigment molecules in a photosystem unit. The absorbed energy is then passed on to the pair of chlorophyll *a* molecules in a reaction center. As a result, electrons from this pair are "moved" in a couple of ways, one physical and one metaphorical. Physically, these electrons are transferred to the primary electron acceptor. You also could think of the initial "distance traveled" by the

Web Tutorial 8.2
Photosynthesis

**Figure 8.4
The Working Units of
Photosynthesis**
Photosystems are multipart units that bring together electrons derived from water and energy derived from the sun. Hundreds of antennae pigments absorb sunlight and transfer solar energy to the photosystem's reaction center. This energy gives a boost to an electron within the reaction center in two ways: It physically moves the electron to the center's primary electron acceptor, and it moves the electron up the energy hill to a more energetic state.

primary
electron
acceptor

e⁻

sunlight

reaction
center

antennae
pigments

photosystem

electrons in a metaphorical way, however: as a movement up the energy hill. The energy from sunlight is pumping the electrons up the hill in photosynthesis.

Energy Transfer in Photosynthesis Works through Redox Reactions

How can electrons move up an energy hill? Recall from Chapter 7 that some substances have a tendency to *lose* electrons to other substances. Any time one substance loses (or "donates") electrons to another, it is said to have been oxidized. Meanwhile, the substance that gained electrons is said to have been reduced. These two reactions always happen together; if one substance is oxidized, another must be reduced. This kind of reduction-oxidation reaction has a shorter name: a *redox reaction*.

Many of the photosynthetic steps you will be seeing are redox reactions. Indeed, you have already seen one. The movement of electrons within the reaction center—from the chlorophyll *a* molecules to the primary electron acceptor—is a redox reaction. The chlorophyll molecules were oxidized by the primary electron acceptor, meaning they lost electrons to it. What happens in the light reactions is a continuation of this energy transfer: electrons are passed on by means of one electron carrier oxidizing another.

As electrons *physically* move through the light reactions in this way, they are also moving both up and down the energy hill—they are becoming first more and then less energetic. If you look at **Figure 8.5**, you can trace their movement up and

down the energy hill as they make their journey. With energy supplied by the sun, electrons are pumped up a couple of formidable energy gradients (in photosystems II and I) only to come partway back down them, as they "seek" their lowest energy state. Critically, they are releasing energy as they fall—just as a boulder releases energy by rolling downhill.

8.3   Stage 1: The Steps of the Light Reactions

With these components and processes in mind, let's trace the steps of the light reactions (see Figure 8.5). The first step is that solar energy, collected by photosystem II's antennae molecules, arrives at the reaction center. This energy then gives a boost to an electron in the reaction center in the two ways noted: The electron *physically* moves to another part of the reaction center complex, the primary electron acceptor. But it is also pumped up the energy hill. With this activity, the reaction center chlorophyll has *lost* an electron. That loss leaves an energy "hole" in this chlorophyll, making it an oxidizing agent. With the energy provided by this imbalance, a special enzyme in the reaction center splits water molecules that lie within the thylakoid compartment. These water molecules are now being oxidized, which means *they* are losing electrons. The electrons travel to the reaction center, where they will be the next electrons in line for an energy boost.

Figure 8.5
Collecting Solar Energy, Boosting Electrons
The solar energy gathered by photosystems II and I is used to energize electrons that exist within the photosystems' reaction centers. Energetically, the electrons are boosted up, and then move down, two energy hills. Physically, they first move to primary electron acceptors and then down electron transport chains until they are at last taken up by NADP$^+$ to form NADPH. The NADPH molecules then transfer the electrons to the Calvin cycle, where they are used to make sugars. When an electron is boosted in photosystem II, the resulting energy imbalance drives the process by which water molecules are split. Electrons derived from the water adjacent to photosystem II then move to its reaction center, where they are the next to be boosted by the sun's energy. The energetic fall of electrons down the electron transport chain between photosystems II and I provides the energy for the synthesis of ATP, which is used to power the Calvin cycle.

A Chain of Redox Reactions and Another Boost from the Sun

By following Figure 8.5 in a general way, you can see what happens next to electrons that are boosted in photosystem II. After arriving at the primary electron acceptor, they fall back down the energy hill as they are transferred through a series of electron transport molecules, each one oxidizing its predecessor. At the bottom of this hill they arrive at photosystem I, which includes a slightly different kind of reaction center. This center is also receiving solar energy, and uses it to boost electrons to a higher energy state. From this energetic state, electrons are transferred down the second energy hill—until they are received by the electron carrier $NADP^+$, which is very much like the electron carrier NAD^+ reviewed in Chapter 7. In accepting electrons, $NADP^+$ becomes reduced to NADPH, an electron carrier that ferries the electrons into the next stage of photosynthesis. This second stage is the Calvin cycle, which will yield the high-energy sugar that is the essential product of photosynthesis.

The Physical Movement of Electrons in the Light Reactions

In this movement up and down the energy hill, the electrons have moved physically through the chloroplast. As **Figure 8.6** shows, they started out in the water of the thylakoid compartment, moved into and then through the thylakoid membrane—handed off at each step by the various electron transport molecules—and then finally ended up in the stroma, attached to NADPH.

8.4 What Makes the Light Reactions So Important?

The steps just reviewed are the essence of the light reactions. To make sure you don't miss the forest for the trees, let's be clear about two momentous things that have taken place within these steps.

The Splitting of Water: Electrons and Oxygen

The first notable event takes place near the start: the splitting of water. Critically, this reaction provides the traveling electrons whose path you've just followed. But it also provides something else: the oxygen that today accounts for more than 20 percent of the Earth's atmosphere. In the water splitting that goes on in photosynthesis, hydrogen atoms are removed from H_2O, while the oxygen is left behind. When two liberated oxygen atoms come together in the thylakoid compartment, the result is O_2—the form of oxygen that exists in our atmosphere. *Here* is where we get the substance that is the breath of life itself for most species, all of it contributed by living things. Given its importance, it is no small irony that oxygen is, in another sense, a kind of green-world refuse—leftovers from the process by which plants strip water of the electrons they need to carry out photosynthesis.

The Transformation of Solar Energy to Chemical Energy

The second major feat that takes place during light reactions is the transformation of solar energy to chemical energy. When the energy of sunlight moves to a chlorophyll molecule in a reaction center, it boosts an electron there from what is known as a ground state to an excited state. Thus far, this has been described as a movement up a metaphorical energy hill. In physical terms, however, this electron is moving farther out from the nucleus of an atom. To appreciate what's special about photosynthesis, consider what the *common* fates are for such excited electrons. One fate is for the electrons to drop back down to the original (and more stable) state, in the process releasing as *heat* the energy they have absorbed. This is the process by which black objects get hot on sunny days. Another possible fate is for falling electrons to release part of their energy as light in the process known as fluorescence.

In photosynthesis, however, the energized electrons are *transferred to a different molecule*—the initial electron acceptors of photosystems II and I. They don't fall back to their ground state, releasing relatively useless heat or light in the process. They are passed on in a redox reaction. This is the bridge to life as we know it. Without this step, the energy of the sun merely makes the Earth warmer. With it, the green world grows profusely; it captures some of the sun's energy and with it builds trunks and grains and leaves. By one reckoning, photosynthesis produces up to 155 billion tons of material each year. This is an amazing amount—about 25 tons for every person on Earth. Electrons are taken from water, boosted to a higher energy state by the sun, and transferred to other molecules. The result is the food that sustains nearly all living things.

Production of ATP

It's also worth noting that a primary function of the fall of electrons between photosystems II and I is a release of energy that is used for the production of ATP. Put together through a process similar to the one you looked at last chapter, this ATP will be used to power the reactions that are coming up in the second stage of photosynthesis. Thus, the end result of the light reactions is that the sun's power has provided energy that is stored in *two* forms: ATP, and the energetic electrons in NADPH. Looking at the big picture, you can see that the *photo* of photosynthesis is an energy-capturing operation.

8.5   Stage 2: The Calvin Cycle

In the second stage of photosynthesis, the energy captured in the light reactions will be *used*. It will power a process by which carbon dioxide, taken from the atmosphere, will be joined to a sugar, with the resulting product energized, thus creating a carbohydrate—which is to say food. To see how this happens, let's begin by taking stock of where the light reactions left off. The short answer is, in the stroma. That's where $NADP^+$ has become NADPH by accepting the energized electrons pouring out from photosystem I. There's also ATP in the stroma, also made from the light reactions.

Energized Sugar Comes from a Cycle of Reactions

Even with the right ingredients, however, it takes more than one step to go from carbon dioxide and a sugar to a sugar that is energetic enough to serve as food. It takes a set of chemical reactions that make up a cycle. This is the **Calvin cycle** or the C_3 cycle, the set of steps in photosynthesis in which energetic electrons are brought together with carbon dioxide and a sugar to produce an energetic carbohydrate. The highlights of this cycle are set forth in **Figure 8.7**. This is the *synthesis* of photosynthesis: a bringing together of elements.

Web Tutorial 8.3
The Calvin Experiments

Figure 8.6
The Light Reactions
The light reactions take place in the thylakoid membranes within the chloroplasts. Electrons are donated by water molecules located in the thylakoid compartments. Powered by the sun's energy, these electrons are passed along the electron transport chain embedded in the thylakoid membrane and end up stored in NADPH in the stroma. An additional product of the splitting of water molecules is individual oxygen atoms, which quickly combine into the O_2 form. This is the atmospheric oxygen that we breathe in.

In its first steps, the Calvin cycle is a process of **fixation**—of a gas being incorporated into an organic molecule. Specifically, carbon dioxide is being fixed into our starting sugar, known as RuBP, which stands for ribulose bisphosphate. From the time they are embryos, plants have small amounts of this sugar in them as a legacy from their parent plants. We could think of it as a sugar that the plant "bootstraps" itself up with, by adding to it carbon dioxide from the atmosphere and energy from the light reactions.

Here are the steps in the Calvin cycle:

1. **Bringing together carbon dioxide and sugar.** The process begins with three molecules of CO_2 (coming in through the leaf stomata) being joined to three molecules of RuBP, which has five carbon atoms. Note that one carbon of CO_2 is being added to a five-carbon molecule, and that this it is being done three times. The result, of course, should be three *six-carbon* molecules. This is the case, but only for a vanishingly brief time. Each six-carbon mole-

cule is so unstable that it is split apart immediately into two *three-carbon* molecules of a substance called 3-phosphoglyceric acid or 3-PGA. The three carbons here give the C_3 cycle its name.

A key player in photosynthesis is the enzyme that brings together CO_2 and RuBP. This massive protein goes under several aliases, but the one used here is **rubisco**. You need to be clear about what it is doing: bringing together in its active site CO_2 and the sugar RuBP. Here is where the small, low-energy gas molecule CO_2 is joined to the ranks of organic molecules, specifically sugars.

2. **Energizing the sugar.** Carbon dioxide has now been added to a sugar; what remains is for this sugar to be energized. These things take place in the next two steps. First, ATP reacts with the molecules of 3-PGA, putting a phosphate group onto each of them. Then NADPH donates a pair of electrons to each of the resulting molecules, yielding six molecules of a substance called glyceraldehyde-3-phosphate or G3P.

3. **The food has arrived.** There should now be a little fanfare, because with this step food has been produced. Note that G3P was synthesized by receiving energetic electrons from NADPH—the electrons that came originally from water and that were boosted up the energy hill by sunlight. G3P thus has more potential energy than did its predecessor in the Calvin cycle. It is precisely this position—a greater distance up the energy hill—that makes food.

Figure 8.7
The Calvin Cycle
CO_2, ATP, and electrons (contained in hydrogen atoms) from NADPH are the input into the Calvin cycle, while a sugar (G3P) is its output.

1. **Carbon fixation.** The enzyme rubisco brings together three molecules of CO_2 with three molecules of the five-carbon sugar RuBP; the three resulting six-carbon molecules are immediately split into six three-carbon molecules named 3-PGA (3-phosphoglyceric acid).

2. **Energizing the sugar.** In two separate reactions, six ATP molecules react with six 3-PGA, in each case transferring a phosphate onto the 3-PGA. The six 3-PGA derivatives oxidize (gain electrons from) six NADPH molecules; in so doing, they are transformed into the energy-rich sugar G3P (glyceraldehyde 3-phosphate).

3. **Exit of product.** One molecule of G3P exits as the output of the Calvin cycle. This molecule, the product of photosynthesis, can be used for energy or transformed into materials that make up the plant.

4. **Regeneration of RuBP.** In several reactions, five molecules of G3P are transformed into three molecules of RuBP, which enter the cycle.

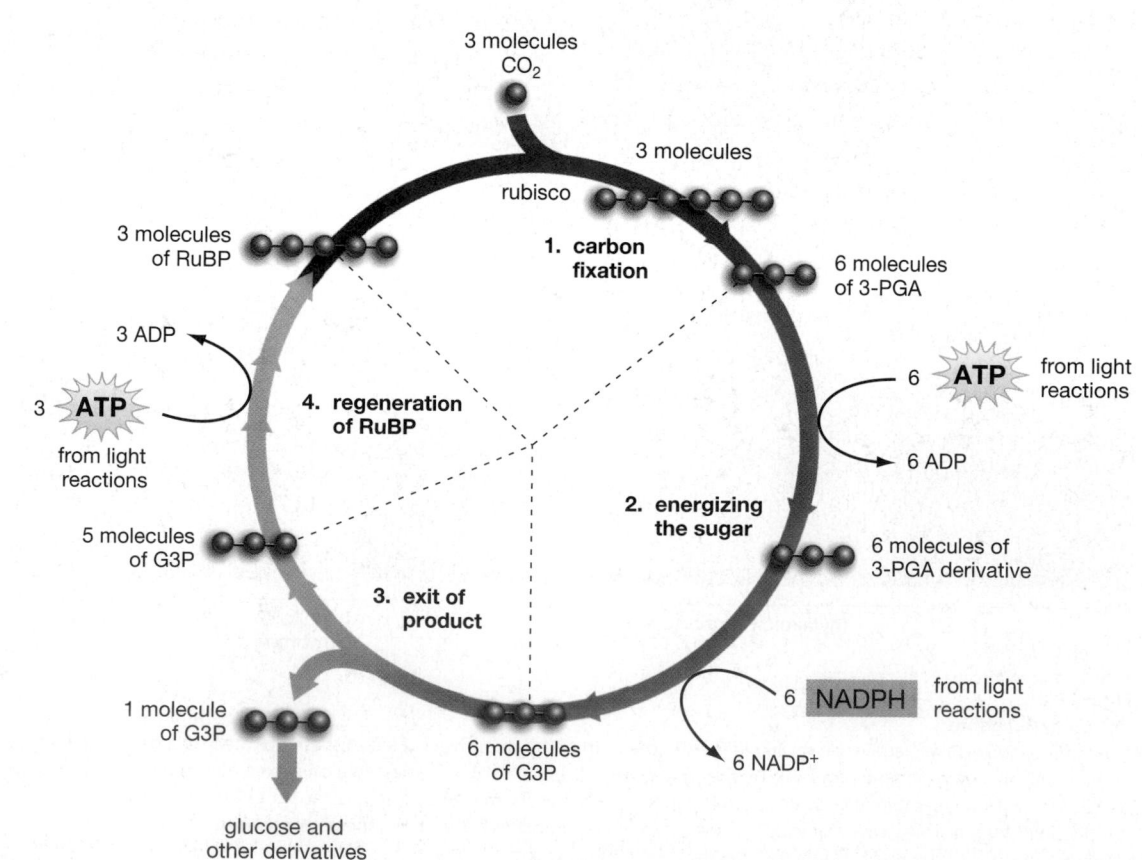

G3P is thus the product of photosynthesis. It is, however, a product that is analogous to steel coming out of a factory: In association with minerals that the plant absorbs through its roots, it can be turned into many things. Put two molecules of G3P together and you get the more familiar six-carbon sugar, glucose. In turn, many molecules of glucose can come together to form the large storage molecules known as starches, familiar to us in such forms as potatoes or wheat grains. Beyond this, sugar is used to make proteins, which are then used as structural components of the plant or as enzymes. Given all this, you may ask, what is the *ultimate* product of photosynthesis? The answer is *the whole plant.*

4. **Regeneration of RuBP.** As you can see from Figure 8.7, the C_3 cycle still has some distance to go after the synthesis of G3P. Critically, only one of the six molecules of G3P will exit as product, while the other five will continue through the cycle to be used in the regeneration of RuBP. This is a process that, as you can see, is powered by the expenditure of more sun-generated ATP. **Figure 8.8** summarizes the process of photosynthesis.

8.6 Photorespiration and the C_4 Pathway

You have now gone through the basic process of photosynthesis. It's necessary, however, to say something about what might be called a *glitch* in this process, and then note a mechanism that plants have evolved to deal with it.

The glitch is called photorespiration, and it concerns a deviation from the process you just went through. Recall that the Calvin cycle begins with the important enzyme rubisco binding with carbon dioxide and then incorporating it into a five-carbon sugar. As it turns out, however, rubisco frequently binds with *oxygen* instead of carbon dioxide. When this happens, less carbohydrate is produced, which means less plant growth.

The amazing thing is how often photorespiration takes place. In C_3 photosynthesis, rubisco may fix up to one molecule of O_2 for every three of CO_2 it incorporates. Worse, when this happens, some of the CO_2 that *has* been fixed by a plant is released by it. It is as if a carpenter building a house took boards that were stored inside and began throwing them out the window.

Photorespiration is especially likely to take place when temperatures rise, because heat prompts the stomata on leaves to close in order to preserve water. The effect of closed stomata, however, is not only that water is kept *in*, but that CO_2 is kept *out*. With a deficit of CO_2, rubisco tends to bind more frequently with oxygen, prompting photorespiration—and plants that simply do not grow as much. With all this

in mind, here is a definition of **photorespiration**: a process in which the enzyme rubisco undercuts carbon fixation in photosynthesis by binding with oxygen instead of with carbon dioxide.

Evolution produced an adaptation that allows some warm-climate plant species to lessen this problem. It is a mechanism that utilizes a special carbon-fixing "front-end" and then a carbon-dioxide shuttle into the Calvin cycle. The so-called C_4 plants that make use of this mechanism (**see Figure 8.9**) don't initially use rubisco to fix carbon dioxide. Rather, they employ a different enzyme that will not bind with oxygen. The immediate product of this reaction is a four-carbon molecule (hence the C_4 cycle's name). A derivative of that molecule moves to a special group of

Figure 8.8
Summary of Photosynthesis in the Chloroplasts of Plant Cells
In the light reactions, solar energy is converted to chemical energy in the thylakoids, and the chemical energy is stored temporarily in the form of ATP and NADPH. Water is required for this reaction, and oxygen is a by-product. The stored chemical energy is in turn used in the Calvin cycle, taking place in the stroma, in which a high-energy sugar is made from carbon dioxide and the sugar RuBP. The sugar can be used for food, or may become part of the plant's structure.

Figure 8.9
Warm-Weather Photosynthesis
Plants such as this sugarcane, shown here in Hawaii, utilize C_4 photosynthesis.

cells and releases the CO_2, which will be used in the Calvin cycle. These special cells are wrapped around leaf veins and are hence named the *bundle-sheath cells* (**see Figure 8.10**). What the C_4 system provides—even at times when little CO_2 may be coming in through the stomata—is a relatively high concentration of CO_2 where it's needed: in the cells where the Calvin cycle takes place. We can thus define **C_4 photosynthesis** as a form of photosynthesis in which carbon dioxide is first fixed to a four-carbon molecule and then transferred to special cells in which the Calvin cycle is undertaken, bundle sheath cells.

The C_4 Pathway Is Not Always Advantageous

The C_4 pathway is known to be employed in about 1,000 species of plants, most notably in some grasses, and in corn, sugarcane, and sorghum. But there are vastly more C_3 than C_4 plants. You might wonder why evolution hasn't, you might say, weeded out C_3 plants in favor of the C_4 variety, since the latter seem to be so much more efficient at photosynthesis. The answer is that C_4 fixation does not confer an across-the-board advantage. It has a cost, which is the expenditure of ATP in shuttling carbon dioxide to the bundle-sheath cells. What this means is that C_4 fixation is advantageous only where the weather is warm enough to bring about a significant increase in photorespiration. Where the weather is cooler, C_4 plants will be out-competed by C_3 species.

8.7 Another Photosynthetic Variation: CAM Plants

When plants live in climates that are not just warm but *dry*, a large part of their survival comes down to retaining water. Photosynthesis, however, works against water retention, because as you have seen, when CO_2 can pass in, water vapor can pass out.

The plants we call succulents—a group that includes most cacti—have a solution for this. It is to close the stomata during the day and open them at night. The plants then carry out C_4 metabolism at night, but only up to a point. They fix carbon dioxide into an initial four-carbon molecule and then stand pat. The CO_2 stays "banked" in them, awaiting the energy of the next day's sun, which will power the production of the ATP they need to carry out the Calvin cycle (**see Figure 8.11**). This is **CAM photosynthesis**, defined as a form of photosynthesis, undertaken by plants in hot, dry climates, in which carbon fixation takes place at night, and the Calvin cycle during the day. This process gets the job done for cactus, pineapple, orchid, and some mint family plants, among others. As you've no doubt guessed, CAM is an acronym; it stands for *crassulacean acid metabolism*. The succulent plant family *Crassulaceae* (which includes jade plants) was the first group of plants in which CAM metabolism was discovered. The three methods of photosynthesis—C_3, C_4, and CAM—are summarized in **Table 8.1**.

How Did We Learn?

It was not until after World War II that scientists pieced together the story of how plants join carbon dioxide to a sugar to create food. As you've seen, this happens through a set of steps that today are called the Calvin cycle. You can read about the man the cycle was named for, Melvin Calvin, and his process of discovery in "Plants Make Their Own Food, But How?" on page 164.

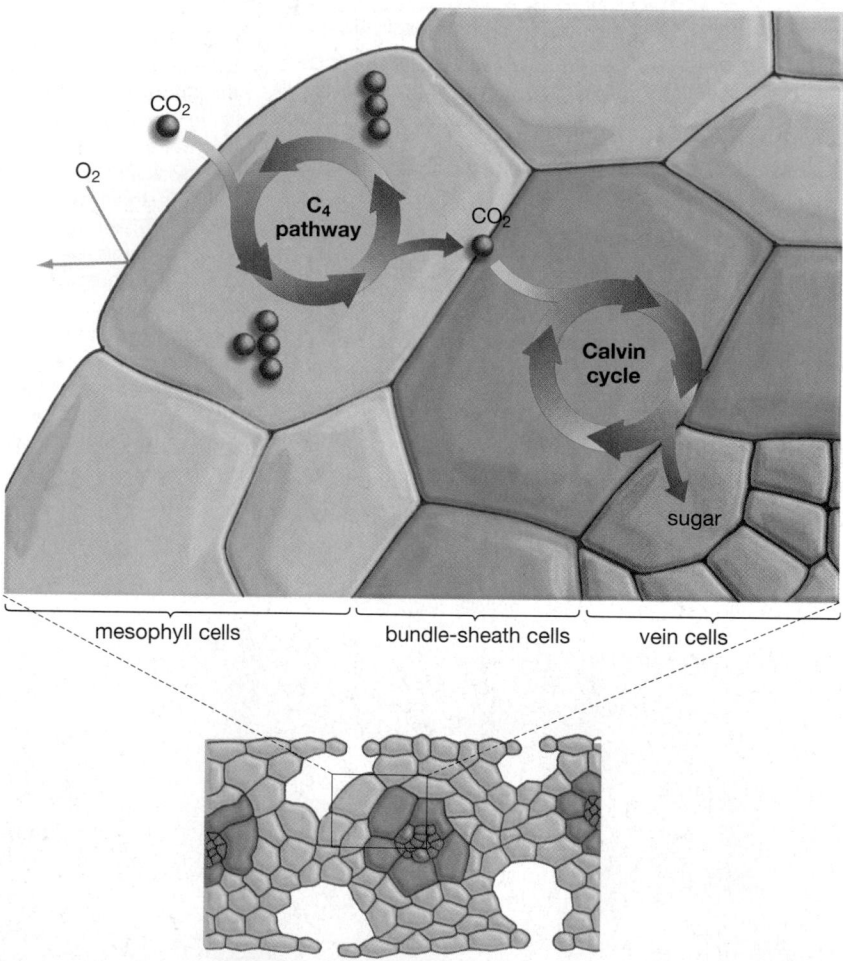

Figure 8.10
C_4 Photosynthesis
C_4 photosynthesis is an adaptation of some warm-climate plants to the problem of photorespiration. Photorespiration occurs when the C_3 enzyme rubisco binds to oxygen rather than carbon dioxide (thereby undercutting the production of sugar). C_4 plants contain a different enzyme in their mesophyll cells that binds to carbon dioxide, but not to oxygen. Then the carbon dioxide is escorted into special bundle-sheath cells, where rubisco can bind to it, thus initiating the Calvin cycle reviewed earlier, meaning the production of sugar can proceed.

Closing Thoughts on Photosynthesis and Energy

Readers who have stayed the course on this account of photosynthesis now know at least one thing very well about it: How complicated it is, with its many components and long metabolic pathways. It's also probably clear by this point why scientists continue to study photosynthesis in such detail. It is the foundation of plant growth, and upon plant growth hinges nothing less than the survival of all animals—including human beings. Without an understanding of this linkage, it's easy to see plants as a set of mute fixtures whose main contribution to human life is aesthetic. But with this knowledge, you can begin to see the central position that plants occupy in the interconnected web of life.

Over the last three chapters, you have learned about the endless back-and-forth of oxygen, carbon dioxide, and energy in the living world. *Cycle* has been a recurring word in this long discussion, because the only one-way trip you've encountered has been the relentless "spillage" of energy from the sun down into heat. Looked at in a cynical way, Earth and its inhabitants constitute a kind of leaky holding tank for energy that comes from the sun. Looked at another way, however, the living world has been able, through pho-

Figure 8.11
Dry-Weather Photosynthesis
Plants such as this saguaro cactus in Arizona utilize CAM photosynthesis, thereby preserving precious water.

tosynthesis, to take the sun's energy and build a remarkable edifice with it. Think of the forms and sheer mass of living material on Earth. One of the most amazing things about this structure is that we humans get to be both a part of it and witnesses to it.

Web Tutorial 8.4
Different Kinds of Photosynthesis

Table 8.1 Three Modes of Photosynthesis

	C$_3$	C$_4$	CAM
Used by:	Majority of plants	Corn, sugarcane (warm environments)	Cactus, pineapple, orchid (dry environments)
Benefits:	Efficient use of ATP	Less photorespiration	Less water loss
Problems:	Photorespiration	Uses up more ATP	Uses up more ATP; hard to "bank" enough CO$_2$
How it works:	mesophyll cell — CO$_2$ → Calvin cycle → sugar	mesophyll cell — CO$_2$ → carbon uptake → Calvin cycle (bundle-sheath cell) → sugar	mesophyll cell — CO$_2$ → carbon storage (night) → Calvin cycle → sugar (day)

How Did We Learn?
Plants Make Their Own Food, But How?

Science constantly is confronted with what are known as "black box" problems. In these problems, researchers know what goes into a process and they know what comes out of it, but what happens *in between* is a mystery. At the conclusion of World War II, plant science had a doozy of a black-box problem. It was clear that plants were starting with carbon dioxide from the air and ending with high-energy carbohydrates, but no one knew what came in between. What were the *intermediate* substances that carbon dioxide was being made part of on the route to food? Getting inside this black box turned out to require a three-part combination: insightful researchers, new scientific techniques, and old-fashioned hard work.

One of the peacetime benefits of World War II's atomic weapons research was that scientists could produce quantities of substances known as *radioactive isotopes*. As you saw in Chapter 2, isotopes result from variations in the number of neutrons an element has in its nucleus. Radioactivity, meanwhile, is the release of radiant energy from atoms undergoing rapid decay. The element carbon is everywhere in nature, and as it turns out, one of its isotopes, carbon-14, is radioactive. Carbon-14 occurs naturally, but the ability to *manufacture* this substance opened a host of possibilities for research in the mid-1940s.

Stepping up to the plate in 1946 to take advantage of these possibilities was a University of California, Berkeley, chemist named Melvin Calvin. Then just 35 years old, Calvin was encouraged by the physicist Ernest Lawrence of Berkeley to apply radiocarbon techniques to organic chemistry research. With carbon-14, Calvin realized, he could *tag* carbon dioxide to find out what it becomes part of during photosynthesis, much as a zoologist might tag a bear with a signaling device to find out where it goes during winter. The radiation that carbon-14 emits might be thought of as a signal whose constant message is: "Here I am."

The steps that Calvin and his colleagues followed were simple in conception but very difficult in execution. They first took some photosynthetic algae and put them in a flask that had light shining on it. Like any photosynthetic organism, these algae would, of course, be taking in carbon dioxide to carry out their work. In this case, however, the carbon dioxide in question contained carbon-14. The trick was to allow the algae to perform a little photosynthesis using this $^{14}CO_2$. Then the algae were plunged into boiling alcohol, which killed them. By the time the plunge was taken, the carbon dioxide would have made it to *some point* in its transformation to carbohydrate; it would

have been incorporated into one molecule in the series of intermediate molecules involved. Stopping photosynthesis at differing points—two seconds after it started, five seconds, and so on—meant stopping the progress of carbon dioxide as it marched through its changes.

All of this would have been for naught, however, without a way to figure out where the carbon was when the process was stopped. This is where the carbon-14 could do its job, but it needed to be joined to another technique that was also newly developed at that time: two-dimensional paper chromatography. If you look at **Figure 1a**, you can see how this technique works. Put a spot of ink on some filter paper and then stick one end of the paper in a solvent—water, for example. The water moves through the paper, carrying different components of the ink along with it at different rates. You can tell something about what the ink is made of by measuring how far its components move through the paper. You can tell still more by doing this in two dimensions: Let the solvent move through the spot one way, then set the paper down at a right angle in a *second* solvent and let it move through in another direction (**Figure 1b**). This is what Calvin and his colleagues did, using as their "ink" the algae that had been killed following photosynthesis.

The paper chromatography left the algae cells drawn out in two directions by the solvents. But where was the original carbon in this material? Because it was radioactively *tagged* carbon, it was sending out its signal saying, "I'm here now." But only a special "receiver" could pick up this signal: photographic film (**Figure 1c**). Setting X-ray film tightly on top of the chromatography paper for long periods—usually about two weeks—caused the radiation from the carbon-14 to expose the film. Spots would show up saying, in effect, "carbon-14 is now here, in this concentration."

There is a wide gap, however, between seeing a black blotch on a piece of film and *identifying* that blotch as a specific substance. The difficulty the researchers encountered can be measured in time—10 years in this case. That's how long it took these workers to complete their investigation. During that time, Calvin and his principal colleagues—postdoctoral researcher Andrew Benson and graduate student James Bassham—worked extraordinarily long hours in deciphering what the downstream products of photosynthesis were and the order in which they were produced.

This long operation was a great success, however. Calvin's team dismantled the black box of carbon fixation, and the information they uncovered can be *used* to aid in such things as increased food production. The set of steps these workers elucidated has variously been referred to as the C₃ cycle, Calvin-Benson cycle, or the Calvin cycle. In 1961, Melvin Calvin received the ultimate in congratulations for a piece of scientific work when he was awarded the Nobel Prize in chemistry for shining a light on photosynthesis.

Figure 1

(a) Paper chromatography in first dimension

Material of interest (algae for Calvin) is put on paper in solution form.

Solvent A moves through paper, separating out components of original material. (Components, shown here as green dots, would probably not be visible in experiments.)

solvent A

(b) Paper chromatography in second dimension

Paper is rotated 90 degrees and put in second solvent.

Component compounds are separated in second dimension. Some compounds contain radioactively labeled carbon.

solvent B

(c) Autoradiography

chromatography

radioactively labeled compounds

film

radioactivity "spots" the film

autoradiograph (developed film)

Chapter Review

Summary

8.1 Photosynthesis and Energy

- Photosynthesis has made possible life as we know it on Earth, because the organic material produced in photosynthesis (a sugar) is the source of food for most of Earth's living things. Photosynthesis also is responsible for the atmospheric oxygen used by many living things in cellular respiration.

8.2 The Components of Photosynthesis

- In plants and algae, photosynthesis takes place in the organelles called chloroplasts, which can exist in great abundance in the mesophyll cells of leaves. The energy for photosynthesis comes mostly from various blue and red wavelengths of visible sunlight that are absorbed by pigments in the chloroplasts. Plant leaves contain microscopic pores called stomata that can open and close, letting carbon dioxide in and water vapor out.
  Web Tutorial 8.1: Properties of Light

- There are two primary stages to photosynthesis. In the first stage, called the light reactions, electrons derived from water are energetically boosted by the power of sunlight. These electrons physically move in this process; they are passed along through a series of electron carriers, ending up as part of the electron carrier NADPH, which carries them to the second stage of photosynthesis. In this second stage, the Calvin cycle, the electrons are brought together with carbon dioxide and a sugar to produce a high-energy sugar, in a process powered by ATP that is produced in the light reactions.
  Web Tutorial 8.2: Photosynthesis

8.3 Stage 1: The Steps of the Light Reactions

- In its first stage, photosynthesis works through a pair of molecular complexes, photosystems II and I. These photosystems are composed partly of antennae molecules—chlorophyll and some accessory molecules—that absorb and transmit solar energy. Other photosystem components include reaction center molecules, which accept both this energy and electrons derived from water; and primary electron acceptors (a part of the reaction centers), to which the electrons move after being energetically boosted.

8.4 What Makes the Light Reactions So Important?

- Two actions of great consequence take place in the light reactions. The first is that water is split, yielding both the electrons that move through the light reactions and the oxygen that organisms such as ourselves breathe in. The second is that the electrons that are derived from the water—and then given an energy boost by the sun's rays—are transferred to a different molecule: the initial electron acceptor. The energetic fall of electrons through the electron transport chain between photosystems II and I also yields energy that produces ATP, which is used to power the second stage of photosynthesis.

8.5 Stage 2: The Calvin Cycle

- In the second stage of photosynthesis, carbon dioxide from the atmosphere is brought together with a sugar, RuBP, by the enzyme rubisco. The resulting compound is energized with the addition of phosphate groups and electrons supplied by the first stage of photosynthesis. The result is the high-energy sugar G3P, which is the product of photosynthesis. All these steps are carried out within a process known as the Calvin or C_3 cycle.
  Web Tutorial 8.3: The Calvin Experiments

- G3P can be used for energy or for plant growth. Everything in the plant ultimately is derived from this sugar, in association with minerals that the plant absorbs through its roots.

8.6 Photorespiration and the C_4 Pathway

- In C_3 plants, the enzyme rubisco frequently binds with oxygen, rather than carbon dioxide. When such photorespiration takes place, no new carbon dioxide is fixed and CO_2 that has been fixed in a plant is lost, thus undercutting productivity in photosynthesis. This problem increases as the temperature rises, because as plants close their stomata to keep in moisture, they also keep out CO_2, thus increasing the likelihood that rubisco will bind with oxygen.

- Some warm-climate plants have evolved a means of dealing with photorespiration. Called C_4 photosynthesis, it employs an enzyme that binds with carbon dioxide but not with oxygen. The carbon dioxide is then shuttled to special bundle-sheath cells in the plant and released, after which it moves into the Calvin cycle. With high levels of CO_2 in the bundle-sheath cells, rubisco binds with CO_2 (and not oxygen), thus greatly reducing photorespiration.

8.7 Another Photosynthetic Variation: CAM Plants

- Dry-weather plants such as cacti employ another form of photosynthesis, CAM photosynthesis. In it, the plant's stomata open only at night, letting in and fixing carbon dioxide that is "banked" until sunrise, when the sun's rays will supply the energy needed to power the Calvin cycle.
  Web Tutorial 8.4: Different Kinds of Photosynthesis

Key Terms

C_4 photosynthesis 161	photosystem 156
Calvin cycle 159	reaction center 156
CAM photosynthesis 162	rubisco 160
chlorophyll *a* 156	stomata 155
chloroplast 155	stroma 156
fixation 160	thylakoid 156
photorespiration 161	thylakoid compartment 156
photosynthesis 154	

Understanding the Basics

Multiple-Choice Questions (answers in the back of the book)

1. In photosynthesis, energy from the sun is being _____ while in the cellular respiration looked at in Chapter 7, energy is being _____.
   a. turned into light ... turned solely into heat
   b. entirely lost to heat ... stored as ADP
   c. stored in carbohydrates ... released from storage in food
   d. absorbed as green light ... stored in carbohydrates
   e. spent as carbohydrates ... stored as carbohydrates

2. Stomata are the _____ on leaves that serve not only to let water vapor out, but to let _____ in.
   a. proteins ... oxygen
   b. cilia ... oxygen
   c. outer cell layers ... sunlight
   d. stems ... carbon dioxide
   e. pores ... carbon dioxide

3. Two important products of the light reactions in photosynthesis are:
   a. electrons, oxygen
   b. electrons, carbon dioxide
   c. chloroplasts, carbon dioxide
   d. rubisco, oxygen
   e. rubisco, carbon dioxide

4. Suppose you become a biologist. On a bright summer day, while studying the rate of photosynthesis in a desert succulent, you discover that its stomata are closed—yet it is producing ATP. This plant must be carrying out
   a. photorespiration
   b. the C_3 cycle
   c. the C_4 pathway
   d. CAM metabolism
   e. CO_2 uptake

5. Most plant photosynthesis occurs in the _____ of leaves.
   a. upper epidermal cells
   b. lower epidermal cells
   c. petioles
   d. stomata
   e. mesophyll cells

6. The essential product of photosynthesis is:
   a. ATP
   b. the enzyme rubisco
   c. the sugar G3P
   d. plant structural proteins
   e. carbon dioxide

7. The electrons boosted to a higher energy level in photosystem II are derived from _____, whose splitting results in the release of the by-product _____.
   a. carbon dioxide, ATP
   b. water, oxygen
   c. NADPH, carbon dioxide
   d. ATP, carbon dioxide
   e. rubisco, oxygen

8. A plant in the sunlight may be performing
   a. photosynthesis
   b. cellular respiration
   c. photorespiration
   d. all of the above
   e. both a and c

9. Is it reasonable to suppose that cells in the petals of a red rose could carry out photosynthesis?
   a. No, the rose petals will absorb green light, rather than scattering it
   b. Yes, the rose petals could absorb blue light, which strongly drives photosynthesis
   c. Yes, by transference of resources from leaves
   d. No, the rose petals would scatter red light, which strongly drives photosynthesis
   e. No, only the cells in leaves photosynthesize

Brief Review

1. Since plants capture energy through photosynthesis, do they need to carry out cellular respiration as well? Why or why not?

2. Sunlight reaching Earth is composed of a spectrum of energetic rays. Describe the rays that make up this spectrum. Which portion of the spectrum drives photosynthesis?

3. What are the component parts of a photosystem?

4. Which would you expect to grow more rapidly—a C_3 plant, a C_4 plant, or a CAM plant? Be careful; there may be more than one correct answer to this question. Explain your answer.

5. The text notes that the fall of electrons between photosystems II and I provides energy used to produce ATP. What is this ATP used for?

Applying Your Knowledge

1. Rubisco has been called the most important protein on Earth. Why should it be regarded as so important?

2. One of the most dramatic environmental changes today is the increase in carbon-dioxide levels in the atmosphere. We usually hear about it in connection with global warming, but that's not the only issue. What effect would increased carbon dioxide have on plants? If more trees are planted, would this stand to have any effect on atmospheric CO_2 levels?

MediaLab

Capturing Sunlight to Make Food: Photosynthesis

You've probably heard songs in which the singers attribute their life, the act of eating and breathing, to their romantic interest. Love is a powerful emotion, but you'd think at least one songwriter would give homage to the event that really does make our lives possible—the process of photosynthesis. Perhaps it

wouldn't sell. The *Web Tutorial* reviews photosynthesis, so that in the following *Web Investigations* you are prepared to gather information on topics closely associated with it. In the *Communicate Your Results* section, you can interpret for yourself how important photosynthesis is in our lives.

The online version of this *MediaLab* can be found in Chapter 8 on your Companion Website (www.prenhall.com/krogh3).

WEB TUTORIAL

The overall process of photosynthesis is often summarized in the following reaction:

water + carbon dioxide + light energy →
glucose + oxygen

As with most biological processes, photosynthesis does not occur in one step, but in a series of reactions. In this *Web Tutorial*, you'll review the three phases of photosynthesis, focusing on reactants and products.

Activity

1. *First, you will learn about how light energy is absorbed by pigment molecules in plants.*

2. *Next, you will discover how light energy is converted to a stored chemical form for transport and later storage.*

3. *Finally, you will investigate the storage of energy in glucose, and test your understanding of photosynthesis.*

After this review, you'll be prepared to apply, extend, and experience some of the consequences of the photosynthetic process in the following *Web Investigations*.

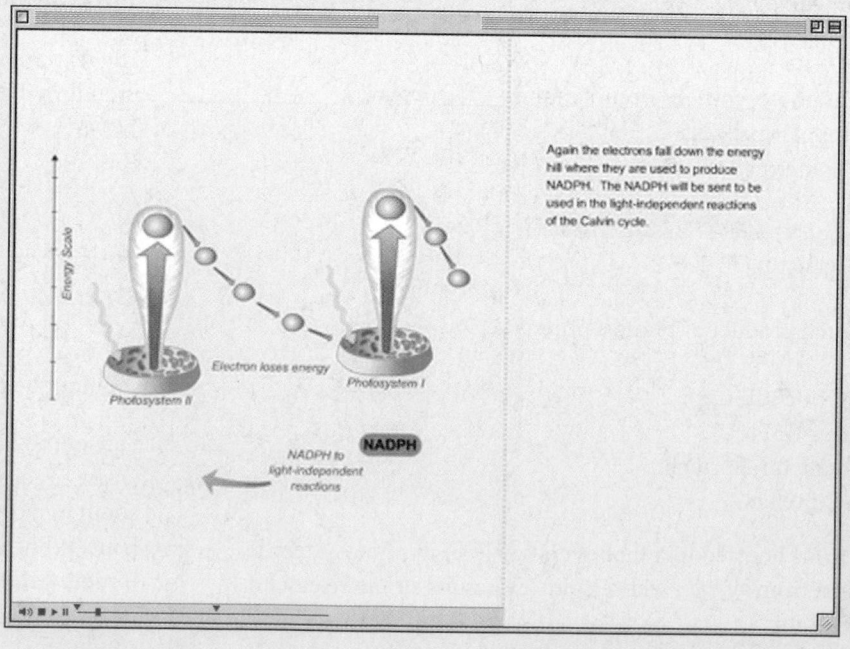

Investigation 1

Estimated time for completion = 10 minutes

If photosynthesis is to occur at all, the plant must be able to intercept light. The better a plant is in intercepting the light, the greater opportunities the plant has to produce food. Select the keyword **LEAVES** on the Website for this *MediaLab* to read an article describing how plants maximize the amount of light they can intercept. At the bottom of that page is a forward link to a discussion of leaf position in a canopy. Review this page. Why have so many plants developed broad, flattened leaves? What is heliotropism, and how does it make plants more efficient? What are sleep movements? Describe the model for leaf orientation in the upper, middle, and lower levels of a leaf canopy.

Investigation 2

Estimated time for completion = 10 minutes

Plants absorb light energy using special molecules called photosynthetic pigments (predominantly chlorophylls). These pigments absorb most of the visible light except for wavelengths in the green part of the spectrum. Consequently, plants appear green. But what happens in the fall when leaves change colors? Why are there so many different colors? And why are the colors more intense some years? Select the keyword **COLORS** on the Website for this *MediaLab* to access a site that will help you answer these questions.

Investigation 3

Estimated time for completion = 15 minutes

You've probably heard of global warming and the greenhouse effect, in which certain gases cause heat to be trapped in the Earth's atmosphere in the same way heat is trapped in a greenhouse. How hot will it be in your community in 100 years? Select the keyword **HOTSPOT** on the Website for this *MediaLab* to view a map showing how much hotter it will be in 50 years by subtracting the annual mean temperatures during 1970–1990 from the predicted temperatures for 2040–2060. One of the major greenhouse gases is carbon dioxide, which has been added to the atmosphere by the burning of fossil fuels. Of course, plants in photosynthesis trap CO_2 out of the atmosphere. Could plants help with global warming? Select the keyword **CO_2** to view changing CO_2 levels over 25 years in Barrow, Alaska; Mauna Loa, Hawaii; Samoa, and the South Pole. What might account for the yearly fluctuations in CO_2 levels? Where fluctuations are the greatest, is there a seasonal difference in plant activity?

COMMUNICATE YOUR RESULTS

Exercise 1

Estimated time for completion = 30 minutes

Using the knowledge from the articles in *Web Investigation 1*, design a plant that can effectively intercept light while keeping the amount of plant tissues to a minimum. Here are some characteristics of this hypothetical plant to keep in mind: The plant grows in a seasonal environment, water conservation is important but not critical, and the plant typically has ten leaves located at five levels on the stem. Draw the leaves for this plant. Also draw a view of the plant from the side and a view of the plant from the top. Describe the decisions you made while creating this plant.

Exercise 2

Estimated time for completion = 15 minutes

If it's fall and the leaves are changing, make a collection of leaves from different species in your area. Otherwise, find pictures of fall leaves and clip or copy them to create a collection. Place these leaves on a poster or in a bound collection. Identify the species of plant as well as possible using available references. For each species, using the leaf's color as a guide, identify the dominant pigment present in the leaf. Is there a pattern of leaf color and plant type? Describe any patterns you observe.

Exercise 3

Estimated time for completion = 60 minutes

In *Web Investigation 3*, you saw an annual fluctuation in CO_2 levels. One possible explanation for the yearly cycle is that increased plant growth decreases atmospheric CO_2 levels during the growing season. How would you test this hypothesis? Prepare a short presentation or poster explaining the initial observation and hypothesis as well as your test, observations, and conclusions. Include your conclusions on how photosynthesis could be used to fight global warming, and how deforestation would contribute to the problem.

9 Genes, Mitosis, and Cytokinesis

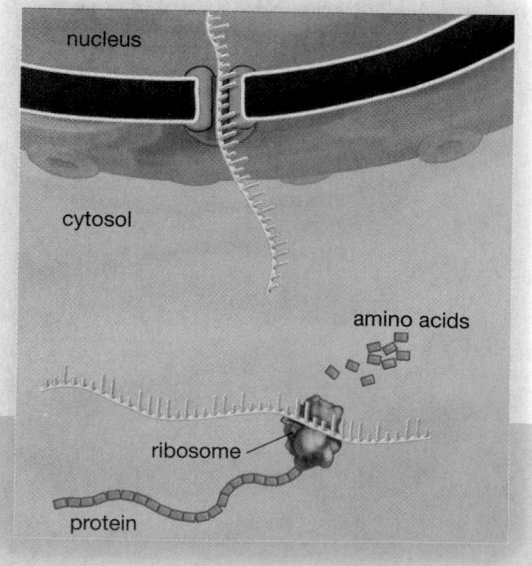

Protein synthesis in action.
(Section 9.1, page 173)

What does a cancer cell look like?
(Essay, page 185)

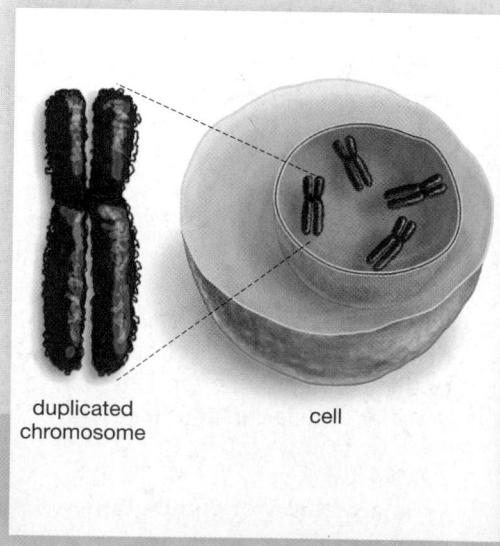

From DNA to the chromosome.
(Section 9.3, page 176)

> **Life depends on information that is stored in DNA. This information is duplicated and then apportioned every time a cell divides.**

Everyone knows how one generation of living things gives rise to another, at least in a general sense. But the details of how this works are not apparent just by looking at Earth's creatures. A brief sexual encounter takes place, and the next thing we know there are new kittens or chicks or babies. Only the encounter and the newborns are obvious; what comes in between is mysterious.

The problem, of course, is that most of the component parts of reproduction are hidden away and, in any event, so small that the process is completely invisible to the naked eye. Given this, it's no wonder that for centuries human beings wondered what it was that one generation passed on so that the next generation could be formed.

A similar kind of puzzlement existed over a related question: What is the mechanism that controls the development of a living thing as it goes from being a microscopic cell to being a human baby in full cry? For that matter, how is it that the adult body is able to build muscle or to repair a minor wound? What, in short, is the mechanism that controls day-to-day physical functioning?

9.1 An Introduction to Genetics

It took roughly a century of hard-won scientific advances for these questions to be answered.

In the end, it turned out that a single substance is central to the reproduction of living things, their development from single cells, and their day-to-day functioning. This substance is deoxyribonucleic acid, a long, vanishingly thin molecule known everywhere today by its acronym, DNA.

DNA contains what is known as an organism's **genome**: the complete collection of that organism's genetic information. This information exists in units called genes that lie along DNA's famous double helix.

How is it that this one molecule can undertake all the tasks just described? To the question about what it is that humans *pass on* in reproduction, the answer is: half of a father's genome and half of a mother's

Going through the cell cycle.
(Section 9.3, page 179)

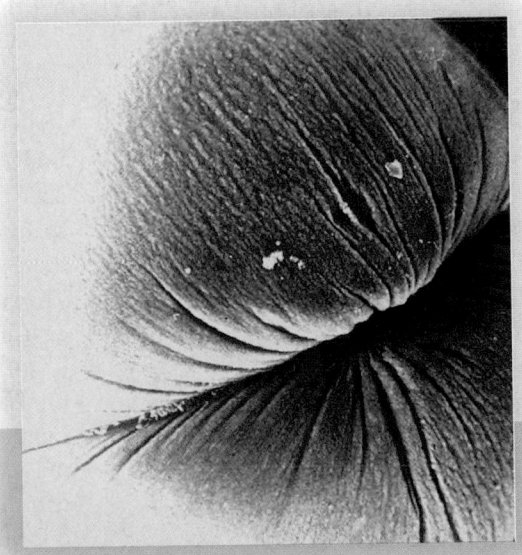

One cell becomes two.
(Section 9.4, page 182)

Plant cell division.
(Section 9.5, page 182)

Figure 9.1
Passing on Genetic Information
Half of each person's genome
comes from the father, and half
from the mother.

genome, both these halves coming together in a fertilized egg to produce a whole, new genome (**see
Figure 9.1**). To the other questions about what controls the development and everyday functioning of
living things, the answer is: the instructions provided
by the genes in the genome.

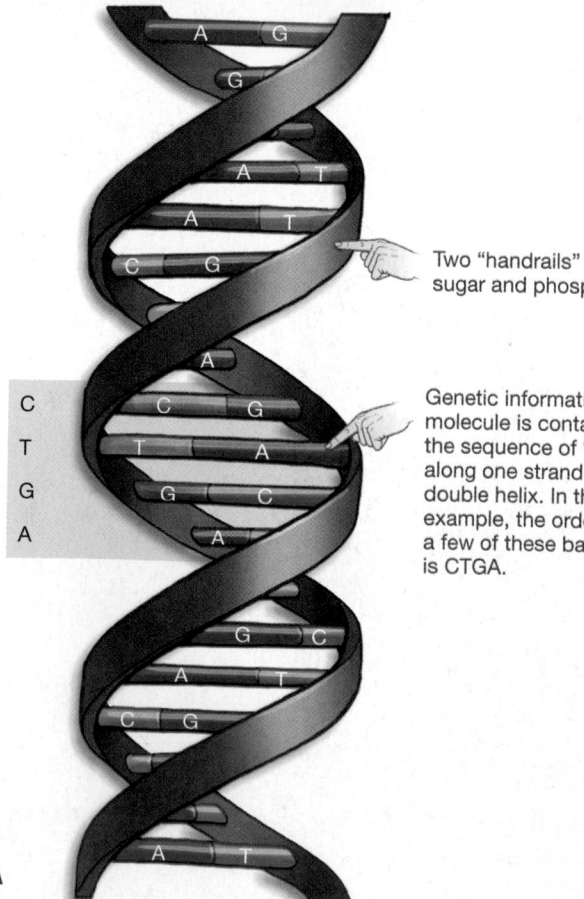

Figure 9.2
**Information-Bearing DNA
Molecule**

Two "handrails" made of
sugar and phosphate.

Genetic information in the
molecule is contained in
the sequence of "bases"
along one strand of the
double helix. In this
example, the order of
a few of these bases
is CTGA.

DNA Contains Instructions for Protein Production

To grasp how genes can control the development and
functioning of living things, note that there are logically two parts to such control. If genes *contain* instructions, something needs to carry them out. As it
turns out, the workers here are proteins; in tremendous diversity and number, they are the working
products of the information contained in genes.

Readers who went through Chapter 3 (on biological molecules) and Chapter 6 (on energy) should
have a good grasp already of what proteins are capable of. As we have seen, there are proteins that form
cartilage and hair; there are communication proteins
that help form the receptors on cells; there are hormonal proteins and transport proteins. Then there
are **enzymes**, the chemically active proteins that speed
up—or in practical terms, *enable*—chemical reactions in living things. Without these protein molecules, almost nothing could get done in the body;
with them, a dazzling set of chemical reactions takes
place every second in every living thing.

What most genes do, then, is contain the information for the production of proteins. In Chapter 14
you'll get the details of how protein production
comes about, but for now let's just look at the essentials of the story. Imagine you are a telegraph operator in the Old West, and your "key" starts tapping
frantically. You leap forward in your chair, listening
for the sound of short and long bursts on the key, and
you begin writing down the letters these sounds
stand for. Here's the message you get:

.—.. — — —.—. —.—   — ....— ..—.

which means:

L o c k   t h e   s a f e

You walk over and do just that. There is thus a
code here, Morse code, that has resulted in some action. In DNA there is likewise a code. But instead of a
code specified in short or long sounds, it is a code
specified in chemical substances. There are four of
these substances, and they lie along the double helix.
They are the "bases" adenine, thymine, guanine, and
cytosine, abbreviated A, T, G, C.

A particular sequence of these bases—usually
thousands of letters long—contains information that
can be acted upon, just as the Morse code did. Only
the action here is the production of a particular protein. One series of A's, T's, C's, and G's contains the
information for the production of one protein, but a
different sequence of A's, T's, G's, and C's specifies a
different protein. These separate sequences of bases
are separate *genes*.

You saw in Chapter 3 that proteins are composed of building blocks called amino acids. The base sequence that makes up a gene, then, is like a message that says, "Give me this amino acid, now this one, then this one, ..." and so on for hundreds of amino acids until a protein is created that folds up and gets busy on some task. This task can be one small part of *forming* a human being—as in embryonic development—or of *maintaining* one, as in an adult. One generation gives rise to another by passing on this entire complement of information.

The Architecture of DNA

It is the architecture of the DNA molecule that makes this protein production process possible. Look at the general scheme of it pictured in **Figure 9.2**. As you can see, DNA looks something like an open, spiral staircase, the handrails of which are a repeating series of sugar (deoxyribose) and phosphate molecules. Meanwhile, the messages you've just been reading about are contained in the steps of the staircase, in the order in which the bases A, T, C, and G are placed along the helix. As you can see, these bases extend inward from both of the DNA rails. The order in which the bases occur *along the rails* is extremely varied. This order is what "encodes" the information for the production of proteins.

The Path of Protein Synthesis

Look now at **Figure 9.3** and see the path that is followed in protein synthesis. The DNA you have been reading about is contained in the nucleus of the cell. The first step is that a stretch of it unwinds there, and its message—the order of a string of bases—is copied onto a molecule called messenger RNA (mRNA). This length of mRNA, which could be thought of as an information tape being dubbed off a "master" DNA tape, then exits from the cell nucleus. Its destination is a molecular workbench in the cell's cytoplasm, a structure called a ribosome. It is here that both message (the mRNA tape) and raw materials (amino acids) come together to make the product (a protein). The mRNA tape is "read" within the ribosome, and as this happens a growing chain of amino acids is linked together in the ribosome in the order called for by the mRNA. When the chain is finished and folded up, a protein has come into existence.

Genetics as Information Management

The story you have been reading about is that of **genetics**, meaning the study of heredity. In reflecting on this story, the first thing to note is that it concerns the storage, duplication, and transfer of *information*. True, it is information encoded in chemical form, but that shouldn't bother us. Information comes in lots of forms; there are the familiar words on a page, but there are also bar graphs, smoke signals, or a baby's smile.

To grasp the fact of genetics as molecular information, think back to Chapter 6, where you looked at a particular protein, an enzyme called lactase that helps break up milk sugar (lactose) into its components of glucose and galactose. In line with what you've seen so far, there is a gene that prompts the production of lactase. This gene's message is copied onto mRNA, which then migrates to a ribosome in the cytoplasm. Lactase is put together there, amino acid by amino acid, and once synthesized, it folds up and gets busy clipping lactose molecules.

Now, consider the role of the gene in this process. It didn't do the lactose clipping; it didn't even migrate to the cytoplasm to be involved in the synthesis of lactase. In this case, its role was more like that of a ... cookbook recipe. It specified this amino acid, then that amino acid, and eventually lactase was produced.

Figure 9.3
The Path of Protein Synthesis

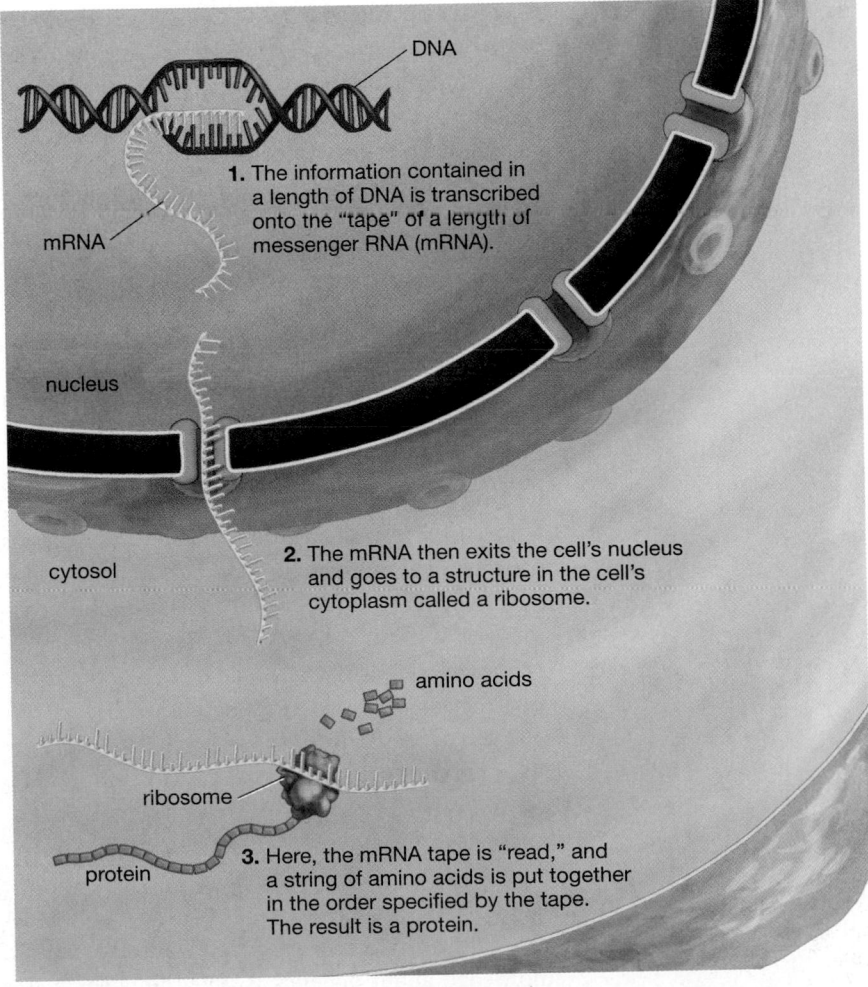

DNA

mRNA

1. The information contained in a length of DNA is transcribed onto the "tape" of a length of messenger RNA (mRNA).

nucleus

cytosol

2. The mRNA then exits the cell's nucleus and goes to a structure in the cell's cytoplasm called a ribosome.

amino acids

ribosome

protein

3. Here, the mRNA tape is "read," and a string of amino acids is put together in the order specified by the tape. The result is a protein.

From One Gene to a Collection

Now, in considering not just one gene, but rather the entire *collection* of genes in a living thing—its genome, in other words—it is easy to see that we are dealing with a vast *library* of information. The size of such a collection can vary, but to give you some idea, the human genome is estimated to include about 30,000 genes. We generally think that information comes to us after birth and from outside the body, but in fact we are born with a volume of information that has been amassed and edited over 3.5 billion years of evolution.

The amazing thing about such collections is that there is not just one copy of them in living things; there may be trillions. Most cells within an organism contain a complete copy of that organism's genome. A given type of cell puts to use (or "expresses") only some parts of this genome, while another type of cell utilizes other parts; but this is merely a way of saying that different genes are active in different cells. This is what distinguishes a liver cell, say, from a bone cell. These cells do different things and, accordingly, need to synthesize different proteins. But *both* kinds of cells have within them the whole genomic library; they merely put different parts of it to use.

Cells duplicate, of course. One cell divides to become two, the two divide to become four, and so on. Given this, if each cell in the body is to have its own copy of the genome, then each time a cell duplicates, the genome that lies within that cell must duplicate as well, prior to the actual cell division. This is just what happens, in a process we'll be reviewing shortly. First, however, let's take a step back and see how genetics as a whole is approached in this book.

The Path of Study in Genetics

From what you've seen so far, it's probably apparent that genetics is very important to biology. It lies at the heart of reproduction, for example, and reproduction is one of the distinguishing features of life. It is also the way life's unimaginable complexity is managed. The information contained in DNA allows living things to be complex, self-sustaining entities in a universe made up mostly of simple, inanimate objects. Given genetics' importance, you'll be looking at it from several angles in this book. First, beginning in this chapter, you will study DNA mostly as it comes packaged in units called chromosomes. Then you will learn how genetics functions in whole organisms, namely Gregor Mendel's famous pea plants. Only later will you return to DNA proper—to its replication and its protein-coding function. Finally, you will see how basic knowledge about genetics is being applied in the brave new world of genetic engineering. Let's begin our tour of these component parts of genetics by seeing how life goes from one cell to many.

9.2   An Introduction to Cell Division

How does a baby grow, or a plant develop, or a wound heal? Always through cell division. As noted in Chapter 4, with the possible exception of viruses, life exists only inside cells. Further, we know that cells come only from other cells. And the *way* cells come from cells is by dividing. To understand the continuity in life, then, we need to have some understanding of how cells divide.

The sheer numbers involved in this process are mind-boggling. In your body, as many as 25 million cell divisions are taking place each second. It is likely that every one of these divisions serves some purpose in maintaining your body; yet there are instances in which cells divide excessively. How does the disease we call cancer take hold? Always through the *unrestrained* division of cells. As you can see in "When Cell Division Runs Amok" on page 184, cancer is intimately related to basic cellular processes.

But why should cells divide at all? That is, why don't they just stay as they are? One answer is that cells die and need to be replaced. In addition, more cells may be needed at one point in life than another. To take one example, the material that makes up human bones is secreted by cells. A growing teenager needs more of this bone material than does, say, a young child. So, where is the teenager going to get this additional material? From additional cells—produced through cell division.

"Cell division" may be a somewhat misleading term if it is taken to mean a simple separation of cellular material, akin to a candy bar being split between two friends. Indeed, a splitting does occur in cell division, but certain parts of the cell must *duplicate* before this happens. Then the duplicated material is parceled out with fine precision, half of it going to one "daughter" cell and half to the other.

What's being duplicated and divided is DNA. Because a cell's full complement of DNA contains such critical information, it would not do for a cell to be left with 50 or 75 percent of this information; rather, it needs the whole thing—no more and no less.

With this in mind, here is the big picture on cell division. First, there is a duplication of DNA; then there is the movement of two precisely matched quantities of it to opposite sides of the "parent" cell; finally there is the splitting of the parent cell into two daughter cells. The duplication of DNA is known as *replication*, the apportioning of it into two identical quantities is known as *mitosis*, and the splitting of the

cell ——
nucleus ——

1. Replication
DNA is duplicated.

2. Mitosis
The two quantities of DNA
are moved to opposite sides
of the parent cell.

3. Cytokinesis
The parent cell splits
into two daughter cells.

Figure 9.4
Overview of Cell Division

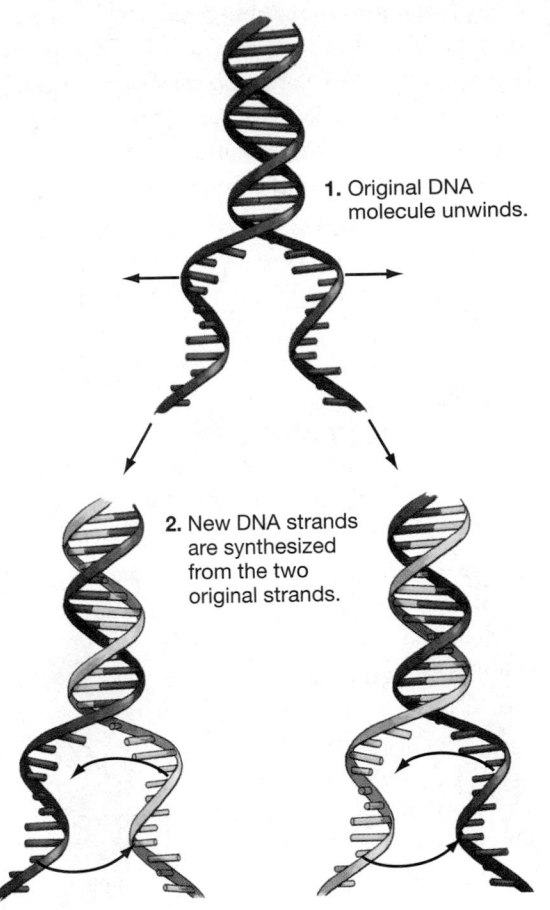

1. Original DNA
molecule unwinds.

2. New DNA strands
are synthesized
from the two
original strands.

Figure 9.5
DNA Replication

(1) A DNA molecule unwinds.

(2) Each of the single strands of
the original molecule (in red)
serves as a template or pattern for
the creation of a second DNA
strand (in pink). Bases on the red
strand pair, one base at a time,
with free-floating bases until an
entire second strand is created.
With this, the quantity of DNA has
effectively doubled.

cellular material is known as *cytokinesis* (**see Figure
9.4**). The goal for the remainder of this chapter is to
learn a little bit about replication and a good deal
more about mitosis and cytokinesis.

The Replication of DNA

So how does the first part of cell division work—the
DNA replication? If you look at **Figure 9.5**, you can
see a simplified representation of the DNA molecule shown in Figure 9.2. Notice that the strands of
the double helix have started to unwind, which is an
initial step in DNA replication (Figure 9.5, step 1).
Each of the two resulting single strands then serves
as a template or pattern upon which a new strand is
created (Figure 9.5, step 2). Earlier, DNA structure
was compared to a spiral staircase. Now think of
that staircase as splitting right down the middle of
its steps (where the A and T or the G and C bases
meet). Then a new *half*-staircase is created that
bonds with one of the old DNA strands; a second
half-staircase is likewise created that bonds with the
second original strand. (These new strands are the

pink ones in Figure 9.5, step 2.) How does this happen? Free-floating DNA bases will bond, one base at
a time, with bases on the original strand. This
process continues down the line until two strands
have been created, each composed of one "old" half-
strand and one "new" half-strand. This replication
process, which doubles the cell's DNA content, takes
place in advance of the cell dividing.

In Chapter 13, you will metaphorically walk
along the rungs of the double helix to grasp the details of this doubling of DNA strands. Right now,
however, you'll be considering DNA on a larger scale,
as it comes *packaged*.

9.3   DNA Is Packaged in Chromosomes

You have thus far conceptualized each cell's DNA as
spiraling out in *one* long double helix; but it does not,
in fact, take that form. Rather, the DNA in each cell
comes divided up and packaged into individual units
of DNA called **chromosomes** (from the Greek for "colored bodies," a name stemming from the dye these
structures absorbed when they were first seen under a
microscope). Different organisms have different
numbers of chromosomes; human cells have 46, for
example, while onion cells have 16. The chromosomes
of eukaryotic organisms, such as ourselves, amount to

Web Tutorial 9.1
The Cell Cycle

DNA "packages" in several senses. They consist not only of DNA itself, but of a protein around which DNA is wrapped. The result is **chromatin**: a molecular complex, composed of DNA and associated proteins, that makes up the chromosomes of eukaryotic organisms. Thus, a number of chromosomes, composed of chromatin, exist in a cell's nucleus, detached but in close physical proximity to one another, and the *collection* of chromosomes makes up nearly the entire complement of a cell's DNA.

If you look at **Figure 9.6a**, you can see how to think about the double helix being packaged into

(a) DNA is packaged in units called chromosomes

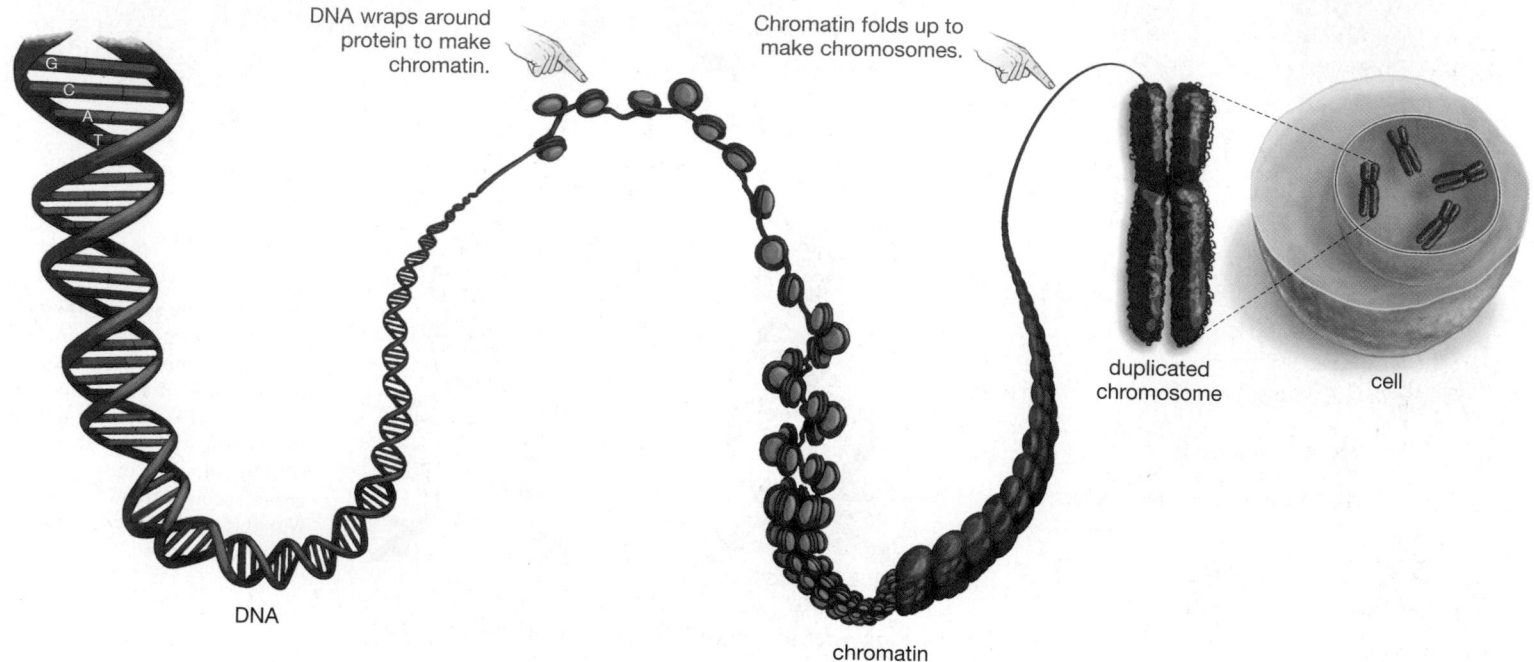

DNA wraps around protein to make chromatin.

Chromatin folds up to make chromosomes.

DNA

chromatin

duplicated chromosome

cell

(b) DNA replication at two levels

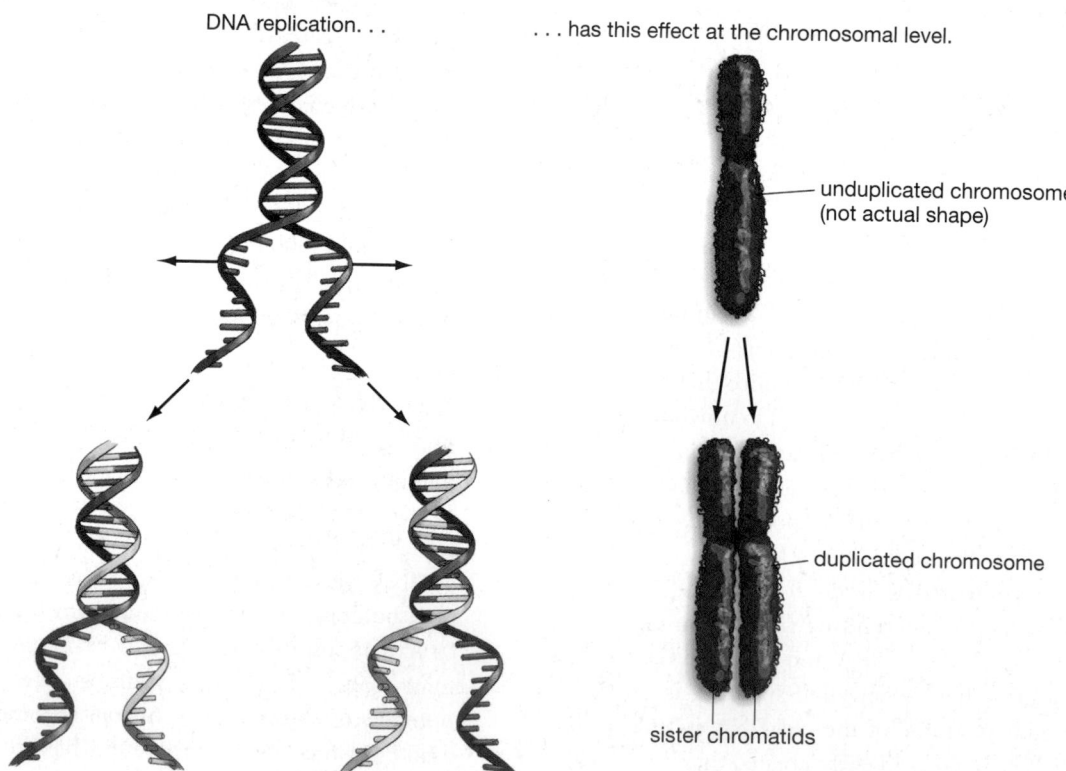

DNA replication. . .

. . . has this effect at the chromosomal level.

unduplicated chromosome (not actual shape)

duplicated chromosome

sister chromatids

**Figure 9.6
Chromosomes and DNA Replication**

(a) The DNA molecule is bound up with proteins, with the resulting combination known as chromatin. This chromatin then makes up structures called chromosomes.

(b) When DNA replicates, the result is two copies of the original DNA molecule. At the chromosomal level, the result of this replication is a single chromosome in duplicated state. The chromosome is composed of two sister chromatids—the two copies of the original DNA molecule. An unduplicated chromosome doesn't actually have the well-defined shape of the chromosome in the figure. It's shown this way merely for purposes of comparison with the duplicated chromosome.

chromosomes. **Figure 9.6b** shows you how to relate the "staircase-splitting" DNA replication just described to what this means at the chromosomal level. When we say that DNA is replicating, this is another way of saying that the chromosomes that DNA helps make up are *duplicating*. Once that has happened, the result is chromosomes in "duplicated state," which means individual chromosomes, each of which is made up of two sister chromatids. Each chromatid is one of the newly replicated DNA double helices, plus its associated proteins, as you can see in Figure 9.6b. More formally, a **chromatid** is one of the two identical strands of chromatin that make up a chromosome in its duplicated state. (It probably goes without saying that despite the name, sister chromatids are neither siblings nor females.)

Matched Pairs of Chromosomes

Chromosomes are detached from one another, but that does not mean they are completely different from one another. In eukaryotes such as ourselves, in fact, chromosomes tend to come in *pairs* that are close, but not exact matches. The 46 chromosomes we have come to us as 23 chromosomes from *each parent*. Critically, with one exception that you'll soon get to, these are 23 matched pairs of chromosomes, each chromosome from the mother matching with one from the father.

Defining a "Matched Pair"

What is a "matched pair" of chromosomes? We have a chromosome 1 that we inherit from our mother, and it contains a set of genes very similar to those that lie on the chromosome 1 we inherit from our father. The same is true for the maternal and paternal copies of chromosome 2, chromosome 3, and so on. Each of us, then, has 23 pairs of **homologous chromosomes**, "homologous" here meaning the same in size and function.

However, homologous chromosomes are not *exactly* alike. Any two of them will contain genes for the same kinds of protein products. If a given paternal chromosome has a gene that codes for hair color, it is a safe bet that the matching *maternal* chromosome will have a gene that codes for hair color. But there can be variations on these genes. A gene on the paternal chromosome may help code for *red* hair, while the gene on the matching maternal chromosome may help code for blonde hair. Nevertheless, both chromosomes have genes that code for hair color, as well as for thousands of other traits, and as such, are said to be homologous.

X and Y Chromosomes

The one exception to the matched-pairs rule in human chromosomes is the so-called sex chromosomes of males. Human females have the 23 pairs of homologous chromosomes mentioned before; 22 of these are *autosomes*, or nonsex chromosomes, and one is a homologous pair of *X* chromosomes that, when present, means a growing embryo will be a female. Males, on the other hand, have the 22 pairs of homologous autosomes and one X chromosome; but then they also have one *Y* chromosome that, when present, means a growing embryo will be a male.

This whole scheme is laid out for you in **Figure 9.7**. There you can see a **karyotype**, or pictorial arrangement of a full set of human chromosomes. There are 46 chromosomes in all, 22 of them matched pairs. In this case, one pair, at lower right, has one X chromosome and one Y chromosome, meaning this is a male.

The chromosomes in Figure 9.7 are in the duplicated state noted earlier, each of them being composed of two sister chromatids. For the sake of clarity, it would be nice to see a picture of some *un*duplicated chromosomes, but we have no pictures that are the counterpart to Figure 9.7. This is

The two chromosomes above each number are a homologous pair (they are the same in size and function).

A human male has one pair of non-homologous chromosomes, X and Y (females have XX).

Figure 9.7
A Karyotype Displays a Full Set of Chromosomes
One member of each chromosome pair comes from the individual's father and the other member from the mother. Each paired set of chromosomes is said to be "homologous," meaning the same in size and function. (The two chromosomes over the number 1 are a homologous pair, the two over number 2, and so forth.) Homologous chromosomes are not exactly alike, however; the genes on them may differ somewhat, meaning the effects they produce will differ. Notice that this karyotype is from a human male; there are 22 pairs of homologous chromosomes and then one X and one Y chromosome (which are not homologous). A female would have two X chromosomes. All the chromosomes are in the duplicated state.

so because chromosomes take on an easily discernable shape only after they duplicate, prior to cell division. As cell division approaches, the DNA-protein complex changes its form; it tightens up, condensing mightily to produce well-defined chromosomes (**Figure 9.8b**). After cell division is complete, the cell's chromosomes return to their relatively formless state, shown in **Figure 9.8a**.

Why this change in form? This condensing before cell division has the same effect as you taking all your scattered belongings and packing them into boxes just before moving from one apartment to another. Remember that DNA is packing up to leave as well, in this case for life in a successor cell. Were it not to tighten into its duplicated chromosomal form, its elongated fibers would get tangled up in the move.

Chromosome Duplication as a Part of Cell Division

With the chromosomes duplicated, you are now ready to look at the process by which they will split up. Before following this path, though, recognize that this separation occurs within the larger process that we are following: the division of the cell as a whole. As you saw in Chapter 5, there are many more things inside a cell than its complement of chromosomes. There are mitochondria, lysosomes, ribosomes, and so forth, and the cytosol in which they are immersed. Together, these things make up the cell's cytoplasm—the material *outside* the nucleus, as opposed to chromosomes,

which lie *inside* the nucleus. With cell division, about half of the cytoplasmic material goes to one daughter cell and half to the other. It is helpful, then, to conceptualize cell division as having two separable components. **Mitosis** is the separation of a cell's duplicated chromosomes prior to cytokinesis. **Cytokinesis** is the physical separation of one cell into two daughter cells. These two processes are part of the big picture of cell division sketched earlier, which now can be stated in a slightly different way. First, chromosomes duplicate; then chromosomes separate and move to opposite sides of the parent cell (mitosis); then the parent cell splits into two daughter cells (cytokinesis).

The Cell Cycle

If you look at **Figure 9.9**, you can see how all these processes are linked over time. The figure illustrates the **cell cycle**: the repeating pattern of growth, genetic duplication, and division seen in most cells. There are two main phases in this cycle. First there is **interphase**: that portion of the cell cycle in which the cell simultaneously carries out its work and, in preparation for division, duplicates its chromosomes. Second, there is **mitotic phase** (or M phase): that portion of the cell cycle that includes both mitosis and cytokinesis.

Interphase and M phase are in turn subdivided into smaller phases. In interphase, first there is G_1, standing for "gap-one." What goes on here are normal cell operations and cell growth. The cell then enters the S or "synthesis" phase, which is the synthesis of DNA, resulting in the duplication of the chromosomes. When this ends, interphase's gap-two or G_2 period be-

(a) DNA in uncondensed form

(b) DNA condensed into duplicated chromosomes

Figure 9.8
DNA Can Be Arranged in Two Ways

(a) Replication occurs when the chromosomes DNA comes packaged in are in a relatively formless state. In this state, the chromatin that makes up the chromosomes has yet to condense into its compact arrangement.

(b) Mitosis occurs after chromatin condenses into the easily discernable shapes of duplicated chromosomes. The micrograph is of color-enhanced duplicated human chromosomes.

Figure 9.9
The Cell Cycle
The three main stages of cell division—DNA replication, mitosis, and cytokinesis—can be seen here in the context of a complete cell cycle. This cycle traditionally is divided into two main phases, interphase and mitotic (or "M") phase, which are in turn divided into other phases. Note that DNA replication—and hence chromosomal duplication—takes place within the S phase of interphase. The average cell spends most of its time in G_1 phase, growing and carrying out its normal cellular functions. Some types of cells, however, cease going through the cell cycle at all, while others progress through it repeatedly and rapidly.

gins, during which there is more cytoplasmic growth and a preparation for cell division. Because DNA synthesis is stopped in G_2 as well as G_1, the word *gap* in G_1 and G_2 can be thought of as a gap in DNA synthesis.

The length of the cell cycle varies greatly from one type of cell to another. In a typical animal cell, the total cell-cycle length averages about 24 hours. Within this cycle, mitotic phase takes up only about 30 minutes. Within interphase, an animal cell spends roughly 12 hours in G_1, 6 hours in S, and 6 hours in G_2. Some cells divide only rarely, while others—such as most nerve cells—don't divide at all. We could think of these cells as existing in an extended G_1 phase. But to

distinguish them from cells that are simply moving through G_1, they are said to be in G_0 phase.

9.4   Mitosis and Cytokinesis

It is the second overarching phase of the cell cycle, mitotic phase, that is the focus for the rest of this chapter. Now the concern is not with how a cell manages its general functions, but with how it *divides*—how it carries out both mitosis and cytokinesis. Mitosis turns out to have four phases, which we'll look at in order, after which we'll review cytokinesis. We will first consider mitosis and cytokinesis as they occur in animal cells.

The Phases of Mitosis

Prophase

The beginning of mitosis marks the end of the cell's interphase (**see Figure 9.10**). The starting state is that the cell's DNA, which replicated during the S phase, has just begun to pack itself into well-defined chromosomes. When we can finally *see* such chromosomes with a microscope, we can say that mitosis has begun, with prophase. Now the packing job continues; before it is done, the DNA will have coiled and condensed into one eight-thousandth of its S-phase length. When this is over in human beings, there are 46 well-defined chromosomes in the nucleus in duplicated state (meaning they are composed of 92 chromatids). Meanwhile, the nuclear envelope—the double membrane surrounding the nucleus—begins to break up.

While this is going on, big changes are taking place outside the nucleus. Recall from Chapter 4 the structures called **microtubules**: protein fibers that are part of the cell's cytoskeleton or internal fiber net-

work. In some of their roles, microtubules can be compared to tent poles that can shorten or lengthen as need be. Throughout mitosis, microtubules stretch the cell as a whole, and physically move the cell's chromosomes around.

In an interphase cell there exists, just outside the nucleus, a **centrosome**: a cellular structure that acts as an organizing center for the assembly of microtubules. This centrosome duplicates, so that now there are two microtubule organizing centers. Now, in prophase, these two centrosomes start to move apart. Where are they going? To the poles. From here on out, it is convenient to think of mitosis and cytokinesis in terms of a global metaphor: The centrosomes migrate to the cellular poles, while the chromosomes first align, and then separate, along a cellular equator called the metaphase plate. Unlike microtubules or the centrosome, the **metaphase plate** is not a structure, but instead is a plane located midway between the poles of a dividing cell. As the centrosomes move apart, they begin sprouting microtubules in all directions. One va-

Web Tutorial 9.2
Mitosis

Mitosis and cytokinesis

chromosomes (each a pair of sister chromatids joined together)

mitotic spindle

metaphase plate

spindle fibers (microtubules)

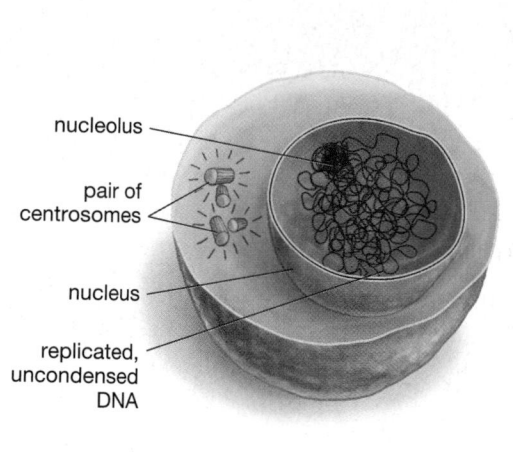

nucleolus

pair of centrosomes

nucleus

replicated, uncondensed DNA

End of interphase

DNA has already duplicated back in S phase. Centrosome has doubled.

Prophase
mitosis begins

The chromosomes take shape as the DNA condenses. The nuclear envelope begins to break down. The two centrosomes begin to move toward the cellular poles, sprouting microtubules as they go.

Metaphase
attachment and alignment

Some microtubules of the mitotic spindle form a cage around the cell's former nucleus while others attach to the sister chromatids and align them at the metaphase plate. Each chromatid now faces the pole opposite that of its sister chromatid.

Figure 9.10
Mitosis and Cytokinesis
The micrographs at the bottom of the figure are pictures of mitosis and cytokinesis in a whitefish embryo.

riety of them forms a football-shaped cage around the nuclear material, while a second variety attaches to the chromosomes themselves. Taken together, the microtubules active in cell division are known as the **mitotic spindle**.

Metaphase

By the time metaphase begins, the nuclear envelope has disappeared completely, and the microtubules that were growing toward the chromosomes now *attach* to them. Through a lively back-and-forth movement, the microtubules align the chromosomes at the equator. With this, each chromatid now faces the pole *opposite* that of its sister chromatid, and each chromatid is attached to its respective pole by perhaps 30 microtubules.

Anaphase

At last the genetic material divides. As you may have guessed, this is a parting of sisters. The sister chromatids are pulled apart, each now becoming a full-fledged chromosome. All 46 chromatid pairs divide at the same time, and each member of a chromatid pair moves toward its respective pole, pulled by a shortening of the microtubules to which it is attached.

Telophase

Telophase represents a return to things as they were before mitosis started. The newly independent chromosomes, having arrived at their respective poles, now unwind and lose their clearly defined shape. New nuclear membranes are forming. When this work is complete, there are two finished daughter nuclei lying in one elongating cell. Even as this is going on, though, something else is taking place that will result in this one cell becoming two.

Cytokinesis

Cytokinesis actually began back in anaphase and is well under way by the time of telophase. It works through the tightening of a cellular waistband that is composed of two sets of protein filaments working

separating chromatids

cleavage furrow

spindle fibers shortening

Anaphase separation

Sister chromatids are moved to opposite poles in the cell, each chromatid now becoming a full-fledged chromosome. The chromatids are moved by the microtubules they are linked to.

Telophase and cytokinesis exit from mitosis

Chromosomes decondense, the mitotic spindle breaks down, and nuclear envelopes form around the two separate complements of chromosomes. Meanwhile, a cleavage furrow begins to form.

Completion of cytokinesis one cell becomes two

The cell membrane pinches together completely, the membranes on either side fuse together, and the one cell becomes two.

Beginning of interphase

These two cells now enter the G_1 phase of interphase.

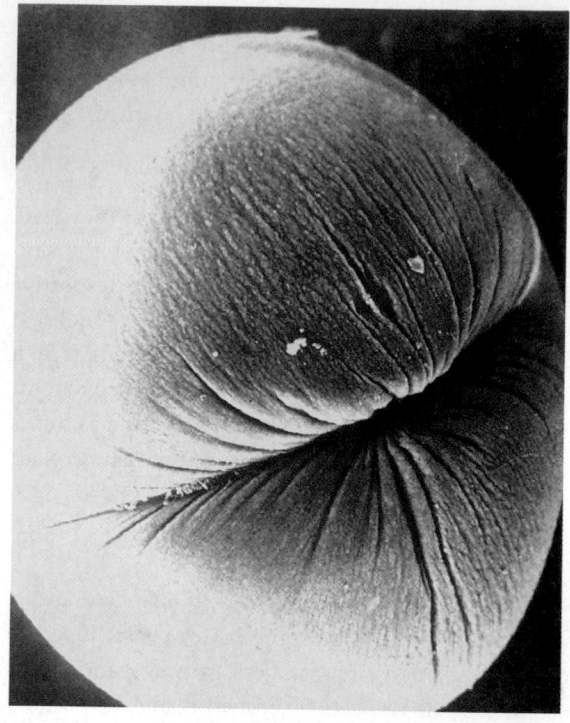

Figure 9.11
Cytokinesis in Animals
Cytokinesis in animal cells begins with an indentation of the cell surface, a cleavage furrow, shown here in a dividing frog egg. (×85)

together. These filaments—the same type that allow your muscles to contract—form a *contractile ring* that narrows along the cellular equator (**see Figure 9.11**). An indentation of the cell's surface (called a cleavage furrow), results from the ring's contraction; consequently, the fibers in the mitotic spindle are pushed closer and closer together, eventually forming one thick pole that is destined to break. The dividing cell now assumes an hourglass shape; as the contractile ring continues to pinch in, one cell becomes two by means of something you looked at in Chapter 4:

membrane fusion. The membranes on each half of the hourglass circle toward each other and then fuse. With this, the two cells become separate. Mitosis and cytokinesis are over, and the two daughter cells slip back into the relative quiet of interphase.

9.5 Variations in Cell Division

Now, we'll look at variations in cell division in certain different types of cells, including plant cells and prokaryotes.

Plant Cells

For the most part, plant cells carry out the steps of mitosis just as animal cells do. In the splitting of cytokinesis, however, plant cells must deal with something that animal cells don't have: the cell wall (see page 86 in Chapter 4). The way animal cells carry out cytokinesis—pinching the plasma membrane inward via the contractile ring—wouldn't work with plant cells, because their thick cell wall lies *outside* the plasma membrane.

The plant cell's solution to cytokinesis is to grow a new cell wall and plasma membrane that run roughly down the middle of the parent cell. If you look at **Figure 9.12**, you can see how this works. A series of membrane-lined vesicles begins to accumulate near the metaphase plate; inside these vesicles is a complex sugar. The vesicles then begin to fuse together; eventually they will form a flat *cell plate* that runs from one side of the parent cell to the other. The membrane portion of the cell plate then fuses with

Figure 9.12
Cytokinesis in Plants
The cell walls of plants are too rigid to form cleavage furrows, as animal cells do when dividing. Therefore, plant cells use a different strategy in cytokinesis. They build a new plasma membrane and cell wall down the middle of the parent cell to separate the two daughter cells from the inside out.

cell wall

vesicles

plasma
membrane

two
daughter
cells

1. Membrane-lined vesicles accumulate near the metaphase plate. The vesicles contain precursors to the cell wall.

2. Vesicles fuse together, forming a cell plate that grows toward the parent cell wall.

3. The newly formed plasma membrane and cell wall fuse with the parent plasma membrane and cell wall, forming two distinct daughter cells.

1. **Bacterial cell** starts with a single, circular chromosome attached to its plasma membrane.

2. The chromosome replicates and the daughter chromosomes attach to different sites on the plasma membrane.

3. The cell membrane and wall grow an extension between the attachment points of the two chromosomes.

4. The cell wall and membrane join together in the middle, resulting in two new cells.

Figure 9.13
Binary Fission in Bacteria
The key to bacterial cell division is that the bacterial chromosome attaches to the cell's plasma membrane. Both daughter chromosomes attach to the plasma membrane, but in different locations. The cell then produces an outgrowth of both plasma membrane and cell wall—called a septum—that grows in from each side of the cell, between the two daughter chromosomes. When the septum runs completely across the cell, it divides the cell in two, leaving one chromosome in each daughter cell.

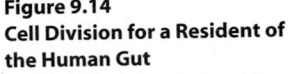

Web Tutorial 9.3
Cell Division for Bacteria

the original plasma membrane of the parent cell, and the result is two new adjacent plasma membranes that split the parent cell in two. Meanwhile, the material enclosed *inside* the cell-plate membrane is the foundation for the new cell-wall segments of the daughter cells.

Prokaryotes

It's also important to recognize that some cells have fundamentally different ways of replicating. The cells of prokaryotes—the bacteria and archaea you looked at in Chapter 4—are a case in point.

If you look at **Figure 9.13**, you can see how cell division works among the prokaryotes. Bacteria are single-celled and have a single, circular chromosome. Bacterial cells do not, however, have their chromosome sequestered inside a nucleus, as with eukaryotic cells, for the simple reason that they *have* no nucleus. Instead, their lone chromosome is attached to their plasma membrane.

A bacterial cell begins its division by duplicating its chromosome, utilizing the same DNA unwinding and replication described earlier. As the daughter chromosomes are completed, however, they attach to *different sites* on the plasma membrane. The cell then begins developing an outgrowth of its plasma membrane and cell wall in between these attachment sites. This outgrowth, called a septum, begins growing from opposite sides of the cell. When the

two septum extensions join in the middle, they divide the one cell into two (**see Figure 9.14**). This process is obviously very different from the eukaryotic mitosis and cytokinesis you looked at. As such, prokaryotic cell division goes under an entirely different name: **binary fission**. The simplicity of binary fission makes for a short cell cycle. Remember how the animal cells we looked at took about 24 hours to go through a cycle? Bacteria can complete their cycle in as little as 20 minutes.

Figure 9.14
Cell Division for a Resident of the Human Gut
E. coli bacteria such as this one exist in great quantity in the human digestive tract, generally harmlessly. It is certain rare varieties of *E. coli*, generally found in food, that have caused outbreaks of sickness and even death in recent years. (×30,000)

When the Cell Cycle Runs Amok: Cancer

The cell cycle reviewed in this chapter is, in one sense, a common natural process: Cells grow; they duplicate their chromosomes; these chromosomes separate; one cell divides into two. This goes on like clockwork, millions of times a second in each one of us. But then one day we learn that an aunt or a grandfather or a friend is experiencing an *unrestrained* division of cells. Things aren't explained to us in this way, of course. We are simply told that someone we know has cancer.

At root, all cancers are failures of the cell cycle. Put another way, all cancers represent a failure of cells to limit their multiplication in the cell cycle. What is liver cancer, for example? It is a damaging multiplication of liver cells. First one, then two, then four, then eight liver cells move repeatedly through the cell cycle, and as their numbers increase, they destroy the liver's working tissues. Given that cancer manifests in this way, it's not surprising that a large portion of modern cancer research is *cell-cycle* research. The logic here is simple: To the extent that uncontrolled cell division can be stopped, cancer can be stopped.

Research done to date has revealed the general outline of the way cells become cancerous. To use a common but apt metaphor, two things are required to bring cells to this state: their accelerators must get stuck and their brakes must fail. The control mechanisms that *induce* cell division must become hyperactive, and the mechanisms that *suppress* cell division must fail to perform. You may have heard a couple of terms used to describe the genetic components of this process. There are normal genes that induce cell division, but

that when mutated can cause cancer; these are the stuck-accelerator genes, called oncogenes. Then there are genes that normally suppress cell division, but that can cause cancer by acting like failed brakes. These are tumor suppressor genes. Note that *both* kinds of genes must malfunction for cancer to get going; indeed, it usually takes a long succession of genetic failures to induce cancer. This is why cancer is most often a disease of the middle-aged and elderly: It can take decades for the required series of mutations to fall into line in a single cell, such that it becomes cancerous.

How do oncogenes interact with tumor suppressor genes? In the normal case, cells will not begin division until prompted to do so by a signal from outside themselves. A protein (called a growth factor) will bind to a cell, setting off a cascade of chemical reactions inside it that triggers division. One of the links in this chemical cascade is a protein called Ras that could be thought of as an old-time railway switch. When Ras is chemically pointed one way (toward "on"), the cell moves through the cell cycle. When it is pointed the other (toward "off"), the cell stays in G_1. The gene that codes for Ras can become mutated, however, and when this happens, the Ras protein changes shape and points in the "on" direction all the time—no matter what signals it is getting from the outside. Thus, *ras* is an example of an oncogene. It normally prompts the cell to divide intermittently; when mutated it prompts the cell to divide continuously.

A cell with a mutated *ras* gene is not doomed to become cancerous, however. What can save it is a good set of brakes, in the form of tumor suppressor genes. The most important of

Variations in the Frequency of Cell Division

There are also variations in cell division among different types of eukaryotic cells. As noted, not all cells divide throughout their existence. Most human brain cells are formed in the first three months of embryonic existence and then live for decades, with relatively few of them ever dividing again. Much the same is true of the leaf cells in plants; they divide only when the leaf is very small, then grow for a time, and then function at this mature size for as long as the leaf lives. At the other extreme, cells located in human bone marrow never *stop* dividing as they produce red

blood cells (which have a short life span). The output here is staggering: about 180 million new red blood cells are produced inside us each minute.

On to Meiosis

The cell division reviewed in this chapter concerns "somatic" cells—the kind that form bone, muscle, nerve, and many other sorts of tissue. Given a distribution this wide, you might well ask: What kind of cells are *not* somatic? The answer is only one kind— the kind that forms the basis for each succeeding generation of sexually reproducing living things.

these genes—one known as *p53*—is so vital to human health that it is sometimes referred to as the "guardian of the genome." In the presence of certain kinds of mutations, *p53* protein levels rise in the cell, and these levels start turning selected genes on and off. The result is the cell's first line of defense against cancer—the cell cycle is shut down until the mutation has been repaired. This shutdown doesn't happen at just any point in the cycle, however. As cancer researchers Leland Hartwell and Ted Weinert discovered in the 1980s, cells have specific *checkpoints* in their cycle. Just as NASA mission control will stop at a defined point in a countdown to see if "all systems are go" for a launch, so a cell has specific points at which it makes sure that all its systems are healthy enough for cell division to continue. The first of its checkpoints comes in G_1, as it is about to enter S phase (during which it doubles its DNA). The second point comes in G_2, as it is about to enter into mitosis and cytokinesis. Thus, if a dividing skin cell, for example, has acquired some mutations in G_1, it will not enter S phase until its DNA repair enzymes have fixed the problem.

But what happens if the DNA damage spotted in G_1 can't be fixed? Then, prompted by *p53*, the cell goes to level-two of its emergency responses: it commits suicide. Through an orderly process called *apoptosis*, the cell shuts down its activities, breaks up, and dies. If you have ever been sunburned, you have probably seen the effects of apoptosis up close. The ultraviolet light in the sun damages the DNA in skin cells. When this damage cannot be fixed with repair enzymes, these cells undergo apoptosis; their remains are the peeling skin that comes with a bad sunburn.

In sum, when genes such as *ras* become mutated, they can lead to an out-of-control cell cycle, but this process can be halted in several ways by tumor suppressor genes such as *p53*. With this, you can probably see what comes next. What will stave off cancer if a cell has *both* a mutated *ras* gene and a mutated *p53* gene? Perhaps nothing, because now the accelerator is stuck and the brakes have failed. As noted, there is generally more to cancer than two mutated genes, but when both *ras* and *p53* malfunction, a cell is well on its way to cancer.

As it turns out, *ras* is probably the most important human oncogene among the hundred or so that have been identified. And *p53* certainly is the most important tumor suppressor gene among the two dozen that have been identified. A mutated *ras* gene is found in about 30 percent of all human cancers, while a mutated *p53* is found in half of all human cancers. As you can imagine, there is intense research interest in both these genes. From 1989 to 2000, more than 17,000 scientific publications were written on *p53* alone. The war on cancer may not have been won, but it certainly is being waged.

Harmful Division
Pictured are two prostate cancer cells in the final stages of cell division.

Chapter Review

Summary

9.1   An Introduction to Genetics

- DNA is an information-bearing molecule that plays a critical role in the reproduction, development, and everyday functioning of living things. DNA contains the information for the production of proteins, which carry out an array of tasks in living things.

- The information in DNA is encoded in chemical substances called "bases," which are laid out along the DNA double helix in four varieties: adenine (A), thymine (T), guanine (G), and cytosine (C). One series of bases contains information for the production of one protein, while a different series of bases specifies a different protein. Each series of protein-specifying bases is known as a gene.

- Protein synthesis begins with the information in a sequence of DNA bases being copied onto a molecule called messenger RNA (mRNA). This molecule moves out of the cell's nucleus to a structure in its cytoplasm called a ribosome. There, the mRNA "tape" is brought together with the building blocks of proteins, amino acids. As the ribosome "reads" the mRNA tape, it strings together a sequence of amino acids called for by the tape. The result is a chain of amino acids that folds into a protein.

- Most of the cells in an organism contain a complete copy of that organism's genome, meaning its collection of genetic information. Before cells divide, their genome must first be copied and the resulting copies apportioned evenly into what will become two daughter cells.

9.2　An Introduction to Cell Division

- Cell division takes place because old cells die and because there are many instances in which an organism needs quantities of new cells above "replacement" level. Cell division includes the duplication of DNA (replication); the apportioning of the copied DNA into two quantities in a parent cell (mitosis); and the physical splitting of this parent cell into two daughter cells (cytokinesis). In DNA replication, the two strands of the double helix unwind, after which each single strand serves as a template for construction of a second, complementary strand of DNA. The result is a doubling of the original quantity of DNA.
  Web Tutorial 9.1:　The Cell Cycle

9.3　DNA Is Packaged in Chromosomes

- DNA comes packaged in units called chromosomes. These chromosomes are composed of DNA and its associated proteins—a combined chemical complex called chromatin. Chromosomes exist in an unduplicated state until such time as DNA replicates, prior to cell division. DNA replication results in chromosomes that are in duplicated state, meaning one chromosome composed of two identical sister chromatids.

- Chromosomes in human beings (and many other species) come in matched pairs, with one member of each pair inherited from the mother, and the other member of each pair inherited from the father. Such homologous chromosomes have closely matched sets of genes on them, though many of these genes are not identical. A given paternal chromosome may have genes that code, for example, for different hair or skin color than the counterpart genes on the homologous maternal chromosome. Human beings have 46 chromosomes—22 matched pairs and either a matched pair of X chromosomes (in females) or an X and a Y chromosome (in males).

- Cell division fits into the larger framework of the cell cycle, meaning a repeating pattern of growth, genetic replication, and cell division. The cell cycle has two main phases. The first is interphase, in which the cell carries out its work, grows, and duplicates its chromosomes in preparation for division. The second is mitotic phase, in which the duplicated chromosomes separate and the cell splits in two.

9.4　Mitosis and Cytokinesis

- There are four stages in mitosis: prophase, metaphase, anaphase, and telophase. The essence of the process is that duplicated chromosomes line up along an equatorial plane of the parent cell, called the metaphase plate, with the sister chromatids that make up each duplicated chromosome lying on opposite sides of the plate. Attached to fibers called microtubules, the sister chromatids are then pulled apart, to opposite poles of the parent cell. Once cell division is complete, sister chromatids that once formed a single chromosome will reside in separate daughter cells, with each sister chromatid now functioning as a full-fledged chromosome.
  Web Tutorial 9.2:　Mitosis

- Cytokinesis in animal cells works through a ring of protein filaments that tightens at the middle of a dividing cell. Membranes on the portions of the cell being pinched together then fuse, resulting in two daughter cells.

9.5　Variations in Cell Division

- Because of their cell walls, plant cells must carry out cytokinesis differently from animal cells. The plant's solution is to grow new cell walls and plasma membranes near the metaphase plate, thus dividing the parent cell into two daughter cells. Prokaryotes such as bacteria employ a process called binary fission: They double their single, circular chromosome, with the two resulting chromosomes attaching to different sites on the plasma membrane. Then an outgrowth of plasma membrane and cell wall, called a septum, begins growing from opposite sides of the cell, in between the two chromosomes. When the two septum extensions join in the middle, they divide the one cell into two.
  Web Tutorial 9.3:　Cell Division for Bacteria

Key Terms

binary fission　183	**genome**　171
cell cycle　178	**homologous chromosomes**　177
centrosome　180	**interphase**　178
chromatid　177	**karyotype**　177
chromatin　176	**metaphase plate**　180
chromosome　175	**microtubule**　180
cytokinesis　178	**mitosis**　178
enzyme　172	**mitotic phase**　178
genetics　173	**mitotic spindle**　181

Understanding the Basics

Multiple-Choice Questions (answers in the back of the book)

1. Proteins serve in living things as:
   a. hormones
   b. enzymes
   c. cell receptors
   d. structural building blocks
   e. all of the above

2. The four bases found along the DNA double helix are
   a. adenine, thymine, guanine, and cytosol
   b. adenine, thyroxine, glucose, and cytosine
   c. adrenaline, thymine, glucosamine, and uracil
   d. adenine, thymine, guanine, and cytosine
   e. none of the above

3. A gene can be described as
   a. a protein that contains enough information to carry out a task
   b. a hormone that prompts some action inside a cell
   c. a series of DNA bases that transfers energy within a cell

d. a series of DNA bases that contains information for production of a protein

e. a protein that delivers information to a ribosome

4. Cell division in bacteria operates very differently from cell division in eukaryotes. Which statement is *incorrect* regarding the cell-division process in bacteria?

   a. bacteria are incapable of rapid cell division
   b. bacteria have a single circular chromosome
   c. the bacterial chromosome is sequestered inside a nucleus
   d. the bacterial chromosome is attached to the plasma membrane during replication
   e. the bacterial chromosome is duplicated before cell division

5. DNA is primarily

   a. a molecule that protects cells from invaders
   b. a molecule that contains information
   c. a molecule that helps transfer energy
   d. a "workbench" on which proteins are put together
   e. a form of protein

6. Prophase has begun when

   a. we can see well-defined chromosomes.
   b. a cleavage furrow has formed.
   c. chromosomes have aligned along the metaphase plate.
   d. chromosomes have duplicated.
   e. sister chromatids have separated.

7. A _____ is composed of two sets of protein filaments that help bring about cytokinesis.

   a. dividing fiber
   b. metaphase plate
   c. spindle
   d. contractile ring
   e. centrosome

8. A root-tip cell in a plant has 22 chromosomes. How many chromatids can be seen during prophase when this cell is undergoing mitosis?

   a. 22
   b. 44
   c. 66
   d. 11
   e. 88

9. The cell cycle is linked to cancer because cancer always entails

   a. too much time spent in S phase
   b. a slow-down in mitosis
   c. unrestrained cell division
   d. a misalignment of chromosomes
   e. not enough time spent in M phase

10. If a cell is not dividing, and has not yet begun replicating its DNA (duplicated its chromosomes), what phase of the cell cycle would it be in?

    a. gap-two (G_2) phase
    b. synthesis (S) phase
    c. gap-one (G_1) phase
    d. prophase
    e. mitotic phase

Brief Review

1. In what way does DNA help form and then maintain our bodies?

2. The drawing shows a cell in a phase of mitosis. What phase is shown? How many chromatids are present in this stage? What is the total number of chromosomes each daughter cell will have?

3. How do mitosis and cytokinesis differ?

4. Name the four phases of mitosis and describe the major events occurring in each phase.

5. What additional cell structure must plant cells deal with when they are undergoing cytokinesis (as compared to animal cells)? Given this difference, how do plant cells carry out cytokinesis?

6. In what way are the 23 pairs of human chromosomes "matched" chromosomes?

7. The protein synthesis pathway—DNA → mRNA → protein—is a very important concept in biology.
   a. What are the information-bearing "building blocks" of DNA?
   b. Where is DNA located in the cell?
   c. What does the "m" in mRNA stand for?
   d. Using this knowledge, what is the function of mRNA, where is it made, and where is it used?"
   e. What are the building blocks of proteins?
   f. Where does protein formation occur?

Applying Your Knowledge

1. Why is it accurate to think of each human being as the owner of a library of ancient information?

2. People who are born with the condition called Down syndrome generally have three copies of a certain chromosome (chromosome 21), rather than the usual two copies. What can you deduce from this regarding the proteins produced by a person with Down syndrome?

3. Given the conceptualization of genetics as information management, what would you predict about the relative size of the human genome as opposed to the genome of a bacterium? What about the human genome compared to that of a flowering plant?

MediaLab

Too Much Division: The Cell Cycle and Cancer

This *MediaLab* is designed to stimulate interest in cell division by allowing you to examine the role of the cell cycle in cancer. To learn more, enter the *Web Tutorial* for an animated review of cell division. Once you have completed this section, you will be guided through a series of *Web Investiga-* *tions*, where you can utilize information on the Internet to examine your own personal risk of contracting cancer, taking into account such factors as inheritance and exposure to environmental carcinogens. Finally, in *Communicate Your Results*, you can evaluate the relevance of these factors.

The online version of this *MediaLab* can be found in Chapter 9 on your Companion Website (www.prenhall.com/krogh3).

WEB TUTORIAL

One cell dividing to create two is crucial for growth, for wound repair, and for creating the next generation of organisms. But if this process is not properly controlled, rogue cancer cells can be produced. You will be reviewing the correct steps in cell division in several interactive exercises as well as observing the consequences of uncontrolled cell division in cancer cells.

Activity

1. *First, you will observe the key to reproduction, the duplication of the genetic information in our DNA.*

2. *You will then review the cycle in which our body duplicates the DNA and other cellular components of existing cells to refresh and replace cells when we grow, or when a wound heals.*

3. *Finally, you can test your knowledge in an interactive exercise where you direct the events of the cell division itself.*

After reviewing the concepts of cell division, you can evaluate your fears and misconceptions about cancer in the *Web Investigations* and apply your knowledge of cell division to achieve a better understanding of cancer.

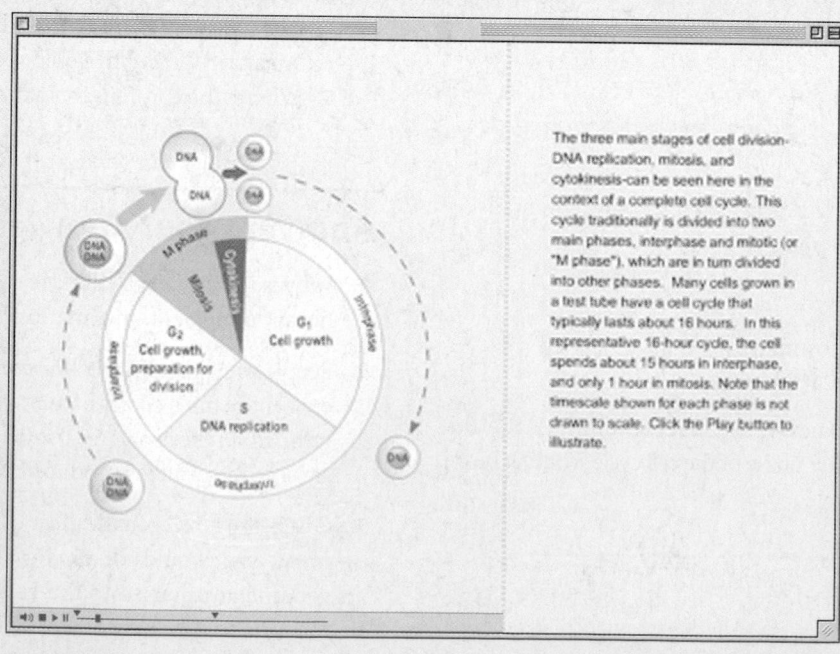

WEB INVESTIGATION

Investigation 1
Estimated time for completion = 15 minutes

Cells can become cancerous (go through accelerated and unregulated division) because they acquire mutations in the genes that normally control the rate at which they travel through the cell cycle. Scientists believe that inheriting a defective gene may predispose a person toward developing some specific cancers. What proportion of cancers are inherited?

Actually, a very small number. In families with these defective genes, the same type of cancer is seen in two or more close relatives, with an earlier-than-usual onset. Select the keyword **INHERITED CANCERS** on your Website for this *MediaLab* to view a list of inherited cancers. Then, select the keyword **PERSONAL HEALTH FORM** to complete a personal health history form, which will likely relieve you of your concern about inheriting these cancers.

Investigation 2
Estimated time for completion = 5 minutes

Daily media warnings expound on evidence that chemicals, drugs, and diet can increase our chances of acquiring cancer. But how can you determine which risk factors are serious, and which may be rare or insignificant? Select the keyword **CANCER RISK FACTORS** on your Website for this *MediaLab* to investigate the relative risk factors in contracting cancer from natural and human-made compounds.

Investigation 3
Estimated time for completion = 5 minutes

How can you tell which cancer you should worry about most, and what are the best preventative measures you can take? Select the keyword **YOUR CANCER RISK** on your Website for this *MediaLab*, and enter your own personal information to find out how to lower your risk of contracting a specific cancer.

COMMUNICATE YOUR RESULTS

How well can scientists predict who will get cancer, when both heredity and the environment are such important factors? In the following exercises, you'll evaluate your own hereditary and environmental cancer risk.

Exercise 1
Estimated time for completion = 15 minutes

Now that you have filled out your personal health history form in *Web Investigation 1*, prepare a 50-word document indicating what type of cancer is found in your family. If it has an earlier-than-normal onset and is not found in two or more close relatives, it is probably not inherited.

Exercise 2
Estimated time for completion = 60 minutes

How can you evaluate the significance of news stories on such substances as chlorinated water or artificial sweeteners as potential cancer causes? After completing *Web Investigation 2*, compose a 250-word essay describing which statement you think is most correct:

1. *Synthetic chemicals manufactured by humans are responsible for more cancers (are more carcinogenic) than are natural compounds like sunlight and natural foods.*

2. *Chemicals found in natural foods and sunlight are more carcinogenic than are synthetic chemicals.*

3. *Both naturally occurring and synthetic chemicals are equally responsible for causing cancer.*

Exercise 3
Estimated time for completion = 15 minutes

In *Web Investigation 3*, you researched your personal chances of developing a specific cancer and what you can do about it. Form a group of your peers, and have each member present one of these factors for each cancer type to the group (for example, dietary changes). In your presentation, be sure to inform the group about some of the most important lifestyle changes that apply.

10 *Meiosis*

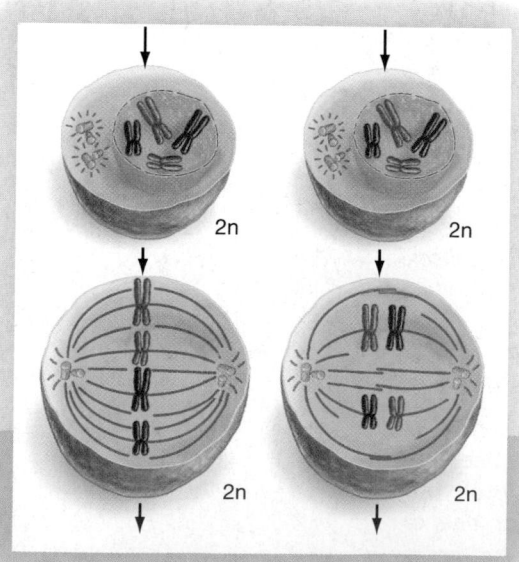

Meiosis and mitosis compared.
(Section 10.2, page 193)

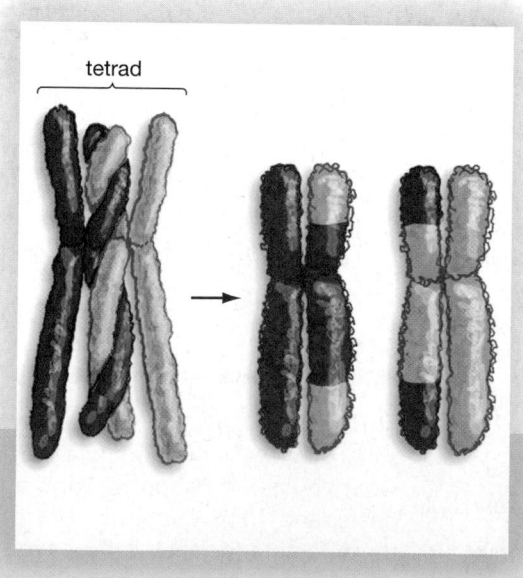

Swapping sections.
(Section 10.2, page 194)

The large X and the small Y.
(Section 10.4, page 199)

A real-life couple—let's call them Jack Fennington and Jill Kent—combine their last names when they get married and thus become Jack and Jill Fennington-Kent. Now, what would happen if the Fennington-Kent's children were to continue in this tradition? Their daughter Susie might marry, say, Ralph Reeson-Dodd, which would make her Susie Fennington-Kent-Reeson-Dodd. If *Susie's* son, John, were to keep this up, he might be fated to become John Fennington-Kent-Reeson-Dodd-Garcia-Lee-Minderbinder-Green, and so on.

This growing chain of names illustrates a kind of problem that living things have managed to address in carrying out reproduction. *Reproduction* in this context does not mean the mitotic cell division you looked at in Chapter 9. Reproduction here means *sexual* reproduction, in which specialized reproductive cells come together to pro-

duce offspring. The cells described in Chapter 9—the ones that undergo mitosis—are known as *somatic* cells, which in animals means all the cells in the organism except for one type. What type is this? Sex cells; cells called *gametes*. These are reproductive cells, known more commonly as eggs and sperm.

Eggs and sperm are not commonly thought of as cells, but that's just what they are, complete with plasma membranes, nuclei, chromosomes, and all the rest (though sperm eventually lose much of this material). Eggs and sperm are *special* cells, however, in that they are not destined to divide like somatic cells and thus make more eggs and sperm. Rather, they will *fuse*—sperm fertilizing egg—to make a zygote, which grows into a whole organism. It is sperm and egg that take part in sexual reproduction and that thus bear some

On the way to a boy or a girl.
(Section 10.4, page 199)

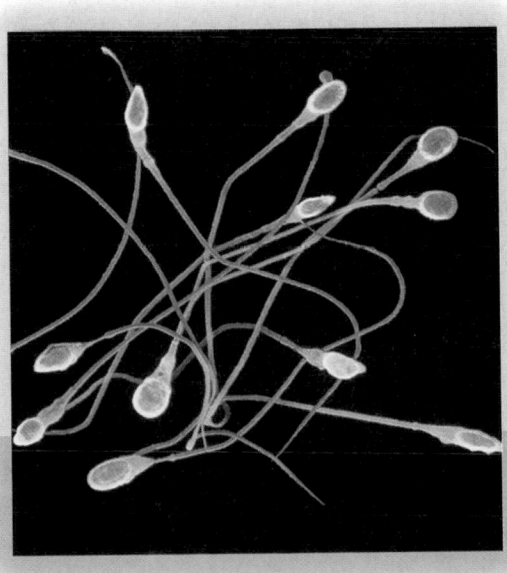

About 250 million of these are made every day.
(Section 10.5, page 201)

End of two journeys.
(Section 10.5, page 201)

relation to the Fennington-Kent problem. Here's how it plays out in humans. Human somatic cells, as you have seen, have 23 pairs of chromosomes or 46 chromosomes in all. If an egg and sperm each brought 46 chromosomes to their *union*, the result would be a zygote with 92 chromosomes. The *next* generation down would presumably have 184 chromosomes, the next after that 368, and so on. This would be about as functional as having Fennington-Kent-Reeson-Dodd-Garcia-Lee-Miderbinder-Green as a last name.

10.1 An Overview of Meiosis

How do chromosomes avoid the problem of doubling with each generation? In sexual reproduction, chromosome union is preceded by chromosome *reduction*. The reduction comes in the cells that give rise to sperm and egg. When these cells divide, the result is sperm or egg cells that have only *half* the usual, somatic number of chromosomes. Human sperm or egg, in other words, have only 23 chromosomes in them. (Not the 23 *pairs* of chromosomes that somatic cells have, mind you; 23 chromosomes.) Each 23-chromosome sperm can then unite with a 23-chromosome egg to produce a 46-chromosome zygote that develops into a new human being. In each generation, then, there is first a halving of chromosome number (when egg and sperm cells are produced), followed by a coming together of these two halves (when sperm and egg unite). This basic pattern holds true for sexual reproduction in all eukaryotes.

Some Helpful Terms

Now here are a few terms that will be helpful. The kind of cell division that results in the halving of chromosome number is called *meiosis*, in contrast with *mitosis*, which you looked at in Chapter 9. In mitosis, there is no halving of chromosome number; just a duplication of chromosomes and then a division of these chromosomes into each of two daughter cells.

In animals, cells that are produced in meiosis—thus getting the half-number of chromosomes—are always reproductive cells, the term for which is **gametes**, as we've seen. Such reduced-chromosome cells are said to be in the haploid state, the term *haploid* literally meaning "single vessel." When egg and sperm unite, however, it marks a return to the *diploid*, or "double vessel" state of cellular existence, meaning 46 chromo-

somes in human beings. (More formally, **haploid** means possessing a single set of chromosomes while **diploid** means possessing two sets of chromosomes.) **Meiosis** can thus be defined as a process in which a single diploid cell divides to produce haploid reproductive cells. Diploid cells are also sometimes referred to as **2n** cells (the "2" here standing for a doubled number of chromosomes), while haploid cells are said to be **1n**. Thus, eggs and sperm are 1n, while the diploid cells that give rise to them are 2n.

In what follows, we will be looking at meiosis as it occurs in human beings; toward the end of the chapter we'll go over some variations on reproduction in other kinds of organisms.

10.2 The Steps in Meiosis

How does the chromosomal halving take place? Let's go over the process of meiosis and see. **Figure 10.1** shows meiosis, in a stripped-down form, as compared to the mitosis described in Chapter 9. As you can see, meiosis includes one chromosome duplication followed by two cellular divisions. This is the key to how the chromosome numbers work out. In mitosis, there was one chromosome duplication and one subsequent division of the doubled chromosomes (into two cells). In meiosis there is one duplication followed by *two* divisions (into four cells). The first of the meiotic divisions is a separation not of chroma*tids*, as in mitosis, but of homologous chromo*somes*. The second meiotic division is then the separation of the chromatids that make up these homologous chromosomes.

But what is this term *homologous*? You may remember from Chapter 9 that homologous chromosomes are chromosomes that are the same in size and function. These chromosomes do similar things, which is to say they have genes on them that code for similar proteins. We have a chromosome 1 that we inherit from our mother, and it is homologous to the chromosome 1 we inherit from our father. Likewise we inherit a chromosome 2 from our mother that is homologous with chromosome 2 from our father, and so forth for 23 pairs. The lone exception to this pairs rule is that the X and Y chromosomes males have are not homologous with one another. Let's walk through the steps of meiosis now. These details will reveal a process that not only divides up genetic material, but provides for a great deal of the diversity

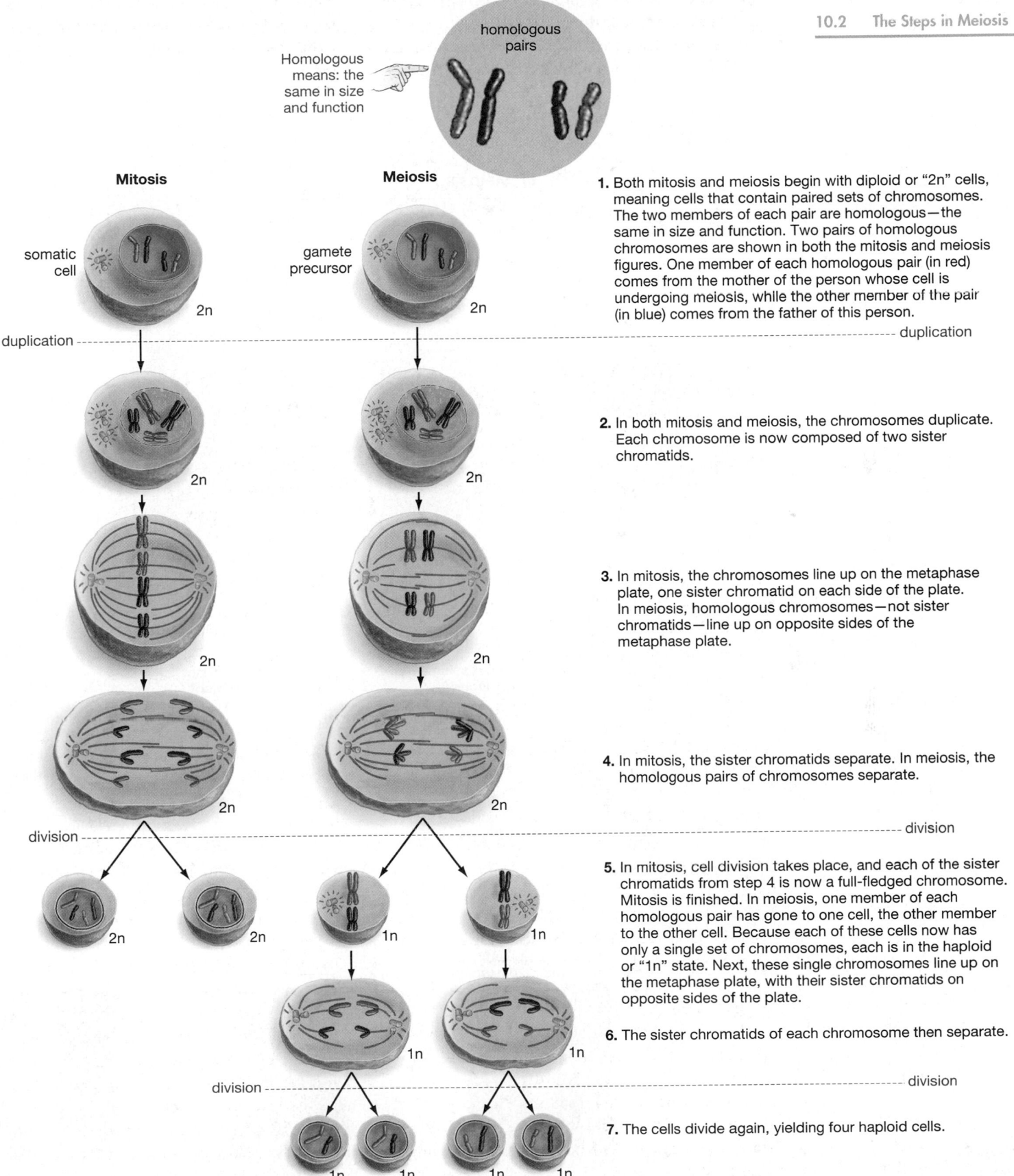

1. Both mitosis and meiosis begin with diploid or "2n" cells, meaning cells that contain paired sets of chromosomes. The two members of each pair are homologous—the same in size and function. Two pairs of homologous chromosomes are shown in both the mitosis and meiosis figures. One member of each homologous pair (in red) comes from the mother of the person whose cell is undergoing meiosis, whlle the other member of the pair (in blue) comes from the father of this person.

2. In both mitosis and meiosis, the chromosomes duplicate. Each chromosome is now composed of two sister chromatids.

3. In mitosis, the chromosomes line up on the metaphase plate, one sister chromatid on each side of the plate. In meiosis, homologous chromosomes—not sister chromatids—line up on opposite sides of the metaphase plate.

4. In mitosis, the sister chromatids separate. In meiosis, the homologous pairs of chromosomes separate.

5. In mitosis, cell division takes place, and each of the sister chromatids from step 4 is now a full-fledged chromosome. Mitosis is finished. In meiosis, one member of each homologous pair has gone to one cell, the other member to the other cell. Because each of these cells now has only a single set of chromosomes, each is in the haploid or "1n" state. Next, these single chromosomes line up on the metaphase plate, with their sister chromatids on opposite sides of the plate.

6. The sister chromatids of each chromosome then separate.

7. The cells divide again, yielding four haploid cells.

Figure 10.1
Meiosis Compared to Mitosis

that exists among living things. The steps of meiosis are illustrated in **Figure 10.2**.

The process starts with the doubling (that is, the replication) of DNA you saw in Chapter 9. DNA dou-bling in meiosis means the same thing as it did in mitosis: All 46 chromosomes in a human cell replicate, yielding 46 chromosomes in duplicated state (meaning they are composed of 92 chromatids).

(a) Meiosis I
Diploid

End of interphase

DNA has already duplicated

Prophase I

Homologous chromosomes link as they condense, forming tetrads.

Crossing over occurs.

Metaphase I

Microtubules move homologous chromosomes to metaphase plate.

Independent assortment occurs.

Anaphase I

Microtubules separate homologo chromosomes (sister chromatids remain together).

First important source of genetic variation

(b) Crossing over

Exchange of parts of non-sister chromatids.

duplicated maternal chromosome

duplicated paternal chromosome

tetrad

sister chromatids

non-sister chromatids

Figure 10.2
Meiosis

(a) The Steps of Meiosis

(b) Crossing Over

(c) Independent Assortment

Meiosis I

The steps of meiosis are separated into two multistep stages, called meiosis I and meiosis II. The big picture here is that in meiosis I, homologous chromosomes are positioned close together, on opposite sides of the cellular equator called the metaphase plate. Then these chromosomes will move apart into different daughter cells. In meiosis II, the chromatids of these now-separated chromosomes will, in turn, separate into different daughter cells.

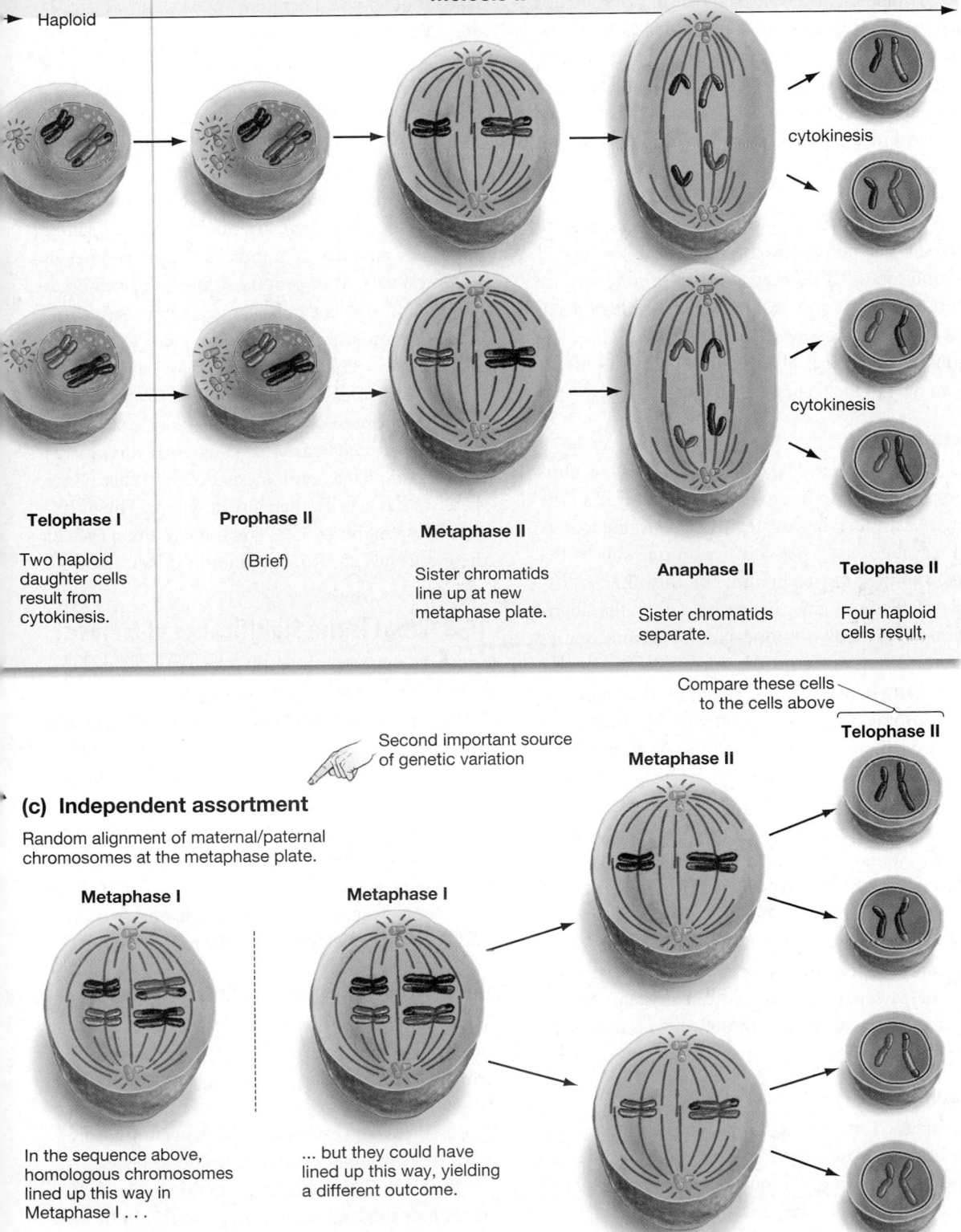

Haploid

Meiosis II

cytokinesis

cytokinesis

Telophase I

Two haploid daughter cells result from cytokinesis.

Prophase II

(Brief)

Metaphase II

Sister chromatids line up at new metaphase plate.

Anaphase II

Sister chromatids separate.

Telophase II

Four haploid cells result.

Compare these cells to the cells above

Telophase II

Second important source of genetic variation

Metaphase II

(c) Independent assortment

Random alignment of maternal/paternal chromosomes at the metaphase plate.

Metaphase I

Metaphase I

In the sequence above, homologous chromosomes lined up this way in Metaphase I . . .

. . . but they could have lined up this way, yielding a different outcome.

Prophase I

Meiosis I begins, in prophase I, with the same appearance of 46 identifiable chromosomes that you observed in mitosis. The first big difference between meiosis and mitosis also appears in prophase I. It is that, in meiosis, *homologous chromosomes pair up*. In mitosis, 46 individual chromosomes condensed, but did not pair up in any way. In meiosis, however, each pair of homologous chromosomes link up as they condense. Maternal chromosome 5, for example, intertwines with *p*aternal chromosome 5, maternal chromosome 6 with paternal 6, and so on. When two homologous chromosomes have paired up in this way, they are called a **tetrad** (see the "Crossing over" section of Figure 10.2).

A critical bit of part-swapping then takes place between the non-sister chromatids of the paired chromosomes. This process is called *crossing over* (or *recombination*), and you'll be looking at it in detail later. Once this crossing over has finished, the homologous chromosomes begin to unwind from one another, though thcy remain overlapped.

Metaphase I

Still existing as tetrads, the homologous chromosomes, attached to microtubules, are moved to the metaphase plate; in this step of meiosis, the maternal member of a given pair lies on one side of the plate and the paternal member on the other. A critical point about this, however, is that the alignment adopted by any one pair of chromosomes bears no relation to the alignment adopted by any other pair. It may be, for example, that paternal chromosome 5 will line up on what we might call side A of the metaphase plate; if so, then maternal chromosome 5 ends up on side B. Shift to chromosome 6, however, and things could just as easily be reversed: The *maternal* chromosome might end up on side A, and the paternal on side B. It is thus a throw of the dice as to which side of the plate a given chromosome lines up on. More important, it is this chance event that determines which *cell* a chromosome joins, because each side of the plate becomes a separate cell once cell division is finished. As you will see, this randomness is critical in the shuffling of genetic material.

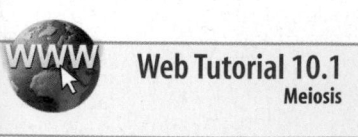

Web Tutorial 10.1
Meiosis

Anaphase I

In anaphase I the paired, homologous chromosomes now begin to move away from each other, toward their respective poles, pulled through the disassembly of the microtubule spindles they are attached to. Though homologous chromosomes have now separated, the sister chromatids that make them up are still together.

Telophase I

With chromosome movement toward the poles completed, the original cell now undergoes cytokinesis, dividing into two completely separate daughter cells. With this, there are two haploid cells, whereas in the beginning there was one diploid cell. (Why are the cells now haploid? Meiosis I moved one set of chromosomes to one cell and the second set to another cell. Therefore, each cell now has only one set of chromosomes.)

Meiosis II

There is little pause for interphase between meiosis I and meiosis II; little time for the daughter cells to regroup and carry on regular metabolic activities. What happens instead is another division—or set of divisions, because there are now two cells. Each of these cells now has 23 duplicated chromosomes in it. After a very brief prophase, these chromosomes line up at a new metaphase plate, with sister chromatids on opposite sides of each plate. What happens next is the same thing that happened in mitosis. The *sister chromatids* now separate, moving toward opposite poles; with this, they assume the role of full-fledged chromosomes. Once this separation is completed, cytokinesis occurs. Where once there were two cells, there are now four. The difference between this process and mitosis is that each of these cells has 23 chromosomes in it instead of 46.

10.3 What Is the Significance of Meiosis?

You have now examined the mechanics of meiosis. But what are the effects of this process? First of all, the "Fennington-Kent" problem noted at the beginning of the chapter has been solved. There will be no 92-chromosome zygotes, because egg and sperm will each bring only 23 chromosomes to their meeting, thus yielding a combined 46 chromosomes in human somatic cells. Just as notable, however, are two kinds of diversity that meiosis brings about. The first of these these is genetic diversity in offspring; the second is a large-scale diversity in the natural world.

Genetic Diversity through Crossing Over

What is genetic diversity? Recall that, back in prophase I of meiosis, the homologous chromosome pairs intertwined for a time and then engaged in something called crossing over (or recombination). In this, there is an exchange of *parts* of chromosomes prior to their lining up at the metaphase plate.

Look at the "Crossing over" section of Figure 10.2 to see how this important process works. In the first stage of meiosis, there is a physical breaking of non-sister chromatids and then a "reunion" of these reciprocal chromosomal sections onto new chromatid partners. With this, what had been a "maternal" chromosome now has a portion of the paternal chromosome within it, and vice versa. Formally, then, **crossing over** can be defined as a process, occurring during meiosis, in which homologous chromosomes exchange reciprocal portions of themselves.

The linkage between crossing over and genetic diversity probably is apparent; the ability of reciprocal lengths of DNA to be exchanged between chromosomes provides a means by which the genetic deck can be reshuffled prior to the formation of gametes. This is so because of what you saw in Chapter 9 about homologous chromosomes: While the genetic information on any two will be similar, it will not be identical. A gene on one chromosome may code for red hair color, but the gene on its homologous chromosome may code for blonde hair color. In crossing over, such genetic variants are being swapped between chromosomes.

Genetic Diversity through Independent Assortment

Another way that meiosis ensures genetic diversity is a crucial event that took place in metaphase I (right after crossing over). It is the random alignment or *independent assortment* of chromosomes at the metaphase plate. (See the "Independent assortment" section of Figure 10.2.) Recall that the alignment of any one pair of homologous chromosomes along the plate bears no relation to the alignment of any other homologous pair. If you looked at, say, chromosome 5, the paternal member of the pair might line up on "side A" of the metaphase plate, meaning maternal chromosome 5 will be on side B. Shift to chromosome 6, however, and things could just as easily be reversed. This random alignment of chromosomes then leads to a random *separation* of them, because a chromosome that lines up on *side* A of the plate will end up in *cell* A, while a chromosome that lines up on side B will end up in cell B. **Independent assortment** can thus be defined as the random distribution of homologous chromosome pairs during meiosis. If we wonder how traits from a mother and father can get "mixed up" in their children, independent assortment joins crossing over in providing an answer. Indeed, for complex creatures such as ourselves, independent assortment assures that, with the exception of identical twins, offspring produced through sexual reproduction will not just be diverse. Each offspring will be *unique*—no other offspring will be exactly like it in genetic terms. Let's see why.

If human beings had only two chromosomes in each cell that went through meiosis—one from the father, one from the mother—there would be only two possible "states" of line-up at the metaphase plate: "maternal on side A" of the plate or "maternal on side B" (with the paternal homologue on the opposite side). The actual number of possibilities, however, is this number of states (2) *raised to the power* of the number of chromosome pairs. Thus, if three chromosome pairs existed, the number of possible outcomes would go to 2^3 or 8 ($2 \times 2 \times 2$). Now get your calculator ready. With the 23 pairs of chromosomes human beings have, the possibilities go to 2^{23}, or about 8 million. General Motors may be able to mix and match engines and upholstery to come up with scores of different models of a given car; but in any given human meiosis, chromosome pairs can line up along the metaphase plate in 8 million different ways. This means any given egg or sperm will be one of about 8 million possible "models." To get a basic idea of how this works out, look at the "Independent assortment" section of Figure 10.2.

Why does this matter? Remember that there are *genes* on these chromosomes, and that the genes on any given paternal chromosome may differ somewhat from those on its matched maternal chromosome. Which chromosome the offspring gets thus makes a difference—in eye color, height, or any of thousands of other characteristics. Given this, each of us is very much affected by the way paternal and maternal chromosomes happened to line up in two very special meioses: those that produced the egg cell and the sperm cell that gave rise to us.

When we add independent assortment to crossing over, it's easy to see why separate children from the same parents can come out looking so different—from each other as well as from the parents themselves (**see Figure 10.3**). Overall, meiosis generates

Figure 10.3
Ensuring Variety
The shuffling of genetic material that occurs during meiosis is the primary reason that children look different from their parents, and from each other.

genetic *diversity*, while its counterpart, mitosis, does not. Mitosis makes genetically exact copies of cells; it *retains* the qualities that cells have from one generation to the next. Meiosis mixes genetic elements each time it produces reproductive cells and thus brings about genetic variation in succeeding generations.

From Genetic Diversity, a Visible Diversity in the Living World

This genetic variation has an importance way beyond that of making siblings look different from each other. It turns out that this diversity is responsible, in significant part, for the fantastically diverse natural world around us. Think of it: two-foot ferns, 100-yard redwood trees, bats, bees, whales, mushrooms. How did the natural world come to be such a remarkably diverse place? The short answer is that evolution is spurred on by the *differences* in offspring that meiosis brings about. Let's see why.

Three frog siblings survive to reproductive age from a clutch of eggs laid by a female and fertilized by a male. Thanks to crossing over and independent assortment, *one* of these frogs may end up having, say, a darker coloration than all the other frogs of its species in its area. In the formation of the eggs and sperm that led to this frog, chromsome parts were swapped (in crossing over) and chromosomes lined up (in independent assortment) in such a way that this frog was the darkest "model" possible, among all the frogs in its population. Further, it happens that, because of shifting rain patterns in this frog's habitat, this dark coloration is starting to be useful for evading predators. This frog will thus survive to have more offspring of its own than do other frogs around it. By being selected for survival in this way—by undergoing what is called natural selection—this frog may have started its population down the road to having a darker coloration.

Now, it's easy to see that coloration is only one of a countless number of traits that could be selected for like this. Taller height in a tree? Diving stamina in a dolphin? Meiosis and sexual reproduction would lead the way to these traits by producing, in one generation after another, *this* tree that grew a little taller or *that* dolphin that dove a little deeper. Just as General Motors provides an array of models for consumers to choose from each year, meiosis and sexual reproduction provide an array of models for *nature* to choose from each generation.

To put a finer point on this, consider the alternative to meiosis and sexual reproduction. Bacteria are single-celled organisms that possess a single, circular chromosome. As you saw in Chapter 9, bacteria divide through the process of binary fission, one bacterium

becoming two in the course of cell division. As it turns out, that's it for bacteria as far as reproduction goes. There is no chromosomal part-swapping or independent assortment of chromosomes in reproduction. And there is no fusion of two gametes from separate organisms, as occurs with eggs and sperm. Instead, there is just an exact duplication of the bacterial chromosome and a splitting of one bacterial cell into two. In general, then, every "daughter" bacterial cell is a genetic replica of its parent cell—a clone of it. What this means is that differences among bacteria are not a built-in feature of their reproduction. Instead, such differences as come to pass are dependent on their DNA mutating (which is rare) or on a form of gene transfer they are capable of (which is intermittent). Natural selection simply does not have as much to choose from in asexually reproducing organisms such as bacteria. Where is the equivalent of our darker-colored frog in a group of bacterial cells descended in a line? How could an equivalent difference come about, given that each bacterium is a clone of its predecessor?

What evidence do we have that sexual reproduction makes a practical difference? Well, consider that bacteria and their fellow single-celled organisms, the archaea, came into existence perhaps 3.8 billion years ago. Then, for 1.8 billion years after that, the living world consisted of nothing *but* bacteria and archaea—it took that long for anything else to evolve from them. We are not sure when sexual reproduction got going, but we have some evidence that it was taking place by 1.2 billion years ago. So, in the last 1.2 billion years, all the fish and birds and trees and fungi and flowers that we see before us developed through sexual reproduction, whereas in the 1.8 billion years after bacteria and archaea got going, they remained pretty much as they were when they began. Though other factors contributed to the ramping up of diversity on Earth, meiosis and sexual reproduction were key players in it. The British geneticist J. B. S. Haldane is said to have remarked that "Evolution could roll on fairly efficiently without sex but such a world would be a dull one to live in." In his statement, we can see the large-scale power of the small-scale processes we've been reviewing.

10.4 Meiosis and Sex Outcome

Let us think now about what meiosis means in relation to passing on sex to offspring. How do humans, in particular, come to be male or female? In humans there is one exception to the rule that chromosomes come in homologous pairs. Human females do indeed have 23 pairs of matched chromosomes, including 22 pairs of "autosomes" and one matched pair of **sex chromosomes**, meaning the chromosomes that determine what sex an individual will be. The sex chromosomes in females are called X chromosomes, and each female possesses two of them. In males, conversely, there are 22 autosomes, one X sex chromosome, and then one Y sex chromosome. It is this Y chromosome that confers the male sex. (See **Figure 10.4** for the differences in the X and Y sizes.)

In meiosis I in a female, the female's two X chromosomes, being homologous, line up together at the metaphase plate. Then these chromosomes separate, each of them going to different cells (**see Figure 10.5**). In males, the non-homologous X and Y chromosomes line up as if they were homologues. Then one resulting cell gets an X chromosome while the other gets the Y chromosome.

Sex determination is then simple. Each of the eggs produced by a female bears a single X chromosome. If this egg is fertilized by a *sperm* bearing an X chromosome, the resulting child will be a female. If, however, the egg is fertilized by a sperm bearing a Y chromosome, the child will be a male.

Because females don't have Y chromosomes to pass on, it follows that the Y chromosome that any male has had to come from his father. Meanwhile, the single X chromosome that any male has had to come from his mother. Females, conversely, carry one X chromosome from their mother and one from their father.

10.5 Gamete Formation in Humans

You've seen that, through meiosis, a single diploid cell gives rise to four haploid gametes. But what are the diploid cells that go through meiosis? As you might expect, there is a whole sequence of actions involved in the process by which egg and sperm are produced—a process known as *gamete formation*. In humans, the starting female cells in gamete formation are known as **oogonia**, while the starting male cells are **spermatogonia**. These are diploid cells

Figure 10.4
The X and the Y
The human X chromosome can be seen on the left, while the human Y chromosome is on the right. The difference in size between them is in part a reflection of the difference in the number of genes each of them contains. The Y chromosome only has about 50, while the X has about 1,500. (Magnified × 10,000)

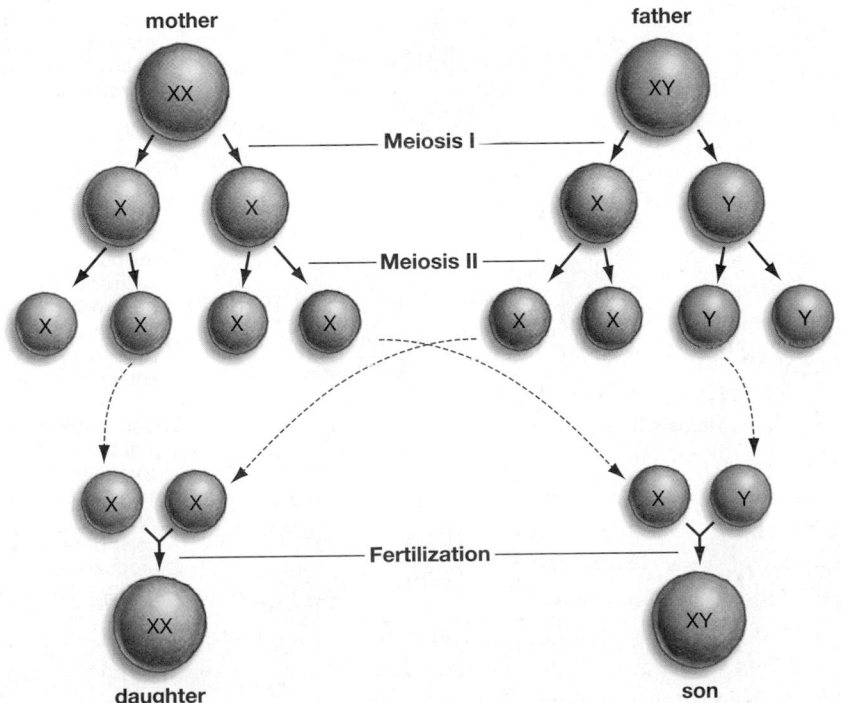

Figure 10.5
Sex Outcome in Human Reproduction

1. Early in meiosis I, the mother's two X chromosomes line up at the metaphase plate (XX). Meanwhile, in the father's meiosis, his X and Y chromosomes line up (XY).

2. The X-X and X-Y pairs then separate into different cells.

3. The chromatids that made up the duplicated chromosomes separate, yielding individual eggs and sperm.

4. Should an X-bearing sperm from the male reach the egg first, the child will be a girl; should the male's Y-bearing sperm reach the egg first, the child will be a boy.

that give rise to two other sets of diploid cells, the **primary oocytes** and **primary spermatocytes**. These then are the cells that undergo meiosis, yielding haploid sperm and egg cells.

Sperm Formation

The starting male spermatogonia exist in the male testes and are capable of giving rise to primary spermatocytes and of generating more spermatogonia. It is this latter, self-generating ability that qualifies spermatogonia as "stem" cells and that allows males to *keep* producing sperm throughout their lives, beginning at puberty. These sperm-producing "factories," in other words, generate not only sperm but more factories as well (**see Figure 10.6**).

The primary spermatocytes that come from spermatogonia go through meiosis I and thus produce the haploid *secondary spermatocytes*. Meiosis II then ensues, and the result is four haploid *spermatids*. These are not yet the familiar, tadpole-like sperm;

those come only after spermatids develop further, a process that takes about 3 weeks. There is thus an assembly-line quality to sperm production. Once a male reaches puberty, he starts producing sperm in this manner, with each sperm moving right through the entire process in a matter of weeks and the process continuing until the male dies. As you'll see, female egg production takes a much different route.

What is the nature of the sperm produced? A given sperm cell must fully develop its best-known feature, its tail-like flagellum. As it turns out, these "tails"—the only such structure in the human body—are composed of none other than the microtubules you have been seeing so much of in cell division. Moving the flagellum in a whip-like motion, microtubules serve to propel the sperm on their journey (**see Figure 10.7**). Sperm also need to "travel light," to which end developing sperm get rid of nearly all the cellular organelles reviewed back in Chapter 4: lysosomes, the Golgi complex, and so forth. A mature

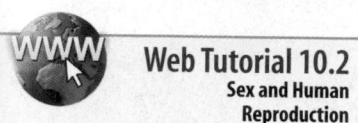

Web Tutorial 10.2
Sex and Human Reproduction

Figure 10.6
Sperm and Egg Formation in Humans

Spermatogenesis

spermatogonium

1. The diploid spermatogonium cell produces a primary spermatocyte.

primary spermatocyte

2. The primary spermatocyte goes through meiosis I, yielding two haploid secondary spermatocytes.

Meiosis I

secondary spermatocytes

3. The secondary spermatocytes go through meiosis II, yielding four haploid spermatids, which will develop into mature sperm cells.

Meiosis II

spermatids

Oogenesis

oogonium

1. Before the birth of the female, a cell called an oogonium develops into a primary oocyte; this cell enters meiosis I, but remains there until it matures in the female ovary, beginning at puberty.

primary oocyte

2. On average, one primary oocyte per month will complete meiosis I. In this process, an unequal meiotic division of cellular material leads to the production of one polar body and one secondary oocyte, which enters into meiosis II.

polar body

secondary oocyte

3. Only secondary oocytes that are fertilized by sperm will complete meiosis II and develop into an egg. The three polar bodies that are produced by meiosis I and II will be degraded.

polar bodies
(will be degraded)

egg

sperm thus amounts to little more than a haploid set of DNA-containing chromosomes in front, a collection of "engines" (mitochondria) in the middle, and a propeller (the flagellum) in the back. About 250 million sperm are made each day, and about that number will be released with each ejaculation. Sperm that are not released will age and eventually are destroyed by the body's immune system.

Egg Formation

The need of male sperm to become stripped-down DNA packages stands in contrast to the needs of female ova or eggs, which must have rich resources of nutrients and building materials in order to sustain life once they have been fertilized. This difference in function is reflected in size: The volume of an egg is 200,000 times the volume of a sperm (**see Figure 10.8** to get an idea of this difference). Accordingly, eggs are created in a process that maximizes cell content, at least for the fraction of eggs that become viable.

Egg formation begins with the cells called the *oogonia* of the female. These may sound like the counterpart to the male spermatogonia, but actually they are very different. Whereas spermatogonia are self-generating stem cells, oogonia are produced in large numbers only up to the seventh month of embryonic life, and none are created after birth. Of the millions produced, most will die while the female is still an embryo; but some survive to become primary oocytes and thus, as diploid cells, enter meiosis I (**see Figure 10.6**).

Amazingly enough, meiosis I is where these oocytes *stay*—for years. Imagine a collection of oocytes in the female ovaries (which are walnut-sized structures just right and left of center in the female pelvic area). Once puberty begins, each oocyte is theoretically capable of maturing into an egg, but an average of only *one* oocyte per month actually starts this maturation process. Which oocyte is this? The one released from the ovary each month in the process called ovulation. All the other oocytes in the ovaries halt their meiosis in prophase of meiosis I. Their chromosomes are duplicated and they have completed crossing over, but they have not yet lined up at the metaphase plate. And this is where things stay for most of the oocytes a female possesses. Only the one oocyte per month that is expelled from the ovary will complete meiosis I and thus enter into meiosis II. Even this meiosis is "arrested," however, until this oocyte is fertilized by a sperm. It is the union with a sperm that prompts the completion of meiosis II. Thus, an oocyte that came into being when a female was an embryo might remain sus-

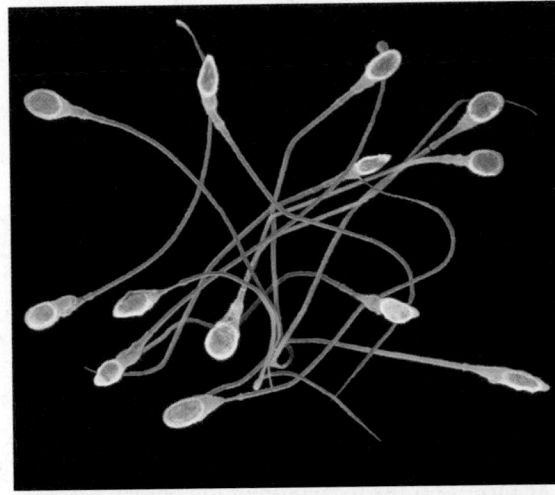

Figure 10.7
Mobile Cells, Bearing Chromosomes
Human sperm, colored to show detail.

Figure 10.8
Big Difference in Size
A human egg surrounded by much smaller human sperm.

pended in the cell cycle for years or even decades. Of the millions of oocytes originally created, only a few hundred will mature even through metaphase I in a woman's lifetime.

How do certain oocytes get "selected" to mature through metaphase I—how do they get selected to be ovulated, in other words? This occurs in connection with an intricate interplay that involves their surrounding tissue, hormones, and the happenstance of timing. You'll read more about this process in Chapter 30.

One Egg, Several Polar Bodies

For the few oocytes selected, the process of going through meiosis I and II means proceeding from one diploid cell to four haploid cells. In this process, however, almost all the cytoplasm will be shunted to *one* of the four cells, the better to build up its stores of nutrients and other cytoplasmic material. This happens in two rounds: meiosis I and meiosis II. When cytokinesis comes in meiosis I, one daughter cell gets almost all the cytoplasm while the second daughter cell gets almost none. This same thing happens in meiosis II. The result? One richly endowed haploid ovum and two, or perhaps three, very small haploid **polar bodies**: nonfunctional cells produced during meiosis in females (Figure 10.6). (Only two polar bodies and the ovum will be the end result if the polar body produced in meiosis I does not continue through meiosis II, which often happens.) The ovum has a chance at taking part in producing offspring, but the polar bodies are bound for oblivion rather than a shot at immortality. They will eventually degrade into their constituent substances.

10.6 Life Cycles: Humans and Other Organisms

The process of the formation of the human gametes called egg and sperm is followed, as you have seen, by the union of these gametes. In humans, the oocyte that is expelled from the ovary makes a slow trip down the female's uterine (or Fallopian) tube, during which time it may encounter a swimming sperm. If it does, the result will be a fertilized egg (or zygote), which then develops into a whole human being. One of the things that will eventually occur in this new human being is the development of another group of eggs or sperm through the process of meiosis. Thus do we see a **life cycle**: the repeating series of steps that occur in the reproduction of an organism. You have looked at the human life cycle, but it's important to recognize that it amounts to only one among many.

Figure 10.9
All-Female Species
Pictured is a Sonoran spotted whiptail lizard, *Cnemidophorus sonorae*, which reproduces through parthenogenesis. Because the eggs these lizards produce are not fertilized by males, they contain only one set of chromosomes, passed on by the mother. Hatchlings develop from these haploid eggs, however, and as a consequence the hatchlings themselves are haploid and genetically identical to the mother. The end result is a species that is entirely female. This lizard was photographed in Arizona.

Not All Reproduction Is Sexual

As noted earlier, human reproduction is **sexual reproduction**: the union of two reproductive cells to create a new organism. But in many other species there is **asexual reproduction** or reproduction that does not involve sex. Asexual reproduction actually is seen in a vast array of organisms. In fact, the only two groupings of living things that *never* carry out asexual reproduction are birds and mammals. Admittedly, asexual reproduction is rare in creatures as complex as fish or reptiles, but it does happen. In the American southwestern desert, for example, there are a few species of whiptail lizard that are entirely female (**see Figure 10.9**). The female whiptail lays haploid eggs, but they are never fertilized. Instead, they develop into haploid clones of her through mitotic cell division. This method of reproduction (called *parthenogenesis*) also results in "drone" male honeybees. Those eggs that a queen bee chooses not to fertilize (with stored-up sperm) develop into drones through parthenogenesis.

Other forms of asexual reproduction also are possible. In fact, you've already been introduced to one of them. Recall that a bacterial cell engages in a form of asexual reproduction, called binary fission, in which it duplicates its single chromosome and then divides in two. Beyond this, anyone who has ever seen a "cutting" taken from a plant knows that a snipped-off stem or branch will, when properly planted, sprout its own roots and grow into an independent plant, complete with the ability to take part in sexual reproduction. This process is called *vegetative reproduction*, and it has a counterpart in the animal world. Cut the arm and part of a central disk from a sea star, for example, and, through *regeneration*, this severed limb will grow into a whole, multi-armed sea star (**see Figure 10.10**).

As we go through the branching tree of life, from more complex creatures to less complex ones, asexual reproduction becomes more common. By the time we reach bacteria, it is the only form of reproduction used. Note that all forms of asexual reproduction produce offspring that are genetically identical to their parents. There is no mixing and matching of chromosomes from different parents in these asexual processes; just a cloning of one genetically identical individual from its parent.

Variations in Sexual Reproduction

Within the framework of sexual reproduction, as you can imagine, there are many variations. For example, separate gametes need not come from separate organisms. Some animals, such as tapeworms, are hermaphrodites, meaning they have both male and female reproductive parts. In some cases, hermaphrodites fertilize themselves, but generally they are fertilized by another member of their species. Most plants contain both male and female parts, and some plants "self-fertilize"—their sperm can fertilize their eggs—as with a pea plant you will be looking at in Chapter 11.

On to Patterns of Inheritance

The tour of cell division over the last couple of chapters has yielded not only a look at how one cell becomes two, but at how chromosomes operate within this process. Given the paired nature of chromosomes and their precisely ordered activity during meiosis, it stands to reason that there would be some predictability or pattern to the passing on of traits. This is the case, as it turns out. And the person who first recognized this pattern was a monk who worked in nineteenth-century Europe in an obscurity he did not deserve.

Figure 10.10
Regenerating the Whole from a Part
A sea star off the coast of Papua New Guinea is regenerating a body and other arms from a piece of one arm and part of its central disk.

Chapter Review

Summary

10.1 An Overview of Meiosis

- In human beings, nearly all cells have paired sets of chromosomes, meaning these cells are diploid. Meiosis is the process by which a single diploid cell divides to produce four haploid cells—cells that contain a single set of chromosomes.

- The haploid cells produced through meiosis are called gametes. Female gametes are eggs; male gametes are sperm. They are the reproductive cells of human beings and many other organisms.

- When the haploid sperm and haploid egg fuse, a diploid fertilized egg (or zygote) is produced, setting into development a new generation of organism.

10.2 The Steps in Meiosis

- In meiosis, there is one round of chromosome replication, followed by two rounds of cell division. There are two primary stages to meiosis, meiosis I and meiosis II. In meiosis I, chromosome duplication is followed by a pairing of homologous chromosomes with one another, during which time they exchange reciprocal sections of themselves. Homologous chromosome pairs then line up at the metaphase plate—one member of each pair on one side of the plate, the other member on the other side. These homologous pairs are then separated, in the first round of cell division, into separate daughter cells. In meiosis II, the chromatids of the duplicated chromosomes are separated into separate daughter cells.

Web Tutorial 10.1: Meiosis

10.3 What Is the Significance of Meiosis?

- Meiosis generates genetic diversity by ensuring that the gametes it gives rise to will differ from one another. In this, it is unlike regular cell division, or mitosis, which produces daughter cells that are exact genetic copies of parent cells.

- Meiosis generates genetic diversity in two ways. First, in prophase I of meiosis, homologous chromosomes pair with each other and, in the process called crossing over or recombination, exchange reciprocal chromosomal segments with one another. Second, in metaphase I of meiosis, there is a random alignment or independent assortment of maternal and paternal chromosomes on either side of the metaphase plate. This chance alignment determines which daughter cell each chromosome will end up in.

- The genetic diversity brought about by meiosis and sexual reproduction is responsible, to a significant extent, for the great diversity of life-forms seen in the living world today. Evolution is spurred on by differences among offspring, and meiosis and sexual reproduction ensure such differences. By contrast, asexual reproduction, as is seen in bacteria and other organisms, produces organisms that are exact genetic copies, or clones, of the parental organism.

10.4 Meiosis and Sex Outcome

- Human females have 23 matched pairs of chromosomes—22 autosomes and two X chromosomes. Human males have 22 autosomes, one X chromosome, and one Y chromosome. Each egg that a female produces has a single X chromosome in it. Each sperm that a male produces has either an X or a Y chromosome within it. If a sperm with a Y chromosome fertilizes an egg, the offspring will be male. If a sperm with an X chromosome fertilizes the egg, the offspring will be female.

10.5 Gamete Formation in Humans

- In humans, the starting cells in male gamete formation, spermatogonia, are diploid cells that give rise to other diploid cells, called primary spermatocytes, that go through meiosis. The result of this meiosis is cells called spermatids that develop into mature sperm. Female gamete formation begins with cells called oogonia, all of which are produced prior to the birth of the female. These give rise to primary oocytes—the cells that will go through meiosis I and II, producing the haploid female ovum or egg. The vast majority of primary oocytes never complete meiosis, however. It is only the single primary oocyte released each month, in the process of ovulation, that completes meiosis I. Only those ovulated oocytes that are fertilized by sperm complete meiosis II.

Web Tutorial 10.2: Sex and Human Reproduction

10.6 Life Cycles: Humans and Other Organisms

- Not all reproduction is sexual reproduction, meaning reproduction that works through a fusion of two reproductive cells. Most types of organisms are capable of asexual reproduction, though such reproduction is rare among more complex organisms and is never carried out by mammals or birds. Asexual reproduction can take several forms. Bacteria reproduce through one form of asexual reproduction, called binary fission, in which a given bacterial cell replicates its single chromosome and then divides in two. Plants can engage in vegetative reproduction; other organisms, such as worms and sea stars, can carry out regeneration in which a new, complete organism can be formed from a portion of an existing one.

Key Terms

Understanding the Basics

Multiple-Choice Questions (answers in the back of the book)

1. In reference to chromosomes, meiosis involves
   a. no duplications, 1 reduction
   b. 1 duplication, 2 reductions
   c. 2 duplications, 1 reduction
   d. 2 duplications, 2 reductions
   e. none of the above

2. Imagine, at prophase of meiosis I, that a diploid (2n) cell that is precursor to the gamete has eight chromosomes. How many chromatids are in the cell?
   a. 16
   b. 8
   c. 4
   d. 2
   e. twice that of mitosis prophase

3. Independent assortment occurs during
   a. prophase I
   b. anaphase II
   c. metaphase I
   d. metaphase II
   e. both c and d

4. Which of the following statements is *not* true regarding egg formation in humans?
   a. Oogonia are not produced until the eleventh or twelfth year.
   b. At the completion of division, one oocyte and two or three polar bodies exist.
   c. In both meiosis I and II, the metaphase plate is shifted to one side of the cell.
   d. An oocyte may take decades to go through the cell cycle.
   e. Each egg contains 23 chromosomes.

5. What are the two sources of genetic diversity in meiosis?
   a. binary fission and regeneration
   b. crossing over and independent assortment
   c. oogenesis and crossing over
   d. spermatogenesis and oogenesis
   e. vegetative reproduction and regeneration

6. Meiosis and sexual reproduction have fostered diversity in the natural world because they
   a. are so accurate in copying genetic information
   b. are nearly certain to produce differences among offspring
   c. are such ancient processes
   d. produce genetic replicas, one generation after another
   e. are used by such a wide range of organisms

7. Eggs are relatively large because they _____; sperm are relatively small because they _____.
   a. must contain spare sets of chromosomes ... function through mobility

b. must contain room for the growing zygote … have only one set of chromosomes

c. must contain room for the sperm … have a short life span

d. must contain nutrients for the zygote … function through mobility

e. exist in a harsh environment … exist in a nurturing environment

8. In prophase I of meiosis,
   a. maternal chromosome 1 joins with maternal chromosome 2.
   b. maternal chromosomes exchange genetic material with other maternal chromosomes.
   c. paternal chromosomes exchange genetic material with other paternal chromosomes.
   d. homologous chromosomes exchange sections.
   e. both c and d are correct.

9. At the completion of meiosis I, each human cell contains
   a. 23 chromosomes, 46 chromatids
   b. 46 chromosomes, 46 chromatids
   c. 46 chromosomes, 92 chromatids
   d. 23 chromosomes, 23 chromatids
   e. none of the above

10. Asexual reproduction is _____ and always results in _____.
    a. found in only a few types of organisms … offspring that are different from parents
    b. found in all types of organisms except mammals and reptiles … offspring that are sometimes genetically identical to parents
    c. reproduction that results from a fusion of two reproductive cells … twice as many offspring as parents
    d. found more commonly in simple organisms than in complex ones … offspring that are genetically identical to parents
    e. found in only a few mammals and birds … offspring that are different from parents

Brief Review

1. Does chromosome reduction take place during meiosis I or II?

2. Is asexual reproduction confined to the plant world?

3. Why are men able to keep producing sperm throughout their lifetime, from puberty forward?

4. How does meiotic cytokinesis in the production of eggs that females produce differ from mitotic cytokinesis?

5. Define and distinguish between somatic cells and gametes.

6. A diploid organism has four chromosomes. Name the phases of mitosis or meiosis shown in the following figures.

7. In what ways does meiosis ensure genetic diversity in offspring?

8. When human egg and sperm come together, how many chromosomes does each kind of gamete have? What is the genetic make-up of the resulting zygote?

Applying Your Knowledge

1. Ultimately, is it the paternal or maternal gamete that delivers the sex-determining chromosome? Describe the process.

2. Mammals have now been cloned by scientists (think of Dolly the sheep). Suppose that half the world's human births were achieved through cloning. How would our world be different?

3. All the bananas we eat come from trees that are produced through "cuttings"—a stem from an existing tree is planted in the ground, resulting in a new tree. Thus, each tree is a clone of another. Why would growers find it advantageous to produce an enormous series of identical clones, rather than using trees that reproduce sexually?

11 Mendel and His Discoveries

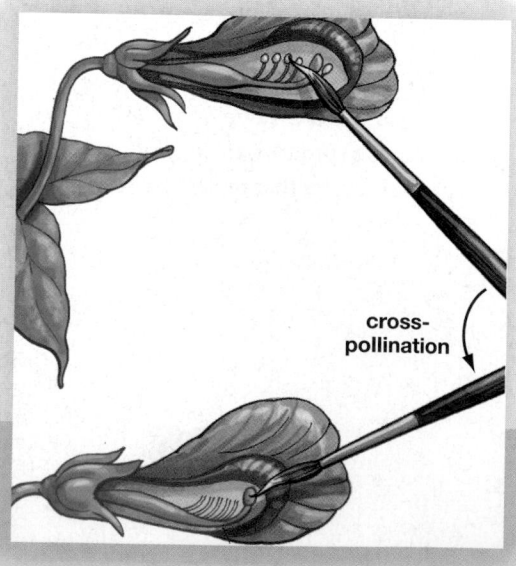

How to cross-pollinate.
(Section 11.2, page 209)

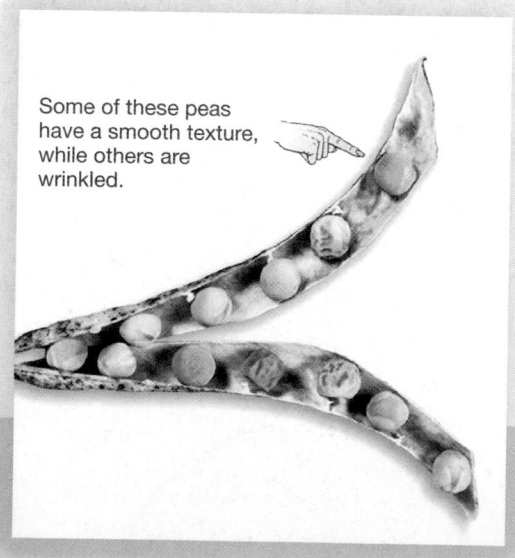

Some of these peas have a smooth texture, while others are wrinkled.

Same pod, different peas.
(Section 11.3, page 211)

mixed   "pure" green

More pea experiments.
(Section 11.4, page 213)

In the Czech Republic, in the oldest part of the city of Brno, stands the former Monastery of St. Thomas. Now a research center, St. Thomas has a small, fenced-in garden that sits just outside its historic living quarters. At one end of the garden stands an ivy-covered tablet, inscribed with a few simple words: "Prelate Gregor Mendel made his experiments for his law here." Visitors to the garden can cast their eyes upward and see the rooms that Gregor Johann Mendel lived in while carrying out his work in the years between 1856 and 1863 (**Figure 11.1**). Mendel labored during this time on a species of common peas, *Pisum sativum*, using tweezers and an artist's paintbrush as his tools. Like many scientific discoverers, Mendel looked at ordinary objects; and as with many scientists, his work was tedious and exacting. Nevertheless, the distance from what Mendel did to what Mendel learned is the distance from the ordinary to the historic.

Coming to adulthood in the mid-nineteenth century, Mendel knew nothing of the elements of genetics we have reviewed so far. Chromosomes and the genes that lie along them had not even been discovered when he was working with his peas; little knowledge existed of meiosis or mitosis, to say nothing of DNA. And as it happened, Mendel himself played no direct role in discovering any of these things. Yet this unassuming monk, the son of eastern European peasant farmers, generally is accorded the title of the father of genetics. What contribution earned him this honor?

Figure 11.1
Austrian Monk and Naturalist Gregor Mendel

maternal paternal
homozygous dominant

maternal paternal
heterozygous

Dominant and recessive.
(Section 11.4, page 215)

↓
F₂ generation

Pollen → SY   Sy   sY   sy

Egg
↓ SY

SS YY   SS Yy   Ss YY   Ss Yy

Sy

SS Yy   SS yy   Ss Yy   Ss yy

sY

Ss YY   Ss Yy   ss YY   ss Yy

sy

Ss Yy   Ss yy   ss Yy   ss yy

Breeding for two characters.
(Section 11.5, page 216)

Genes and environment.
(Section 11.10, page 222)

11.1 Mendel and the Black Box

Mendel's achievement was to comprehend what was going on inside what might be called the "black box" of genetics without ever being able to look inside that box himself. Science is filled with so-called black-box problems, in which researchers know what goes *into* a given process and what comes *out*. It is what is going on in between—in the black box—that is a mystery. In the case of genetics, what lies inside the black box is DNA and chromosomes and meiosis, and so forth—all the component parts of genetics, in other words, and the way they work together. Because of the timing of his birth, Mendel had no knowledge of any of these things. Until Mendel, however, nobody had looked carefully at even the starting and ending points of this black-box problem: at what went in and what came out. Mendel's original pea plants represented the "input" side to the black box of genetics, while the offspring he got from breeding these plants represented the output. By looking carefully at generations of parents and offspring—at both sides of the box, in a sense—Mendel was able to infer something about what had to be going on within. As you will see, his main inferences were correct: (1) that the basic units of genetics are material elements; (2) that these elements come in pairs; (3) that these elements (today called genes) can retain their character through many generations; and (4) that gene pairs *separate* during the formation of gametes.

These insights may sound familiar, because all of them were approached from another direction in Chapters 9 and 10. Here are the lessons you went over then:

1. Genes are material elements—lengths of DNA.

2. In human beings, genes come in pairs, residing in pairs of homologous chromosomes.

3. Chromosomes make copies of themselves, thus giving the genes that lie along them the ability to be passed on intact through generations.

4. In meiosis, homologous chromosomes line up next to each other and then *separate*, with each member of a pair ending up in a different egg or sperm cell.

By observing generations of pea plants and applying mathematics to his observations, Mendel inferred that something like this had to be happening in reproduction. Because Mendel was the first to perceive a set of principles that govern inheritance, we date our knowledge of genetics from him.

11.2 The Experimental Subjects: *Pisum sativum*

Beginning work in his monastery garden after a period of study in Vienna, Mendel managed to pick, in *Pisum sativum*, a nearly perfect species on which to carry out his experiments. If you look at **Figure 11.2**, you can see something of the life cycle of this garden pea. Note that what we think of as peas in a pod are seeds in this plant's ovary. Each of these seeds begins as an unfertilized egg, just as a human baby begins as a maternal egg that is unfertilized. Sperm-bearing pollen, landing on the plant's stigma, then set in motion the fertilization of the eggs.

Importantly, *Pisum* plants can *self*-pollinate. The anthers of a given flower release pollen grains that land on that flower's stigma. Each seed that develops from the resulting fertilizations can then be planted in the ground and give rise to a new generation of plant. The way to think of the seeds in a pod is as

Figure 11.2
Life Cycle of the Pea Plant

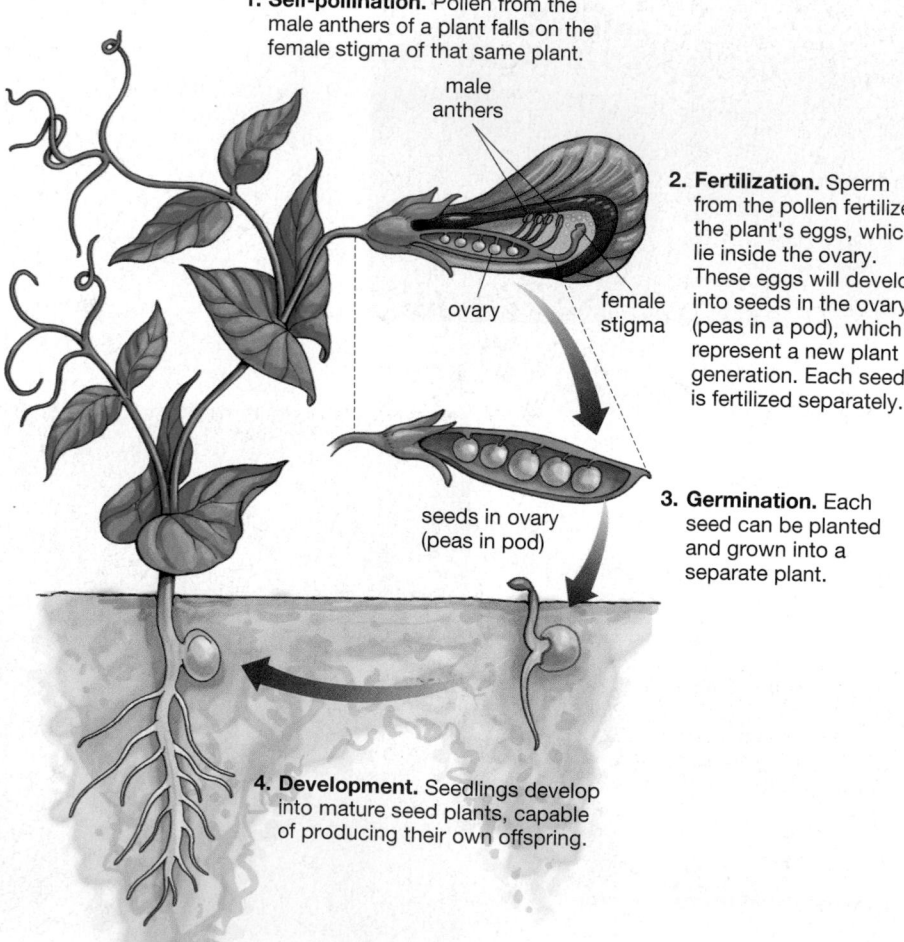

1. **Self-pollination.** Pollen from the male anthers of a plant falls on the female stigma of that same plant.

male anthers

2. **Fertilization.** Sperm from the pollen fertilize the plant's eggs, which lie inside the ovary. These eggs will develop into seeds in the ovary (peas in a pod), which represent a new plant generation. Each seed is fertilized separately.

ovary

female stigma

3. **Germination.** Each seed can be planted and grown into a separate plant.

seeds in ovary (peas in pod)

4. **Development.** Seedlings develop into mature seed plants, capable of producing their own offspring.

multiple offspring from separate fertilizations—one pollen grain fertilizes this seed, another pollen grain fertilizes another. This is why, as you'll see, seeds that are in the same pod can have different characteristics.

Though the pea plants can self-pollinate, Mendel could also **cross-pollinate** the plants at will—he could have one plant pollinate another—by going to work with his tweezers and paintbrushes, as shown in **Figure 11.3**.

In directing pollination, Mendel could control for certain attributes in his pea plants—qualities now referred to as *characters*. If you look at **Table 11.1** on page 210, you can see that there were seven characters in all—such things as stem length, seed color, and seed shape. Note that each of these characters comes in two varieties. There are yellow or green seeds, for example, and purple or white flowers. Such character variations are

**Figure 11.3
How to Cross-Pollinate Pea Plants**

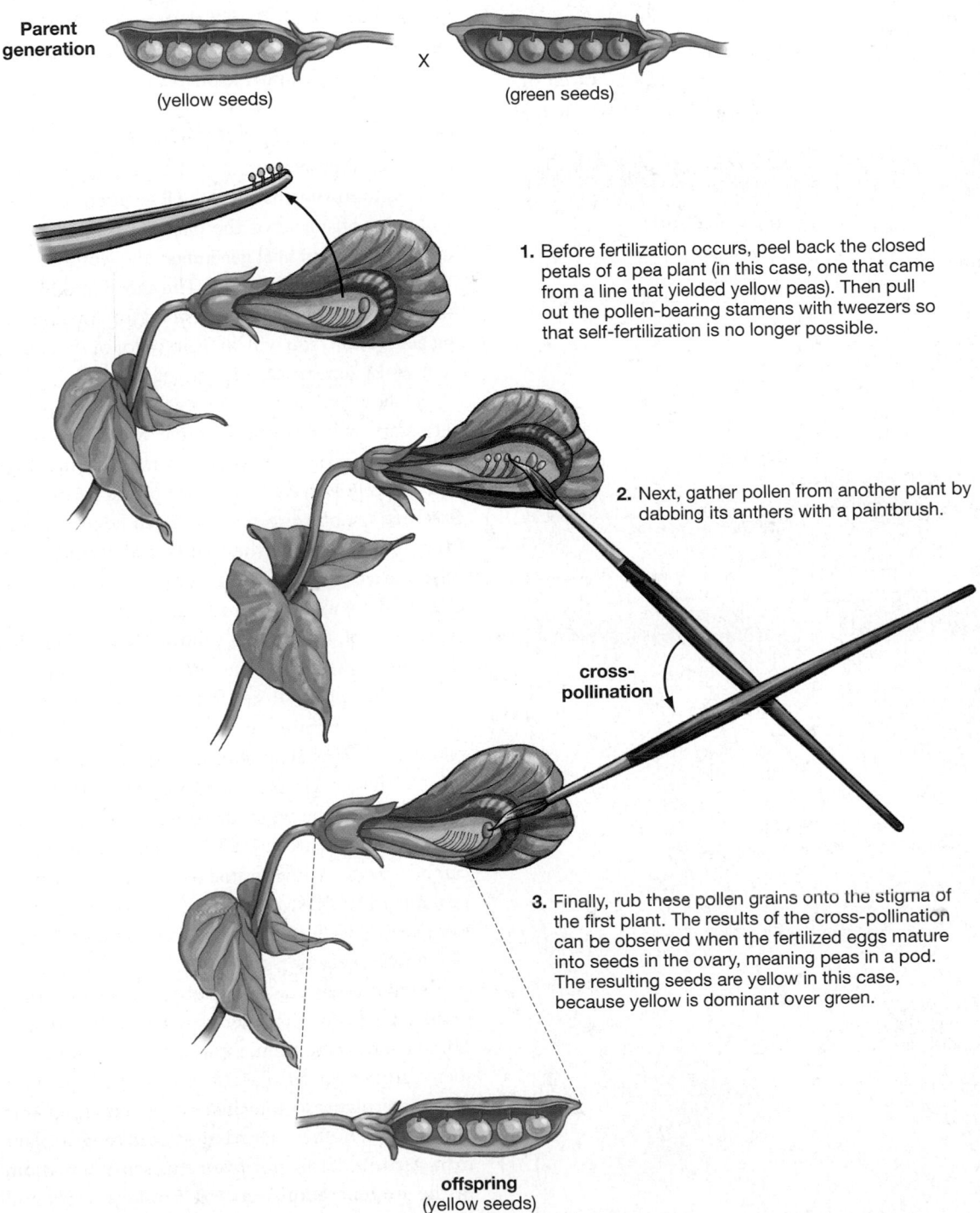

Parent generation

(yellow seeds)   X   (green seeds)

1. Before fertilization occurs, peel back the closed petals of a pea plant (in this case, one that came from a line that yielded yellow peas). Then pull out the pollen-bearing stamens with tweezers so that self-fertilization is no longer possible.

2. Next, gather pollen from another plant by dabbing its anthers with a paintbrush.

cross-pollination

3. Finally, rub these pollen grains onto the stigma of the first plant. The results of the cross-pollination can be observed when the fertilized eggs mature into seeds in the ovary, meaning peas in a pod. The resulting seeds are yellow in this case, because yellow is dominant over green.

offspring
(yellow seeds)

known as *traits*. Mendel referred to each of these variations as being either a "dominant" or a "recessive" trait, as the table shows. For now, you can think of a recessive trait as one that tends to remain hidden in certain generations of pea plants. A dominant trait, meanwhile, can be thought of as a trait that tends to appear in those same generations. You'll get a formal definition of dominant and recessive later.

Web Tutorial 11.1
Mendel's Experiments

Phenotype and Genotype

Now let's put these traits in another context. Taken together, traits represent what are called **phenotypes**. Broadly speaking, a phenotype is a physiological feature, bodily characteristic, or behavior of an organism. In the context of Mendel, phenotype means the pea plant's visible physical characteristics. Purple flowers are one phenotype, white flowers another; yellow seeds are one phenotype, green seeds another. Meanwhile, any phenotype is in significant part determined by an organism's underlying **genotype**, meaning its genetic makeup.

11.3 Starting the Experiments: Yellow and Green Peas

Mendel began by making sure that his starting plants "bred true" for the phenotypes under study. That is, he assured himself that, for example, all of his purple-flowered plants would produce nothing but generations of purple offspring.

Parental, F₁, and F₂ Generations

The **parental generation** in such experiments is often referred to in shorthand as the **P** generation. Meanwhile, the offspring of the parental generation are known as the **first filial generation**, the word *filial* indicating a son or a daughter. The shorthand for first filial is F_1. The F_x form can be used for any succeeding generation. You will be seeing a lot of the second filial, or F_2 generation, for example.

So how did Mendel proceed with his plants? Let's start with just one example. Mendel took, for his P generation, some plants from a line that bred true for yellow seeds and other plants from a line that bred true for green seeds. Then he took pollen from one variety of the plants and fertilized the other variety, as seen in Figure 11.3. The plants fertilized in this way then produced their own seeds—every one of which was yellow. (Remember that although these seeds were developing within the pods of the parental generation, they represented the new generation—the F_1 generation.) Getting all yellow seeds was an interesting result in itself. Because each seed in a pea-plant pod is fertilized separately, it *can* be the case that a given pod will contain both yellow and green seeds. (Other pea characters can be variable within a pod as well, as you can see in **Figure 11.4**.) Yet all the seeds in this generation were yellow, indicating that yellow was a dominant trait and green a recessive one.

Having viewed these results, Mendel then planted his F_1 seeds and let plants grow from them. These plants were then allowed to *self*-pollinate—sperm from a given plant fertilized the eggs from that same plant, so that instead of "crossing" one plant with another, Mendel was crossing a plant with itself. What he got from this self-pollination, in the F_2 generation, was 6,022 yellow seeds and 2,001 green seeds.

Table 11.1 Pea-Plant Characters Studied by Mendel		
Character studied	**Dominant trait**	**Recessive trait**
Seed shape	smooth	wrinkled
Seed color	yellow	green
Pod shape	inflated	wrinkled
Pod color	green	yellow
Flower color	purple	white
Flower position	on stem	at tip
Stem length	tall	dwarf

Some of these peas have a smooth texture, while others are wrinkled.

Figure 11.4
Variation within a Pea Pod
Since each garden pea is fertilized separately, individual peas within a pod can have different character traits.

The Power of Counting

In counting the seeds, Mendel was taking a giant step forward. Why? Experimenters before Mendel had gotten the kind of results he had. What they did not do, however, was undertake a careful *counting* of their results and then analyze the results in terms of proportions.

Looking at the specific results, two things stand out. First, green seeds disappeared in F_1, but came back in F_2. Recall that there was not a green seed to be found in the F_1 generation pods, but in F_2, there are 2,001 of them. Second, green seeds came back in F_2 as a *specific proportion* of the seeds as a whole. The F_2 generation isn't divided 50/50, half-yellow and half-

green; instead, there are roughly 3 yellow seeds for every 1 green seed—or to put it another way, a 3:1 ratio of yellow to green seeds. As it turned out, Mendel got the same result with each of the seven characters he was studying, as you can see in **Table 11.2**. Note that the 3:1 ratio is a proportion of dominant to recessive traits—more yellow seeds than green, more purple flowers than white. It was *solely* the dominant traits that appeared in the F_1 generation, but in the F_2 generation the dominants are simply appearing in greater proportion than the recessives.

Interpreting the F_1 and F_2 Results
What did Mendel learn from these results?

No "Blending" in Inheritance
For one thing, he saw that inheritance for his peas was not a matter of the "blending" of their characteristics. For example, the flower colors purple and white were retained as just that. No intermediate phenotypes—say, pink flowers—resulted from the cross in any generation. This finding ran contrary to the notion, popular in Mendel's time, that two given traits would blend into a homogenous third entity, as coffee and milk will blend together.

Dominant and Recessive Elements Come in Pairs
Beyond this finding, it was apparent that, dominance notwithstanding, plants could retain the *potential* for recessive phenotypes, even though those phenotypes might not appear in a given generation. Mendel's F_1 plants had no green seeds, but in F_2 the green seeds were back. It was reasonable to assume, therefore, that the yellow-seed F_1 plants retained a green-seed

Dominant trait	Recessive trait	Ratio of dominant to recessive in F_2 generation
Smooth seed	Wrinkled seed	2.96:1 (5,474 smooth, 1,850 wrinkled)
Yellow seed	Green seed	3.01:1 (6,022 yellow, 2,001 green)
Inflated pod	Wrinkled pod	2.95:1 (882 inflated, 299 wrinkled)
Green pod	Yellow pod	2.82:1 (428 green, 152 yellow)
Purple flower	White flower	3.14:1 (705 purple, 224 white)
Flower on stem	Flower at tip	3.14:1 (651 along stem, 207 at tip)
Tall stem	Dwarf stem	2.84:1 (787 tall plants, 277 dwarfs)
	Average ratio, all traits:	**3:1**

Table 11.2 Ratios of Dominant to Recessive in Mendel's Plants

element, which got expressed only in the F₂ generation. Finally, because his phenotypes came in pairs, it was reasonable for Mendel to hypothesize that the elements likewise came in pairs.

If you think Mendel's *pairs of elements* sound suspiciously like the "pairs of genes" on homologous chromosomes we've seen before, you are right. However, it's time to start referring to these "matched pairs of genes" in scientific terminology. It is more accurate to think of matched pairs of genes as alternative forms of a single gene. The proper name for an alternative form of a gene is an **allele**. Thus the pea plant had a single gene for seed color that came in two alleles—one of which coded for yellow seeds, the other of which coded for green seeds. These alleles resided on separate homologous chromosomes.

Figure 11.5
(a) Mendel's P Generation Crosses
(b) Examples of Punnett Squares

11.4 Another Generation for Mendel

Having seen recessive phenotypes reappear in F₂, Mendel decided to extend his breeding. In his next experiment, he took a set of F₂ generation seeds— all of them yellow—planted them and let the plants they grew into self-pollinate. Then he looked at the color of the F₃ seeds contained in the pods of these plants. What he found was that, of 519 plants grown, 166 yielded only yellow seeds, while the remaining 353 plants had a mixture of yellow and green seeds in the pods, in the familiar 3:1 ratio. But when he similarly took F₂ green seeds, planted them, and let them self-pollinate, these plants produced nothing but green seeds.

(a) P generation crosses

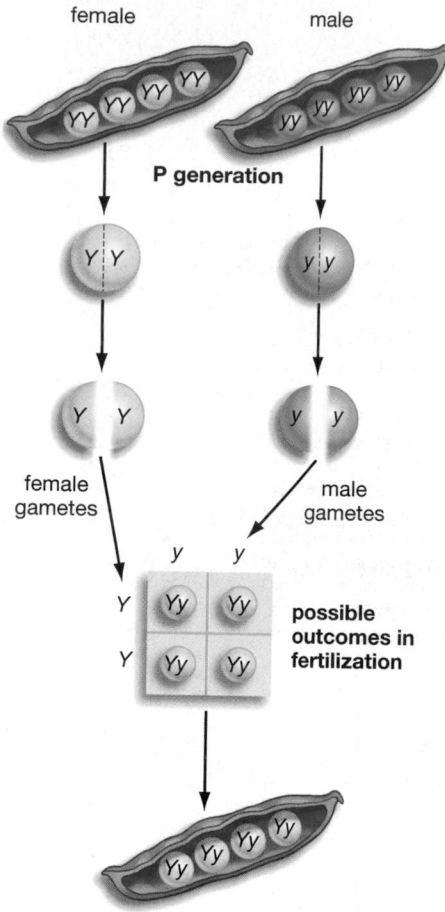

1. Female gametes are being provided by a plant that has the dominant, yellow alleles (*YY*); male gametes are being provided by a plant that has the recessive, green alleles (*yy*).

2. The cells of the pea plants that give rise to gametes start to go through meiosis.

3. The two alleles for pea color, which lie on separate homologous chromosomes, separate in meiosis, yielding gametes that each bear a single allele for seed color. In the female, each gamete bears a *Y* allele; in the male, each bears a *y* allele.

4. The Punnett square shows the possible combinations that can result when the male and female gametes come together in the moment of fertilization. (If you have trouble reading the Punnett square, see Figure 11.5b). The single possible outcome in this fertilization is a mixed genotype, *Yy*.

5. Because *Y* (yellow) is dominant over *y* (green), the result is that all the offspring in the F₁ generation are yellow, because they all contain a *Y* allele.

What could have caused these results? The answer was the underlying elements Mendel had hit upon, meaning the alleles for the color gene. When he planted his yellow seeds, some of them yielded all-yellow offspring, but others yielded mixed (green and yellow) offspring. He reasoned that there must be *two kinds* of yellow plants: Those that are "pure" yellow (the 166 that yielded solely yellow seeds) and those that were "mixed" yellow (the 353 that produced both yellow and green seeds). Pure yellow had *nothing but* yellow alleles within, and would produce nothing but yellow seeds when self-pollinated. Meanwhile, the mixed yellow would have one yellow and one *green* allele within, and thus would produce pods that contained seeds of both colors. Finally, the green seeds had nothing but green alleles and thus produced nothing but green seeds.

Mendel's Generations in Pictures

Let's make these points clearer by reviewing all three generations of experiments schematically.

The F₁ Generation

It will be helpful to introduce a convention here. Let us refer to dominant and recessive alleles by uppercase and lowercase letters, with uppercase used for dominant types and lowercase used for recessive types. Thus a "pure" yellow-seeded plant, having *two* yellow alleles, would be symbolized as *YY*. Meanwhile, pure green-seeded plants are *yy*, while mixed

(b) How to read a Punnett square

1. A *p* gamete from the male combines with a *p* gamete from the female to produce an offspring of *pp* genotype (and white color).

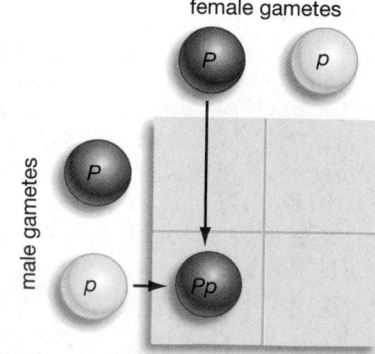

2. A *p* gamete from the male combines with a *P* gamete from the female to produce an offspring of *Pp* genotype (and purple color).

seeds are *Yy*. Let us say, just as an example, that female gametes are being supplied by a plant that is *YY*, while male gametes are coming from a plant that is *yy*. In meiosis, as you've seen, homologous chromosomes separate. This happens in the pea plants, meaning that each of these plants will contribute *one member* of its gene pair to its respective gametes—the *YY* female contributing a *Y* gamete, and the *yy* male contributing a *y* gamete. When these gametes fuse in the moment of fertilization, the result is a *Yy* hybrid in the F₁ generation. If you look at **Figure 11.5**, you will be introduced to a time-honored way to represent such outcomes, the Punnett square, and see Mendel's F₁ results symbolized as well.

Note that, because *Y* is dominant, all the seeds in the F₁ offspring pods will have a yellow *phenotype*, even though every one of these seeds contains a mixed *genotype*. (Every one is *Yy*.) It takes only one *Y*

allele for a seed to be yellow; for a seed to be green, then, it must have two *y* alleles.

The F₂ Generation

Next come the F₁ crosses that yielded the F₂ generation. The starting point here is the F₁ seeds, which are all of the mixed *Yy* type, as you can see in **Figure 11.6**. Meiosis then occurs in the gamete precursors, which results in a separation of these alleles: Half the gametes now contain *Y* alleles and the other half *y*. You can see from the figure why this cross can now give us back the green-seed phenotype, on average in a 1:3 proportion with yellow seeds. Note that there are twice as many mixed-genotype seeds (*Yy*) as either variety of pure seed (*YY* or *yy*). Important mathematical principles underlie this outcome. You can read more about them in "Proportions and Their Causes." on the next page.

Figure 11.6
From the F₁ to the F₃ Generation

From the F₁ to the F₂ generation

The starting point is the F₁ generation, a set of seeds that all have the *Yy* genotype. These seeds are planted and the plants go through meiosis, yielding the gametes shown around the Punnett square. When these gametes come together in self-fertilization, the possibilities include *YY* and *yy* combinations, as well as the *Yy* combination seen in the F₁ generation. The existence of *yy* individuals is the reason green seeds reappear in the F₂ generation. Because *Y* is dominant, the green phenotype could not appear in seeds that had even a single *Y* allele.

From the F₂ to the F₃ generation

With three starting genotypes (*YY, Yy, yy*) the F₂ generation yields plants that have these three genotypes, though there are more F₂ plants of "mixed" genotype than of either "pure" genotype.

Proportions and Their Causes: The Rules of Multiplication and Addition

To be a good songwriter, a person needs to be both a good musical composer and a good lyricist. Of all the people who decide to take up songwriting, say that 1 in 10 is a good composer and that 1 in 10 is a good lyricist. Now, what is the probability that a person who takes up songwriting will be *both* a good composer and a good lyricist? The answer to this question turns out to have relevance to all kinds of questions in our world, including the results that Gregor Mendel got.

When Mendel examined the F_2 pods that contained the F_3 seeds, he found that there were many more pods that had mixed seed colors within (yellow and green) than pods whose seeds were either all-yellow or all-green. It was the F_1 meiosis that set the stage for this outcome, as you can see here:

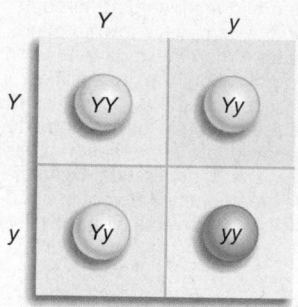

The Punnett square provides an intuitive visual sense of why things turned out the way they did. Meiosis in the F_1 plants produced twice as many mixed F_2 seeds (Yy) as either type of "pure" seeds (YY or yy). It's even more helpful, however, to understand a principle that underlies this outcome. A simple coin-tossing example can illustrate what is at work. Suppose that you are going to throw two coins in the air—a nickel and a dime. What is the likelihood that *both* coins will come up heads? There is only one way to get this result:

1. Nickel = heads; dime = heads

Now consider tossing the two coins and specifying a *mixed* result. There are *two* ways that this condition can be satisfied:

1. Nickel = heads; dime = tails
2. Dime = heads; nickel = tails

The seeds are in the same situation. What is the likelihood of getting a "pure" yellow seed? As you can see by looking again at the Punnett square, there is only one way to get this: female Y, male Y. Now consider specifying a mixed result. There are two ways to get this: female y, male Y; and female Y, male y.

The Rule of Multiplication

In order to state a principle that can generalize to any situation, let's look at this concept in a more formal way. What are the odds of tossing up one coin and getting heads? Fifty-fifty, right?

What are the odds of tossing up two coins and having both come up heads?

This means a 50 percent chance, which equals 0.5. Now what are the odds of tossing up two coins and having both come up heads? A principle called the **rule of multiplication** comes into play here. It states that the probability of any *two* events happening is the product of their respective probabilities. In this case, the probability for each head coming up is 0.5, so the equation is $0.5 \times 0.5 = 0.25$, or a 25 percent probability of two heads.

The Rule of Addition

Now what is the probability of getting one coin that comes up heads and one that comes up tails—when either of them can be heads or tails? When an outcome can occur in two or more *different* ways, as is the case here, the probability of this happening is the *sum* of the respective probabilities. This principle is known as the **rule of addition**. The probability of nickel = heads, dime = tails is the same 0.25 probability you saw in the rule of multiplication. But the probability of nickel = tails, dime = heads is also 0.25. The probability that *either* of these outcomes will take place is thus $0.25 + 0.25 = 0.50$, or 50 percent.

All this gives us a way to figure the songwriter probability—or any set of independent probabilities. Remember the stipulation that 1 in 10 aspiring songwriters is a good composer and 1 in 10 is a good lyricist. Thus, under the rule of multiplication, $0.10 \times 0.10 = 0.01$, meaning 1 in 100 will be good at both composing and lyric writing.

The F₃ Generation

Finally, in Figure 11.6, you can see why Mendel got the results he did when he went from F₂ to F₃. Recall that when Mendel planted and self-fertilized his *yellow* F₂ seeds, he got 519 plants, of which 166 produced nothing but yellow seeds. Now you can see why: These were not only phenotypically yellow; they were "pure" yellow in terms of genotype (*YY*). Mendel also got 353 plants that produced both yellow and green seeds. This is because the seeds these plants grew from were of mixed genotype (*Yy*); in reproduction, their offspring would be of both pure (*YY, yy*) and mixed (*Yy*) genotype. Finally, when Mendel planted and self-fertilized *green* F₂ seeds, all the plants that resulted from these seeds bred true for green seeds, because all of them began as *yy*. **Figure 11.7** illustrates how the three genotypes discussed here yield only the two phenotypes of yellow or green.

The Law of Segregation

For inheritance to work this way, Mendel saw something we noted earlier: That, though plant cells may contain *two* copies (alleles) of a gene relating to a given character, these copies must *separate* in gamete formation. How else could two *Yy* parents ever give rise to *yy* (or *YY*) progeny, unless the *Yy* elements could first separate (in the parents) and then recombine in different ways (in the offspring)? Thus did Mendel derive his insight, sometimes called Mendel's First Law or the **Law of Segregation:** Differing characters in organisms result from two genetic elements (alleles) that separate in gamete formation, such that each gamete gets only one of the two alleles. As noted, the physical basis for this law, which Mendel knew nothing of, is the separation of homologous chromosomes during meiosis.

Homozygous and Heterozygous Conditions

It's time to add a couple more terms to the concepts you have been considering. There is scientific terminology for the genotypically "pure" and "mixed" organisms noted earlier. An organism that has two identical alleles of a gene for a given character is said to be **homozygous** for that character (as with *YY* or *yy*). An organism that has differing alleles for a character is said to be **heterozygous** for that character (as with *Yy*). You often see homozygous used in combination with the terms dominant and recessive. For example, a *yy* plant is a *homozygous recessive*, while a *YY* is a *homozygous dominant* (**see Figure 11.8**). Knowledge of these terms puts you in a position to understand formal definitions of dominant and recessive. **Dominant** is a term used to desig-

Three genotypes yield . . .

two phenotypes.

yellow   green

Figure 11.7
Three Genotypes Yield Two Phenotypes
The two alleles for seed color (*Y* = yellow and *y* = green) can result in three genotypes (*YY, Yy, yy*), but these can yield only two phenotypes (yellow and green).

nate an allele that is expressed in the heterozygous condition. In a heterozygous pea plant (*Yy*), the yellow allele (*Y*) is expressed, meaning it is dominant over the green allele (*y*). **Recessive** is a term used to designate an allele that is not expressed in the heterozygous condition. The green allele (*y*) is recessive because it is not expressed when it exists heterozygously with the yellow allele (*Yy*).

possible pairing of homologous chromosomes

dominant allele

recessive allele

location of gene for seed color

maternal paternal   maternal paternal   maternal paternal
homozygous dominant   **heterozygous**   **homozygous recessive**

yellow seeds   yellow seeds   green seeds

Figure 11.8
Chromosomes and Phenotypes
The figure shows how alleles on chromosomes yielded the pea-color phenotypes that Mendel observed.

11.5 Crosses Involving Two Characters

Thus far, the subject has been how pea plants come to differ in *one* of their characters, seed color. When people breed organisms for a single difference such as this, looking to see how the offspring will come out, the procedure is known as a **monohybrid cross.** Mendel, however, went on to ask: What happens if you breed organisms for *two* characters? What happens, in other words, if you undertake what is known as **dihybrid cross**? The question Mendel was seeking to answer in carrying out his dihybrid crosses was: Do given characters travel together in heredity, or do they travel separately? If you get one character passed on to a plant, do you necessarily get the other?

Crosses for Seed Color *and* Seed Shape

One dihybrid cross that Mendel performed involved, for its first character, the yellow and green seeds you've become so familiar with. In addition, this cross involved a second character of these seeds: their shape, which can be smooth or wrinkled (as you saw in Figure 11.4). It's clear that yellow color is dominant to green and, as Table 11.1 shows, smooth seed shape is dominant to wrinkled. We have been denoting the alleles for seed color as Y for yellow and y for green. In the same fashion, let us now denote seed-shape alleles as S for smooth and s for wrinkled.

You can see, in **Figure 11.9a**, what the phenotypic outcomes were for these crosses from the P to F_1 gen-erations. In the F_1 generation, all the seeds were smooth and yellow. When the F_1s were self-pollinated, however, the F_2 phenotypes that resulted came out as 315 smooth yellow seeds; 108 smooth green seeds; 101 wrinkled yellow seeds; and 32 wrinkled green seeds. These numbers work out to a 9:3:3:1 ratio, meaning 9 parts smooth yellow; 3 parts smooth green; 3 parts wrinkled yellow; and 1 part wrinkled green.

A Hidden, Underlying Ratio

For Mendel, these imposing figures represented another opportunity to perceive something about how the black box of genetics operated. He realized early on that this ratio might be a composite, hiding an underlying reality for each of the *single* characters

**Figure 11.9
Phenotype Ratios in a Dihybrid Cross**

(a) Results of Mendel's dihybrid cross

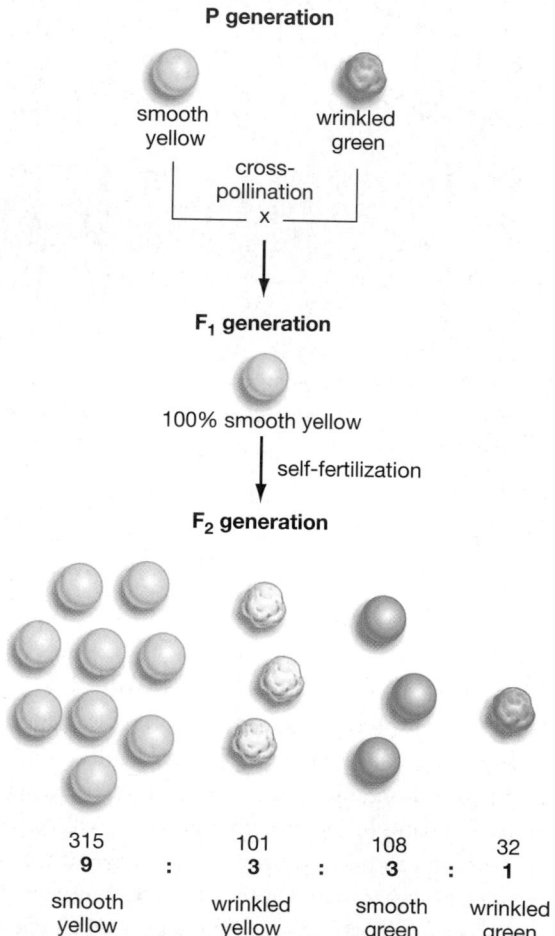

In one of his dihybrid crosses, Mendel cross-bred plants that had smooth yellow seeds with those that had green wrinkled seeds. The result was a generation of plants that all had smooth yellow seeds. When these plants self-fertilized, the result was an F_2 generation that had the phenotypes shown in a 9:3:3:1 ratio.

(b) Why Mendel got these results

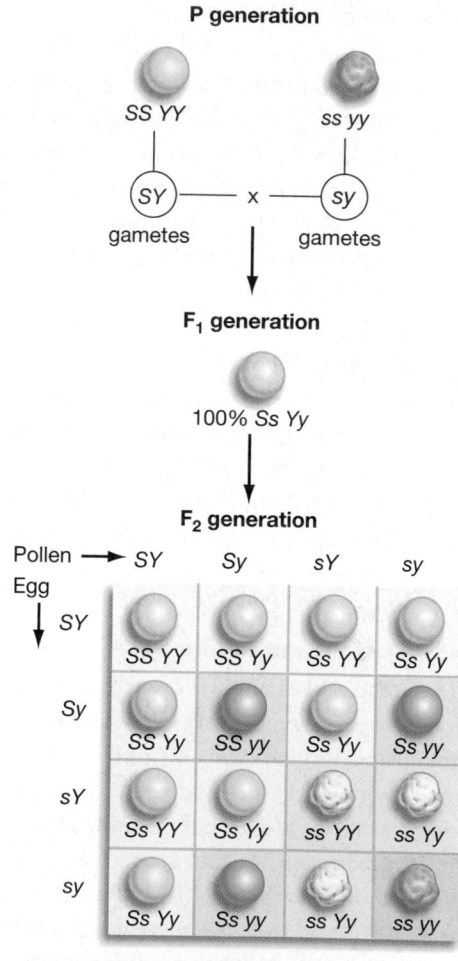

The Punnett square demonstrates why Mendel got the 9:3:3:1 phenotypic ratio in his dihybrid cross. Nine combinations yield smooth yellow seeds, 3 yield smooth green seeds, 3 yield wrinkled yellow seeds, while only 1 results in a wrinkled green seed.

he was studying. Think for a second, as Mendel did, of only one of these characters, the color of the seeds. Here, the result is:

315 (smooth) yellow seeds	108 (smooth) green seeds
<u>101</u> (wrinkled) yellow	<u> 32</u> (wrinkled) green
416 yellow seeds	140 green seeds

This equals a yellow:green ratio of about 3:1. In other words, the familiar 3:1 ratio in the F_2 generation still holds. It held as well when Mendel looked only at seed *shape*. This suggested something to Mendel that turned out to be another of his major insights: that characters—in this case, seed shape and seed color—are transmitted *independently* of one another. When these two characters were being crossed at the same time, the results for each were the same as when they were crossed as single characters in the earlier experiments. Thus, one character's transmission did not appear to affect the other's.

Understanding the 9:3:3:1 Ratio

Still, what's the basis of the formidable 9:3:3:1 ratio that Mendel got in his dihybrid cross, with its mixture of wrinkled yellows, smooth greens, and so forth? This is simply a more complex example of the kind of outcomes you saw earlier with the aid of the Punnett square. If you look at the square in **Figure 11.9b** and start adding up internal squares *by phenotype*, Mendel's 9:3:3:1 ratio starts making sense. You can see, for example, where the 1 in the ratio comes from: There is only 1 part wrinkled green seeds, because it is only the *sy* (pollen) and *sy* (egg) combination that yields this phenotype. Likewise, you will get three parts wrinkled yellow seeds by adding up the three possible male and female gamete combinations that could bring this about.

The Law of Independent Assortment

This outcome could only come about, however, if Mendel's fundamental insight about dihybrid crosses was correct: that characters were being transmitted independently of one another. If one character had affected another's transmission, these ratios would have been very different. This insight of Mendel's is now known as Mendel's Second Law, or the **Law of Independent Assortment**. It states that during gamete formation, gene pairs assort independently of one another.

Independent Assortment and Chromosomes

Now recall that the underlying physical basis for this law was set forth in Chapter 10: In meiosis, pairs of homologous chromosomes *assort independently* from one another at the metaphase plate. It may be, for example, that paternal chromosome 5 will line up on side A of the metaphase plate; if so, then maternal chromosome 5 ends up on side B. For chromosome 6, however, things could just as easily be reversed: The *maternal* chromosome might end up on side A, and the paternal on side B (see Figure 10.2, page 194.) The genes for Mendel's seed color exist on the plant's chromosome 1, while the genes for seed shape exist on its chromosome 7. Because these are separate chromosomes, they assort independently at the metaphase plate, meaning they are passed on independently to future generations.

11.6 Reception of Mendel's Ideas

When Mendel finished his experiments, he delivered two lectures on them to a local scientific society in 1865. It would be nice to report that the society members' jaws dropped open once Mendel let them in on how inheritance worked in the living world, but no such thing happened. His findings were ultimately published in a scientific journal that was distributed in Germany, Austria, the United States, and England. Mendel even took it upon himself to get 40 reprints of his paper, thereafter sending some out to various scientists in an effort to spark some exchange on his findings. All to no avail. His work sank nearly without a trace, finally to be rediscovered in 1900, 16 years after his death. Today, the consensus within the scientific community is that nobody cared about Mendel's findings in his own time simply because nobody grasped their significance (see "Why So Unrecognized?" on the next page).

This poor early reception notwithstanding, Mendel's insights have stood the test of time. For certain kinds of phenotypes, his rules of inheritance are extremely reliable. To this day, biologists will begin an observation by noting that "Mendelian rules tell us that . . . " or "Mendelian inheritance operates here." Even allowing that he had intellectual predecessors, the fact is that Mendel did not just *add* to the discipline of genetics; he founded it.

11.7 Incomplete Dominance

Mendel knew as well as anyone that the rules he discovered did not apply in all instances of inheritance. In his peas, crossing white- and purple-flowered plants resulted in an F_1 generation in which all flowers were purple. In some other species, however, the results are different. Crossing a true-breeding red-flowered *snapdragon* with a true-breeding white-flowered snapdragon produces neither red- nor white-flowered F$_1$ snapdragons, but *pink* snapdragons (**see Figure 11.10**). This might seem to indicate that inheritance can indeed work through the blending of genetic traits—a notion that Mendel's work had quashed. Blending is not taking place, however. When breeding is continued through the F$_2$ generation, red and white flowers come back, along with the pink, in a ratio of 1 part red, 2 parts pink, 1 part white. This 1:2:1 ratio demonstrates that red and white alleles have not irretrievably blended into pink, but rather have come together in F$_1$, only to separate out again in F$_2$. Still, how can the pink F$_1$ snapdragons be explained?

Genes Code for Proteins

First, think about what genes do: They contain information regarding the production of proteins. In the case of colors, such proteins can bring about the formation of pigments. This is the case with the snapdragons; they have a gene for color, and one of the alleles of this gene brings about the production of red pigment. Meanwhile, the second allele of this gene is nonfunctional—it brings about the production of no pigment at all. Two of the red alleles, then, yield a red color, while one red allele produces only enough pigment to yield a pink color. Neither the red nor the white allele, therefore, is completely dominant; each is thus said to have **incomplete dominance**, meaning a genetic condition in which the heterozygote phenotype is intermediate between either of the homozygous phenotypes.

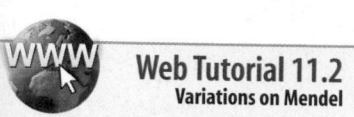

Web Tutorial 11.2
Variations on Mendel

Figure 11.10
How Red and White Yield Pink: Incomplete Dominance in Snapdragons

RR
red

rr
white

P generation

1. The starting plants are a snapdragon homozygous for red color (*RR*) and snapdragon homozygous for white color (*rr*).

Rr
100% pink

F$_1$ generation

2. When these plants are crossed, the resulting *Rr* genotype yields only enough pigment to produce a flower that is pink—the only phenotype in the F$_1$ generation.

sperm

R   *r*

R

RR   *Rr*

egg

r

Rr   *rr*

F$_2$ generation

3. In the F$_2$ generation, alleles combine to produce red, pink, and white phenotypes.

1 : 2 : 1
red   pink   white

Why So Unrecognized?

"If fame belonged to me, I could not escape her—if she did not, the longest day would pass me on the chase," wrote Emily Dickinson in 1862, in seeming ambivalence about becoming a published poet. Dickinson's words came in a letter to Thomas Higginson, who had recently advised her against seeking publication of her verses on grounds that they were not yet strong enough. Higginson was the second, and as it turned out, last person to disparage Dickinson's efforts to publish her poetry. After his advice was offered, Dickinson kept her own company as a writer; by the time she died, only a close circle around her had seen her work.

Half a world away, Dickinson had a counterpart of sorts in her contemporary, Gregor Mendel (born eight years before her, and deceased two years before). Like Dickinson, Mendel had something special to offer the world. But it was an offer made to a world that was not prepared to listen. Mendel died in obscurity in 1884, his work appreciated by, so far as we can tell, no one but himself. Indeed, 34 years were to pass between publication of his research results and recognition of their significance. Yet from the time his work was rediscovered in 1900, Mendel has been treated with great respect, such that today he is generally recognized as the founder of genetics.

How, then, could Mendel's work have gone unrecognized in his own time? A couple of easy but **unsatisfying** answers are that he labored in a scientific backwater (in the hinterland of the Austrian empire) and that his results were published in an obscure scientific journal.

Mendel appears to have been a victim of his own originality.

Even granting these points, a good number of scientists still had access to Mendel's report—if not by reading it in the journal that published it, then by receiving one of the reprints of it that Mendel himself mailed out. If fame didn't follow from such exposure, why not simple recognition by at least one person?

The answer appears to be fairly straightforward: Mendel wasn't appreciated in his lifetime by anyone because he wasn't comprehended in his lifetime by anyone. Indeed, intense exposure to his ideas seemed to make no difference in this regard. Consider that he carried on a seven-year correspondence regarding his work with a famous botanist, Carl Nägeli, during which time Nägeli, like everyone else, seemed to miss the significance of Mendel's experiments entirely. Assuming that nineteenth-century scientists were as bright as those in the twenty-first century, how could this have happened?

First, Mendel himself did not make much of the principles of heredity he uncovered. In his long paper, he punctuates a great deal of detail about his experiments with some understated formulations of general principles. In itself, this is not surprising. Scientists often let data "speak for themselves," resting assured that their colleagues will not miss a major point, however subtly it may be presented. Most scientists can do this, however, because they are confident that their colleagues will be *looking* for major points in their papers. In Mendel's case, nobody was looking for points about how heredity worked because scarcely anybody but Mendel had a concept of pure heredity. As contemporary geneticists Daniel L. Hartl and Vitezslav Orel have observed, in the minds of nineteenth-century scientists, heredity was merely a part of development—the process by which a fertilized egg becomes a fully formed organism. Mendel, meanwhile, thought of heredity as operating under its own independent set of rules, after which he went on to say what those rules were. Mendel thus delivered an answer to a question that nobody had asked: How does heredity work?

Other barriers existed to understanding as well. Mendel used mathematics to derive his insights on genetics, an approach that was novel in the biology of his day. Beyond this, in 1859 Charles Darwin's *On the Origin of Species* had been published, an event that sent scientists scurrying to look for "continuous," or subtle variations between organisms—a phenomenon that they thought might shed some light on evolution. Conversely, Mendel's paper, coming seven years later, talked about pairs of seemingly unchangeable genetic elements that gave rise to such either/or features as smooth or wrinkled seeds. It was difficult to fit such elements into a scheme of gradual evolutionary transformation.

Looking over all these factors, Mendel appears to have been, in essence, a victim of his own originality. (This again puts him in the company of Emily Dickinson, whose language was too idiosyncratic for her early readers.) There is a saying that it doesn't pay to be more than 10 minutes ahead of your time. Gregor Mendel had the misfortune of being about 34 years ahead of his.

11.8 Lessons from Blood Types: Codominance

The notion of genes as protein-producing entities can help us steer through another variation on Mendelian inheritance, this one having a great importance for variety in the living world. When people speak of blood "types," what they mean is types of proteins that cover the surface of red blood cells. These surface proteins come in many different varieties, the two most important of which are designated A and B (**see Figure 11.11**).

Blood types are completely under genetic control, with a single gene that lies on chromosome 9 determining what blood type a person will have—A, B, AB, or O. There are two copies of this gene in each individual, because there are two copies of chromosome 9 in each individual—one inherited from the mother, the other inherited from the father. Thus, there exists the possibility for *alleles*, or gene variants in each individual.

Now, a single person could have two alleles that code for type A protein, or a person could have both alleles coding for type B molecules. In the first case a person would have type A blood, and in the second type B blood. However, a person could have one allele that codes for the type A molecule *and* one that codes for type B, in which case that person would have type AB blood. Finally, a person could have two alleles that are inactive—that code for neither surface protein— and would thus have type O blood.

Getting Both Types of Surface Proteins

What's new in this case is, first, another aspect of the idea of dominance in alleles. In the blood types, *both* the A and B alleles produce proteins (for the cell-surface molecules). People who are heterozygous for these alleles thus do not get a phenotype that, like pink flowers, lies halfway between A and B. They get both the A and B proteins on the surface of their blood cells. Alleles that have this kind of independent effect result in **codominance**: a condition in which two alleles of a given gene have different phenotypic effects, with both effects manifesting in organisms that are heterozygous for the gene.

Dominant and Recessive Alleles

All this gets us to an important point, which is the relationship between dominant and recessive alleles. In common speech the word *dominance* is used all the time to mean "bringing another under submission by means of superior power." Alleles, however, are not locked in a power struggle with one another. Alleles contain information for the

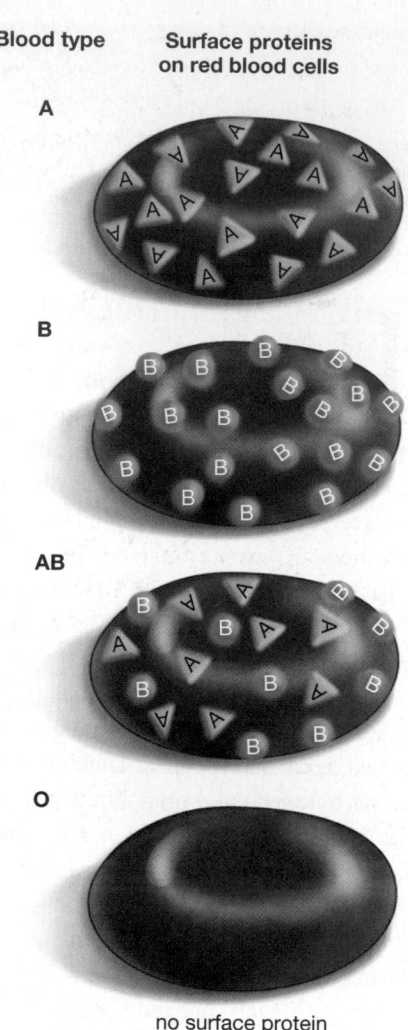

Blood type   **Surface proteins on red blood cells**

A

B

AB

O

no surface protein

Figure 11.11
Human Blood Types
The familiar A, B, O human blood-typing system refers to proteins on the surface of red blood cells. People whose blood is "type A" have A proteins on their blood cells. It is also possible to have only B proteins (and be type B); to have both A and B proteins (and be type AB); or to have none of these proteins (and be type O).

production of proteins. Such proteins (or lack of them) can create dominant phenotypes (smooth peas), incompletely dominant phenotypes (pink snapdagons), or codominant phenotypes (AB blood). "Dominance," then, just refers to the ways in which a given allele is expressed. But as you've seen, a *recessive* allele is not eliminated by being paired with a dominant allele—it simply isn't expressed in a given generation. When this generation gives rise to another, the recessive allele will be passed on intact, at which point it may be expressed. When the pea plant's recessive green allele was passed on, for example, it was expressed when brought together with another green allele. This has relevance for traits more familiar to us. People seem to have an idea that human blond hair, to give one example, eventually will cease to exist because the genes for it are recessive to dark hair. The alleles for blond hair are, however, not disappearing. To the extent that alleles for it come together in reproduction, there will always be blond-haired people.

11.9 Multiple Alleles and Polygenic Inheritance

ABO blood types have one more lesson for us. In Mendel's seed shapes, there were two phenotypic variants: smooth and wrinkled. In blood types, there were four: A, B, AB, and O. As you know, no one person can have more than *two* alleles for a given gene. As a result, a person may be, say A and B, but he or she cannot be A, B, and O. It is thus only in a *population* of humans that the full range of ABO alleles can be found. And therein lies the lesson. In a population, alleles can come not just in two, but in many variants.

When three or more alleles of the same gene exist in a population, they are known as **multiple alleles**. Such alleles are important in and of themselves, for they can bring diversity to traits that are governed by single genes (such as human blood types). Their more general significance comes, however, in con-

nection with traits that are controlled not by one gene, but by many. Recall that seed texture in Mendel's peas was governed by a single gene (which had smooth and wrinkled allelic variants). This situation is, however, the exception rather than the rule in the living world. Most traits are governed by many genes. The human traits of height, weight, eye color, and skin color are each controlled by several genes. In the wider living world, the color of a wheat grain, the length of an ear of corn, and the amount of milk a cow gives are all controlled by many genes acting together. The term for such genetic influence is **polygenic inheritance**, meaning the inheritance of a genetic character that is determined by the interaction of multiple genes, with each gene having a small additive effect on the character.

When we have many genes contributing some small increment to a trait, the result is what you see in **Figure 11.12**. Human beings don't come in two heights, or three or four; they display what is known as a "continuous variation" in height, each person being just barely taller or shorter than the next. Continuous variation also holds true for human skin color. Human beings don't really have "black" or "white" or "red" skin. Instead they have skin that comes in a *range* of hues, in which one color shades

(a) Continuous variation in human height

(b) The bell curve

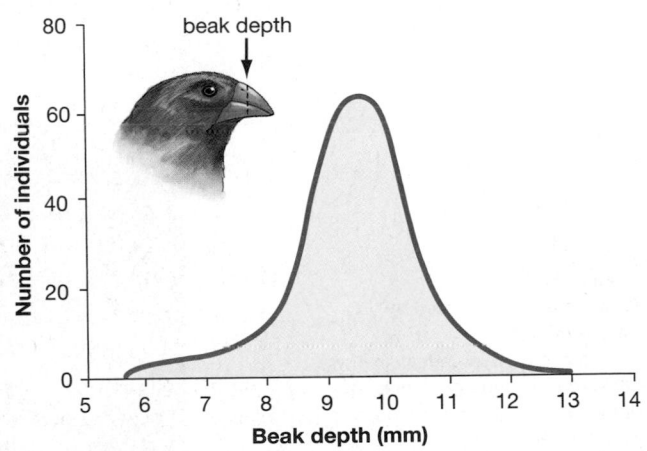

Figure 11.12
Continuous Variation and the Bell Curve

(a) Mendel's pea seeds may have been green or yellow, but traits such as human height do not have this either/or quality. Human heights exist in a range, with no fixed increments between heights of individuals. Such "continuous variation" results from polygenic inheritance, in which each of several genes contributes a small additive effect to a character. University of Connecticut students in the picture have been arranged by height to show how continuous variation works in this one human trait. Note that the group as a whole takes on the shape of a bell. The students' heights are distributed in a pattern that creates a bell curve.

(b) A bell curve can also be seen in this graph, which plots the average beak depth of a population of Darwin's finches from the Galápagos Islands. Note how most of the finches had beak depths close to the average depth of the population as a whole.

imperceptibly into another. Likewise, trees of a given species come in a range of heights, and the beaks of birds come in a range of lengths. Polygenic inheritance creates this fine-grained diversity.

Now, note something else about Figure 11.12a. Most of the students fall in the middle range of heights in the group. Put another way, there are fewer tall or short students than there are students of medium height. This height distribution means that the group as a whole takes on a kind of shape—a bell shape. This is, in fact, the famous **bell curve**, meaning a distribution of values that is symmetrical, and largest around the average. Most biological traits manifest in this way. Look, for example, at the beak depths in a group of Darwin's finches in Figure 11.12b. Graphs like this just confirm what we know intuitively—that traits in living things cluster around what is average, rather than what is extreme.

In polygenic inheritance, with its many genes and alleles, gene interactions are so complex that predictions about phenotype are a matter of *probability*, not certainty. Human height is largely under genetic control, and there are means of trying to predict the height of children based on the height of their parents. (The starting point generally is to add together the height of the parents and divide the result by two.) All that such predictions can do, however, is specify that if parents are of a given height, then there is a certain probability that their children will fall into a given range of heights. Think how different this is from the situation with Mendel's peas. There, you could confidently predict that a given cross would yield, say, all green peas.

11.10 Genes and Environment

Scientists work awfully hard at trying to determine the probabilities for certain polygenic outcomes—those related to disease. In carrying out this work, they are essentially doing what Mendel did: observing traits in a parental generation and then observing traits in the parents' offspring. Such work is the basis for the warnings we sometimes hear about how much a person's risk for a particular cancer goes up if that person has a relative who has contracted the disease. With polygenic illnesses such as cancer, however, it is difficult to separate the genetic factors from what are called "environmental" factors. What's an environmental factor? Any external influence that is favorable or unfavorable for the development of a trait in an organism. Smoking, for example, is an environmental factor that influences development of lung cancer. Indeed, smoking is responsible for about 90 percent of all lung-cancer cases. Even so, only a minority of smokers ever contract lung cancer. Why do some smokers get this disease while others are spared? A large part of the answer is genetic susceptibility: the genetic makeup of some individuals makes them more susceptible to the environmental influence of smoking. Thus, we can see genes and environment working together to create the outcome of lung cancer. And this is almost always the case in nature. For polygenic traits—which is to say, most traits—it is rare for genes to be the sole determining factor.

A clear example of how genes and environment work together can be seen in **Figure 11.13**, which shows pictures of the most popular species of hydrangea flower, *Hydrangea macrophylla*. Any garden-

Figure 11.13
Flower Color Is Affected by Environment
Both the blue hydrangeas in the background and the pink hydrangeas in the foreground are from the same species (*Hydrangea macrophylla*). Yet they have different coloration because of different chemical conditions in their soil. (The soil the blue plants are in is more acidic than the soil the pink plants are in.) This is but one example of how genes and environment work together to produce the traits we see in living things. The plants are blooming along a wall in Salem, Oregon.

er could start with a blue hydrangea, like the one in the picture on the left, take a "cutting" from it, do a little preparatory work, plant the cutting in the ground, and get a whole new hydrangea plant as a result. For our purposes, the important point is that this second plant is a clone of the first. It is not produced by mixing eggs and sperm; it is an exact genetic replica of the first plant. It can, however, be a plant with *pink* flowers instead of blue if some garden lime is mixed into its surrounding soil. It's possible, therefore to have two hydrangea plants with the exact same genotype, but with very different phenotypes— pink or blue flowers. The message here is one of genetic limitation. Genotype specifies only so much about phenotype. Protein products that bring about a blue plant in one environment will bring about a pink plant in another. Across the natural world, things generally work this way. Genes do not come with an unvarying ability to bring about an effect. Rather, genes and environment work together to create the phenotypes we see in living things.

11.11   One Gene, Several Effects: Pleiotropy

You've seen that many genes can work together to produce one effect, such as human height. It is also possible, however, for a single gene to have many effects. This is frequently the case, actually, for the simple reason that the processes of living things are so interrelated.

The phenomenon of one gene having many effects is called **pleiotropy**. Many examples of this phe-

nomenon exist; one of the more interesting, perhaps, is a debilitation known as *fragile-X syndrome*, which is the most common cause of inherited mental retardation. The *X* in its name refers to the X chromosome. *Fragile* comes from the break on the long arm of the X chromosome that can be seen in people who suffer from the syndrome. Fragile-X is now thought to be caused by a defect in a single gene, dubbed *FMR-1* by the team of researchers who discovered it.

The upshot of this defect is that fragile-X victims lack a functional *FMR-1* gene, which is to say their *FMR-1* does not appear to prompt production of any protein. One clear result of this is mental retardation; people with fragile-X commonly have an IQ of about 40–70 (as opposed to the norm of 100). For our purposes, fragile-X also has effects that seemingly stand far afield from mental retardation. Those with fragile-X often have an abnormally long face; large, protuberant ears, and (when male) large testicles. This broad range of effects, seemingly stemming from the inactivation of a single gene, contains a message: Genes normally work together in an interrelated web, rather than functioning under a one-gene → one-phenotype model.

On to the Chromosome

This completes the survey of Mendel's work and the variations on his ideas of inheritance. As you have seen, Mendel's work lay dormant for some decades in the nineteenth century. What sent scientists scurrying back to his findings were experiments on those tiny entities you have looked at in detail before: chromosomes, the subject of the next chapter.

Chapter Review

Summary

11.1   Mendel and the Black Box

- Gregor Mendel was the first person to comprehend some of the most basic principles of genetics. He reached these understandings in the mid-nineteenth century, working in what is now the Czech Republic and using as his experimental subjects a species of garden pea, *Pisum sativum*.

11.2   The Experimental Subjects: *Pisum sativum*

- Mendel looked at seven characters in his plants—such attributes as seed color and texture. In his plants, each of these characters came in two varieties or traits, one of them dominant, the other recessive. His experiments involved breeding pea plants, starting with plants that had a given set of traits and then observing which of those traits showed up in succeeding generations.

- A phenotype is any physiological feature, bodily characteristic, or behavior of an organism. In Mendel's plants, purple flowers were one phenotype and white flowers were another. Phenotypes in any organism are in significant part determined by that organism's genotype, meaning its genetic makeup. Mendel realized that the phenotypes in his plants were being controlled by what we would today call their genotypes.

Web Tutorial 11.1: Mendel's Experiments

11.3   Starting the Experiments: Yellow and Green Peas

- Mendel realized that it was possible for organisms to have identical phenotypes—for all his pea plants to have yellow seeds, for example—and yet to have differing underlying genotypes.

- One of Mendel's central insights was that the basic units of genetics are material elements that, in his pea plants, came in pairs. These elements, today called genes, come in alternative forms called alleles. One member of an allele pair resides on one chromosome, while the other allele resides on a second chromosome that is homologous to the first.

- Another of Mendel's insights was that genes retain their character through many generations, rather than being "blended" together. Genes that coded for green pea color, for example, were retained in their existing form over many generations.

11.4 Another Generation for Mendel

- A third insight of Mendel's was that alleles separate prior to the formation of gametes. Though Mendel did not know it, the physical basis for this is that the alleles he was observing resided on homologous chromosomes, which always separate in meiosis. An organism that has two identical alleles of a gene for a given character is said to be homozygous for that character. An organism that has differing alleles for a character is said to be heterozygous for that character. Dominant means: expressed in the heterozygous condition (as with the yellow color of peas, expressed in the heterozygous Yy condition). Recessive means: not expressed in the heterozygous condition (as with the green color of peas in the Yy condition).

11.5 Crosses Involving Two Characters

- Mendel observed that the genes for the different characters he studied were passed on independently of one another. This was so because the genes for these characters resided on separate, non-homologous chromosomes. The physical basis for what he found is the independent assortment of chromosomes during meiosis.

11.6 Reception of Mendel's Ideas

- Gregor Mendel published his work, but the significance of it was never recognized in his lifetime. It was only rediscovered 16 years after his death, in 1900.

11.7 Incomplete Dominance

- Not all inheritance works through the principles Mendel perceived in his peas. Incomplete dominance operates when neither allele for a given gene is completely dominant, with the result that heterozygous genotypes can yield an intermediate phenotype (such as pink snapdragons).
  Web Tutorial 11.2: Variations on Mendel

11.8 Lessons from Blood Types: Codominance

- In some instances, differing alleles of the same gene will have independent effects, rather than one allele being dominant over the other. Such is the case with the genes that code for the human blood proteins, A and B. Neither of the alleles for these proteins is dominant over the other. Rather, a person can have a genotype that produces either or both of the proteins, or neither of them.

11.9 Multiple Alleles and Polygenic Inheritance

- Human beings and many other species can have no more than two alleles for a given gene, each allele residing on a separate, homologous chromosome. Many allelic variants of a gene can, how-

ever, exist in a population. Most traits in living things are governed not by one gene but by many, with these genes often having several allelic variants. The term for such genetic influence is polygenic inheritance, meaning the inheritance of a genetic character that is determined by the interaction of multiple genes, with each gene having a small additive effect on the character.

- Polygenic inheritance produces continuous variation in phenotypes, meaning there are no fixed increments of difference between individuals. Human skin, for example, comes in a range of colors in which one color shades imperceptibly into the next.

- The traits produced in polygenic inheritance tend to manifest in bell-curve distributions, in which most individuals display near-average trait values, rather than extreme trait values. Gene interactions and gene-environment interactions are so complex in polygenic inheritance that predictions about phenotypes are a matter of probability, not certainty.

11.10 Genes and Environment

- The effects of genes can vary greatly in accordance with the environment in which the genes are expressed. An organism's genotype and environment interact to produce that organism's phenotype.

11.11 One Gene, Several Effects: Pleiotropy

- Genes work in an interrelated fashion, such that a single gene is likely to have multiple effects. Pleiotropy is a phenomenon in which one gene has many effects.

Key Terms

Understanding the Basics

Multiple-Choice Questions (answers in the back of the book)

1. The first filial generation, or F_1, results when
   a. two P generation organisms are crossed
   b. the progeny of a P generation is crossed
   c. a P generation is crossed with an F_2 organism
   d. an F_3 organism is crossed with an F_2 organism
   e. both a and d

2. When Mendel crossed pure-breeding yellow peas with pure-breeding green peas, the F_1 generation contained
   a. all yellow peas
   b. all green peas
   c. green and yellow peas
   d. green, wrinkled peas
   e. both b and d

3. A very important characteristic of the garden peas used by Mendel was that
   a. each trait examined had more than two different varieties.
   b. all yellow peas had the same genotype.
   c. the F_1 generation always resulted in a 1:1 phenotypic ratio.
   d. all crosses resulted in a 1:3 genotypic ratio.
   e. the plants had the ability to self-fertilize.

4. If a cross is made between a pure-breeding green, smooth ($yySS$) plant, and a pure-breeding yellow-wrinkled ($YYss$) plant, what is the result?
   a. all green, wrinkled peas
   b. all yellow, wrinkled peas
   c. all yellow, round peas
   d. yellow wrinkled; green wrinkled
   e. none of the above

5. If plants in a cross have the following genotypes ($YYRr \times yyRr$), the correct term for the type of cross is:
   a. recessive cross
   b. dominant cross
   c. monohybrid cross
   d. dihybrid cross
   e. codominant cross

6. Mendel's first law states:
   a. During the formation of gametes, gene pairs demonstrate independent assortment.
   b. During the formation of gametes, genetic elements (alleles) segregate from each other.
   c. The probability of any two events happening is the product of their respective probabilities.
   d. If an organism is pure-breeding for any trait, it will display incomplete dominance.
   e. Mendel did not write any laws regarding genetics.

7. In the ABO blood system in human beings, alleles coding for the A and B proteins are codominant, while the O allele is recessive to both A and B. In a paternity dispute, a type AB woman claimed that one of four men was the father of her type A child. Which of the following men could be the father of the child on the basis of the evidence given?
   a. type A
   b. type B
   c. type O
   d. type AB
   e. any of them

8. Mendel's second law states that
   a. No organism can have more than two alleles for a given character.
   b. No two organisms can ever be genetically identical.
   c. Organisms will tend to be heterozygous for most traits, rather than homozygous.
   d. The way one gene pair assorts during gamete formation will affect the way other gene pairs assort.
   e. Gene pairs assort independently of one another during gamete formation.

9. Which of the following is true about polygenic inheritance?
   a. It is the exception rather than the rule in living things.
   b. Its outcomes are always predictable.
   c. It is never seen in human beings.
   d. It produces phenotypes that grade smoothly into one another.
   e. It produces only homozygous individuals.

10. Which of the following is true regarding the effects of genes and environment on phenotypic variation?
    a. Gene expression will always be greatest in the native environment.
    b. Gene expression is not affected by a change in environment.
    c. Phenotypes are based only on environmental influences.
    d. Environment may easily affect genotype, not phenotype.
    e. The phenotypes of genetically identical organisms may vary in different environments.

Brief Review

1. What are the differences between:
   a. phenotype and genotype?
   b. dominant and recessive?
   c. codominance and incomplete dominance?

2. True or False: When Mendel conducted his genetic research, neither DNA nor chromosomes had been discovered.

3. What genetic principle is demonstrated in the fragile-X syndrome? Explain how this principle differs from the relationship between genes and physical outcomes that Mendel observed in his pea plants.

4. In a case of Mendelian genetics where one gene affects one trait, how many different genotypes may represent a dominant phenotype (for example, yellow pea color)?

5. If a heterozygous yellow pea plant is crossed with a homozygous green pea plant, what percentage of the progeny peas will be yellow?

6. What term is now given to Mendel's "element of inheritance"?

7. What two laws are credited to Mendel and his research?

8. Using the symbols A, a, B, and b, what Mendelian crosses would result in the following phenotypic ratios?
   a. 1:1
   b. 3:1
   c. 1:1:1:1
   d. 9:3:3:1

Applying Your Knowledge

1. Stands of aspen trees often are a series of genetically identical individuals, with each succeeding tree growing from the severed shoot of another tree. Using what you've learned of genetics in this chapter, would you expect one aspen tree in a stand to differ greatly from another in its phenotype? Would you expect each to look exactly like the next in terms of phenotype?

2. The ABO blood-typing system mentioned in the text has great practical significance because the human immune system will attack blood-cell surface proteins that it recognizes as "foreign"— that is, proteins that a person does not have on his or her own blood cells. Given this, what is the "universal donor" blood type? What is the "universal recipient" type?

3. If, as the text states, the effects of genes can be expected to vary in accordance with the environment in which these genes work, would you expect this phenomenon to be applicable to human genes, such as those that help produce such traits as height, weight, or introversion and extroversion?

Genetics Problems

One of Mendel's many monohybrid (single character) crosses was between a true-breeding (homozygous) parent bearing purple flowers and a true-breeding (homozygous) parent bearing white flowers. All the offspring had purple flowers. When these offspring were allowed to self-fertilize, Mendel observed that their offspring occurred in the ratio of 3 purple-flowered:1 white-flowered plants. The allele determining purple flowers is symbolized P and the allele determining white flowers is symbolized p. Use this information to answer the following questions.

1. What are the genotypes of the parents?
   a. $PP; pp$
   b. $PP; Pp$
   c. $Pp; Pp$
   d. $pp; pp$

2. Which generation has only purple-flowered plants?
   a. P
   b. F_1
   c. F_2
   d. F_3

3. Which generation tells you which of the traits is dominant?
   a. P
   b. F_1
   c. F_2
   d. F_3

4. How many phenotypes are present in the F_2 generation?
   a. 1
   b. 2
   c. 3

5. How many different genotypes are present in the F_2 generation?
   a. 1
   b. 2
   c. 3

6. Mendel allowed the white-flowered F_2 plants to self-fertilize. What proportion of these F_2 plants produced only white-flowered offspring?
   a. none
   b. $\frac{1}{4}$
   c. $\frac{1}{3}$
   d. $\frac{3}{4}$
   e. all

7. Mendel allowed the purple-flowered F_2 plants to self-fertilize. What proportion of these F_2 plants produced only purple-flowered offspring?
   a. none
   b. $\frac{1}{4}$
   c. $\frac{1}{3}$
   d. $\frac{3}{4}$
   e. all

8. If a heterozygous purple-flowered pea plant is crossed with a homozygous white-flowered plant, what proportion of offspring will be white-flowered?
   a. none
   b. $\frac{1}{4}$
   c. $\frac{1}{2}$
   d. $\frac{3}{4}$
   e. all

9. Given what you know about the alleles that determine purple and white color in pea flowers, why is it possible to have a purple-flowered heterozygote, but not a white-flowered heterozygote?

10. In considering flower color in pea plants, we are dealing with _____ gene(s) and _____ allele(s).
   a. 1; 1
   b. 1; 2
   c. 1; 4
   d. 2; 1
   e. 2; 2

11. The next three questions require you to apply rules of probability.
    a. In a toss of two coins, what is the chance of obtaining two heads?
       (1) 0
       (2) 12.5 percent
       (3) 25 percent
       (4) 50 percent
       (5) 75 percent
    b. What rule of probability was used to determine the chance of obtaining two heads?
    c. Now, use this rule to solve the following problem. In a cross between two purple-flowered heterozygotes 75 percent of their offspring are expected to be purple-flowered. In a cross between two heterozygotes with yellow-colored seeds, 25 percent of their offspring are expected to be green. If two purple-flowered, yellow-seeded individuals, each heterozygous for both genes, are crossed, what proportion of their offspring are expected to be purple-flowered with green seeds?

12. By observing flower color in snapdragons, is it possible to unambiguously determine the genotype? Is the same true for flower color in peas? Why or why not?

13. If the alleles for snapdragon flower color were codominant, instead of incompletely dominant, a possible phenotype for a heterozygous individual would be:
    a. pure red flowers
    b. pure pink flowers
    c. pure white flowers
    d. a checkerboard pattern of red and white regions on flowers

14. If two individuals with AB blood type marry, what proportion of their children are expected to have AB blood type?
    a. none
    b. 0.25
    c. 0.50
    d. 0.75
    e. all

MediaLab

Where Did I Get This Nose? Understanding Mendelian Genetics

Can you roll your tongue? Is there a cleft in your chin? What is the color of your eyes? These and countless other characteristics that make you a unique individual were determined by the traits you inherited from your parents. In this *MediaLab*, you'll firmly establish your understanding of the rules governing the inheritance of simple genetic traits. In the *Web Tutorial*, you will work through these rules using some of Gregor Mendel's original genetic studies of peas. In the *Web Investigation*, you can practice these rules of probability with your own family, and make predictions about the inheritance of these traits in the *Communicate Your Results* section.

The online version of this *MediaLab* can be found in Chapter 11 on your Companion Website (www.prenhall.com/krogh3).

The online version of this *MediaLab* can be found in Chapter 11 on your Companion Website (www.prenhall.com/krogh3).

WEB TUTORIAL

It is obvious to most people that physical traits are inherited in families. But the rules that govern them were a mystery until a nineteenth-century Augustinian friar, Gregor Mendel, discovered the pattern behind inheritance of traits, by conducting breeding experiments on garden peas. With this *Web Tutorial*, you can review Mendel's experiments in order to lay the foundation for applying these rules to human genetics.

Activity

1. First, you will examine how different versions of a trait (like green versus yellow seed color) are passed from parents to offspring, and how rules of probability can explain the outcome.

2. Then you will learn to use a Punnett square, a chart that shows all possible combinations of alleles in the offspring of any parents, allowing you to predict the chances of inheriting one or more different traits.

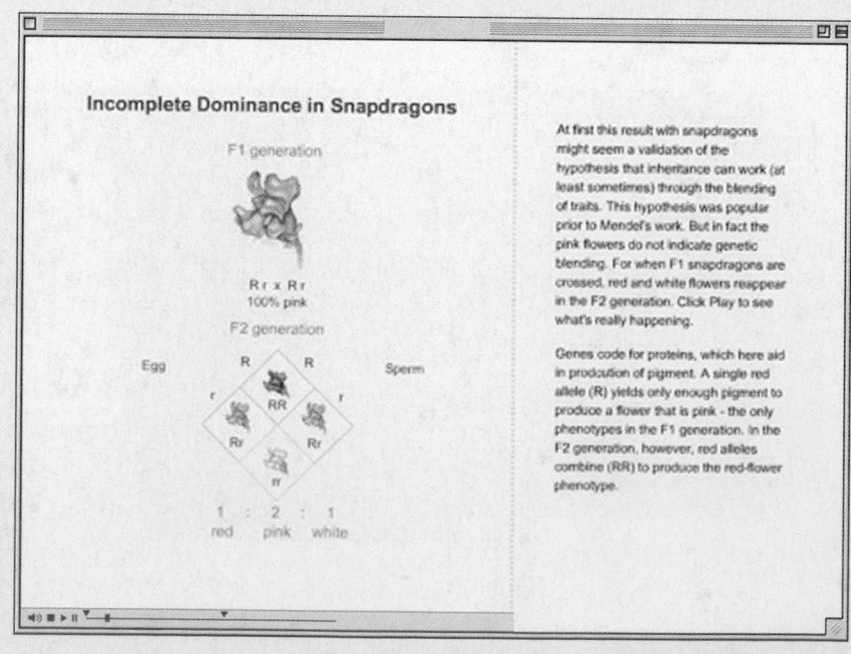

Investigation 1

Estimated time for completion = 10 minutes

Most complex human genetic traits are not as simple to understand as the pea traits that Mendel studied. For example, researchers have found that children of two obese parents have an 80 percent chance of being obese. Can we conclude that it is due to their genes, or is it due to their environment? Maybe people are more likely to overeat and not exercise if their parents exhibit these behaviors. Select the keyword **OBESITY** on the Website for this *MediaLab*, to read an article on the linkage between genes and obesity.

Investigation 2

Estimated time for completion = 20 minutes

Before the introduction of DNA testing, ABO blood type was commonly used as evidence in paternity tests. Select the keywords **BLOOD TYPE** on the Website for this *MediaLab* and read a tutorial about the inheritance of blood type. Then, try your hand at answering some questions on blood type by clicking next on the keywords **ABO QUESTIONS**, and then select the blood-type questions on the genetics quiz.

Investigation 3

Estimated time for completion = 20 minutes

Understanding the inheritance of Mendelian traits is just the beginning of understanding how genes help shape our identity. Our appearance, health, and even behavior is strongly influenced by our genes. Currently under way is a multinational project, called the Human Genome Project, which is intended to uncover all of the genes located on all the human chromosomes. Select the keyword **GENOME** on the Website for this *MediaLab* to view a current map of all the human genes that have been located thus far. Select a chromosome and read as much information as you can about a human disease-causing gene that has been located there. What is the name of the gene, and what disease does it cause? Is there a genetic test available for the gene? Has identifying the gene helped create any new therapies?

Now that you have practiced some of Mendel's laws in the preceding investigations, apply and extend your abilities by addressing some genetics problems.

COMMUNICATE YOUR RESULTS

Exercise 1

Estimated time for completion = 15 minutes

How much of our behavior, personality, even physical appearance is due to our genes, and how much is due to our environment? Having read the evidence given in the article in *Web Investigation 1* for a genetic basis for obesity, what is your conclusion about how our weight is determined? Be prepared to discuss this with several of your peers by answering the following questions: In your mind, what was the most convincing point in the article? How did the researchers control for environmental differences versus genetic differences? Can you really assume that two individuals, even siblings, are ever raised with the same environment? How many participants would need to be included in this type of study to make it statistically significant?

Exercise 2

Estimated time for completion = 20 minutes

You just learned how to use ABO blood type to determine parentage. Now find out your own blood type and the blood type of your parents, and try to determine your family's genotypes. If you don't know your blood type, you can find it out easily when you donate blood at your local blood drive. Create a problem like the ones from the **ABO QUESTIONS** in *Web Investigation 2*, and then generate a Punnett square showing all possible blood-type genotypes for the children of your family. What is your phenotype? Genotype? If your parents had more children, what is the probability that they could donate blood for you?

Exercise 3

Estimated time for completion = 15 minutes

Prepare a 50-word description of the gene you investigated in *Web Investigation 3* to inform your classmates about the current state of human genetics research.

12 Chromosomes and Inheritance

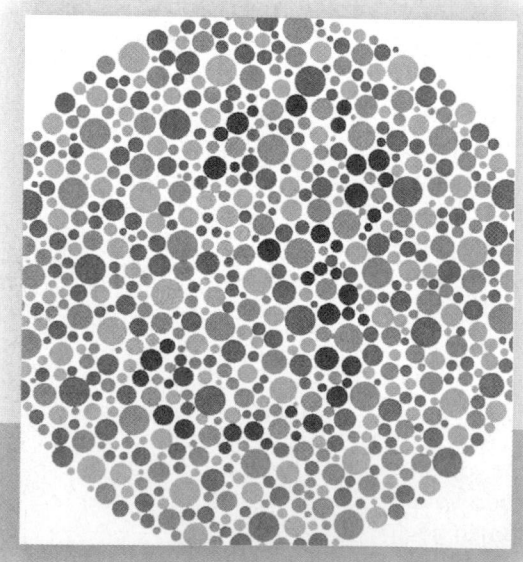

What number do you see?
(Section 12.1, page 232)

A dominant disorder.
(Section 12.2, page 234)

Nondisjunction in meiosis I

A mistake in meiosis.
(Section 12.5, page 237)

The common condition known as Down syndrome is almost always caused by the inheritance of an extra chromosome. But how can a parent who does not have an extra chromosome pass one on to a son or daughter? The gene that causes sickle-cell anemia seems also to offer some protection against malaria. How can it have both effects? The chromosomal makeup of women offers them a kind of protection against being color blind. Why should this be so?

From these questions, it may be apparent that chromosomes and the genes on them are centrally involved in issues of human health. You saw last chapter that chromosomal activity lies at the root of several of the genetic principles that Gregor Mendel uncovered. Mendel's "pairs of elements," which separate in reproduction, had as their physical basis the pairs of homologous chromosomes—one inherited from the male, one from the female—that first pair up and then separate from one another in meiosis. The differing traits that Mendel investigated so thoroughly, such as yellow or green peas in a pod, had as their physical basis the pairs of *alleles* or differing forms of a gene that lie on homologous chromosomes.

But there are aspects of chromosomal functioning that Mendel's work scarcely touched on. For one, there is the issue of sex chromosomes. As noted in Chapter 10, the sex of human beings is determined by their chromosomal makeup. Human females have two X chromosomes, while human males have one X and one Y chromosome. But apart from conferring sex, what part do these special chromosomes play in heredity?

Next, how do the terms *dominant* and *recessive* that you looked at last chapter play out with respect to human disease? And how can genetically based diseases be traced through generations of a family?

Finally, you saw in Chapter 10 that a critical step in meiosis is the *crossing over* (or recombination) that occurs early in it. In this process, homologous chromosomes first intertwine and then swap pieces of themselves, after which they separate in meiosis. But what happens when chromosomes fail to properly carry out this part swapping or separation? The short answer is that such mistakes are responsible for a number of the afflictions that affect human beings, including Down syndrome.

Translocation.
(Section 12.6, page 241)

Down syndrome's signature.
(Essay, page 241)

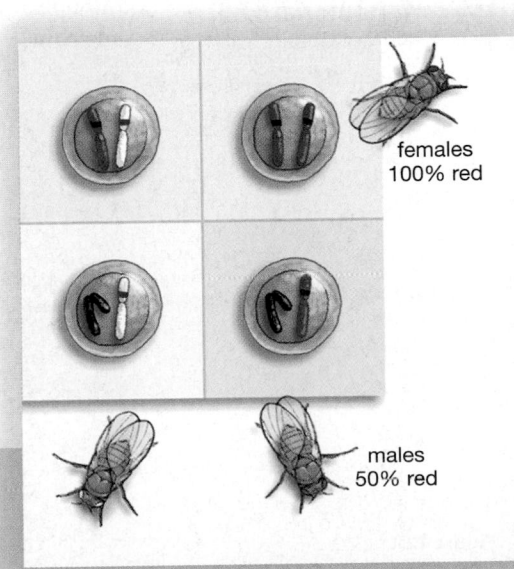

Only the males had white eyes.
(Essay, page 243)

So, in this chapter you will look at sex chromosomes, dominant and recessive disease genes, tracing diseases through generations, and diseases caused by chromosomal mistakes. All the disorders that will be reviewed are transmitted through so-called "Mendelian" inheritance, meaning they are all disorders in which a single gene or chromosome means the difference between sickness and health. In contrast, many widespread diseases, such as heart disease and cancer, are polygenic—they are based on many genes working in concert, with a given set of faulty genes only predisposing a person toward sickness, rather than ensuring it. Let's start now with sex and heredity.

12.1 X-Linked Inheritance in Humans

Minor cuts are simply an irritation to most of us, but for people suffering from the condition known as hemophilia, such cuts can be life threatening. Hemophilia is a failure of blood to clot properly. A group of proteins interact to make blood clot, but about 80 percent of hemophiliacs lack a functioning version of just one of these proteins (called Factor VIII). Genes contain the information for the production of proteins, of course, so at root hemophilia is a genetic disease—a faulty gene is causing the faulty Factor VIII protein. This same process is at work in a couple of other well-known afflictions: the disease called Duchenne muscular dystrophy, and a far less serious condition, red-green color blindness. These disorders have more in common than being genetically based, however. All of them are known as *X-linked* disorders, because the genes that cause them lie on the X chromosome. As it turns out, X-linked disorders claim more male victims than female. Why should this be so? A look at color blindness can provide the answer.

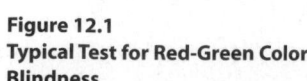

Web Tutorial 12.1
X-Linked Recessive Traits

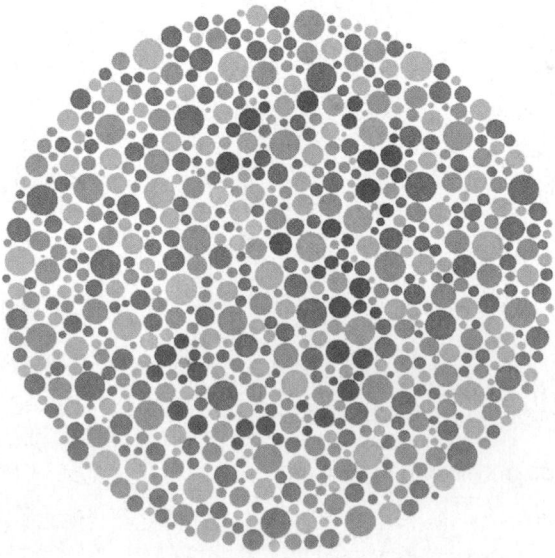

Figure 12.1
Typical Test for Red-Green Color Blindness
If you do not see a number inside the large circle, you may have this recessive trait.

The Genetics of Color Vision

Despite its name, "color blindness" almost never means a *total* inability to perceive color. Rather, it most often means an inability to distinguish among certain shades of red and green (**Figure 12.1**). To understand how color vision can malfunction in this way, it's important to understand how it commonly works. When light enters our eyes, it travels to the back of them and lands on a group of cells (called cones) that have within them molecules called pigments. A pigment is simply a substance that strongly absorbs a given color of light. The pigments in cone cells turn out to be molecules composed of two main parts, one of which is a protein called opsin. Because genes code for proteins, it's easy to see how color blindness is genetically based: We have genes that are coding for the protein portions of our light-absorbing pigments. More specifically, we have a gene that codes for blue-absorbing pigment, and it lies on chromosome 7; and then we have genes that code for both red- and green-absorbing pigments, and they lie very close to one another on the X chromosome. A red-green color-blind person, then, is one in whom these X-located genes fail to code for the proper pigment proteins.

Alleles and Recessive Disorders

In the normal case, as you've seen, a given gene comes in two variant forms or *alleles* in each person. One allele for a gene might reside on, say, the chromosome 1 we inherit from our mother; if so, the second allele for this gene will reside on the chromosome 1 we inherit from our *father*. There is therefore a kind of backup system in human genetics: genes come in pairs of alleles that lie on separate, homologous chromosomes. If one allele for a given trait is defective, there will usually exist a second, functional allele for that same trait on a homologous chromosome.

This genetic structure usually works fine when a condition is a so-called **recessive disorder**, meaning a genetic disorder that will not exist in the presence of a functional allele. In such a condition, a person does not have to have *two* functional alleles; a single "good" allele will do. And red-green color blindness turns out to be a recessive disorder: a person who has even one functional allele for red pigment and one functional allele for green pigment will not be color blind. So why do men suffer more from this condition than women? Because men have no backup: they have only one allele for red pigment and one allele for green pigment because they have only one *X chromosome* (and one Y). Meanwhile, women have two X chromosomes. If the pigment alleles are defective on one of their chromosomes, the alleles on their other X chromosome will still provide them with full color vision.

Given this, think about the interesting way that color blindness is passed along. Say there is a mother who is not color blind herself, but who is heterozygous for the trait. That is, she has functional color alleles on one of her X chromosomes but dysfunctional alleles on her other X chromosome. Should her son happen to inherit this second X chromosome, he will be color blind, because the X chromosome he got from his mother is his *only* X chromosome (**Figure 12.2**). Meanwhile, a daughter who inherited this chromosome would likely be protected by her second X chromosome—the one she got from her father. Not surprisingly, then, more males are color blind than females. About 8 percent of the male population has some degree of color blindness, while for females the figure is about half a percent. Women enjoy a similar protection in connection with other X-linked disorders, such as hemophilia and muscular dystrophy.

12.2 Autosomal Genetic Disorders

The X and Y chromosomes are, of course, only two of the chromosomes in the human collection, and any chromosome can have a malfunctioning gene on it. The chromosomes other than the X and Y chromosomes are called *autosomes*, as you've seen. A recessive dysfunction related to an autosome is thus known as an **autosomal recessive disorder**. (For a list of all the disorders you'll be looking at and more, see **Table 12.1**.)

Figure 12.2
The Value of Having Two X Chromosomes
The mother in the figure is not herself color blind but has one dysfunctional set of red-green alleles (represented by the red X), which she passes on to one son and one daughter. The daughter is not color blind because she has inherited, from her father, a second X chromosome—one that has functional red-green alleles. Meanwhile the son is color blind because his only X chromosome is the flawed one he inherited from his mother. (The other son, shown in the square's lower-left cell, is not color blind because he has inherited his mother's functional alleles.)

Table 12.1 Selected Examples of Human Genetic Disorders		
Type	**Name of condition**	**Effects**
X-linked recessive disorders	Hemophilia	Faulty blood clotting
	Duchenne muscular dystrophy	Wasting of muscles
	Red-green color blindness	Inability to distinguish shades of red from green
Autosomal recessive disorders	Albinism	No pigmentation in skin
	Sickle-cell anemia	Decreased oxygen to brain and muscles
	Cystic fibrosis	Impaired lung function, lung infections
	Phenylketonuria	Mental retardation
	Tay-Sachs disease	Nervous system degeneration in infants
	Werner syndrome	Premature aging
Autosomal dominant disorders	Polydactyly	Extra fingers or toes
	Campodactyly	Inability to straighten little finger
	Huntington disease	Brain tissue degeneration
Aberrations in chromosome number	Down syndrome	Mental retardation, shortened life span
	Turner syndrome	Sterility, short stature
	Klinefelter syndrome	Dysfunctional testicles, feminized features
Aberrations in chromosome structure	Cri-du-chat syndrome	Mental retardation, malformed larynx
	Fragile-X syndrome	Mental retardation, facial deformities

Web Tutorial 12.2
Some Human Genetic Disorders

Sickle-Cell Anemia

A well-known example of an autosomal recessive disorder is sickle-cell anemia, which affects populations derived from several areas on the globe, including Africa. In the United States it is, of course, most widely known as a disease affecting African Americans. The "sickle" in the name comes from the curved shape that is taken on by the red blood cells of its victims. Red blood cells carry oxygen to all parts of the body; in their normal shape they look a little like doughnuts with incomplete holes. When they take on a sickle shape, however, red cells clog up capillaries, resulting in decreased oxygen supplies to brain and muscle (**Figure 12.3**). In the United States, the average life expectancy for men with the condition is 42 years; for women, it is 48 years.

The question is, what causes a red blood cell to take on this lethal, sickled shape? There is a protein, called hemoglobin, that carries the oxygen within red blood cells. The vast majority of people in the world have one form of hemoglobin, called hemoglobin A; but sickle-cell anemia sufferers have another form of this protein, hemoglobin S, which coalesces into crystals that distort the cell.

Now, how is sickle-cell anemia passed from parents to offspring? Because it is a recessive condition, any child who gets it must inherit *two* alleles for it—one allele from the mother, one from the father, each of them coding for the hemoglobin S protein. This means, of course, that both parents must themselves have at least one hemoglobin S allele; both parents must be at least heterozygous for the trait. In this situation, the laws governing inheritance of this disorder are simply those of Mendel's monohybrid cross: a child of these two parents has a 25 percent chance of inheriting the disorder. You can look at the Punnett square in **Figure 12.4a** to see how this works out.

It's important to note the status of the parents in this example. They are heterozygous for a recessive debilitation, meaning they do not suffer from the condition themselves because they are protected by their single "good" allele. Each of them is, however, a **carrier** for the condition: a person who does not suffer from a recessive genetic debilitation, but who carries an allele for it that can be passed along to offspring. In this respect, they are just like the mother in the color-blindness example.

Malaria Protection: Hemoglobin S as a Useful Protein

Sickle-cell anemia offers another lesson in connection with the notion of hemoglobin S as a "faulty" protein. It is in fact quite a functional protein in certain circumstances; namely, when it appears heterozygously (with hemoglobin A) in people who live in regions where malaria is common. The most severe form of malaria is caused by a single-celled parasite that is transmitted into human beings by the *Anopheles* mosquito. Traveling through the bloodstream, these parasites invade and ultimately destroy red blood cells. For reasons we still don't understand, having hemoglobin S in one's system makes red blood cells resistant to invasion. Thus, it is likely that hemoglobin S became as widespread as it is because of its value in resisting malaria. The price of this resistance, however, is that some offspring are not heterozygous for hemoglobin S. They are homozygous for it, meaning they have sickle-cell anemia.

Dominant Disorders

Though sickle-cell anemia is an autosomal disorder and red-green color blindness an X-linked disorder, both are recessive disorders. That is, a person with even a single properly functioning allele will not suffer from them. However, there are also **dominant disorders**: genetic conditions in which a single faulty allele can cause damage, even when a second, functional allele exists. This leads to the concept of an **autosomal dominant disorder**, simply meaning a dominant genetic disorder caused by a faulty allele that lies on an autosomal chromosome. There is, for example, an autosomal dominant disorder called Huntington disease. Affecting about 30,000 Americans, it results in both mental impairment and uncontrollable spastic

Figure 12.3
Healthy Cells, Sickled Cell
Three normal red blood cells flank a single sickled cell. (×7400)

(a) Sickle-cell anemia: transmission of a recessive disorder.

Sickle-cell anemia is a recessive autosomal disorder; both the mother and father must carry at least one allele for the trait in order for a son or a daughter to be a sickle-cell victim. When both parents have one sickle-cell allele, there is a 25 percent chance that any given offspring will inherit the condition.

👉 25% probability of inheriting the disorder

Figure 12.4
Transmission of Recessive and Dominant Disorders

(b) Huntington disease: transmission of a dominant disorder.

👉 50% probability of inheriting the disorder

In Huntington disease, if only a single parent has a Huntington allele there is a 50 percent chance that a son or daughter will inherit the condition.

movements called *chorea*. Perhaps its most famous victim was the American folksinger Woody Guthrie. Like most Huntington sufferers, Guthrie did not begin to show symptoms of the disease until well into adulthood—*after* he had children, who then may have had the disease passed along to them. You can look at the Punnett square in **Figure 12.4b** to see how the inheritance pattern of an autosomal dominant disease, such as Huntington, differs from that of an autosomal recessive illness. Because a parent need only pass on a single Huntington allele for a son or

daughter to suffer from the condition, the chances of any given offspring getting the disease from a single affected parent are one out of two.

12.3 Tracking Traits with Pedigrees

Confronted with a medical condition, such as Huntington, that is running through a family, scientists find it helpful to construct a medical **pedigree**, defined as a familial history. Normally set forth as diagrams, medical pedigrees do more than give a family history of a disease. They can be used to ascertain whether a condition is dominant or recessive, and X-linked or autosomal. This can help establish probabilities for *future* inheritance of the condition—something that can be very helpful for couples thinking of having a child.

If you look at **Figure 12.5**, you can see a simple pedigree for albinism: a lack of skin pigmentation, which is known to be an autosomal recessive condition. In the figure, you can see some of the standard symbols used in pedigrees. A circle is used for a female and a square for a male. Parents are indicated by a horizontal line connecting a male and a female, while a vertical line between the parents leads to a lower row that denotes the parents' offspring. This second row— a horizontal line of siblings—has an order to it: oldest child on the left, youngest on the right. A circle or square that is filled in indicates a family member who has the condition (in this case albinism), while a symbol that is half filled in indicates a person known to be heterozygous for a recessive condition (a carrier). One of the strengths of a pedigree is that it can sometimes tell researchers which persons are heterozygous carriers of a recessive condition. Remember that a carrier does not display *symptoms* of the condition. So how can a pedigree reveal this?

Take a look at Figure 12.5. The only thing that would be apparent from actually seeing any of the people in the pedigree is that two of them—a female in generation II and a male in generation III—have the condition of albinism. But a little knowledge of Mendelian genetics also allows some other deductions. If the condition had been dominant, then it would have manifested itself in at least one of the parents on the left in generation I. Because this was not the case, it is fair to deduce that this is a recessive condition. The fact that it is recessive, however, means that *both* parents in generation I had to be carriers for the allele—both have to be heterozygous for the condition, which is why their symbols can be half shaded in. Things are less clear with the parents on the right in generation I. One of their sons did not manifest the condition himself, but went on to have a son who did.

From this, we know that the son in generation II had to have been heterozygous for the condition. But from which parent did this son get his albinism allele? Either, or both, of his parents in generation I could have been heterozygous for the condition and yet between them, only have passed along a single albinism allele.

This mixture of certainty and uncertainty leads to the genotype labeling you see in the figure, with *A* representing the dominant "normal" allele and *a* representing the recessive albinism allele. We know, for example, that both parents on the left in generation I had to be *Aa*, but all we can say for sure about the parents on the right in the same generation is that at least one of them was a carrier.

12.4 Aberrations in Chromosomal Sets: Polyploidy

All of the maladies you've looked at so far have resulted from dysfunctional genes that exist among a standard array of chromosomes. In humans this array is 22 pairs of autosomes and either an XX combination (in females) or an XY (in males). Meanwhile, Mendel's peas had 7 pairs of chromosomes, and the common fruit fly has 4 pairs. Whatever the *number* of chromosomes, note the similarity in all these species: Their chromosomes come in pairs; or to put it another way, they all have two *sets* of chromosomes, meaning the organisms that posses them are diploid.

In many situations, however, organisms don't end up with the two sets of chromosomes that are standard for their species. This is called **polyploidy**: a condition in which one or more entire sets of chromosomes has been added to the genome of a diploid organism.

You may wonder how a human being could end up with more than two sets of chromosomes. After all, in meiosis, sperm and egg end up with just one set of chromosomes in them. When they later fuse, in the moment of conception, the result is then two sets of chromosomes in the fertilized egg. But what if *two* sperm manage to fuse with one egg? The result is a fertilized egg with three sets of chromosomes, and the outcome is polyploidy. Normally an egg lets in only one sperm, and it blocks the others hovering about with a kind of chemical gate-slamming mechanism. But occasionally more than one sperm manages to make it in. Human polyploidy can also get started before fertilization, when meiosis malfunctions and gives a single egg or sperm two sets of chromosomes, meaning there will be three sets in total when egg and sperm fuse.

Polyploidy actually is tolerated well in some organisms. Indeed, it has come about countless times in

**Figure 12.5
A Hypothetical Pedigree for Albinism through Three Generations**

plant species and generally gives rise to perfectly robust plants. In human beings, however, polyploidy is a disaster. Perhaps only 1 percent of human embryos with the condition will survive to birth, and none of these babies lives long. Concerns about chromosome number in living persons, then, center not on addition or deletion of whole sets of chromosomes, but rather on the gain or loss of *individual* chromosomes.

12.5 Incorrect Chromosome Number: Aneuploidy

The condition called **aneuploidy** is one in which an organism has either more or fewer chromosomes than normally exist in its species' full set. Put another way, aneuploidy is a condition in which an organism has one chromosome too many, or one too few. Among human genetic malfunctions, aneuploidy is unusual in that it occurs quite commonly and yet goes largely unrecognized. This is so because it most often occurs not in fully formed human beings, but in embryos. A would-be mother may know only that she is having a hard time getting pregnant. What she may not know is that she actually *has* been pregnant—perhaps several times—but that aneuploidy has doomed the embryo in each case. Doomed it in what way? The most common outcome of aneuploidy is a pregnancy that ends in miscarriage. And many of these miscarriages happen so early in a pregnancy that a woman never realizes she was pregnant; the microscopic embryo may simply be part of material that is discharged, perhaps with

the woman's next menstrual period. Even when a miscarriage is recognized as such, tests can seldom be run that can identify aneuploidy as the cause. But by undertaking careful examinations of thousands of pregnancies, scientists have concluded that aneuploidy is responsible for about 30 percent of miscarriages. And how common is miscarriage? One 1988 study found that 31 percent of embryos miscarry after they have been implanted in the woman's uterus. A small proportion of embryos do manage to survive aneuploidy, but even in these instances there are consequences. Down syndrome is one of the outcomes of aneuploidy.

Aneuploidy's Main Cause: Nondisjunction

What brings about the harmful condition of aneuploidy? The cause usually is a phenomenon known as **nondisjunction**, which simply means a failure of homologous chromosomes or sister chromatids to separate during meiosis. If you look at **Figure 12.6**, you can see how this works. Note that it can occur either in meiosis I or in meiosis II. In meiosis I, two homologous chromosomes, on the opposite side of the metaphase plate, can be pulled to the *same* side of a dividing cell, producing daughter cells with imbalanced numbers of chromosomes. Conversely, nondisjunction can take place in meiosis II, by means of sister chromatids going to the same daughter cell after failing to "disjoin" (hence the cumbersome term *nondisjunction*). Such actions then produce an egg or sperm that has 24 or 22 chromosomes instead of the standard haploid number of 23; after union with a normal egg or sperm, this re-

Figure 12.6
A Mistake in Meiosis Brings about an Abnormal Chromosome Count
Nondisjunction can occur either in meiosis I or meiosis II, when either chromosomes or chromatids fail to separate properly. When it occurs in meiosis I, 100 percent of the resulting gametes will be abnormal; when it takes place in meiosis II, only 50 percent will be abnormal.

Normal	Abnormal	Abnormal

Nondisjunction in meiosis I

Nondisjunction in meiosis II

| 23 | 23 | 23 | 23 | 24 | 24 | 22 | 22 | 23 | 23 | 22 | 24 |

100% of gametes get normal number of chromosomes   100% of gametes get abnormal number of chromosomes   50% normal   50% abnormal sults in an embryo that has either 47 or 45 chromosomes, instead of the standard 46.

The effect of this is that the embryo has a genetic imbalance—one that perhaps can be made clear by an analogy. Imagine that while baking chocolate chip cookies, you decided to increase the amount of flour called for in the recipe. This change might be of little consequence if you increased all the other ingredients in the same proportion. If, however, you increased nothing but the flour, the final product would be hard and flavorless because the ingredients in it would be unbalanced. An added chromosome has this same effect: it unbalances the proportions of *biological* ingredients (the proteins) that help produce and maintain a living thing.

The Consequences of Aneuploidy

As noted, embryos with the wrong number of chromosomes are not likely to survive. Setting aside aneuploidies that affect the X and Y chromosomes, *all* aneuploidies result in miscarriage except for those that give an embryo an additional chromosome 13, 18, or 21. It is the gain of an additional chromosome 21 that causes the most well known outcome of aneuploidy in human beings. **Down syndrome** is, in some 95 percent of cases, a condition in which a person has three copies of chromosome 21, rather than the standard two. Ninety percent of these cases come about because of nondisjunction in egg formation, with the remaining 10 percent caused by nondisjunction in sperm formation. Seen in about 0.1 percent of all live births, Down syndrome results in an array of effects: smallish, oval heads, IQs that are well below normal, infertility in males, short stature and reduced life span in both sexes.

It is well known that when women pass the age of about 35, their risk of giving birth to a Down syndrome child increases dramatically. It seems less well known that even at maternal age 40, the odds of conceiving such a child are less than 1 in 100 (**Figure 12.7**). Scientists are not certain why the mother's age should figure so prominently in Down syndrome, though several hypotheses have been put forward to account for this. Most scientists agree that one piece of the puzzle is something you saw in Chapter 10: that in egg development, the process of meiosis generally stretches on for decades. Any given egg that develops in a woman starts meiosis I before the woman is born, but it may not complete this meiosis until she is, say, in her thirties. In the intervening decades, this egg's cellular machinery has aged, perhaps to the point that it can no longer separate its chromosomes or chromatids properly.

Abnormal Numbers of Sex Chromosomes

Aneuploidy can affect not only autosomes but sex chromosomes as well, meaning the two X chromosomes that females have and the X and Y chromosomes that males have. Embryos often survive sex chromosome aneuploidies, but the result, once again, is usually debilitations. An example is Turner syndrome, which produces people who are phenotypically female, but who have only one X chromosome. Such females, then, have only 45 chromosomes, rather than the usual 46. Their state is sometimes referred to as XO, the "O" signifying the missing X chromosome. The absence of a second sex chromosome causes a range of afflictions. Females with Turner syndrome have ovaries that don't develop properly (which causes sterility), they are generally short, and they often have brown spots (called nevi) over their bodies.

Turner syndrome results from a loss of a chromosome, but all manner of sex chromosome *additions* can also take place. There are, for example, XXY men, who while phenotypically male in most respects, tend

(a) Living with Down syndrome

(b) Maternal age and Down syndrome risk

Mother's age	Chances of giving birth to a child with Down syndrome
20	1 in 1925
25	1 in 1205
30	1 in 885
35	1 in 365
40	1 in 110
45	1 in 32

Figure 12.7
Down Syndrome: Increasing Risk with Age
(a) An adolescent girl with Down syndrome works with her teacher.
(b) The risk of giving birth to a Down syndrome child increases dramatically past maternal age 35.

to have a number of feminine features: some breast development, a more feminine figure, and lack of facial hair. When coupled with other characteristics (such as tall stature and dysfunctional testicles), the result is a condition called Klinefelter syndrome.

Beginning in the late 1960s, it became possible to test developing fetuses for genetic abnormalities. In recent years, however, reproductive technology has moved beyond testing. Prospective parents can now choose, from a group of embryos they have created, embryos that do not have any recognizable genetic defects. You can read more about this in "PGD: Screening for a Healthy Child" on the next page.

12.6 Structural Aberrations in Chromosomes

Aberrations can occur *within* a given chromosome, sometimes resulting from interactions *between* chromosomes. A frequent cause of such change is that pieces of chromosomes can break off from the main chromosomal body. Such a chromosomal fragment may then be lost to further genetic activity, or it may rejoin a chromosome—either the one it came from or another—often to harmful effect. These structural aberrations may come about spontaneously, but they may also be caused by exposure to such agents as radiation, viruses, and chemicals.

Deletions

A chromosomal **deletion** occurs when a chromosome fragment breaks off and then does not rejoin any chromosome. Such an event might take place during meiosis in a parent whose own somatic cell chromosomes were perfectly normal. In such an instance, a healthy parent could pass along a complement of 23 chromosomes, one chromosome of which would be missing a segment. If the deleted piece were large enough, the zygote would likely not survive. You can see how critical even a portion of a chromosome is by looking at children who suffer from a rare condition, called *cri-du-chat* ("cry of the cat") syndrome, which results from the deletion of the far end of the "short arm" of chromosome 5. If you look at **Figure 12.8**, you can see a **karyotype**—a visual image of a chromosome set—that shows you this deletion. Children born with the cri-du-chat condition exhibit a host of maladies, among them mental retardation and an improperly constructed larynx that early in life produces sounds akin to those of a cat.

Inversions and Translocations

When a chromosome fragment rejoins the chromosome it came from, it may do so with its orientation "flipped," so that the fragment's chemical sequence is out of order. This is an inversion: a chromosomal abnormality that comes about when a chromosomal fragment that rejoins a chromosome does so with an inverted orientation (see **Figure 12.9** on page 241). A translocation is a chromosomal abormality that occurs when two chromosomes that are not homologous exchange pieces, leaving both with improper gene sequences, which can have phenotypic effects.

Duplications

There is, of course, a perfectly normal process of chromosomal part swapping—crossing over. But consider what might happen if two homologous chromosomes exchanged *unequal* pieces of themselves in crossing over. One would lose genetic material while the other would gain it. Because these are homologous (meaning paired) chromosomes, the fragment added to the latter chromosome would duplicate some of the material it already has. This is but one of the ways in which

Figure 12.8
Chromosomal Deletion
(a) A five-year-old boy affected by cri-du-chat syndrome, which results from a chromosomal deletion. Note the small head and low-set ears.
(b) Karyotype of a person with cri-du-chat syndrome. Note, in chromosome 5, the abnormality in the homologous chromosome on the right. It lacks a section that is present in the left chromosome.

(a) Cri-du-chat syndrome

(b) Cri-du-chat karyotype

Chromosome with portion deleted

PGD: Screening for a Healthy Child

Is the baby OK?" In a life full of questions, it's possible that none carries more weight than this one. In most cases the answer will be reassuring, but in some it will be devastating. Small wonder, then, that scientists constantly are trying to perfect ways to know in advance whether a newborn will be healthy. You have seen that a large number of debilitating human conditions have genetic causes. Further, you know that nearly every kind of cell in a person's body contains a complete copy of that person's genome, or set of genes. Therefore, to check on someone's genetic well-being, all that is necessary is to have access to a small collection of that person's cells. And such cells exist, of course, in embryos as well as in newborn babies and adults. Thus, it's not hard to see what the procedure would be for prenatal genetic testing: Gather embryonic cells and examine their DNA and chromosomes.

This kind of testing has been going on, in ever-more refined forms, since the late 1960s. From that time until quite recently, however, most prospective parents who got bad news from a genetic test had two choices: abort the fetus, or bring a child with an incurable condition into the world. Now, an ever-growing number of reproductive clinics are providing a third choice. Parents who are willing to undertake so-called in vitro fertilization—fertilization of the mother's eggs in a laboratory—can have each one of the early-stage embryos that results from this process tested for genetic trouble. Of this initial group of embryos, only those found to be genetically healthy are candidates to be inserted back into the mother. The hope is that at least one of them will implant in the mother's uterus and result in a child.

This process, called pre-implantation genetic diagnosis or PGD, can be used by couples who have no known genetic risk factors, but who are simply having a hard time conceiving a child. As the main text notes, a large proportion of human embryos have genetic defects (such as aneuploidy). Moreover, some couples may be particularly prone to producing such embryos, which generally are washed away in miscarriages. PGD allows couples to screen their embryos for genetic problems before implantation in the uterus, thus greatly upping their chances of bringing a child to term.

PGD can also be used, however, in connection with couples who are *likely* to produce a child with genetic defects. In an extreme example, imagine a prospective father who knows he is fated to fall victim to Huntington disease because he has been found to carry the defective Huntington allele. Since Huntington is a dominant disorder, his odds of passing the disease along to one of his children are one in two. With PGD, only those embryos without the harmful allele would be selected for implantation.

Of course, more conventional means of genetic screening, such as amniocentesis, can provide information about conditions such as Huntington, but there is a difference. In amniocentesis, cells are obtained from an embryo that has been developing in a mother's uterus for a minimum of 14 weeks. By the time the results of amniocentesis are in, more than four months of a nine-month pregnancy may have elapsed. Most prospective parents would make a distinction between aborting a four-month-old fetus on the one hand or not implanting a four-day-old embryo on the other. Of course, not everyone feels this way. For some people, all embryos represent human life; therefore, producing an embryo, and then not using it, amounts to taking a human life. And in PGD, embryos have two fates: those that are not implanted are eventually destroyed.

Right now, some clinics allow parents to use PGD to choose the sex of their child.

Beyond this issue, PGD also raises another ethical question: What limits should be placed on choosing from among embryos? Right now, some clinics allow parents to use PGD to choose the *sex* of their child. If this seems disturbing, consider that, with our expanding knowledge of genetics, it may be possible in the future to select for a tall child or a blond-haired child. Prospective parents who would never abort a fetus to get such an outcome might not object to choosing from among embryos to get it, particularly since more embryos must be produced than will be used. Parents may think: Since a selection process is going to take place anyway (for healthy genes), why not select for things like hair color as well?

Such questions become less abstract with a little knowledge of how PGD works. Many of its steps are those that occur with any in vitro fertilization (IVF). The starting point for IVF is to administer to the prospective mother a group of hormones that stimulate formation of a large group of eggs in her ovaries. (These eggs are the oocytes you looked at in Chapter 10.) Anywhere from a week to two weeks later, a physician uses a needle attached to an ultrasound guide to remove the mature eggs from the ovaries. Though numbers vary, it would not be uncommon for 10 or 12 eggs to be recovered in this process. The husband then provides sperm to fertilize the eggs, with this fertilization taking place in a laboratory.

Three days after fertilization, each egg has divided into an eight-cell embryo. If you look at **Figure 1a**, you can see what comes next: using a tiny hollow tube called a pipette, a physician gently suctions one of the eight cells away from the others. (Embryonic cells are so undifferentiated at this point that the loss of any one of them does not interfere with development of the others into a child.) The cell that is removed provides the DNA for testing. If you look at **Figure 1b**, you can see the results of one of the tests. Recall that children born with

Down syndrome generally have a third copy of chromosome 21. It is possible to *test* for a third chromosome 21 by preparing DNA "bases" that will latch onto the unique set of DNA bases that exist on chromosome 21. Moreover, these "homing" DNA bases are fluorescent—they light up. The result is what you see in the figure: the prepared bases have latched onto three chromosome 21's in these embryonic cells; they have revealed that, had this embryo been implanted in the mother, the result would have been a child with Down syndrome.

By use of this test and others, embryos produced through IVF are ranked according to their health. Parents then choose from among them, selecting perhaps three or four that will be transferred back into the mother by a physician.

(a)

(b)

Figure 1

(a) Removing a Cell for Testing
A human embryo at the eight-cell stage (center), being manipulated to have one of its cells removed for pre-implantation genetic diagnosis. A pipette at left holds the embryo while a smaller pipette at right gently suctions off one cell from it. The cell's genetic material is then checked for abnormalities. If this embryo is determined to be normal, it may be inserted back into the mother's uterus, where it can develop into a baby.

(b) Down Syndrome Diagnosed
Genetic testing of this embryo has revealed that each of its cells has three copies of chromosome 21, indicated by the red areas in the nuclei of the cells. Such an embryo would develop into a child with Down syndrome. The red areas represent fluorescently labeled DNA that has bound or "hybridized" with regions of DNA specific to chromosome 21.

genetic duplication can take place. Such duplication is something of a double-edged sword. For individuals, it may have no effect at all, though large duplications can have negative effects, such as mental retardation. For the living world as a whole, however, duplication has been vital, because of its role in evolution. Just as adding a bedroom to a house might free up an existing bedroom, such that it could be turned into, say, a den, so adding a gene to a chromosome can "free up" an existing gene, such that it can be altered through mutation and go on to produce a new protein for an organism. At least half our genes are members of "gene families" that arose through gene duplication.

How Did We Learn?

For scientists to understand the chromosomal afflictions you've looked at in this chapter, they had to understand the basic linkage between chromosomes and inheritance. A scientist from Columbia University was the single most important figure in deepening our knowledge of this subject. You can read about his work in "Thomas Hunt Morgan" beginning on the next page.

Figure 12.9
Chromosomal Structural Changes

Deletion

Inversion

Translocation

Duplication

How Did We Learn?
Thomas Hunt Morgan: Using Fruit Flies to Look More Deeply into Genetics

Gregor Mendel used pea plants in his work, but generations of researchers after him have employed a common fruit fly, *Drosophila melanogaster*, in trying to unravel the secrets of genetics. One of the earliest *Drosophila* workers was a Kentuckian named Thomas Hunt Morgan, who greatly deepened our understanding of heredity with work he began in 1908 in his lab at Columbia University.

The *Drosophila* fly has a lot going for it as an experimental subject: It is small, it has unusually large chromosomes, and it has what is known as a short generation time. Whereas Mendel got one generation of pea plants a year, Morgan got one generation of *Drosophila* every 12 days or so. In practical terms, this meant that Morgan's group had to wait at most a month to see the results of their experiments.

Lessons from a Mutation: White-Eyed Flies

Morgan's path to discovery began with a chance event. One day he looked into one of the empty milk bottles in which he kept his flies and saw something strange: Among numerous normal or "wild-type" *Drosophila* with red eyes was a single male with white eyes (**see Figure 1**). Morgan correctly assumed that the variation he saw had come about because of a spontaneous genetic change or "mutation" in the fly. He then crossed his white-eyed male with females that he knew bred true for red eyes, and got all red-eyed flies in the F$_1$ generation. No surprise there; it simply looked as though red eyes were the same type of dominant trait that Mendel had seen in, for example, his yellow peas. Indeed, when Morgan went on to breed the F$_1$ generation—those that had mixed red and white alleles—he got a 3:1 red-to-white ratio in the F$_2$ generation. But the strange thing was that every white-eyed fly was a *male*. Why should that be?

(a) Eye of red-eyed *Drosophila*   **(b)** Eye of white-eyed *Drosophila*

Figure 1
The Mutation Morgan Saw

The importance of Morgan's insight was that he had linked a particular trait to a particular chromosome, which was a first.

As it turns out, sex chromosomes exist in *Drosophila* as they do in human beings: Females have two X chromosomes, while males have one X and one Y. Doing further experiments on these flies, Morgan eventually decided that the gene for eye color had to lie on a *particular* chromosome: the X chromosome. Why? Any fly that was white-eyed had to have only white-eyed alleles (because white was recessive). Normally, of course, this would mean *two* white-eyed alleles, but there was an exception: Males could be white-eyed if they had but a single white allele—because they have only a *single X chromosome*. You can look at **Figure 2** to see how this plays out schematically. The importance of Morgan's insight was not that he had grasped something about eye color in the fly. It was that he had linked a particular trait to a particular chromosome, which was a first.

On to DNA

For several chapters, you've been looking at genetics from the viewpoint of the genetic packages called chromosomes. Important as chromosomes are, it's probably been apparent that the real genetic control lies with the units that help

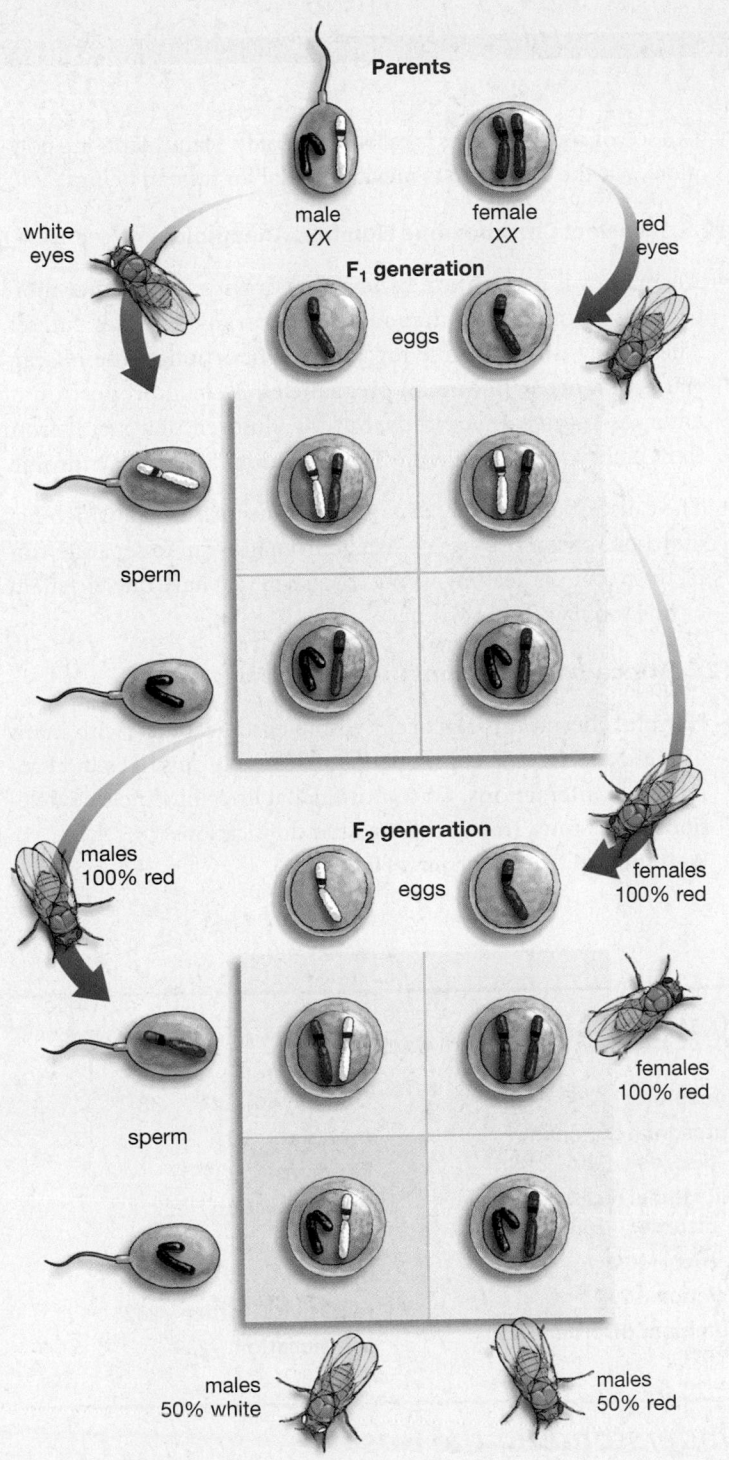

When Traits Separate: Recombination

Continuing with *Drosophila* breeding work, Morgan and his colleagues soon were finding all kinds of mutations in the flies. There was, for example, a mutation for "miniature" wings, as opposed to full ones. This trait followed the rules described earlier for the white-eyed mutation and accordingly was deemed to be an X-linked characteristic. Not surprisingly, the white-eyed and miniature-winged mutations tended to be transmitted *together* when both of these mutations were bred for, because the genes for both of them lay on the same chromosome. The question was, though, did genes on the same chromosome *always* travel together? Surprisingly, the answer was no. For example, miniature wings were usually passed on together with white eyes, but not always. Sometimes one trait would appear in an offspring but the other would not. Since genes for these traits were on one chromosome, how did they get separated from one another?

A paper published in Europe in 1909 gave Morgan a clue. Viewing cells under a microscope, F. A. Janssens had observed chromosomes entwining with each other during an early phase of meiosis. Given this and his own data, Morgan made a creative leap. He suggested that chromosomes can swap parts with each other during their meiotic intertwining. Sound at all familiar? Remember, in the Chapter 10 review of meiosis, the discussion of the phenomenon known as crossing over? Here, with Morgan, is the insight that led to this now-established tenet of science. Appropriately enough, insights such as these won Morgan a Nobel Prize in 1934.

Web Tutorial 12.3
Morgan's Flies

Figure 2
Why All Morgan's White-Eyed F₂'s Were Males
The F₂ female flies that inherited one white-eyed X-chromosome allele also inherited a second red-eyed X allele, making them red-eyed. However, the males inheriting the white-eyed allele had no second X chromosome. Instead, they inherited a Y chromosome—which has no genes on it for eye color—leaving them white-eyed.

make them up: the DNA sequences we call genes. As you've seen, it is genes that make pea-plant flowers purple or white—and that give a person Huntington disease or not. It's time to explore just what these genes are and how they operate.

Chapter Review

Summary

12.1 X-Linked Inheritance in Humans

- Certain human conditions, such as red-green color blindness and hemophilia, are called X-linked conditions, because they stem from dysfunctional genes located on the X chromosome. Men are more likely than women to suffer from these conditions because men have only a single X chromosome. A woman with, for example, a dysfunctional blood-clotting allele on one of her X chromosomes usually will be protected from hemophilia by a functional allele that lies on her second X chromosome.

- Hemophilia and red-green color blindness are examples of recessive genetic conditions, meaning conditions that will not exist in the presence of functional alleles.

- Given the nature of recessive genetic conditions, persons who do not suffer from such conditions themselves may yet possess an allele for it, which they can pass on to their offspring. Such persons, referred to as carriers of the condition, are heterozygous for it—the alleles they have for the trait differ, one of them being functional, the other being nonfunctional.
Web Tutorial 12.1: X-Linked Recessive Traits

12.2 Autosomal Genetic Disorders

- Sickle-cell anemia is an example of a recessive autosomal disorder. It is autosomal because the genetic defect that brings it about involves neither the X nor Y chromosome. It is recessive because persons must be homozygous for the sickle-cell allele in order to suffer from the condition—they must have two alleles that code for the same sickle-cell hemoglobin protein.

- Some genetic disorders are referred to as dominant disorders, meaning those in which a single allele can bring about the condition, regardless of whether a person also has a normal allele.
Web Tutorial 12.2: Some Human Genetic Disorders

12.3 Tracking Traits with Pedigrees

- In tracking inherited diseases, scientists often find it helpful to construct medical pedigrees, meaning familial histories that normally take the form of diagrams. Pedigrees allow experts to make deductions about the genetic makeup of several generations of family members.

12.4 Aberrations in Chromosomal Sets: Polyploidy

- Human beings and many other species have diploid or paired sets of chromosomes. In human beings, this means 46 chromosomes in all: 22 pairs of autosomes and either an XX chromosome pair (for females) or an XY pair (for males). The state of having more than

two sets of chromosomes is called polyploidy. Many plants are polyploid, but the condition is inevitably fatal for human beings.

12.5 Incorrect Chromosome Number: Aneuploidy

- Aneuploidy is a condition in which an organism has either more or fewer chromosomes than normally exist in its species' full set. Aneuploidy is responsible for a large proportion of the miscarriages that occur in human pregnancies. A small proportion of embryos survive aneuploidy, but the children that result from these embryos are born with such conditions as Down syndrome.

- The cause of aneuploidy usually is nondisjunction, in which homologous chromosomes or sister chromatids fail to separate correctly in meiosis, leading to eggs or sperm that have one too many or one too few chromosomes.

12.6 Structural Aberrations in Chromosomes

- Harmful aberrations can occur within chromosomes, with many of these aberrations coming about because of mistakes in chromosomal interactions. Chromosomal aberrations include deletions, inversions, translocations, and duplications.
Web Tutorial 12.3: Morgan's Flies

Key Terms

aneuploidy 237	Down syndrome 238
autosomal dominant disorder 234	inversion 239
	karyotype 239
autosomal recessive disorder 233	nondisjunction 237
carrier 234	pedigree 235
	polyploidy 236
deletion 239	recessive disorder 232
dominant disorder 234	translocation 239

Understanding the Basics

Multiple-Choice Questions (answers in the back of the book)

1. Much genetic information can be derived from pedigrees (family genetic histories). Such information is especially helpful in connection with humans because
   a. humans cannot be crossed experimentally
   b. other animals have long life spans
   c. we know relatively little about human genetics
   d. humans have so many chromosomes
   e. humans are too complicated

2. Sickle-cell anemia patients have a different form of _____, which leads to _____.
a. hemoglobin, increased muscle activity
b. a sex chromosome, sterility
c. pigment, color blindness
d. skin cell, nevi
e. hemoglobin, decreased oxygen transport

3. Individuals most protected against malaria are those who
a. are heterozygous for sickle-cell anemia (one hemoglobin A, one hemoglobin S)
b. are homozygous for sickle-cell anemia (two hemoglobin S)
c. are hemophiliacs
d. are homozygous for hemoglobin A
e. both a and c

4. Inheritance of a dominant autosomal disorder differs from inheritance of an autosomal recessive disorder in that:
a. A dominant disorder may be passed on only if both parents are affected.
b. A dominant disorder is evident only if the offspring is homozygous for the allele.
c. A dominant disorder is more often seen in females.
d. A dominant disorder may be passed on even if only one parent is affected.
e. both b and d

5. An individual having 44 autosomes and one X chromosome would be classified as:
a. polyploid
b. aneuploid
c. having Klinefelter syndrome
d. having Turner syndrome
e. both b and d

6. A human embryo with 69 chromosomes would
a. die in the womb or shortly after birth
b. be considered polyploid
c. have fewer problems than a plant with the same condition
d. both a and b
e. all of the above

7. Which of the following statements is *not* true regarding Down syndrome?
a. Affected individuals usually have three copies of chromosome 21.
b. The condition is usually caused by nondisjunction in egg formation.
c. A woman over 35 increases her chance of having a Down syndrome child to 1 out of every 40 births.
d. Approximately 0.1 percent of all live births are children with Down syndrome.
e. The physical characteristics associated with the disorder include mental retardation, male infertility, short stature, and reduced life span.

8. Nondisjunction can occur in
a. meiosis I or mitosis
b. mitosis or meiosis II
c. only meiosis II
d. only meiosis I
e. either meiosis I or II

9. A carrier is a person who
a. suffers from a recessive disorder
b. is heterozygous for a recessive disorder
c. is homozygous for a recessive disorder
d. does not suffer from a recessive disorder but possesses an allele for it
e. b and d

10. What do all human males inherit from their mother?
a. an X chromosome
b. genes for red-green color vision
c. two X chromosomes
d. all of the above
e. a and b only
f. Turner syndrome
g. none of the above

Brief Review

1. How can the serious genetic defect known as aneuploidy be both widespread and relatively unrecognized?

2. In sex-linked diseases, which gender is more frequently affected—male or female? Why?

3. Why can people with red-green color blindness still see other colors, such as blue?

4. Compare and contrast the four chromosome structural aberrations discussed in this chapter: deletions, inversions, translocations, and duplications.

5. Given the following situations, answer accordingly:
a. A human cell with 47 chromosomes has probably undergone _____.
b. A cell duplicates DNA, but fails to undergo cytokinesis. This would lead to _____.

6. Why would a person with Klinefelter syndrome exhibit both male and female features?

7. Certain genotypes may be advantageous in specific situations. Give an example of a heterozygous genotype that is advantageous over either homozygous genotype. (Hint: especially in mosquito-infested areas.) Why is this the case?

Applying Your Knowledge

1. The text notes that an alternate allele of the hemoglobin gene can cause sickle-cell anemia when a person is homozygous for this allele, but that a person who is heterozygous for the allele actually can derive a benefit from it—protection from malaria. In the United States, 8 percent of African Americans are carriers for the sickle-cell allele, while in central Africa the figure is 20 percent. What could account for this difference?

2. The text notes that the technique known as pre-implantation genetic diagnosis (PGD) allows prospective parents to screen embryos not only for serious genetic defects such as Down syndrome, but for traits that may be regarded as more or less desirable, such as male or female gender. What limits, if any, should be placed on parents' ability to choose from among embryos for traits such as this?

3. Thinking back to what you learned in Chapter 10 about how sperm are produced, why is it that the cells that give rise to sperm undergo nondisjunction less frequently than the cells that give rise to eggs?

Genetics Problems

1. A man who is a carrier for sickle-cell anemia, a recessive genetic disease, marries a normal, noncarrier woman. What proportion of their children are expected to be afflicted with sickle-cell anemia?

2. Hemophilia is an X-linked recessive disease that prevents blood clotting. If a woman who is a carrier for hemophilia marries a normal man, what proportion of their sons are expected to have hemophilia? What is the chance that their first child will have hemophilia? (Remember, the sex of this child is unknown until birth.)

3. Neurofibromatosis is a genetic disorder associated with an allele of one autosomal gene. Individuals with neurofibromatosis have uneven skin pigmentation and skin tumors. A man with neurofi-

bromatosis marries a normal woman who does not carry the allele for this disorder. The couple has 5 children, 3 of whom have neurofibromatosis. The most likely explanation for this outcome is that neurofibromatosis is a _____ trait and the man is _____.
   a. recessive; homozygous recessive
   b. recessive; heterozygous
   c. dominant; homozygous dominant
   d. dominant; heterozygous
   e. a and b are both possible explanations

Consider the following pedigree for a human autosomal trait. (Note that in pedigrees, generations are indicated by Roman numerals and individuals within a generation are numbered from left to right with Arabic numerals.)

4. Is the allele that determines this trait dominant or recessive? Explain your reasoning.

5. Using symbols A and a for the dominant and recessive alleles, respectively, what is the genotype of the affected male in the second generation (individual II-3)?

6. What is the genotype of this individual's mate?

7. If female III-2 marries a heterozygous man, what proportion of their children are expected to have this trait?

8. Consider the following pedigree, which posits a fantasy gene for ear shape, symbolized by P for the regular allele or p for a pointy-shaped allele if this is an autosomal trait; or by X^+ for the regular allele or X^p for the pointy allele if this is an X-linked trait.

   This pedigree indicates the trait is most likely inherited as an:
   a. autosomal dominant
   b. autosomal recessive
   c. X-linked dominant
   d. X-linked recessive

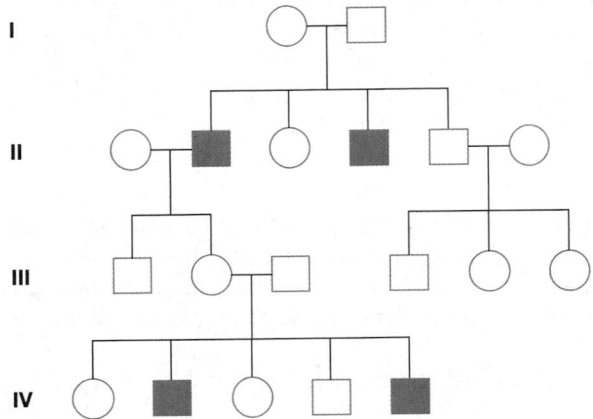

9. What is the genotype of individual I-1?

10. If a woman who is a carrier for this trait married individual III-1, what proportion of their children are expected to show this trait? What proportion of their sons are expected to show this trait?

11. Construct a pedigree to answer the following question. Red-green color blindness is an X-linked recessive trait. A woman who has a color blind mother and a father with normal color vision marries a man with normal vision. This couple has a son. What is the chance that the son is color blind?

12. Hyperphosphatemia, a disease that causes a form of rickets (abnormal bone growth and development), is inherited as an X-linked dominant trait. A woman who is heterozygous for the disease allele marries a normal man. What proportion of their sons will have hyperphosphatemia? What proportion of their daughters will have hyperphosphatemia? If hyperphosphatemia were an X-linked recessive trait, how would your answer differ?

MediaLab

Do We Know Too Much? Human Genetic Testing

Collum is an 8-month-old baby with an incurable neurodegenerative disorder. In a few short weeks, he changes from a playful, robust infant to being unable to lift his head, to move, and eventually even to breathe. When reading heart-breaking parental accounts about battling these kinds of rare conditions, you may ask why it happens, what medical science is doing for a cure, and if it could happen to your child. Doctors have recently discovered the cause of many of these illnesses; unfortunately, they are genetic mutations passed from parent to child during conception. Today there are few treatment options for repairing mutations. With this discouraging news, the only solace may be that we can now predict the chance of a future child or grandchild suffering the same fate. Given what you know about human genetics from reading Chapter 12, can you predict your child's chance of inheriting some disorder? In the following *Web Tutorial*, you will review the three patterns of inheritance of genetic mutations, so that in the *Web Investigation* you can analyze your skills as a human geneticist.

This *MediaLab* can be found in Chapter 12 on your Companion Website (www.prenhall.com/krogh3).

WEB TUTORIAL

Human genetics uses Mendel's rules about the probability of inheriting a specific genetic characteristic and extends them to predicting inheritance of human diseases. This *Web Tutorial* will lead you through the three main patterns of inheritance seen in human genetics.

Activity

1. First, you will learn about the special inheritance pattern seen for mutations on the X chromosome.

2. Then, you will learn how to create a Punnett square to predict the chance of a child inheriting a recessive or dominant condition caused by a mutation on one of human chromosomes 1-22, which are called autosomes.

3. Next, you will examine one of the most serious genetic disorders, chromosomal mutations, and see how they occur.

4. Finally, you will test your ability to use a pedigree to discern the passage of a genetic trait through a family.

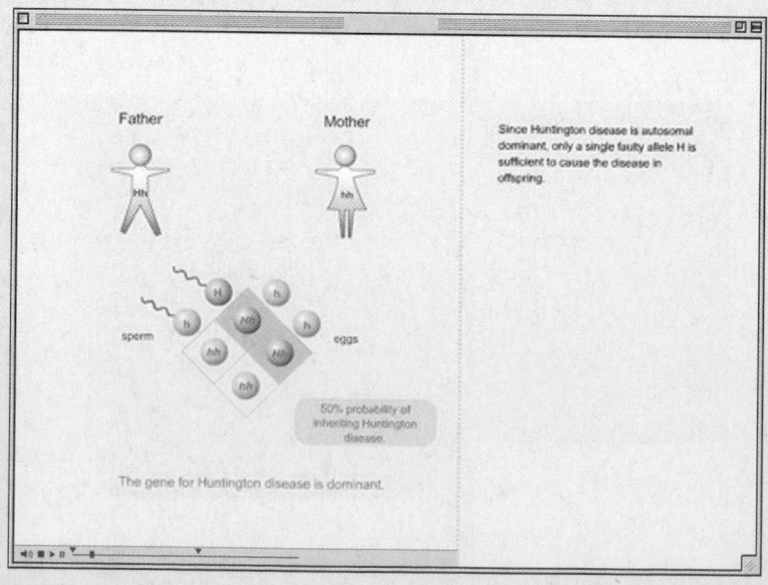

Father   Mother

Since Huntington disease is autosomal dominant, only a single faulty allele H is sufficient to cause the disease in offspring.

sperm   eggs

50% probability of inheriting Huntington disease.

The gene for Huntington disease is dominant.

Investigation 1
Estimated time for completion = 10 minutes

Genetic counselors are health professionals who specialize in disseminating information on over 4,000 different inherited human diseases. They take detailed family histories, review basic genetics, and counsel patients on the likelihood of inheriting one of thousands of disorders, while dealing with the emotional and sometimes moral issues involved. How do you know if you should see a genetic counselor? Would you understand the basic genetics they explained to you? Click on the keyword **COUNSELOR** on the Website to read an article describing gene testing.

Investigation 2
Estimated time for completion = 5 minutes

In the future portrayed in the 1997 movie *Gattaca*, prenatal genetic screening helps couples choose the perfect child, free from mutations that would predispose heart disease, low IQ, or even myopia. Click on the keyword **GATTACA** on the Website to visit the future and try your hand at designing your offspring. What would you select for your child's height, weight, health problems, and even IQ if you could?

Investigation 3
Estimated time for completion = 5 minutes

How close is science getting to science fiction? In *Web Investigation 2*, you tried to design the perfect child. How many of the traits like Alzheimer's, drug addiction, arthritis, even height that you listed as undesirable in your family can now be tested for? Click on the keyword **GENETESTS** on the Website. When you get there, you will do a Link-In Search to see a list of all the genes in the GeneTests databank. To do this, when the screen opens, simply leave the disease name blank and click on "Submit the Disease Name." You can then investigate one of the hundreds of genetic mutations for which genetic tests are currently available. Pick one of the genetic diseases that runs in your family, and investigate the state of research into treatments and predictive gene testing.

Now that you have investigated the current science of genetic testing, comment on what you learned and how it has influenced your feelings on some of the emotional issues involved.

Exercise 1
Estimated time for completion = 15 minutes

If someone could test your DNA and tell you what diseases you would likely suffer from in 25 years, would you want to know the results? Using the article from *Web Investigation 1*, compose a 250-word paper supporting or refuting your personal decision to know the results of your own gene test. Use examples, including the specific disease you would be tested for, the actual likelihood of contracting the disease if you have a positive test, how this knowledge could help you avoid dying from the disease, and how you think having this knowledge would affect you and your family.

Exercise 2
Estimated time for completion = 5 minutes

Is it even possible to design the perfect child using your genetic background? If there are undesirable traits in your family, you may need to add beneficial genes from outside your gene pool. The checklist from the *Gattaca* website uses questions similar to those a genetics counselor might ask you about your family health history. List all the "undesirable" inherited traits that run in your family.

Exercise 3
Estimated time for completion = 5 minutes

In *Web Investigation 3*, you looked at one of the hundreds of human diseases with a genetic component, such as familial breast cancer, that may run in your family and can currently be tested for. Prepare a 250-word report for your own family members about the current state of knowledge on this disease and the tests available. Describe the disease, and indicate how much of the severity of symptoms is due to environmental influences like diet and how much to genetic mutations. If a DNA test is available, indicate whether you would like to know the results of the test, and if the test can accurately predict who will get the disease.

13 DNA Structure and Replication

James Watson.
(Section 13.2, page 252)

Francis Crick.
(Section 13.2, page 252)

The double helix.
(Section 13.3, page 254)

> **DNA serves as a storehouse of information for living things. Scientists could not understand how DNA could play this role until they understood how all of its component parts fit together.**

"In research the front line is almost always in a fog," wrote Francis Crick in his 1988 memoir, *What Mad Pursuit*. Crick has first-hand knowledge of this. In 1953, with James Watson, he discovered the structure of DNA, an effort that brought him to the front line of research, which is where he has remained ever since. Crick's book makes clear what a tremendous difference there is between learning something about nature and discovering something about it. In learning, dozens of voices stand ready to instruct; there are books, lectures, videos, CDs—a world of well-organized information. The person who seeks to discover something about nature, meanwhile, is confronted with silence. Nature goes on: Cells divide, chromosomes condense, birds migrate. But *why* do these things operate the way they do? All the researcher has as a guide are the things themselves, working away. The trick is to devise some test (called an experiment) that can make nature's routine operations yield up information. In this process of teasing out truth, knowledge is gained in very small increments. Scientists are like the first people down a darkened maze of tunnels; they must make their way exceedingly slowly, feeling each square inch of wallspace as they go, after which they can only leave lights on *behind* them (in the form of their scientific papers, books, and so forth).

13.1 What Do Genes Do, and What Are They Made of?

To get a feel for the process of discovery, consider the state of genetics early in the twentieth century. By 1920, it had been demonstrated beyond any doubt that genetic information resided on chromosomes. Within a decade or so, by looking at some abnormally large fly chromosomes, scientists could observe in great detail such chromosomal processes

DNA replication begins.
(Section 13.3, page 255)

One kind of mutation.
(Section 13.4, page 257)

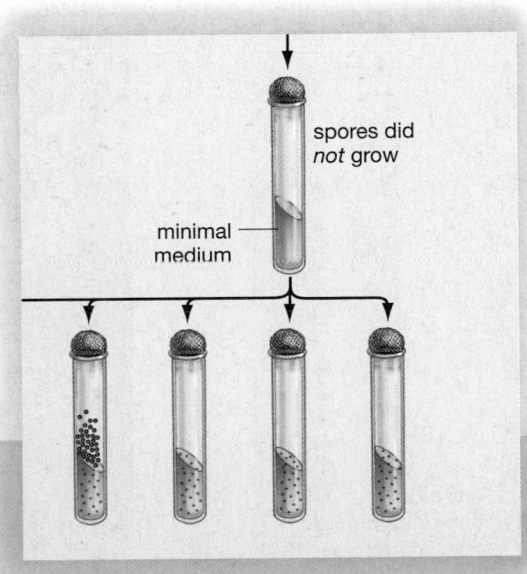

A famous experiment.
(Essay, page 259)

as crossing over. By viewing the banding patterns on these chromosomes, they could even identify the rough location of some genes.

Yet what was a gene? What was the physical nature of this unit of heredity, and how did it work? No one knew. Because genes are much smaller than the chromosomes on which they reside, there was no hope of simply viewing one under a microscope. In observing chromosomes, scientists were only "looking" at genes in the way that any of us is "looking" at lunar rocks by glancing up at the moon. Through the 1920s and 1930s, then, genes could be described only in vague, functional terms, as in: A gene is an entity that lies along a chromosome and brings about a phenotypic trait in an organism (for example, the green or yellow peas of Mendel's experiments).

Things were to clear up somewhat in the ensuing years. The seminal achievement in genetics in the late 1930s and early 1940s was a more concrete description of what genes do: They bring about the production of proteins. The central achievement in genetics from the mid-1940s to the early 1950s was strong evidence indicating what genes are composed of: deoxyribonucleic acid, or DNA for short.

DNA Structure and the Rise of Molecular Biology

By the early 1950s, a key question became *how* DNA carried out its genetic function. To find out, scientists had to piece together its exact chemical structure. This investigation turned out to be a watershed event in biology. Just as opening a mechanical watch and observing how its parts fit together would allow a person to understand how the watch works, so deciphering the structure of DNA allowed biologists to understand how genetics works at its most fundamental level. How could a section of DNA specify a protein? How could genetic information be copied? The structure of the DNA molecule suggested answers to these questions, as you'll see.

Apart from what this investigation uncovered, the inquiry itself stood as a symbol of a new era in biology. When Gregor Mendel did his experiments with peas, he was looking at whole organisms. When T. H. Morgan was doing his work with *Drosophila* flies, he was interested in whole chromosomes, which he knew to be composed of several types of molecules. In the early 1950s, however, the search turned to a single molecule. How was DNA structured, and how did this structure allow it to carry out its various func-

Figure 13.1
Young and Famous
James Watson, on the left, and Francis Crick, with a model of the DNA double helix, shortly after they published their paper on the molecule's structure.

tions? Biological research of this sort has grown ever more important in the decades since the 1950s. It is today known as **molecular biology**: the investigation of life at the level of its individual molecules.

13.2   Watson and Crick: The Double Helix

James Watson and Francis Crick may not be instantly recognized scientific names in the way that, say, Albert Einstein or Louis Pasteur are, but there's a certain public awareness that these two researchers did something important in connection with DNA (**Figure 13.1**). What they did was present to the world, in 1953, the structure of DNA: Atom-by-atom, bond-by-bond, this is how DNA fits together, they said in unveiling DNA's now-famous configuration, the double helix.

The two were a seemingly unlikely pair to make an epochal scientific discovery. Watson, an American, was a 23-year-old who was scarcely more than a year out of graduate school, and Crick, an Englishman, was a 35-year-old just then working on his doctorate when the two met in the fall of 1951 at Cambridge University in England. Ending up together by coincidence at the same laboratory, they realized in short order their mutual interest in the structure of DNA and, to the neglect of projects they were supposed to be working on, they began several rounds of model building and brainstorming that resulted in their breakthrough.

Watson and Crick were greatly aided in their investigation by the work of others. Though the DNA molecule was too small to be seen by even the most powerful microscopes of the time, something about its structure could be inferred from a technique called *X-ray diffraction*. In this process, a purified form of a molecule is bombarded with X rays. The way these rays scatter upon impact then reveals something about the structure of the molecule.

If you look at **Figure 13.2**, you can see the results of some X-ray diffraction. As you can imagine, it takes a highly trained observer to be able to deduce anything about the structure of a molecule from such an image. Fortunately for Watson and Crick, such a person was working just up the road from them. She was Rosalind Franklin, a researcher at King's College in London and one of the handful of individuals then skilled in performing X-ray diffraction on DNA. She and her colleague, Maurice Wilkins, were themselves working on the structure of DNA at the time, as

were other researchers in America. Thus did Watson, at least, regard the search for DNA structure to be a race between several teams, a fact that concentrated his efforts wonderfully. In 1962 Watson, Crick, and Wilkins were awarded the Nobel Prize in Medicine or Physiology for their work on DNA. Rosalind Franklin died of cancer in 1958 at the age of 37. Nobel Prizes are not awarded posthumously; it's unknown what would have happened had she lived.

Let's start now to look at DNA's structure, which will put you in a position to appreciate the achievement of Watson, Crick, and their fellow researchers.

Web Tutorial 13.1
DNA

(a) Rosalind Franklin

(b) X-ray diffraction image of DNA

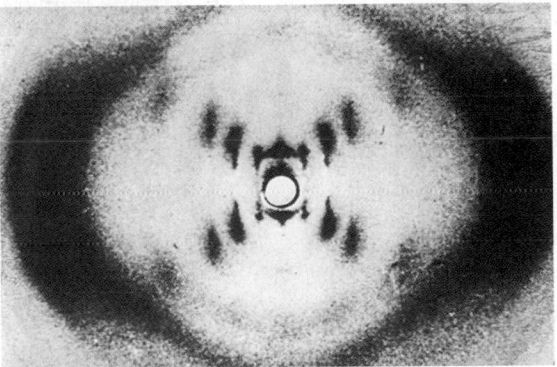

Figure 13.2
(a)   DNA Investigator
Rosalind Franklin, whose work in X-ray diffraction was important in revealing the structure of the DNA molecule.

(b)   Imaging DNA
One of Franklin's X-ray diffraction images of DNA. The "cross" formed of dark spots indicated the molecule had a helical structure.

13.3 The Components of DNA and Their Arrangement

If you look at **Figure 13.3**, you can see the component parts of DNA. First, there is a phosphate group, and second, a sugar called *deoxyribose*. Third, there are four possible DNA "bases": adenine guanine, thymine, and cytosine—A, G, T, and C, for short. When you link together a phosphate group, a deoxyribose molecule and one of the four bases, you get the basic building block of DNA, the *nucleotide*, one of which is boxed in the larger DNA molecule in the figure.

When you look at this larger figure as a whole, you can see that the double-helix looks something like a spiral staircase. By focusing on its exterior "handrails,"

you can see how sugar and phosphate fit together to form a kind of chain, with its links going: sugar-phosphate-sugar-phosphate (symbolized in the figure by S and P). The "steps" lying between these handrails are composed of DNA's bases. As the figure shows, each of the bases amounts to a *half*-stair-step, if you will. Each extends inward from one handrail of the double helix and then is joined to a base extending inward from the *other* handrail of the DNA molecule. (The bases are linked via hydrogen bonds, symbolized by the dotted lines in the figure.)

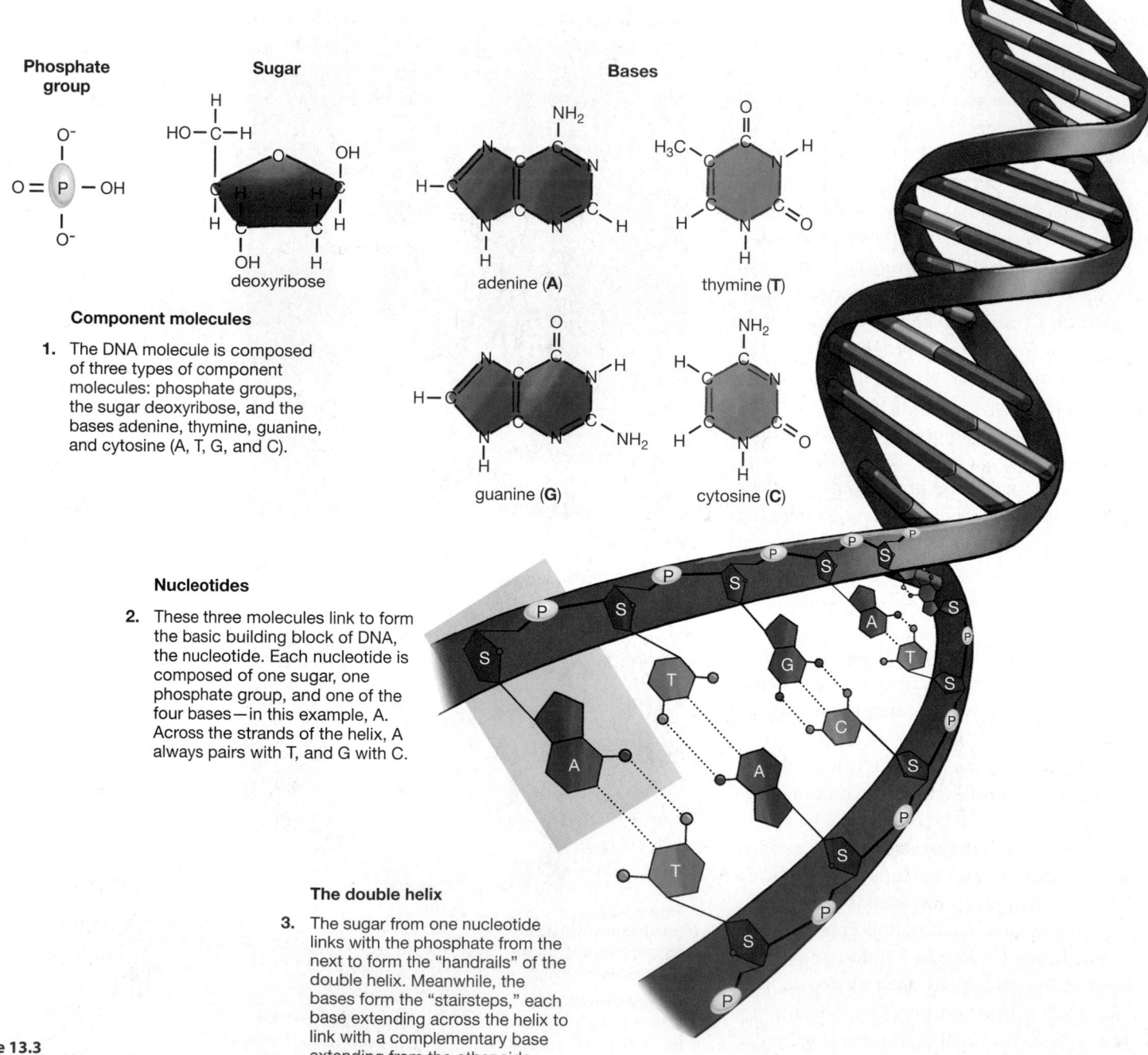

Phosphate group

Sugar

deoxyribose

Bases

adenine (**A**)

thymine (**T**)

guanine (**G**)

cytosine (**C**)

Component molecules

1. The DNA molecule is composed of three types of component molecules: phosphate groups, the sugar deoxyribose, and the bases adenine, thymine, guanine, and cytosine (A, T, G, and C).

Nucleotides

2. These three molecules link to form the basic building block of DNA, the nucleotide. Each nucleotide is composed of one sugar, one phosphate group, and one of the four bases—in this example, A. Across the strands of the helix, A always pairs with T, and G with C.

The double helix

3. The sugar from one nucleotide links with the phosphate from the next to form the "handrails" of the double helix. Meanwhile, the bases form the "stairsteps," each base extending across the helix to link with a complementary base extending from the other side.

**Figure 13.3
The Structure of DNA**

The figure shows some examples of one base being paired with another. At the bottom, for example, an A base on the left is paired with a T base on the right. Go two sets of nucleotides up and a G on the left is being paired with a C on the right. This turns out to be one of the fundamental rules about DNA structure. If you viewed a billion DNA *base pairs*, as they're called, you would find the same thing: A always pairing with T, and G always pairing with C, across the helix. (Any two bases that can pair together in this way are said to be *complementary*; thus A is complementary to T, and G is complementary to C. Likewise, you can have complementary chains of DNA.)

The Structure of DNA Gives Away the Secret of Replication

It was DNA's very structure that suggested the answer to one of the great questions of genetics: How is genetic information passed on? To put this another way, how does a cell make a copy of its own DNA? As you've seen, a full complement of our DNA is contained in nearly every cell in our body. Yet cells divide, and the daughter cells contain exactly the same DNA complement as the parent cell. This means that genetic information is passed on by means of DNA being copied, with one copy of this molecule ending up in each daughter cell. Indeed, such copying extends to the formation of egg and sperm cells, meaning this is the way genetic information is passed on from one *generation* to the next. But how could this work?

The structure Watson and Crick discovered suggested a way. We've observed that A must always pair with T, and G with C, across the two strands of the double helix. This rule, Watson and Crick saw, meant that each single strand of DNA could serve as a *template* for the synthesis of a new single strand (**see Figure 13.4**). Each A on an old strand would specify the place for a T on the new, each G on the old a place for C on the new, and so forth. All that was required was for the two old strands to separate—splitting the stair steps right down the middle—and for new strands to be synthesized that were complementary to the old. As it turned out, this was exactly how things worked, as you'll see shortly.

The Structure of DNA Gives Away the Secret of Protein Production

The second thing the structure suggested was a partial answer to another great question of genetics: How the molecule of heredity could be versatile enough to specify the dazzling array of proteins that all living things produce. The handrails of DNA's double helix are monotonous—phosphate, sugar, phosphate, sugar. But the bases can be laid out along these handrails in an extremely varied manner. A has to pair with T and G with C *across* the helix; but *along* the handrails, the bases can come in any order. Look at the top drawing in Figure 13.4 and see the order this hypothetical group of bases comes in; starting from the bottom right, A-G-C-T-A-C. Strung together by the thousands, these bases can specify a particular protein, just as in Morse code a series of short and long clicks can specify a particular word.

The Building Blocks of DNA Replication

You have already looked briefly at the basic process by which DNA is copied or "replicated," but we now need to review some of the details of this process. The basic steps here are straightforward. The essential building block of DNA is the unit called the **nucleotide**, which can be seen in the box in Figure 13.3. Every nucleotide contains one sugar and one phosphate group. What differentiates one nucleotide from another is the base

Figure 13.4
DNA Replication
The result of DNA replication is two identical molecules of DNA, whereas the process began with one.

1. DNA to be replicated

2. Strands separate

3. Each strand now serves as a template for the synthesis of a separate DNA molecule as free nucleotides base-pair with complementary nucleotides on the existing strands.

Order of bases encodes information for protein production.

4. This results in two identical strands of DNA.

that is attached to it; in this case the base is A, but as you can see, others have T, C, or G.

Figure 13.4 shows the process of DNA replication in overview. Note that the first thing that happens is that the joined strands of the double helix unwind, separating from one another. The nucleotides on each of the single strands are then paired with free-floating nucleotides that line up in new, complementary strands. Because *both* strands of the original double helix are being paired with new strands, the end product is two double helices, where before there was one.

You can see in Figure 13.4 that the addition of nucleotides moves in differing directions on the two strands. This is so because of something you can see in Figure 13.3: the two strands of the double helix have opposite orientations. Note that the sugars of the right-hand strand, for example, are upside down relative to the sugars of the left-hand strand. (If the strands were people, we would think of them as lying head to *foot* relative to each other.) Because new nucleotides can be added to only one end of a DNA strand—what's known as the three-prime end—the nucleotides are added in different directions.

DNA Replication: Something Old, Something New

It's worth drawing a little finer point on one aspect of this process: Each resulting double helix is a combination of the old and the new. Each has one "parental" strand of DNA and one newly synthesized complementary strand. This combination is conceptually important because it is how life builds upon itself. You can see this illustrated in **Figure 13.5**.

Eventually, the two double helices are fully formed. A little later they part company, during mitosis, with each newly formed double helix moving into a separate cell and thereafter serving as an independently functioning segment of DNA. (At the chromosomal level, the newly replicated helices form the

core of something you've seen a lot of in the last few chapters: sister chromatids, which eventually part and become independent chromosomes.)

However simple this process may sound in overview, its details are enormously complicated. As you might imagine, such a process could not proceed without enzymes to catalyze it. To name just two groups of them, there are enzymes called *helicases* that unwind the double helix, separating its two strands to make the bases on them available for base pairing. There is also another group of enzymes, collectively known as **DNA polymerases**, that move along each strand of the double helix, joining together nucleotides as they are added—one by one—to form the new, complementary strands of DNA.

Editing Out Mistakes

The base pairing that goes on in replication happens hundreds, then thousands, then millions of times in a given stretch of DNA: Free-standing A's are aligned with complementary T's, while C's are aligned with G's. Given the numbers of base pairs involved, the amazing thing is how few mismatches there are by the time the process is completed. The error rate in DNA replication—the rate at which the *wrong* bases have been brought together—might be only one in every billion bases by the end of replication. Yet *during* replication, such a mistake might be made once in every 100,000 bases. Obviously, to start with one number of mistakes but to end up with far fewer, the cell's genetic machinery has to be capable of correcting its errors.

This happens partly through the services of the versatile DNA polymerases, which are able to perform a kind of DNA editing: They remove a mismatched nucleotide and replace it with a proper one. Interestingly enough, this happens through a kind of backspacing. Normally the DNA polymerases are moving along a DNA chain, linking together recently arrived nucleotides. When an error is detected, however, they stop, move "backward," remove the incorrect nucleotide, put in the correct one, and then move forward again.

13.4 Mutations: Another Name for a Permanent Change in DNA Sequence

With this consideration of alterations in DNA structure, you have arrived at an important concept: that of a **mutation**, which can be defined as a permanent alteration of a DNA base sequence. Such alterations come about because the cell's various DNA error-correcting mechanisms are not foolproof; they do not correct all the mistakes that occur.

DNA's makeup can be altered in many ways. A slight change in the chemical form of a base might,

Figure 13.5
How Life Builds on Itself
Each newly synthesized DNA molecule is a combination of the old and the new. An existing DNA molecule unwinds, and each of the resulting single strands (the old) serves as a template for a complementary strand that will be formed through base pairing (the new).

old

new

for example, cause a G to link up across the helix with a T (instead of with its normal partner, C), as you can see in **Figure 13.6**. Then, in a subsequent round of DNA replication, the cell might "repair" this error in such a way that a permanent mistake is introduced: An A-T pair now exists, whereas the original sequence had a G-C pair. Permanent mistakes like these are called **point mutations**, meaning a mutation of a single base pair in the genome. Such mutations stand in contrast to the kind of whole-chromosome aberrations presented in Chapter 12, though these also qualify as mutations under some definitions.

In what way are mutations "permanent"? Think of how DNA replication works. Before any cell can divide, it must first make a copy of its complement of DNA. Should this DNA contain an uncorrected mistake, it too will be copied again and again with each succeeding cell division. Most mutations have no noticeable effect on an organism; and, as you'll see, mutations are vital to the process of evolution. But the concept of mutation is quite rightly fearful to us, because in relatively rare instances, mutations can have disastrous effects.

Examples of Mutations: Cancer and Huntington

A cancerous growth is a line of cells that has undergone a special kind of mutation—one that causes the affected cells to proliferate wildly. As an example, the skin cancer known as melanoma causes skin cells called melanocytes to start dividing very rapidly. For our purposes, the question is: How does this process get going? In 2002, British scientists looked at numerous lines of melanoma cells that had been taken from cancer patients. They found that 59 percent of these cells contained a mutation in a gene called *BRAF*. This gene, like all others, amounts to a sequence of DNA nucleotides—a sequence of C's, T's, A's, and G's. When the British scientists looked at how the *BRAF* gene had actually mutated, they found that in 80 percent of cases, there had been a single change: an A had been substituted for a T at *BRAF*'s 1,796th nucleotide. What they found, in other words, was a point mutation, nearly two thousand bases within the sequence of nucleotides that makes up the *BRAF* gene. And the effect of this mutation? It produces a protein that is a slightly altered version of the normal BRAF protein. This protein is altered enough, however, that it keeps melanocytes moving through the cell-division cycle, causing them to multiply wildly.

Cell proliferation is not the only kind of trouble mutations can bring about. Those of you who read Chapter 12 are familiar with the Huntington disease that causes spastic movements, severe de-

mentia, and usually death among its victims. In all people there is a gene, called *IT15*, that has within it a number of repeats of a particular "triplet" of bases, CAG. People with 37 or fewer CAG repeats in their *IT15* gene are fine; they will suffer no illness at all from the gene. People with 39 CAG repeats, however, probably will develop Huntington, though their first symptoms are not likely to appear until they are 66; people who have 50 or more repeats will descend into dementia at an average age of 27. Unlike the case with cancer, however, the Huntington mutation does not cause cells to multiply wildly. Instead, the mutated *IT15* gene creates a faulty protein called huntingtin, which cannot be broken down by nerve cells and ends up building up inside them, eventually killing them. Because Huntington is caused by a repeating group of three nucleotides, it is referred to as a "trinucleotide repeat" disease. At least eight other diseases of the nervous system fall into this category.

Heritable and Non-Heritable Mutations

Though Huntington disease and melanoma are both caused by mutations, there is an important distinction to be made between them. Most mutations come about in the body's **somatic cells**, which is to say cells that do not become eggs or sperm. This is the case with the mutations that bring about melanoma. Conversely, some mutations arise in **germ-line cells**, meaning the cells that do become eggs or sperm. This is the case with the Huntington mutation. The important point here is that germ-line cell mutations are *heritable*—they can be passed on from one generation to the next, in the ways reviewed in Chapter 12. In contrast, though a line of melanoma cells may be quite harmful, it is separate from the line of cells that

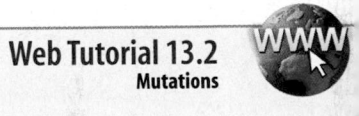

Web Tutorial 13.2
Mutations

Figure 13.6
One Route to a Mutation

Starting DNA	Incorrect base-pairing	Mutation

G C	G C	G C
T A	T A	T A
C G	C G	C G
G C	G T	A T ← Point mutation
C G	C G	C G
T A	T A	T A

1. In replicating a cell's DNA, mistakes are sometimes made, such that one base can be paired with another base that is not complementary to it (G with T in this case).

2. The next time a cell replicates its DNA, the replication repair mechanism may "fix" this error in such a way that a permanent alteration in the DNA sequence results. The original G will be replaced, instead of the wrongly added T. The result is an A-T base pair, whereas the cell started with a G-C base pair.

gives rise to eggs or sperm. For this reason, melanoma cannot be passed on from one generation to the next.

What Causes Mutations?

A critical question, of course, is what causes DNA to mutate? One answer is so-called environmental insults. The chemicals in cigarette smoke are powerful *mutagens*, meaning substances that can mutate DNA. So is the ultraviolet light that comes from the sun. To look at the latter example in a little more detail, ultraviolet light is a form of radiation that can link adjacent T's together in a single strand of DNA; sometimes it even causes both strands of the DNA helix to break. When this latter damage takes place in a cell, one of three things can happen. First, enzymes can successfully repair the damage. Second, the cell will recognize that this damage *cannot* be repaired, in which case the cell will commit suicide in the process known as apoptosis. Third, the enzymes will not repair the damage, but the cell will fail to initiate apoptosis. In this instance, the *failed* repair action may mean permanent change in base sequence—a mutation, in short.

Not all mutations are caused by environmental influences. Mutations happen simply as random, spontaneous events. Molecules collide in a cell, for example, causing DNA damage. The very process of eating and breathing produces so-called free radicals that can damage DNA. And the DNA replication machinery itself may introduce errors, irrespective of any outside influences.

Once such errors occur, it is understandable that some of them will go uncorrected, simply because of the size of the replication operation. When a human cell divides, billions of DNA base pairs have to be copied. And some 25 million cells are dividing each second in human beings. The surprise, therefore, is not that mistakes happen, but that so *few* of them happen, and that fewer still become permanent. (Recall the one-in-a-billion error rate in DNA replication that was observed earlier.) After learning about the kinds of effects mutations can have on organisms, however, you can understand why this error rate is so low: Life as we know it could not exist with a *high* error rate, at least in the portions of genome that code for proteins. Remember that within 3 billion A's, T's, G's, and C's, the substitution of a single A for a single T can help bring about melanoma. How could life exist if such mistakes were common?

The Value of Mistakes: Evolutionary Adaptation

While it's true that, for individuals, mutations can have a negative effect, for the living world as a whole mutations have been vitally important because of a role they play in evolution. It turns out that germ-line muta-

tions are the only means by which completely new genetic information can be added to a species' genome, in the form of new alleles (meaning variant forms of a gene). Organisms can combine *existing* alleles, in myriad ways. Think of meiosis, with its chromosomal part swapping (crossing over) and reshuffling of chromosomes (independent assortment). Valuable as these processes are, no amount of genetic recombination could have produced, for example, the eyes that some living things possess. To go from no eyes to eyes, there had to have been some mutations along the line—some accidental reorderings of DNA sequences such that entirely new proteins were produced. Such adaptations are vital to living things, given their struggle to get along in environments that are constantly changing. If environments change, species need to change too, in order to survive. And the only way major changes can come about is through mutations. You'll be looking at this topic again in the evolution unit of this book. For now, however, isn't it interesting to ponder the fact that the living world adapts partly through its mistakes?

How Did We Learn?

It may be clear to us today that genes are information-bearing units and that the information they contain is used to produce proteins. But 60 years ago, things were not so clear. Indeed, scientists had to work hard to attain this insight. To find out more about their efforts, see "Getting Clear about What Genes Do" on the next page.

On to How Genetic Information Is Put to Use

Back in Chapter 9, you saw that since antiquity, human beings have speculated about how one generation of living things can give rise to another—about *how* it is that life goes on. The questions posed by the Greeks, by scientists in the Renaissance, by Mendel and Morgan and others were finally answered in the 1950s and 1960s, when scientists came to understand DNA replication at the molecular level. The something-old, something-new quality to this replication—parental DNA strands serving as templates for new strands—was the detailed answer to the ancient question of how the qualities of living things can be passed down through generations.

Splendid as this function is, it is only one of the two great tasks carried out by our genetic machinery. You have just reviewed the process by which genetic information is replicated; now let's look at the process by which this information is used. How can a stretch of DNA bring about the production of a protein? You'll see in the chapter coming up.

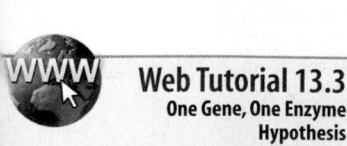

Web Tutorial 13.3
One Gene, One Enzyme
Hypothesis

How Did We Learn?
Getting Clear about What Genes Do: Beadle and Tatum

In the 1930s, biologists were confused not only about what genes were made of (DNA) but also about what it was that genes did. We now know that a large part of what they do is contain the information for the production of proteins, including the reaction-hastening proteins called *enzymes*. But it took work over a period of years by Stanford University researchers George Beadle and Edward Tatum to make this clear. Their experimental subject was a red fungus, the bread mold *Neurospora*.

Following the Growth of a Fungus

Research scientists are always looking for ways to control the confusing conditions of nature in order to tease out the rules it plays by. Beadle and Tatum's control mechanism was, first, to *induce* genetic mutations in *Neurospora* spores by bombarding them with X-rays. These mutated spores were then transferred one at a time into test tubes, where the second element of control came in. Natural or "wild type" *Neurospora* can manufacture or "synthesize" most of what they need to live, given just a few basic biological molecules in their surroundings. But could the descendants of the *mutated* group of *Neurospora* do this? Could they be put in a so-called minimal medium—a liquid environment that forces the fungus to manufacture almost all its necessary biological molecules—and still multiply into a thriving colony? The answer for many of the mutant strains was no. The mutations these organisms had undergone had rendered them unable to synthesize some substance that they needed to thrive. By being selective about *adding* substances to the minimal media, Beadle and Tatum could tell what substance the mutant cells were unable to synthesize. If they added the right thing, the colony would grow, as you can see in **Figure 1**. Thus, they reasoned, whatever substance they added was the substance a mutated strain could no longer synthesize on its own. For some of the mutant strains, the missing substance turned out to be the amino acid arginine.

We now know that arginine is produced in one of the metabolic pathways reviewed in Chapter 6. In such a pathway, a precursor compound is modified several times in a chain, with a different enzyme facilitating each step of the operation. By selectively supplying different strains of mutant *Neurospora* with arginine's *precursor* substances, Beadle and Tatum could discern the step at which the arginine metabolic pathway had been blocked. One strain required only precursor A to produce arginine, for example, while another strain required precursors A and B. In the tradition of T. H. Morgan, the researchers linked these blockages to genes on three separate *Neurospora* chromosomes. The summary result then was clear. A given *Neurospora* strain had become a mutant by having its genes altered through radiation. As a result, it no longer carried out the transformation of, say, precursor A to precursor B. It took an

enzyme to facilitate this transformation. What genes were doing, then, was bringing about the production of enzymes.

The One-Gene, One-Enzyme Hypothesis

Eventually, a famous label was applied to these experimental results: The *one-gene, one-enzyme hypothesis*. What each gene does is call up production of one enzyme, which undertakes a particular metabolic task. Though the notion of what a gene is has now been broadened, the essential insight was not only correct, it was critical. With it, scientists at last understood what genes were doing. For this work, which they completed in 1941, Beadle and Tatum shared in the Nobel Prize in 1958.

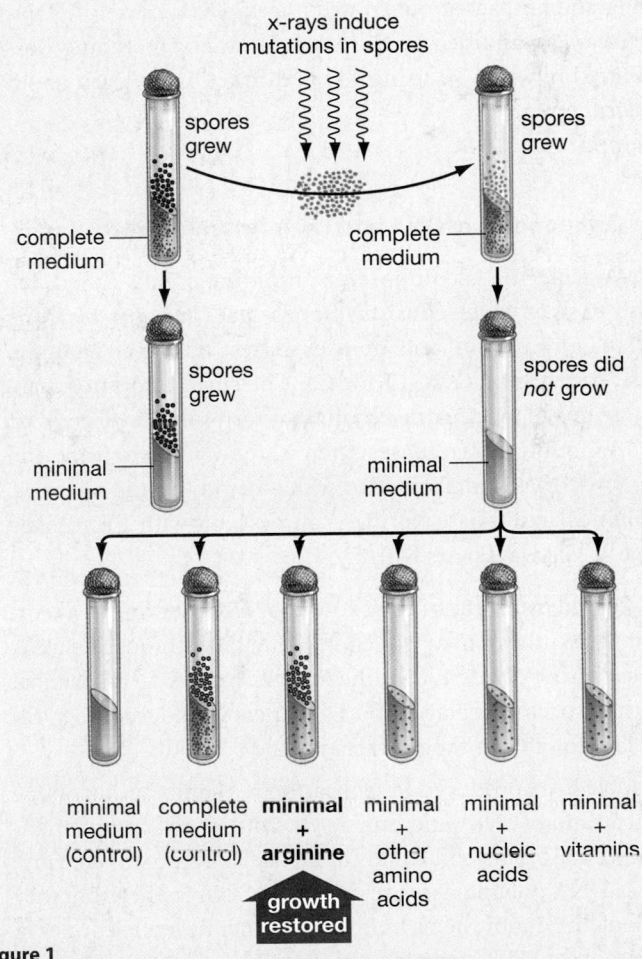

Figure 1
Beadle and Tatum Experiment with Mutated Spores
Using spores of the fungus *Neurospora*, Beadle and Tatum found that some mutated versions of the spores could not grow in a medium that required them to synthesize all their biological molecules. By selectively adding molecules to this "minimal medium," they demonstrated that the mutation was preventing the spores from producing certain compounds, among them the amino acid arginine. By tracing the metabolic pathway leading to arginine, Beadle and Tatum realized that the *Neurospora* genes that had been made dysfunctional were coding for enzymes that facilitated the steps leading from the precursors of arginine to arginine itself.

Chapter Review

Summary

13.1 What Do Genes Do, and What Are They Made of?

- James Watson and Francis Crick discovered the chemical structure of DNA in 1953. This event ushered in a new era in biology because it allowed researchers to understand some of the most fundamental processes in genetics.

- In trying to decipher the structure of DNA, Watson and Crick were performing work in molecular biology. This is the investigation of life at the level of its individual molecules. Molecular biology has grown greatly in importance since the 1950s.

13.2 Watson and Crick: The Double Helix

- Watson and Crick met in the early 1950s at Cambridge University in England and set about to decipher the structure of DNA. Their research was aided by the work of others, including Rosalind Franklin, who was using X-ray diffraction to learn about DNA's structure.
  Web Tutorial 13.1: DNA

13.3 The Components of DNA and Their Arrangement

- The DNA molecule is composed of building blocks called nucleotides, each of which consists of one sugar (deoxyribose), one phosphate group, and one of four bases: adenine, guanine, thymine, or cytosine (A, G, T, or C). The sugar and phosphate groups are linked together in a chain that forms the "handrails" of the DNA double helix. Bases then extend inward from the handrails, with base pairs joined to each other in the middle by hydrogen bonds. In this base pairing, A always pairs with T across the helix, while G always pairs with C.

- DNA is copied by means of each strand of DNA serving as a template for the synthesis of a new, complementary strand. The DNA double helix first divides down the middle. Each A on an original strand then specifies a place for a T in a new strand, each G specifies a place for a C on the new strand, and so forth.

- Each double helix produced in replication is a combination of one parental strand of DNA and one newly synthesized complementary strand. This is how life builds upon itself. A group of enzymes known as DNA polymerases are central to DNA replication; they move along the double helix, bonding together new nucleotides in complementary DNA strands.

- DNA can encode the information for the huge number of proteins utilized by living things because the sequence of bases along DNA's handrails can be laid out in an extremely varied manner. A collection of bases in one order encodes the information for one protein, while a different sequence of bases encodes the information for a different protein.

13.4 Mutations: Another Name for a Permanent Change in DNA Sequence

- The error rate in DNA replication is very low, partly because repair enzymes are able to correct mistakes. When such mistakes are made and then not corrected, the result is a mutation: a permanent alteration in a cell's DNA base sequence.

- Most mutations have no effect on an organism, but when they do have an effect, it is generally negative. Cancers result from a line of cells that have undergone types of mutations that cause them to proliferate wildly.

- Some mutations come about in the body's germ-line cells, meaning cells that become eggs or sperm. Such mutations are heritable: They can be passed on from one generation to another. The gene for Huntington disease, which is expressed in nerve cells, is a heritable, mutated form of a normal gene.
  Web Tutorial 13.2: Mutations
  Web Tutorial 13.3: One Gene, One Enzyme Hypothesis

Key Terms

DNA polymerase	256	**nucleotide**	255
germ-line cell	257	**point mutation**	257
molecular biology	253	**somatic cell**	257
mutation	256		

Understanding the Basics

Multiple-Choice Questions (answers in the back of the book)

1. James Watson and Francis Crick
   a. proved that DNA contains information for the production of proteins
   b. elucidated the nature of genetic mutations
   c. discovered DNA
   d. proved that chromosomes were made partly of DNA
   e. discovered the structure of DNA

2. The type of biological study that was exemplified through the discovery of DNA structure is called
   a. detailed biology
   b. component biology
   c. microscopic biology
   d. elemental biology
   e. molecular biology

3. The components of the DNA handrails are _____ and _____.
   a. nucleotides, phosphates
   b. sugars, nucleotides

c. sugars, bases

d. sugars, phosphates

e. none of the above

4. Which of the following combinations is an example of a nucleotide?

a. sugar + phosphate + adenine

b. sugar + phosphate + guanine

c. sugar + phosphate + thymine

d. sugar + phosphate + cytosine

e. all of the above

5. Which of the following DNA sequences contains a mismatched base pair?

a. TCAA
   AGTT

b. CAGC
   GTCG

c. GATA
   CTCT

d. AATT
   TTAA

e. GACG
   CTGC

6. If cytosine makes up 26 percent of the nucleotides in a sample of DNA from an organism, then adenine would make up what percent of the bases?

a. 26

b. 52

c. 28

d. 24

e. It cannot be determined from the information provided

7. If DNA's structure is compared to a spiral staircase, then its stairsteps would be

a. phosphate-sugar-phosphate chains

b. free-floating DNA bases bonded together randomly

c. chromatin

d. paired DNA bases, always linking A and T, or G and C

e. none of the answers above is correct

8. DNA polymerases work to

a. unwind the double helix during replication

b. cause mutations in DNA

c. join together nucleotides in a growing, complementary DNA strand

d. correct errors in DNA base sequences during replication

e. both c and d

9. Watson and Crick made their momentous discovery about DNA in _____.

a. 1943

b. 1953

c. 1921

d. 1973

e. 1962

10. How are the base pairs of the DNA double helix linked together?

a. phosphate bonds

b. hydrogen bonds

c. carbon–carbon bonds

d. sugar bonds

e. basic bonds

Brief Review

1. How does the phrase "something old, something new" describe the method of DNA replication employed by the cell?

2. What did Watson and Crick's discovery reveal that was so important?

3. True or False: DNA polymerases work only in a forward direction.

4. What is a mutation? Are all mutations harmful?

5. What is the nature of the Huntington disease mutation, and what is its effect at a cellular level?

Applying Your Knowledge

1. Given the following DNA sequence, determine the complementary strand that would be added in replication:

   ATTGCATGATAGCC

2. Why does a germ-line mutation carry greater potential significance than a somatic mutation?

3. A gene's nucleotide bases are known to be composed of 15 percent guanine. What percentages of each of the other three bases are contained in the same gene?

4. Why is it important that DNA replication have a low error rate?

5. Would you expect cancer to arise more often in types of cells that divide frequently (such as skin cells) or in types of cells that divide rarely or not at all (such as nerve cells)? Explain your reasoning.

14 Genetic Transcription, Translation, and Regulation

Transferring information.
(Section 14.2, page 265)

The triplet code.
(Section 14.4, page 269)

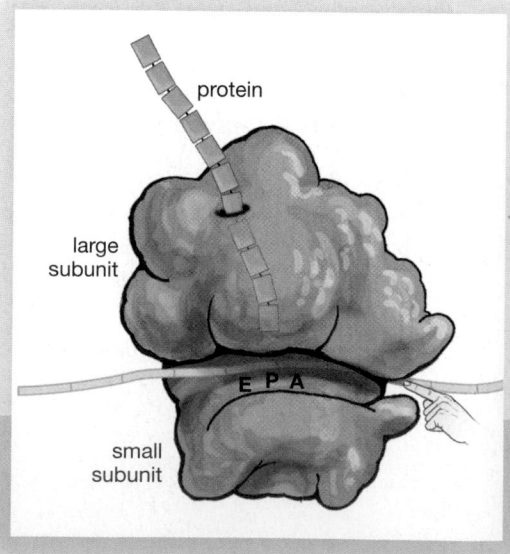

A ribosome.
(Section 14.4, page 271)

The scientific advance that was reviewed in Chapter 13, the discovery of the structure of DNA in 1953, bears some comparison to the birth of Napoleon: Both events had momentous consequences, but not for a while. Only slowly did the discoveries come that, in time, were seen as hinging on James Watson and Francis Crick's work. So significant were these advances, however, that the years between 1953 and 1966 are now regarded by some scholars as a kind of golden age of genetics; a time when basic findings about this field came fast and furious, such that by the mid-1960s scientists had at last grasped the essentials of how the genetic machinery works.

These discoveries were made in connection with both of the two great tasks of genetics: on the one hand, the copying or "replication" of DNA that you reviewed in Chapter 13; on the other, the means by which DNA's genetic infor-

mation brings about the production of proteins. The first task has to do with how genetic information is preserved; the second with how genetic information is utilized. This second task is the subject of this chapter.

14.1 The Structure of Proteins

Because you'll be dealing extensively with proteins here, now may be a good time to review some basic information about them. As you saw in Chapter 3, proteins fit into the "building blocks" model of biological molecules. The blocks in this case are amino acids. String a number of these together and you have a **polypeptide** chain, which then folds up in a specific three-dimensional manner, resulting in a protein. Proteins are likely to be made of hundreds of amino acids strung together, often in several linked polypeptide chains.

Mass production.
(Section 14.4, page 273)

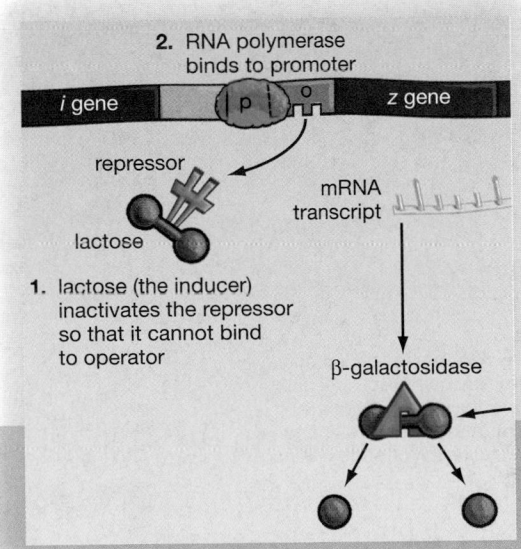

Genetic regulation in action.
(Section 14.5, page 275)

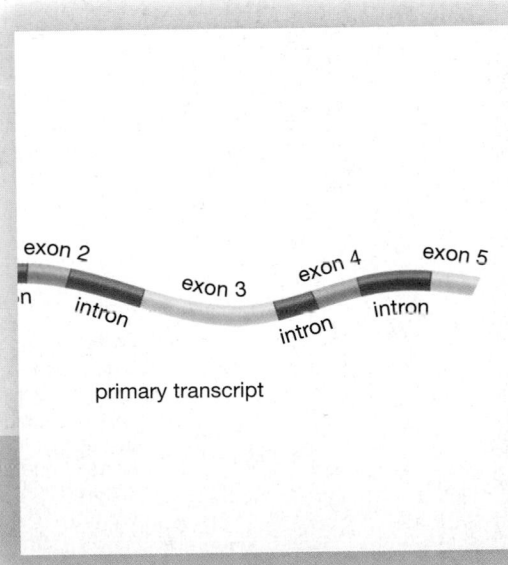

Ready for editing.
(Section 14.5, page 277)

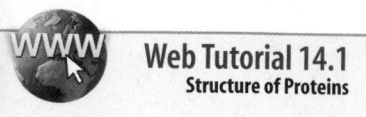

Synthesizing Many Proteins from 20 Amino Acids

Though there are hundreds of thousands of different proteins, each one of them is put together from a starting set of a mere 20 amino acids. If you wonder how such diversity can proceed from such simplicity, think of the English language, which has thousands of words, but only 26 letters in its alphabet. It is the *order* in which letters occur that determines whether, for example, "cat" or "act" is spelled out; just so, it is the order of amino acids that determines what protein is synthesized.

If you look at **Figure 14.1a**, you can see the chemical structure of two free-standing amino acids, glycine (gly) and isoleucine (ile). If you look at **Figure 14.1b**, you can see that these two amino acids are the first two that occur in one of the two polypeptide chains that make up the unusually small

protein we call insulin. **Figure 14.1c** then shows a three-dimensional representation of insulin—the folded-up form this protein assumes before taking on its function of moving blood sugar into cells. A list of all 20 primary amino acids and their three-letter abbreviations can be found in **Table 14.1**.

For our purposes, the question is: How do the chains of amino acids that make up a protein come into being? How do gly, ile, val, and so forth come to be strung together in a specific order to create this protein? You know from what you've studied so far that genes can be thought of as "recipes" for proteins, and that these recipes are set forth as a series of chemical "bases"— the A's, T's, C's, and G's that lie along a DNA strand. How, then, do we get from *this* series of DNA bases to *that* series of amino acids—to a protein? Let's find out.

Figure 14.1
The Structure of Proteins

glycine **(gly)**

isoleucine **(ile)**

(a) Amino acids

The building blocks of proteins are amino acids such as glycine and isoleucine, which differ only in their side-chain composition (light colored squares).

H_3N^+ — gly | ile | val | glu | gln | cys | cys | ala | ser | val | cys | ser | leu | tyr | gln | leu | glu | asn | tyr | cys | asn — C

(b) Polypeptide chain

These amino acids are strung together to form polypeptide chains. Pictured is one of the two polypeptide chains that make up the unusually small protein insulin.

(c) Protein

Polypeptide chains function as proteins only when folded into their proper three-dimensional shape, as shown here for insulin. Note the position of the glycine and isoleucine amino acids in one of the insulin polypeptide chains (colored light green).

Table 14.1 Amino Acids

Amino Acid	Abbreviation
Alanine	ala
Arginine	arg
Asparagine	asn
Aspartic acid	asp
Cysteine	cys
Glutamine	gln
Glutamic acid	glu
Glycine	gly
Histidine	his
Isoleucine	ile
Leucine	leu
Lysine	lys
Methionine	met
Phenylalanine	phe
Proline	pro
Serine	ser
Threonine	thr
Tryptophan	trp
Tyrosine	tyr
Valine	val

The destination of this mRNA is a molecular workbench in the cell's cytoplasm, a structure called a ribosome. More formally, a **ribosome** is an organelle, located in the cell's cytoplasm, that is the site of protein synthesis. At the ribosome, both the recipe (the mRNA tape) and the raw materials (amino acids) come together to make the product (a protein). As the mRNA tape is "read" within the ribosome, something grows from it: a chain of amino acids that have been linked together in the ribosome in the order specified by the mRNA. When the chain is finished and folded up, a protein has come into existence. And how do amino acids get to the ribosomes? They are brought there by a second type of RNA, transfer RNA (tRNA).

As may be apparent from this account, protein synthesis divides neatly into two sets of steps. The first set is called **transcription**: the process by which the genetic information encoded in DNA is copied onto messenger RNA. The second set is called **translation**: the process by which information encoded in messenger RNA is used to assemble a protein at a ribosome. Let's look in more detail now at both of these processes, starting with transcription.

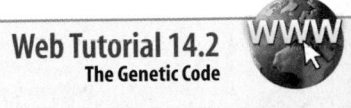

Web Tutorial 14.2
The Genetic Code

Figure 14.2
The Two Major Stages of Protein Synthesis

14.2 Protein Synthesis in Overview

In overview, the process of protein synthesis can be described fairly simply. In eukaryotic organisms such as ourselves, the DNA just referred to is contained in the nucleus of the cell. The first step is that a stretch of it unwinds there, and its message—the order of a string of A's, T's, C's and G's—is copied onto a molecule called messenger RNA (mRNA). This length of mRNA, which could be thought of as an information tape being copied off a "master" DNA tape, then exits from the cell nucleus (**see Figure 14.2**).

Transcription

1. In transcription, a section of DNA unwinds and nucleotides on it form base pairs with nucleotides of messenger RNA, creating an mRNA "tape."

2. This segment of mRNA then leaves the cell nucleus, headed for a ribosome in the cell's cytoplasm, where translation takes place.

Translation

3. Joining the mRNA tape at the ribosome are amino acids, brought there by transfer RNA molecules. The length of messenger RNA is then "read" within the ribosome. The result? A chain of amino acids is linked together in the order specified by the mRNA tape.

4. When the chain is finished and folded up, a protein has come into existence.

14.3 A Closer Look at Transcription

From what's been reviewed so far, you can see that a key player in transcription (and translation) is RNA, whose full name is ribonucleic acid. If you look at **Figure 14.3**, you can see just how similar RNA is to DNA. For one thing, RNA has the sugar and phosphate "handrail" components you saw in DNA last chapter. Then, in both molecules, this two-part structure is joined to a third element, a base.

There are, however, differences between DNA and RNA. For one, RNA is usually single-stranded, whereas DNA is structured in two strands that form its famous double helix. Beyond this, recall that any given DNA building block or "nucleotide" has one of four bases: adenine, guanine, cytosine, or thymine (A, G, C, or T). RNA utilizes the first three of these, but then substitutes uracil (U) for the thymine (T) found in DNA.

Passing on the Message: Base Pairing Again

Given the chemical similarity between DNA and RNA, it's not hard to see how DNA's genetic message can be passed on to messenger RNA: Base pairing is at work again. Recall from Chapter 13 how DNA is replicated. The double helix is unwound, after which bases along the now-single DNA strands are paired up with complementary DNA bases. Every T on a single DNA strand is paired with a free-floating A, and every C is linked with a G, thus yielding a complementary DNA *chain*. Because of RNA's similarity to DNA, the bases RNA has can also form base pairs with DNA. The twist to this RNA-DNA base pairing is that each *A* on a DNA strand links up with a *U* on the RNA strand, instead of the T that would be A's partner in DNA-to-DNA base pairing. The length of RNA that results from the process of transcription is called a *primary transcript*. With all this in mind, here's a more formal definition of **messenger RNA**

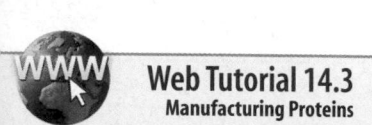

Web Tutorial 14.3
Manufacturing Proteins

(a) Comparison of RNA and DNA nucleotides

(b) Comparison of RNA and DNA three-dimensional structure

Figure 14.3
RNA and DNA Compared
(a) Each building-block nucleotide of both DNA and RNA is composed of a phosphate group, a sugar—ribose in RNA, deoxyribose in DNA—and one of four bases. RNA and DNA both utilize the bases adenine, guanine, and cytosine (A, G, and C), but RNA utilizes the base uracil (U) instead of the thymine (T) that DNA utilizes.
(b) Both RNA and DNA amount to linked chains of these nucleotides. The "handrails" of both RNA and DNA are composed of the sugar molecule of one nucleotide linked to the phosphate molecule of the next nucleotide (thus the S-P-S-P labeling). The "stair steps" stemming from the handrails are formed by the bases of the nucleotides, as with the G and C bases extending inward at the top of the DNA strand. While DNA is double-stranded, RNA generally is single-stranded.

(mRNA): a type of RNA that encodes, and carries to ribosomes, information for the synthesis of proteins. You can see how transcription works by looking at **Figure 14.4.** It will come as no surprise to you that an enzyme is critically involved in this process. **RNA polymerase**, as this complex of enzymes is known, actually undertakes two critical tasks: It unwinds the DNA sequence and then strings together the chain of RNA nucleotides that is complementary to it, thus producing the primary transcript.

Messenger RNA Processing

In prokaryotes such as bacteria, transcription works just as you've seen so far: messenger RNA is synthe-sized directly from a DNA template. It turns out, however, that in eukaryotes such as ourselves, there is an intervening step between getting an initial RNA nucleotide chain and getting a finished mes-senger RNA molecule. Just as a writer's first draft must undergo some editing before it is a finished work, so the original RNA chain must undergo some editing before it is referred to as messenger RNA. This is so because the starting DNA sequences in eukaryotes are not made up of a continuous se-ries of bases that code for one amino acid after an-other. Instead, coding sequences of DNA are interspersed with *non*-coding sequences. The initial RNA chain synthesized from the DNA is a copy of

1. RNA polymerase unwinds a region of the DNA double helix.

RNA nucleotides

RNA

DNA

2. RNA polymerase begins assembling RNA nucleotides on the DNA template.

RNA

3. The completed portion of the RNA transcript separates from the DNA. Meanwhile, RNA polymerase unwinds more of the untranscribed region of the DNA.

RNA

4. The RNA transcript is released from the DNA, and the DNA is rewound into its original form. Transcription is completed.

Figure 14.4
Transcription Works through Base Pairing
Thanks to their chemical similarity, DNA and RNA can engage in base pairing, and this base pairing is how RNA transcripts are synthe-sized. The enzyme complex RNA polymerase undertakes two tasks in transcription: It unwinds the DNA sequence to be transcribed, and it brings together RNA nu-cleotides with their complemen-tary DNA nucleotides, thus producing an RNA chain.

both kinds of sequences, but this soon changes. The original RNA chain—the primary transcript—undergoes a kind of molecular editing in which non-coding sequences are snipped out, and the remaining coding sequences are spliced back together. You can see this pictured in **Figure 14.5**. The product of this editing is the messenger RNA molecule. The portions of the primary transcript that are edited out in this process are called *introns* (because they are *int*ervening sequences). Meanwhile, the portions of the primary transcript that are left in during editing are called *exons* (because most of these sequences are *ex*pressed as proteins). Of course, these two kinds of sequences have counterparts in the original DNA. Thus, we can define an **intron** as that part of a primary transcript (or the DNA encoding it) that is removed in mRNA editing. And we can define an **exon** as that part of a primary transcript (or the DNA encoding it) that is retained during mRNA editing.

Taking a step back from this, the message is that eukaryotic DNA has sequences—the introns—that do not code for protein, and that don't even make it into the final mRNA chain. This, of course, raises the question: What are introns doing in DNA in the first place? As you can see in "Making Sense of 'Junk' DNA" on page 280, clues are steadily emerging about the function of these sequences.

A Triplet Code

Thus far, you have been looking at what might be called the flow of genetic information (from DNA to mRNA). A separate issue in protein synthesis, however, has to do with the linkage between DNA and mRNA on the one hand and amino acids on the other. Think of this as scientists did in the 1950s. Allowing that DNA bases are coding for amino acids in a protein, a primary question that arose was: How *many* DNA bases does it take to code for each amino acid? It seemed clear that the answer was not one. Because there are only four DNA bases (A, T, C, and G), if each coded for its own amino acid, only four amino acids could have been incorporated into proteins, as opposed to the 20 that actually are. Nor could the answer be two, because the number of possible amino acids this number could yield up was only 16. Thinking that nature probably would work as economically as possible, the South African–born biochemist Sydney Brenner suggested that DNA worked in a *triplet code*, meaning that each *three* DNA bases specified a single amino acid. Brenner turned out to be right. As **Figure 14.6** shows, each three bases in a DNA sequence pairs with three mRNA bases, but each group of three mRNA bases then codes for a *single* amino acid. Each coding triplet of mRNA bases is known, appropriately enough, as a **codon**.

Once scientists knew that protein production worked by means of a triplet code, they were confronted with a different question: If you have a given three bases, *which* amino acid do they specify? In Morse code, the sounds .__. (short-long-short) code for the letter *P*. But if we know that a given mRNA codon has the base sequence UCC, what *amino acid* does this code for? Today we know that the answer is serine (ser), but at one time this was not clear at all. Indeed, it took years for scientists to figure out all the linkages between codons and amino acids. When this work was completed, however, the result was the **genetic code**, which can be defined as the inventory of linkages between nucleotide triplets and the amino acids they code for. If you look at "Learning to Read Nature's Rule Book" on page 278, you can learn more about the nature and importance of this code.

14.4 A Closer Look at Translation

With a length of RNA having first been transcribed from a length of DNA, having been edited, and having then moved to a ribosome as mRNA, many of the players are in place for translation—the second stage

Figure 14.5
Editing Out Non-Coding Sequences

In eukaryotes, lengths of DNA that are transcribed contain sequences that code for amino acids as well as sequences that do not code for them. Both kinds of sequences are copied onto primary transcripts of RNA. Once this is done, however, the non-coding sequences (called introns) are removed by enzymes through the editing process shown, while the coding sequences (called exons) are spliced back together. The result is a messenger RNA molecule.

primary transcript

exon 1   intron   exon 2   intron   exon 3

enzymes cut out the introns

enzyme

messenger RNA

The Triplet Code

Figure 14.6
Triplet Code
Each triplet of DNA bases codes for a triplet of mRNA bases (a codon), but it takes a complete codon to code for a single amino acid.

of protein production. What's also needed, however, are the building blocks of proteins, amino acids. As noted, they are brought to ribosomes by a second form of RNA, called transfer RNA (or tRNA).

The Nature of tRNA

If you look at **Figure 14.7**, you can see why tRNA is aptly placed within the translation phase of protein synthesis. When, in common discourse, we think of a *translator*, we think of someone who can communicate in *two* languages. Transfer RNA effectively does this. One end of each tRNA molecule links with a specific *amino* acid, which it finds floating free in the cytoplasm. Then, transferring this amino acid to the ribosome, this tRNA molecule bonds with a *nucleic* acid—a triplet of bases on the mRNA that is moving through the ribosome. Thus, tRNA is bonding

Web Tutorial 14.3
Manufacturing Proteins

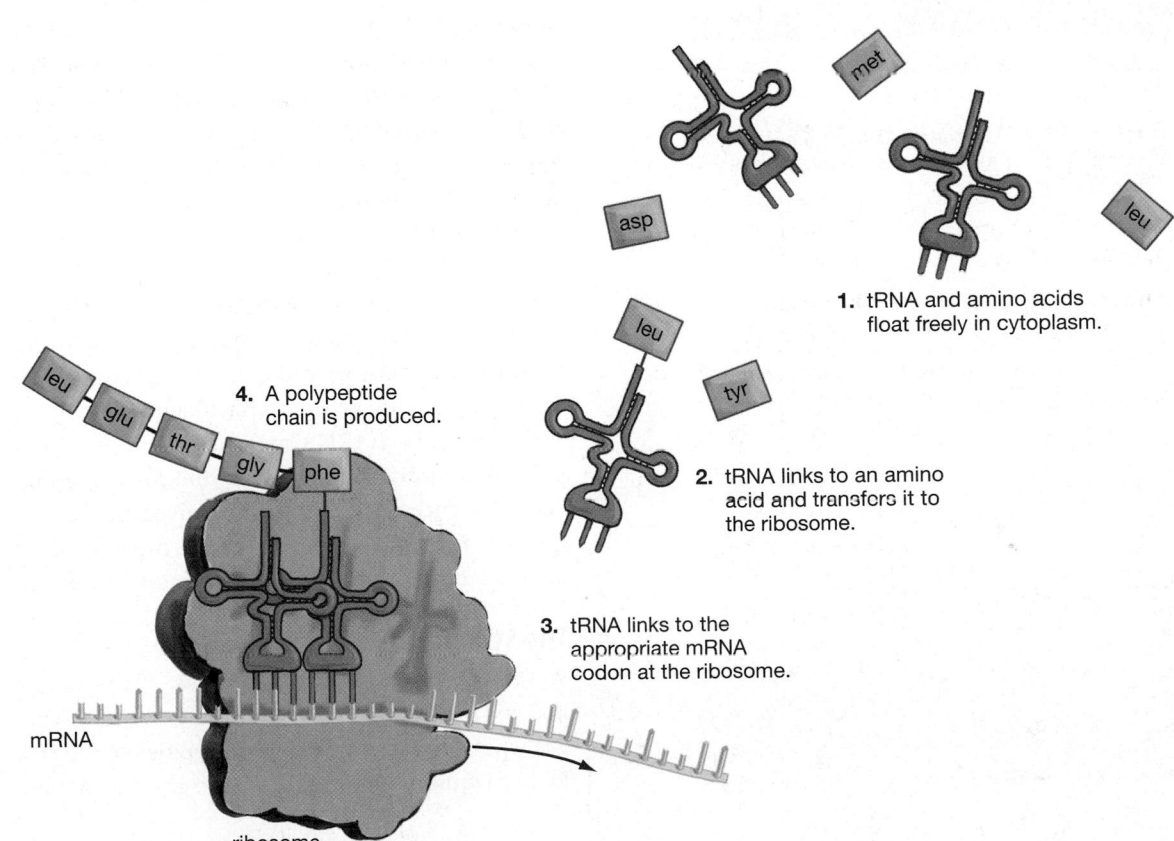

1. tRNA and amino acids float freely in cytoplasm.

2. tRNA links to an amino acid and transfers it to the ribosome.

3. tRNA links to the appropriate mRNA codon at the ribosome.

4. A polypeptide chain is produced.

mRNA

ribosome

Figure 14.7
Bridging Molecule
Transfer RNA (tRNA) molecules link up with amino acids on the one hand and mRNA codons on the other, thus forming a chemical bridge between the two kinds of molecules in protein synthesis. They also transfer amino acids to ribosomes, as shown in the steps of the figure.

(a) Transfer RNA binding

arg

amino acid attachment site

tRNA
molecule

mRNA attachment site

anticodon

C G A
codon

mRNA

(b) The 3-D shape of tRNA

hydrogen bonds

G C U
anticodon

Figure 14.8
The Structure of Transfer RNA
(a) In this two-dimensional model of transfer RNA, one end of the tRNA molecule can be seen bonding to a specific amino acid (arg), while the other end bonds to its counterpart mRNA codon (CGA).

(b) This three-dimensional model of tRNA shows the molecule in the "folded up" form it takes when carrying out its dual-bonding function.

with two very different kinds of molecules—amino acids on the one hand, nucleic acids on the other—thereby serving as a translator between them. **Transfer RNA (tRNA)** can be defined as a form of RNA that, in protein synthesis, bonds with amino acids, transfers them to ribosomes, and then bonds with messenger RNA.

Figure 14.8a provides a more detailed look at how transfer RNA carries out this function. You can see that it bonds with an mRNA codon by means of three bases it possesses, called an **anticodon**. At its other end (the 12 o'clock position in the figure), there is an attachment site for the amino acid. Each tRNA molecule is specific for a particular amino acid, meaning the correct amino acid sequence will result from a given mRNA sequence. **Figure 14.8b** gives you a more realistic idea of what tRNA looks like in its folded-up form.

The Structure of Ribosomes

You've now been introduced to almost all the players that will be active in protein synthesis at the ribosome. But what is the structure of the ribosome itself? If you look at **Figure 14.9**, you can begin to get an idea. Note

Table 14.2 Types of RNA

Type of RNA	Functions in	Function
Messenger RNA (mRNA)	Nucleus, migrates to ribosomes in cytoplasm	Carries DNA sequence information to ribosomes
Transfer RNA (tRNA)	Cytoplasm	Provides linkage between mRNA and amino acids; transfers amino acids to ribosomes
Ribosomal RNA (rRNA)	Cytoplasm	Structural component of ribosomes

(a) Large and small ribosomal units

protein

large
subunit

small
subunit

E P A

mRNA

Ribosomes are composed
of two subunits that come
together during translation.

(b) Binding sites in the ribosome

protein

large
subunit

small
subunit

mRNA

E   P   A
site   site   site

A simplified cross section
of the ribosome illustrates
the E, P, and A sites where
tRNA molecules bind
during translation.

Figure 14.9
The Structure of Ribosomes

that ribosomes are composed of two "subunits"—one larger than the other—both made of a mixture of proteins and yet another type of RNA, **ribosomal RNA (or rRNA)**. The two subunits may float apart from another in the cytoplasm until prompted to come together by the process of translation. You can see that when the subunits have been joined, there exist three binding sites (which it is convenient to think of as slots), one of them an "E" site, the next a "P" site, and the third an "A" site. You'll be looking at their roles

shortly. **Table 14.2** sets forth the three types of RNA reviewed so far that are active in protein synthesis.

The Steps of Translation

With all the players introduced, let's see how translation works. To keep things simple, we'll follow the process as it occurs in prokaryotes. Our starting point is an mRNA transcript that is ready to begin binding with a ribosome. Meanwhile, nearby tRNA molecules have linked to their appropriate amino acids.

mRNA Binds to Ribosome, First tRNA Arrives

In this first step, the mRNA chain arrives at the ribosome and binds to the ribosome's small subunit (see Figure 14.10). The mRNA codon AUG is the usual "start" codon for a polypeptide chain. Next, a tRNA molecule with the appropriate anticodon se-

The steps of translation

1. A messenger RNA transcript binds to the small subunit of a ribosome as the first transfer RNA is arriving. The mRNA codon AUG is the "start" sequence for most polypeptide chains. The tRNA, with its methionine (met) amino acid attached, then binds this AUG codon.

2. The large ribosomal subunit joins the ribosome, as a second tRNA arrives, bearing a leucine (leu) amino acid. The second tRNA binds to the mRNA chain, within the ribosome's A site.

3. A bond is formed between the newly arrived leu amino acid and the met amino acid, thus forming a polypeptide chain. The ribosome now effectively shifts one codon to the right, relocating the original P site tRNA to the E site, the A site tRNA to the P site, and moving a new mRNA codon into the A site.

4. The E site tRNA leaves the ribosome, even as a new tRNA bonds with the A site mRNA codon, and the process of elongation continues.

Figure 14.10
The Steps of Translation

quence (UAC) binds to this AUG codon. This tRNA arrives bearing its appropriate amino acid, which is methionine (met). Following this, the large ribosomal subunit becomes part of the ribosome, providing the ribosome's A, P, and E binding sites.

Polypeptide Chain Is Elongated

Now amino acids will start to be joined together in a chain. As you can see, this elongation process begins with a second incoming tRNA molecule binding to an mRNA codon in the A site. Because it happens to be a CUG codon, a tRNA with a GAC anticodon binds to it. This tRNA comes bearing the amino acid leucine (leu). Next, the met amino acid attached to the tRNA in the P site bonds with the leu amino acid attached to the tRNA in the A site. In this process, the bond is broken between met and its original tRNA.

Once this occurs, a kind of molecular musical chairs ensues: The ribosome effectively shifts one codon to the right. With this, the tRNA that had been in the P site is relocated to the E site. What does the *E* stand for? Exit. The tRNA in this site bears no amino acid now; soon it will be ejected from the ribosome altogether. Meanwhile, the tRNA that had been in the A site moves to the P site, and a new codon shifts into the now-vacated A site. You can see what comes next: A tRNA bonds with this new codon in the A site. Soon, the growing polypeptide chain will bond with *this* tRNA's amino acid, and the process will continue.

Termination of the Growing Chain

There are three separate codons that don't code for any amino acid, but that instead act as stop signals for polypeptide synthesis. Any time one of these "termination" codons moves into the ribosome's A site, it doesn't bind with an incoming tRNA, but instead brings about a severing of the linkage between the P-site tRNA and the polypeptide chain. Indeed, the whole translation apparatus comes apart at this point, with the polypeptide chain being released to fold up and be processed as a protein. Translation has been completed.

Speed of the Process; Movement through Several Ribosomes

How fast does this process go? Very fast. An *E. coli* bacterium can string together up to 40 amino acids per second, meaning that an average-sized protein of about 400 amino acids could be put together in 10 seconds. Note, however, that mRNA tapes often are read not by one ribosome, but by many. As you can see in **Figure 14.11**, several ribosomes—perhaps scores of them—might move over a given mRNA transcript, with the result that identical polypeptide chains grow out of each ribosome. This greatly increases the number of proteins that can be put together in a given period of time.

What Is a Gene?

This trip through transcription and translation has made it possible for you to get a more accurate definition of the most basic unit in genetics, the gene. Thus far, a gene has been viewed as a length of DNA that codes for a protein. But recall that ribosomes are made partly of RNA. Where does this ribosomal RNA come from? Just like messenger RNA, ribosomal RNA must be coded for by DNA. A segment of DNA unwinds and then forms base pairs with RNA nucleotides to produce an RNA sequence. Only this is a *ribosomal* RNA sequence that doesn't code for anything; it simply migrates to the cytoplasm to become part of a ribosome. So great is the cell's need for ribosomes that there is an entire section of the nucleus (called the nucleolus) whose DNA is constantly being

(a)

(b)

Figure 14.11
Mass Production
(a) An mRNA transcript can be translated by many ribosomes at once, resulting in the production of many copies of the same protein.

(b) A micrograph of this process in operation. The figure shows two mRNA strands with ribosomes spaced along their length. In the upper strand, translation is under way and polypeptides can be seen emerging from the ribosomes.

transcribed for rRNA. Likewise, there are sections of DNA that code for transfer RNA, which also migrates to the cytoplasm to be involved in translation. Note that in the case of both transfer RNA and ribosomal RNA, DNA is being transcribed. But the ultimate *product* of this transcription is not a protein; it's RNA in two forms. With all this in mind, here is a more accurate definition of a gene: A **gene** is a segment of DNA that brings about the transcription of a segment of RNA.

14.5 Genetic Regulation

The basic understanding you now have of how genes code for proteins leaves a critical question unanswered: Why does a given gene turn on or off? Why does transcription of this gene begin, or not begin? Most genes don't simply stay "on." The cells in our pancreas, for example, turn out the protein insulin *intermittently*—in response to what we've eaten—rather than ceaselessly transcribing the gene for insulin. So, what are the start and stop signals for this protein-synthesizing machinery? For that matter, why is it that only *pancreatic* cells turn out insulin when almost all other cells in the body possess copies of the insulin gene? To come to an understanding of these things, you need to learn something about how protein synthesis is regulated.

DNA Is the Cookbook, Not the Cook

We have thus far thought of the "genome" or genetic inventory of a living thing as a kind of cookbook, containing recipes (DNA sequences) that lead to products (proteins) that undertake a wide variety of tasks (hastening chemical reactions, serving as receptors). It's tempting to go from these ideas to thinking that DNA is the boss, at least for the metabolic processes lying outside our conscious control. After all, it's giving "orders" for the body to put together these all-important proteins, isn't it?

Well, sticking with the metaphor, a cookbook does not give orders; it merely contains information, which an *agent* (called a cook) then carries out. It becomes clear that DNA is not the cook when you consider that by itself, DNA can't synthesize anything. Think back to transcription. The DNA double helix does not unwind itself, nor does it bring RNA nucleotides into alignment with its own bases, nor does it snip out introns in the primary transcript, nor does it affect any of the other steps you looked at. Instead, all these tasks are carried out by enzymes, which are *proteins*. (Recall that the protein complex known as RNA poly-

merase is central in carrying out the steps of transcription.) DNA is indeed the cookbook, but it is powerless to prepare its own recipes. A critical insight is that, through chemical bonding, information comes *to* the double helix as well as from it, in a process known as genetic regulation.

A Model System in Genetic Regulation: The Operon

Genetic regulation actually can occur at any step in the protein synthesis process. But our main focus here will be on regulation as it occurs in transcription—the copying of the DNA information onto a length of RNA. The essential question is: What factors stand to facilitate or impede this process? What factors stand to make it more or less likely that RNA polymerase will latch onto a length of DNA and then go down the line, pairing DNA bases up with complementary RNA bases? To get an idea, you'll look at what's known as a "model" regulatory system in a model organism. The system is called the *operon*, and the organism is the *Escherichia coli* bacterium.

Jacques Monod and François Jacob's Experiments

Jacques Monod and François Jacob were two French researchers, who in the 1950s wanted to learn how genes turn on and off in living creatures. By then it was clear that in most cases, genes didn't simply *stay* on. The activity of at least some genes had to be *inducible*, meaning triggered by conditions in the organism's environment. One means of inducement seemed clear; scientists had known for many years that bacteria would synthesize certain enzyme proteins only if the substance these enzymes worked on (their "substrate") was present in the bacterial cell. Accordingly, Monod and Jacob focused on a group of enzymes that allow *E. coli* first to obtain the sugar lactose and then to break it down into two simple sugars. This latter step is a clipping operation in which lactose (commonly known as milk sugar) is broken into its component simple sugars, galactose and glucose.

In the simplified version of this operation that we'll look at, two genes are involved in *E. coli* lactose metabolism. As you can see in **Figure 14.12a**, there is a *y* gene that codes for a so-called *permease* enzyme, which transports lactose into the cell. Then there is a *z* gene, which codes for the enzyme beta-galactosidase (or *β*-galactosidase), which does the lactose clipping mentioned before. (A third, *a* gene seems to be part of the system, but no one has yet discovered what it does.)

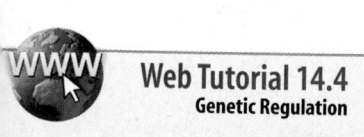

Web Tutorial 14.4
Genetic Regulation

Activity Induced by Lactose

The genes involved in lactose metabolism were known to be inducible, and the *inducer*—the substance that prompted their activity—was known to be lactose. Put simply, in the presence of lactose, these genes turned on. Yet what was the control mechanism here? The experiments of Jacob and Monod eventually led them to propose that *E. coli*'s lactose metabolism is governed by an elegant multipart genetic system that they dubbed the *operon*.

(a) Structure of the lac operon system

A simplified structure of the lac operon system. The system consists of (left to right) an *i* gene that codes for a repressor protein (the two green crosses); RNA polymerase, shown bound to the DNA strand's promoter region (P); a region of the DNA strand called the operator (O); two genes and their protein products: The *z* gene that codes for the lactose-clipping beta-galactosidase enzyme; and the *y* gene, which codes for a permease enzyme, which transports lactose into the cell. (The *a* gene, while part of the system, codes for a protein whose function is unknown.)

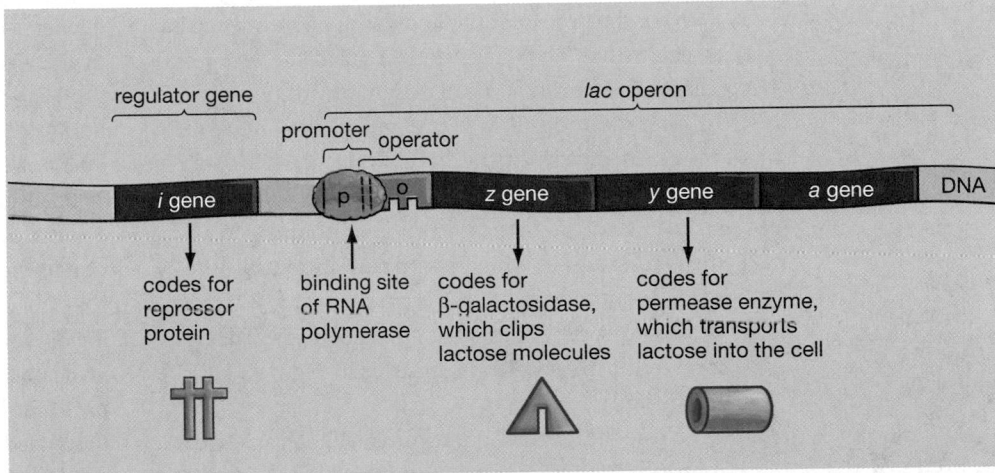

(b) When lactose is absent ...

The repressor protein binds to the operator and prevents RNA polymerase from ever beginning transcription of the lactose-processing enzymes.

(c) When lactose is present ...

The repressor is inhibited from binding with the operator, thus allowing transcription and hence production of the lactose-processing enzymes.

Figure 14.12
Genetic Regulation in Action

In the *lac* operon, the *z*, *y*, and *a* genes are transcribed as a unit onto a single messenger RNA transcript. "Upstream" from the *z* gene is a segment of DNA known as the promoter sequence. Any **promoter sequence** is the site on a segment of DNA to which RNA polymerase attaches prior to beginning transcription. Note, in the figure, however, that *in between* the promoter site and the *z* gene sequence is a region that Jacob and Monod called the *operator*. This sequence of DNA can exist in one of two states. In one, it is bound to a protein called a *repressor*, which effectively *blocks* the binding of RNA polymerase to the promoter, thus shutting down transcription. In the other state, it is unbound—free of the repressor—in which case transcription can proceed. Because the repressor is a protein, it is itself the product of a gene (the *i* gene) that lies just a little farther yet upstream. (You can see it in Figure 14.12a, on the left.)

Now, the critical question is: What causes the repressor either to bind with the operator (thus halting transcription) or to stay clear of it (thus allowing transcription)? The answer is the absence or presence of lactose. If you look at **Figure 14.12b**, you can see how this plays out. The critical factor is that the repressor protein has *two* binding sites. One of them binds to the operator, as already noted, but the other binds to *lactose*. When this lactose binding takes place, a repressor that is bound to an operator changes shape; like a clothespin that's been pinched, it opens up and is released from the operator site. The result? RNA polymerase is no longer blocked, meaning it can bind to the promoter site and begin transcription of the *z*, *y*, and *a* genes. They produce their enzymes, and lactose metabolism proceeds. When all the lactose has

been broken down, however, the repressor molecules return to their original shape—meaning the shape that can bind to the operator—thereby shutting down gene transcription.

With their insights about this system, Jacob and Monod elucidated a great deal about gene regulation. First, they confirmed the existence of genetic sequences whose sole functions are *regulatory*. Think of it: The *i* gene sequence codes for a protein, but it is a protein whose function is to allow DNA transcription to go forward, or to turn it off. Meanwhile, the operator DNA segment doesn't code for a protein at all; instead it exists as a binding site for this repressor protein. Such regulatory sequences stand in distinction to the DNA segments that code for end-product proteins—in this series, the *z*, *y*, and *a* genes. Next, the operon concept confirmed the nature of *feedback* mechanisms that operate in genetic regulation. The proteins that are produced through DNA's instructions feed back on the DNA molecule itself, thus helping to control the production of other proteins.

The *lac* operon concept has been deepened since this original understanding was arrived at. In particular, it was found that a completely different protein (called CAP) had to bind with DNA upstream from the *lac* promoter for RNA polymerase to readily bind with the *lac* promoter site. Looked at one way, the CAP protein facilitates the *lac* operation, while the repressor protein blocks it. And with this added layer of control, you can see the basic elements that operate in almost all transcription regulation, no matter how elaborate it may get (and it gets very elaborate). Some molecules are going to facilitate the binding of RNA polymerase to the promoter, while other molecules are going to impede this binding. Transcription is controlled by the sum of all these influences.

Figure 14.13
Not as Much Difference as We Thought
At one time, scientists assumed that the human genome contained about 100,000 genes. Genome sequencing revealed, however, that the human genome probably contains about 30,000 genes. This is only about 11,000 more genes than the tiny roundworm *C. elegans*, and about 17,000 more than the *Drosophila* fruit fly. Scientists can make comparisons among genomes because, though the human genome has gotten most of the attention, the genomes of several other organisms have now been sequenced as well, including those shown here.

Saccharomyces cerevisiae
(baker's yeast)

Drosophila melanogaster
(fruit fly)

Caenorhabditis elegans
(roundworm)

Arabidopsis thaliana
(mustard plant)

Estimated number of genes:

6,034

13,061

19,099

25,000

Another Layer of Control: Alternate Splicing

If we ask how the genetic machinery is able to turn out its fabulous array of proteins, an additional layer of control can be found in a step leading to protein synthesis that comes after the transcription we've just gone over. When biologists completed the first stage of the Human Genome Project in 2001, one of the surprises was that the human genome was shown to contain far fewer genes than the 100,000 that had been the standard estimate for years. The teams that sequenced the human genome came up with consensus estimates of about 30,000 genes (though some scientists still believe the number could be twice that). The 30,000 figure actually held a double surprise because it meant that, contrary to our previous assumptions, human beings do not have five times or ten times as many genes as, say, fruit flies or roundworms. If you look at **Figure 14.13**, you can see that we humans—with our vision, speech, and 100 trillion cells—probably have only 11,000 more genes than the microscopic roundworm *C. elegans*, which is eyeless, speechless, and made up of 959 cells.

Once this was recognized, the challenge to science was to understand how human beings do so much more with their 30,000 genes than *C. elegans* does with its 19,000. One part of the answer seems clear: Human beings have a relatively high proportion of multifunctional genes, meaning genes capable of coding for more than one protein. If you look at **Figure 14.14**, you can see the "alternative splicing" process by which organisms such as ourselves can get different proteins from a single gene. Note that the introns you looked at earlier aid in this process by dividing genes into "modules" that can be spliced together in different ways. This is one more indication of the valuable role these non-coding sequences play in human genetics. By some estimates, 60 per-

cent of human genes may undergo alternate splicing. The upshot of this is that, though we probably have only 30,000 genes, we may have hundreds of thousands of proteins functioning within us.

14.6 The Magnitude of the Genetic Operation

Our 30,000 genes are contained in a genome that is about 3.2 billion base pairs long. To make this large number a little less abstract, consider the following exercise. If we took the base sequence of the human genome and simply arrayed the single-letter symbols for the bases on a printed page, going like this:

AATCCGTTTGGAGAAACGGCCCTATTG
GCAGCAAGGCTCTCGGGTCGTCAACG
CGTATTAAACATATTTCAAGGCTCTA …

it would take about 1,000 telephone books, each of them 1,000 pages long, merely to record it all. We're talking, then, about an unbroken series of these base symbols that goes on for a million pages. That is one measure of the size of the human genome. Simply maintaining this genome—making sure that it is passed on from one cell and generation to another—requires that all of these 3.2 billion bases be faithfully copied each time a cell divides. (They have to be copied twice, actually, because we have two copies of each chromosome.) When we start thinking about *using* this genome—about producing proteins from it—all the layers of genetic regulation sketched out earlier (and more) come into play. Genes help bring about proteins; some of these proteins feed back on other genes and control their production of other proteins; RNA sequences get

Figure 14.14
Alternative RNA Splicing
The human genome may contain only 30,000 genes, but that does not mean these genes code for only 30,000 proteins. Through the process of alternative RNA splicing, it is possible for a single gene to code for several proteins. In the figure, a single primary transcript, containing five exons or protein-coding portions, has been transcribed from a single gene. The human genetic machinery can then splice these exons together in alternative ways to yield different proteins—A or B in the figure.

Learning to Read Nature's Rule Book: The Genetic Code

Like scholars trying to extract meaning from an ancient written language, biologists in the early 1960s were trying to extract meaning from an ancient molecular language. They knew that triplets of mRNA bases were coding for amino acids, but what was the linkage? If you had a given triplet, which amino acid did it code for? Though it took them the better part of a decade to find out, eventually they succeeded. If you look at **Figure 1**, you can see a summation of their work—the genetic code in its entirety. Let's look a little closer at this code to understand its nature and significance.

One of the notable things about the code is that not every mRNA triplet in it codes for an amino acid. Note, in Figure 1, that three mRNA codons specify "stop" codes that bring an end to the synthesis of a polypeptide chain. One triplet (AUG) specifies a special amino acid, methionine (met), which serves as the starting amino acid for most polypeptide chains. Note also that the genetic code is redundant. The amino acid phenylalanine (phe), for example, is coded for not only by the UUU triplet, but by UUC as well. Indeed, almost all the amino acids are coded for by more than one mRNA codon. Leucine (leu) and serine (ser) are coded for by no fewer than six.

With the deciphering of these linkages, scientists were handed a powerful tool: If they knew one "end" of a genetic linkage, they instantly were given insight into the other. If they saw, with-in a protein suspected of causing disease, an abnormally high number of "repeats" of the amino acid glutamine (gln), they knew just who the culprit was: an mRNA sequence that had with-in *it* an abnormally high number of repeats of the triplet CAG (or CAA). And this, in turn, led directly to the faulty DNA sequence—they could start looking for a DNA sequence whose telltale signature was the faulty series of repeats. With the cracking of the code, knowing the protein meant being able to make predictions about DNA sequences and vice versa. It was as if scientists had been given a critical page from a book called *Important Rules of Nature.*

A second lesson from the code was that it revealed how unified life is at the genetic level. As biologists looked among various species at the linkages between DNA sequences and amino acids, they found that with only a few exceptions, the genetic code is universal in all living things. This means that the base triplet CAC codes for the amino acid histidine, whether this coding is going on in a bacterium or in a human being.

This insight turned out to be important in two ways. First, it is evidence that all life on Earth is derived from a single ancestor. How else can we explain all of life's diverse organisms sharing this very specific code? Such a complex molecular linkage—this triplet equals that amino acid—is extremely unlikely to have evolved *more* than once. What seems likely is that

spliced in different ways, yielding different proteins from the same original transcript, and so forth.

The obvious message here is that the human genetic operation is unimaginably complex. But it turns out that humans are not special in this regard. If we were to walk through the genetic operation of even a humble bacterium, you would see that its complexity is only slightly less stunning than ours. What's important to recognize is that this complexity is necessary because it *enables life.* Living things must obtain energy, they must grow, they must respond constantly to their environ-ment, they must reproduce, and they must coordi-nate all these activities. Only an incredibly sophis-ticated system of information storage and use could allow a self-contained entity to do all these things. And genetics is exactly such a system. With each twitch of a muscle or swig of a soft drink, in-formation repositories called genes are opened or closed within us, setting in motion the delivery of the tiny working entities called proteins—or stop-ping delivery of them, if that's what is called for. Not surprisingly, we are nowhere close to having a complete understanding of how any genetic sysit came to be employed in an ancient common ancestor, after which it was passed on to all of this organism's descendants—every creature that has subsequently lived on Earth. Note, then, that this code has been passed on from one generation to the next, and from one evolving species to the next, for billions of years. We humans share in an informational linkage that stretches back billions of years and runs through all the contemporary living world.

Apart from this, the universality of the genetic code has a very practical consequence. It means that genes from one organism can function in another. This has both good and bad consequences for human beings. First the bad: Viruses that cause diseases ranging from colds to AIDS can "hijack" the human cellular machinery for their own purposes, precisely because their genes function in human cells. (The human cellular machinery will put together proteins whether these proteins are called for by human or viral DNA.) Now the good news: Using "biotechnology" processes you'll be learning about in Chapter 15, human beings can today use viruses and bacteria to manufacture all kinds of products, including medicines such as human insulin and human growth hormone. In these cases, human genes are being put to work inside microorganisms. This transferability of genes from one species to another has, as its basis, the universality of the genetic code.

Figure 1
The Genetic Code Dictionary
If we know what a given mRNA codon is, how can we find out what amino acid it codes for? This dictionary of the genetic code offers a way. Say you want to confirm that the codon CGU codes for the amino acid arginine (arg). Looking that up here, C is the first base (go to the C row along the "first base" line), G is the second base (go to the G column under the "second base" line) and U is the third (go to the codon parallel with the U in the "third base" line).

tem works. But, as one scientist has said, we are at "the end of the beginning" of our understanding—we understand the process in outline; now it's on to the details.

Biotechnology Is Next

You have seen in this chapter that DNA is only one of the molecules governing protein synthesis. But saying that something is simply one part of a chain is not saying it is not powerful. DNA may "only" be the cookbook, but think of the profound effect this single function stands to have. Following the metaphor, think how different a pie would be if an editing error in a recipe resulted in the insertion of the word *cinnamon* where *sugar* should be (and if our cook had to insert the cinnamon). Now imagine the change for the better if you could *change the recipe* to include sugar instead of cinnamon. The ability to manipulate DNA's instructions lies at the heart of what is commonly called biotechnology. This exciting, promising area of biology is the subject of Chapter 15.

enzyme

Making Sense of "Junk" DNA

Imagine that you pick up a book, a novel, that begins: "It was the best of times, it was the the the pzknlku ljkh uiop nk; lkj bhji; lkjhjoiugh qpmzxd kjhb olkjb worst of times." Reading on, you see that things go on like this for hundreds of pages, right to the end. Baffled? So were scientists when, in 1977, they discovered that eukaryotes such as ourselves have genetic "books" that are filled with passages of such seeming nonsense.

You've already seen that the "sense" side to an organism's "genome," or store of genetic material, is the information contained in that organism's DNA. Such information comes in the form of A's, T's, C's, and G's that code for proteins. If a genome were nothing *but* sense, one "coding" triplet of these bases would follow another in succession, with only some housekeeping sequences in between them. What scientists began perceiving in the late 1970s, however, is that it is the *coding* sections of the genome that are few and far between. For many years following the 1970s revelations, estimates were that only 3 to 5 percent of the human genome coded for protein. Then, with the unveiling of the human genome sequence in early 2001, the estimates dropped again: At most, a mere 1.5 percent of the human genome seems to code for protein. To gain some perspective on this, consider that, while the DNA in any of our cells would stretch to about 6 feet in length if uncoiled, only about 1 inch of this length is DNA that codes for proteins.

So, what is all this non-coding DNA? Some portions are the housekeeping or "regulatory" sequences of DNA noted in the text, while other portions—at the tips of chromosomes—play a part in keeping chromosomes intact. Some DNA, however, has no known function at all and thus, years ago, was given a name that has stuck: junk DNA.

Such "junk" can be thought of as existing in two locations. First, there are the introns mentioned earlier, most of which are non-coding nucleotide strings *within* gene sequences. Introns bear some comparison to the nonsense strings in the first paragraph, in that they interrupt related strings of bases that *do* code for a given protein. It would not be unusual for a gene to contain half a dozen introns, with these intervening sections comprising 90 percent of the bases in the sequence.

Junk DNA can also lie, however, *in between* segments that code for genes. Some of this junk can be stupendously monotonous. For example, there are some 30,000 to 50,000 short segments of DNA in the human genome that consist of nothing more than a couple of bases repeated over and over, as in: CACACACACA …

Chapter Review

Summary

14.1 The Structure of Proteins

- Proteins are composed of building blocks called amino acids. A string of amino acids is called a polypeptide chain. Once such a chain has folded into its working three-dimensional shape, it is a protein. Though there are hundreds of thousands of different proteins, all of them are put together from a starting set of 20 amino acids. It is the order in which the amino acids are linked in a polypeptide chain that determines which protein will be produced.
Web Tutorial 14.1: Structure of Proteins

14.2 Protein Synthesis in Overview

- There are two principal stages in protein synthesis. The first stage is transcription, in which the information encoded in DNA is copied onto a length of messenger RNA (mRNA), which in eukaryotes moves from the cell nucleus to structures in the cytoplasm called ribosomes. The second stage is translation, in which amino acids are linked together at the ribosomes in the order specified by the mRNA sequence.
Web Tutorial 14.2: The Genetic Code

14.3 A Closer Look at Transcription

- The information in DNA is transferred to messenger RNA through complementary base pairing. Each "C" nucleotide in a segment of DNA being transcribed results in a "G" nucleotide being added to a segment of RNA, and so forth. The length of RNA that results from this base pairing is called a primary transcript. The enzyme RNA polymerase unwinds the DNA sequence to be transcribed and then strings together the chain of RNA nucleotides that is complementary to it, thus producing the primary transcript.

- Within eukaryotic gene sequences, lengths of DNA that code for amino acids are interspersed with lengths that do not code for amino acids. Both types of sequences are copied onto the primary transcript. This chain then undergoes a form of editing in which non-coding sequences are removed and coding sequences are spliced back together. The product of this editing is a messenger RNA molecule. An intron is that part of a primary transcript (or the DNA that encodes it) that is removed during mRNA editing. An exon is that part of a primary transcript (or the DNA that encodes it) that is retained during mRNA editing. The function of introns is being investigated.

This latter sequence, a molecular broken record, would certainly seem to fit the definition of junk, if by that we mean something so useless that it might as well be thrown away. And yet, research in recent years has cast doubt on whether any sequence in the genome is insignificant in this way. It is true that many sequences do not code for protein, but that does not mean that they serve no function at all.

Some DNA has no known function at all and thus, years ago, was given a name that has stuck: junk DNA.

Consider, for example, a sequence in the genomes of primates that was long thought to be the essence of junk. Known as the Alu repeat, this sequence is about 280 base pairs long, which is not particularly extensive in the context of the 3-billion-base-pair human genome, until you consider that about 1 million *copies* of Alu are believed to be dispersed throughout the human genome. Thus, this sequence alone makes up nearly 10 percent of our genome—far more than all the coding regions put together.

The Alu repeat is thought to be derived from a sequence in the primate genome that was capable of making copies of itself that could be inserted elsewhere in the genome. Under this view, the Alu sequence was a kind of squatter capable of multiplication. It did no particular harm to its "host" genome, but it did no good for it either. It simply made more and more copies of itself, which continued to be inserted into the primate genome. Thus, the Alu repeat was thought of as falling into a particular category of junk DNA, *selfish DNA*, meaning DNA whose only function is to replicate itself.

But is this true? Human Genome Project researchers found that older Alu segments—those that came into the primate genome earlier in evolutionary history—tend to congregate near the gene-rich areas of the human genome. It's hard to explain why a sequence that is junk would link up with genes over evolutionary time unless that sequence was working with the genes in some fashion—perhaps helping to regulate them. Beyond this observation, researcher Carl Schmid of the University of California, Davis, has found that in mice, a close genetic relative of the Alu repeat is activated when mice become physiologically stressed by, for example, being made to drink lots of alcohol. The impression scientists are getting is that, while the Alu repeat may have arrived originally as a genetic squatter, it has long since been conscripted into duty by the genome.

The seeming usefulness of something as repetitive and long-winded as the Alu repeat calls into question the whole notion of "junk" DNA. One view is that there is no junk DNA; there is only human ignorance of the functions that various DNA segments serve. Another view, however, is that there really are vast stretches of human and other genomes that serve no function at all—not even the function of making more copies of themselves, as many sequences of junk DNA seem to have lost this ability. With the entire human genome sequence in hand, we may be on the road to finding out where the truth lies.

- Each three coding bases of DNA pair with three RNA bases, but each group of three mRNA bases then codes for a single amino acid. Each triplet of mRNA bases that codes for an amino acid is called a codon. The inventory of linkages between base triplets and the amino acids they code for is called the genetic code.
  Web Tutorial 14.3: Manufacturing Proteins

14.4 A Closer Look at Translation

- Transfer RNA serves as a bridging molecule in protein synthesis, thanks to its ability to bond with both amino acids and nucleic acids (in the form of mRNA). A given tRNA molecule bonds with a specific amino acid in the cell's cytoplasm and then transfers that amino acid to a ribosome in which an mRNA transcript is being "read." There, another portion of the tRNA molecule, called an anticodon, bonds with the appropriate codon in the messenger RNA chain.

- Ribosomes, the complex "workbenches" of protein synthesis, are composed of proteins and ribosomal RNA (rRNA). Each exists as two subunits in the cytoplasm that come together only with the initiation of protein translation. Each bears A, P, and E binding sites to which tRNA molecules bond, thus facilitating the synthesis of an amino acid chain.

- Translation works by means of a succession of tRNA molecules arriving at a ribosome, bound to their appropriate amino acids, and then bonding to their appropriate codon in the mRNA transcript. As this process takes place, the succession of amino acids is linked together into a polypeptide chain.

- In addition to messenger RNA, transfer RNA and ribosomal RNA are transcribed from sequences of DNA. It is thus appropriate to think of a gene as an entity that does more than code for proteins. A gene can be defined as a segment of DNA that brings about the transcription of a segment of RNA.

14.5 Genetic Regulation

- The production of a given protein can be facilitated or impeded at any point in the protein synthesis pathway. This process is called genetic regulation. A critical point in genetic regulation comes during transcription, when various factors can either facilitate or impede the binding of RNA polymerase to a DNA promoter sequence. One example of transcription regulation is the bacterial *lac* operon system, which regulates the metabolism of lactose. The *lac* operon provides examples of DNA sequences that are purely regulatory. It also provides an example of feedback in genetics, in which proteins that result from transcription go on to bond with DNA sequences, thereby controlling the production of other proteins.

- The human genome contains an estimated 30,000 genes—only about 11,000 more genes than exist in the primitive roundworm *C. elegans*. Human complexity is partly attributable to the fact that most human genes appear to be able to code for more than one protein, through the process known as alternative splicing of RNA transcripts.

Web Tutorial 14.4: Genetic Regulation

14.6 The Magnitude of the Genetic Operation

- Life is made possible by the fantastic ability of genetic systems to store and use information.

Key Terms

anticodon 270	promoter sequence 276
codon 268	ribosomal RNA (rRNA) 271
exon 268	ribosome 265
gene 274	RNA polymerase 267
genetic code 268	transcription 265
intron 268	transfer RNA (tRNA) 270
messenger RNA (mRNA) 266	translation 265
polypeptide 263	

Understanding the Basics

Multiple-Choice Questions (answers in the back of the book)

1. A chain of _____ results in a polypeptide chain that folds up into a _____.
   a. RNA bases ... transcript
   b. amino acids . ... gene
   c. proteins . ... ribosome
   d. DNA bases ... gene
   e. amino acids ... protein

2. How does DNA differ from RNA?
   a. DNA uses the bases A, T, C, G; RNA uses the bases A, U, C, G.
   b. DNA is a double-stranded molecule; RNA is usually single-stranded.
   c. DNA is a nucleic acid; RNA is a protein.
   d. a and b

3. The press reported recently that, within a large liver cancer tumor, doctors found small bone fragments, fingernails, and skeletal muscle tissue. What can you infer from this about the tumor cells?
   a. that they are functioning normally
   b. that genetic regulation in them has broken down
   c. that cancerous cells need many different kinds of tissue

   d. that the cells came originally from bone-, fingernail-, and muscle-generating tissue
   e. that liver cells can give rise to many kinds of tissue

4. What mRNA sequence signals the start of a sequence to be translated?
   a. ATG
   b. UGA
   c. AUG
   d. UAG
   e. UAA

5. An intron is:
   a. a portion of a primary transcript or DNA that is transcribed that does not contribute to mRNA
   b. the structure in the cytoplasm that is the site of protein synthesis
   c. the coding portion of a length of DNA or a primary transcript of RNA
   d. always a non-coding sequence of bases, as found either in DNA or a primary transcript
   e. both a and d

6. Which of the following statements is true regarding ribosomes?
   a. They are composed of two separate units, each made of rRNA combined with protein.
   b. They are used to translate the mRNA sequence into a protein composed of amino acids.
   c. They have three different sites for tRNA binding.
   d. a and b only
   e. all of the above

7. Why can transfer RNA be referred to as a "bridging" molecule?
   a. It forms a chemical bridge between DNA and messenger RNA.
   b. It creates the linkage between the base pairs of the double helix.
   c. It links species through evolution.
   d. It links ribosomes together.
   e. It forms chemical bonds with both amino acids and messenger RNA.

8. A typical protein might be _____ amino acids long and could be produced in as little as _____ in translation.
   a. 50 ... five minutes
   b. 50,000 . ... five hours
   c. 5 ... five seconds
   d. 400 ... 10 seconds
   e. 4,000 ... four minutes

9. The *lac* operon provided an example of feedback in genetic regulation. What was feeding back onto what?
   a. A protein produced through transcription and translation of one gene went on to regulate transcription of a different gene.
   b. Ribosomes produced through the information encoded in DNA went on to serve as the sites of protein synthesis.
   c. Messenger RNA strands synthesized as a complement to DNA went on to reduce DNA transcription.

d. Transfer RNA molecules limited translation at the ribosomes.

e. Transfer RNA molecules sped up translation in mitochondria.

10. The genetic code is an inventory of which _____ specify(ies) which _____.

    a. three mRNA bases ... amino acid

    b. mRNA base . ... amino acid

    c. amino acids ... proteins

    d. polypeptide chain ... protein

    e. three DNA bases ... three mRNA bases

Brief Review

1. What two great tasks are carried out by our genetic machinery?

2. What are the three types of RNA discussed in this chapter? What do their abbreviations stand for? What are their functions?

3. What is the difference between transcription and translation?

4. During transcription, DNA neither unwinds itself nor pairs its own bases with complementary RNA bases. How are these tasks accomplished?

5. What is the difference between introns and exons?

6. Why is it inaccurate to conceptualize DNA as the sole controller of a cell's production of proteins?

7. How many DNA bases does it take to code for an RNA codon? How many amino acids does an RNA codon code for?

Applying Your Knowledge

1. Why does the activity of at least some genes need to be inducible?

2. Given the following sequence of mRNA, what would the resulting amino acid sequence be?

    AUGAAACGGGGACCAAUGGAUAACUAA

3. In a hypothetical situation, you have identified a new species that uses six bases, instead of three, in its genetic code. It has also been discovered that the proteins this species forms are made up of 220 amino acids. To ensure that each amino acid has a separate and distinct encoding sequence, how many bases need to be included in each codon?

MediaLab

Can We Stop the Cycle? DNA to RNA to Protein

We take for granted our control over bacteria and viruses, confident that we can stop them dead with a simple antibiotic or antiviral medication. But, did you know that these medications work to control the same critical steps of transcription, translation, and protein manufacture that occur in our cells? In the *Web Tutorial* of this *MediaLab*, you'll review the cellular activities needed to manufacture proteins, so that in the *Web Investigation*, you can analyze the subtle differences between our cells and their invaders. These differences can be exploited in our fight against the enemies within us, as you'll see in the *Communicate Your Results* section.

This *MediaLab* can be found in Chapter 14 on your Companion Website (www.prenhall.com/krogh3).

WEB TUTORIAL

Every single one of the thousands of different proteins made by a cell is created in the same way, and the steps are similar in all cells. This *Web Tutorial* leads you step-by-step through the protein production pathway.

Activity

1. First, you will review the two major stages in protein synthesis: (a) copying the information of DNA into RNA so that it can exit the nucleus, and (b) the actual manufacture of protein on ribosomes in the cytoplasm.

2. Next, you'll try your hand at directing these processes, by gathering all the ingredients needed to transcribe DNA and translate the resulting RNA message into protein.

Now that you have reviewed the steps in protein synthesis, you can continue to the next section and investigate how blocking these critical steps can cripple an organism—and in the process, save our lives.

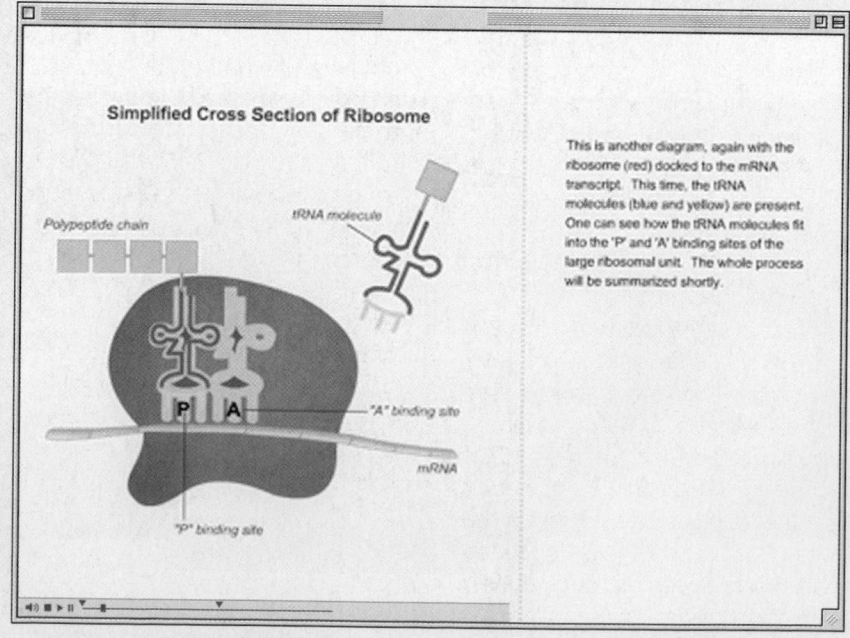

WEB INVESTIGATION

Investigation 1
Estimated time for completion = 5 minutes

If you still think that the steps in making a protein are confusing, maybe you would like to try a step-by-step interactive demonstration. Select the keywords **DNA WORKSHOP** from your Website to visit a site that allows you to take part in coordinating the manufacture of proteins. Click on "*DNA WORKSHOP ACTIVITY*" once you reach the site, and try your hand at using DNA in replication and in protein synthesis.

Investigation 2
Estimated time for completion = 5 minutes

You just saw two uses for DNA, replication and transcription. DNA to RNA to protein is called the central dogma because all cells use the same steps in protein synthesis. HIV, the virus that causes AIDS, is a retrovirus, meaning it carries its genetic material as RNA, not DNA. Click on the keyword **HIV** from your Website to view a step-by-step overview of HIV infection. How can HIV replicate its genetic information or transcribe RNA without DNA?

Investigation 3
Estimated time for completion = 15 minutes

By now, you understand how all proteins are made; but what would happen if you stopped protein synthesis—death? Yes, but a death you can rejoice in—the death of your enemies. Enemies in this case include opportunistic bacteria that can invade your tissues and cause disease or death. Many antibiotics work by stopping transcription or translation of proteins. Read about bacteria and antibiotics by clicking on the keywords **ANTIBIOTICS ATTACK** from your Website, and you'll discover how a wide range of antibiotics act to defeat bacteria.

COMMUNICATE YOUR RESULTS

Exercise 1
Estimated time for completion = 5 minutes

Make a table of the similarities and differences between replication and protein synthesis that you observed in *Web Investigation 1*. Include the following: When are the two processes performed? What process occurs in both? Where? What enzymes are involved? What is the result in both cases?

Exercise 2
Estimated time for completion = 5 minutes

HIV uses a special viral enzyme called *reverse transcriptase* as a critical part of its life cycle. The popular anti-HIV drug AZT works by preventing reverse transcriptase functioning. Describe what would happen to a cell that was infected with HIV when AZT is used. AZT is a thymine analog, meaning a look-alike; the only difference is that it has an N-atom on the important carbon in the ribose sugar that is needed to make covalent bonds between nucleotides. Why would this structure affect reverse transcription?

Exercise 3
Estimated time for completion = 15 minutes

You think your fever and sore throat are caused by a streptococcal infection (strep throat). Your friend offers you penicillin left over from his last bacterial infection. Would it even work on your sore throat if you really did have an infection of streptococcus? How does penicillin work to kill bacterial cells, but not harm your cells? If you found out your infection was more serious (pneumonia) and the culprit was *Mycoplasma pneumoniae*, would the penicillin be effective? You decide to try a wide-spectrum antibiotic that kills many species of bacteria by preventing translation or transcription. What would your pharmacist and doctor recommend to block transcription, or translation, by binding and inactivating ribosomes? Why doesn't this hurt your own translation and transcription?

15 *Biotechnology*

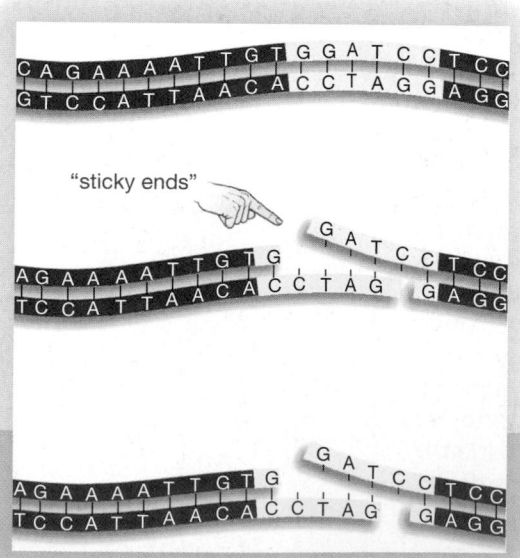

Snipped by restriction enzymes.
(Section 15.2, page 290)

transformation

replication

Bacterial protein factories.
(Section 15.2, page 291)

Hello, Dolly!
(Section 15.3, page 293)

During summertime in America, many a suburban and country resident takes pride in growing a lush, green lawn. The bane of weekend life for many of these same people, however, is that these lawns need to be mowed so often. For millions of Americans, one of the givens in life—right up there with paying taxes and dying—is the necessity of regularly cutting the grass.

Now, however, this given may be up for grabs. A giant American lawn products company currently is field testing a strain of grass that has been genetically engineered to make it grow slowly—so slowly that it might need to be cut only twice from spring through fall. And this "low-mow" trait may be just one of several changes in store for grass. By manipulating grass genes, it should be possible for grass to come in different *colors* (reds, blues, various greens) or to stay green even in a drought.

When you hear the word "biotechnology," designer grass may not immediately come to mind. But in this one product, it's possible to see most of the elements that make biotechnology seem both so promising and yet so threatening. Note that designer grass:

- Shakes up our notions of what is possible in the world.
- Has a big commercial potential. The market for low-mow grass has been estimated at a whopping $10 billion per year.
- Could have a personal impact. If brought to market, low-mow grass would affect not only businesses (think of golf courses) but personal lives as well. It would mean a change in how our lawns look and how we spend our time.
- Has critics who would like to see it go away entirely. The American Society of Landscape Architects petitioned the U.S. Department of Agriculture to suspend low-mow field tests until the department determined that pollen from the grass won't mix or "hybridize" with strains of natural grasses. The fear is that low-mow traits could spread, with unknown ecological consequences.

How it was done.
(Section 15.3, page 294)

embryo

surrogate mother

Dolly

Can extinction be reversed?
(Section 15.3, page 296)

microarray

An array of possibilities.
(Section 15.5, page 300)

(a) A tobacco plant glows in the dark. A firefly gene spliced into the plant has allowed it to produce the firefly's fluorescent enzyme, luciferase.

(b) Bigger salmon faster. All the Atlantic salmon in the picture are about 14 months old, but the salmon on the left grew to 3 kilograms in this time-frame, while the other salmon won't reach this "market weight" for another year. The difference? Scientists from the biotech firm Aqua Bounty Farms spliced a DNA sequence from an ocean pout into the salmon's genome . At maturity, however, the genetically engineered salmon will weigh no more than the wild variety.

(c) Mother and clone. The Italian foal in the foreground, named Prometea, is a clone of the mare standing by her. DNA was extracted from skin cells of the mare and then put into an egg whose DNA had been removed. In a twist on the cloning procedure, the resulting embryo was then implanted back into this very mare, who went on to give birth to Prometea. In genetic terms, the two horses could be thought of as identical twins.

(d) Human medicine from goats. A firm called GTC Biotherapeutics has specialized in splicing DNA into the genomes of goats. The result is goat's milk that contains therapeutic human proteins, among them a protein called AT3 that prevents the formation of blood clots.

Figure 15.1
Biotechnology in Many Forms

If the word "revolution" can be defined as "overturning an established order," then surely biotechnology is ushering in a revolution. To judge for yourself, look at the pictures in **Figure 15.1**. Our assumption may be that human beings and goats are fundamentally separate varieties of living things. But note that the goats in Figure 15.1 have a *human* gene in them. As a result, the milk they give contains a medically useful human protein. Our assumption may be that fireflies glow and that plants don't. But note that the tobacco plant in Figure 15.1 is all lit up, thanks to a firefly gene that has been spliced into it. If biotechnology were about nothing more than this kind of genetic "mixing" between species, it would be important enough. But as you'll see, its reach is much broader yet. It affects the criminal justice system, the diagnosis of illness, and even the preservation of endangered species.

15.1 What Is Biotechnology?

The term biotechnology is familiar to most of us, but what does it really mean? In the broadest sense, **biotechnology** can be defined as the application of technology to natural biological processes. One such process involves the way a cell copies its DNA every time it divides. In the 1980s, a California scientist realized there was a way to use technology to exploit this natural copying, such that a tiny DNA sample could rapidly be copied over and over, thus yielding a relatively large DNA sample. One result of this "PCR" process is that police can now recover, from the tiniest specks of blood or tissue, enough DNA to get a "match" in a criminal case. (Even a licked postage stamp can yield enough DNA to get a conviction.) Like other biotech processes we'll be looking at, PCR was a marriage of biological and technological insight. By the time you finish this chapter, you'll see why "biotechnology" is such an appropriate term.

Because biotechnology is so varied, any account of it has to be limited to a few examples chosen from among thousands that exist. In this chapter, we will consider four aspects of biotechnology—aspects that overlap one another somewhat, but that are nevertheless distinct. These are:

- Transgenic biotechnology—the splicing of DNA from one species into another
- Reproductive cloning—the production of mammals through cloning
- Forensic biotechnology—the use of biotechnology to establish identities (of criminals, of crime victims, and so forth)
- Personalized medicine—the development of medical treatments that are tailored to individuals in accordance with their unique genetic makeup

Let's start now by reviewing an area of biotechnology in which genes are moved from one organism to another.

15.2 Transgenic Biotechnology

Human beings grow to their full height under the influence of human growth hormone (HGH), which normally is secreted by the human pituitary gland. HGH's role in promoting growth is, of course, most important during childhood and adolescence. A faulty pituitary gland can greatly reduce the amount of HGH young people have in their system, leaving them abnormally short. For years, the only way to get HGH was to laboriously extract it from the pituitaries of dead human beings, a practice that not only yielded too little HGH to go around but that also turned out to be unsafe.

Enter biotechnology, which in the mid-1980s produced synthetic HGH in the following way. Using collections of human cells, the gene for HGH was snipped out of the human genome and inserted into the *E. coli* bacterium. Each bacterium that took on the HGH gene began transcribing and then translating this gene, which is to say turning out a small quantity of HGH. These bacteria were then grown in vats by the billions. The result? Collectible quantities of HGH, clinically indistinguishable from that produced in human pituitary glands, manufactured by a biotech firm, and shipped to pharmacies worldwide.

Note that in this process, a gene was taken from one species (a human being) and spliced into another species (a bacterium). With this, the bacterium became a **transgenic organism**: an organism whose genome has stably incorporated one or more genes from another species. This same phenomenon is repeated time and time again in biotechnology. The goats in Figure 15.1 are transgenic—they incorporated a human gene into their genome. The tobacco plant in Figure 15.1 is transgenic—it incorporated a firefly gene into its genome. But how is this possible? How do you cut DNA out of one genome and paste it into another? To get an answer, we'll take a walking tour of some basic biotech processes. As a starting point, imagine that as with human growth hormone, the goal is to produce quantities of a hypothetical human protein through the use of a living organism.

A Biotech Tool: Restriction Enzymes

In the early 1970s it became possible for scientists to cut genomes at particular places, with the discovery of **restriction enzymes**. These are enzymes, occurring naturally in bacteria, that are used in biotechnology to cut DNA into desired fragments. (In nature, bacteria use them to cut up the DNA of invading viruses.) In isolating restriction enzymes, scientists found that many of them had a wonderful property: They didn't just cut DNA randomly; they cut it at very specific places. Here is how it works with an actual restriction enzyme called *Bam*HI. The two strands of DNA's double helix are

Web Tutorial 15.1
**Restriction Enzymes
and Plasmids**

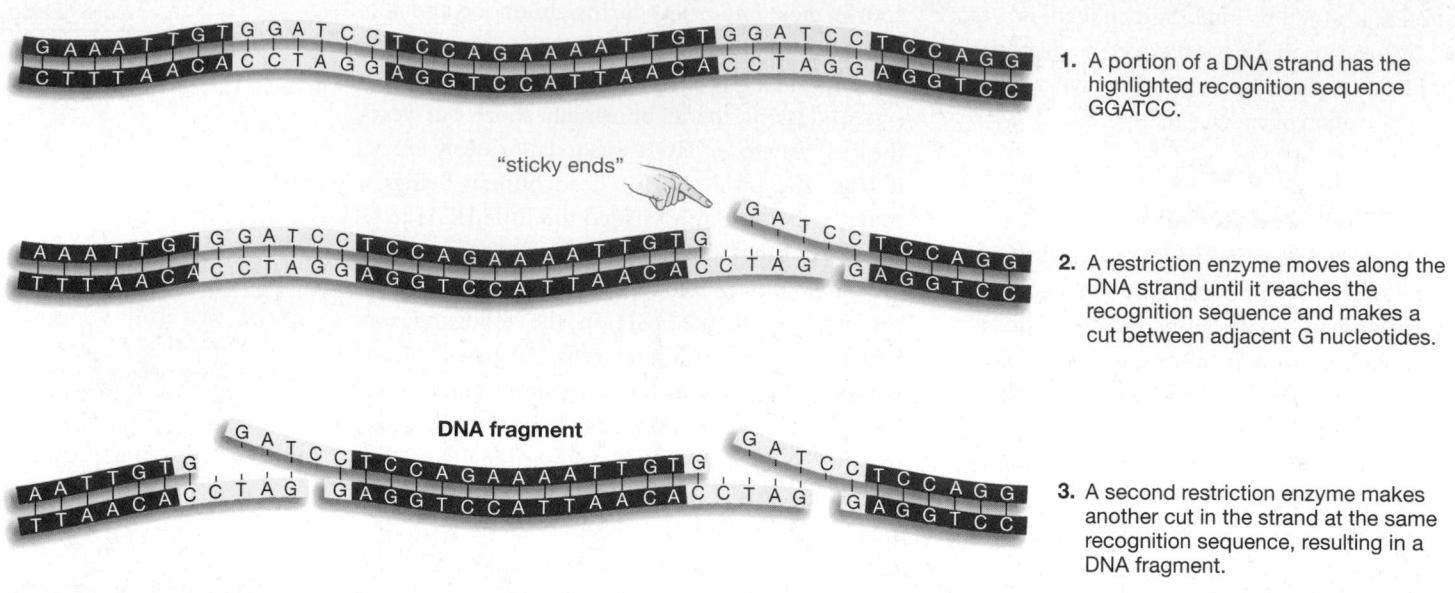

1. A portion of a DNA strand has the highlighted recognition sequence GGATCC.

"sticky ends"

2. A restriction enzyme moves along the DNA strand until it reaches the recognition sequence and makes a cut between adjacent G nucleotides.

DNA fragment

3. A second restriction enzyme makes another cut in the strand at the same recognition sequence, resulting in a DNA fragment.

Figure 15.2
The Work of Restriction Enzymes

complementary, as we've seen, and they also happen to run in opposite directions. Thus, the sequence GGATCC would look like **Figure 15.2** if we were viewing both strands of the helix.

Now, the *Bam*HI restriction enzyme will move along the double helix, leaving the DNA alone *until* it comes to this series of six bases, known as its *recognition sequence*, and here it will make identical cuts on both strands of the DNA molecule, always between adjacent G nucleotides. When another *Bam*HI molecule encounters another GGATCC sequence, it too makes cuts, which effectively is like making a second cut in a piece of rope, giving us rope *fragments*.

*Bam*HI's recognition sequence may be GGATCC, but another restriction enzyme will have a *different* recognition sequence, and will make its cuts between a different pair of bases. Indeed, nearly 1,000 different restriction enzymes have been identified so far, which cut in hundreds of different places. The fact that they make cuts at so many specific locations has given scientists a terrific ability to cut up DNA in myriad ways.

Note that with *Bam*HI, each of the resulting DNA fragments has one strand that protrudes. Restriction enzymes that make this kind of cut are particularly valuable, for they produce "sticky ends" of DNA, so named because they have the potential to *stick to* other complementary DNA sequences. In the fragment on the lower-left in Figure 15.2, for example, the protruding sequence CTAG could now easily form a base pair with *any* piece of DNA whose sequence is the complemen-

tary GATC. So great is the need for restriction enzymes that they can now be ordered from biochemical suppliers, much as a person might order a set of socket wrenches from a hardware store.

Another Tool of Biotech: Plasmids

From the overview of manufacturing human growth hormone, recall that the human gene for HGH was inserted into *E. coli* bacteria, which then started turning out quantities of this protein. The question is, How did this human gene get into a bacterium? Several methods of transfer are available, but for now let's focus on a specific kind of DNA delivery vehicle. As it turns out, bacteria have small DNA-bearing units that lie *outside* their single chromosome. These are the **plasmids**, extrachromosomal rings of bacterial DNA that can be as little as 1,000 base pairs in length (**see Figure 15.3**). Plasmids can replicate independently of the bacterial chromosome; but just as important for biotech's purposes, they can *move into* bacterial cells.

How do plasmids do this? Bacteria are capable of taking up DNA from their surroundings, after which this DNA will function—that is, code for proteins—inside the bacterial cells. Appropriately enough, this process is known as **transformation**: a cell's incorporation of genetic material from outside its boundary. Some bacterial cells are naturally adept at transformation, while others, such as *E. coli*, can be induced to perform it by means of chemical treatment. Critically, plasmid DNA can be taken in via transformation and continue to function, as plasmid DNA, inside the bacteria.

Using Biotech's Tools: Getting Human Genes into Plasmids

At this point, you know about a couple of tools in the biotech tool kit: restriction enzymes and the transformation process involving plasmids. Let's now see how they work together. As you can see in **Figure 15.4**, the process starts with a gene of interest in the human genome. The first step is to use restriction enzymes on this human DNA. Knowing, say, the starting and ending sequence of the gene of interest, a restriction enzyme is selected that allows part of the genome to be cut into a manageable

bacterium

bacterial chromosome

plasmid

**Figure 15.3
Transfer Agent**
Plasmids are small rings of bacterial DNA that are not a part of the bacterial chromosome. They can exist outside bacterial cells and then be taken up by these cells. This artificially colored micrograph shows a type of plasmid, from *E. coli* bacteria, that is commonly used in genetic engineering.

**Figure 15.4
How to Use Bacteria to Produce a Needed Human Protein**

human cell containing
gene of interest

DNA

protein synthesis

human protein of interest

bacterial chromosome

plasmid

bacterium

Use same restriction enzyme to snip plasmid.

1. Use restriction enzymes to snip gene of interest from the isolated human genome.

2. Insert gene into plasmid (complementary sticky-ends will fit together).

recombinant DNA

transformation

3. Transfer the plasmid back into bacterial cell.

replication

4. Let bacterial cells replicate. Harvest and purify the human protein produced by the plasmids inside the bacterial cells.

bacterial clones

fragment including this sequence of interest, preferably in a sticky-ended form.

Here's where the beauty of restriction enzymes really comes into play. If the same restriction enzyme is now used on the DNA of isolated *plasmids*, the result is *complementary* sticky ends of plasmid and human DNA. In other words, these segments of human and plasmid DNA, through sticky-ended base pairing, fit together like puzzle pieces.

When the DNA fragments are mixed with the "cut" plasmids, that's just what happens: Human and plasmid DNA form base pairs, and the human DNA is incorporated into the plasmid circle. With this, a segment of DNA that was once part of the human genome has now been *re-combined* with a different stretch of DNA (the plasmid sequence). This process gives us the term **recombinant DNA**, defined as two or more segments of DNA that have been combined by humans into a sequence that does not exist in nature.

Getting the Plasmids Back inside Cells, Turning out Protein

To this point, what has been done is to produce a collection of independent plasmids having a human gene as part of their makeup. Remember, though, the goal is to turn out quantities of whatever protein the human gene is coding for. To do this requires a vast quantity of plasmids working away, which means working away *back inside* bacterial cells, and it's here that transformation comes into play. If the plasmids are put into a medium containing specially treated bacterial cells, a few of these cells will take up plasmids through transformation (at which point these cells have become transgenic, as noted earlier). Once this happens, the plasmids start *replicating* along with the bacterial cells themselves. As one bacterial cell becomes two, two become four, and so on, the plasmids are replicating away as well. And as the cell count reaches into the billions, collectible quantities of the protein begin to be turned out via instructions from the human gene inserted into the plasmid DNA.

A Plasmid Is One Kind of Cloning Vector

In this example, plasmids were the vehicle that served to take on some foreign DNA and then to ferry it into working bacterial cells. Note, however, that plasmids are only one vehicle among several that can be used. Collectively, such vehicles are known as **cloning vectors**, meaning self-replicating agents that serve to transfer and replicate genetic material. Next to plasmids, the most common cloning vector is a type of virus that infects bacteria—a bacteriophage.

Real-World Transgenic Biotechnology

The example we just went over concerned a hypothetical medicine, but lots of actual medicines are being produced through biotechnology today. By one industry count, more than 150 biotechnology drugs and vaccines have been approved by the U.S. Food and Drug Administration. We've already touched on one biotech medicine: the human growth hormone that is produced inside the *E. coli* bacterium. As it turns out, *E. coli* is something of a workhorse in medical biotech. Human insulin and several kinds of cancer-fighting compounds are also produced through it.

E. coli and its fellow bacteria are not the only "bioreactors" used in medical biotechnology, however. Yeast, hamster cells, and even mammals are utilized as well. Goats of the type pictured in Figure 15.1 produce several kinds of proteins in their milk, including one called AT3 that prevents the formation of blood clots. You might wonder why large, expensive goats would be used to turn out proteins when bacteria are available. The answer is that lactating goats naturally produce a tremendous amount of protein, in the form of the proteins that help make up their milk. Through genetic manipulation, scientists can tie the production of *human* proteins to the goat's natural production of its milk proteins, and the result is a bonanza: A single goat can produce over a kilogram (2.2 pounds) of needed human protein per year. You also might wonder how a human gene can be spliced into a goat genome. Human DNA is injected into goat embryos when they are at the one-cell stage.

Genetically Modified Food Crops

Transgenic organisms do more than produce medicines. You may have heard of genetically modified or "GM" food crops. It won't surprise you to hear that most of these crops are transgenic. If you look at **Figure 15.5**, you can see a transgenic rice that has been dubbed "golden rice" because of its ability to produce its own beta carotene, which the human body coverts to vitamin A. Conventional rice does not contain beta carotene, and this fact has health consequences. The World Health Organization estimates that half a million children go blind each year from vitamin A deficiency and that one to two million children die from it. No one claims that golden rice can completely solve this problem, but the hope is that it can help alleviate it. Golden rice is transgenic in more ways than one: Genes from both a bacterium and a daffodil have been spliced into it, thus enabling it to produce the beta carotene.

Field tests are just beginning on golden rice, but several other transgenic food crops are in full commercial production right now. Indeed, in the United States 80 percent of all soybeans, 70 percent of all cotton, and 38 percent of all corn crops currently are genetically modified in one way or another. In general, the purpose of transgenic crops is to get greater crop yields with less use of chemical pesticides and herbicides. No other biotech product has sparked as much controversy as GM crops, however. We'll review some of the issues surrounding GM crops in the chapter's concluding section.

15.3 Reproductive Cloning

You may have noticed that the word *cloning* popped up in the discussion of transgenic biotechnology. Thanks to movies and recent real-life events, this word has taken on some sinister implications, as if biological cloning were inherently a Frankenstein-like procedure. But it need be no more threatening than the process of making copies of a single gene. To **clone** simply means "to make an exact genetic copy of." An individual clone is one of these exact genetic copies. Thus, in the biotech world, the gene for human growth hormone is cloned by means of being snipped out of the human genome and then copied within bacterial cells. A collection of such cells can be thought of as a single clone, because all of them are genetically identical. (One bacterium splits into two, and both "daughter" cells are genetic replicas of the parent cell.)

Cloning can involve not just bacteria, however, but larger organisms as well. Human beings actually have been making clones for centuries, though by low-tech rather than high-tech methods. A "cutting" taken from a plant and put into soil can sometimes grow into a whole new plant. When this happens, there is no mixing of egg and sperm. The new plant comes entirely from one individual—the original plant—and thus meets the definition of a clone, in that it is an exact genetic copy of another entity.

All this said, in recent years biotechnology has greatly expanded the range of what can be cloned. The potential for such cloning appears to be very broad indeed—something that has inspired both great optimism and great concern. Biotechnology has now joined with various reproductive technologies to produce clones not just of genes or cells or plants, but of mammals, with the starting cells for these mammals coming from *adult* mammals. The most famous example is Dolly the sheep, cloned by researcher Ian Wilmut and his colleagues in Scot-

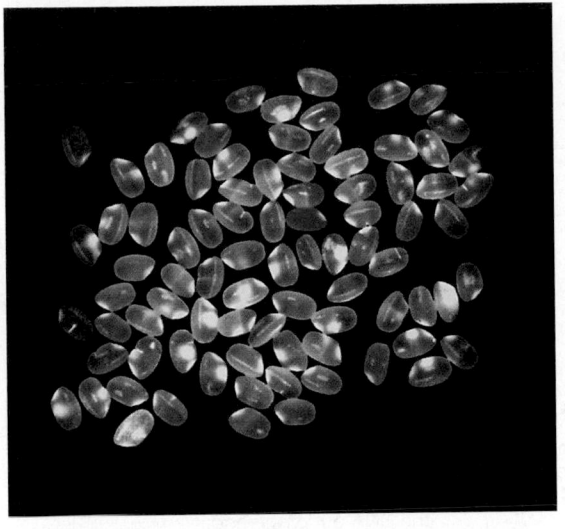

Figure 15.5
A More Nutritious Rice
Grains of the genetically engineered "golden rice" stand out next to grains of ordinary rice. The rice has a golden color because it is able to produce its own beta carotene, which the human body converts into Vitamin A.

land in 1997 (**see Figure 15.6**). This is **reproductive cloning**: cloning intended to produce genetically identical adult animals. Powerful in its own right, it gains added potential when combined with the basic biotech processes you've been reviewing.

Reproductive Cloning: How Dolly Was Cloned

Dolly the sheep, who died in 2003, was a clone as that term is defined: She was, to a first approximation, an exact genetic replica—in this case, of an-

Web Tutorial 15.2
Recombinant DNA

Figure 15.6
Revolutionary Sheep
Dolly, the first mammal ever cloned from an adult mammal, is shown here as a young sheep with her surrogate mother. Note that Dolly is white-faced, like the sheep she was cloned from, while her surrogate mother is black-faced.

white sheep

1. A cell was taken from the udder of a six-year-old white sheep and then allowed to divide many times in the laboratory. Meanwhile an egg was taken from a second black-faced sheep.

udder cells

2. One of the resulting udder cells was selected to be the "donor" cell for the cloning. Meanwhile, using a slender tube called a *micropipette*, researchers sucked the DNA out of the egg.

DNA

3. The donor cell and egg were put next to each other, and an electric current was applied to the egg cell.

black-faced sheep

egg cell

4. This caused the two cells to fuse and prompted an activation that reprogrammed the donor-cell DNA. This caused the fused cell to start developing as an embryo.

embryo

5. After some incubation, the embryo was implanted in a third sheep, which served as the surrogate mother.

surrogate mother

Dolly

6. This mother gave birth to Dolly the sheep, which grew into an adult.

Figure 15.7
How Dolly Was Cloned

other sheep. Here's how she was produced (**see Figure 15.7**). A cell was taken from the udder of a six-year-old adult sheep and then grown in culture in the laboratory, meaning that the original cell divided into many "daughter" cells. While this was going on, researchers took an *egg* from a second sheep and removed its nucleus, meaning they removed all its nuclear DNA. Then they placed the udder cell (which had DNA) next to the egg cell (which did not have DNA) and applied a small

electric current to the egg. This had two effects: It caused the two cells to fuse into one, and it mimicked the stimulation normally provided when a *sperm* cell fuses with an egg. With this, the udder cell DNA began to be reprogrammed. As a result of this reprogramming, the fused cell started to develop as an embryo. (Though the egg cell had its DNA removed, it still contained all kinds of egg-cell proteins whose normal function is to trigger development of an embryo. It was these factors still in the egg that reprogrammed the donor-cell DNA.) After the embryo had developed to a certain point, the researchers implanted it in a third sheep, which served as a surrogate mother. The result, 21 weeks later, was the lamb Dolly, who went on to give birth to two sets of her own lambs.

Every cell in Dolly had DNA in its nucleus that was an exact copy of the DNA in the six-year-old donor sheep. Thus Dolly was a clone of that sheep. There was no second parent contributing chromosomes to Dolly, no mixing of genetic material at the moment of conception—just a copying of one individual from another.

Cloning and Recombinant DNA

Once Dolly was born, science was off to the races in terms of producing clones of mammals. To date, horses, mules, cows, pigs, cats, and mice have been cloned—all of them essentially through the same process that was used with Dolly. But to what end? That is, why are scientists cloning these animals? Well, to use Dolly as an example, Ian Wilmut and his colleagues were not so much interested in cloning a sheep as they were in coupling the power of reproductive cloning to the techniques of recombinant DNA that you just looked at. The workers at Wilmut's research institute went on to produce Polly the sheep, who was not only a clone, but a clone who had had a human gene inserted into her genome and was thus able to produce a blood-clotting protein useful to hemophiliacs. A *group* of such clones would be valuable because they all would have the same starting genetic set—the same genome—and thus would all be able to produce the blood-clotting protein. The power of cloning is the power to produce one organism after another that has the same traits. Cloning makes it possible to sidestep the *mixing* of traits that comes with sexual reproduction.

Human Cloning

Reproductive cloning may interest scientists because of its potential to yield products such as medicines. It has captured the attention of the average person, however, because it raises the possibility of *human* cloning. For reasons noted below, human cloning seems less likely now than it did a couple of years ago. Nevertheless, it is still possible that in the near future, a person will be produced not through sex, but through cloning. How could a person be cloned? Pretty much through the same method used with Dolly—take a cell from an adult human being, fuse this cell with an enucleated human egg cell, and implant the fused cell in the uterus of a woman willing to bring the resulting embryo to term.

The prospect of a human clone is so dizzying that it's worthwhile to think about what such a person would represent in biological terms. He or she would be a genetic replica of the person who provided the donor cell with the DNA in it. One helpful way to think of this person's biological status is in terms of a more familiar concept: that of an identical twin. As it happens, identical twins also are genetic replicas of one another. Early in a human pregnancy, separate cells from an embryo start forming as two separate human beings, and the result is identical twins. Cloning is a *different* means of producing genetically identical individuals, but the critical point is that a donor and a clone would be no more alike than two identical twins. Indeed, we would expect DNA donors and their clones to be *less* alike than identical twins. This is so because identical twins usually share similar environments—in the womb, in the home, and so on—while donor and clone would likely grow up in very different environments.

Be this as it may, the prospect of a human clone still has the power to stun us—generally to repulse us, to judge by news reports. It now appears, however, that nature's rules may get in the way of human cloning. For several years after Dolly was produced, scientists puzzled over the fact that they could not clone a *primate* and have it live past the early embryonic stage. In 2003, scientists discovered what the problem was. In primate cells, proteins that help control cell division are concentrated in the very part of the egg cell that is removed in the cloning procedure. The result is that, when cells divide in a primate clone, the chromosomes are misapportioned—some cells get too many chromosomes while others get too few. An embryo cannot survive such a genetic imbalance. As a result, we have no cloned primates so far, and no clear idea of whether we will get one.

Saving Endangered Species

Could *Jurassic Park* someday become a reality through cloning? That is, could scientists recover some dinosaur DNA and use it to produce a living dinosaur via the cloning process we've just gone over? The chances are slim, for the simple reason that DNA degrades over time, and dinosaurs have been gone a *long* time—the last of them died 65 million years ago. The DNA of animals who died only a few thousand years ago is so fragmentary that nothing could be cloned from it. If you think about it, however, even if intact dinosaur DNA could be found, there would still be another problem. Recall that in Dolly's case, donor DNA from a sheep had to be placed in a sheep egg that had its nucleus removed. Where are the dinosaur eggs that could be used for dinosaur cloning? There aren't any, of course. But scientists working today have dealt with this very problem in trying to bring back species who have *recently* gone extinct, or who are threatened with extinction.

If you look at **Figure 15.8**, you can see a picture of a Spanish mountain goat called a bucardo. There are no longer any living bucardos, as the last one was killed in January of 2000 when a tree fell on it. Fortunately, just months before this goat's death, scientists took tissue samples from it and preserved them. One problem in bringing back the bucardo through cloning involves the *Jurassic Park* question: Where do you get a bucardo egg, given that there are no more bucardos? Scientists from a U.S. company called Advanced Cell Technology (ACT) believe they have an answer. Donor DNA cells can fuse with eggs from *closely related* species, thus bringing about a clone. Indeed, ACT has already pulled this trick off with a threatened ox-like species, called a gaur, that is found in India and Southeast Asia. In 2000, a cell taken from a male gaur was fused with an enucleated egg from a common cow. In January 2001, a seemingly healthy gaur was born to a surrogate mother (once again, a cow). The gaur died shortly after birth, but the cause apparently was unrelated to the cloning. It seems possible, then, that severely threatened species could have their numbers increased through cloning, while other species might be brought back to the world *following* extinction. Is biotechnology exciting or what?

15.4 Forensic Biotechnology

After New York's World Trade Center (WTC) was destroyed on September 11, 2001, public officials had to undertake the grim task of trying to identify all the victims of the attack, and to do so quickly, so as to provide some sense of closure to the victims' loved ones. In the weeks following the attack, therefore, officials collected samples of DNA not only from WTC victims, but from the toothbrushes and razors of persons who were missing since the tragedy and hence *presumed* to be victims. They also collected DNA from relatives of these presumed victims. With this DNA database in hand, workers then made an effort to match one kind of DNA with another—to match the DNA found on a toothbrush, for example, with the DNA from a WTC victim.

In 1998, then-President Bill Clinton publicly denied allegations that he had been sexually involved with a young intern at the White House, Monica Lewinsky. The matter might have stayed right there—Ms. Lewinsky saying one thing, the president saying another—except that Ms. Lewinsky had preserved a dress with a stain on it that she said came from the president's semen. The FBI subsequently extracted DNA from this stain and soon thereafter took a sample of blood from the president. Eventually, the FBI reported on the odds that anyone *but* the president was the source of the semen. These turned out to be roughly 7.8 trillion to one. With this, the president ceased to make claims about not having had sex with Ms. Lewinsky.

High-profile cases such as these are the most visible manifestation of a huge change that has come about in the way society *identifies* persons—criminals, biological fathers, and victims, most notably. In the criminal arena, the most highly valued type of physical evidence today is not fingerprints; it is tiny bits of human tissue from which DNA can be extracted. But how do police use DNA to get a "match" in a criminal case? Let's find out.

The essence of "forensic DNA typing," as it is known, is to get two sets of physical samples—first, a sample left by the perpetrator in such forms as blood or semen; and second, a blood sample from a suspect. By comparing the DNA patterns of both samples, forensic scientists can establish odds as to whether the suspect *is* the perpetrator. (Conversely, it would be possible to use a victim's blood sample and test it against, for example, blood found on the suspect's clothing.)

The Use of PCR

When forensic DNA typing first came into use in the 1980s, a significant limitation on it was that relatively *large* samples of human tissue had to be obtained in order to get enough DNA to work with. Eventually, however, this problem was all but eliminated by something called the **polymerase**

Figure 15.8
Is Extinction Forever?
This Spanish mountain goat, the bucardo, is now extinct, but scientists hope to bring the species back through reproductive cloning.

chain reaction (PCR): a technique for quickly producing many copies of a specific segment of DNA. Thanks to PCR, if a criminal so much as licks an envelope and leaves it behind, police can retrieve enough DNA to get a match.

The PCR process is very simple in outline. Four kinds of materials are mixed together to carry it out. The first of these is a quantity of DNA itself. Then there is a collection of DNA nucleotides and DNA polymerase (which, remember, goes down the line on single-stranded DNA, affixing nucleotides to available bases). Finally, there are two DNA "primer" sequences—short sequences of single-stranded DNA that act as signals to DNA polymerase, saying "start adding nucleotides here."

The first step in the process is that the starting quantity of DNA is heated until the two strands of DNA's double helix separate, resulting in two single strands of DNA (**see Figure 15.9**). As the heated DNA mixture cools, primers will attach to each of the now-separate strands of DNA. Then the DNA polymerases go down the line, starting from the primers, linking nucleotides to the template DNA and thus producing strands that are complementary to the original strands. The result is *two* double-stranded lengths of DNA, both identical to the original double strand. In short, the DNA sample has been doubled in one copying "cycle." Then the entire process of heating and cooling is repeated. Since each copying cycle takes only 1–3 minutes, by the time 90 minutes have passed, millions of copies can be created. Moreover, thanks to the specificity of primers, the sequence that is copied can be limited to a small sequence of interest within the larger genome. So useful is PCR that it is employed not just in forensic biotechnology, but in countless facets of biological research. We are focusing here on one specific use for PCR, but it has so many applications that in 1993, its inventor, Kary Mullis, was awarded the Nobel Prize in Chemistry for his achievement.

Finding Individual Patterns

Once PCR has done its job, the police have enough DNA to begin looking for the individual patterns within it—one set of patterns found in the crime-scene DNA, one set of patterns seen in the suspect's DNA. But what are these patterns that each of us carries? Human genomes are filled with short sequences of DNA that are repeated over and over, from 3 to 50 times, like this:

TCAT TCAT TCAT TCAT TCAT

This TCAT example is not hypothetical. It is an actual *short tandem repeat* (or STR) that police de-

partments use in today's DNA typing. The usefulness of STRs is that, at a given location in the genome, one person will have one number of tandem repeats, while another person is likely to have a *different* number of repeats, like so:

Individual 1: TCAT TCAT TCAT TCAT

Individual 2: TCAT TCAT TCAT TCAT TCAT TCAT

Now, the chances are small that two unrelated individuals will have an identical number of repeats at even one location in the genome. But modern forensic DNA typing looks at STR repeats at 13 different locations. Imagine yourself, then, as a forensic investigator who is reviewing both DNA from a crime scene and DNA from a suspect in the crime. At genomic location 1, the STR patterns are:

Web Tutorial 15.3
PCR: Rapid
Copying of DNA

Figure 15.9
DNA Copying Machine
The polymerase chain reaction (PCR) makes copies of a given length of DNA very quickly.

1. A researcher selects a DNA region of interest.

double-stranded DNA

2. The DNA is heated, causing the two strands of the double helix to separate.

single-stranded DNA

primers

3. As the mixture cools, short DNA sequences called *primers* form base pairs with complementary DNA sequences on their respective strands.

4. DNA polymerase goes down the line, synthesizing complementary DNA strands. The end result is a doubling of the original DNA.

double-stranded DNA

5. The process is repeated many times, doubling the amount of DNA each time.

Crime scene: TCAT TCAT TCAT TCAT

Suspect: TCAT TCAT TCAT TCAT

The chances are small that both the suspect and crime-scene samples just happened to have the same number of repeats at this genomic location. If the STR patterns continue to line up this way at the other 12 locations, then the case is all but closed: The suspect almost surely is the perpetrator, because the odds of any two people having identical STR patterns at 13 locations are astronomically small.

It's important to recognize that this kind of DNA evidence can be used to prove innocence as well as guilt. DNA testing regularly exonerates not only suspects, but people who have been *convicted* of crimes. In the past 15 years, more than 130 prisoners who were jailed for various offenses have been freed on the basis of DNA testing. If you look at **Figure 15.10**, you can see one way that short, repeating DNA sequences can be visualized in criminal cases. (For more on DNA visualization, see "Visualizing DNA" on the next page.)

Beyond matching a known suspect to a crime scene or victim, forensic DNA typing has another power. Increasingly, it is allowing police to make so-called *cold hits*. All 50 states now require criminals convicted of violent crimes to provide DNA samples. Capitalizing on this the FBI has put together a national database of the DNA profiles of these criminals. Given this, imagine a situation in which a crime is committed, and no suspect was identified, but in which a DNA sample was retrieved. A DNA profile will be produced from this sample—a profile that can be matched against all those that are stored in the DNA database. If the profile from the crime scene matches a criminal's stored profile, that in itself is sufficient evidence to make an arrest. Looking to the future, if both technical and legal issues can be worked out, police may be able to do DNA typing and database searching right at a crime scene. Imagine being a police officer at such a location. You spot a small amount of blood, get technicians to analyze it on the spot, and check the resulting STR profile against the national database. The computer comes up with a match, and you walk away from a crime scene with a printout that contains the name and last known address of the person you intend to arrest for the crime.

15.5 Personalized Medicine

Pharmaceutical drugs are supposed to save us from illness rather than cause it, of course. But a study published in 1998 reported that, in a single year in the United States, serious *adverse* drug reactions were seen in 2.2 million instances and resulted in over 100,000 deaths. Such reactions actually turn out to be a leading cause of hospitalization and death. How can we predict who will suffer an adverse reaction and who won't? Pharmaceutical companies must subject potential drugs to years of safety testing, but some individuals inevitably will slip beneath the radar of such testing.

But why should this be? Why should a given drug affect different people in different ways? This question is pertinent not just to the issue of safety, but to the issue of effectiveness. Take two patients with the same kind of cancer, give them both the same drug to fight the cancer, and their outcomes might be very different—even to the point of one patient living and one dying. Lots of factors can come into play in such cases, but one factor that is being intensively studied is genetic variability.

One of the things that the Human Genome Project revealed is the degree to which human beings differ from one another in their genetic makeup. Take two people who are not related and, on average, their genomes will differ by 1 base pair in a thousand. Each of these individual variations is called a single-nucleotide polymorphism, or SNP. Today, millions of SNPs have been "mapped" in the genome. Most of them lie outside the regions of the genome that code for proteins and thus have little relevance to medicine. But some do lie within DNA's protein-coding regions, and scientists are focusing intensely on these. A research group in San Diego, for example, is looking at hundreds of people who suffer from high blood pressure and who are being treated for their condition with a standard array of drugs. The twist in this study is that the *genomes* of these patients are also being analyzed, with an eye toward examining any SNP patterns that emerge. It may be that patients who share an SNP-pattern 1 will do better on one

Murderer's shirt   Victim's blood

Figure 15.10
Telltale Stains
A defendant in this real-life murder case claimed that blood stains found on his clothing (see the rows under "shirt") came from his own blood rather than from the blood of a young woman who was stabbed to death. The DNA evidence said otherwise. Look at the pattern in the row under V (for victim) and see how closely it matches the pattern in the shirt rows. The probability that the blood on the defendant's clothing came from anyone but the victim was 1 in 33 billion. (Courtesy of Cellmark Diagnostics, Inc., Germantown, Maryland)

Visualizing DNA

Web Tutorial 15.4
DNA Size and Sequencing

I n working with DNA, scientists need a way to compare one segment of DNA to another. This means that lengths of DNA need to be visualized in some way. But how can something as small as a segment of DNA be visualized? Let's find out.

Running DNA through a Gel

There is a material used in biotechnology, called a gel, that in some ways is like the food gelatins we're used to. Running through a gel are a series of microscopic spaces (or "pores"). Given this, the gel acts like a sifter: Substances such as DNA can pass through it, but only with some coaxing and at a controlled rate.

The starting length of DNA might be a whole genome's worth, but more likely will be some subset of a genome. Whatever the case, the process begins with using a restriction enzyme to chop up a DNA sample into a quantity of fragments. When the DNA from many cells is cut up with the restriction enzyme, the result is a huge number of identical copies of fragment 1, a huge number of copies of fragment 2, and so on. As you know, restriction enzymes don't make evenly spaced cuts throughout a length of DNA; they cut at specific recognition sequences. Thus fragment 1 will be a different size than fragment 2, which in turn will be a different size than fragment 3, and so on.

The question is, how do researchers learn the size of each fragment? The answer comes from a DNA sprint through the pores in the gel. As you can see in **Figure 1**, a chamber is used that has two special features. First, it has electrodes at each end—one negative and one positive—and second, it has a series of indentations, or "wells," located on the same end of the tray as the negative electrode.

The process begins with forming a gel in a tray. Then the tray containing the gel is placed in a solution that conducts electricity.

The collection of DNA fragments is then added to the wells, which lie on the end of the tray *opposite* that of the positively charged electrode. And here's the key: DNA itself is negatively charged. Given that opposites attract in electricity, the DNA fragments are drawn to the positively charged end of the gel. But to get there, they must make it through the gel. Given this obstacle, it is the *smallest* of the fragments that will travel the farthest in a given amount of time, while the largest of the fragments will travel the least amount of distance.

Learning the Size of the Fragments

What this means is that the fragments are separated out by size. A fragment that is, say, one thousand nucleotides long will make it farther through the gel than a fragment that is two thousand nucleotides long. Researchers can *see* where each fragment has ended up in the gel, because, after running the gel, they add a fluorescent dye that binds to the DNA. The result is a series of bands within the gel (similar to supermarket bar codes), with each band representing a collection of DNA fragments of the same size. The size of each fragment is learned by putting, in one "lane" of the gel, a series of "reference fragments," meaning fragments of known size. If one of the reference fragments was 10,000 nucleotides long, and if one of the sample's fragments traveled far enough through the gel to line up perfectly with it, the researchers know that their sample fragment is roughly 10,000 nucleotides long as well.

This technique of sizing DNA fragments is called *gel electrophoresis*, a name that makes sense considering the gel that's used, the electricity, and the fact that *phoresis* is a Greek word meaning "to be carried."

Figure 1
Visualizing Lengths of DNA
In gel electrophoresis, negatively charged DNA fragments travel through the porous gel toward the positive end of the tray when a charge is applied to the gel. Large fragments, however, do not travel as far in a given amount of time as small fragments. Thus the fragments separate out by size. The first "stripe" at the top of a lane represents a collection of fragments of a given size, the second stripe a second collection of fragments of a smaller size, and so on.

drug, while patients who have an SNP-pattern 2 will do better on another drug. Why? Because these genetic differences could lead to differences in the way the patients metabolize the drugs they are taking.

It's easy to see that such SNP analysis could get more personalized over time. Conceivably, each of us could have an "SNP profile" that physicians could match up against any number of disease treatments and drugs. The questions the physicians would ask would be: Is this drug safe for a person with this SNP profile? Is this treatment likely to be the most effective treatment for a person with this SNP profile? Note, however, that a personalized genetic profile might also reveal genetic *susceptibility* to diseases. We'll return to this subject later, but for now just ask yourself: Who should have access to genetic profiles?

Microarrays: Catching Genes in the Act

As you know, the outcome of genetic activity is the production of proteins. Given this, another way to personalize medicine would be to look not at a person's genome, but at what that person's genome is *doing*. The question here is what genes within the person's genome are being "expressed" at a given point in time? Which genes are actively coding for proteins? A technological advance called DNA microarrays now allows researchers to take "snapshots" of the genetic activity going on within individual cells.

Recall that, for any protein to be produced, a gene will first code for a messenger RNA (mRNA) that ferries the gene's information to a ribosome, where the protein is actually put together. Thus, if you know which mRNAs are in the cytoplasm of a cell, you know which *genes* are active in that cell. Of course, a cell is likely to have thousands of different mRNAs in its cytoplasm at any one time. So how could you learn what all of them are? You can put a microarray to work, as shown in **Figure 15.11a** on page 301.

Each microarray "chip" is a glass slide smaller than a postage stamp. Through use of the same photolithography technique that is used to make computer chips, thousands of tiny "spots" of single-stranded DNA are applied to a microarray chip, with each spot in effect containing multiple copies of a single gene. In the example shown, two different cells are being compared, one of them a cancerous cell from a breast-cancer patient, the other a normal breast cell. In the microarray procedure, mRNAs are isolated from each of these cells. Then these mRNAs are converted into a more stable nucleic acid, complementary DNA (cDNA). Critically, the cDNAs derived from the cancerous cell are fluorescently labeled red, while the cDNAs derived from the normal, "control" cell are labeled green.

Given your knowledge of complementary base pairing, you may be able to guess what comes next. When the cDNAs are poured onto the microarray, they will hybridize or bond with complementary DNA segments that are on the chip. But what are these complementary segments? Individual genes. And each cDNA molecule is complementary to *one* of these genes (because each cDNA represents a gene that was expressed back in the cell). Therefore, when a cDNA bonds with an individual gene on the chip, this is in effect a message saying, "This gene is active in this cell right now."

Recall, however, that we are comparing gene activity in two cells. Every time a red-labeled cDNA from the cancerous cell bonds with its complementary DNA, it adds to the red light that will be seen on a DNA spot when a laser is shined on it. Every time a green-labeled cDNA from the normal cell bonds to its complementary DNA, a small amount of green light will be added to a spot. A computer can calculate the *ratio* of red to green light at any one spot, and the result is what you see at the bottom of the figure. Genes in the cancerous cell that are strongly active, relative to genes in the control cell, show up as red dots. Genes in the cancerous cell that have weak activity relative to the control show up as green dots. Meanwhile, yellow dots indicate genes in the two cells that are equally active, and black dots indicate genes that are inactive in both cells.

You probably can see one use for this right away. At given points in time, what genes are active in a cancer cell, as opposed to a normal cell? Researchers would like to know about this in the same way that an army officer would like to know how an enemy's forces are being utilized over time.

But there's a more individualized aspect to microarrays as well. No two cancer patients will have exactly the same kind of tumor; different tumors will express different genes. Under a microscope, these tumors may look the same, but they are not the same in terms of gene expression. And such expression can affect how aggressive a tumor is, and how it responds to a given treatment. Imagine, then, using microarrays to develop "expression profiles" for individual tumors. This is now being done all the time. It has been done in Europe in recent years for breast-cancer tumors, and the results have been encouraging. Women whose tumors had one kind of expression profile were found to be more likely to have a recurring cancer than women whose tumors had another profile. As a result, trials are now underway in which women are being assigned to get one kind of *treatment* or another, based on what kind of expression profile their tumor had. As you can imagine, individualized genetic snap-

(a) How microarrays work

1. Each spot in the microarray contains multiple copies of a single gene.

2. Messenger RNA (mRNA) sequences are obtained, in this case from cancerous breast cells and normal breast cells. These mRNAs are converted to complementary DNA (cDNA) sequences, which are applied to the chip. The cancer cell cDNAs have been fluorescently labeled red, while the normal cDNAs have been labeled green.

cDNAs derived from **normal cell** mRNAs

cDNAs derived from **cancer cell** mRNAs

microarray

There are thousands of dots like this on each microarray

3. The cDNAs bond or "hybridize" with the genes that are on the chip, as shown below. When a laser light is shined on the chip, the pattern of hybridizing is revealed in a series of colored dots on a computer display. The colors indicate which genes are most active in cancerous cells as compared to normal cells.

chip DNA strands (genes)

cDNAs from **cancer cells** hybridizing with chip DNA

cDNAs from **normal cells** hybridizing with chip DNA

cDNAs from **both kinds of cells** hybridizing with chip DNA

cDNAs from **neither cell types** hybridizing with chip DNA

This gene is most active in cancer cells

This gene is most active in normal cells

This gene is equally active in both cell types

This gene is not active in either cell type

(b) How microarrays look

**Figure 15.11
Microarray Technology**

A small portion of a microarray display, with individual DNA spots visible. This microarray was used to study gene expression in baker's yeast.

shots are not limited to cancer; all kinds of human diseases can be analyzed through them. And this technology is still young. In the future, physicians will be able to take account of the genetic activity within us in ways that we can't yet imagine.

15.6 Controversies in Biotechnology

Having learned something about biotechnology, consider the following question. Let us suppose that through biotechnology, you could fashion an egg-laying chicken that had no eyes and no legs. If you could do such a thing, would you? On a less theoretical level, a safer, cheaper human growth hormone is now available thanks to biotechnology. But who should get human growth hormone? Should it be reserved for children who are truly short, or should it be made available to children who are simply shorter than they'd like to be? And if, in the future, it becomes possible to manipulate qualities other than height—say hair or eye color—what limits should be placed on the use of these techniques? Do we face the prospect of "designer human beings," and if so, do cosmetic traits get apportioned out strictly in accordance with who can pay for them? It's hard to tell whether society will have to grapple with such issues in the future, simply because it's impossible to know where biotechnology might lead us. But there are plenty of current controversies in biotechnology. Here's a brief look at a few of them.

Genetically Modified Foods

No biotechnology issue has raised more furor than that of genetically modified foods. Consider that the "golden rice" reviewed earlier had to be grown in a greenhouse in Switzerland that was made grenade-proof because of fear it might be attacked by opponents of "GM" foods. What is this controversy about? In a nutshell, proponents of GM foods see in them the potential to feed a hungry world and to lessen the environmental damage caused by such human practices as pesticide application. Opponents of them see the potential to harm human health and wreak havoc on Earth's ecosystems.

If you look at **Figure 15.12**, you can see a case in point in this battle. Pictured are two sets of cotton plants, one set genetically modified, the other not. The modified plants are transgenic. They contain genes from a bacterium, called *Bacillus thuringiensis*, that is found naturally in the soil and that produces proteins that are toxic to a number of insects. Collectively, these proteins constitute a natural insecticide known as Bt, which has been sprayed on crops for years, mostly by "organic" farmers, meaning those who do not use human-made pesticides or herbicides. Enter biotechnology firms, which in the 1990s spliced *Bt* genes into crop plants, with the result that these plants—corn, cotton, and potatoes—now produce their *own* insecticide. The results have in some ways been an environmentalist's dream. In one survey conducted in the American Southeast, farmers who planted *Bt* cotton reduced the amount of chemical insecticides they applied to their fields by 72 percent. They did this, moreover, while increasing cotton yields by more than 11 percent.

Despite such benefits, we can also see, in the use of *Bt* seeds, the qualities that make environmentalists uneasy about GM crops in general. Those few insects that survive in *Bt*-enhanced fields are likely to give rise to populations resistant to the natural toxin. This raises the prospect of a valued natural insecticide losing its effectiveness against insects over the long run. So alarming is this possibility that the U.S. Environmental Protection Agency requires that at least 20 percent of any given farmer's crops must be non-*Bt* plants. The idea is to create non-*Bt* "refuges" near the *Bt* fields that will harbor bugs that have not built up a resistance to *Bt*. These bugs will then mate with *Bt*-resistant bugs, thus helping to ensure that *Bt* resistance does not spread.

Meanwhile, another fear is that some GM crops will take on the role of "super-plants" that will spread by means of their pollen fertilizing nearby plants. (This is the same threat landscape architects see in low-mow grass, for example.) Then there is the idea that the foods made from GM crops could set off allergic reactions in consumers or have other adverse health effects on them. There is no evidence that GM foods have caused either health or environmental problems so far. But European countries have been concerned enough about these issues that, since 1998, they have enforced a moratorium on the planting of any new commercial GM crops.

Cloning

The ethical issues connected to cloning center almost entirely around human cloning. There is near-universal agreement that it would be unethical to attempt to clone a human being with the intention of having it develop from embryo to child to adult. This is so in part because the reproductive cloning of any mammal is currently a hit-or-miss process. Hundreds of attempts may be required to produce a viable embryo that can be successfully implanted in a uterus and brought to term. And the clones that are produced often have physical defects or are abnormally large at birth.

Even if each attempt at cloning a horse or a cat resulted in a healthy individual, however, science would still be confronted with the fundamental question of whether it is ethical to clone a human being. While the answer from almost all scientists seems to be no, a few scientists from several countries have expressed an interest in human cloning. As such, the possibility of its taking place cannot be ruled out.

Genetic Profiles

As noted, in the future it might be possible for people to get genetic profiles of themselves—inventories of the SNPs that make their genome unique. Such a profile might well reveal the susceptibilities that individuals have to genetically linked diseases, however, and this is where the controversy starts. The worst-case scenario is that individuals could be branded as disease-prone by reason of their genetic profiles, with

Figure 15.12
Built-in Resistance to Pests
The cotton plants on the left have had genes spliced into them from the bacterium *Bacillus thuringiensis*. These genes code for proteins that function as a pesticide. Meanwhile, the cotton plants on the right are not transgenic in this way—they have not had genes from another organism spliced into them. Both stands of cotton were under equal attack from insects, but the *Bt*-enhanced plants fared much better.

the result that employers would not want to hire them and insurers would not want to insure them. (An extreme version of this kind of genetic discrimination is portrayed in the film *Gattaca*.)

Because a small number of genetically based diseases can be tested for currently, this issue has some relevance right now. Certainly governments are acting as if genetic discrimination is a current threat. Most states have enacted laws that prohibit the use of genetic information in the issuance of medical insurance policies; most have passed laws prohibiting employment discrimination based on genetics; and President Clinton signed an executive order prohibiting the federal government from making any decision to hire, promote, or dismiss a worker based on genetic information. Thus far, however, there is little evidence that any institutions have had an interest in carrying out genetic discrimination in connection with employment or health insurance.

The most contentious area in this debate seems to be life insurance, which is special in that it is seen less as a "right" than a consumer option. As a result, life insurance has not been subject to the same kind of government regulation as has health insurance or employment practice. Imagine what would happen, though, if individuals could know, through genetic testing, that they were at significant risk of an early death, but that insurance companies were forbidden to know the genetic background of any of their life-insurance applicants. The result would be droves of disease-susceptible people signing up for life insurance, dying young (on average), and thus driving up life-insurance rates for everyone. Such are the economic issues that come with the new world of science and technology.

On to Evolution

In touring the strands of DNA's double helix, you've had many occasions to see how this microscopic molecule can profoundly affect our macroscopic world. DNA replicates, it mutates, it is passed on from one generation to the next. And some organisms will have more *success* in passing on their DNA—in reproducing, in other words—than will others. This latter fact has been critical in bringing about the huge variety of life-forms that Earth houses, from bacteria to bats to trees. Over billions of years, genetics has interacted with Earth's myriad environments to produce the grand story of life. That story is called evolution, and it is the subject of the next four chapters.

Chapter Review

Summary

15.1 What Is Biotechnology?

- Biotechnology is the application of technology to natural biological processes. Innovations in biotechnology result from insights that are both biological and technological in nature.

15.2 Transgenic Biotechnology

- A transgenic organism is an organism whose genome has stably incorporated one or more genes from another species. Many biotechnology products are produced within transgenic organisms. Human growth hormone, for example is produced within a bacterium that has been made transgenic by means of incorporating a human gene.

- Restriction enzymes are proteins derived from bacteria that can cut DNA in specific places. Plasmids are small, extrachromosomal rings of bacterial DNA that can exist outside of bacterial cells and that can move into these cells through the process of transformation.
Web Tutorial 15.1: Restriction Enzymes and Plasmids

- Human DNA can be inserted into plasmid rings. Scientists use the same restriction enzyme on both the human DNA of interest and the plasmids. Complementary "sticky ends" of the fragmented human and plasmid DNA will then bond together, thus splicing the human DNA into the plasmid. This produces recombinant

DNA: two or more segments of DNA that have been combined by humans into a sequence that does not exist in nature.

- Once plasmids have had human DNA spliced into them, the plasmids can then be taken up into bacterial cells through transformation. As these cells replicate, producing many cells, the plasmid DNA inside them replicates as well. These plasmids are producing the protein coded for by the human DNA that has been spliced into them. The result is a quantity of the human protein of interest.

- Plasmids are one type of cloning vector, meaning a self-replicating agent that, in cloning, functions in the transfer of genetic material. Viruses known as bacteriophages are another common cloning vector.

- A large number of medicines and vaccines are produced today through transgenic biotechnology. Transgenic organisms that are used for this purpose include not only bacteria but also yeast, hamster cells, and mammals such as goats. Transgenic food crops are planted in abundance today in the United States. These genetically modified or GM crops are a subject of great controversy.

15.3 Reproductive Cloning

- A clone is a genetically identical copy of a biological entity. Genes can be cloned, as can cells and plants. Reproductive cloning is the process of making adult clones of animals. Dolly the sheep was a reproductive clone. Today, reproductive cloning of mammals is carried out through variants of the process that was used with Dolly: An egg cell has its nucleus removed and is fused with an adult cell containing a nucleus and, therefore, DNA. The fused cell then starts to develop as an embryo and is implanted in a surrogate mother.

- Reproductive cloning can work in tandem with various recombinant DNA processes. Reproductive clones may be made transgenic and produce proteins of interest to humans.

- It is possible that a human being might be cloned in the near future though, for technical reasons, such cloning seems less likely today than it did a few years ago.

- It appears possible that severely threatened animal species could have their numbers increased through reproductive cloning and that species recently made extinct might be brought back from extinction through cloning.
  Web Tutorial 15.2: Recombinant DNA

15.4 Forensic Biotechnology

- Identities of criminals, biological fathers, and disaster victims often are established today through the use of DNA. Forensic DNA typing is the use of DNA to establish identities in connection with legal matters, such as crimes.

- The polymerase chain reaction (PCR) is a technique for quickly producing many copies of a segment of DNA. It is useful in situations, such as crime investigations, in which a large amount of DNA is needed for analysis, yet the starting quantity of DNA is small.
  Web Tutorial 15.3: PCR: Rapid Copying of DNA

- Forensic DNA typing usually works through comparisons of short tandem repeat (STR) patterns that are found in all human genomes. Police will, for example, compare the STR pattern in a suspect's DNA with the STR pattern in DNA extracted from a crime scene.
  Web Tutorial 15.4: DNA Size and Sequencing

15.5 Personalized Medicine

- The genomes of any two unrelated human beings differ, on average, by one base pair per thousand. Each of these individual variations is called a single-nucleotide polymorphism or SNP. Researchers today are trying to find out if individuals might react differently to drugs or other medical treatments based on the SNP patterns in their genome.

- DNA microarrays are research devices that allow scientists to take a "snapshot" of the genetic activity going on at a given moment in a given type of cell. Through microarrays, scientists can learn which genes are being expressed in one type of cell, relative to another. Microarrays are being used today to develop "expression profiles" of cells—profiles that show the pattern of gene expression that is taking place in specific cells, such as cancer cells.

15.6 Controversies in Biotechnology

- Society is increasingly having to grapple with issues that biotechnology is raising. For example, what limits should there be on modifying organisms other than humans? What limits should be placed on the cosmetic modification of humans?

- No aspect of biotechnology has been as controversial as the production of genetically modified food (GM food). Critics charge that GM foods are potentially dangerous to human beings and to the environment. Proponents of GM foods say these foods are of enormous potential to benefit humanity and the environment.

- Two of the fears most commonly expressed about GM foods are that they stand to cause allergic or other adverse health reactions in some people, and that as crops they may spread uncontrollably, through hybridization with wild plants. There is no evidence thus far that GM foods are having either effect.

- Genetic testing may be used in the near future to diagnose genetic susceptibility to a broad range of diseases. There is concern that individuals diagnosed as genetically susceptible will be subject to genetic discrimination, either by insurance companies or by employers.

Key Terms

biotechnology 289	**recombinant DNA** 292
clone 293	**reproductive cloning** 293
cloning vector 292	**restriction enzyme** 289
plasmid 290	**transformation** 290
polymerase chain reaction (PCR) 296	**transgenic organism** 289

Understanding the Basics

Multiple-Choice Questions (answers in the back of the book)

1. How is biotechnology defined?
   a. the technical advances made by researchers in biology over the last decade
   b. the study of technical biology
   c. the application of technology to natural biological processes
   d. the process of cloning genes
   e. the use of commercialization in biological research

2. In transgenic biotechnology involving bacteria, which sequence of events would be followed in the process of harvesting a protein of interest?
   a. Replicate cloning vectors in host cells; isolate gene that codes for protein; insert gene into vector; harvest protein of interest; transform the vector into bacteria.
   b. Transform vector into bacteria; isolate gene that codes for protein; replicate vectors in host cells; insert gene into vector; harvest protein of interest.

c. Harvest protein of interest; isolate gene that codes for protein; insert gene into vector; replicate vectors in host cells; transform the vector into bacteria.

d. Isolate gene that codes for protein; insert gene into vector; replicate vectors in host cells; transform the vector into bacteria; harvest protein of interest.

e. Isolate gene that codes for protein; insert gene into vector; transform the vector into bacteria; replicate vectors in host cells; harvest protein of interest.

3. The most common way to visualize DNA molecules is to employ gel electrophoresis. The reason the DNA molecule migrates from one end of a gel electrophoresis tray to another is that:
   a. DNA is a very small molecule
   b. DNA is naturally active
   c. DNA molecules are negatively charged; the opposite ends of the trays are positively charged
   d. DNA molecules are positively charged; the opposite ends of the trays are negatively charged
   e. None of the above is correct

4. Criminal investigators who want to make copies of a DNA sequence from a crime do so through
   a. the polymerase chain reaction
   b. transformation
   c. gel electrophoresis
   d. DNA sequencing
   e. microarrays

5. Which of the following has biotechnology helped accomplish?
   a. genetically engineered medicines
   b. identification of criminals
   c. cloning of mammals
   d. genetically engineered crops
   e. all of the above

6. Which of the following is an example of a transgenic organism?
   a. E. coli bacterium with a human gene inserted
   b. Dolly the sheep
   c. rice with bacterium and daffodil genes inserted
   d. all of the above
   e. a and c only

7. Dolly the sheep was cloned by means of
   a. applying an electric current to an egg and sperm in a laboratory
   b. taking an embryo from one sheep and implanting it in another
   c. taking a cell from an adult sheep and fusing it with a sheep egg that had its DNA removed
   d. inserting new genes into an existing mammary cell
   e. getting sperm to fuse with egg outside a living sheep

8. The basis of personalized medicine is that
   a. genes can be moved from one organism to another
   b. individual human genomes differ slightly from one another
   c. cloning genes is so easy
   d. cloning mammals has become routine
   e. individual human genomes are exactly the same

9. Microarrays provide
   a. specific lengths of DNA
   b. knowledge of which genes are being expressed in a given cell
   c. a way to reliably sequence entire genomes
   d. a means for inserting genes into genomes
   e. a way to compare crime-scene and suspect DNA

10. What is a clone?
    a. an exact genetic copy of a gene or organism
    b. a cell that can take up plasmids
    c. a segment of DNA of a specified length
    d. an offspring produced by test-tube fertilization
    e. a segment of DNA that can prime the polymerase chain reaction

Brief Review

1. Why is it useful to have organisms such as bacteria turning out human proteins?

2. Wolf-like marsupials called Tasmanian tigers became extinct in the 1930s. What would be the key to bringing the Tasmanian tiger back through cloning?

3. Why is the polymerase chain reaction (PCR) so valuable?

4. Why are restriction enzymes that cut to produce sticky ends useful? If the following piece of DNA were cut with BamHI, what would the fragment sequences be?

   ATCGGATCCTCCG
   TAGCCTAGGAGGC

5. Why did Dolly the sheep end up looking like the sheep that "donated" the udder cell, rather than the sheep that donated the egg?

Applying Your Knowledge

1. One of the motives put forth for human cloning is that people want to replace children or other loved ones who have died. To what extent could a clone of a loved one be a replacement for that person? If the technique had then been available, should doctors in the nineteenth century have preserved the DNA of Abraham Lincoln for cloning?

2. One of the concerns mentioned in the chapter regarding the use of genetic technology centers around privacy issues such as "genetic discrimination." Once we improve our ability to screen the human genome for disease susceptibility, is there any level of testing that should be required by society as a means of reducing health care costs or reducing transmission of genetic diseases across generations?

3. Should society demand that there be no risks to genetically modified foods before it allows them to be developed? Does any significant technology have no risks associated with it?

MediaLab

Holding Out Promise or Peril? Biotechnology

Biotechnology promises to create new pharmaceuticals (even replacement organs), improve livestock yields, and even reduce the need for pesticides and herbicides in agriculture. However, many people question whether scientists are proceeding at a rate outdistancing careful, cautious evaluation. Using genetically manipulated organisms for food has met great resistance in Europe, where it is called Frankenfarming—a reference to Mary Shelley's Dr. Frankenstein and the famous monster he created by combining human corpses. To learn more, enter the *Web Tutorial* for an animated review of the major techniques used to swap DNA between species. Don't be intimidated by the technology; the animations will unveil the simplicity of the techniques. In the *Web Investigation* and *Communicate Your Results* sections, you will evaluate and discuss different perspectives on the value of biotechnology—its promise, or perhaps its threat.

The online version of this *MediaLab* can be found in Chapter 15 on your Companion Website (www.prenhall.com/krogh3).

WEB TUTORIAL

The process of manipulating DNA has little of the mystique displayed in science fiction. It is more akin to the mundane process of cooking. This *Web Tutorial* will lead you through some common techniques of biotechnology.

Activity

1. *First, you will learn about restriction enzyme digestion and how plasmids help introduce foreign DNA into bacterial hosts.*

2. *Next, you will learn about how the techniques of gel electrophoresis and the polymerase chain reaction are used to create and organize DNA fragments.*

3. *Finally, you will investigate the real-life science fiction where these techniques are used in forensics and in cloning.*

Although the techniques are trivial, the result is not. Scientists are tinkering with the exact blueprint of an entire organism, of which only a small fraction is understood. Many people fear that scientists may make unforeseen changes that could irrevocably alter our lives.

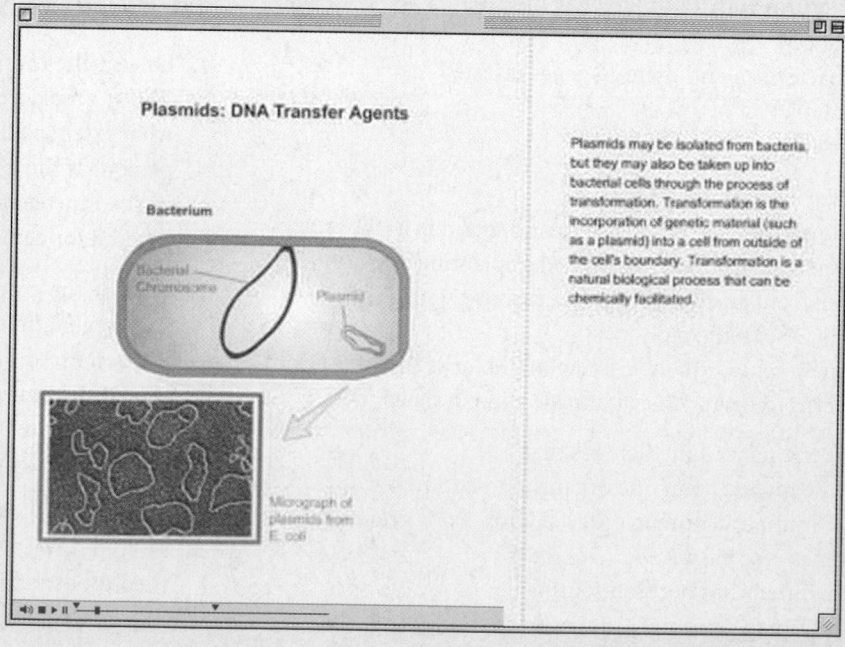

Plasmids: DNA Transfer Agents

Bacterium

Bacterial Chromosome

Plasmid

Plasmids may be isolated from bacteria, but they may also be taken up into bacterial cells through the process of transformation. Transformation is the incorporation of genetic material (such as a plasmid) into a cell from outside of the cell's boundary. Transformation is a natural biological process that can be chemically facilitated.

Micrograph of plasmids from E. coli

Investigation 1

Estimated time for completion = 15 minutes, followed by keeping a diet diary for 24 hours

Currently, 38 percent of corn, 80 percent of soybeans, and 70 percent of cotton grown in the United States are the product of genetic engineering—transferring DNA from foreign species to create plants more resistant to insect pests or herbicides. Could you be using some of these foods? Select the keyword **GE FOODS** from the Website for this *MediaLab* to read a list of genetically engineered agricultural products that are currently marketed and sold. Then select the keyword **GE DIET** to see if you are eating any of these products. Keep a diet diary for one day to see how many genetically engineered foods you may be eating.

Investigation 2

Estimated time for completion = 15 minutes

Today, biotech food is one of the most explosive environmental issues in Europe, where protesters have destroyed crops they call Frankenplants, and insisted that food labels contain warnings if they contain genetically engineered products. Mean-while, most Americans are already serving these foods for dinner. This may be the first time you have realized that fact, because the FDA has ruled that these genetically altered plants do not need to carry special labels warning consumers. Select the keywords **GE PROTESTS** and **FDA GE POLICY** from your Website for this *MediaLab* to read about both sides of the issue.

Investigation 3

Estimated time for completion = 15 minutes

Genetic engineering has already demonstrated its potential for great good, by alleviating diseases in countless hemophiliacs, diabetics, cancer sufferers, and immune-compromised children. These diseases are treated by pharmaceuticals manufactured in transgenic organisms—for example, pigs who have the human gene for human hemoglobin that is used in blood transfusions. Select the keyword **CHOCOLATE COW** on your Website for this *MediaLab* to test your knowledge of the techniques used to create transgenic organisms by creating cows that make chocolate milk. Then select the keyword **TRANSGENIC HEMOGLOBIN** to visit a more serious site describing the creation of transgenic pigs for blood donation.

COMMUNICATE YOUR RESULTS

Now that you have been introduced to the level of genetically engineered products you come into contact with daily, use the following questions to analyze and communicate your feelings on the subject of biotechnology.

Exercise 1

Estimated time for completion = 5 minutes

You created a record of your diet for 24 hours. What percentage of your diet could be from genetically engineered crops? How do you feel about it?

Exercise 2

Estimated time for completion = 20 minutes

The promise of lowering the use of pesticides and herbicides in growing genetically engineered food would appear to be a dream come true for organic farmers and environmental groups. However, environmental groups have organized a letter-writing campaign to force the FDA to inform consumers about genetically engineered food on ingredient labels. Do you think food labels should include information that identifies ingredients derived from genetically engineered foods? Form a group and compose a letter to the FDA supporting your position.

Exercise 3

Estimated time for completion = 30 minutes

What are some ethical concerns about using animals to replace human organs or to provide human medications? Write an essay defending or refuting this statement: "It is not only ethically appropriate, but it would be unethical not to pursue creating transgenic organisms to provide blood substitutes as a way to save human lives." Consider these facts: Recombinant hemoglobin from livestock would cost less than human blood, and it would be free from HIV. Currently only 5 percent of Americans are blood donors; at this rate, it is estimated that by 2030 we will have a shortfall of 4 million units of blood. Over 60 million pigs are slaughtered for food each year, and our nation's donor blood needs could be entirely met by 1.2 million pigs.

16 Charles Darwin, Evolutionary Thought, and the Evidence for Evolution

Charles Darwin.
(Section 16.2, page 311)

Fantastic voyage.
(Section 16.2, page 312)

Island of discovery.
(Section 16.4, page 314)

Charles Darwin is the person most responsible for deepening our understanding of how life evolved on Earth. Evidence uncovered from his time to ours has confirmed his insights.

Standing in a coastal redwood grove in California, we see trees stretching hundreds of feet into the air and wonder: Why are they so tall? Watching a nature program on television, we observe the exquisite plumage of the male peacock, but are puzzled that such a *cumbersome* display could exist on a creature that has to be wary of predators. Leafing through a book, we discover that the color vision of honeybees is most sensitive to the colors that exist in the very flowering plants they pollinate. We wonder: Can this be an accident?

For as long as humans have existed, people have asked questions like these. Yet for most of human history, even the most informed individuals had no way to make *sense* of the variations that nature presented. Why does the redwood have its height or the peacock its plumage? Through the middle of the nineteenth century, the answer was likely to be either a shrug of the shoulders or a statement such as: "The creator gave unique forms to living things for reasons we can't understand."

Jumping ahead to our own time, modern-day biologists would give different answers to these questions. Their replies would be something like this:

- Redwoods (and trees in general) are so tall because, over millions of years, they have been in competition with one another for the resource of sunlight. Individual trees that had the genetic capacity to grow tall got the sunlight, flourished, and thus left relatively many offspring, which made for taller trees in successive generations.

- Extravagant plumage exists on male peacocks because it is attractive to *female* peacocks when they are choosing mating partners. Such finery is indeed cumbersome and carries a price (in lack of mobility), but this price is outweighed by the value of the feathers. Over time, the peacock ancestors with more attractive plumage mated more often and thus sired more offspring than peacocks who had less impressive plumage. This made for successive generations of peacocks with more elaborate plumage.

- It is not an accident that honeybee eyesight is most sensitive to the colors that exist in the flowering plants they pollinate. Both bees and flowering plants flourish because of their interactions with one another—bees get food and flowers get pollinated. It is likely that flower color, or bee vision, or both, were *modified* over time to maximize this interaction.

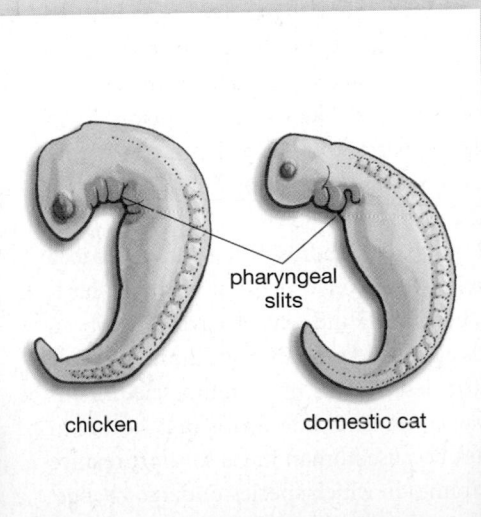

A clue to common descent.
(Section 16.6, page 316)

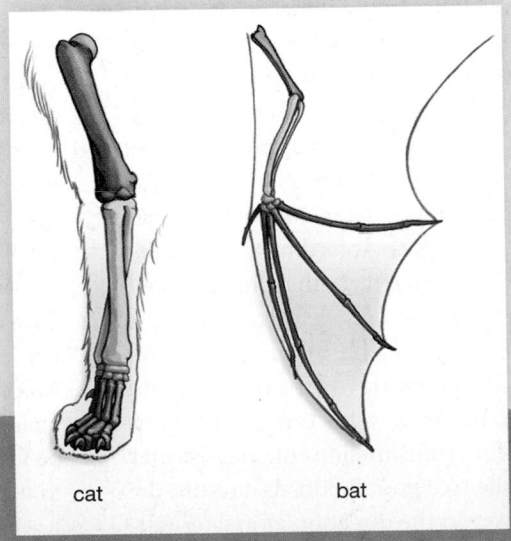

How is a cat like a bat?
(Section 16.9, page 319)

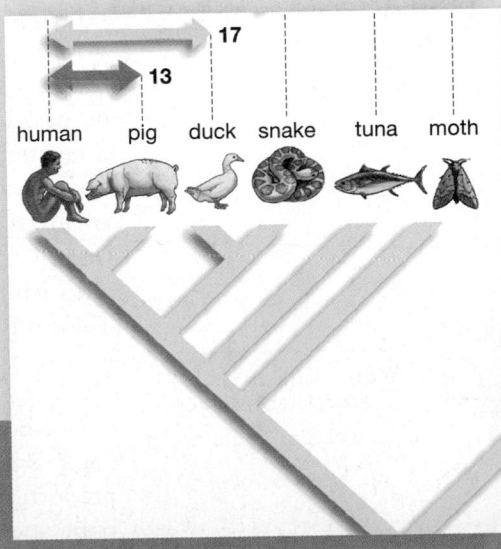

Tracking evolution.
(Section 16.9, page 322)

Comparing contemporary answers such as these to that single nineteenth-century answer, you might well ask: What is it that came *in between*, so that we no longer must simply stand in puzzled wonderment before the diversity of nature?

16.1 Evolution and Its Core Principles

What intervened was a set of intellectual breakthroughs in the mid-nineteenth century that today go under the heading of the *theory of evolution*. Two principles lie at the core of this theory.

Common Descent with Modification

One of these principles has been labeled **common descent with modification.** It holds that particular groups, or species, of living things can undergo modification in successive generations, with such change sometimes resulting in the formation of new, separate species—one species separating into two, these two then separating further. If you had a videotape of this "branching" of species and then ran it *backward*, what you'd eventually see is a reduction of all these branches into one, meaning that all living things on Earth ultimately are descended from a single, ancient ancestor. Evolution itself can have several definitions. In this chapter, we will think of it as synonymous with common descent with modification. In Chapter 17, you'll get a more technical definition of it.

Natural Selection

Descent with modification is joined to a second evolutionary principle, **natural selection**: A process in which the differential adaptation of organisms to their environment selects those traits that will be passed on with greater frequency from one generation to the next. In the redwood example, trees that grew taller were better adapted to their environment than shorter trees, in that the taller trees got more sunlight. Accordingly, the taller trees left more offspring than the shorter trees. These offspring would likewise tend to inherit the genetic capacity to grow tall, meaning they too would have more offspring than other trees of *their* generation. In this way, the trait of tallness is being *selected* for transmission to ever-greater proportions of the tree population. As a result, the population evolves in the direction of greater tallness. As you will see, there are other processes that shape evolution, but none is as important as natural selection.

The Importance of Evolution as a Concept

Evolution is not just important to biology; it is central to it. If biology were a house, evolution's principles would be the mortar binding its stones together. Why? Because all life on Earth has been shaped by evolution's key principles, natural selection and common descent with modification. This is easy to see once you think about any given organism. Take your pick: a fish, a tree, a human being? *All* of them evolved from ancestors, all of them ultimately evolved from a common ancestor, and natural selection was the primary process that shaped their evolution.

Given this, the theory of evolution provides a means for us to understand nature in all its buzzing, blooming complexity. It allows us to understand not just things that are familiar to us, such as the forms of the redwoods and peacocks, but all manner of *new* natural phenomena that come our way. When physicians observe that strains of infectious bacteria are becoming resistant to antibiotics, they don't have to ask: How could this happen? General evolutionary principles tell them that organisms evolve; that bacteria are capable of evolving very quickly (because they can produce many generations a day); and that antibiotic resistance is simply an evolutionary adaptation.

Evolution Affects Human Perspectives Regarding Life

So far-reaching is the theory of evolution that its importance stretches beyond the domain of biology and into the realm of basic human assumptions about the world. Once persuasive evidence for the theory had been amassed, it meant that human beings could no longer view themselves as something *separate* from all other living things. Common descent with modification tells us that we are descended from ancestors, just like other organisms. Thus we sit not on a pedestal, viewing the rest of nature beneath us, but rather on one tiny branch of an immense evolutionary tree.

Beyond this, evolution meant the end of the idea of a *fixed* living world, in which, for example, birds have always been birds and whales have always been whales. Birds are the descendants of dinosaurs, while whales are the descendants of medium-sized mammals that walked on land. Life-forms only *appear* to be fixed to us, because human life is so short relative to the time frames in which species undergo change.

Finally, in evolution human beings are confronted with the fact that, through natural selection, life has been shaped by a process that has no mind and no goals. Like a river that digs a canyon, natural selec-

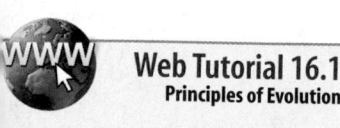

Web Tutorial 16.1
Principles of Evolution

tion shapes, but it does not design; it has no more "intentions" than does the wind. Trees that received more sunlight left more offspring, and thus trees grew taller over time. This is not a "decision" on the part of nature; it is an outcome of impersonal process. And if evolution has no consciousness, it follows that it can have no morals. This force that has so powerfully shaped the natural world is neither cruel nor kind, but simply indifferent.

16.2 Charles Darwin and the Theory of Evolution

How did such a far-reaching theory come into existence? Those who have read through the unit on genetics in this book know that the basic principles of that field were developed over the course of about a century by a large number of scientists. In contrast, a single person—nineteenth-century British naturalist Charles Darwin—is credited with bringing together the essentials of the theory of evolution (**see Figure 16.1**).

Darwin's Contribution

Darwin's contribution was twofold. First, he developed existing ideas about descent with modification while providing a large body of evidence in support of them. Second, he was the first to perceive that descent with modification is primarily driven by the process of natural selection.

To be sure, the study of evolution has been refined and expanded since Darwin. And it should be noted that before Darwin had ever published anything on his theory, a contemporary of his, fellow Englishman Alfred Russel Wallace, independently arrived at his insight about the importance of natural selection to evolution. (This makes Wallace the co-discoverer of this principle.) Yet, there is universal agreement that it is Charles Darwin who deserves primary credit for providing us with the core ideas that exist in evolutionary biology even today.

Darwin's Journey of Discovery

Darwin was born on February 12, 1809, in the country town of Shrewsbury, England. He was the son of a prosperous physician, Robert Darwin, and his wife, Susannah Wedgwood Darwin, who died when Charles was eight. Young Charles seemed destined to follow in his father's footsteps as a doctor, being sent away to the University of Edinburgh at age 16 for medical training. But he found medical school boring, and his medical career came to a halt when, in the days before anesthesia, he found it unbearable to watch surgery being performed on children. His fa-

ther then decided that he should study for the ministry. At the age of 20, Darwin set off for Cambridge University to spend three years that he later recalled as "the most joyous in my happy life." Darwin's happiness came in part from the fact that theology at Cambridge took a backseat to what had been his true passion since childhood: the study of nature. From his early years, he had collected rock, animal, and plant specimens and was an avid reader of nature books. His studies at Cambridge did yield a divinity degree, but they also gave Darwin a solid background in what we would today call life science and Earth science.

An Offer to Join the Voyage of the *Beagle*

Darwin's training, and the contacts he made at school, came together in one of the most fateful first-job offers ever extended to a recent college graduate. One of Darwin's Cambridge professors arranged to have him be the resident naturalist aboard the HMS *Beagle*, a ship that was to undertake a survey of coastal areas

Figure 16.1
Scientist of Great Insight
Charles Darwin, late in his life. (Painting by John Collier, 1883. London, National Portrait Gallery. ©Archiv/Photo Researchers.)

around the world (**see Figure 16.2**). If you look at **Figure 16.3,** you can trace the *Beagle's* journey. In addition to numerous stops on the east coast of South America (the ship's primary survey site), the *Beagle* also stopped briefly at the remote Galapagos Islands, about 970 kilometers or 600 miles west of Ecuador—a visit you'll learn more about later.

Thus did Darwin spend time on a research vessel—five years in all—beginning in England two days after Christmas 1831 and ending back there in October 1836. Just 22 when he left, he was prone to seasickness; he had to share a 10-by-15-foot room with

two other officers; he was not a traveler by nature; and the journey was dangerous (three of the *Beagle's* officers died of illness during it). Yet Darwin was happy because of the work he was doing: looking, listening, collecting, and thinking about it all. Here he is writing about a part of coastal Brazil:

> A most paradoxical mixture of sound and silence pervades the shady parts of the wood. The noise from the insects is so loud that it may be heard even in a vessel anchored several hundred feet from the shore; yet within the recesses of the forest a universal silence appears to reign. To a person fond of natural history such a day as this brings with it a deeper pleasure than he can ever hope to experience again.

Figure 16.2
What the *Beagle* Looked Like
A reconstruction of the *HMS Beagle,* sailing off the coast of Tierra del Fuego in South America.

16.3 Evolutionary Thinking before Darwin

Darwin beheld these sights and sounds at a time when change was in the air with respect to ideas about life on Earth.

Charles Lyell and Geology

The single book Darwin took with him when he boarded the *Beagle* was the first volume of Charles Lyell's *Principles of Geology,* published in 1830 and bearing a message that even Lyell's fellow scientists found hard to accept: that geological forces *still operating* could account for the changes geologists could see in the Earth's surface. (As Darwin put it, "that long lines of inland cliffs had been formed, the great valleys excavated, by the agencies which we still see at work.") Under this view, Earth had not been put into final form at a moment of cre-

Figure 16.3
Journey into History
The main mission of *HMS Beagle's* 5-year voyage of 1831–1836 was to chart some of the commercially promising waters of South America. Charles Darwin served on board the ship as a resident naturalist and companion to ship's captain Robert FitzRoy. Darwin observed nature and collected specimens throughout the ship's journey, but for purposes of the theory of evolution, the ship's most important stops came in 1835 on the Galapagos Islands, west of South America. The *Beagle* had a complex itinerary; for example, it stopped twice at the Falkland Islands off the southeast coast of South America, once in 1833 and again in 1834.

(a) Strata of sedimentary rock with fossils embedded

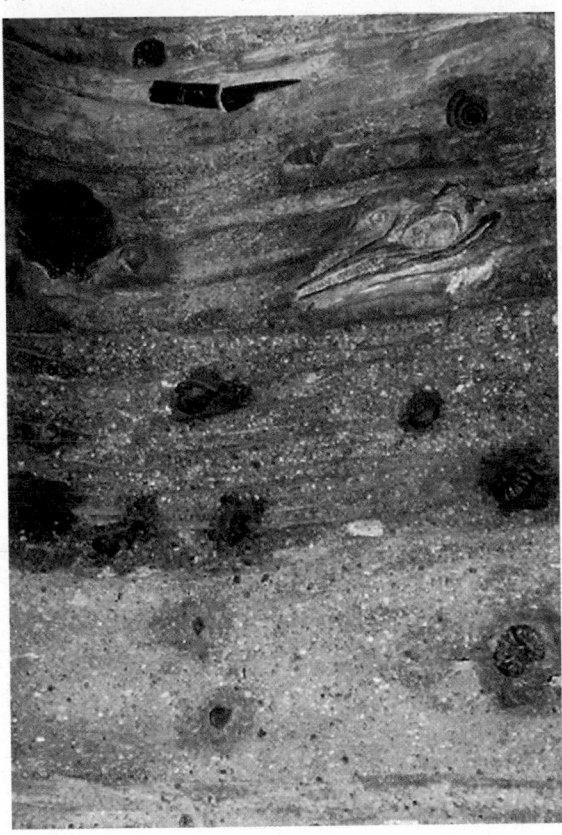

(b) Fossilized sea urchin, at least 65 million years old

Figure 16.4
Geologic Strata and Their
Contents

ation, but rather was steadily undergoing change. If such a thing were possible for the Earth itself, why not for the creatures that lived on it? (**See Figure 16.4.**)

Jean-Baptiste de Lamarck and Evolution

An idea along this line *had* been proposed, by the French naturalist Jean-Baptiste de Lamarck, in a book published in 1809. Lamarck believed that organisms changed form over generations through what has been termed the inheritance of acquired characteristics. Ducks or frogs did not originally have webbed feet, he said, but in the act of swimming they stretched out their toes in order to move more rapidly through the water. In time, membranes grew between their toes, effectively becoming webbing; critically, this characteristic was passed along to their offspring (**see Figure 16.5**). Over time, he believed, an animal would acquire enough changes that one species would diverge into two, with this branching extending all the way to human beings. In his work, Lamarck lent support to a *means* of evolution that we know today is false. (Animals don't pass along traits in accordance with the activities they carry out.) Yet note what he got right: that organisms can evolve; that one kind of organism can be ancestral to a different kind of organism.

Georges Cuvier and Extinction

Another French scientist, Georges Cuvier, in examining the fossil-laden rocks of the Paris Basin early in the nineteenth century, provided conclusive evidence of the extinction of species on Earth. This was a radical notion at the time, because many Christians believed that the creator would never allow one of his creatures to perish. (One amateur fossil collector who believed this was Thomas Jefferson.) This much about extinction Cuvier got right. However, seeing in his rock layers seeming "breaks" in the sequence of animal forms—a layer of simple forms would be followed by a layer of more complex forms as he went from older to newer layers—he held that there had been a series of catastrophes, such as floods, that wiped out life in

Figure 16.5
The Duck's Feet
Jean-Baptiste de Lamarck proposed that new species evolve through a branching evolution, which is correct. He also proposed, however, that one of the forces driving this evolution is the inheritance of acquired characteristics, which does not take place. Under Lamarck's view, common at the time, a duck got its webbed feet because of activities it carried out during its lifetime, and this change was then passed on to its offspring.

given areas, after which the creator had carried out *new* acts of creation, bringing more complex life-forms into being with each act.

If you were to survey a broad swath of scientific thought leading up to Darwin, you'd repeatedly find what you've seen with Lamarck and Cuvier: a given scientist getting things *partly* right and partly wrong (which is almost always the way in science). The result was a rich mix of scientific findings and fanciful speculation that existed in Darwin's world as he boarded the *Beagle*. He himself believed at the time that species were fixed entities; that they did not change over time.

16.4 Darwin's Insights Following the *Beagle*'s Voyage

Darwin observed and collected wherever he went, but the most important stop on his journey took place nearly four years into it, when the *Beagle* stopped for a scant five weeks at the remote series of volcanic outcroppings called the Galapagos Islands (**see Figure 16.6**). There, in the dry landscape, amidst broken pieces of black lava, he saw strange iguanas and tortoises and mockingbirds that varied from one island to another. He shot and preserved several of these mockingbird "varieties" for transport back home, along with a number of small birds that he took to be blackbirds, wrens, warblers, and finches.

Figure 16.6
The Galapagos Islands
Galapagos is Spanish for *tortoise*. A part of Ecuador, the islands are still an important site of evolutionary research. Here a giant tortoise moves through the Alcedo Volcano area on one of the islands, Isabela.

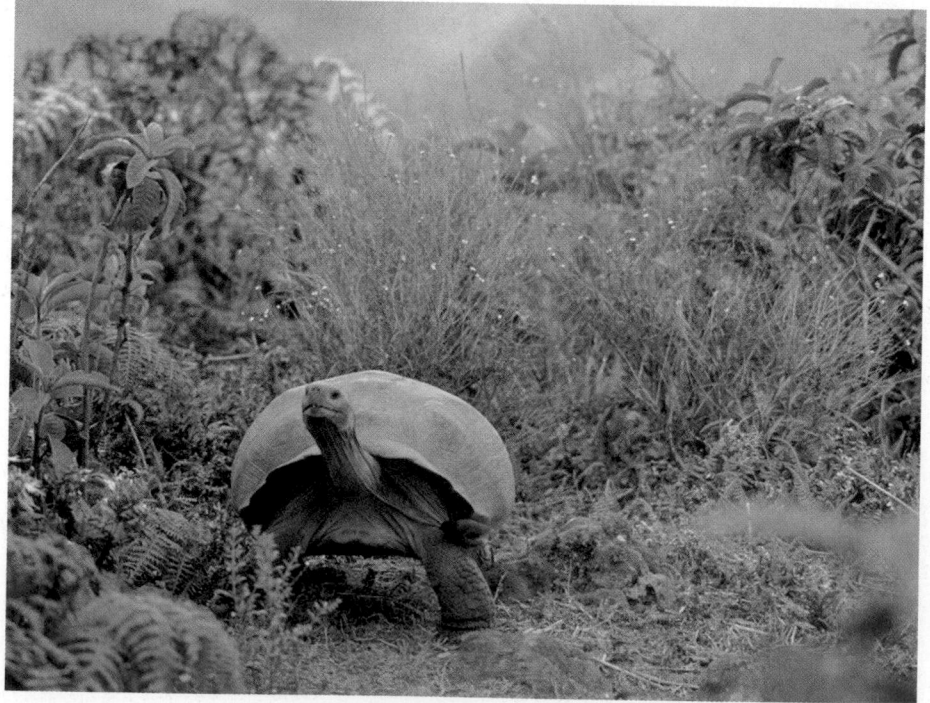

Perceiving Common Descent with Modification

Arriving back in England in October of 1836, Darwin soon donated a good deal of his *Beagle* collection to the Zoological Society of London. If there was a single most important flash of insight for him regarding descent with modification, it came when one of the Society's bird experts gave him an initial report on the birds he had collected on the Galapagos. Three of the mockingbirds were not just the "varieties" that Darwin had thought; they were separate species, as judged by the standards of the day. Beyond that, the small birds he had believed to be blackbirds, finches, wrens, and warblers were all finches—separate species of finches, each of them found nowhere but the Galapagos (**see Figure 16.7**).

With this, Darwin began to see a pattern: The Galapagos finches were related to an ancestral species that could be found on the mainland of South America, hundreds of miles to the east. Members of that ancestral species had come by air to the Galapagos and then, fanning out to separate islands, had diverged over time into separate species. Thus it was with Galapagos tortoises and iguanas and cactus plants as well; they had common mainland ancestors, but on these islands, had diverged into separate species. Darwin began to perceive the infinite branching that exists in evolution.

Perceiving Natural Selection

But what drives this branching? In England and set on a career as gentleman naturalist, Darwin married and settled in London for a time before moving to a small village south of London, where he would live out his days (**see Figure 16.8**). Two years after his homecoming, inspiration on evolution's key process came to him not from looking at nature, but from reading a book on human population and food supply—*An Essay on the Principle of Population,* by T. R. Malthus. As Darwin later wrote in his autobiography:

> I happened to read for amusement Malthus on Population, and being well prepared to appreciate the struggle for existence which everywhere goes on ... it at once struck me that under these circumstances favourable variations would tend to be preserved and unfavourable ones to be destroyed.

Thus did natural selection occur to Darwin as the driving force behind evolution. *Organisms* that had "favorable variations" were preserved (they lived and left many offspring) while those that had unfavorable variations were destroyed (they left fewer offspring or none at all). As a result, over generations, organisms evolved in the direction of the favorable variations.

You might think that, with two major insights in place—common descent with modification and natural selection—Darwin would have rushed to inform the world of them. In fact, more than 20 years were to elapse between his reading of Malthus and the 1859 publication of his great book, *On the Origin of Species by Means of Natural Selection*. In between, though incapacitated much of the time with a mysterious illness, Darwin published on geology, bred pigeons, and spent eight years studying the variations in barnacles—activities that each had relevance to his theory, and that yet constituted a kind of holding pattern for him as he contemplated informing the world of a theory that he knew would be controversial. Darwin finally got to work on what he thought would be his "big species book" in 1856.

16.5 Alfred Russel Wallace

Two years after Darwin began this labor, half a world away and unbeknownst to him, a fellow English naturalist lay in a malaria-induced delirium on an Indonesian island. Alfred Russel Wallace made a living collecting bird and butterfly specimens from the then-exotic lands of South America and Southeast Asia, selling his finds to museums and collectors. He had thought long and hard (and even published) about how species originate. Now, shivering with malarial fever in a hut in the tropical heat, with the question on his mind again, Wallace came upon the very insight that had come to Darwin 20 years earlier: Natural selection is the process that shapes evolution. Recovering from his illness, Wallace wrote out his ideas over the next few days

and sent them to a scientific hero of his in England—Charles Darwin! He asked Darwin to read his manuscript and submit it to a journal if Darwin thought it worthy.

Darwin was stunned as he faced the prospect of another man being the first to bring to the world an insight he thought was his alone. Nevertheless, he would not allow himself to be underhanded with the younger scientist. He informed some of his scientist friends about his plight, and (without informing Wallace) they arranged for both Wallace's paper and some of Darwin's letters, sketching out his ideas, to be presented at a meeting of a scientific society in London on July 1, 1858. The readings before the scientific society turned out to have little immediate effect, but they did prod Darwin into working on what would become *On the Origin of Species*, published some 16 months later. This event had a great effect. Indeed, it set off a thunderclap whose reverberations can still be heard today.

16.6 Descent with Modification Is Accepted

Sparking both scorn and praise, Darwin's ideas were fiercely debated in the years after 1859. At least within scientific circles, however, it did not take long for common descent with modification to be accepted. Fifteen years or so after *On the Origin of Species* was published, almost all naturalists had become convinced of it, and it's not hard to see why. With evolution as a framework, so many things that had previously seemed curious, or even bizarre, now

Figure 16.7
One of Darwin's Finches
Geospiza fuliginosa feeds on sedge seeds in the Galapagos Islands.

Figure 16.8
Where *On the Origin of Species* Was Written
In this study in his house in rural England, Charles Darwin conducted scientific research and wrote his ground-breaking work, *On the Origin of Species by Means of Natural Selection*.

made sense. For example, years before *Origin* was published, scientists had known that, at a certain point in their *embryonic* development, species as diverse as fish, chickens, and humans all have structures known as pharyngeal slits (**see Figure 16.9**). In fish, these structures go on to be *gill* slits; in humans they develop into the eustachian tubes, among other things. The question was: Why would such different animals share this common structure in embryonic life? With evolution, the answer became clear. All of them shared a common vertebrate *ancestor*, who had the slits. The vertebrate ancestral line had branched out into various species, yet elements of the common ancestor persisted in these different species in their embryonic stage.

In bringing together countless "loose ends" such as this, evolution became the mortar that unified the study of the living world. (It's interesting to think of biologists from this period as readers who start going over a detective novel a *second* time, saying, "Of course!" and "Why didn't I see that?") Given this, scientists had little trouble accepting the *fact* of evolution—that is, the occurrence of descent with modification. But the primary process that Darwin said was driving evolution, natural selection, was not embraced so quickly. Indeed, the twentieth century would be almost halfway over before it was generally accepted.

16.7 Darwin Doubted: The Controversy over Natural Selection

The essential stumbling block for the theory of evolution by natural selection was this. It asserted that traits can vary in ways that confer reproductive advantages on given individuals, and that these variations can be passed on from one generation to the

next. With the trees considered earlier, the trait was height, and the variation that conferred a reproductive advantage was greater height. In a given environment, therefore, added height represents a *difference* that allows some members of the species to leave more offspring than others, leading eventually to a taller species over all. But in the middle of the nineteenth century, no one could imagine how such differences could reliably be passed down over many generations. Even scientists of the time could not understand this, because they had no grasp of the field that we today call genetics.

Coming to an Understanding of Genetics

Those of you who have read the genetics section of this book may remember, from Chapter 11, that a trait such as tree height is likely to be governed by many genes working in tandem, with each of these genes coding for a protein that has some small, additive effect on height. Indeed, such multigene or "polygenic" inheritance is at work with most of the traits in living things. (See "Multiple Alleles and Polygenic Inheritance" in Chapter 11, page 221.) A tree's "height genes" will be shuffled in countless ways when tree egg and sperm are formed, and when they fuse in fertilization. As a result, gene combinations that yield particularly tall trees will come together in certain instances. In addition, outright mutations—alterations in genetic information—can take place, showing up as new physical traits, one of them being a taller tree. Most important for our purposes, whatever the genetic information is, it *persists;* it is passed on largely intact from one generation to another in the small informational packets we call genes. The result is small physical differences that can be reliably passed on from one generation to the next.

Figure 16.9
Different Embryos, Same Structure
(Adapted from M. K. Richardson, 1997.)

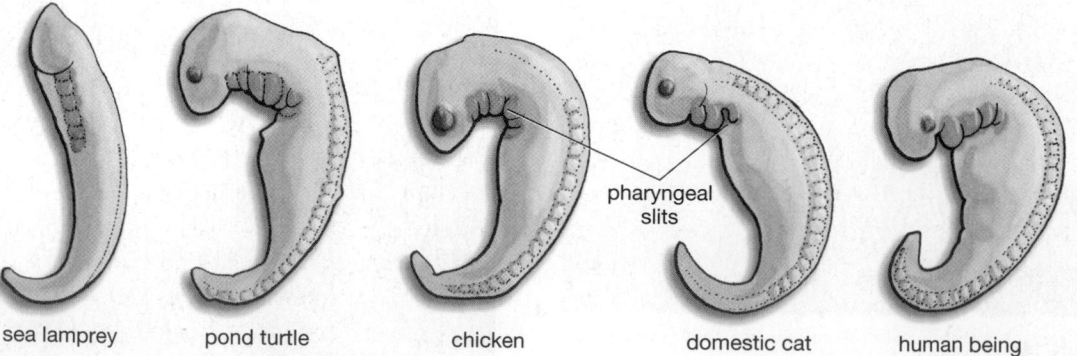

Pharyngeal slits exist in these five vertebrate animals ...

pharyngeal slits

sea lamprey   pond turtle   chicken   domestic cat   human being

... evidence that all five evolved from a common ancestor.

Darwin could not have imagined a better mechanism for carrying out natural selection as he had envisioned it. The problem was that neither he nor anyone else in his time knew that things worked like this. Most nineteenth-century scientists believed that inheritance worked through a "blending" process akin to mixing different-colored paints. If you blend red and blue paint, for example, you get something that lies halfway between them, purple. Under such a system, differences in traits would not be preserved over time; they would be averaged into oblivion. Blending would work to make groups of organisms the *same*, not to allow differences among them. How could natural selection work if there were no persistent differences to select from?

Vindicating Natural Selection's Role in Evolution

The vindication of natural selection required, first, a demonstration (by Gregor Mendel) that inheritance doesn't work by blending. Rather, it works through the transmission of the stable genetic units we now call genes. Then, in the early part of the twentieth century, came the demonstration that, through polygenic inheritance, genes could account for very small physical differences that arise within a given population. Trees come in a *range* of heights, with the differences in this range governed by the combinations of individual genes described earlier.

Darwin Triumphant: The Modern Synthesis

Advances in genetics such as this were later joined to other types of evolutionary research, such that in the period roughly from 1937 to 1950 there took place what is known as the **modern synthesis**: The convergence of several lines of biological research into a unified evolutionary theory. Taxonomists reported on how species are distributed throughout the world. Mathematical geneticists provided guidance on how evolution *could* work, given the shifting around of genes among organisms. Paleontologists studied evolution in the fossil record. Critically, these different types of scientists were involved in a process of "mutual education" with one another; the findings of geneticists, for example, were now known to taxonomists, and vice versa. The upshot was a greatly deepened understanding of how evolution works—an understanding that provided conclusive evidence for Darwin's assertions about the importance of natural selection. The architect of evolutionary theory had been vindicated nearly 100 years after publishing his great work. (For another example of evolution's explanatory power, see "The Evolution of Skin Color" on page 320.)

16.8 Opposition to the Theory of Evolution

So, why are Darwin's essential insights so widely believed to be correct? We'll now review some of the evidence for these insights, but first a word about why this is desirable. When you studied cells in this book, you did not review the "evidence for cells." Nor did you go over the "evidence for energy transfer" when studying cellular respiration, nor the "evidence for lipids" when studying biological molecules. What makes evolution different from these topics?

The False Notion of a Scientific Controversy

Evolution has an unusual status among major biological subdisciplines. Almost alone among them, its findings are regularly challenged as being unproven or simply wrong. For the average person, who can't be bothered with the details of such a controversy, these attacks make it appear that the theory of evolution is not a body of knowledge, solidly grounded in evidence, but rather a kind of scientific guess about the history of life on Earth.

What Is a Theory?

Several factors are critical in allowing the continued appearance of a "scientific debate" on the validity of the theory of evolution, when in fact none exists. The first of these has to do with a simple misunderstanding regarding terminology. You saw in Chapter 1 that, to the average person, the word *theory* implies an idea that certainly is unproven and that may be pure speculation. In science, however, a theory is a general set of principles, supported by evidence, that explains some aspect of the natural world. Accordingly, we have Isaac Newton's theory of gravitation, Albert Einstein's general theory of relativity, and many others. Lots of principles go into making up the theory of evolution, some of them on surer footing than others. Over time, however, some of these principles have achieved the status of established fact—we are as sure of them as we are sure that the Earth is round. Among these principles are the fact that evolution has indeed taken place and the fact that this has occurred over billions of years.

The Nature of Historical Evidence

A second factor that provides an opening for the opponents of evolution is the nature of the evidence for it. If you were called upon to provide the "evidence for cells" referred to earlier, a look through a microscope at some actual cells might be enough to stop this "debate" in its tracks. Conversely, one of evolution's most important manifestations—radical transformations of life-forms—can never be observed in this way, because these transformations take place over vast expanses of time. Asking to "see" the equivalent of a dinosaur evolving into a bird before you'll believe it is like asking to see the European colonization of North America before you'll acknowledge it.

Evolution is taking place right now, all around us, but the evidence for evolution is *historical* evidence to a degree that is not true of, say, the study of genetics or of photosynthesis. Any ancient historical record is fragmentary, and evolution's historical record is ancient indeed. The fossils that scientists analyze are what remain from hundreds of millions of years of weathering and decay. Such an incomplete record leaves room for a great deal of interpretation among scientists—far more than is the case in purely experimental science. This interpretation has to do, however, with the *details* of evolution, not with its core principles. It has to do with what group descended from what other; with the rate at which evolution has proceeded, or with the role that pure chance has played in evolution. It does not have to do with *whether* evolution has occurred.

16.9 The Evidence for Evolution

So, what makes scientists so sure about the core principles of evolution? In any search for truth, we are more comfortable when lines of evidence are internally consistent and then go on to agree with *other* lines of evidence. The evidence for evolution satisfies both criteria. If we were to find even a single glaring inconsistency within or between lines of evidence, the whole body of evolutionary theory would be called into question. But no such inconsistencies have turned up yet, and scientists have been looking for them for about 145 years.

Radiometric Dating

One claim of evolutionary theory, as you have seen, is that evolution proceeds at a leisurely pace, with billions of years having elapsed between the appear-

ance of life and the present. Yet how do we know that Earth isn't, say, 46,000 years old, as opposed to the 4.6 billion that scientists believe it to be? The conceptual bedrock upon which we have determined the age of the Earth and its organisms is **radiometric dating**: a technique for determining the age of objects by measuring the decay of the radioactive elements they contain. As volcanic rocks are formed, they incorporate into themselves various elements that are in their surroundings. Some of these elements are radioactive, meaning they emit energetic rays or particles and "decay" in the process.

With such decay, one element can be transformed into another, the most famous example being uranium-238, which becomes lead-206 through a long series of transformations. The critical thing is that this transformation proceeds at a fixed *rate*; it is as steady as the most accurate clock imaginable. It takes 4.5 billion years for half a given amount of uranium-238 to decay into lead-206 (hence the term *half-life*). When such a transformation takes place in a cooled rock, the original or "parent" element is trapped within the rock, as is the "daughter" element, and the atoms of both elements can be counted. Therefore, comparing the *proportion* of a parent element to the daughter element in a rock sample provides a date for the rock with a fair amount of precision. This is so because of the fixed rate, noted earlier: It takes a set amount of time for a given number of parent atoms to yield the number of daughter atoms found in a sample. There are now more than 40 different radiometric dating techniques used, each of them employing a different radioactive isotope. (See Chapter 2, page 22, for information on isotopes.) Some of these isotopes have very long half-lives (as with uranium-238), but some have relatively short half-lives. Given the range of such "radiometric clocks," scientists have been able to date objects from nearly the formation of the Earth to the present, though there are some gaps in the picture.

Fossils

Today, one line of evidence for evolution is the similarity of fossil types by sedimentary layers. Looking at the same geologic layers of sediment worldwide, scientists find similar types of fossils, with a general movement toward more complex organisms as they go up through the newer strata. In Chapter 1, it was noted that scientific claims must be *falsifiable*; they must be open to being proved false upon the discovery of new evidence. The fossil record presents a falsifiable claim. For example, creatures called trilobites (**see Figure 16.10**) had a long run on Earth, existing in the ancient oceans from about 500

Figure 16.10
Ancient Organism, Now Extinct
Shown is a fossilized trilobite, a kind of arthropod that became extinct long before the animals known as primates came to exist. This fossilized trilobite dates from about 370 million years ago and was found in present-day Morocco.

whale   cat

bat   gorilla

Figure 16.11
Four Animals, One Forelimb Structure
Whales, cats, bats, and gorillas are all descendants of a common ancestor. As a result, the bones in the forelimbs of these diverse organisms are very similar despite wide differences in function. Four sets of homologous bones are color-coded for comparison. Note that in each case there is one upper bone, joined to two intermediate bones, joined to five digits.

million years ago until some 245 million years ago, when they became extinct. By contrast, the evolutionary lineage that humans are part of, the primates, *began* about 60 million years ago. If scientists were to find, in a single fossil bed, fossils of trilobites existing side by side with those of early primates, our whole notion of evolutionary sequences would be called into question. No such incompatible pairing has happened, however, and the strong betting is it won't. Given this, the line of fossil evidence is internally consistent, but there's more. When we compare fossil placement with the dates we get from radiometric dating, we get excellent agreement *between* these two lines of evidence. We don't find trilobites embedded in sediments that turn out to be 60 million years old.

Comparative Morphology and Embryology

Morphology is the study of the physical forms that organisms take, while **embryology** is the study of how animals develop, from fertilization to birth. As it turns out, the evidence provided for evolution by comparative embryology was touched on earlier, in noting the pharyngeal slits that exist in the embryos of creatures as diverse as fish and humans.

In comparative morphology, some classic evidence for evolution is seen in the similar forelimb structures found in a very diverse group of mammals—in a whale, a cat, a bat, and a gorilla, as seen in **Figure 16.11**. Such features are said to be **homologous**, meaning the same in structure owing to inheritance from a common ancestor. Look at what exists in each case: one upper bone, joined to two intermediate bones, joined to five digits. Evolutionary biologists postulate that the four mammals evolved from a com-

mon ancestor, adapting this 1-2-5 structure over time in accordance with their varying needs.

Evidence from Gene Modification

In the genetics unit you saw that every living thing on Earth employs DNA and utilizes an almost identical "genetic code" (*this* triplet of DNA bases specifies *that* amino acid). At the very least, this means there is a unity running through all earthly life; it is also consistent with the idea that all life on Earth ultimately had a single starting point—the single common ancestor mentioned earlier.

In recent years, molecular biology has also provided another check on what scientists have long believed to be true about evolutionary relationships—about which species are more closely related and about how long it's been since they've shared a common ancestor. All genes amount to a sequence of A, T, G, and C bases along DNA's double helix. And there are some genes that do very similar things in different organisms. There is, for example, a gene called *hedgehog* that helps regulate embryonic development in the *Drosophila* fruit fly, and a gene called *sonic hedgehog* that helps regulate embryonic development in mice.

Though the *hedgehog* and *sonic hedgehog* genes are similar, we would not expect them to be identical. This is so because gene base sequences *change* over time through the process of mutation. If the *rate* of this change is constant, then mutations are like a molecular clock that's ticking, with the passage of a given amount of time, you get a set number of mutations. Given this, the longer it has been since two organisms shared a common ancestor, the greater the number of base differences we should see in the sequence of genes like *hedgehog* and *sonic hedgehog*.

The Evolution of Human Skin Color

Dark-skinned Kenyans, lighter-skinned Algerians, and fair-skinned Norwegians. Everyone knows that as you travel from the equator to the poles, human skin color tends to go from darker to lighter. But why should this be so? Two California researchers have made a case that human skin color results from a precarious position we humans are in with respect to sun exposure: if we get too much sun, we suffer one kind of damage; if we get too little, we suffer another. These competing influences, the researchers say, have worked through natural selection to make human skin lighter in some populations and darker in others.

Nina Jablonski and George Chaplin of the California Academy of Sciences believe that all human beings are involved in a balancing act with respect to sun exposure. On the one hand, people who get too little sun may have a hard time making enough vitamin D, meaning their bones cannot grow properly and their immune system starts to break down. On the other, people who get too much sun deplete their body's supply of a B vitamin called folic acid. When this happens in grown men, the result may be low sperm counts. When it happens in pregnant women, the result may be babies that have devastating "neural tube" defects—nervous system damage caused by the failure of the fetal spine to close properly during development.

The vitamin D part of this story has been understood in outline for decades. Vitamin D allows calcium to be absorbed by the intestines, and calcium, in turn, allows bones to grow strong. Human beings can get vitamin D from food, but they can also get it from sun exposure; the ultraviolet portion of sunlight prompts the body to turn cholesterol into vitamin D.

Since the 1960s, researchers have hypothesized that vitamin D's connection with sunlight has pushed human beings toward developing *lighter* skin. Why? The pigment that turns human skin dark, melanin, has the effect of blocking UV light absorption. Therefore, in a place like Scandinavia, where there is less sun during the year, it would be advantageous to have less melanin in the skin, as this would mean lighter skin, more UV absorption, and more vitamin D production. If skin color were based solely on this factor, however, we would expect all human beings to have the fair skin of Scandinavians. They clearly don't, so what other factors might be at work in pushing human beings toward *darker* coloration?

Nina Jablonski was prompted to think about this in the early 1990s because of a fortuitous set of circumstances. She was then at the University of Western Australia, whose researchers were among the first to discover the link between a lack of folic acid in expectant mothers and neural tube defects in their children. (So strong is this connection that, by the late 1990s, the U.S. and Canadian governments ordered that flour and other grain products be "fortified"

with folic acid.) While at the university, Jablonski was asked to give a lecture on the biology of human skin color. In doing research for her talk, she ran across a 1978 *Science* magazine paper which noted that fair-skinned people who are exposed to sun-like levels of ultraviolet light can suffer drastic reductions in the amount of folic acid in their system. Making a mental note of this, she went on, a few weeks later, to attend a seminar at the university on the link between folic acid and neural tube defects. Now it all came together. For some years, scientists had speculated that folic acid levels might have something to do with darker skin, but *how* could these two things be linked? Now Jablonski thought she knew: Sunlight could lower folic acid levels, and low folic acid levels could bring about neural tube defects. As an evolutionary anthropologist, she realized that these two factors could easily work with a third to bring about different human skin colors. What was the third factor? Natural selection.

Imagine two women—human mothers on the sunny African savannah, say, 50,000 years ago, both of them pregnant. One of them has enough melanin in her skin to block the sun's UV rays such that her supply of folic acid remains high. As a result she delivers a normal, healthy child. The other mother, however, has insufficient pigment for the UV blockage. As a result, she delivers a child with a neural tube defect. This second child will not live long enough to have children of its own. The first child, however, *will* go on to have children; it has been *selected*, if you will, to have offspring, who themselves are likely to be dark-skinned. When this process is repeated with many generations of children, the result is a population of dark-skinned people.

Jablonski published a short paper on the possible link between folic acid and dark skin in 1992 and there the matter stayed until 1996, when she saw a paper by an Argentine pediatrician describing how three healthy women under his care had given birth to children with neural tube defects after using tanning beds in the early weeks of their pregnancy. Spurred on by this information, Jablonski and her research colleague (and husband) George Chaplin set out to find evidence that would confirm or disprove a hypothesis they had arrived at: that skin color is a result of a push-pull between retaining enough folic acid (for nervous-system development) and making enough vitamin D (for proper bone development). From that time to this, they say, all the evidence they have uncovered supports this idea.

On the vitamin D side, a question the two researchers wanted to answer was: How much sun do you have to get for your body to start making this vitamin? Fortunately, scientists in Boston had answered that question for their area by exposing human skin, day after day, to sunlight on the roof of a hospital, and then measuring its vitamin D production. Combining information from this work

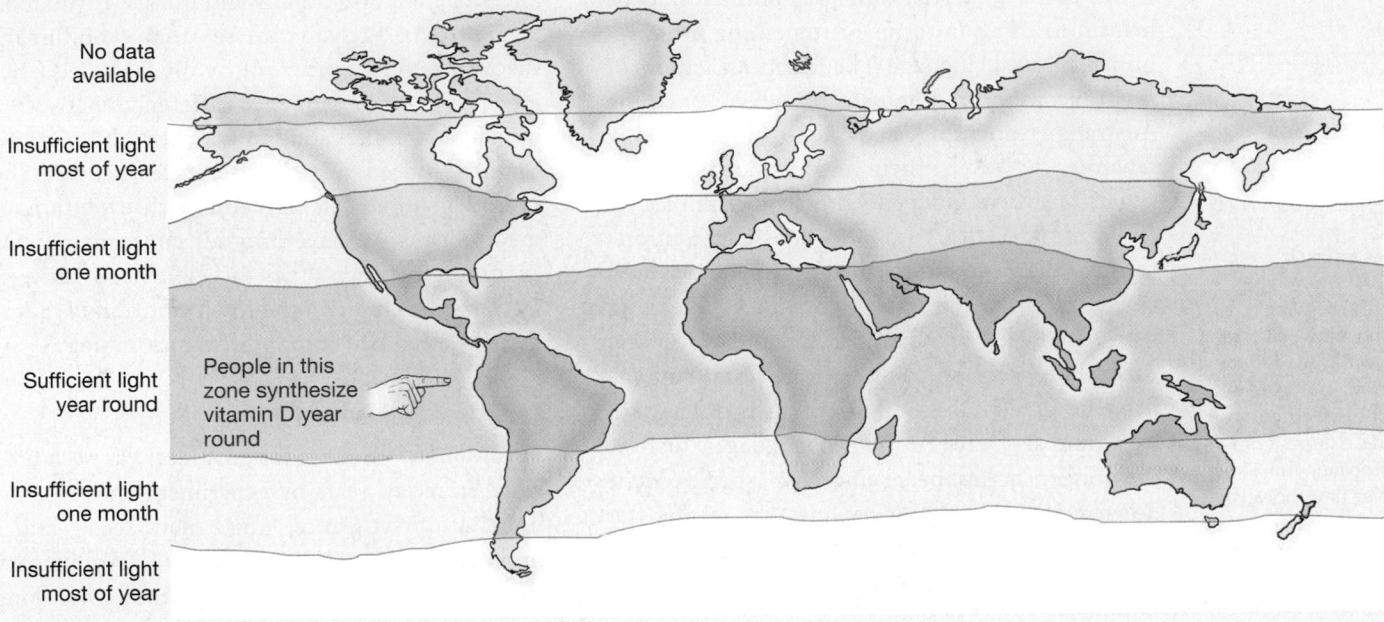

Figure 1
Ultraviolet Light and Vitamin D
Does the sun provide enough ultraviolet light to produce the vitamin D human beings need? In some parts of the world it does, but in others it does not. Note that in northern Europe there is insufficient UV light for vitamin D production most of the year, but that near the equator UV light is sufficient all year round.

with satellite data on the amount of UV radiation that falls around the world allowed Jablonski and Chaplin to construct what you see in **Figure 1**—a map dividing the world into three kinds of areas: those in which enough sunlight falls to allow people to synthesize vitamin D all year long; those in which vitamin D cannot be synthesized at least one month out of the year; and those in which there is not enough UV light, averaged throughout the year, to satisfy human vitamin D needs.

With this, the researchers were able to make predictions about how dark the skin of various peoples should be in given areas, based on the amount of UV light that falls there. Then these predictions were checked against *actual* skin colors for the areas. The result? The deeper the ancestral roots of a population in a given area, the more likely it was that this population's skin color would match the color predicted for it. The ancestors of the !Kung tribesman on the left in **Figure 2** came to the southern Africa thousands of years ago, while the ancestors of the Zulu woman on the right came to the area about 1,000 years ago from equatorial Africa. Thus, natural selection has had longer to work on the !Kung population than on the Zulu population and has given the !Kung a lighter skin color that is a better fit with the relatively cool climate of the region.

Beyond these findings, the researchers believe that their hypothesis may help explain another aspect of human skin color: why, in all cultures, men tend to have slightly darker skin than women. This difference, of perhaps 3 to 4 percent, may exist because men need slightly higher folic acid levels than women. Lack of folic acid in mice and rats causes their sperm produc-

tion to drop so much that they become infertile. Meanwhile, human males who are given folic acid experience a rise in sperm count. "Men need to protect their folic acid levels year-round," Jablonski says, whereas women are most at risk for low levels only during pregnancy. If so, then in the slight differences between male and female skin color, we can see the results of an ancient push-pull. Standing in the middle of this, acting as the judge of what works and what doesn't, is the no-nonsense process of natural selection.

Figure 2
Adaptation to UV Levels
The !Kung tribesman on the left is a member of the Khoisan ethnic group, which came to southern Africa thousands of years ago. By contrast, the woman on the right is part of the Zulu ethnic group, which came to southern Africa from equatorial Africa about 1,000 A.D. The Zulus have thus had less time to adapt to the lower levels of UV radiation that prevail in southern Africa. As a result, their skin is still the darker color common to the indigenous peoples of equatorial Africa.

To better understand this last point, it may be helpful to think in terms of something more familiar: natural language. The European settlers of Australia were predominately English. Once the Australians and English became fundamentally *separate*, however, their manner of speaking began to evolve independently. For example, we could think of the word *outback* as a "mutation" in Australian speech. Meanwhile, England would be developing its own "mutations," meaning words not used in Australia. And the longer the Australians went on being separate from the English, the greater the number of such differences we would see between the two languages. Just so, the longer it has been since two species went down separate evolutionary lines, the greater the number of base differences we would see in similar *genes* they have, as measured by the different mutations each has acquired.

This gene-modification hypothesis has been put to the test in connection with a gene that codes for an enzyme called cytochrome *c* oxidase, which exists in organisms as different as humans, moths, and yeasts. Going into this experiment, evolutionary theory predicted that there should be fewer DNA base-pair differences between the cytochrome *c* oxidase genes of, say, a human and a duck than between a human and a moth, because all the *other* evidence we had told us that humans and ducks share a more recent common

ancestor than do humans and moths. If you look at **Figure 16.12**, you can see that evolutionary theory was fully borne out by the DNA sequencing. There are 17 sequence differences between a human and a duck, but 36 between a human and a moth. Indeed, all the differences between the species pictured fall into line with evolutionary theory. Thus we have another confirmation for evolution between lines of evidence—between DNA sequencing *and* the fossil record *and* radiometric dating *and* comparative morphology.

Experimental Evidence

Finally, much evidence for evolution has been provided in recent years by experiment and observation. At first glance, this may seem rather improbable because as you've seen, evolutionary change can often be perceived only over long stretches of time. Scientists have devised clever ways to catch evolution in the act, however.

Consider the experiments of John Endler, who believed that the male guppies he was studying were being pulled in two directions by natural selection. On the one hand, those who were larger and had brighter coloration were chosen more often by females for mating. On the other, these very characteristics made the males more vulnerable to predators. Endler saw that he could test natural selection by putting some guppies in a predator-free environment. In only a few generations, the males evolved brighter coloration and larger tails. When Endler then reintroduced predators into this population, things went the other way; over several generations, the males evolved smaller tails and less brilliant colors. Both of these outcomes are precisely what evolutionary theory would predict. In both instances the guppies evolved in a direction that would maximize their reproductive success—more mates with the brighter colors in the predator-free environment, and a longer life (and hence more reproduction) with the drab coloration they evolved in the predator-laden environment.

On to How Evolution Works

Given the abundance of evidence for evolution, biologists long ago stopped asking whether it occurred. The really interesting questions for decades have been: Through what means has evolution proceeded? At what pace? In what direction, if any? These are the questions this text will address in the next three chapters.

Figure 16.12
Using Molecules to Track Evolution
Diverse organisms—such as yeast, moths, and pigs—all have genes that code for an enzyme called cytochrome *c* oxidase. These organisms inherited cytochrome *c* oxidase genes from a common ancestor many millions of years ago. Over time, however, the cytochrome *c* oxidase genes have undergone mutations that have altered the sequence of their DNA "building blocks," called bases. The longer it has been since any two species shared a common ancestor, the more differences there should be in their cytochrome *c* oxidase bases. There are 13 differences between the bases found in human cytochrome *c* oxidase genes and those found in pigs, but there are 66 differences between the human and yeast genes. (Data from Whitfield, Philip. 1993. From *So Simple a Beginning: The Book of Evolution*. New York: Macmillan: Maxwell Macmillan International.)

Number of DNA nucleotide base differences in the cytochrome *c* oxidase gene

Large number of base differences between humans and yeast — 66, 36, 31, 20, 17, 13 — Small number of base differences between humans and pigs

human pig duck snake tuna moth yeast

Chapter Review

Summary

16.1 Evolution and Its Core Principles

- Within the theory of evolution, a key principle is that of descent with modification. This principle describes the process by which species of living things can undergo modification over time, with such change sometimes resulting in the formation of new, separate species. All species on Earth have descended from other species, and a single, common ancestor lies at the base of the evolutionary tree.

- A second key principle in the theory of evolution concerns natural selection: a process in which the differential adaptation of organisms to their environment selects those traits that will be passed on with greater frequency from one generation to the next.

- The theory of evolution has an importance beyond the domain of biology. Through it, human beings have become aware that (1) they are descended from other varieties of living things, and (2) the organisms that populate the living world are not fixed entities, but instead are constantly undergoing change.
  Web Tutorial 16.1: Principles of Evolution

16.2 Charles Darwin and the Theory of Evolution

- Charles Darwin deserves primary credit for the theory of evolution. He developed existing ideas about descent with modification while providing a large body of evidence in support of them. And he was the first to perceive that natural selection is the primary process that drives evolution.

- Darwin's insights were inspired by the research he carried out during a five-year voyage he took around the world on the ship *HMS Beagle*, beginning in 1831.

16.3 Evolutionary Thinking before Darwin

- Some of Darwin's ideas can be traced to the work of Charles Lyell, Jean-Baptiste de Lamarck, and Georges Cuvier, who respectively noted the dynamic geological nature of the Earth, the possibility of descent with modification, and the extinction of species on Earth.

16.4 Darwin's Insights Following the *Beagle*'s Voyage

- Darwin understood descent with modification for several years before he comprehended that natural selection was the most important process driving it. It was his reading of a work by Malthus that sparked his realization about natural selection.

16.5 Alfred Russel Wallace

- English naturalist Alfred Russel Wallace is the co-discoverer of the principle that evolution is shaped by natural selection.

16.6 Descent with Modification Is Accepted

- Descent with modification was accepted by most scientists not long after publication of Darwin's *On the Origin of Species by Means of Natural Selection* in 1859. Scientists accepted it because it explained so many facets of the living world.

16.7 Darwin Doubted: The Controversy over Natural Selection

- The hypothesis that natural selection is the most important process underlying evolution was not generally accepted until the middle of the twentieth century. Its acceptance hinged on a modern synthesis in the theory of evolution that brought together lines of evidence from genetics, the fossil record, and the distribution of organisms throughout the world.

16.8 Opposition to the Theory of Evolution

- Even today the theory of evolution is regularly challenged as being unproven or simply wrong. One factor leading to the appearance of a "scientific debate" over evolution is confusion about the meaning of the word theory. Though the average person may equate "theory" with speculation, in science, a theory is a general set of principles, supported by evidence, that explains some aspect of the natural world.

16.9 The Evidence for Evolution

- Five principal lines of evidence are consistent with the theory of evolution. First, radiometric dating indicates that the Earth is greater than 4 billion years old. Second, the placement of fossils is consistent with the theory of evolution and with radiometric dating. Third, the theory of evolution explains the common occurrence of homologous physical structures in different organisms. Fourth, the theory of evolution is consistent with variations found in the DNA sequences of various organisms. Fifth, experimental demonstrations of evolution have been carried out in the laboratory and in nature.

Key Terms

common descent with
  modification 310

embryology 319

homologous 319

modern synthesis 317

morphology 319

natural selection 310

radiometric dating 318

Understanding the Basics

Multiple-Choice Questions (answers in the back of the book)

1. In science, a theory is
   a. an untested hypothesis
   b. a general set of principles, supported by evidence, that explains some aspect of the natural world
   c. speculation about the natural world, based on general knowledge of a field
   d. an observation
   e. the first idea proposed to explain some aspect of the natural world

2. Which of the following are central ideas in the theory of evolution by natural selection? (Select all that apply.)
   a. Organisms vary in traits that affect their reproduction.
   b. Descent with modification occurs over generations.
   c. Evolution has a goal.
   d. Traits that aid in reproduction will become more widespread in succeeding generations.
   e. Traits that are acquired during the life of an individual contribute to evolution.

3. Which of the following observations provide evidence for evolution? (Select all that apply.)
   a. Monkey and trilobite fossils are never found in the same fossil beds.
   b. Athletic training can produce an increase in muscle mass.
   c. DNA sequences of genes shared by various species vary in accordance with predictions about how related those species are.
   d. Almost all organisms use a common genetic code.
   e. Species whose adult forms look very different may have similar features in embryonic life.

4. During the formulation of his theory of evolution by natural selection, Darwin brought together ideas and results from several disciplines. Match the person with the phrase that describes his work.
   a. Lyell   catastrophic extinction and new creations explain fossil record
   b. Wallace   inheritance of acquired characters
   c. Lamarck   natural selection is differential survival or reproduction
   d. Cuvier   geological forces observable today caused changes in Earth

5. Some of the following structures are homologous with each other. Which ones are they, and which two do not belong to this group?
   a. whale flipper
   b. insect leg
   c. bat wing
   d. cat forelimb
   e. octopus tentacles

6. The discovery of _____ provided critical evidence for natural selection to be widely accepted as the chief mechanism driving evolution (select one):
   a. methods for radiometric dating
   b. extinctions in the fossil record
   c. genes as the cause of disease
   d. genes as the units of inheritance
   e. fossil bacteria

7. Important implications of the theory of evolution by natural selection include (select all that apply):
   a. All organisms, including humans, are descended from a common ancestor.
   b. The biological world is constantly evolving.
   c. Nature designs things intentionally.
   d. The characteristics of organisms are molded by an impersonal process without a goal.
   e. Humans are just a small part of the tree of life.

8. John Endler performed an experiment involving guppies in which he demonstrated evolution driven by natural selection that worked through a predator-prey relationship. Which of the following are true statements about the results of his experiments? (Select all that are correct.)
   a. Males with longer tails and brighter coloration were more frequently eaten by predator fish.
   b. Females preferred to mate with dull-colored males.
   c. When predator fish were added to a population that had not previously had predators, males with dull coloration were favored by natural selection.
   d. When predators were removed, the average brightness of male tails in the population increased.
   e. When predators were removed, the average brightness of females increased.

Brief Review

1. What is homology, and why does it provide evidence for evolution?

2. How does the evidence presented in Figure 16.12 support the conclusion that humans are more closely related to pigs than to yeast?

3. Describe two examples in which agreement among different lines of evidence provides evidence for evolution.

4. What is one observation that Darwin made in the Galapagos that influenced his thinking about evolution, and why was it important? Would he have been as likely to formulate his theory had he not had the opportunity to sail on the *Beagle*? Why or why not?

Applying Your Knowledge

1. Using evolutionary principles, explain why large ears might be expected to evolve in a terrestrial plant-eater such as a rabbit or deer, but not in an aquatic mammal such as a seal.

2. Explain the evolutionary steps by which bacteria may become resistant to antibiotics, using the core requirements for evolution by natural selection.

3. Critics of the theory of evolution say it leaves no room for human purpose, since the theory asserts that human beings evolved through a process—natural selection—that has no goals or intentions. Does the theory undercut the idea of purpose in human life?

17 *Microevolution*

Route to new genetic information.
(Section 17.3, page 330)

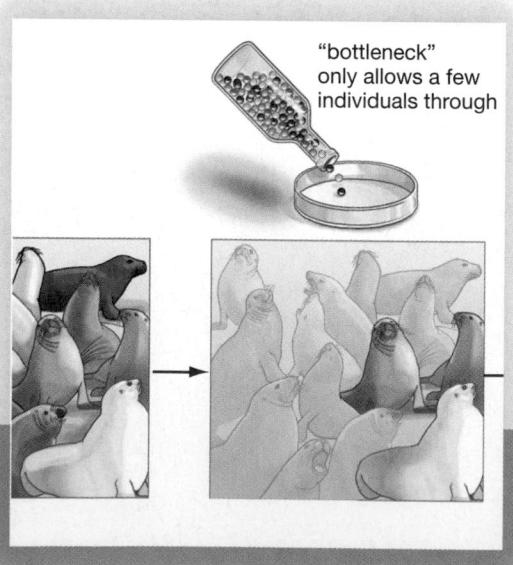

"bottleneck" only allows a few individuals through

The bottleneck effect.
(Section 17.3, page 332)

Ladies, take your pick!
(Section 17.3, page 333)

When people think of the word *evolution*, what generally comes to mind is the grand sweep of evolution: The story of how microorganisms were the first life-forms; of how dinosaurs came and went; of how human beings arose as newcomers on the planet. It is quite a story, to be sure, but to fully appreciate it we need to look first not at these *outcomes* of evolution, but rather at evolution's *processes*. How do generations of organisms become modified over time? That's the subject of this chapter. When you understand it, you'll be in a position to comprehend evolution on its grander scale.

17.1 What Is It That Evolves?

In approaching the topic of how organisms become modified over generations, the first question is: What is it that evolves? If you think about it, it's pretty clear that it is not individual organisms. A tree may inherit a mix of genes that makes it slightly taller than other trees, but if this tree is considered in isolation, it is simply one slightly taller tree. If it were to die without leaving any offspring, nothing could be said to have evolved, because no persistent quality (added height) has been passed on to any group of organisms.

In Chapter 16 you were introduced to the idea of a **species**, which can briefly be defined as a group of organisms who can successfully interbreed with one another in nature, but who don't successfully interbreed with members of other such groups. You might think that it is species—such as horses or American elm trees—that evolve. Indeed, scientists often speak this way when they refer, for example, to an amphibious mammal having evolved into today's whales. But this is a kind of shorthand whose inaccuracy becomes apparent when species are considered as they live in the real world.

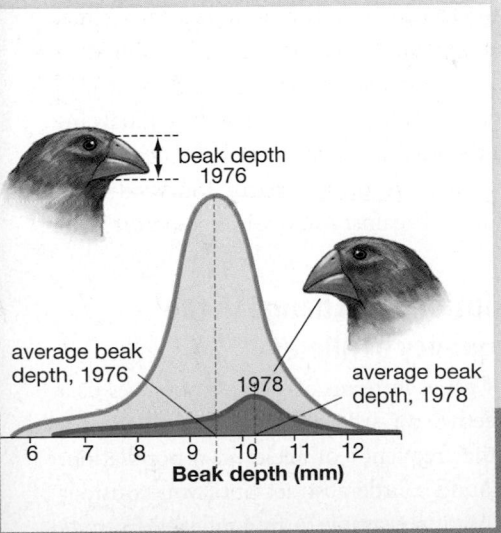

Surviving a drought.
(Section 17.4, page 336)

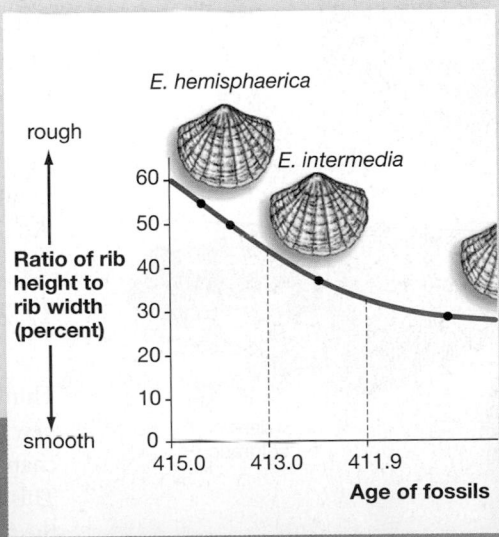

Evolving towards smoothness.
(Section 17.5, page 339)

No medium beaks.
(Section 17.5, page 339)

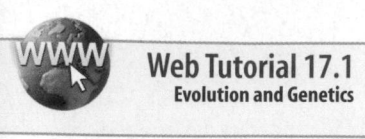

Web Tutorial 17.1
Evolution and Genetics

Figure 17.1
Evolution within Populations

(a) A hypothetical species of frog lives and interbreeds in one expanse of tropical forest.

(b) After several years of drought, the forest has been divided by an expanse of barren terrain. The single frog population has thus been divided into two populations, separated by the barren terrain. The two frog populations now have different environmental pressures, such as the kinds of predators each faces, and they no longer interbreed; after many generations their coloration diverges as they adapt to the different pressures.

Populations Are the Essential Units That Evolve

Think of a hypothetical species of frogs living in, say, equatorial Africa in a single expanse of tropical forest. Suppose that a drought persists for years, drying up the forest such that this single lush range is now broken up into two ranges separated by an expanse of barren terrain (**see Figure 17.1**). When the separation occurs, there is still only a single species of frog; but that species is now divided into two *populations* that are geographically isolated and hence no longer interbreeding. Each population now faces the natural selection pressures of its *own* environment—environments that may differ greatly even though they are nearly adjacent. One area may get more sun, while the other has a larger population of frog predators, for example. Thus, each population stands to be modified individually over time—to evolve. What is it that evolves? The essential unit that does so is a **population**, which can be defined as all the members of a species that live in a defined geographic region at a given time.

original
coloration

(a) Original environment

(b) Altered environment

lighter
coloration

population B

expanse of
barren terrain

darker
coloration

population A

The question then becomes, *how* do populations evolve? The population of frogs that has more predators may, over many generations, evolve a coloration that makes them less visible to predators. But how does this slightly different coloration come about? Through genes. A given frog may be unable to change its spots, but *generations* of frogs can have theirs changed through the shuffling, addition, and deletion of genetic material.

Genes Are the Raw Material of Evolution

Recall from Chapter 11 that the genetic makeup of any organism is its **genotype**—and that a genotype provides an underlying basis for an organism's **phenotype**, meaning any observable traits that an organism has, including its physical characteristics and behavior. Many genes are likely to be involved in producing a phenotype such as coloration. In sexually reproducing organisms, *each* of these coloration genes will likely come in two variant forms, called **alleles**, with offspring inheriting one allele from their father and one from their mother (**see Figure 17.2**). Though both alleles help code for coloration, one may result in slightly lighter or darker coloration than the other.

Genes don't just come in two allelic variants, however; they can come in many. In most species, no one organism can possess more than two alleles of a given gene, but a *population* of organisms can possess many allelic variants of the same gene (which is one reason human beings don't just come in one or two heights, but in a continuous *range* of heights.)

When the concept of a population is put together with that of genes and their alleles, the result is the concept of the **gene pool**: all the alleles that exist in a population. This gene pool is the raw material that evolution works with. If evolution were a card game, the gene pool would be its deck of cards. Individual cards (alleles) are endlessly shuffled and dealt into different "hands" (the genotypes that individuals inherit), with the strength of any given hand dependent upon what game is being played. (Survival in a drought? Survival against a new set of predators?)

17.2 Evolution as a Change in the Frequency of Alleles

Thinking of genes in terms of a gene pool gives us a new perspective on what evolution is at root: a change in the frequency of alleles in a population. This may sound a little abstract until you consider the frog coloration example. A frog inherits, from its mother and father, a coloration that allows it to evade predators slightly more successfully than other frogs of the same generation. It thus lives longer and leaves more offspring than the other frogs. It is successful in this way because of the advantageous set of alleles it inherited. Because this frog is more successful at breeding, its alleles are being passed to the *next* generation of frogs in relatively greater numbers than the alternative alleles carried by less successful frogs. Thus, this frog's alleles are increasing in frequency in the frog population. In looking at any example of evolution in a population over time, you would find this kind of change in allele frequency as its basis, assuming a stable environment.

With this perspective in mind, you're ready for a definition of **microevolution**: A change of allele frequencies in a population over a relatively short period of time. Why the *micro* in microevolution? Because evolution *within* a population is evolution at its smallest scale. This conception of microevolution allows you to understand the formal definition of evolution promised to you last chapter. **Evolution** can be defined as any genetically based phenotypic change in a population of organisms over successive generations. Taking a step back, the large-scale *patterns* produced by microevolution eventually become visible, as with the evolution of, say, mammals from reptiles. This is **macroevolution**, defined as evolution that results in the formation of new species or other groupings of living things.

17.3 Five Agents of Microevolution

So, what is it that causes microevolution? Put another way, what causes the frequency of alleles to change in a population? In the frog-coloration example, a familiar process was at work: natural selection. The frog's coloration allowed the frog to evade predators, thus helping the frog to produce more offspring than did other frogs. This particular coloration was thus *selected* for greater transmission to future generations. With this selection, allele frequencies began to be altered in the frog population. Over generations, the alleles for protective coloration increased relative to other sets of alleles.

Natural selection is not the only process that can change allele frequencies, however. There are five "agents" of microevolution that can alter allele frequencies in populations. These are mutation, gene flow, genetic drift, nonrandom mating, and natural selection. You can see these processes summarized in **Table 17.1**. (For a review of how scientists tell whether one of these processes actually is at work changing allele frequencies, see "Detecting Evolution: The Hardy-Weinberg Principle," on p. 340.) We'll now look at each of these agents of change in turn.

Figure 17.2
Genetic Basis of Evolution
Many genes can produce a trait such as body coloration, and each gene often has many alleles or variants. Each individual in a population, however, can possess only two alleles for each gene, one allele inherited from its mother and one inherited from its father. The two frogs in the figure both have maternal and paternal copies of chromosome 3 that house genes for coloration. The chromosomes of the two frogs may differ, however, in the allelic variants they have of these genes. The frog with dark coloration may possess alleles a_1 and a_2 while the light-colored frog may possess alleles a_2 and a_4 of this same gene.

Table 17.1 Agents of Change: Five Forces That Can Bring about Change in Allele Frequencies in a Population

Agent	Description
Mutation	Alteration in an organism's DNA; generally has no effect or a harmful effect. But beneficial or "adaptive" mutations are indispensable to evolution.
Gene flow	The movement of alleles from one population to another. Occurs when individuals move between populations or when one population of a species joins another, assuming the second population has different allele frequencies than the first.
Genetic drift	Chance alteration of gene frequencies in a population. Most strongly affects small populations. Can occur when populations are reduced to small numbers (the bottleneck effect) or when a few individuals from a population migrate to a new, isolated location and start a new population (the founder effect).
Nonrandom mating	Occurs when one member of a population is not equally likely to mate with any other member. Includes sexual selection, in which members of a population choose mates based on the traits the mates exhibit.
Natural selection	Some individuals will be more successful than others in surviving and hence reproducing, owing to traits that give them a better "fit" with their environment. The alleles of those who reproduce more will increase in frequency in a population.

Mutations: Alterations in the Makeup of DNA

As you saw in the genetics unit, a mutation is any permanent alteration in an organism's DNA. Some of these alterations are heritable, meaning they can be passed on to future generations. Mutations can be as small as a change in a single base pair in the DNA chain (a point mutation) or as large as the addition or deletion of a whole chromosome or parts of it. Whatever the case, a mutation is a change in the informational set an organism possesses (**see Figure 17.3**). Looked at one way, it is a change in one or more alleles.

The rate of mutation is very low in most organisms; during cell division in humans, it might be just one DNA base pair per billion. And of the mutations that do arise, very few are beneficial or "adaptive." Most do nothing, and many are harmful to organisms. Thus mutations usually are not working to *further* survival and reproduction, as the frog-coloration alleles did. Given this, they generally are not likely to appear with greater frequency in successive generations. The upshot is that mutations are not likely to account for much of the change in allele frequency that is observed in any population.

But a few mutations occur that are adaptive. These genetic alterations are something like creative thinkers in a society: They are rare but very important. Such mutations are the only means by which *new* genetic information comes into being—by which new proteins are produced that can modify the form or capabilities of an organism. The evolution of eyes or wings had to involve mutations. No amount of shuffling of *existing* genes could get the living world from no eyes to eyes. Of course, no mutation can bring about a feature such as eyes in a single step; such changes are the result of many mutations, followed by rounds of genetic shuffling and natural selection, generally over millions of years.

Gene Flow: When One Population Joins Another

Allele frequencies in a population can also change with the mating that can occur after the arrival of members from a *different* population. This is the second microevolutionary agent, **gene flow**, meaning the movement of genes from one population to another. Such movement takes place through **migration**, which is the movement of individuals from one population into the territory of another. Some populations of a species may truly be isolated, such as those on remote islands, but migration and the gene flow that goes with it are the rule rather than the exception in nature. It may seem at first glance that migration would be limited to animal species, but this isn't so. Mature plants may not move, but plant seeds and pollen do; they are carried to often-distant locations by wind and animals (**see Figure 17.4**). Of course, for a migrating population to alter allele frequencies of another population, its gene pool must be different from that of the population it is joining.

Genetic Drift: The Instability of Small Populations

To an extent that may surprise you, evolution turns out to be a matter of chance. You can almost see the dice rolling in the third microevolutionary agent, genetic drift. Imagine a hypothetical population of 10,000 individuals. An allele in this gene pool is carried by one out of ten of them, meaning that 1,000 individuals carry it. Now imagine that some disease sweeps over the population, killing half of it. Say that this allele had nothing to do with the disease, so the illness might be expected to decimate the allele carriers in rough accordance with their proportion in the population. If this were the case, 5,000 individuals in the population would survive, and 1 in

Web Tutorial 17.2
Agents of Change

(a)

Normal   **Point mutation**

correct
nucleotide sequence   incorrect
nucleotide sequence

(b)

Normal   **Deletion**

complete
chromosome 5   incomplete
chromosome 5

Figure 17.3
Basis of New Genetic Information
A mutation is any permanent alteration in an organism's DNA. Examples of mutations include **(a)** point mutations, in which the nucleotide sequence is incorrect and **(b)** deletions, in which part of a chromosome is missing.

(a) Hawaiian silversword

(b) Tarweeds in California

North America

gene flow

Hawaiian Islands

Pacific Ocean

Figure 17.4
Migration in Plants
Brought about by volcanic eruptions, the Hawaiian Islands have always been surrounded by the Pacific Ocean. Therefore all the plant species existing on the islands today are descended from species that were introduced to the islands through one means or another—human activity, wind currents, water currents, or animal dispersal of seeds and pollen. **(a)** Hawaiian silverswords are derived from **(b)** a lineage of California plants commonly known as tarweeds.

10—or about 500 of them—could be expected to be carriers of this allele. Let us say, however, that just by chance, *550* of the allele carriers were killed, thus leaving the surviving population of 5,000 with only 450 allele carriers. In that scenario, the frequency of the allele in this population would drop from 10 percent to 9 percent (**see Figure 17.5a**).

Now for the critical step. Imagine the same allele, with the same 1-in-10 frequency, only now in a population of *10*. There is now but a single carrier of the allele, and that individual may not be one of the 5 members of the population to survive the disease. In this case, the frequency of this allele drops from 10 percent to zero (**see Figure 17.5b**). It can be replaced

(a) Large population = 10,000
(allele carriers in red)

allele frequency = $\frac{1,000}{10,000}$ = 10%

50% of population survives, including 450 allele carriers

allele frequency = $\frac{450}{5,000}$ = 9%

little change in allele frequency
(no alleles lost)

(b) Small population = 10
(allele carriers in red)

allele frequency = $\frac{1}{10}$ = 10%

50% of population survives, with no allele carrier among them

allele frequency = $\frac{0}{5}$ = 0%

dramatic change in allele frequency
(potential to lose one allele)

Figure 17.5
Genetic Drift

(a) In a hypothetical population of 10,000 individuals, 1 in 10 carries a given allele. The population loses half its members to a disease, including 550 individuals who carried the allele. The frequency of the allele in the population thus drops from 10 percent to 9 percent.

(b) A population of 10 with the same allele frequency likewise loses half its members to a disease. Because the one member of the population who carried the allele is not a survivor, the frequency of the allele in the population drops from 10 percent to zero.

only by a mutation (which is extremely unlikely) or by migration from another population. Assuming that neither happens, no matter how this population grows in the future, in genetic terms it will be a different population than the original in that it lost this allele. The allele might be helpful or harmful, but its adaptive value doesn't matter. It has been eliminated strictly through chance. This is an example of **genetic drift**: the chance alteration of allele frequencies in a population, with such alterations having the greatest impact on small populations. It is true that some genetic drift has taken place in the larger population, but consider how small the effect is. The allele simply went from a 10 percent frequency to a 9 percent, with no loss of allele. Chance events can have much greater effects on small populations than on large ones.

Two scenarios, common in evolutionary history, produce the small populations that are most strongly affected by genetic drift. Populations can be greatly reduced through disease or natural catastrophe; or a small subset of a population can migrate elsewhere and start a new population. The first of these scenarios is called the *bottleneck effect*; the second is called the *founder effect*. Let's have a look at both of them in turn.

The Bottleneck Effect and Genetic Drift

The **bottleneck effect** can be defined as a change in allele frequencies in a population due to chance following a sharp reduction in the population's size. Real populations, or even species, can go through dramatic reductions in numbers. For example,

northern elephant seals, which can be found off the Pacific coast of North America, were prized for the oil their blubber yielded and thus were hunted so heavily that by the 1890s, fewer than 50 animals remained. Thanks to species protection measures, the seals' numbers have rebounded somewhat in recent decades. But genetically, all the members of this species are very similar today, because they all descended from the few seals who made it through the nineteenth-century bottleneck. What occurs in these reductions is a "sampling" of the original population—the "sample" being those who survived the devastation (**see Figure 17.6**).

The reason allele frequencies change in such an event has to do with the nature of probability and sample size. Imagine a box filled with M&M's candies, with equal numbers of red, green, and yellow M&M's inside. You close your eyes and grab a handful of M&M's and pull out 12. With such a small sample, you might get, say, six reds, four greens, and two yellows, rather than the four-of-each-kind that would be expected from probability. If you pulled out *120* M&M's, conversely, your reds, greens, and yellows would be much more likely to approach the 40-of-each-kind that would be expected. In just such a way, a small sample of *alleles* is likely to yield a gene pool that's different from the distribution found in the larger population.

The Founder Effect and Genetic Drift

Genetic drift can also result from the **founder effect**, which is simply a way of stating that when a small subpopulation *migrates* to a new area to start a new

Figure 17.6
The Bottleneck Effect
Northern elephant seals were hunted so heavily by humans that in the 1890s, fewer than 50 animals remained. The population has grown from the few survivors (represented here by the three seals in the second frame), but the resulting genetic diversity of this population is very low. (Seal coloration for illustrative purposes only.)

"bottleneck" only allows a few individuals through

Original population, original allele frequency.

Hunting of seals in late 1800s greatly reduced population size.

Surviving population had different allele frequency and little genetic diversity.

This different allele frequency is reflected in today's population.

population, it is likely to bring with it only a portion of the original population's gene pool. This is another kind of sampling of the gene pool, in other words; but in this case it's caused by the migration of a few individuals rather than the survival of only a few. This sample of the gene pool now becomes the founding gene pool of a new population. As such, it can have a great effect; whatever genes exist in it become the genetic set that is passed on to all future generations, as long as this population stays isolated.

The power of the founder effect can be seen most clearly when a founding population brings with it the alleles for rare genetic diseases. There is, for example, a very rare genetic affliction of the eyes called *cornea plana* that results in a misshapen cornea—the first structure of the eye through which light passes. The result can be impaired close-range vision and a general clouding of eyesight. Cornea plana is known to affect only 113 people worldwide. The strange thing is that 78 of these people are in Finland, most of them in an area in northern Finland. Current research indicates that about 400 years ago, a small population arrived in this isolated area, with at least one member of this population carrying the recessive allele that causes this affliction. Since then, this allele has continued to profoundly affect subsequent generations in the area. This will always be the case if the descendants of a founder population stay relatively isolated over time—that is, if the descendents breed mostly among themselves.

From this and the earlier examples, you may have perceived by now that there is an inherent value in genetic diversity; you can read about this in "Lessons from the Cocker Spaniel," on page 334.

Nonrandom Mating: When Mating Is Uneven across a Population

You've looked at mutation, gene flow, and genetic drift as agents of change with respect to allele frequencies in a population. Now let's look at a fourth agent, **nonrandom mating**, which is simply mating in which a given member of a population is not equally likely to mate with any other given member.

Some forms of nonrandom mating do not directly affect allele frequencies. Such is the case with **assortative mating**, which occurs when males and females that share a particular characteristic tend to mate with one another. Humans practice assortative mating, in that short individuals tend to pick short mates, while tall individuals tend to pick tall mates. Such mating tends to bring similar alleles together ("short" with short, etc.) but it does not directly alter the frequency of alleles in a population.

Nonrandom mating does affect allele frequency, however, when some members of a population mate *more* than others. In practice, this is mating based on *phenotype*, which you may recall is any observable trait in an organism, including differences in appearance and behavior. It is the appearance of particularly nice plumage on a male peacock that makes female peacocks choose it for mating, rather than another male, while it is the behavior of strutting and chest-swelling in a male sage grouse that causes a succession of female grouse to mate with it rather than nearby competitors (**see Figure 17.7**). These are examples of **sexual selection**, defined as a form of nonrandom mating that produces differential reproductive success, based on differential success in obtaining mating partners. It's easy to see that if one male mates four times as much as the average male of his generation, his alleles stand to increase proportionately in the next generation.

Differential mating success among members of one sex in a species often is based on choices made by members of the opposite sex in that species. In general, it is females who are doing the choosing in these situations. Differential mating success can also, however, be based on differences in combative abilities that give individuals of one sex (generally males) greater access to members of the opposite sex. Sexual selection has something in common with natural selection, in that both processes result in some individuals passing along more of their genes to future generations than others. But while natural selection has to do with differential survival and reproductive capacity (and hence reproduction), sexual selection has to do with differential *mating* (and hence reproduction). In sum, sexual selection is a form of nonrandom mating that can affect allele frequencies in populations.

Figure 17.7
Sexual Selection
Individuals in some species choose their mates based on appearance or behavior. Female sage grouses prefer to mate with males who put on superior "displays," which include sounds, a kind of strutting, and a puffing up of their chests. Here, two males display before females on a sage grouse breeding ground.

Lessons from the Cocker Spaniel:
The Price of Inbreeding

"Marry afar" is advice given by the pygmy men of Africa, by which they mean, "marry a woman who lives far from your home." The pygmies point to the hunting rights a man acquires in distant territory by marrying a woman from a remote region, but there is another benefit to this practice as well: It helps ensure genetic diversity among the pygmies. When pygmies from remote locations marry, it cuts down on the chances of "inbreeding," meaning mating in which close relatives produce offspring. Inbreeding can have harmful effects not only in humans, but in any species.

What are these effects? Well, consider what has happened in the United States with "purebred" dogs (**Figure 1**), which is to say dogs that over many generations have been bred solely with members of their own breed (cocker spaniels mating only with cocker spaniels, and so forth). In the mid-1990s it was estimated that up to one-fourth of all U.S. purebred dogs had some sort of serious genetic defect—ranging from improper joint formation to heart defects, to deafness. We also have a good deal of experimental evidence from other animals on the effect of inbreeding. In one instance, a group of white-footed mice that had been inbred and then let out into the natural environment survived at only 56 percent the rate of a group of genetically diverse mice. As already noted, negative biological outcomes can appear in humans too;

for that reason, many Western societies have made it illegal for first cousins to marry (although the actual harm that comes from first-cousin marriages has recently been judged to be minimal).

Why does inbreeding cause such trouble? As you've seen, every organism has a whole series of genes, almost all of which come in two variant forms, or alleles, one allele inherited from the father and one from the mother. In all organisms, a very small proportion of these alleles is potentially harmful or even lethal. But in most instances such alleles are recessive. *One* defective allele is not enough to cause trouble, because the second differs from it and provides sufficient information for the organism to function properly. Alleles that differ are said to be heterozygous, whereas alleles that are identical are homozygous.

In the mid-1990s it was estimated that up to one-fourth of all U.S. purebred dogs had some sort of serious genetic defect.

So how do these biological facts play out in inbreeding? Imagine two seals, brother and sister, that have mated together because their population has been so reduced. Imagine that their mother had a recessive allele that brings about a heart defect, and that this allele oc-

Natural Selection: Evolution's Adaptive Mechanism

You've already gone over a good deal about natural selection in this review of evolution, but it's time now to look at it as the last agent of change in microevolution. First, what is meant by natural selection? Here is a short definition: **Natural selection** is a process in which the differential adaptation of organisms to their environment selects those traits that will be passed on with greater frequency from one generation to the next. What does this mean in practice? Here is what biologist Julian Huxley had to say about it almost 60 years ago.

Since there is a struggle for existence among individuals, and since these individuals are not all alike, some of the variations among them will be advantageous in the struggle for survival, others unfavorable. Consequently, a higher proportion of individuals with favorable variations will on the average survive, a higher proportion of those with unfavorable variations will die or fail to reproduce themselves.

By this process, the traits of those who are more successful in reproducing will become more widespread in a population—as the alleles that bring about these traits increase in frequency from one generation to the next.

A key concept here is that of **adaptation**, meaning a modification in the structure or behavior of organisms over generations in response to environmental change. Environmental change may come to a population (through streams drying up, for example), or a population may come to environmental change (through migration). Either way, natural selection is the process that pushes populations to adapt to new environmental conditions. The frog population noted at the outset of the chapter adapted to a new predator, for example, by evolving a darker coloration.

Among the five agents of microevolution, natural selection is the only one that consistently works to adapt organisms to their environment. Genetic drift is random; it could as easily work against an adaptive trait as for it. Although mutations can have an adaptive effect, they more often have no effect or even a

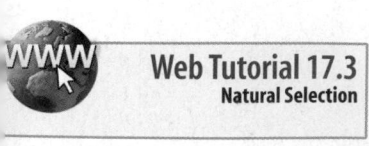

Web Tutorial 17.3
Natural Selection

curs in only one out of every hundred seals. There is a one-in-two chance that the mother will pass this allele on to any one of her offspring, and let's say it happened with the male and female here: Both brother and sister have inherited the defective allele. When *they* mate, the chance that either of them will pass along the defective allele to their offspring is likewise one out of two. More important, however, the chance that *both* of them will pass the allele along—producing an offspring with two defective alleles—is one out of four. If, on the other hand, the brother had mated with an unrelated member of the population, the chances of this union passing along two copies of this defective allele are one in *four hundred*.* Why the difference? Because the unrelated female had only a one-in-a-hundred chance of having the allele in the first place, whereas the sister had a one-in-two chance of getting it from her mother.

The essence of this lesson, as you may have realized, is that inbreeding has brought together identical alleles—the recessive homozygous alleles that are required for many genetic diseases. Random breeding, meanwhile, tends to keep homozygous alleles apart. It tends to preserve genetic diversity, to put it another way.

You might think from this that there are no uses for genetic *similarity*, but consider what human beings have been doing for centuries

with dog breeding. Cocker spaniels did not come about by accident. Dogs that had cocker spaniel features were bred together for many generations, ultimately giving us today's dog. It was the *novel features* of the spaniel that people wanted, and novel features are often the result of homozygous recessives coming together. While the breeding done to produce American cocker spaniels has resulted in dogs with cute, floppy ears, the unintended effect of this practice is a breed that is also prone to ear infections and a "rage syndrome" that can result in unprovoked aggression, even against familiar humans.

We don't value the seal's heart condition the way we value the spaniel's floppy ears, but looked at one way it too is a novel feature, made possible by the pairing of homozygous recessives.

Figure 1
Result of Generations of Controlled Breeding

---

*Remembering the rule of multiplication from Chapter 11, to calculate the odds of passing on two defective alleles in the random mating example, take the son's chances of passing along the allele (1 in 2, or 50 percent, or 0.5) × 0.01 (the chance of his female partner *having* the allele) × 0.5 (the chance of her passing the allele along). This works out to 0.0025, which equals 1 in 400. For the brother-and-sister mating, the figures are 0.5 (the chance of the brother passing it along) × 0.5 (the chance of the sister passing it along), which equals 0.25—or 1 in 4.

---

negative effect. Gene flow doesn't necessarily bring in genes that are better suited to a given environment. And nonrandom mating has to do with the ways mating partners are selected, not with matching individuals to environment.

Natural selection is, however, constantly working to modify organisms in accordance with the environment around them. As such, it is generally regarded as the most important agent in having shaped the natural world—in having given zebras their stripes and flowers their fragrance.

17.4 What Is Evolutionary Fitness?

Even the strongest supporters of natural selection as a shaping force would not maintain that it is working to produce perfect organisms. The concept of "fitness" is helpful here, if only to clear up some misconceptions. To a biologist, **fitness** means the success of an organism in passing on its genes to offspring *relative* to other members of its population at a particular time. An organism cannot be deemed "fit," even if it has 1,000 offspring. It can only have *more or*

less fitness relative to other members of its population (who might have 900 or 1,100 offspring). This has to do, once again, with allele frequencies in a gene pool. No matter how many offspring an individual has, its allele frequencies will increase in a population only if it has *more* offspring than other members of its generation. Thus, fitness is a measure of impact on allele frequencies in a population.

This concept then gets us to the notion of "survival of the fittest," and the misunderstandings that arise from it. The phrase can be taken to imply the existence of superior beings; that is, organisms that are simply "better" than their counterparts, with images of being faster, more muscular, or smarter coming to mind. In fact, however, evolutionary fitness tells us nothing about organisms being *generally* superior, and it certainly tells us nothing about the value of any particular capacity, be it brawn or brain. All it tells us about are organisms who are better than others in their population at passing along their genes in a given environment at a given time. An accurate phrase, as others have pointed out, would not be "survival of the fittest,"

Figure 17.8
A Product of Evolution on the Galapagos
A male of the finch species *Geospiza fortis*, which is native to the Galapagos Islands.

Figure 17.9
Who Survives in a Drought?
A large percentage of the population of *Geospiza fortis* died on a Galapagos Island, Daphne Major, during a drought in 1977. Peter and Rosemary Grant observed in 1978 that individuals who survived the drought had a greater average beak depth than average individuals surveyed before the drought, in 1976. Individuals with larger beaks were better able to crack open the large, tough seeds that were available during the drought. The offspring of the survivors likewise had larger average beak size than did the population before the drought. Thus, evolution through natural selection was observed in just a few years on the island.

but rather "survival of those who fit—for now." Let's look at a real-life example of natural selection to see why this is true.

Galapagos Finches: The Studies of Peter and Rosemary Grant

When Charles Darwin stopped at the Galapagos Islands in 1835, some of the animal varieties he collected were various species of finches. Over the years, biologists kept coming back to "Darwin's finches" because of the very qualities Darwin found in them: They seemed to present a textbook case of evolution, with their 13 species having evolved from a single ancestral species on the South American mainland. Yet for more than 100 years after Darwin, it was a puzzle for scientists to figure out how Darwin's posited mechanism of evolu-

tion, natural selection, could have been at work with the finches. This changed beginning in the 1970s, when the husband-and-wife team of Peter and Rosemary Grant began a painstakingly detailed study of the birds.

Natural selection in the finches came into sharp focus in 1977, when a tiny Galapagos island, Daphne Major, suffered a severe drought. Rain that normally begins in January and lasts through July scarcely came at all that year. This was a disaster for the island's two species of finches; in January 1977 there were 1,300 of them, but by December the number had plunged to fewer than 300. Daphne's medium-sized ground finch, *Geospiza fortis*, lost 85 percent of its population in this calamity. The staple of this bird's diet is plant seeds. When times get tough, as in the drought, the size and shape of *G. fortis* beaks—their beak "morphology"— begins to define what one bird can eat as opposed to another (**see Figure 17.8**). In *G. fortis*, larger body size and deeper beaks turned out to make all the difference between life and death in the drought of 1977. Measuring the beaks of *G. fortis* who survived the drought, the Grant team found they were larger than the beaks of the population before the drought by an average of some 6 percent. This was a difference of about half a millimeter, or roughly two-hundredths of an inch; by such a difference were the survivors able to get into large, tough seeds and make it through the catastrophe, eventually to reproduce (**see Figure 17.9**).

This is natural selection in action, but there is more to be learned from the Grant study, which is to say *evolution* made visible. The Grant team knew that beak depth had a high "heritability" in the finches, meaning that beak depth is largely under genetic control. As it turned out, the *offspring* of the drought survivors had beaks that were 4 to 5 percent deeper than the average of the population before the drought. In other words, the drought had preferentially preserved those alleles from the starting population that brought about deeper beaks, and the result was a population that evolved in this direction.

But the Grant study yielded one more lesson. In 1984–1985 there was pressure in the opposite direction: Few large seeds and an abundance of small seeds provided an advantage to *smaller* birds, and it was they who survived this event in disproportionate numbers.

Lessons from *G. fortis*

So, where is the "fittest" bird in all this? There isn't any. Evolution among the finches was not marching toward some generally superior bird. Different traits were simply favored under different environmental conditions. Secondly, there is no evolutionary movement toward combativeness or general intelligence here. Survival had to do with size—and not necessarily *larger* size at that. Looking around in nature, it's

Figure 17.9 chart:

beak depth
1976

average beak depth, 1976

1978

average beak depth, 1978

Number of individuals

Beak depth (mm)

Shift of average beak depth following drought

true that some showcase species, such as lions and mountain gorillas, gain success in reproduction by being aggressive. And it's true that our own species owes such success as it has had to intelligence. But in most instances, it is not brawn or brain that make the difference; it is something as seemingly benign as beak depth and its fit with the environment.

Finally, consider how imperfect natural selection is at the genetic level. Suppose the smaller *G. fortis* that disproportionately died off in 1977 also disproportionately carried an allele that would have aided just slightly in, say, long-distance flying. In the long run this might have been an adaptive trait, but it wouldn't matter. The flight allele would have been *reduced* in frequency in the population (as the smaller birds died off) because flight distance didn't matter in 1977, beak depth did. Evolution operates on the phenotypes of whole organisms, not individual genes. As such, it does not work to spread *all* adaptive

traits more broadly. Instead, the destiny of each trait is tied to the constellation of traits the organism possesses. Genes are "team players," in other words, that can only do as well as the team they came in on.

17.5 Three Modes of Natural Selection

In what directions can natural selection push evolution? As noted in Chapter 11, a character such as human height is under the control of many different genes and is thus **polygenic**. Such polygenic characters tend to be "continuously variable." There are not one or two or three human heights, but an innumerable number of them in a range. (See "Multiple Alleles and Polygenic Inheritance" on p. 221.) When natural selection operates on characters that are polygenic and continuously variable, it can proceed in any of three ways. The essential question here is: Does natural selection favor what is average in a given character, or what is extreme? (**See Figure 17.10.**)

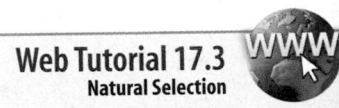

Web Tutorial 17.3
Natural Selection

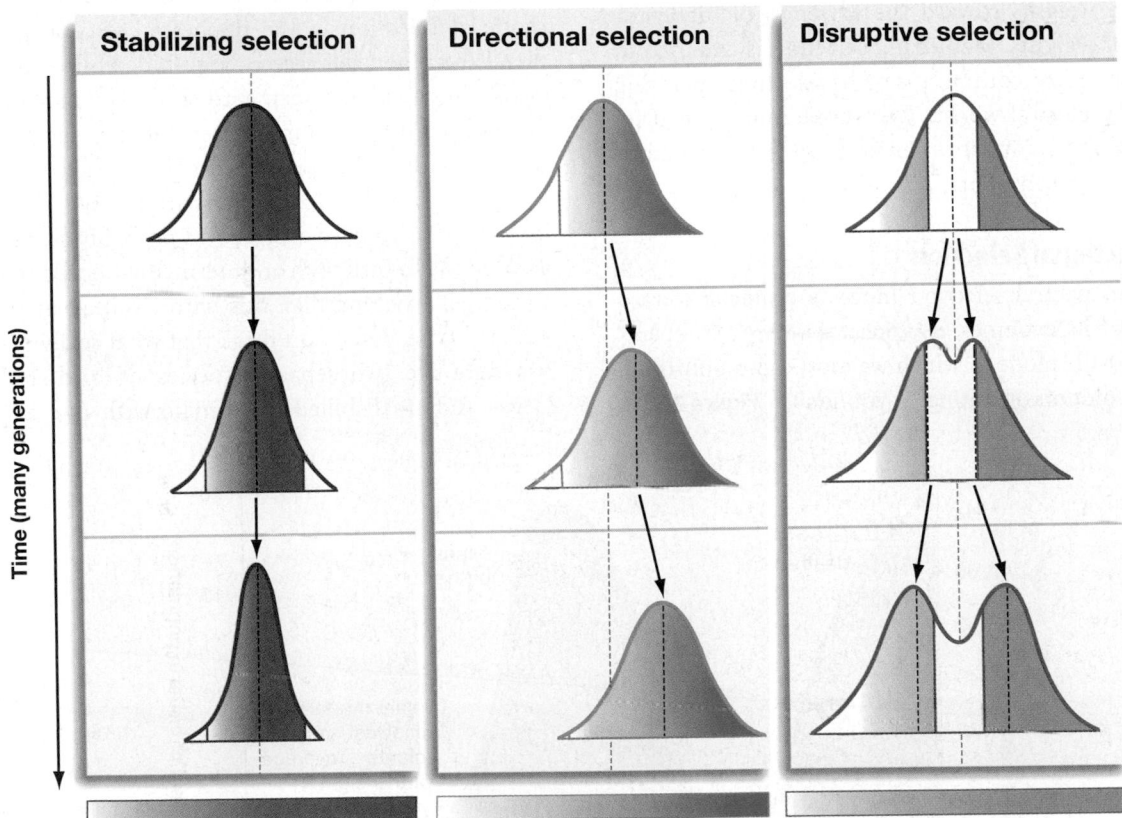

Range of a particular characteristic (in this instance, lightness or darkness of coloration)

In stabilizing selection, individuals who possess extreme values of a characteristic—here, both the lightest and the darkest colors—are selected against and die or fail to reproduce. Over succeeding generations, an increasing proportion of the population becomes average in coloration.

In directional selection, one of the extremes of a characteristic is better suited to the environment, meaning that individuals at the other extreme are selected against. Over succeeding generations, the coloration of the population moves in a directon–in this case toward darker coloration.

In disruptive selection, individuals with average coloration are selected against and die. Over succeeding generations, part of the population becomes lighter, while part becomes darker, meaning the range of color variation in the population has increased.

Figure 17.10
Three Modes of Natural Selection

Stabilizing Selection

In **stabilizing selection**, intermediate forms of a given character are favored over extreme forms. A clear example of this is human birth weights. If you look at **Figure 17.11**, you can see, first, the weights that human babies tend to be. Notice that there are not only relatively few 3-pound babies, but relatively few 9-pound babies as well. A great proportion of birth weights fall at the average or "mean" of a little less than 7 pounds. Now look at the infant-mortality curve. Infant deaths are highest at both extremes of birth weight; low-birth-weight babies *and* high-birth-weight babies are more at risk than are average-birth-weight babies (though low birth weight poses the greater risk). Put another way, the children most likely to survive (and reproduce) are those carrying alleles for intermediate birth weights. Thus, natural selection is working to make intermediate weights even more common. It is not working to move birth weights toward the extremes of higher or lower weights. Stabilizing selection is assumed to be the most common type of selection operating in the natural world. This should not be surprising, because most organisms are well adapted to their environments.

Directional Selection

When natural selection moves a character toward *one* of its extremes, **directional selection** is in operation—the mode in which we most commonly think of evolution operating. If you look at **Figure 17.12**,

you can see an example of directional selection that took place over a very long period of time—about 10 million years—involving evolution toward smoothness of shells in certain species of brachiopods.

Disruptive Selection

When natural selection moves a character toward *both* of its extremes, the result is **disruptive selection**, which appears to occur much less frequently in nature than the other two modes of natural selection. This mode of selection is visible in the beaks of yet another kind of finch. A species of these birds found in West Africa (*Pyrenestes ostrinus*) has a beak that comes in only two sizes. Thomas Bates Smith, who has studied the birds, has observed that if human height followed this pattern, there would be some Americans who are 4 to 5 feet tall, and some who are 6 to 7 feet tall, but no one who is 5 to 6 feet tall (**see Figure 17.13**).

The environmental condition that leads to this mode of selection in the finches is, once again, diet. When food gets scarce, large-billed birds specialize in cracking a very hard seed, while small-billed birds begin feeding on several soft varieties of seed, with each type of bird being able to outcompete the other for its special variety. Given how these birds have evolved, it's probably safe to assume that a bird with an intermediate-sized bill would get less food than one with a bill of either extreme type. You might think that what really exists here are two separate species of bird, but large- and small-billed birds mate with one an-

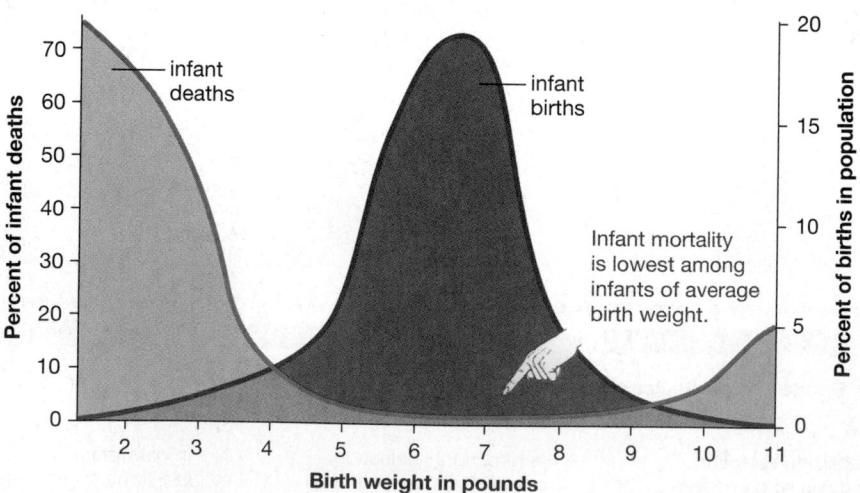

Figure 17.11
Stabilizing Selection: Human Birth Weights and Infant Mortality
Note that infant deaths are more prevalent at the upper and lower extremes of infant birth weights.

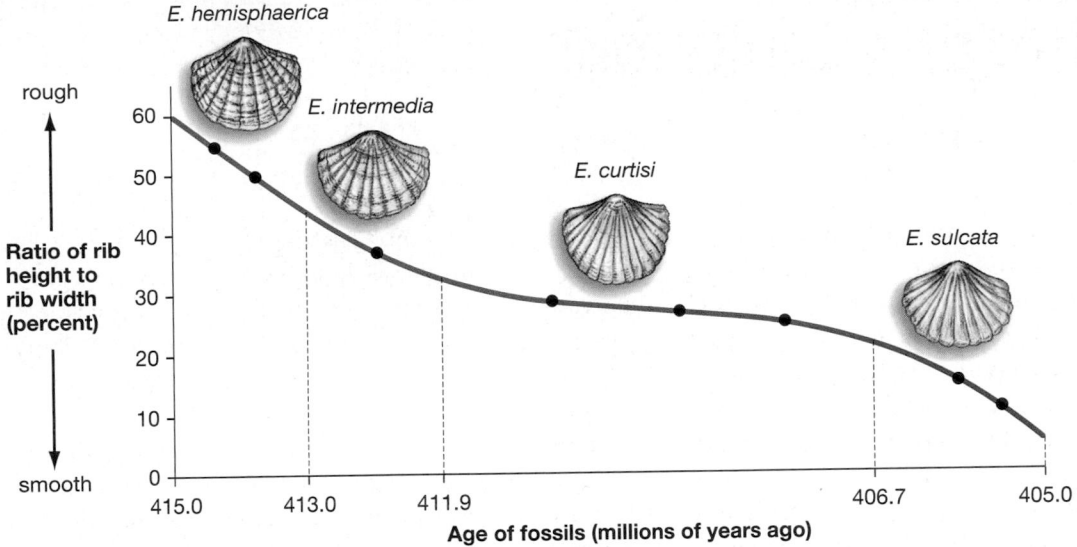

Figure 17.12
Directional Selection: Evolving toward Smoothness
Over a period of 10 million years, beginning about 415 million years ago, directional selection operated on these brachiopods, such that their shells became progressively smoother over time. (Adapted from Ziegler, A.A. 1966. The Silurian Brachiopod *Eocoelia hemisphaerica* (J. de C. Sowerby) *Palaeontology* 9:523-524. Reproduced by permission of The Palaeontological Association.)

Figure 17.13
Disruptive Selection: Evolution That Favors Extremes in Two Directions
Finches of the species *Pyrenestes ostrinus*, found in West Africa. Birds of this species have beaks that come in two distinct sizes—large and small.

other. Bill size seems to be under the control of a single genetic factor, so that bills are able to come out either large or small. This genotype was presumably shaped by natural selection over generations, such that any alleles for intermediate-sized bills were weeded out.

On to the Origin of Species

Stabilizing selection does what it says: It stabilizes given traits of a population, thereby keeping it a single entity. However, both disruptive and directional selection can serve as the basis for speciation—for bringing about the transformation of a single species into one or more *different* species. How is it, though, that such speciation works? And how do we classify the huge number of species that are the outcome of evolution's myriad branchings? These are the subjects of the next chapter.

Detecting Evolution:
The Hardy-Weinberg Principle

How can scientists tell when evolution is taking place? As you've seen, evolution always entails a change in allele frequencies in a population. And there are five primary "agents" of allele frequency change—processes such as genetic drift and natural selection. So, how can scientists tell when one of these agents actually is at work? They can employ a procedure—a kind of test—devised early in the twentieth century by a British mathematician, Godfrey Hardy, and a German physician, Wilhelm Weinberg. Working independently, Hardy and Weinberg arrived at an insight, now called the Hardy-Weinberg principle, that today is used routinely not just in evolutionary biology, but in fields like public health as well.

The starting point for the Hardy-Weinberg principle is its assertion that, in a sufficiently large population, allele frequencies will *not* change unless one of the five agents is at work. A population whose alleles are not being altered by one of the agents is said to be at *Hardy-Weinberg equilibrium*—a state in which the population's allele frequencies remain constant, generation after generation. Let's walk through an example now that shows how a population at Hardy-Weinberg equilibrium stays the same. Along the way, you'll see the kinds of insights that are made possible by the Hardy-Weinberg principle.

Imagine a hypothetical species of plant whose flowers come in two colors, red and white, and say that we are looking at a population of 100 of these individuals. Further, we know from breeding these plants that red results from a dominant allele for a gene, while white results from a recessive allele for that gene. In the tradition of Mendel, we signify the red allele as *R* and white as *r*. Finally, we have sampled this population's DNA and found that *R* has a frequency of 78 percent, while *r* has a frequency of 22 percent. What does "frequency" mean in this context? It means that if we looked at the gametes of these plants—their eggs and sperm—78 percent of them would contain a dominant *R* allele while 22 percent would contain a recessive *r* allele. Now, keep your eye on this 78:22 allele frequency, because that is what we are primarily interested in. The essential question is: When we look at the *next* generation of plants, will the allele frequencies in it remain 78:22? Or do allele frequencies change merely by virtue of reproduction? Hardy and Weinberg say no; in a large population, an agent of change is required to alter allele frequencies. Let's find out.

To see what happens in the next generation, we need to calculate the *genotypes* of our starting generation, which Hardy-Weinberg allows us to do. What is a genotype in this context? Each egg or sperm may contain only *one* allele for a gene—in this case *R* or *r*—but in diploid organisms such as flowering plants, egg and sperm fuse in fertilization, thus bringing alleles together to create an organism that has *two* alleles for each gene—one from the male, one from the female. In this context, then, genotype means the combination of *R* and *r* alleles that an individual possesses. Now, what possible combinations could a given individual have? An easy way to visualize them is to return once again to the Punnett squares that were used in Chapter 11. Imagine, in the parental generation, a male and female that are both heterozygous for the color gene—each of them has one *R* allele and one *r* allele. In this case, our Punnett square looks like this:

Possible genotypes in the population

So, the possible genotypes in the next generation are *RR*, *Rr*, or *rr*. (Further, note that because the *r* allele is recessive, only the *rr* genotype yields white flowers, signified by the white flower in the square.) But how do we calculate the genotype frequencies that will come about from this range of possibilities? How do we calculate what percentage of the population will have the *RR* genotype, for example, based on the allele frequencies we started with? The heart of the Hardy-Weinberg principle, the Hardy-Weinberg equation, allows us to do this. To generalize beyond the case of our red- or white-flowered plants, let's use a couple of conventional symbols in the equation: *p* will stand for the frequency of the more common *R* allele, and *q* will stand for the frequency of the less common *r* allele. The Hardy-Weinberg equation then looks like this:

The Hardy-Weinberg equation...	p^2	+	$2pq$	+	q^2
Applied to this example means...	R^2	+	$2Rr$	+	r^2
And this yields the...	frequency of the RR genotype	+	frequency of the Rr genotype	+	frequency of the rr genotype

This formula says: If we take the frequency of the R allele and square it (R^2), we will get the frequency of the RR genotype in the population. Well, we know that the frequency of the R allele in the population is .78, so this means .78 × .78, which equals .6084. This is another way of saying that 60.84 percent of the population should have the genotype RR. Next, doubling $R \times r$ ($2Rr$) yields the genotype frequency of individuals that are heterozygous for the gene, meaning the plants that are the Rr genotype. This works out to 34.32 percent of the population. Finally, taking r times itself (r^2) yields the frequency of the rr genotype, which works out to be 4.84 percent of the population.

Though this formula has allowed us to work out genotype frequencies for the population, we have, in a sense, merely taken Mr. Hardy and Mr. Weinberg's word that things work like this. A question you may well be asking yourself at this point is: *why* do these particular mathematical steps reveal this information? Why, for example, should squaring the percentage of R alleles in the population tell us what the percentage of RR genotypes is in this population? To grasp the logic that's at work, it's important to understand that the Hardy-Weinberg equation deals with *probabilities*. It starts with a set of allele frequencies in a population and then says, given these, what are the probabilities of getting various genotypes? The particular steps that the formula uses to answer this question can perhaps best be understood by looking at a more familiar set of probabilities, those that come with flipping a coin.

When we flip a coin, what is the probability that heads or tails will come up? Fifty-fifty or 0.5, right? Now, what are the chances that when we flip two coins, *both* will come up heads? The answer is contained in something covered in Chapter 11, the rule of multiplication (see page 214). This rule states that the probability of any two events happening is the *product* of their respective probabilities. In the case of our coin toss, this means the respective

probabilities of each of our tosses, 0.5 × 0.5, which equals 0.25—so we have a 25 percent chance of getting two heads.

Now, it's important to recognize that the 50–50 odds that exist in coin tossing actually stem from an initial set of *frequencies*. There are heads, which have a frequency of 0.5 in our population of coins, and there are tails, which likewise have a 0.5 frequency. But there are other frequencies besides 0.5—and other probability exercises to run besides flipping coins. In our *flowering plant* population, we have frequencies of *alleles*. These are 0.78 for R and 0.22 for r. If the probability of getting one R allele is 0.78, then the rule of multiplication tells us that the probability of getting two R alleles in an organism is 0.78 × 0.78, or to put it another way, 0.78^2. This latter number is simply a specific value for p^2 in the Hardy-Weinberg equation of $p^2 + 2pq + q^2$. You can easily see that the rr genotype frequency is similarly derived from q^2, which in this case means 0.22^2.

But what about the middle term in the equation, the $2pq$ that gives us the percentage of Rr genotypes in the plant population? Look at the Punnett square again; you can see that there are *two* ways a plant could end up with the Rr genotype—male R and female r, or female R and male r. When an outcome can occur in two or more different ways, something called the rule of addition comes into play. It states that the probability of a given outcome is the *sum* of its respective probabilities. In this case, the probability of getting one R and one r is 0.78 × 0.22. But this same probability can happen in two different ways (Rr and rR), so the formula for it is (0.78 × 0.22) + (0.78 × 0.22). Of course, since we are adding two identical numbers, another way of stating this is 2 × (0.78 × 0.22). Thus do we get the middle term of the Hardy-Weinberg equation, $2pq$, where the p is 0.78 and the q is 0.22. With this, we can see the basis of the whole equation, which plays out this way in our example:

The Hardy-Weinberg equation...	p^2	+	$2pq$	+	q^2
In this case means...	0.78 × 0.78	+	2 × (0.78 × 0.22)	+	0.22 × 0.22
Which yields the answers...	0.6084	+	0.3432	+	0.0484

(continued)

(continued from previous page)

So, we can see from this example that 60.84 percent of the population is likely to be *RR*, 34.32 percent *Rr*, and 4.84 percent *rr*.

Now we have only one more step to go, which is to calculate expected allele frequencies in the *second* generation, based on the first-generation genotype frequencies that we got. This is just a matter of unpacking, we might say, the genotype frequencies. To calculate what the *R* allele frequencies will be, we start by dividing the 0.3432 *Rr* genotype in half—yielding 0.1716—because half the alleles in this genotype are, by definition, *R* (and the other half *r*). Then we add to this number all of the .6084 alleles in the *RR* genotype, because all these alleles are *R*. To get the frequency of *r* alleles, we take the 0.1716 figure and add to it the 0.0484 figure for the *rr* genotype. Thus:

$$R = 0.6084 + 0.1716 = 0.78$$
$$r = 0.0484 + 0.1716 = 0.22$$

Hopefully, these last two figures look familiar because they are, in fact, the allele frequencies we started with in the first generation. Thus Hardy-Weinberg has demonstrated that allele frequencies do not change from one generation to the next simply as a matter of reproduction.

To grasp the importance of this lack of change, imagine that you are a geneticist who has sampled a human population for the frequency of an allele suspected of contributing to disease in young adults. With your allele frequencies in hand, you run your Hardy-Weinberg equation to get the genotype frequencies for this population. Now the critical step: You sample the population for its *actual* genotype frequencies and find that they don't match the Hardy-Weinberg prediction. You discover that there are fewer people in the population with the homozygous recessive (*qq*) genotype frequency than predicted by Hardy-Weinberg. This means that at least one of the agents noted earlier in the chapter has to be at work. One or more of them is disturbing Hardy-Weinberg equilibrium. Among the possibilities is that the agent at work is natural selection. The *qq* genotype may in fact contribute to people to dying younger, and hence having fewer children. This could be why there are fewer people with this genotype in the population than predicted by the formula.

Hardy-Weinberg, then, can tell scientists not only about evolution, but about human health. Indeed, it can reveal information about human health in several ways. Recall that, in our flowering plant example, the equation showed that 4.84 percent of the population should have the *rr* genotype. This turns out to be another way of saying that 4.84 percent of the flowers should be *white*. All the rest should be red, because all the rest have at least one dominant red allele (*R*), which is all it takes to be red. In a simple genetic scenario such as this, then, Hardy-Weinberg allowed us to derive not only genotype frequencies, but phenotype frequencies—what percentage of plants will have what characteristics. Phenotypes can, however, just as easily have to with human health as flower color. What percentage of the U.S. caucasian population is likely to have cystic fibrosis, as a result of being homozygous for its recessive allele? The answer, 1 in every 2,000 individuals, is provided by Hardy-Weinberg.

Chapter Review

Summary

17.1 What Is It That Evolves?

- A population is defined as all the members of a species living in a defined geographical area at a given time. Natural selection acts on individuals, but it is populations that evolve.

17.2 Evolution as a Change in the Frequency of Alleles

- Genes may be found in variant forms, called alleles. In most species, no individual will possess more than two alleles for a given gene, but a population may possess many such allelic variants. The sum total of alleles in a population is referred to as that population's gene pool.

- The basis of evolution is a change in the frequency of alleles within a population (a phenomenon that includes the appearance of new alleles through mutation). Evolution at this level is called microevolution.
Web Tutorial 17.1: Evolution and Genetics

17.3 Five Agents of Microevolution

- Five evolutionary forces can result in changes in allele frequencies within a population. These agents of microevolution are mutation, gene flow, genetic drift, nonrandom mating, and natural selection.

- Mutation happens fairly infrequently, and most mutations either have no effect or are harmful; yet rare adaptive mutations are vital to evolution in that they are the only means by which entirely new genetic information comes into being.

- Gene flow, the movement of genes from one population to another, takes place through migration, meaning the movement of individuals from one population into the territory of another.

- Genetic drift, the chance alteration of allele frequencies in a population, has its greatest effects on small populations. Genetic drift works on small populations in two ways. The first of these is the bottleneck effect, defined as a change in allele frequencies due to chance during a sharp reduction in a population's size. The second is the founder effect: the fact that when a small subpopulation migrates to a new area to start a new population, it is likely to bring with it only a portion of the original population's gene pool.

- Nonrandom mating is mating in which a given member of a population is not equally likely to mate with any other member. Sexual selection is a form of nonrandom mating that can directly affect the frequency of alleles in a gene pool. It occurs when differences in reproductive success arise because of differential success in mating.

- Some individuals will be more successful than others in surviving and hence reproducing, owing to traits that better adapt them to their environment. This phenomenon is known as natural selection. Natural selection is the only agent of microevolution that consistently acts to adapt organisms to their environments. As such, it is generally regarded as the most powerful force underlying evolution.

Web Tutorial 17.2: Agents of Change

17.4 What Is Evolutionary Fitness?

- The phrase "survival of the fittest" is misleading, because it implies that evolution works to produce generally superior beings who would be successful competitors in any environment. Evolutionary fitness, however, has to do only with the relative reproductive success of individuals in a given environment at a given time. One individual is said to be more fit than another to the extent that it has more offspring than another. But individuals are not born with invariable levels of fitness; instead, fitness can change in accordance with changes in the surrounding environment.

17.5 Three Modes of Natural Selection

- Natural selection has three modes: stabilizing selection, directional selection, and disruptive selection. Stabilizing selection moves a given character in a population toward intermediate forms and hence tends to preserve the status quo; directional se-

lection moves a given character toward one of its extreme forms; and disruptive selection moves a given character toward two extreme forms.

Web Tutorial 17.3: Natural Selection

Key Terms

adaptation	334	genotype	328
allele	328	macroevolution	329
assortative mating	333	microevolution	329
bottleneck effect	332	migration	330
directional selection	338	natural selection	334
disruptive selection	338	nonrandom mating	333
evolution	329	phenotype	328
fitness	335	polygenic	337
founder effect	332	population	328
gene flow	330	sexual selection	333
gene pool	328	species	327
genetic drift	332	stabilizing selection	338

Understanding the Basics

Multiple-Choice Questions (answers in the back of the book)

1. In most populations of living things, each individual has ____ copies of each gene, which may be the same or different allelic variants. A population may have _____ allelic variants for a given gene.
   a. 1, 2
   b. 2, 4
   c. 2, many
   d. 1, many
   e. 2, 2

2. Match the terms with their meanings:
   a. gene pool   a variant form of a gene
   b. allele   the set of all alleles in a population
   c. allele frequency   the genetic makeup of an organism
   d. genotype   exchange of genes between populations
   e. gene flow   the relative representation of a given form of a gene in a population

3. Which of the following statements is true of microevolution? (Select all that apply.)

a. It is a change in allele frequency within populations.
b. It is caused by inheritance of characters acquired during the life of an organism.
c. It is seen when some allelic variants cause individuals to have increased reproductive success.
d. It always leads to adaptation.
e. It is caused only by natural selection.

4. Agents of change in allele frequency in populations include (select all that apply):
   a. genetic drift
   b. meiosis
   c. mutation
   d. segregation
   e. natural selection

5. Agents that consistently produce adaptive evolution (adaptation) include (select all that apply):
   a. genetic drift
   b. mutation
   c. meiosis
   d. natural selection
   e. gene flow

6. Mutations are (select all that apply):
   a. generally beneficial
   b. changes in the genetic material that may be inherited
   c. always caused by changes in single base pairs of DNA
   d. the ultimate source of new genetic variation
   e. prone to occur with great frequency

7. In stabilizing selection, _____ individuals have the highest fitness:
   a. large
   b. intermediate
   c. bright
   d. extreme
   e. small

8. Match the agent of evolution to its description:
   a. mutation — chance alterations of allele frequencies in a small population
   b. gene flow — a process in which the fit of an organism with its environment selects those traits that will be passed on with greater frequency from one generation to the next
   c. natural selection — movement of alleles between populations by migration
   d. genetic drift — genetic drift due to a few colonizing drift genotypes
   e. founder effect — changes in the genetic material

9. When an insect population becomes resistant to insecticides, this is an example of a response to _____ selection.
   a. disruptive
   b. stabilizing
   c. sexual
   d. directional
   e. random

10. Finches in the Galapagos experienced _____ selection on beak depth following a drought, while the African finch *P. ostrinus* experiences _____ selection on beak size because it eats either very small, soft seeds or much larger, hard seeds.
    a. stabilizing; directional
    b. sexual; disruptive
    c. directional; disruptive
    d. disruptive; directional
    e. stabilizing; disruptive

11. A large lizard population (1,000 individuals) on the coast contains mostly individuals that are plain brown, but a few have white spots. Coloration is genetically determined. One day during a storm, two spotted lizards hitch a ride on a piece of driftwood to a nearby island, where they join a population of 100 lizards, some of which are spotted and some of which are plain brown. The island's lizard population allele frequency has thus changed due to
    a. natural selection
    b. mutation
    c. gene flow
    d. nonrandom mating
    e. inbreeding

Brief Review

1. Explain the statement, "Individuals are selected, populations evolve."

2. What is a gene pool, and why do changes in gene pools lie at the root of evolution?

3. What are the five causes of allele frequency changes (microevolution), and how does each work?

4. Why is evolutionary fitness always a measure of relative fitness in a population?

5. Why is natural selection the only agent of evolution that consistently produces adaptation?

6. Is the evolutionary fitness of an individual expected to be the same or different in different environments? How did the Grant's study of beak depth of finches after the drought and then again in 1984–1985 provide a real example of this?

Applying Your Knowledge

1. Cheetahs have long legs relative to other large cats. However, leg length in a cheetah population is more likely to be under stabilizing rather than directional selection. Why?

2. The text notes that natural selection is the process that pushes populations to adapt to environmental change. Is natural selection still going on in human populations? Why or why not?

3. Explain why genetic drift may be important when captive populations of animals or plants are started with just a few individuals.

4. Two moth populations of the same species utilize different host plants. One rests on leaves and has evolved a green color that allows it to escape predation by blending in with the leaves. The other population rests on tree trunks, and is brown in color. The colors of these moths are genetically determined by different alleles of the same gene. What would be some consequences of migration of moths leading to gene flow between these two populations?

MediaLab

Are Bacteria Winning the War?
Natural Selection in Action

The last time your doctor prescribed an antibiotic for you, was it for a common cold or a real bacterial infection? If you had a bacterial infection, the first antibiotic might not have worked. Why not? You may have been infected with a strain of bacteria resistant to that antibiotic. The rise and spread of drug-resistant bacteria are consequences of natural selec-

tion—evolution in action. The *Web Tutorial* will help you review how the environmental conditions can mold populations by natural selection. The following *Web Investigation* introduces the serious threat of evolving antibiotic-resistant bacteria. In the *Communicate Your Results* section, you can look for causes and solutions to this new problem.

This *MediaLab* can be found in Chapter 17 on your Companion Website (www.prenhall.com/krogh3).

WEB TUTORIAL

In any population, organisms vary. In a group of bacteria, for example, there may be some rare antibiotic-resistant members. When the environment changes, let's say you take a prescribed antibiotic, and natural selection acts. All the sensitive bacteria die, leaving the antibiotic-resistant bacteria to thrive, thus changing the makeup of the population. This is just one of three types of natural selection that are animated in this activity.

Activity

1. First, you will see how evolution, the modification of a trait in a population over time, is based in the change in frequencies of alleles for that trait.

2. Next, you will compare the three types of natural selection—directional, stabilizing, and disruptive selection—and see how they might act to change allele frequencies.

   Use the Internet in the following *Web Investigations* to view modern examples of natural selection, including antibiotic resistance in bacteria, and see how natural selection affects us all.

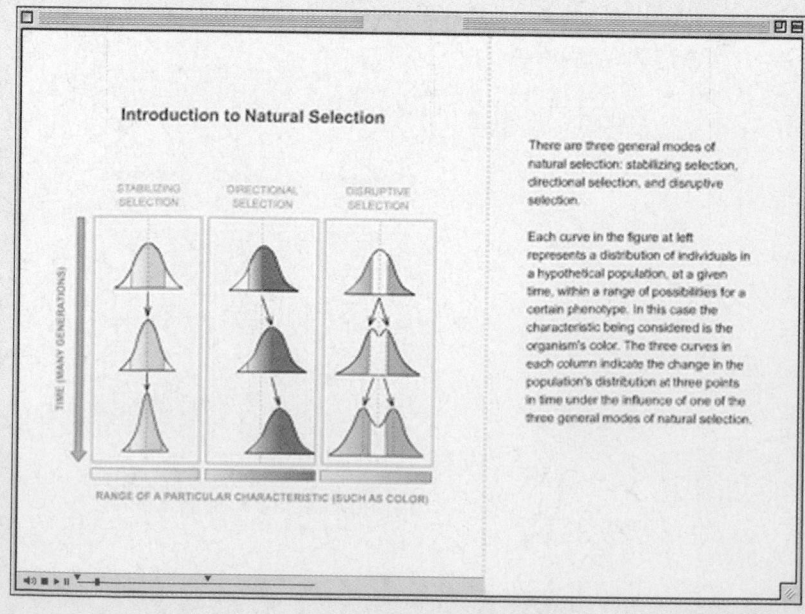

WEB INVESTIGATION

Investigation 1
Estimated time for completion = 20 minutes

Why should people care if antibiotic resistance occurs in bacteria? Read an online article by selecting the keyword **ANTIBIOTIC RESISTANCE** on your Website for this *MediaLab*. Note the biological causes of antibiotic (or antimicrobial) resistance, and the problems predicted. Two factors seem to be operating in this situation: antibiotic resistance by the bacteria in the context of natural selection, and the overuse (and misuse) of antibiotics by people.

Investigation 2
Estimated time for completion = 5 minutes

It's not just bacteria; many microbes have evolved to overcome the medical arsenals hurled against them. Americans were even beginning to see AIDS as a chronic but manageable disease after the introduction of the combination drug therapies that decimated the virus to nearly unde-

tectable levels. Now, however, many are finding these treatments no longer effective, and drug companies must develop new therapies. You can view the current state of several drug-resistant microbes by selecting the keyword **CDC** or **HIV** on your Website for this *MediaLab*.

Investigation 3
Estimated time for completion = 10 minutes

The curse of most infections isn't usually the direct damage inflicted by the virus, but rather the body's defensive response and the accompanying symptoms like runny nose, sneezing, fever, pain, even diarrhea. From an evolutionary standpoint these maybe very beneficial. Select the keyword **EVOLVED DEFENSES** on your Website for this *MediaLab* to read about several examples ranging from morning sickness to coughing.

Now that you have seen some real-life examples, do some of the following exercises to gain an understanding of the factors influencing natural selection and human diseases.

COMMUNICATE YOUR RESULTS

Exercise 1
Estimated time for completion = 15 minutes

What will happen when antibiotics are rendered useless against more and more antibiotic-resistant bacteria? What should we be doing to stop this trend? Using information from *Web Investigation 1*, compile a list of bacterial species that have developed antibiotic resistance, and indicate when. How has natural selection been a factor in the development and spread of antibiotic resistance? Write a list of common guidelines that you could use in explaining this problem to your friends and family. Include suggestions for stopping the spread of antibiotic resistance—and the consequences if we do not.

Exercise 2
Estimated time for completion = 15 minutes

In *Web Investigation 2*, you read about the emerging threat of drug-resistant microbes. Prepare a short presentation of one example to add to a list created by other students. Include the type of natural selection involved, the organism, and what science is doing about solving the problem.

Exercise 3
Estimated time for completion = 10 minutes

So you took some over-the-counter remedy for your common cold; but is it really best to completely obliterate those miserable symptoms? Using the article from *Web Investigation 3*, explain why or why not. Why might evolved defenses like runny noses, fevers, and diarrhea actually be beneficial for survival of our species? How did they evolve? Are the costs of these defenses actually worth it?

18 *Macroevolution*

Endangered or not?
(Section 18.1, page 350)

New species in a generation.
(Essay, page 355)

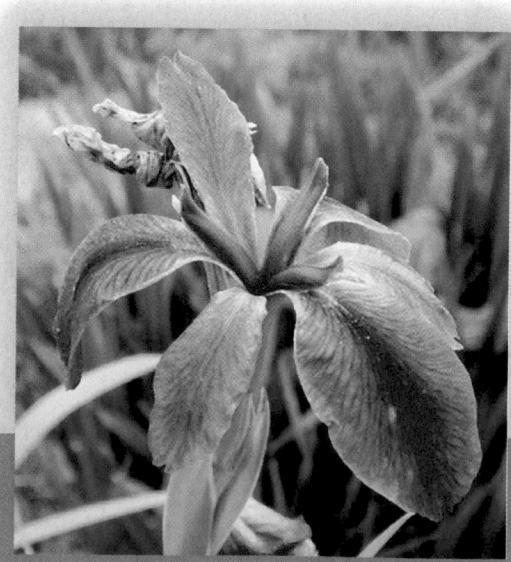

Derived from three species.
(Section 18.2, page 357)

New species come about when populations of existing species cease to breed with one another. Each new species that arises constitutes another branch on life's family tree. Scientists are trying hard to figure out what this tree looks like.

How many types of living things are there on Earth? How many varieties of life-forms are there that we can recognize as being fundamentally different from one another? It may surprise you to learn that we haven't the foggiest idea. The lowest estimate is about four million species, but higher-end estimates often come in at 10 to 15 million and the highest of them all is 100 million. Scientists simply have been unable to catalogue the vast diversity that exists on our planet. In 250 years of digging, netting, bagging, and observing they have identified about 1.8 million species—a large number, to be sure, but only a fraction of the species that actually exist, even if our lowest estimates are correct.

Since no one knows how many species there are, let's suppose that there are "only" 4 million on Earth. Isn't this number staggering? This seems particularly true given its starting point. A single type of organism arose perhaps 3.8 billion years ago, branched into two types of organisms, and then the process continued—branches forming on branches—until at least 4 million different types of living things came to exist on Earth. Now here's the real surprise: These are just the *survivors*. The fossil record indicates that more than 99 percent of all species that have ever lived on Earth are now extinct. Branching indeed.

The questions to be answered in this chapter are: How does this branching work? How do we go from the microevolutionary mechanisms explored in Chapter 17 to the actual divergence of one species into two? And how do we classify the creatures that result from this branching?

18.1 What Is a Species?

The category of life that's been mentioned so far, the species, has a great importance not only to biology, but to society in general. If we allow that some bacteria are harmful to human beings while others are helpful, that some varieties of rice carry disease-resistance genes while others do not, that some species of birds are endangered while others are not, then it follows that there must be some means of distinguishing one of these groupings from another (**see Figure 18.1** on next page). The whole notion of knowing something about the natural world begins to break down if we can't say *which* grouping it is that is endangered or harmful.

Jerky and smooth speciation.
(Section 18.3, page 359)

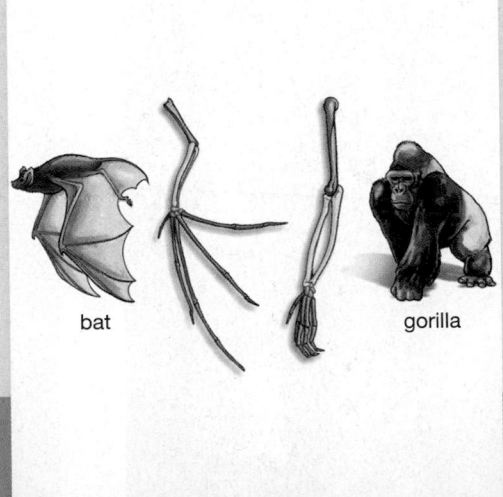

Same structure, different creatures.
(Section 18.4, page 362)

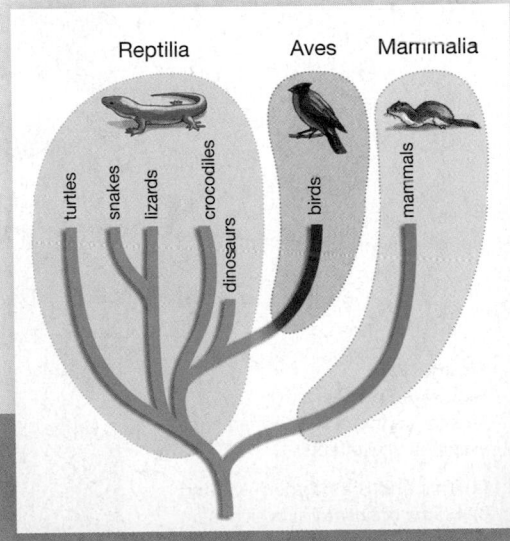

Reptilia   Aves   Mammalia

turtles snakes lizards crocodiles dinosaurs birds mammals

Are birds reptiles?
(Section 18.5, page 365)

349

Over the centuries, human beings have devised various ways of defining the groups now called species. But in science today, the most commonly accepted definition stems from what is known as the **biological species concept**, which uses breeding behavior to make classifications. We actually looked at a version of the biological species concept in Chapter 17. Here it is again, as formulated by the evolutionary biologist Ernst Mayr:

> Species are groups of actually or potentially interbreeding natural populations which are reproductively isolated from other such groups.

Note that the breeding behavior Mayr talks about can be real or potential. Two populations of finch may be separated from one another by geography, but if, upon being reunited in the wild, they began breeding again, they are a single species. Note also that Mayr stipulates that species are groups of *natural* populations. This is important because breeding may take place in captivity that would not in nature. No one doubts that lions and tigers are separate species; yet they will mate in zoos, producing little tiglons or ligers (depending on whether the father was a tiger or a lion). In natural surroundings, however, they apparently have never interbred, even when their ranges overlapped centuries ago.

You might think that, with the biological species concept in hand, scientists would be able to study any organism and, by discerning its breeding behavior, pronounce it to be a member of this or that species. Nature is so vast and varied, however, that this doesn't always work. We can't look at the breeding activity of the single-celled bacteria or archaea, for example, because they don't *have* any breeding behavior; they multiply instead by simple cell division. (Microbiologists define bacterial and archaeal groupings by sequencing their DNA or RNA and looking for the degree to which these sequences are the same.) Then there are separate species that sometimes interbreed in nature, producing so-called hybrid offspring as a result. Such mixing between species happens more in the plant world than the animal, but it does take place in both. If species are supposed to be "reproductively isolated" from one another, what are we to make of these crossings? (Mayr points out that it is *populations* in his definition that are reproductively isolated, not individuals, and that whole populations do tend to stay within their species confines.)

Despite these difficulties, the biological species concept provides a useful way of defining the basic category of Earth's living things. Bacteria and archaea notwithstanding, most multicellular species carry out sexual reproduction at least part of the time, and relatively few species outside the plant kingdom regularly

(a) Endangered species

(b) Not endangered

Figure 18.1
Separate Entities
The concept of a species can have very practical effects.

(a) This bird is a northern spotted owl (*Strix occidentalis*), which is an endangered species, protected by federal law.

(b) This bird is a barred owl (*Strix varia*), which is not endangered.

produce hybrids. Moreover, this species concept is rooted in a critical behavior of organisms themselves—mating, which controls the flow of genes. And as you saw in Chapter 17, it is the change in the genetic makeup of a population (a change in its allele frequencies) that lies at the root of evolution.

18.2 How Do New Species Arise?

Having defined a species, let's now see how one variety of them can be transformed into another in the process called **speciation**: the development of new species through evolution. As you've observed, a single species can diverge into two species, the "parent" species continuing while another branches off from it. A key question for scientists is: What brings this branching evolution about? The answer has to do with the flow of genes reviewed in Chapter 17. As you saw then, evolution within a population means a change in that population's allele frequencies. Now imagine *two* populations of a single species of bird, with one being separated from the other—say, by one of them having flown to a nearby location. To the extent that they continue to breed with one another, with individuals moving between the locations, each population will *share* in whatever allele frequency changes are going on with the other population. Hence the two populations will evolve together, remaining a single species. Now imagine that the migration stops between the two populations. Each population continues to undergo allele frequency changes, but it no longer shares these changes with the other population. Alterations in form and behavior may accompany allele changes, and these alterations may pile up over time. Coloration or bill lengths may change; feeding habits may be transformed. After enough time, should the two populations find themselves geographically reunited, they may no longer freely interbreed. At that point, they are separate species. Speciation has occurred.

The critical change here came when the two populations quit interbreeding. For scientists, the key question thus becomes: Why would this happen? What could drastically reduce interbreeding, and hence gene flow, between two populations of the same species?

The Role of Geographic Separation: Allopatric Speciation

In the preceding example, a very clear factor reduced gene flow between the bird populations: They were separated geographically. And geographical separation turns out to be the most important starting point in speciation.

Populations can become separated in lots of ways. On a large scale, glaciers can move into new territory, cutting a previously undivided population into two. Rivers can change course, with the result that what was a single population on one side of the river may now be two populations on different sides of it. On a smaller scale, a pond may partially dry up, leaving a strip of exposed land between what are now two ponds with separate populations. Such environmental changes are not the only ways that populations can be separated, however. Part of a population might *migrate* to a remote area, as did the bird population, and in time be cut off from its larger population. For a real-life example of how migration can bring about speciation, **see Figure 18.2**.

When geographical barriers divide a population and the resulting populations then go on to become separate species, what has occurred is **allopatric speciation**. *Allopatric* literally means "of other countries"

18.2 How Do New Species Arise?

Web Tutorial 18.1
Speciation

Figure 18.2
Speciation in Action
Millions of years ago, the salamander *Ensatina eschscholtzii* began migrating southward from the Pacific Northwest. When it reached the Central Valley of California—an uninhabitable territory for it—populations branched west (to the coastal range) and east (to the foothills of the Sierra Nevada mountains). Over time, the populations took on different colorations as they moved southward. By the time the two populations were united in Southern California, they differed enough, genetically and physically, that they either did not interbreed or produced infertile hybrid offspring when they did. (Salamanders are falsely colored in drawing for illustrative purposes.)

1. The original population started in the north and migrated southward.

2. The population split to the east and west of the Central Valley. Then two populations began to evolve independently.

3. Evolution of eastern population.

4. Evolution of western population.

Central Valley

5. The east and west populations came back together in Southern California, but could no longer interbreed (or produced infertile hybrid offspring).

(see Figure 18.3). Look along the banks on either side of the Rio Juruá in western Brazil, and you will find small monkeys, called tamarins, that differ genetically from one another in accordance with how wide the river is at any given point. Where it is widest, the members of this species do not interbreed, while at the narrow headwaters they do. Are the nonbreeding populations on their way to becoming separate species? Perhaps, but only if gene flow is drastically reduced between them, probably for a very long time.

Reproductive Isolating Mechanisms Are Central to Speciation

While geographical separation is the most important factor in getting speciation going, it cannot bring about speciation by itself. Following geographical separation, two populations of the same species must then undergo physical or behavioral changes that will *keep* them from interbreeding, should they ever be reunited. Allopatric speciation thus operates through a one-two process: first the geographic separation, then the development of differing characteristics in the two resulting populations. These are characteristics that will *isolate* them from each other in terms of reproduction.

Thus arises the concept of **reproductive isolating mechanisms**, which can be defined as any factor that, in nature, prevents interbreeding between individuals of the same species or of closely related species. Geographic separation is itself a reproductive isolating mechanism, because it is a factor that prevents interbreeding. But, because the mountains or rivers that are the actual barriers to interbreeding are outside of or *extrinsic to* the organisms in question, geographic separation is called an **extrinsic isolating mechanism**. For allopatric speciation to take place, what also must occur is the second in the one-two series of events: The evolution of *internal* characteristics that keep organisms from interbreeding. Such characteristics are referred to as **intrinsic isolating**

mechanisms: evolved differences in anatomy, physiology, or behavior that prevent interbreeding between individuals of the same species or of closely related species.

Six Intrinsic Reproductive Isolating Mechanisms

What are these intrinsic mechanisms? A list of the most important ones is presented in **Table 18.1**. An easy way to remember them is to think about what sequence of events would be required for fertile offspring to be produced in any sexually reproducing organism. First, organisms that live in the same area must encounter one another; if they don't, the "ecological isolation" mechanism is in place. If they do encounter one another, they must then mate in the same time frame; if they don't, then temporal isolation is in place, and so on.

Ecological Isolation

Two closely related species of animals may overlap in their ranges and yet feed, mate, and grow in separate areas, which are called *habitats*. If they use different habitats, this means they may rarely meet up. If so, gene flow will be greatly restricted between them. Lions and tigers *can* interbreed, but they never have in nature, even when their ranges overlapped in the past. One reason for this is their largely separate habitats: Lions prefer the open grasslands, tigers the deep forests.

Temporal Isolation

Even if two populations share the same habitat, if they do not mate within the same time frame, gene flow will be limited between them. Two populations of the same species of flowering plant may begin releasing pollen at slightly different times of the year. Should their reproductive periods cease to overlap altogether, gene flow would be cut off between them.

Figure 18.3
Geographical Separation—Leading to Speciation?
These two varieties of squirrel had a common ancestor that at one time lived in a single range of territory. Then the Grand Canyon was carved out of land in Northern Arizona, leaving populations of this species separated from one another, about 10,000 years ago. In the area of the Grand Canyon, **(a)** the Abert squirrel lives only on the Canyon's south rim, while **(b)** the Kaibab squirrel lives on the north rim. It's unclear whether these two varieties of squirrel would be reproductively isolated if reunited today—that is, whether they are now separate species—but the geographical separation they have experienced is the first step on the way to allopatric speciation.

(a) Abert squirrel, south rim of Grand Canyon

(b) Kaibab squirrel, north rim of Grand Canyon

Behavioral Isolation

Even if populations are in contact and breed at the same time, they must choose to mate with one another for interbreeding to occur. Such choice is often based on specific courtship and mating displays, which can be thought of as passwords between members of the same species. Birds must hear the proper song, spiders must perform the proper dance, and fiddler crabs must wave their claws in the proper way for mating to occur.

Mechanical Isolation

Reproductive organs may come to differ in size or shape or some other feature, such that organisms of the same or closely related species can no longer mate. Different species of alpine butterfly look very similar, but their genital organs are different enough that one species cannot mate with another.

Gametic Isolation

Even if mating occurs, offspring may not result if there are incompatibilities between sperm and egg or between sperm and the female reproductive tract. In plants, the sperm borne by pollen may be unable to reach the egg lying within the plant's ovary. In animals, sperm may be killed by the chemical nature of a given reproductive tract, or may be unable to bind with receptors on the egg.

There is one form of gametic isolation, called *polyploidy*, that is very important in plants and that may have played a part in giving rise to the vertebrate evolutionary line that we humans are part of. You can read about it in "New Species through Genetic Accidents" on the next page.

Hybrid Inviability or Infertility

Even if offspring result, they may develop poorly—they may be stunted or malformed in some way—or they may be infertile, meaning unable to bear offspring of their own. A well-known example of such infertility is the mule, which is the infertile offspring of a female horse and a male donkey (see Figure 18.4).

Sympatric Speciation

Thus far, you have looked at the development of intrinsic reproductive isolating mechanisms strictly as a second step in speciation—one that follows a geographic

Figure 18.4
Mules Are Infertile Hybrids
Even though mules cannot themselves reproduce, humans frequently cross horses and donkeys to produce mules in order to take advantage of their exceptional strength and endurance. Chromosomal incompatibilities between horses and donkeys leave the mules sterile.

Table 18.1 Reproductive Isolating Mechanisms

Extrinsic isolating mechanism		**Geographic isolation** Individuals of two populations cannot interbreed if they live in different places (the first step in allopatric speciation).
Intrinsic isolating mechanisms		**Ecological isolation** Even if they live in the same place, they can't mate if they don't come in contact with one another.
		Temporal isolation Even if they come in contact, they can't mate if they breed at different times.
		Behavioral isolation Even if they breed at the same time, they will not mate if they are not attracted to one another.
		Mechanical isolation Even if they attract one another, they cannot mate if they are not physically compatible.
		Gametic isolation Even if they are physically compatible, an embryo will not form if the egg and sperm do not fuse properly.
		Hybrid inviability or infertility Even if fertilization occurs successfully, the offspring may not survive, or if it survives, may not reproduce (e.g., mule).

New Species through Genetic Accidents: Polyploidy

In the chapter so far, speciation has been portrayed as something that takes place over many generations. But plants have a means of speciating in a single generation. It is called *polyploidy*, and it is very important in the plant world; more than 100,000 species of flowering plants in existence today are thought to have been brought about through it. Beyond this, polyploidy may have had a great importance in the evolution of animals. Evolutionary biologists currently are debating whether a polyploidy "event" helped speed the rise of animals with backbones—the vertebrates, such as ourselves. As you'll see, whenever polyploidy comes about, it helps speed up evolution for reasons we'll get to.

How does polyploidy work? Here is one of the ways. From the genetics unit, you may recall that human beings have 23 pairs of chromosomes, *Drosophila* flies four pairs, and Mendel's peas seven. Whatever the *number* of chromosomes, the commonality among all these species is that their chromosomes come in *pairs*, which is the general rule for species that reproduce sexually.

As noted at the start of the chapter, plants are more adept than animals at producing "hybrids," with the gametes from two *separate* species coming together to create an offspring. Often these offspring are sterile, however, because when it comes time for them to produce *their* gametes (the counterparts to human sperm or eggs), the sets of chromosomes they inherited from their different parental species may not "pair up" correctly in meiosis, owing to differences in chromosome number or structure.

Now comes the accident. Suppose that, back when it was first created as a single-celled zygote, the hybrid offspring carried out the usual practice of doubling its chromosome number in preparing for its initial cell division. Now, however, the cell fails to actually divide; whereas it was supposed to put half its complement of chromosomes into one daughter cell and half into another, it doesn't do this. It doubles the chromosomes, but keeps them all in one cell. Equipped with *twice* the usual number of chromosomes, this single cell then proceeds to undergo regular

cell division, meaning that every cell in the plant that follows will have this doubled number of chromosomes. Critically, this plant will have doubled both its *sets* of chromosomes—the set it got from parental species A and the set it got from species B. If you double a set, by definition every member of that set now has a partner to pair with in gamete formation. Thus the roadblock to a hybrid producing offspring has been removed; the chromosomes can all pair up.

This pairing up yields gametes (eggs and sperm), which can then come together and fuse thanks to another capability of plants. Recall that many plants can *self-fertilize*. A single plant contains male gametes that can fertilize that same plant's female gametes. Thus the plant with the doubled set of chromosomes can fertilize itself, theoretically beginning an unending line of fertile offspring. This line of organisms is "reproductively isolated" from either of its parental species because it has a different number of chromosomes than either parental species. With reproductive isolation, we have a *separate species*; and with self-fertilization, we have a species that can perpetuate itself.

Did polyploidy speed the evolution of our own vertebrate line?

A multiplication of the normal two sets of chromosomes to some other set number is known as **polyploidy**; here we have speciation by polyploidy, which is one type of sympatric speciation. The importance of this in the plant world is immense. Many of our most important food crops are polyploid, including oats, wheat, cotton, potatoes, and coffee. Indeed, the type of polyploid speciation we've looked at—which begins with a hybrid offspring—often produces bigger, healthier plants. As a result, breeders have developed ways to artificially induce polyploidy.

But what about animals? The self-fertilization that some plants are capable of does not exist among more complex animals. As a result, polyploidy that can be maintained over gener-

separation of populations. As it happens, however, intrinsic reproductive isolating mechanisms can develop between two populations in the *absence* of any geographic separation of them. If these isolating mechanisms reduce interbreeding between the populations

sufficiently, speciation can take place. What occurs in this situation is not allopatric speciation, however; it is **sympatric speciation**, which can be defined as any speciation that does not involve geographic separation. (*Sympatric* literally means "of the same country.")

ations is extremely rare in the animal kingdom. But in the course of hundreds of millions of years of evolution, it clearly has been maintained several times. An extremely important polyploidy event may have occurred about 500 million years ago, just as vertebrate animals were evolving from invertebrates. A controversial hypothesis holds that this event doubled the chromosomal set of our invertebrate ancestors, thus greatly accelerating the pace of their evolution.

How can polyploidy speed up evolution? Think of it this way. If you added an extra room to a house, that would give you the flexibility to transform, say, an existing bedroom into a den. Now, if you add genes to a genome, as polyploidy does, that provides the *genome* with a kind of flexibility: the flexibility to have one kind of gene transformed into another. Where once an organism would have but two copies of a given gene—one allele from each parent—with polyploidy it has four. With this change, one pair of these alleles can mutate without causing harm to the organism because the *other* pair of alleles can carry out their function all by themselves. And in a few cases, alleles that mutate will produce new proteins that can help transform an organism—that can help it evolve down different lines. Polyploidy, then, provides for a tremendous increase in the genetic capacity to evolve. And it provides this capacity in a single generation.

Polyploidy in Wheat

Two different species of wheat exist in nature, with slightly different "genomes" or complements of DNA.

1. Gametes (eggs and sperm) are formed in the different species.

2. These gametes fuse, in fertilization, to form a zygote—a single cell that will develop into a new plant. Such a mixed-species or "hybrid" zygote generally develops into a sterile plant, because its chromosomes cannot pair up correctly when the plant produces its own gametes during meiosis.

3. In this case, however, the zygote doubles its chromosomes in preparation for cell division, but then fails to divide. With this doubling, each chromosome now has a compatible homologous chromosome to pair with during meiosis. This is the polyploidy event.

4. Gamete formation then takes place in the plant.

5. These gametes from the same plant then fuse, because this is a self-fertilizing plant. With this, a new generation of wheat plant has been produced—one that is a different species from either parent generation, because each of the parent species has two pairs of chromosomes, while this new hybrid species has four pairs.

Sympatric speciation has been a contentious subject in biology for years. One form of sympatric speciation is the polyploidy reviewed in "New Species through Genetic Accidents." But setting polyploidy aside, most biologists thought for years that if sympatric speciation took place at all, it was of trivial importance. By the mid 1990s, however, new evidence had convinced some of the most prominent researchers in evolutionary biology that sympatric speciation does have significance in the broader picture of speciation.

Sympatric Speciation in a Fruit Fly

To see how sympatric speciation works, consider one of its best-studied examples, a species of fruit fly named *Rhagoletis pomonella*. Prior to the European colonization of North America, *R. pomonella* existed solely on the small, red fruit of hawthorn trees (**see Figure 18.5**). The Europeans brought *apple* trees with them, however, and by 1862 some *R. pomonella* had moved over to them. It seemed to at least one mid-nineteenth-century observer, however, that with the introduction of apples there had arisen separate varieties of the flies—what are sometimes called apple flies and haw flies—with each variety courting, mating, and laying eggs almost exclusively on its own type of tree. A modern researcher named Guy Bush led the way, beginning in the early 1960s, in investigating whether this was the case, and the answer turned out to be yes. The two varieties of flies are separated from each other in all these ways. In one study undertaken on them, only 6 percent of the apple and haw flies interbred with one another. The apple and haw *R. pomonella* are not separate species yet, but they certainly give indication of being in transition to that status.

For our purposes, the first thing to note is that this separation has not come about because of *geographic* division. The apple and hawthorn trees that the two varieties of flies live on may scarcely be separated in space at all. Given this, how did this single species move toward becoming two separate species? Bush offers a likely scenario, based on a critical difference between the hosts the two species live on. Apples tend to ripen in August and September, while hawthorn fruit ripens in September and October. In the sum-

mer, all fruit flies emerge as adults after wintering underground as larvae, after which they fly to their host tree to mate and lay eggs in the fruit.

Bush believes that about 150 years ago (when hawthorns were hosts to all the flies), some individuals in a population of *R. pomonella* experienced either a mutation or perhaps a chance combination of rare existing alleles. In either event, this change did two things: It caused these flies to emerge slightly *earlier* from their underground state than did most flies; and it drew these flies to the smell of *apples* as well as hawthorns. Because apples mature slightly earlier than the hawthorn fruit, these flies had a suitable host waiting for them. More important, these flies would have bred *among themselves* to a high degree. Recall that the other flies were emerging later, and the adult fly only lives for about a month. Thus, the variant alleles were passed on to a selected population in the next generation. Today, the apple *R. pomonella* flies indisputably do emerge earlier than the hawthorn flies. This is one of the things that ensures reproductive isolation between the two groups; their periods of mating don't fully overlap.

Such a lack of overlapping mating periods may sound familiar, because it is one of the intrinsic reproductive isolating mechanisms you looked at earlier. (It is temporal isolation.) You also can see ecological isolation in operation with these flies. Though the two types of flies live in the same area, they meet up with relatively little frequency, because they have different habitats (hawthorn vs. apple trees). In short, these populations have developed intrinsic reproductive isolating mechanisms without ever having been separated from one another geographically. They are headed toward speciation, but in this case it is sympatric speciation.

Speciation through Hybridization

Sympatric speciation can also take place, at least in plants, through the hybridization mentioned earlier, wherein egg and sperm from different species come together to produce offspring. As you can imagine, if plant species A occupies one habitat, and a closely related plant species B occupies another nearby habitat, there will be a so-called "hybrid zone" running between these two habitats where both plants exist and fertilize each other by means of wind-borne pollen. In some instances, healthy hybrid offspring can be produced from this mixing of different species' gametes. However, most hybrid offspring are infertile; they grow, but like mules, they will be incapable of giving rise to a *succeeding* generation of plants.

In rare instances, however, hybrids will be able to have fertile offspring of their own, not by mating

**Figure 18.5
A Species Undergoing Sympatric Speciation?**
The fruit-fly species *Rhagoletis pomonella*, pictured here on the skin of a green apple, may be undergoing speciation.

(a) One parental species

(b) Another parental species

(c) Hybrid species

Figure 18.6
Evolving from Several Species
Louisiana's *Iris nelsonii* plant, on the right, is thought to have evolved through the hybridization of three other *Iris* species. One of these is *Iris fulva,* on the left, and another is *Iris hexagona* in the middle.

with hybrids of their type, but by mating with one or more of the *parental* species that gave rise to them. Should hybrids get established in this way, their genetic complement will change over time. As they exchange alleles with several parental species, they may develop a genome that isolates them from any one of these species, but that allows them to produce fertile offspring by mating with hybrids of their own kind. Once this happens, a new species has come into being. If you look at **Figure 18.6**, you can see *Iris nelsonii*, a hybrid species that grows in Louisiana, and two of the three parental species it came from.

To sum up, the most common form of speciation, allopatric speciation, takes place when a geographic separation is followed by the development of intrinsic reproductive isolating mechanisms. A less common form of speciation, sympatric speciation, occurs when these isolating mechanisms develop in the absence of geographic separation.

Two special means of sympatric speciation are speciation through polyploidy and speciation through hybridization.

18.3 When Is Speciation Likely to Occur?

The horseshoe crab (**see Figure 18.7**) is not really a crab at all, but instead is distantly related to land-dwelling arthropods such as spiders and scorpions. (It lacks the antennae that real crabs possess, but it *has* the pincers around the mouth that all spiders and scorpions do.) Horseshoe crabs have been around in something like their modern form for more than 300 million years. They exist today in a scant four or five species, each one of which is pretty much like the others. The crabs live in the shallow oceans off North America and Asia, pushing through sand or mud to feed on everything from algae to small-bodied invertebrate animals.

(a) Modern horseshoe crab

(b) Fossilized horseshoe crab

(c) Galapagos finch

Figure 18.7
Different Groups of Organisms Undergo Different Rates of Speciation

Because horseshoe crabs look essentially the same today as they did 300 million years ago, some scientists have called them "living fossils." Compare the modern organism, on the left, with the fossil at center, which is at least 145 million years old. By contrast, the Galapagos finches have diversified tremendously, forming 13 species in as little as 100,000 years.

Now consider the Galapagos (or Darwin's) finches you looked at in Chapter 17. There are *thirteen* of these species on the small Galapagos archipelago, all of them derived from a single species of South American finch that arrived on one of the islands perhaps 100,000 years ago.

Think of the difference between horseshoe crabs and Darwin's finches. The former have remained almost unchanged for more than 300 million years throughout the world, while the latter diverged into 13 different species in the last 100,000 years in a small cluster of islands off South America.

Specialists and Generalists

Why the great differences in rate of speciation here? Two general principles are at work. First, as Niles Eldredge has pointed out, horseshoe crabs are *generalists*: Their diet is extremely diverse; they will eat plants and small animals but will also scavenge for debris on the ocean bottom. By contrast, you saw in Chapter 17 how *specialized* some of the Galapagos finches are in their feeding behavior—particularly when food has become scarce because of drought conditions, as happens on the islands. In such times, species might exist on a single variety of plant seed. Species that are tied in this way to a particular food or environmental condition must adapt in connection with changes in them or face extinction. Think of how quickly the bills of the *Geospiza fortis* population on Daphne Major evolved toward greater depth when having a deeper bill meant the difference between life and death (see Chapter 17, page 336). By definition, this kind of adaptation means change—and change is what speciation is all about. By contrast, the horseshoe crab shifts from one food to another, depending on what is available, not adapting greatly in response to changes in any one food source.

New Environments: Adaptive Radiation

The second lesson offered by horseshoe crabs and finches concerns the kinds of environments that induce speciation. The Galapagos islands were formed by volcanic eruptions that brought the islands above the ocean's surface only about 5 million years ago. At that time, these volcanic outcroppings gave new meaning to the word *barren*. For a brief time, the islands were utterly sterile, with no life on them. Very quickly, however, life did come to the islands, with bacteria, fungi, plant seeds, and tiny animals landing on the islands, all being borne by air or ocean currents. The South American finches obviously did not arrive until much later; but by then, with lots of large plant species well established, what these birds

encountered was an environment rich with possibility, for there were *no birds of their kind* on the islands. Imagine that you are a graphic artist, working in a big city with lots of other graphic artists, most of whom specialize in this or that (magazines, Internet websites, etc.). Now you and a few other graphic artists move to a new city in which there are few graphic artists, but a good number of *possibilities* for graphic arts work. You would thus be able to specialize fairly easily—filling a *niche* or working role in this new environment—because many of these niches would not yet have been taken. Just so did Darwin's finches rush in to fill previously unoccupied niches on the Galapagos Islands—this plant seed, this insect, this mating environment.

Such a situation is ripe with possibilities for change (meaning speciation) because, while niches are in flux, there is a good deal of shaping of species to environment. But more of this occurred on the Galapagos, because this niche-filling was taking place on 25 separate *islands*. The birds can fly from one island to another, but the water between the islands nevertheless represents a geographic barrier to bird interbreeding, and you know what follows from this: allopatric speciation.

The Galapagos finches exemplify something known as **adaptive radiation**: the rapid emergence of many species from a single species that has been introduced to a new environment. The finches radiated out to fill new niches on the islands, with populations adapting to the environments over time. In summary, two conditions that are conducive to speciation are specialization (of food source or environment) and migration to a new environment, particularly when there are no closely similar species in that environment.

Is Speciation Smooth or Jerky?

Charles Darwin knew that in looking at large-scale evolutionary changes, what is striking in the fossil record is the lack of "transitional forms," meaning fossils that demonstrate the incremental changes that took place as one species branched from another, in a line going from A to B to C to D. Darwin thought that this was simply a problem of not having collected enough fossils in the right places; that in time, the transitional forms would show themselves. To a certain extent, Darwin was right. In recent years, scientists have been unearthing fossils that show clear transitional forms—for example, in the evolution of whales from a medium-sized, four-legged land mammal.

These kinds of advances notwithstanding, when we look at the fossil record as a whole, there are still more gaps than Darwin would have been comfortable with. Indeed, the fossil record seems to speak against the mode of evolution as Darwin had envisioned it. He imagined evolution as a series of infinitesimally small changes accumulating in a slow, steady way in populations of a species until in time one species could be seen to have diverged into two.

What the fossil record exhibits again and again, however, is not evidence of slow, steady change in a species. Rather, there are indications of enormous lengths of time in which so-called *stasis* occurs—in which species stay exactly the same or undergo some minute modifications. After this long stasis, there appears to be an *abrupt* change to a new species.

In 1972, two young scientists proposed that it was time to take the fossil record at face value. Why isn't it plausible, they said, that species experience stasis for long periods of time, after which speciation then takes place in relatively brief bursts? This is the **theory of punctuated equilibria** proposed by Stephen Jay Gould and Niles Eldredge. (Periods of stasis are the equilibrium that species generally live in, with these then being "punctuated" by the speciation events.)

So, how rapid is speciation under this view? It can take place in thousands of years rather than the millions during which a species is in stasis. If that is the case, it would explain why there are so few transitional forms in the fossil record: They aren't around for long enough to leave many fossils (**see Figure 18.8**).

There has been great debate about the theory of punctuated equilibria ever since it was proposed. Some scientists have supported it, others have opposed it. Its detractors (sometimes called "gradualists") have noted that only the "hard parts" of species (bone and so forth) are preserved in the fossil record, while much evolutionary change must concern "soft parts." Other critics allege that the theory proposes nothing new, but merely puts terminology to ideas that already existed (in population genetics) about how rapidly species can evolve.

Some recent experimental evidence is consistent, however, with the idea of punctuated equilibria. Relying on the ability of bacteria to reproduce rapidly, scientists looked at 10,000 generations of them over a period of 4 years—freezing samples at various points in time. They found that these cells tended to stay the same size for hundreds of generations and then evolve to a larger average size very quickly. Other researchers have asked how much *genetic* change is required to bring about speciation and found that, in comparing two species of flowering plant at least, the answer is very little. They found that changes in as few as eight genetic locations may account for the differences seen between two species of monkey flower that differ in color and according-

ly attract different pollinators. If so few changes are required for speciation, then it could proceed more rapidly than if many changes were necessary.

One possibility is that speciation is both jerky (punctuated) and smooth (gradual), depending on the species and the characteristics being examined. Changes in "morphology" or physical structure are based on genetic changes, as you have seen. It could be that genetic changes are gradual, while the resulting morphological changes come about in spurts.

18.4 The Categorization of Earth's Living Things

This chapter began by noting the importance of the species concept—of being able to say that this organism is fundamentally separate from that. To have a species concept means, of course, that there has to be some means of *naming* separate species. You have probably noticed that most of the species considered in this chapter have been referred to by their scientific names; you didn't just look at a fruit fly, but rather *Rhagoletis pomonella*. To the average person, such names may be regarded as evidence that scientists are awfully exacting—or just plain fussy. Why the two names? Why the Latin? Can't we just say fruit fly?

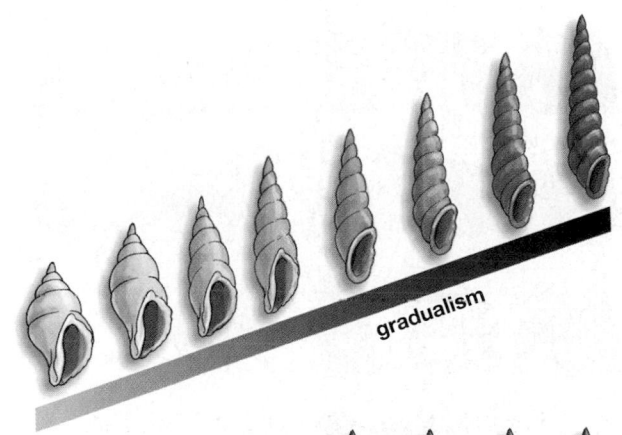

According to the gradualism model, speciation occurs through gradual change over long periods of time.

According to the punctuated equilibria model, long periods of stasis may periodically be "punctuated" by rapid bursts of speciation.

**Figure 18.8
Is Speciation Smooth or Jerky?**

To take these questions one by one, scientists can't just say "fruit fly" for the same reason a person can't say "the guy in the white shirt" while trying to identify a player at a tennis tournament. There are lots of guys in white shirts at tennis tournaments, and there are lots of different kinds of flies in the world. It is important to be able to say *which* fly we are talking about. The importance of this can be seen with *Rhagoletis pomonella* itself, which is a major pest in the apple industry. Tell some apple growers that you have spotted flies on their apples and you may get a shrug of the shoulders; tell them you have spotted *R. pomonella* and you may get a very different reaction.

The Latin that is used stems from the fact that this naming convention was standardized by the Swedish scientist Carl von Linné in the eighteenth century, at a time when Latin was still used in the Western world in scientific naming. (In fact, Linné is better known by the Latinized form of his name—Carolus Linnaeus.)

Linnaeus recognized the confusion that can result from having several common names for the same creature, and thus devoted himself to giving specific names to some 4,200 species of animals and 7,700 species of plants—all that were known to exist in his time. Many of the names he conferred are still in use today.

The fact that there are *two* parts to scientific names—a **binomial nomenclature**—points to the central question of groupings of organisms on Earth. Consider the domestic cat, which has the scientific name *Felis domestica*. The first part of its name is its genus, *Felis*, which designates a group of closely related but still separate species. It turns out that, worldwide, there are five other species of small cat within the *Felis* genus, such as the small cat *Felis nigripes* ("black-footed cat") found in Southern Africa.

Taxonomic Classification and the Degree of Relatedness

The practical importance of the genus classification is that, if we know that two organisms are part of the same genus, then to know something about one of them is to know a good deal about the other. But what is the basis for placing organisms in such a category? Modern science classifies organisms largely in accordance with how closely they are *related*. In this context, "related" has the same meaning as it does when the subject is extended families. If people have the same mother, they are more closely related than if they shared only a common *grandmother*, which in turn makes them more closely related than if they had only a common great-great grandmother, and so on.

In the same way, species can be thought of as being related. Domestic dogs (*Canis familiaris*) are very closely related to gray wolves (*Canis lupus*), with all dogs being descended from these wolves. Indeed, by some reckonings dogs and gray wolves are the same species (*Canis lupus*), because they will interbreed in nature. Such differences as exist between them are the product of a mere 15,000 years or so of the human domestication of dogs. It may be, then, that 15,000 years ago there was but *one* species (the gray wolf) that gave rise to both today's wolf and today's dog. A close relation indeed.

Domestic dogs are also related, however, to domestic *cats*; if we look far back enough in time, we can find a single group of animals that gave rise to both the dog and cat lines. This does not mean going back 10,000 years, however; it means going back perhaps 60 million years. So there is a big difference in how closely related dogs and wolves are, as opposed to dogs and cats. Establishing such *degrees* of related-

Linnaean System of Classification

Kingdom (Animalia)

Phylum (Chordata)

Class (Mammalia)

Order (Carnivora)

Family (Felidae)

Genus (Felis)

Species (Felis domestica)

Figure 18.9
Classifying Living Things
The classification of the house cat, *Felis domestica*, based on the Linnaean system.

ness is the most important task of the scientific classification system. There is a field of biology, called **systematics**, that is concerned with the diversity and relatedness of organisms; part of what systematists do is try to establish the truth about who is more closely related to whom. They study the evolutionary history of groups of organisms.

Setting aside for the moment the difficulty in *determining* what such evolutionary histories are, there obviously is a tremendous cataloguing job here, given the number of living and extinct species mentioned earlier. Given this diversity, a method of classifying organisms, called a *taxonomic system*, is employed in order to classify every species of living thing on Earth. There are eight basic categories in use in the modern taxonomic system: **species, genus, family, order, class, phylum, kingdom**, and **domain**. The organisms in any of these categories make up a grouping of living things, a **taxon**.

A Taxonomic Example: The Common House Cat

If you look at **Figure 18.9**, you can see how this taxonomic system works in connection with the domestic cat. As noted, this cat is only one species in a genus (*Felis*) that has five other living species in it. The genus then is a small part of a family (Felidae) that has 17 other genera in it (panthers, snow leopards, and others). The family is then part of an order (Carnivora) that includes not only big and small

"cats," but other carnivores, such as bears and dogs. On up the taxa we go, with each taxon being more inclusive than the one beneath it until we get to the highest category in this figure, the kingdom Animalia, which includes all animals. (Later you'll look at the "supercategory" above kingdom, called domain; but for simplicity's sake, kingdom is the highest-level taxon considered here.)

Constructing Evolutionary Histories

So how do systematists go about putting organisms into these various groups? What evidence do they use in constructing their evolutionary histories? They rely on radiometric dating, the fossil record, DNA sequence comparisons—all the things reviewed in Chapter 16 that are used to chart the history of life on Earth.

If you look at **Figure 18.10**, you can see the outcome of some of this work, an evolutionary "tree" for one group of organisms, in this case one of the major groups of mammalian carnivores. You can see that the tree is "rooted," about 60 million years ago, with an ancestral carnivore whose lineage then split two ways: to dogs on the one hand and everything else on the other. One interesting facet of this evolutionary history is how closely related bears are to the aquatic carnivores. All such histories are hypotheses about evolutionary relationships, with each such hypothesis known as a **phylogeny**.

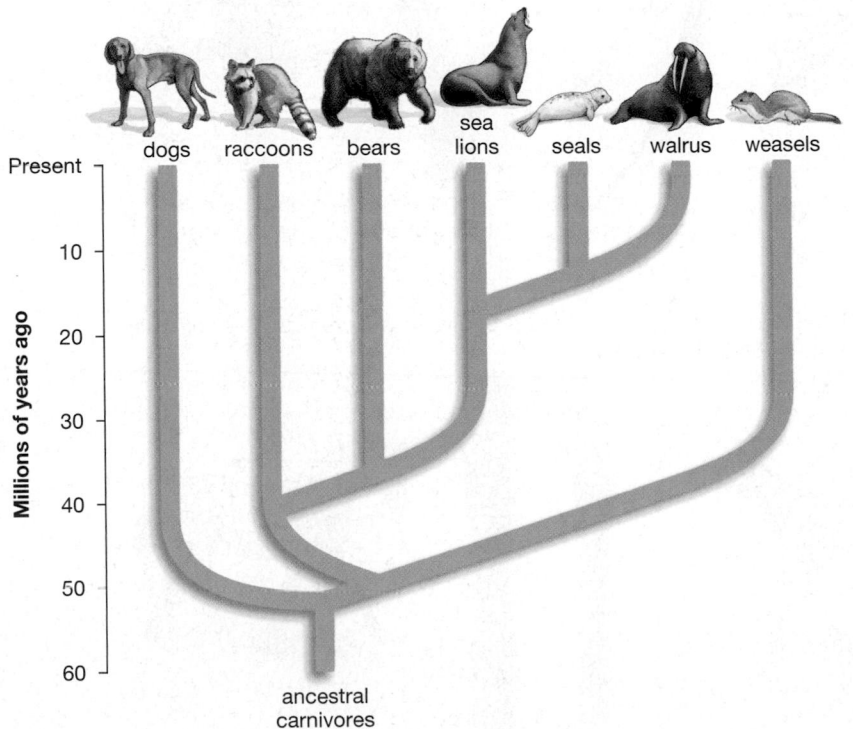

Figure 18.10
A Family Tree for a Selected Group of Mammalian Carnivores

Obscuring the Trail: Convergent Evolution

One of the things that makes the interpretation of evolutionary evidence difficult is that similar features may arise *independently* in several evolutionary lines. A bedrock of systematic classification is the existence of **homologies**, which can be defined as common structures in different organisms that result from a shared ancestry. In Chapter 16, a strong homology was noted in forelimb structure that exists in organisms as different as a gorilla, a bat, and a whale. If you look at **Figure 18.11**, you can see the gorilla and the bat again.

Now, however, consider an extinct group, the litopterns, that once lived in what is now Argentina. Like the modern-day horse, they roamed on open grasslands. Over the course of evolutionary time they developed legs that were extraordinarily similar to the horse's, right down to having an undivided hoof. In fact, litopterns are only very distantly related to the horse; but the leg similarities were enough to fool at least one nineteenth-century expert who thought he had found in litopterns the ancestor to the modern horse.

What is exhibited in the legs of the litoptern and horse is an **analogy**: a feature in different organisms that is the same in function and superficial appearance. When nature has shaped two separate evolutionary lines in analogous ways, what has occurred is **convergent evolution**. (Both the litoptern and horse lines converged in their development of similar legs.) But analogous features have nothing to do with common descent; they merely show that the same kinds of environmental pressures lead to the same kinds of designs. (There are only so many leg structures that work well for grass-eating mammals that roam over long distances, so it's not surprising that natural selection would have pushed two separate evolutionary lines toward a similar leg shape.) The problem for systematics

(a) Homology: Common structures in different organisms that result from common ancestry

bat

bones of wing   bones of arm

gorilla

(b) Analogy: Characters of similar function and superficial structure that have *not* arisen from common ancestry

litoptern

one-toed foot

horse

one-toed foot

Figure 18.11
Related, as Opposed to Similar

(a) Bats and gorillas have the same bone composition in their forelimbs—one upper bone, joined to two intermediate bones, joined to five digits—because they share a common ancestor. Of course, these forelimbs are used today for very different functions.

(b) Horses and the extinct litopterns have long legs and one-toed feet that serve the same function, but these features were derived independently in the two creatures—in separate lines of descent.

is that analogy can be confused with homology; analogies can make us believe that organisms share common ancestry when in fact they do not.

18.5 Classical Taxonomy and Cladistics

Given difficulties such as convergent evolution and a less-than-perfect fossil record, systematists over the years have been driven to devise several methodologies for producing phylogenies. The essential question they have asked is: What means of *interpreting* the evidence will give us the most accurate picture of how Earth's living and extinct organisms are related?

One of the methodologies for interpreting evidence actually predates the field of systematics and most of the techniques used in it. Handed down from the time of Darwin, this methodology is sometimes called *classical taxonomy* (or descriptive taxonomy). In thinking about animals in Earth's family tree, classical taxonomists would look first and foremost at the physical form or "morphology" of the animals in question, as preserved in the fossil record, and compare it to the morphology of modern animals. Skull shape, "dentition" (teeth patterns), limb structure, and much more would be considered. They would also look at *where* the ancient forms existed, compared to modern forms. More recently, they have been using molecular techniques, such as comparing DNA or protein sequences in different living species to determine the relatedness among them. In essence, classical taxonomists would look at how many similarities one group has with another and, on that basis, try to judge relatedness among them. The word *judge* is used advisedly here, because at the end of the day in the classical system, subjective judgments usually need to be made about who is more closely related to whom. It is a matter of weighing one piece of evidence against another, but who's to say which piece of evidence is more important? In addition, as you'll see, classical taxonomy sometimes makes a distinction between the phylogenies it establishes and the taxonomic categories into which it puts different organisms.

Another System for Interpreting the Evidence: Cladistics

The subjectivity inherent in classical taxonomy helped bring about the formation of another system for establishing relatedness. Developed in the 1950s by the German biologist Willi Henning, it is called **cladistics** (from the Greek *klados*, meaning "branch"). In practice, cladistics has become the core of most of the phylogenetic work going on today.

In **Figure 18.12** you can see a **cladogram**, which is an evolutionary tree constructed within the cladistic system. Note that there is a very simple branched line and that no time scale is attached to it, as was the case with the evolutionary tree of carnivores. Cladistics concerns itself first with lines of descent—with the *order* of branching events. Once this order has been established, efforts can be made to fix events in time, but that is a secondary concern. First and foremost, this cladogram is a proposed answer to the question: Among the animals lizard, deer, lion, and seal, which two groups of animals have the most recent common ancestor? Then, which other two have the *next* most recent common ancestor, and so on. By extension, the question is: Who is more closely related to whom? Note that these questions are being asked about only four of the five animals listed. You'll get to the role of the hagfish in a moment.

Cladistics Employs Shared Ancestral and Derived Characters

The starting point for cladistic analysis is the difference between so-called ancestral characters and derived characters. If you look at any group of species (any taxon), its **ancestral characters** are those that existed in an ancestor common to them all. There are about 50,000 species of animals on Earth that possess a dorsal vertebral column (better known as a backbone). The ancestor to all fishes, reptiles, and mammals had such a feature, which makes the vertebral column an ancestral character for all these groups. On the other hand, only *some* vertebrates then went

Figure 18.12
A Simple Cladogram
Among the lizard, deer, lion and seal, which two are most closely related? The tentative answer displayed in this cladogram is the lion and the seal. The basis for this assertion is the number of unique or "derived" characters these two creatures share compared to any other two organisms under consideration. (They share three characters: tetrapod structure, mammary glands, and carnivorous feeding.) Such a system pays no attention to superficial similarities among organisms. Like fish, seals swim in the water; but they share far more derived characters with lions than they do with fish—enough to persuade scientists that seals have returned to the water in relatively recent times, following a period in which their ancestors lived on land.

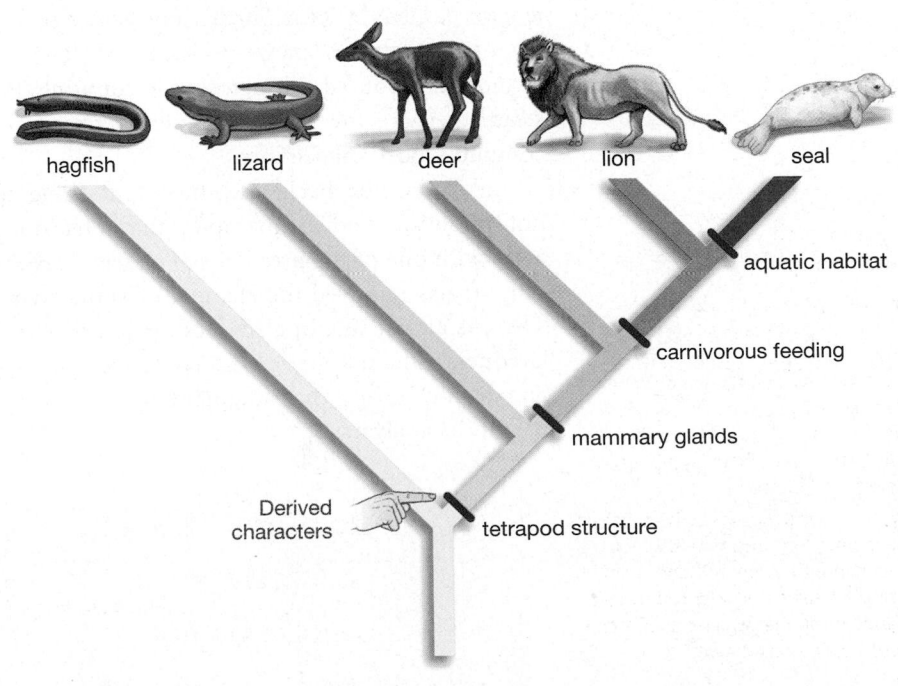

hagfish   lizard   deer   lion   seal

aquatic habitat

carnivorous feeding

mammary glands

Derived characters   tetrapod structure

on to become animals that have four limbs (and are thus tetrapods). The tetrapod feature is thus a **derived character** of the vertebrate state; it is a character *unique* to taxa descended from a common ancestor.

In Figure 18.12, you can see a continuation of this process of ever-more selective grouping in that only some mammals are carnivorous feeders, and only some members of this taxon are *aquatic* mammalian carnivores. The presumption in cladistics is that shared derived characters are evidence of common ancestry and that the *more* derived characters any two organisms share, the more recently they will have shared a common ancestor, compared to other organisms under study. At its most fundamental level, cladistics becomes a matter of counting shared derived characters. Seals and lions share *three* derived characters (tetrapod structure, mammary glands, and carnivorous feeding), while the lizard has only one derived character that it shares with all the other animals (tetrapod structure). Cladistics infers from this that the lion and the seal have a more recent common ancestor than do any other two groups in the cladogram—that their branching from this common line of descent came later than any other branching in the line. And the hagfish? It is a starting-point organism for the mammalian carnivores, known as an *out-group*. If we are to say that the animals under consideration have derived characters, they must be derived *compared to* some other organism—in this case, the hagfish.

The examples here employ visible, physical traits, but in practice modern cladistics relies heavily on comparisons among molecular sequences, such as the number of shared, derived base pairs in lengths of DNA or RNA. Furthermore, since cladistics often compares many species, its phylogenies cannot be produced through simple counting; instead, they are the result of multiple rounds of computer-aided calculations.

Taking a step back, the important thing to note about the cladistic method is that it has done away with one of the problems of classical taxonomy: It has removed the element of subjectivity. There is a firm rule in cladistics for inferring relatedness—the number of shared derived characters—which means that judgment need not play a part in its analyses.

Should Anything but Relatedness Matter in Classification?

Strictly speaking, cladistic analysis is not about the classification of Earth's living things. Rather, cladistics is concerned solely with establishing lines of descent. Once these are established, categories can be overlaid on them. Having looked at various cladograms, we could say that this group constitutes a class called "Reptilia," while this group constitutes a class called "Amphibia." But cladistics *per se* is not concerned with this. If the question, however, is not just phylogeny, but how to *categorize* Earth's organisms, then it's not clear that cladistic analysis always provides the most sensible categories.

To appreciate this point, consider the following question. Who is more closely related: lizards and crocodiles on the one hand, or birds and crocodiles on the other? It may surprise you to learn that, in terms of phylogeny, it is birds and crocodiles. Birds split off from a dinosaur-crocodile line within the last 200 million years or so, while the split between the lizard and crocodile lines came far earlier. *Classical* taxonomy says that, despite this, crocodiles, lizards, dinosaurs, and turtles belong in one class (Reptilia), while birds belong in another (Aves; **see Figure 18.13**). Its implicit assumption is that, in classifying creatures, something counts *besides* evolutionary relationships—in this case, the special qualities of birds (flight, warm-bloodedness). Cladistics, meanwhile, says that the only criterion for placement is phylogeny. It holds that a given taxon needs to contain all the descendents stemming from a particular branch point—in this case the branch point that leads to both reptiles and birds. If you think that both sides in this debate are making sensible arguments, then you understand why it is so difficult to come up with a universally accepted means of classifying Earth's living things.

On to the History of Life

The millions of species that exist on Earth today took billions of years to evolve. During that time, life went from being exclusively microscopic and single-celled to being the staggeringly diverse entity it is today. How did this happen over time? And how did we go from no life to life? And what is the order of appearance for life's living things? These are the subjects of Chapter 19.

(a) Classical view of relationships among tetrapods

(b) Cladistic view of relationships among tetrapods

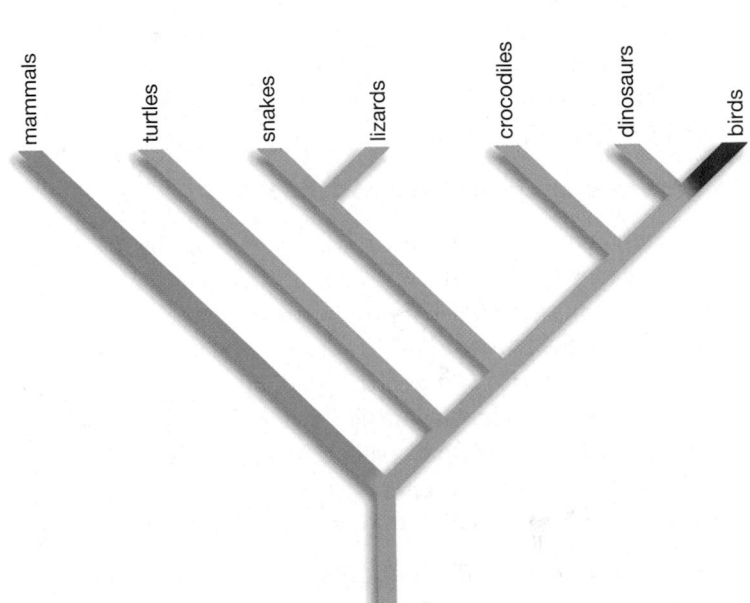

Figure 18.13
Are Birds Reptiles?

(a) Classical taxonomy employs three classes, Aves, Mammalia, and Reptilia, for birds, mammals, and reptiles. Thus, crocodiles and birds are in separate classes—a recognition on the part of classical taxonomists of the unique features of birds, such as feathers.

(b) In cladistic analysis, by contrast, birds are grouped very closely with crocodiles and dinosaurs, in recognition of the recent shared ancestry of the three groups. The only consideration in this system of classification is who is more closely related to whom.

Chapter Review

Summary

18.1 What Is a Species?

- The most accepted definition of a species is derived from the biological species concept: "Species are groups of actually or potentially interbreeding natural populations that are reproductively isolated from other such groups." Earth's organisms are so varied that this definition does not apply to all of them.

18.2 How Do New Species Arise?

- Branching evolution occurs when a single "parent" species diverges into two species, the parent species continuing while a second species arises from it. Branching evolution is based on reductions in gene flow between populations of the same species. To the extent that gene flow is maintained between two geographically separate populations, they will experience similar allele frequency changes, meaning they will evolve together. When gene flow is drastically reduced, however, the populations will evolve separately. When evolution has altered the physical or behavior characteristics of the populations enough that they can no longer interbreed, even if reunited, speciation has occurred.

- Geographical separation is the most important factor in reducing gene flow between populations of the same species. Such separation can come about because of a change in environment—a river may change course, for example—or because of the migration of part of a population. When geographic separation plays a part in the evolution of a species, allopatric speciation is said to have occurred.

- Geographical separation cannot bring about speciation by itself. Following geographical separation, populations of the same species must develop internal characteristics that will keep them from interbreeding, should they be reunited. Such characteristics are referred to as intrinsic isolating mechanisms. There are six such isolating mechanisms: ecological, temporal, behavioral, mechanical, gametic isolation, and hybrid inviability or infertility.

- Speciation that occurs in the absence of geographical separation is called sympatric speciation. Like allopatric speciation, sympatric speciation always entails the development of intrinsic reproductive isolating mechanisms.

- There are two special forms of sympatric speciation. One is speciation through hybridization—a relatively rare phenomenon that is most important in plants. The other is polyploidy: a doubling of the number of chromosomes in a species that can bring about speciation in one generation. Polyploidy has been especially important in plant speciation, but it has played a part in animal evolution as well.

Web Tutorial 18.1: Speciation

18.3 When Is Speciation Likely to Occur?

- Speciation is more likely to occur when a species is highly specialized with respect to a food source or other environmental condition. Speciation is also more likely to occur when a species is introduced to an environment in which few other species of its kind exist. Such an environment has many available working roles or niches available to the new species—a situation that leads to rapid specialization, which in turn leads to speciation. This series of events is known as adaptive radiation: the rapid emergence of many species from a single species that has been introduced to a new environment.

- There is considerable debate among evolutionary biologists regarding the pace of evolution. Under one view, called the gradualist model, evolution proceeds at a slow, steady rate; under another view, called the punctuated equilibria model, organisms undergo long periods of "stasis" or little change, followed by relatively brief episodes of rapid speciation.

18.4 The Categorization of Earth's Living Things

- In science, a two-name or "binomial" nomenclature is used for each of Earth's species. The first name designates the genus, or group of closely related organisms, that the species is a member of; the second name is specific to the species. Genus and species fit into a larger framework of *taxonomy*, meaning the classification of species. Going from least to most inclusive, the eight commonly used groupings in this taxonomy are species, genus, family, order, class, phylum, kingdom, and domain.

- Species are put into these categories largely on the basis of relatedness—species that are closely related are in the same genus; species that are distantly related may only be in the same phylum or kingdom. The biological discipline of systematics is concerned with establishing degrees of relatedness among both living and extinct species.

- Systematists establish evolutionary histories or "phylogenies" by reviewing various kinds of evidence, including radiometric dating, the fossil record, and DNA sequence comparisons. Based on this evidence, they determine the evolutionary history of a given species.

- In establishing phylogenies, one of the things systematists look for is homologous structures: common structures in different organisms that result from a shared ancestry. One problem with their use is that they can be confused with analogous structures: similar features that developed independently in separate lines of organisms (as with the legs of modern horses and extinct litopterns).

18.5 Classical Taxonomy and Cladistics

- One method of determining phylogeny, classical taxonomy, establishes evolutionary relationships among living and extinct organisms in accordance with such factors as physical form, distribution, and molecular similarities; but classical taxonomy employs subjective judgments in deciding on what weight to give one piece of evidence as opposed to another. The phylogenetic system known as cladistics does away with this element of subjectivity by following a firm rule for inferring relatedness. It counts the number of shared derived characters two organisms have, meaning the features they uniquely share that are derived from another group of organisms.

- Cladistics is centrally concerned with establishing lines of descent, though species can be put into taxonomic categories that are derived from cladistic analysis. Classical taxonomy holds that, in putting organisms into various categories, factors other than phylogeny ought to be taken into account. Cladistics holds that the only criterion for taxonomic placement is phylogeny—a group must contain all descendants stemming from a given branch point.

Key Terms

adaptive radiation 358	intrinsic isolating
allopatric speciation 351	mechanism 352
analogy 362	kingdom 361
ancestral character 363	order 361
binomial nomenclature 360	phylogeny 361
biological species concept 350	phylum 361
cladistics 363	polyploidy 354
cladogram 363	reproductive isolating
class 361	mechanisms 352
convergent evolution 362	speciation 351
derived character 364	species 361
domain 361	sympatric speciation 354
extrinsic isolating mechanism 352	systematics 361
family 361	taxon 361
genus 361	theory of punctuated
homology 362	equilibria 359

Understanding the Basics

Multiple-Choice Questions (answers in the back of the book)

1. In the biological species concept, the factor that defines a species is
   a. geographical separation
   b. reproductive isolation
   c. hybridization
   d. cladogenesis
   e. its behavior

2. In allopatric speciation (select all that apply):
   a. Allele frequency changes are shared between populations.
   b. Populations are geographically isolated.

c. Gene flow between populations is greatly reduced by physical barriers.

d. Geographically isolated populations accumulate genetic changes over time that eventually block successful interbreeding.

e. Populations are directly adjacent.

3. Factors that can be problems in determining the true relationships among organisms may include (select all that apply):

a. homologous traits

b. analogous traits

c. convergent evolution

d. poor fossil record

e. shared derived traits

4. Possible intrinsic reproductive isolating mechanisms include (select all that apply):

a. mating at different times of year or times of day

b. geographical isolation

c. incompatibility between eggs and sperm that prevent fertilization

d. singing a different mating song than another species

e. producing fertile hybrids

5. Match the reproductive isolating mechanism with the means by which it works:

a. temporal isolation — populations live in different environments

b. ecological isolation — populations are separated by physical barriers

c. geographical isolation — mating occurs at different times of day or year

d. gametic isolation — egg and sperm do not fuse

e. hybrid sterility — progeny of a cross are unable to reproduce

6. In ocean-dwelling creatures such as sea urchins or corals, sperm and eggs are released into the water by males and females, and fertilization occurs externally. If several closely related species of coral live in the same location, what reproductive isolating mechanisms are likely to be effective at preventing interbreeding? (Select all that apply.)

a. behavioral isolation

b. gametic isolation

c. temporal isolation

d. ecological isolation

e. hybrid infertility

7. Order the following categories into the appropriate biological hierarchy, with the least inclusive category first.

a. family

b. species

c. phylum

d. genus

e. class

8. Adaptive radiations (select all that apply):

a. are most likely to occur on mainlands

b. are examples of rapid speciation that occurs when a number of ecological niches have not been filled

c. concern the evolution of heat loss in vertebrates experiencing stressful climates

d. are exemplified by the Galapagos finches

e. often occur on islands

9. Which pair of animals is probably most closely related evolutionarily?

a. animals in the same genus

b. animals in the same order

c. animals in the same family

d. animals in the same phylum

e. animals in the same class

Brief Review

1. What is convergent evolution, and why is it a problem for phylogenetic analyses?

2. Contrast the gradual and punctuated equilibria models of long-term evolution. What type of evidence has been used to support the punctuated equilibria theory?

3. Describe one major difference between allopatric and sympatric speciation. What is one thing that they have in common?

4. State the biological species concept.

5. Why is the evolution of intrinsic reproductive isolation mechanisms required for two groups to be called separate species? Why isn't simple geographical isolation sufficient?

Applying Your Knowledge

1. Living things are classified into a set of hierarchical categories. Why is this more useful to biologists than simply giving everything a one-word name (or a number) and eliminating some of the categories?

2. Populations of some kinds of organisms may be isolated by a barrier as small as a roadway, while other organisms require a much larger physical barrier to block gene flow. What features of organisms might determine how readily they become geographically isolated? What impact might these features have on how often or how rapidly speciation is likely to occur in these groups?

3. In an adaptive radiation, one species may colonize a previously empty environment, such as an island, and diversify evolutionarily into a set of closely related species that occupy a very wide range of habitats. For example, in the Darwin's finches on the Galapagos Islands, one species fills the role of woodpecker by using a stick to tap on trees and dig out insects. Do you think that such a species would have been likely to evolve in an area that already had woodpeckers? Why or why not?

19 *The History of Life on Earth*

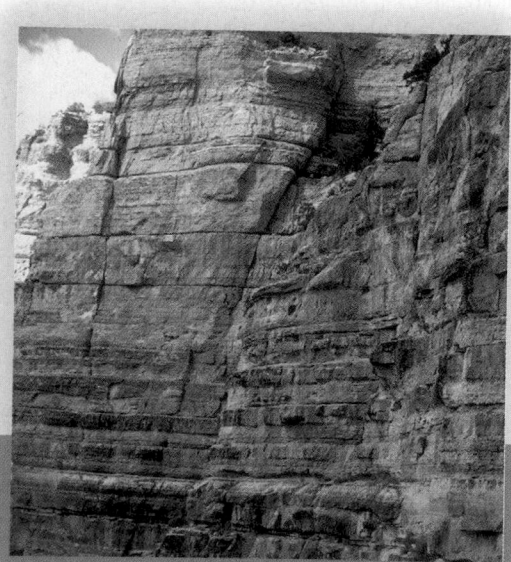

The history of life written in layers of rock.
(Section 19.1, page 371)

North America

Africa

live lizard

South America

live lizard

Parting company
(Essay, page 373)

One of the earliest-evolving groups of plants.
(Section 19.6, page 381)

> **Life started out small perhaps 3.8 billion years ago and stayed that way for a long time. Eventually it exploded into a multitude of forms that came to include human beings.**

Within 5 minutes of its birth, a newborn wildebeest on the plains of central Africa can be off and running with its herd (**see Figure 19.1**). By contrast, human infants probably will not be able to take a step by themselves until they are about a year old. Female lions reach sexual maturity at about 3 years, and killer whales at about 7, but in human hunter-gatherer societies, reproduction generally begins at age 18 or 19. Even in comparison to our fellow mammals, humans mature at a notably slow rate.

At first glance, it might seem puzzling that our evolution took this turn. From what we have learned of natural selection, wouldn't it make sense that survival would *decrease* for offspring that developed more slowly? What is the fitness payoff in having young that are essentially helpless for several years and then immature for many more? Here is one possible answer. As a species, we have survived not so much because of our physical capabilities, but because of our wits. Our success is the product of our remarkable capacity to *learn*. But learning takes time, and it is arguably best undertaken by minds that remain for a long time in what might be called a state of flexible immaturity. (Think of how easily young children acquire a second language in comparison with adults.) Among our human ancestors, it may be that those who survived tended to be those who could learn the most. And who could learn the most? Those who took the longest to mature.

Under this view, we carry our evolutionary heritage with us in the form of delayed maturity. We did not leave this heritage behind in the African savanna, where human beings first evolved; we can see it every time we look at a 2-year-old. In the same way, we can see evolutionary vestiges in us from a much earlier time as well. Note the way we walk, our *left arm* swinging forward as our *right leg* does the

Figure 19.1
No Time to Lose
A newborn wildebeest struggles to its feet immediately after its birth on the plains of Africa. Wildebeest predators, such as hyenas, often concentrate their efforts on the newborn.

On the way to flowering plants.
(Section 19.6, page 383)

What Is a Primate?
(Section 19.7, page 386)

The artistic flowering of early humans.
(Section 19.8, page 394)

Figure 19.2
Our Evolutionary Heritage
The gait exhibited by almost all four-limbed animals, including human beings, stems from the reversing S-pattern that our evolutionary ancestors used in getting around when they were making the transition from aquatic to terrestrial life. Here a salamander employs this same motion in getting from one place to another.

same. Almost all four-limbed animals walk this way. One view is that we inherited this from the elongated, four-finned fish we evolved from. They came onto the muddy land by slithering in an S-pattern, the left-front fin going back as the left-rear fin went forward, then the reverse (**see Figure 19.2**).

Note the sweep of evolution in all this. Maturation is with us from one period, walking style from another. If we look at the genetic code—*this* DNA sequence specifying *that* amino acid—we have within

Figure 19.3
A Timescale for Earth and Its Living Things

Mya	Relative time scale	Era	Period	Epoch	Million years ago (Mya)	Notable events	Major extinction events
0				Recent	0.01	Historic time	
65		Cenozoic	Quaternary	Pleistocene	1.65	Extinction of many large mammals; modern humans appear	
245				Pliocene	5	Early humans emerge (genus *Homo*)	
544			Tertiary	Miocene	23	Grasses replace forests in drier areas	
				Oligocene	35	Rise of several modern mammals	
				Eocene	56	Earliest whale fossils; first horses	
				Paleocene	65	First primate fossils / Extinction of dinosaurs; mammals begin to flourish	Cretaceous extinction
		Mesozoic	Cretaceous		145	Angiosperms replace gymnosperms in many habitats	
			Jurassic		210	First bird fossil (*Archaeopteryx*) / First flowering plants (Angiosperms)	Triassic extinction
			Triassic		245	First dinosaurs and mammals	Permian extinction
		Paleozoic	Permian		290	First mammal-like reptiles	
			Pennsylvanian		320	First insect flight	
			Mississippian		360	First reptiles / First gymnosperms	Devonian extinction
			Devonian		408	First seed-bearing plants / First insects	Ordovician extinction
			Silurian		440	Early jawed fishes / First fossils of land animals	
			Ordovician		505	First plant fossils / First fungus fossils	Cambrian extinction
			Cambrian		544	First fossil of chordate (ancestors of vertebrates) / Cambrian explosion (expansion of animal diversity)	
		Precambrian			600	First animal fossils	
					1,500	Possible date for first multicellular life	
					2,000	First eukaryotic fossils	
					2,300	First oxygen accumulation in atmosphere	
					3,200	Early bacterial fossils	
					3,800	Possible evidence of earliest life on Earth	
4,600					4,600	Earth is formed	

Relative time scale: Paleozoic · Mesozoic · Precambrian

us a heritage that stretches back to the beginning of life on Earth, because this code is shared by nearly every living thing. Under this view, evolution is not some abstract process that lies separate from us; on the contrary, it is with us in every step we take. But how has evolution proceeded in its long sweep down the ages? Starting with the spark of life itself, how did it produce the range of creatures that inhabit the Earth? In this chapter, you'll begin to find out.

19.1 The Geological Timescale: Life Marks Earth's Ages

We can start this inquiry by getting a sense of life's timeline. The Earth, which is home to all the life we know of, came into being about 4.6 billion years ago. Given the human life span of 80-plus years, 4.6 billion years is an unimaginably long time. Indeed, it's a long period of time relative to any time frame we know of. The universe as a whole is thought to be 14 billion years old at most, so the Earth's history stretches back a third of the way to the beginning of time.

In measuring something as long as 4.6 billion years, it obviously won't do to think in terms of individual years, so scientists use something called the geological timescale, which you can see in **Figure 19.3**. It divides earthly history into broad *eras*, shorter *periods*, and shorter-still *epochs*. The scale begins with the formation of the Earth (at the bottom of the figure), and runs to "historic time," meaning time in the last 10,000 years.

But what do the demarcations in this timescale indicate? What, for example, is the distinction between the Permian period you can see at the middle left of Figure 19.3, and the Triassic period that followed it? Remember that back in Charles Darwin's time, there was no radiometric dating of materials—no using the decay of uranium, for example, to provide absolute dates for any fossils that might be found. Hence, no one could say whether a fossil was 10 million or 100 million years old. Geologists of the time did know, however, that sedimentary rocks had been put down in layers (or strata), with the oldest strata on the bottom and the youngest strata on top (**see Figure 19.4**). And as it turned out, each stratum tended to have within it a group (or "assemblage") of fossils that was unique to it. The result was that each stratum and its fossils could be assigned a *relative* date—each was older than this stratum, but younger than that one. Since fossils helped define the geological strata, it's not surprising that scientists marked off the geological timescale in accordance with the *transitions* they saw in fossil forms. The Permian period is considered different from the Triassic period because, with move-ment from one to the other, a different set of life-forms appears, as recorded in the fossil record.

Features of the Timescale

Now a couple of notes on the timescale. First, it may surprise you to learn what the basis is for many of the transitions in it: death on a grand scale, in the form of "major extinction events." Six of these events are noted in Figure 19.3 (over on the right), with all of them defining the end of an era or period. The most famous extinction event, the **Cretaceous Extinction**, occurred at the boundary between the Cretaceous and Tertiary periods. This was the extinction, aided by the impact of one or more giant asteroids, that brought about the end of the dinosaurs, along with many other life-forms. The greatest extinction event of all, however, occurred earlier, in the boundary between the Permian and Triassic periods. This was the **Permian Extinction**, in which as many as 96 percent of all species on Earth were wiped out (see "Physical Forces That Have Shaped Evolution" on the next page).

This is not to say, however, that all Earth's eras or periods are marked off by extinctions. The transition between the Precambrian and Paleozoic eras marks not a major extinction, but a seeming explosion in the diversity of animal forms. Nevertheless, this so-called Cambrian Explosion, which you'll read about later, is just a different kind of transition in living things.

Web Tutorial 19.1
Evolutionary
Timescales

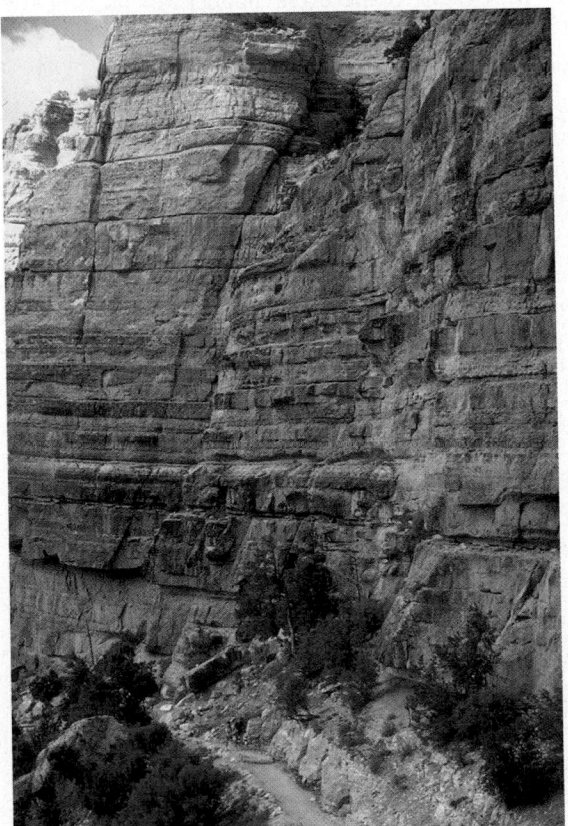

Figure 19.4
Revealing Layers
The history of life can be traced through fossilized life-forms found in layers of sediment, seen here in America's Grand Canyon.

Physical Forces and Evolution

Climate Change

The living world is very much affected by the physical forces operating on the Earth. You can see this in connection with the mass extinctions we noted in the main text. What has caused these extinctions? Evidence links at least four of those listed in Figure 19.3 to episodes of global climate change, specifically global cooling. (The four are the Ordovician, Devonian, Permian, and Cretaceous extinctions.) All kinds of things happen with global cooling. Glaciers develop, wiping out everything in their path and tying up huge amounts of water in ice. This reduces sea levels, thereby killing many organisms that live on the continental shelves. The oceans themselves get colder, particularly at greater depths, which is its own kind of killing event. As may be apparent, loss of habitat is intimately tied to the issue of global climate change. Global cooling is not the only factor involved in mass extinctions, but it is thought to be the most important factor.

Extraterrestrial Objects

In the public mind, the Cretaceous Extinction that finished off the dinosaurs had a single, nearly instantaneous cause: the explosive impact of an enormous asteroid, 10 kilometers (6.5 miles) in diameter, that struck Mexico's Yucatan Peninsula 65 million years ago. There is no doubt that this catastrophic event happened; what is in doubt is that it was the sole or even predominant cause of the Cretaceous Extinction. For one thing, fossil evidence indicates that many Cretaceous life-forms, including the dinosaurs, were in severe decline *before* the asteroid struck. Secondly, as just noted, we have evidence that global cooling occurred in Cretaceous times. If there is a consensus view on this issue, it is that one or more asteroids probably were responsible for the nearly instantaneous demise of some species, but that in other cases they were merely the final blow in extinctions that already were under way.

At the very least, the Cretaceous Extinction shows that evolution can be affected by sudden, catastrophic events that have nothing to do with Earth's normal physical processes. A fascinating point is raised by this: Fitness, in the evolutionary sense, can change in an eyeblink. The qualities that made the dinosaurs so dominant in the Triassic period were of no use once the asteroid struck. The game of survival had changed. Now *other* qualities came to the fore in survival. Among these may have been small size, which mammals had, perhaps to their great benefit.

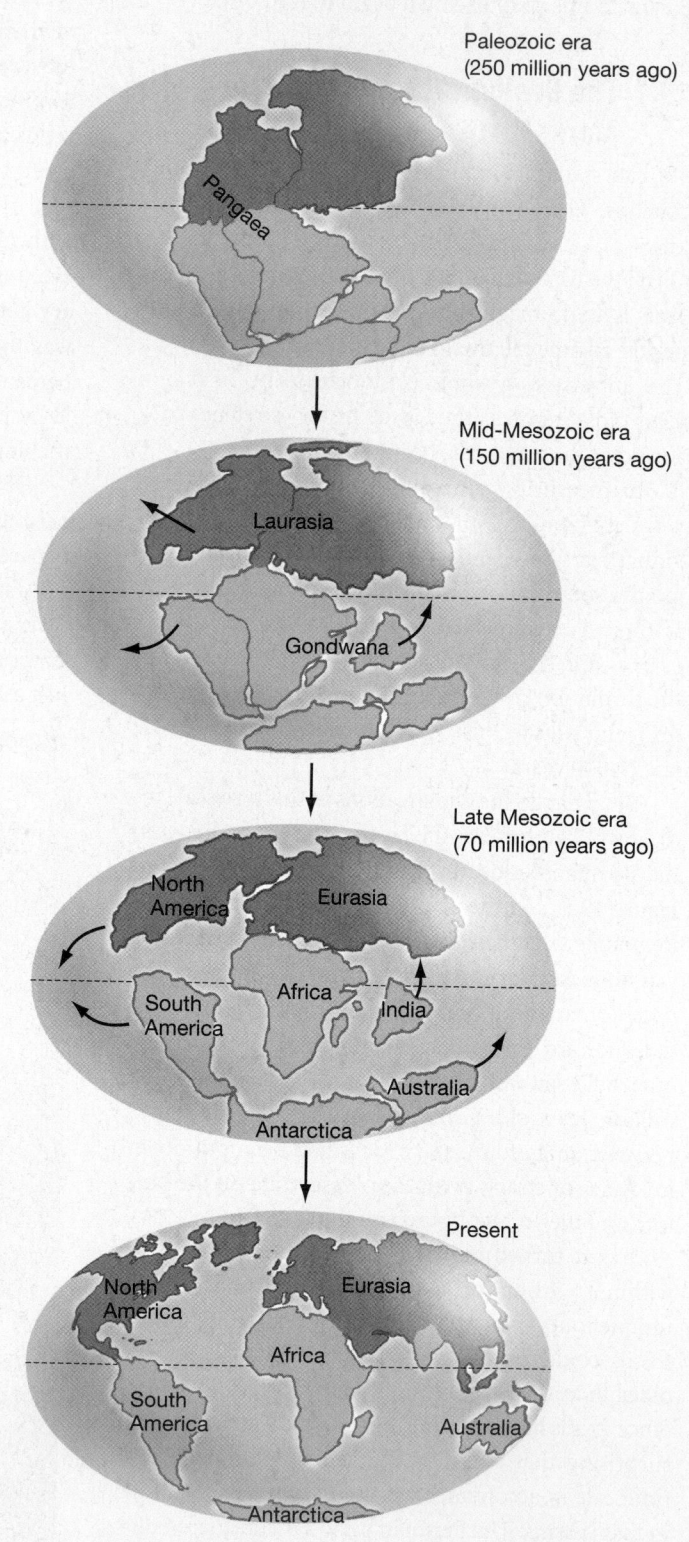

Figure 1
Continental Drift
During Earth's history, the tectonic plates that make up the surface layer of Earth have moved with respect to one another, causing the continents to spread apart and slam together.

Continental Drift

As noted in Chapter 18, the primary engine driving speciation is the geographic separation of populations. Geographic separation was described as taking place in scales that were both small (a stream changing course) and large (a glacier's movement). It turns out that geographic separation can take place on a much larger scale yet, in that whole *continents* have come together and separated again during Earth's history.

If you look at **Figure 1**, you can see the landmasses of the world as they have existed at four separate times: 250 million years ago, 150 Mya, 70 Mya, and the present. In the first of these, nearly all the Earth's continental mass was part of a single supercontinent, Pangaea, which stretched from the South to North Pole. By the Early Cretaceous, Pangaea was separating along the lines you see in the figure. This in turn gave way to our current division which, like its predecessors, is a configuration in flux.

These maps are only four "snapshots" in a process of **continental drift**, or the movement of continents in geological time, that has produced lots of other alignments. How does such movement come about? In essence, the Earth's crust and part of its upper mantle are divided into a series of plates that move laterally over the globe. The movement of these plates can be thought of in terms of a conveyor belt. Halfway between North America and Europe there is a long underwater mountain chain, the Atlantic Ridge. This ridge has in its middle a deep valley that forms the border between the North American and Eurasian Plates. Hot material in the Earth's interior is constantly being moved up into the valley from either plate, after which, as new crust, it moves eastward on one side of the ridge but westward on the other. What we have, then, is a spreading of the ocean floor in opposite directions. *Continents* sit atop this spreading material, and they are being moved in opposite directions—Europe to the east, North America to the west—as if they were objects on conveyor belts (**see Figure 2**).

The Impact of Continental Drift on Evolution

Continental drift has had profound effects on evolution. As noted, global cooling has been the most significant force behind mass extinctions. But what causes global cooling? One factor is the development of glaciers, which as it turns out can grow only when continents are located at or near the Earth's poles. This *was* the case 300 million years ago, then it was *not* the case 200 million years ago, and now it is again. By moving landmasses on and off the poles, continental drift has helped change the climate.

Continental drift has had a second profound effect on evolution, in that it has brought about the separation and mixing of living *populations*. For example, the breakup of the supercontinent Pangaea eventually meant the creation of island continents such as Australia and Antarctica. Until the coming of humans, Australia had scarcely any placental mammals—mammals whose embryos are nourished by a placenta (see Chapter 30). Since prehistoric times, however, Australia has had an abundance of marsupial (or "pouched") mammals, such as kanga-

(a) Paleozoic era Pangaea (250 million years ago)

(b) Today

Figure 2
Similar fossils are found on the east coast of South America and the west coast of Africa. How can this be?

(a) 250 million years ago, the two continents were contiguous and formed part of the giant continent Pangaea.

(b) Animals that were alive then are now found as fossils on opposite sides of the ocean because the ocean floor has been spreading westward and eastward along the central Atlantic Ridge. The ocean floor is spreading because hot material from the Earth's interior is constantly being moved up into the central Atlantic Ridge, even today.

roos and koalas. We can read evolutionary history in this distribution. As traditional theory has it, marsupials developed in Pangaea before its breakup, in what is now North America and Western Europe, and spread to Australia across land bridges to what is now Antarctica. (See the first and second drawings, Figure 1.) Meanwhile, placental mammals were spreading too; but few were able to reach the Australia-Antarctic landmass before it broke away from Pangaea. In effect, placental mammals missed the Antarctic-Australian boat. This idea has been challenged recently, because some ancient placental teeth have been found in Australia. One possibility is that mammals evolved in the south and then migrated to the north.

Now, when did some of these transitions come about? You might think that a transition such as a sudden increase in animal forms would have occurred very early in life's history, but the Cambrian Explosion took place 544 million years ago. This is a long time ago, to be sure, but life is thought to have begun 3.8 *billion* years ago. (Another way of writing this is 3,800 million years ago or 3,800 Mya). There may not have been an animal on the planet for 3.2 billion years after life got going—nor any plants either. Life was single-celled to begin with and, 2 billion years later, it still consisted of nothing but microbes. In the Precambrian era, life evolved at such a slow pace that we scarcely have words for it. ("Glacial" greatly overstates things.) Conversely, if the fossil record is correct, all the birds, reptiles, fish, plants, and mammals that exist today came about in the last 16 percent of evolutionary time—the last 600 million years of life's 3.8-billion-year span. As you'll see, our own species, *Homo sapiens*, is an extreme latecomer in this series of events. (For a look at why various "arrival dates" are uncertain, see "Fossils and Molecular Clocks: Dating Life's Passages" on page 376.)

What Is Notable in Evolution Hinges on Values

One final word about the timescale and the path you will follow in this chapter. Picking out the "notable events" in evolution is inevitably an exercise in making value judgments. The notable events covered in this chapter will lead you along a line that begins with microscopic sea creatures and ends with human beings. The value judgment guiding this path is that students have a great interest in knowing about their own evolution, and that the path to humans arguably presents the broadest sweep of evolutionary development. Such a course of study may leave the impression, however, that all of evolution amounts to a march toward the development of human beings, who then get to occupy the highest branch of an evolutionary tree.

In reality, we occupy one ordinary branch among a multitude of branches. Under notable events in the Cenozoic era, the table could just as easily have listed milestones in the evolution of fish or birds, or the emergence of social insects such as bees. These creatures have continued evolving in the modern era, along with our own species, but in lines separate from us. Focusing on a line that leads to humans is like focusing on a railroad route that leads from, say, Baltimore to Denver, while ignoring the multitude of lines that intersect with it or that are separate from it. We regard the Baltimore–Denver route as special because we are *interested* in it, but that does not mean

that it is fundamentally *different* from any other line. Some special qualities have evolved in human beings, but the same could be said for almost any species. In phylogenetic terms, we simply lie at the tip of one evolutionary branch, while bees lie at another, and cactus plants lie at still another.

The Kingdoms of the Living World Fit into Three Domains

In tracing the history of life, you'll be looking to some extent at all the major life-forms that have evolved on Earth. Thus it will be helpful to have at the outset a sense of what these major life-forms are. This book employs a system of three *domains* of life, which then have within them "kingdoms," as noted in Chapter 18. The three domains are Archaea, Bacteria, and Eukarya.

Archaea is a domain of life populated entirely by microscopic, single-celled organisms, many of which live in "extreme" environments, such as boiling-hot vents on the ocean floor. **Bacteria** is likewise a domain of single-celled microscopic creatures, but these are the bacteria that are more familiar to us. The third domain, **Eukarya**, then includes all the organisms that are most familiar to us—plants, animals, and fungi—along with another group that is less familiar, the protists. (The protist kingdom has within it lots of single-celled water dwellers, but also includes some large organisms, such as giant sea kelp.)

19.2 How Did Life Begin?

Taking a historical approach to tracing life on Earth, the first question that arises is one of the toughest: How did life begin? Darwin himself thought about this and imagined that life began in what he called a "warm little pond" in the early Earth. Well, maybe; but the *very* early Earth had no warm little ponds. What it had was an environment more akin to hell on Earth.

You have seen that Earth was formed about 4.6 billion years ago. This took place in a process of "accretion," in which ever-larger particles clumped together: cosmic dust to gravel, gravel to larger balls, larger balls to objects the size of tiny planets. One consequence of such development was that the accretion now called Earth was periodically being slammed into by *other* large accretions—meteorites and comets and proto-planets. One of these objects was as large as Mars, and the result of its impact on the Earth, 100 million years after Earth formed, may have been the creation of our moon. There were no oceans at this time, and Earth was so hot that it was covered with a layer of molten rock. Here are biologists Christopher Wills and Jeffrey Bada writing in *The Spark of Life* about the young planet:

> Earth at this stage must have been a spectacular planet, its thick atmosphere swirling with color as Jupiter's atmosphere does today. The day side would have been dazzling, and the darkness of the night side would have been dispelled periodically by the flashes of huge lightning storms and the fitful, red glow of mighty volcanic eruptions. Occasionally, bright explosions would blaze up out of the haze surrounding the planet, as [objects] the size of Mount Everest plunged down to strike the surface.

The bombardment of Earth seems to have slowed by about 3.8 billion years ago. With this change, we are left with a large question about what the planet was like. Scientists believe that the sun shone some 20–30 percent less brightly then than it does now. So one of two things is possible. If Earth's atmosphere contained a sufficient concentration of "greenhouse" gases, such as methane and carbon dioxide, then it would have remained a warm place—perhaps even a broilingly hot place. Conversely, if the concentration of these gases was low, then the Earth was frozen over in a global glaciation. Even the seas may have been frozen to a depth of a few hundred meters.

These two views lead to varying ideas about where life could have arisen. It may have originated in a *cold* little pond—one that was under a glacier—but then again, it may have gotten started in just the opposite environment: a hot-water environment, as we'll see. A third possibility is that something like Darwin's warm little pond did exist, in the form of tide pools at the edge of an ancient ocean. As different as all of these environments are, note that all of them are aqueous environments. Life got going in water.

A requirement of any of these environments is that they had to have in them the chemical raw materials that could be used in forming life's critical molecules. You saw in Chapter 3 that life's informational molecules (DNA and RNA) are composed of certain kinds of building blocks (nucleotides), while its proteins are composed of other kinds of building blocks (amino acids). The raw materials for such building blocks could have been the gases methane and ammonia. These substances certainly would have been spewed out (or "outgased") by Earth's early volcanoes. The question is whether they would have been quickly broken down in the ultraviolet light, coming from the sun, that bathed the early Earth's atmosphere.

Figure 19.5
Space Travelers
Fragments of the Murchison meteorite, which landed on the township of Murchison in Australia in 1969. The meteorite contained water and organic molecules such as amino acids. Some scientists hypothesize that organic materials like these could have seeded life on Earth.

Some scientists believe that building blocks such as amino acids could have arrived ready-made, delivered by the meteorites and comets that smashed into the young Earth. It's clear, from meteorites that have landed on Earth in recent decades, that such objects *can* carry organic molecules (**see Figure 19.5**). It appears unlikely, however, that such accidental "seeding" from outer space could have brought a sufficient *quantity* of organic materials to get life going.

Life May Have Begun in Very Hot Water

A third possibility for the supply of organic materials is that they came from the methane and hydrogen sulfide that gush out even today from deep-sea vents on the floors of the world's oceans. Interestingly enough, there are creatures living near these vents today. Some of these are microscopic archaea and bacteria that thrive at temperatures of 105° Celsius (247° Fahrenheit), which is above the temperature at which water boils (see **Figure 19.6**). To judge by some of the molecular sequencing that has produced life's family tree, the very oldest organisms on Earth may be "hyperthermophiles" such as these. Various lines of evidence, including the fact that these organisms live around the

Figure 19.6
Hot Habitat
Material pours forth from a hot-water vent on the floor of the Atlantic Ocean. The fluid being emitted is mineral-rich enough to support bacteria and archaea that in turn form the basis for a local food web.

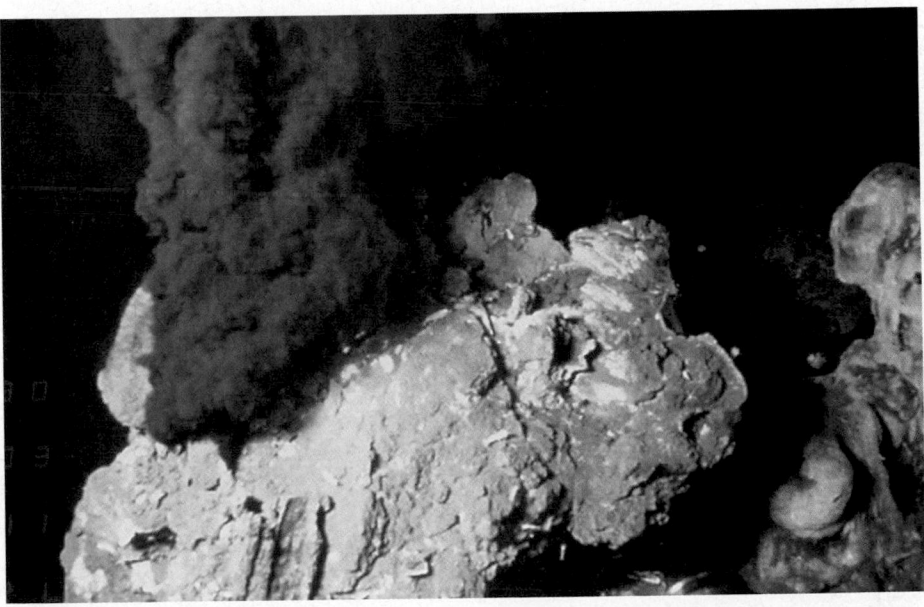

145 First bird fossil (*Archaeopteryx*)
210 First flowering plants (Angiosperms)
245 First dinosaurs and mammals

Fossils and Molecular Clocks: Dating Life's Passages

The geological timescale in Figure 19.3 has a lot of "firsts" in it—first reptiles, first dinosaurs, and so forth. But how can scientists assign even a rough date to the first appearance of a life-form? Through radiometric dating, they can assign dates to *fossils* of life-forms (see Chapter 16, page 318). But that's not the same thing as assigning a date for the *appearance* of a life-form, meaning the date at which it first branched off from an existing group, in the way that reptiles did from amphibians. Imagine that an ancient fossil can be dated radiometrically. What are the chances that this creature was one of the *earliest* organisms of its kind? The answer is, slim to none. Because if an organism was one of the first of its kind to exist, by definition it was one of only a few that existed. And a small "starting set" of this sort is unlikely to leave any fossils. (Think of postage stamps. If only 10 copies of a stamp were originally made a century ago, the chances of one of them existing today are very small. If 10,000 were made, conversely, the chances of one existing go up considerably.) What fossils generally indicate is an *abundance* of a given species—an abundance that can only come about long after the species first appeared.

Beyond this, fossils themselves are a limiting factor in determining when different life-forms first appeared. Recall that one of the ways that relatedness among species is determined is by looking for similarities in their physical characteristics, as detailed in their fossils. But when it comes to Earth's early one-celled life-forms (such as bacteria), fossils can be few to begin with, and those that exist may not differ much in appearance. So, how can scientists begin to construct family trees for Earth's most ancient living things?

One answer, which scientists hit upon in the 1960s, is to use a different kind of dating method than the molecular clocks reviewed in Chapter 16 (see page 319). By comparing molecular sequence differences between living creature A and living creature B, scientists could begin to calculate how long it had been since they shared a common ancestor—how long it was since they branched off into separate species, in other words. How is this possible? Imagine knowing that two streams you are near result from the branching of one stream at some point off in the distance. Further, imagine that you know the *rate* at which these streams are diverging from each other—one stream going in this direction, the other going in that.

You may not be able to travel the whole distance to see the branching point itself, but because you know the rate at which the streams are parting company, you can predict the point at which they diverge. Molecular clocks give scientists a rate of divergence among groups of species, which can be used to infer their branching points.

Molecular dating work was aided tremendously beginning in the 1960s by a scientist named Carl Woese of the University of Illinois who realized that one particular molecule, ribosomal RNA (rRNA), exists in all living things in a standard form. This meant that rRNA sequences could be used as a common molecular clock to measure very ancient lineages. Today, it is not just rRNA, but DNA and proteins as well that are used as molecular clocks to judge when various species arose. The result has been nothing less than a revolution in constructing life's family trees. One of the most robust scientific enterprises of today is the use of molecular clocks to try to "infer phylogenies"—to develop family trees, complete with the dates of the branching points on them.

The problem with this is that the "molecular dates" that are derived often differ drastically from the "fossil dates." The oldest primate fossils we have are about 55 million years old. Meanwhile, molecular dating tells us the earliest primates arose about 90 Mya. You would *expect* the molecular date to be older than the fossil date, because the oldest primate fossil is not likely to be the oldest primate. But should the dates differ by 35 million years? Is it reasonable to expect that primates left no fossils at all for the first 35 million years of their existence? Closer to home, the earliest undisputed dog fossils we have date from 14,000 years ago, but molecular sequencing says dogs arose from wolves 135,000 years ago.

In these cases, as in many others, fossil and molecular scientists disagree about where the truth lies. The molecular scientists think the fossil scientists need to look for earlier fossils; meanwhile, the fossil scientists think the molecular scientists need to recalibrate their molecular clocks. Of course, no matter what method is used, we could never hope to develop precise dates for events that occurred so far in the past; estimates and uncertainty simply come with the territory in developing the history of life. Hopefully in the future, however, science will undergo its own convergence, giving us a clearer picture of how old the branches are on life's family tree.

right sorts of organic materials, leads to an idea that has a good deal of support among origin-of-life researchers. It is that life began in the "prebiotic soup" of hot-water systems—in the deep-sea vents or the kind of hot-spring pools that exist in Yellowstone Park (**see Figure 19.7**).

On the other hand, there are respected researchers who feel that, whatever the deep-sea vents may have had in the way of life-inducing qualities, their scalding temperatures would have obliterated any early self-replicating molecules, which were bound to be fragile. A much more likely first home for life, these researchers feel, are sheltered stretches of ancient ocean beaches, where the combination of tides and the composition of shoreline rocks would have "sorted" organic materials in accordance with their adhesiveness and other qualities. In this environment, the right initial combination of materials could have come together and then been joined by fresh materials, delivered continuously by the ocean waves.

Wherever life began, it cannot have been created in a single step from basic compounds such as methane and hydrogen sulfide. There is a huge gap between these materials and organisms as complex as the archaea. If organic molecules did not come from outer space, early Earth had to be a kind of natural chemical lab in which ever more complex organic molecules were produced from simpler ones. A major portion of origin-of-life research involves creating, in the laboratory, simulations of early Earth environments and then watching to see if life's building blocks will come together in them. Scientists now have scenarios that can account for the creation of most, but not all, of these compounds.

The RNA World

Any living thing must have at least one critical feature: the ability to reproduce itself. Today, a key player in reproduction is DNA. In Chapter 14, you saw that our "genome," or inventory of DNA, can be thought of as a kind of cookbook containing recipes (DNA sequences) that lead to products (proteins) that undertake a wide variety of tasks. Yet, as noted there, though DNA is the cookbook, it is not the cook. When it comes time for DNA to be copied, the double helix cannot unwind itself nor pair its bases up nor do anything else. Instead, all these tasks are carried out by the *proteins* known as enzymes. Hence there is a chicken-and-egg dilemma: Enzymes can't be produced without the information contained in DNA, but DNA can't copy itself without the activity of enzymes. So, how did life get going if neither thing can function without the other?

In the late 1960s, researchers hit on a solution that has come to have a good deal of support. In early life-forms, a *single* molecule performed both the DNA and enzyme roles. This molecule was RNA (ribonucleic acid), which was portrayed back in Chapter 14 as a kind of genetic middleman, ferrying DNA's information to the sites where proteins are put together. A critical piece of evidence about RNA's role in early life came in 1983, when researchers discovered the existence of enzymes that are composed of RNA instead of protein: **ribozymes**. These molecules can encode in-

formation *and* act as enzymes (by, for example, facilitating bonds that bind RNA units together).

This evidence leads researchers to the presumed existence of the "RNA world"—an early living world that consisted solely of self-replicating RNA molecules. But there are questions about this RNA world. One of them is how it came into being in the first place. RNA is so complex, and so fragile, that many researchers believe it had to have taken over the role of a simpler, sturdier precursor. There are several candidates for this role, though none has proven itself yet.

The Step at Which Life Begins

The critical step in life's development comes in imagining RNA or its precursor beginning to carry out this replication. *This* is the step at which life can be said to have begun. Given a molecule that can make copies of itself, a line of such molecules can come into existence. Given the *mistakes* that are bound to take place in such copying, molecules can be produced that differ slightly from one another in being, say, more resistant to the elements. Molecules that have such an advantage will leave more daughter molecules, which might just as well be called offspring. What happens, in short, is natural selection among self-replicating molecules. This selection, of course, leads to evolution among these molecules, and with evolution life begins to diversify into the innumerable forms we see today.

Web Tutorial 19.2
RNA-like Self Replication

Figure 19.7
Only Seemingly Inhospitable
The hot-water Grand Prismatic Pool in Yellowstone National Park, shown here in an aerial view, gets its blue color from several species of heat-tolerant cyanobacteria. The colors at the edge of the pool come from mineral deposits. The "road" at the top of the pool is a walkway for visitors.

Once replication got going, we were still a long way from life as we know it today. Even the most primitive contemporary living things are encased in the protective linings; and they can get rid of wastes, react to their environments, and so forth. Whatever the sequence of events, once life's elaborations are joined to replication, we move from simple molecules to the cellular ancestors of today's organisms.

19.3 The Tree of Life

Once life was established, how did it evolve? If you look at **Figure 19.8**, you can see the biggest picture of all, which scientists produced by doing the kind of ribosomal RNA sequences note in Dating Life's passages on page 376. At the bottom you see a "universal ancestor," which is the organism—or perhaps a cooperative group of organisms—that gave rise to all current life. The evolutionary line that leads from the universal ancestor then branches out to yield, on the one hand, the domain Bacteria and, on the other, a line that leads to both the domain Archaea and the domain Eukarya. Archaea were long thought of as simply a different kind of bacteria, but recent research has shown these organisms to be distinct from bacteria in fundamental ways. Nevertheless, there are great similarities. Bacteria and archaea are

Figure 19.8
The Universal Tree of Life
The universal ancestor at the base of the tree gave rise to two domains of organisms whose cells lack nuclei—Bacteria and Archaea. The third domain of life is the Eukarya, whose earliest kingdom was the protists. From these protists all plants, animals, and fungi evolved.

essentially single-celled, and no archaeic or bacterial cell has a nucleus. Conversely, *all* the organisms in the domain Eukarya have nucleated cells, and are thus "eukaryotes."

As noted earlier, domain Eukarya has four "kingdoms" within it that you'll be learning about. Looking at the tree, you can see that the earliest kingdom in Eukarya is Protista—mostly one-celled, water-dwelling creatures—and it is from Protista that the other three eukaryotic kingdoms evolve. An unknown species within Protista gave rise to all the fungi that exist on Earth today; another grouping of protists called the choanoflagellates probably gave rise to all of the animal kingdom; and the protists we call green algae gave rise to all of today's plants. Note that, though it's common to think of plants and fungi as being alike, fungi and animals actually are more closely related than are fungi and plants.

19.4 A Long First Period: The Precambrian

With this picture in mind, let's start tracing life from its cellular beginnings. As noted, living things started small and stayed that way for a long, long time. Recall that the Earth was formed about 4,600 Mya. The earliest evidence we have of life is not a fossil but instead a kind of chemical signature of life left in the barren, frozen Isua rocks of Greenland (**see Figure 19.9**). Carbon trapped in these 3,700 to 3,800-million-year-old rocks is of a type produced only by living things. This evidence is controversial, but carbon signatures indicating photosynthesis are abundant beginning at 3,500 Mya, and microfossils found in Western Australia indicate that by 3,200 Mya, filament-type bacteria existed there. Most authorities believe that life existed by 3,800 Mya, or at the latest by 3,500 Mya. All of this life was of two types, bacteria or archaea, and all of it seems to have existed in the ancient oceans.

Once the bacteria and archaea got going, the long, slow Precambrian era had began. It was probably almost 2 billion years before any other life-form came into existence. When the first *multi*celled organisms appeared isn't clear. Certainly they exist by the time we have the first fossil evidence for animals, which is 600 Mya. But molecular clock studies put their evolution much further back, perhaps about 1,500 Mya. Even supposing this latter figure is right, note the big picture here. It took about 900 million years for life to appear after the Earth was formed; but then it took another 2.3 billion years to get from these single-celled life-forms to multicelled life-forms. Some authorities

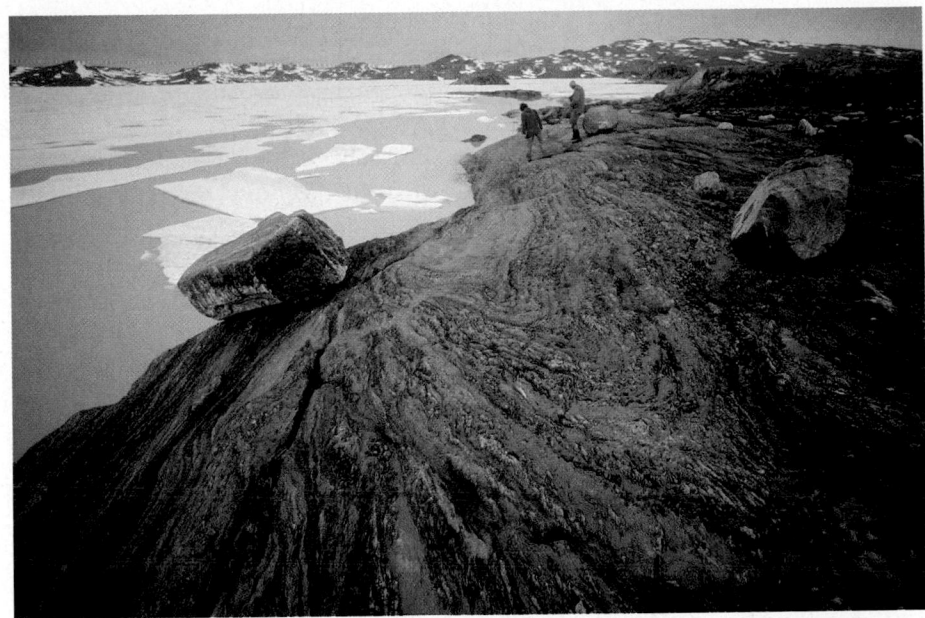

Figure 19.9
Looking at the Oldest Rocks
The rocks at Isua, Greenland are believed to be the oldest in the world. In examining them, scientists have found possible chemical signatures of life that have been dated to nearly 3.8 billion years ago.

say this is evidence that the real hurdle in evolution was not the initiation of life, but rather the initiation of complex, multicellular life. What is certain is that evolution took its time in the Precambrian. The years rolled by in the millions, the land was barren, and the oceans were populated mostly by creatures too small to see with the naked eye.

Notable Precambrian Events

None of this is to say, however, that "nothing happened" in the Precambrian era. Those of you who have read Chapter 8 know how critical photosynthesis is for life on Earth. This capability first came about in the Precambrian era—and fairly early in the era at that.

Photosynthesis began in bacteria at least by the time the first bacterial fossils left their imprint, about 3,200 Mya. This event was a turning point. Had this capacity not been developed, evolution would have been severely limited, for the simple reason that there would have been so little to eat on Earth. The earliest organisms subsisted mostly on organic material in their surroundings, but the supply of this material was limited. In photosynthesis, the sun's energy is used to *produce* organic material—in our own era, the leaves and grasses and grains on which all animal life depends. Large organisms require more energy and, through photosynthesis, a massive quantity of energy-rich food was made available.

One particular kind of photosynthesis, again beginning in the Precambrian, had a second dramatic impact on evolution. One very early type of bacteria, the *cyanobacteria*, were the first organisms to produce *oxygen* as a by-product of photosynthesis. For us the word oxygen seems nearly synonymous with the word life, but until about 2,300 Mya there was almost no oxygen in the atmosphere. When it finally did arrive, through the work of the cyanobacteria, its effect was anything but life-giving. For most organisms it was a deadly gas, producing what has been termed an "oxygen holocaust" and establishing a firm rule for life on Earth: Adapt to oxygen, stay away from it, or die.

In the creatures that adapted to oxygen, we find one of the most interesting stories in evolution. Those of you who went through Chapter 7, on cellular energy harvesting, will recall that most of the energy that eukaryotes get from food is extracted in special structures within their cells, called *mitochondria*. Though mitochondria are tiny organelles within eukaryotic cells, they have characteristics of free-living *cells*, specifically free-living bacterial cells. As it turns out, that is probably what they once were. Ancient bacteria that could metabolize oxygen took up residence in early eukaryotic cells and eventually struck up a mutually beneficial relationship with them (**see Figure 19.10**). The bacteria benefited from the eukaryotic cellular machinery, and the eukaryotes got to survive in an oxygen-rich world. In a second bacterial invasion, algae and their plant descendants got not only mitochondria, but the chloroplasts in which photosynthesis is carried out (see "Endosymbiosis" in Chapter 4, page 84).

The oxygen revolution then had one more momentous consequence. Molecules of oxygen came together to form the gas called *ozone*, which rose through the atmosphere to form the ozone layer, giving Earth, for the first time ever, protection against the ultraviolet radiation that comes from the sun. Marine creatures had been shielded from this radiation by the ocean itself, but prior to the formation of the ozone layer, there was no chance for life to develop on *land*.

19.5 The Cambrian Explosion

As the Precambrian was coming to a close, life consisted of bacteria, archaea, and many kinds of protists, most of which lived in the ocean. By about 600

Mya, however, we get the first fossil evidence of *animals* in the seas. The term "animal" here fits our common sense definition: They all are multicelled organisms, and they get their nutrition from other organisms or organic material.

There currently is a debate about whether the earliest animal fossils represent a line of creatures that died out, or are instead related to today's animals. Whatever the case, these early animals can be seen as a kind of early stirring; a first blip on the screen bringing news of something big to come. To judge by the fossil record, about 60 million years after the emergence of these animals, we get it. A tidal wave of new animal forms, the like of which has never been seen before or since in evolution. This is the **Cambrian Explosion**, which began about 544 Mya.

Recalling the taxonomic system you went over in Chapter 18, you may remember that just below the "domain" and "kingdom" categories there is the **phylum**, which can be defined informally as a group of organisms that share the same body plan. There are at least 36 phyla in the animal kingdom today, some of these being Porifera (sponges), Arthropoda (insects, crabs), and Chordata (ourselves, salamanders). With one exception, the fossil record indicates, every single one of these came into being in the Cambrian Explosion. This seeming riot of sea-floor evolution was actually more extensive than even this implies, in that a good number of phyla that *don't* exist today—phyla that have become extinct—also seem to have first appeared in the Cambrian. Some of these creatures are so bizarre, it's surprising that Hollywood hasn't mined the Cambrian archives for new ideas on monsters (**see Figure 19.11**). As if all this weren't enough, the Cambrian Explosion appears to have taken place in a very short period of time relative to evolution's normal pace—perhaps as little as 5 million years.

But did it? The Cambrian Explosion is so extreme that one of the primary challenges to evolutionary biology has been to explain why such a thing came about—or why it came about only once. Note the series of events: only a few animal forms before the Cambrian, then the explosion, then almost no new animal forms since. In the 1990s, several lines of evidence suggested something else: that animal forms actually began to diverge well back in the *Pre*cambrian. Under this view, all the Cambrian Explosion amounted to was an explosion of forms big and hard enough to leave *fossils*. The forms themselves appeared earlier and more gradually, this idea goes, but were too small and fragile to leave imprints behind. And indeed, molecular clock studies suggest that animals appeared as far back as 1.5 billion years ago.

Figure 19.10
Adapting to Oxygen
The "powerhouses" of our cells—the organelles called mitochondria—have several characteristics of free-standing bacteria.

(a) There is general agreement among scientists that our mitochondria originally were bacteria that invaded eukaryotic cells many millions of years ago. These bacteria benefited from the eukaryote's cellular machinery, and the cell benefited from the bacteria's ability to metabolize oxygen.

(b) Over time, the bacteria came to be integrated into the host cells, replicating along with them. Two symbiotic organisms had now become a single organism.

(c) Today, the mitochondria in your cells turn the energy from food into a form that allows you to run, think, and turn the pages of this book. These artificially colored mitochondria functioned in a liver cell of a mouse.

(a)

eukaryotic cell

bacterial cell

(b)

eukaryotic cell

mitochondrion

(c)

If the Cambrian Explosion did in fact occur, what could have sparked it? Lots of ideas have been proposed; one of the best-received is that the explosion was triggered by the rise in atmospheric oxygen. To get bigger creatures, you need more oxygen, and levels of atmospheric oxygen may have reached a critical threshold about this time. Once larger forms *could* appear, adaptive radiation took place on a grand scale. So many niches were available that there was an explosion of forms. Once all the basic niches were taken, however, this frenzy of new forms not only came to a stop, it was pruned back (in the sense that some Cambrian phyla became extinct).

19.6 The Movement onto the Land: Plants First

The teeming seas of the early Cambrian period stand in sharp contrast to what existed on land at the time, which was no life at all except for some hardy bacteria. Earth was simply barren—no greenery, no birds, no insects. When multicelled life did come to the land, the first intrepid travelers were plant-fungi combinations. (Even today, most plants have a symbiotic relationship with fungi, the plants providing fungi with food through photosynthesis, the fungi providing plants with water and mineral absorption through their filament extensions.) Exactly when this transition onto land took place is a matter of debate. The earliest undisputed fossil evidence we have of plants and fungi on land dates from 460 Mya, meaning these organisms had become abundant by that time. But when did they first appear? New molecular work estimates that land (or "terrestrial") fungi have been around for 1.3 billion years. These fungi couldn't have existed without plants—since they need them to live—which would mean that plants were on land at this time too. The general transition here began with marine algae in the ocean, then continued with freshwater algae, then freshwater algae that came to exist in *shallow* water, living partially above the waterline. When the transition to full-time living on land came, it was to damp environments.

Adaptations of Plants to the Land

Such a change required a lot of adaptation. Aquatic algae did not have to deal with water loss or the crushing effects of gravity, but land plants did. One of the plants' responses to the water problem was to evolve a waxy outer covering, called a *cuticle*, that could retain moisture. Meanwhile, an initial response to gravity was to stay low. Some of the most primitive land plants are mosses that often hug the ground like so much green carpet (**see Figure 19.12**).

Figure 19.11
Life on the Ancient Sea Floor
The Cambrian Explosion resulted in a multitude of new animal forms. In this artist's interpretation of the fossil evidence, a number of now-extinct Cambrian animals are shown in their ancient sea-floor habitat. Two of these are Anomalocaris, raising up with the hooked claws, and Hallucigenia, on the sea floor with the spikes extending from it.

Then there was the problem of reproduction. When green algae reproduce sexually, their gametes (eggs and sperm) float off from them as individual cells, after which they are brought together by ocean currents or the cells' own movement. Once this happens, the resulting embryos develop completely on their own. An embryo left to mature by itself on land, however, would dry out and perish. Plants adapted to the land by developing a protective housing for embryos; in a plant, embryos mature *within* a parent.

Figure 19.12
Lying Low
Moss covering rocks along a stream in Tennessee's Great Smoky Mountains National Park. Mosses are members of the earliest-evolving group of plants, the bryophytes.

Another Plant Innovation: A Vascular System

If you look at **Figure 19.13**, you can see how the major divisions of plants evolved. The most primitive land plants, the **bryophytes** (represented by today's mosses), had no vascular structure—meaning a system of tubes that transports water and nutrients. Plants without such a system have very limited structural possibilities. They can grow out, but they lack ability to grow *up* very far, against gravity. By contrast, the ancestors of today's ferns developed a vascular system; with this, over the ensuing 100 million years, a variety of **seedless vascular plants** evolved, including huge seedless trees such as club mosses, some of them 40 meters tall, which is about 130 feet.

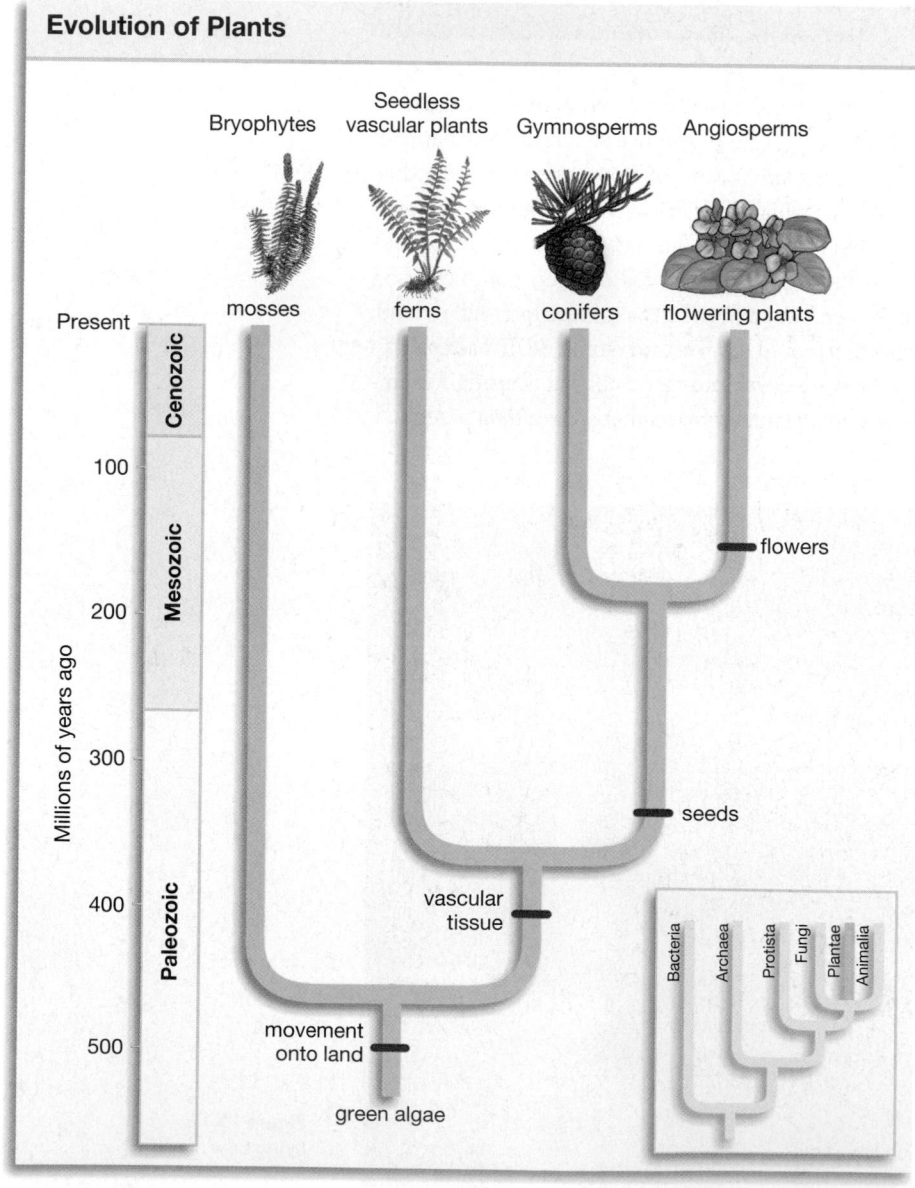

Figure 19.13
How Plants Evolved
The tree of life for bryophytes, seedless vascular plants, gymnosperms, and angiosperms.

Plants with Seeds: The Gymnosperms and Angiosperms

Even as the seedless vascular plants were reaching their apex, a revolution in plants was well under way as some of them developed *seeds*. With the first seed plants, offspring no longer had to develop within a delicate plant on the forest floor. Instead they developed within a seed, which can be thought of as a reproductive package that includes not only an embryo (brought about when sperm fertilized egg), but food for this embryo, and a tough outer coat.

The living descendants of the first seed plants are **gymnosperms**—today's pine and fir trees, for example—whose seeds are visible in the well-known pinecone. Gymnosperms also represent the final liberation of plants from their ocean past. Mosses and ferns had sperm that could make the journey to eggs only through water. Not much water was needed; a thin layer would do, as with the last of a morning's dew on a fern leaf. With seed plants, however, the water requirement is gone entirely. Sperm are encased inside pollen grains, which can be carried by the *wind*. Think how far a windblown pollen grain could disperse compared to a sperm moving across a watery leaf. Several types of gymnosperms developed beginning about 350 Mya. Today, gymnosperm trees cover huge stretches of the Northern Hemisphere.

The Last Plant Revolution So Far: The Angiosperms

At the time the dinosaurs reigned supreme among land animals, the first flowering on Earth occurs, with the development of flowering plants, also known as **angiosperms**. Evolving about 165 Mya, the angiosperms eventually succeed the gymnosperms as the most dominant plants on Earth. Today there are about 700 gymnosperm species, but some 260,000 angiosperm species, with more being identified all the time. Angiosperms are not just more numerous than gymnosperms, they are vastly more diverse as well. They include not only magnolias and roses, but oak trees and cactus, wheat and rice, lima beans and sunflowers. If you look at **Figure 19.14**, you can see the fossilized impression of what may be an early flowering plant, dating from 125 Mya, along with an artist's conception of what it looked like.

19.7 Animals Follow Plants onto the Land

The movement of plants onto the land made it possible for animals to follow. With plants came food and shelter from the sun's rays. Recalling the division of the animal kingdom into various phyla, it was the phylum of arthropods that first moved to land. About 440 Mya—20 million years after the first plant fossils were laid down—a creature similar to a modern centipede laid down the oldest set of terrestrial animal tracks we know of. It makes sense that arthropods were the first animals to come onto land, because the hallmark of all of them is a tough external skeleton (an "exoskeleton"), which can prevent water loss and guard against the sun's rays.

Other kinds of arthropods, the insects, came on land some 50 million years after the first arthropod immigrants. The insect pioneers were wingless, perhaps being something like modern silverfish. Insect flight would not develop for tens of millions of years more, but when it did insects had the skies to themselves for 100 million years. The more primitive flying insects are represented today by dragonflies, whose wings cannot be folded back on their body (**see Figure 19.15**). The compactness that came with foldable wings gave later insects the advantage of being able to get into small spaces. (Think of a common housefly.) In both winged and wingless forms, the insects took to the land with a vengeance. About 1.4 mil-

lion species of living things have been identified on Earth to date, of which *half* are insects. For millions of years, the insects and their fellow arthropods were the only animals on land—but this would change.

Vertebrates Move onto Land

You'll recall that back at the time of the Cambrian Explosion, almost all animals existed on the ancient ocean floor. Within just a few million years, however, animals with backbones, known as vertebrates, were moving throughout the ocean; several of them were primitive, now extinct, orders of fishes. About 450 Mya, we get the rise of the family of fishes, the gnathostomes, that are the ancestors of nearly all the fish species still alive today, from sharks to gars to goldfish. Critically, gnathostomes are the first creatures to have jaws. With the development of jaws, these vertebrates and their descendants (one of whom is us) could securely grasp all kinds of things; big chunks of food, to be sure, but also offspring and inanimate objects. The new foods that became available to those with jaws allowed the gnathostomes to outgrow their jawless vertebrate relatives.

Primitive Fish First

It was a particular, later-arriving type of gnathostome, the "lobe-finned" fishes, that represent the transitional organisms between sea life and land life. The lobed *fins* these creatures possessed are the precursors to the

Figure 19.14
A Possible Early Flowering Plant
In 2002, a team of Chinese and American scientists announced the discovery of *Archaefructus sinensis*, whose fossilized, 125-million-year-old impression can be seen at left. The plant clearly had angiosperm-like traits—for example, the male reproductive structures known as anthers. Yet it had no petals. One hypothesis is that it represents a transitional form in the evolution of angiosperms from lake-dwelling herbaceous plants. If so, it stands to overturn the long-held hypothesis that angiosperms evolved from woody gymnosperms. On the right is an artist's conception of what *A. sinensis* looked like.

Figure 19.15
The First to Take Flight
Dragonflies, such as this dew-covered individual, are descendants of the insects that first developed the ability to fly. Flying insects that evolved later could fold their wings back, as with today's housefly.

four *limbs* that are found in all tetrapod vertebrates, including ourselves (**see Figure 19.16**). It is a line of such tetrapods—the amphibians, the reptiles, and the mammals—that you'll follow for the rest of your walk through evolution. Here is the order of emergence among these forms. The lobe-finned fish give rise to amphibians, and early, salamander-like amphibians give rise to reptiles. Early reptiles then diverge into several lines, one leading to the dinosaurs and another leading to mammals. Dinosaurs eventually die out, of course, but before they do, a lineage that will live on—the birds—diverges from them (**see Figure 19.17**).

Amphibians and Reptiles

In **Figure 19.18**, you can see an artist's rendering of *Ichthyostega*, one of the earliest-known amphibians, which has a tail much like that of its lobe-finned ancestors. *Amphibian* literally means "double life," which is appropriate because in these creatures we can see the pull of both the watery world from which they came and the land onto which they moved. Modern-day frogs can serve as an example here. Many species of frog spend their adult lives as air-breathing land dwellers, but must return to the water to reproduce. Female frogs deposit eggs directly into the water, and the males then deposit sperm on top of them. The young that survive from this clutch go on to live as swimming tadpoles, complete with gills and a tail. After a time, however, both these features disappear, even as lungs start to develop, along with ears for hearing and legs for hopping. The tadpole has become a frog—a double life indeed.

A Critical Reptilian Innovation: The Amniotic Egg

In the transition from amphibian to *reptile*, there is a severing of the amphibian ties to the water through a new kind of protection for the unborn. Amphibian eggs require a watery environment; lacking any sort of outer shell, they dry out if taken out of the water, thus killing the embryo inside. The early reptiles solved this problem with the remarkable adaptation of the **amniotic egg**: an egg that has not only a hard outer casing, but an inner padding in the form of egg "whites" and a series of membranes around the growing embryo. These membranes help supply nutrients and get rid of waste for the embryonic reptile. With this hardy egg, the tie to the water had been broken; reptiles could move *inland*.

Amphibians were the sole terrestrial vertebrates for about 30 million years, beginning about 350 Mya. We think of these creatures now in terms of small frogs and salamanders, but the amphibians that roamed the Earth in the Pennsylvanian period were often the size of modern-day pigs or crocodiles. The carnivores among them probably fed on small early reptiles, but reptiles ultimately became the hunters rather than the hunted. Thriving everywhere from water to dry highlands, reptiles grew in numbers and diversity.

One line of reptiles evolved, about 220 Mya, into the most fearsome creatures ever to walk the Earth—the dinosaurs. For 155 million years, no other land creatures dared challenge them for food or habitat. Not all dinosaurs were huge, and many did not eat meat. Yet even a leaf eater such as *Apatosaurus* must have commanded a good deal of respect, because it measured more than 26 meters, or 85 feet, from head to tail and weighed more than 30 tons. By comparison, a modern African elephant may weigh about 7 tons.

From Reptiles to Mammals

Scurrying about in the underbrush when the dinosaurs reigned supreme were several species of insect-eating animals, none bigger than a rat. These

(a) Ray-finned fish   **(b)** Lobe-finned fish   **(c)** Amphibian

Figure 19.16
Vertebrates onto Land

(a) Our ray-finned fish ancestors lacked bones in their fins.

(b) The lobe-finned fish that evolved from ray-finned fish had small bones in their fins that enabled them to pull out of the water and support their weight on tidal mudflats and sandbars.

(c) Finally, the early amphibians lost ray fins altogether, and had only bones in their limbs.

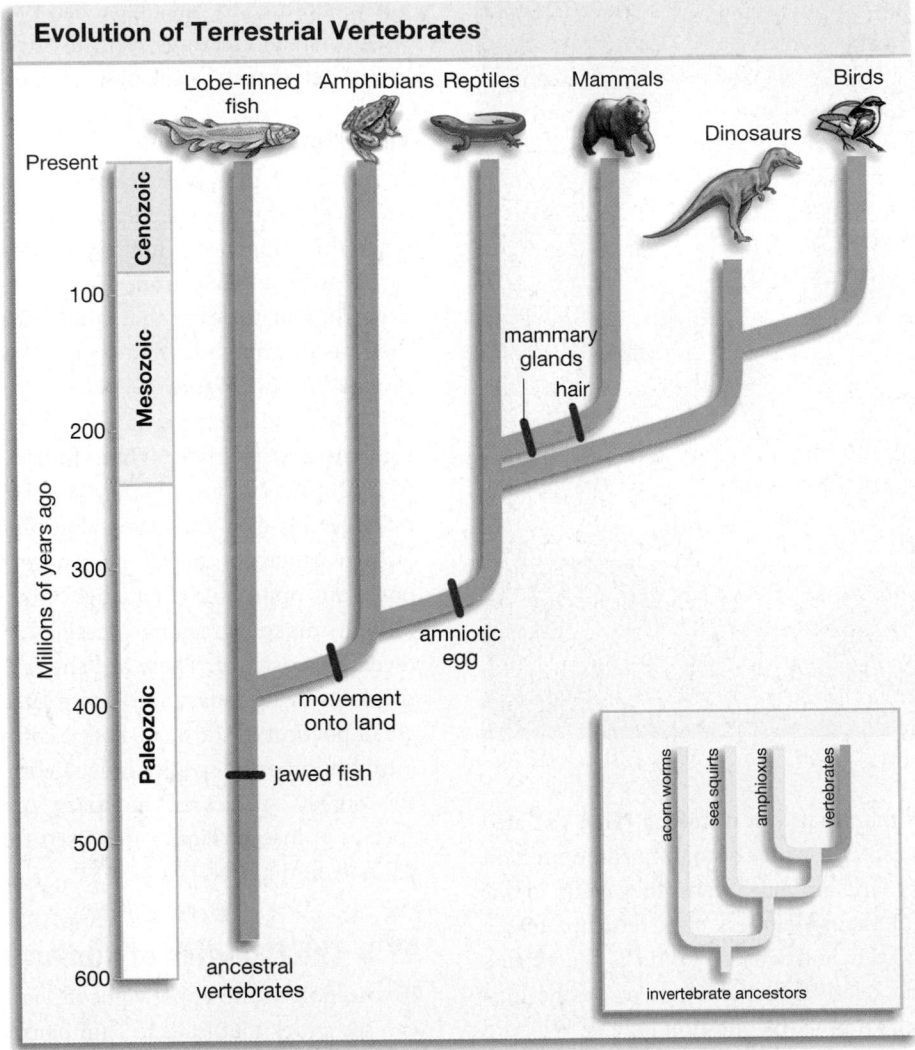

Figure 19.17
How Terrestrial Vertebrates Evolved
A tree of life for lobe-finned fish, amphibians, reptiles, mammals, and birds.

animals fed their young on milk derived from special female mammary glands, however. In addition, they probably possessed fur coats over their skins—an important feature for animals restricted to feeding at night, when the dinosaurs were less active. These were the mammals, the first of which appeared about 210 million years ago—about 10 million years after the dinosaurs arose. In an example of being "born at the wrong time," these small mammals then lived in the shadow of the reptilian behemoths for more than 100 million years. Toward the end of the Cretaceous period, they began to radiate out into more environments and consequently evolved into more forms. At that point fate intervened: The asteroid that helped bring the reign of the dinosaurs to a crashing close 65 Mya also

Figure 19.18
Transitional Animal
An artist's conception of *Ichthyostega*, one of the earliest known amphibians, seen at upper left climbing on the log and at center. Sometimes thought of as a "four-legged fish," *Ichthyostega* spent most of its time in water and probably used its back legs mostly for paddling. All land creatures with backbones, including human beings, ultimately trace their ancestry to tetrapod fishes such as *Ichthyostega*.

Figure 19.19
Primate Characteristics
These modern-day lemurs in Madagascar exhibit several characteristics common to most primates: Opposable digits that enable grasping, front-facing eyes that allow binocular vision, and a tree-dwelling existence.

brought the mammals out of hiding. They radiated into niches far and wide, becoming the dominant form of large land animal, a status they retain to this day. Some of their members even returned to the sea, as with seals and whales. (Who is the whale's closest living relative? It turns out to be the hippopotamus.) An obvious question here is: Why did the mammals survive the Cretaceous Extinction while the dinosaurs died out? Alas, we have no clear answers. Pure size may have had something to do with it; small creatures seem to survive extinction events better than large ones.

The Primate Mammals

A species of placental mammals gave rise to the order of mammals called *primates*, though exactly when this happened is not clear. The oldest primate fossils we have date from 55 Mya, but it will not surprise you to learn that molecular work places their origins much further back—at about 90 Mya. If you look at **Figure 19.19**, you can see, in the lemur of Madagascar, a modern-day descendant of these earliest primates. Three things characteristic of most primates are apparent in this picture: large, front-facing eyes that allow for binocular vision (which enhances depth perception); limbs that have an opposable first digit, like our thumb (which makes grasping possible); and a tree-dwelling existence. There are about 230 species of primates living today (**see Figure 19.20**), which is a small portion of the 4,600 species of mammals. It's a tiny number of species indeed compared to, say, the 60,000 species of molluscs, or the 750,000 species of insects. **Figure 19.21** sets forth a possible primate family tree.

19.8 The Evolution of Human Beings

If you look to the upper right in Figure 19.21, you can see a fork that leads to chimpanzees on the one hand and human beings on the other. Down at the branching point of this fork is a presumed "com-

(a) A prosimian

(b) A New World monkey

(c) A great ape

Figure 19.20
Several Types of Primates

(a) A loris from India (*Loris tardigradus*) is representative of an early primate lineage, the prosimians, that includes llemurs.

(b) A woolly spider monkey (*Brachyteles arachnoides*) from the Atlantic rain forest in Brazil. Note the tail, which is capable of grasping objects. Only New World monkeys have such tails.

(c) A lowland silverback gorilla (*Gorilla gorilla*), native to Africa.

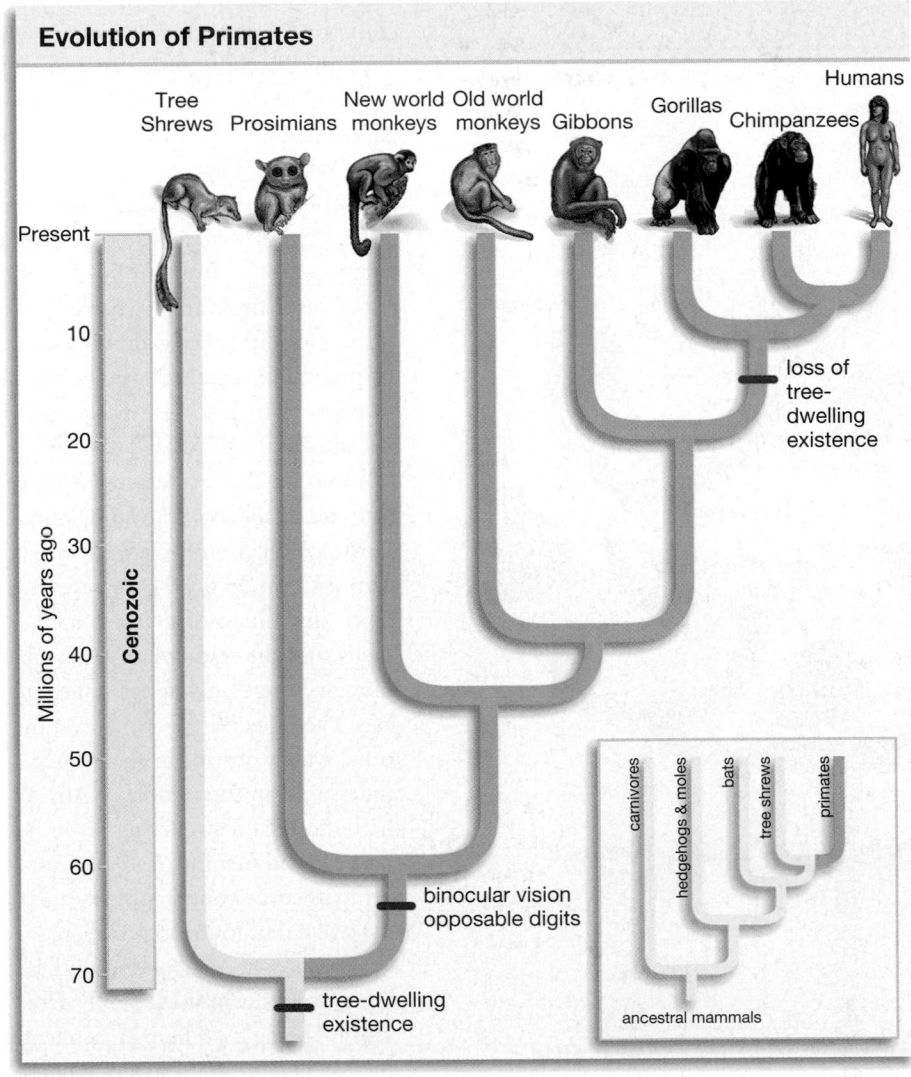

Evolution of Primates

Tree Shrews · Prosimians · New world monkeys · Old world monkeys · Gibbons · Gorillas · Chimpanzees · Humans

Present

Millions of years ago

Cenozoic

10

20

loss of tree-dwelling existence

30

40

50

carnivores · hedgehogs & moles · bats · tree shrews · primates

60

binocular vision opposable digits

70

tree-dwelling existence

ancestral mammals

**Figure 19.21
How Primates May Have
Evolved**

mon primate ancestor"—a single species that gave rise to both the chimpanzee family tree and the human family tree. By working backward through a set of primate molecular clocks, geneticists have determined that this branching probably occurred between 6 and 7 million years ago.

This split, of course, raises the question: Who was the common primate ancestor? We know that it was not the equivalent of a modern-day chimpanzee; today's chimpanzees did not arise until about the same time modern humans did. All we can say is that it was an ape-like creature whose closest living relatives include not only ourselves and chimpanzees, but gorillas and the chimp-like primates known as bonobos.

Figure 19.21 might leave the impression that it only took a couple of speciation events to go straight from the primate ancestor to modern human beings and chimpanzees. But the line extending up to hu-

mans is something like a satellite image of a river: it shows only the river's general outline, instead of its turns and branches. For a kind of close-up of the line leading to human beings, look at **Figure 19.22** on the next page. In it, you can see one possible way in which the human lineage might have evolved, from the common primate ancestor to modern *Homo sapiens*.

It's important to note at the outset that the human family tree in Figure 19.22 represents just one hypothesis, among many that have been proposed, for how human beings evolved. The problem in constructing such a tree is not with the dates you see that are lined up with the species; most of them are solid. And the problem is not with the individual species; we have fossils of all of them. The problem comes with *connecting* the species: who arose from whom? There is scarcely a branching point or line of connection in Figure 19.22 that all authorities agree to, and even many of the species and genus names in it are

Evolution of Human Beings

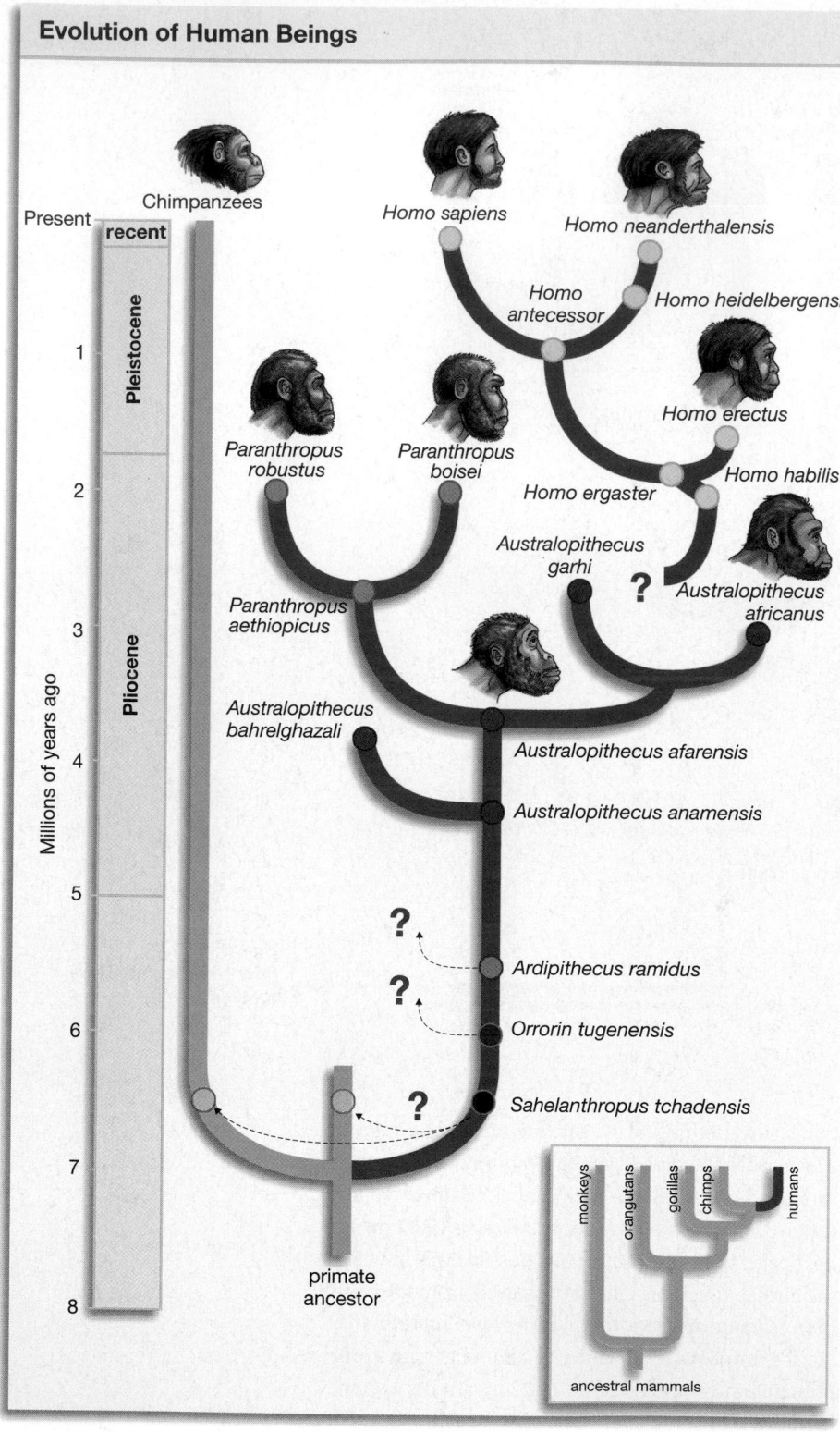

Figure 19.22
A Possible Family Tree for Human Beings

eage. Without family trees, human evolution can become an incomprehensible set of Latin names.

Debates about where an animal species belongs in a family tree are normally carried out in scientific papers and conferences, away from the public spotlight. When it comes to the human lineage, however, the public *cares* about who goes where, for the same reason that any of us would care about whether our family ancestors came from Ireland or Peru. Hence, major fossil finds are the subjects of major newspaper stories. And the scientists who make these finds are pressed for details about the meaning of their discoveries, as if they were private detectives who had just shown up with a load of family secrets.

Who are these researchers? There are archaeologists and geneticists who study human origins, along with biological anthropologists, who sequence ancient and modern DNA. However, the central evidence in human-origins research has always been fossils, and the researchers who seek out and analyze human-lineage fossils are called paleoanthropologists. These scientists go wherever the fossils are likely to be, which can mean the French countryside, but can also mean the middle of Africa's Sahel desert or the bottom of a sweltering pit in Spain. There, they can be found turning over handfuls of earth in an effort to uncover bone fragments and rock impressions that will tell us more about where we came from.

The ultimate goal of this work is the construction of an accurate human family tree, with the word "family" being used here in its scientific sense. All the species in Figure 19.22 are members of the taxonomic family *Hominidae*, which is to say the family of manlike primates. Every member of the *Hominidae* family is referred to as a **hominid**, including human beings.

What are some of the notable features of this tree as it's been constructed so far? Well, if you look at the root of Figure 19.22, you'll notice it that starts with one species, the primate ancestor. Up at the top is our species, *Homo sapiens*. In between these two points, there is a kind of bush-like branching of the various genera and species. Now here's the interesting thing: Every species in this tree is extinct except for our own. Numerous species arose in the human family tree over the past 6 or 7 million years, but all of them are gone except us. If you could take a time machine back 50,000 years, you would find, in Africa and elsewhere, fully modern human beings, which is to say hominids who physically are indistinguishable from us. But in Europe you would also find stocky Neanderthals (species *Homo neanderthalensis*), and over in the Far East you would find the dwindling remnants of a once far-flung species, *Homo erectus*. Jump forward another 10,000 years and all the *H. erectus* are

matters of dispute. (Is the *Paranthropus* genus at center left really its own genus, or should the species in it be included in the nearby *Australopithecus* genus?) Given these uncertainties, you might ask, why produce such trees at all? Scientists have use for them because they provide a starting point for analyzing the human lineage. We have use for them because they provide a starting point for *understanding* this lin-gone; jump forward another 13,000 and all the Neanderthals are gone. Today, only we *Homo sapiens* remain among the hominids.

Another way to think of this tree is in terms of relative time frames. An "ancient" civilization, such as that of Egypt, stretches back perhaps 5,000 years. Yet the Neanderthals disappeared from the face of the Earth 22,000 years before Egyptian civilization began, and they had been in existence for 200,000 years. Even so, the Neanderthals were late-comers among the hominids. Recall that the *Hominidae* line stretches back as far as 7 million years. Thus, human evolution took a great deal of time, even when dated just from the last primate ancestor. On the other hand, when we consider the entire sweep of evolution, all hominids are late-comers. If we allow that life on Earth began 3.8 billion years ago, and think of all of evolution as taking place in one 24-hour day, then the most ancient of the hominids evolved in the last $2\frac{1}{2}$ minutes of that day. And modern human beings? We arose at most 200,000 years ago, which means we have only been around for the last 5 seconds of Earth's evolutionary day.

Yet another way to think of human evolution is in terms of *where* it took place. The message here is quite straightforward: For perhaps 70 percent of the time we hominids have been around, we lived and died solely in Africa. This is clear because the earliest hominid fossils found *outside* of Africa date to only 1.75 Mya. Meanwhile, all the early and mid-period hominid fossils have been unearthed on the African continent, as you can see in **Figure 19.23**.

As little as 10 years, ago, a finer point could have been put on this: It was not just in Africa, but in *East* Africa that most hominid evolution took place. Until the mid-1990s, all early- and middle-period hominid fossils were found in a swath of Africa that runs from the eastern portion of South Africa up through the Great Rift Valley that traverses modern Kenya, Tanzania, and Ethiopia. Then, in 1995, a French researcher named Michel Brunet announced that he had turned up hominid fossils in Chad, some 2,500 kilometers west of the Great Rift Valley. In 2002, Brunet and his colleagues stunned the research world when they announced that they had found a very primitive hominid in Chad, a creature they dubbed *Sahelanthropus tchadensis* but who they informally refer to as Toumaï. If Toumaï's status as a hominid is confirmed, it pushes the geographical range of early human ancestors across much of the African continent.

The Toumaï fossils actually were remarkable in another way. They capped a period of two years in which the root of the hominid family tree was pushed back by more than 2 million years. Prior to

Figure 19.23
Hominid Fossil Sites in Africa
All of the oldest hominid fossils have been found on the African continent.

2000, the oldest putative hominid fossil was dated at 4.4 million years old. Then, in rapid succession, all three of the species you can see at the base of the tree in Figure 19.22 were announced by different teams of researchers. With the Toumaï find, hominid fossils were pushed back to between 6 and 7 Mya. As you may recall, molecular anthropologists have calculated that the human and chimpanzee lines only split at about 7 Mya at most. One possibility, then, is that Brunet's

Toumaï is a creature that lies right at the base of the hominid family tree. Another possibility, however, is that Toumaï is not a hominid, but belongs in the line of primate ancestors (which is why it's marked with dotted lines and a question mark in Figure 19.22). How do scientists determine placements like these? Let's see.

Interpreting the Evidence

If you look at **Figure 19.24**, you can see part of the *S. tchadensis*/Toumaï fossils that Brunet and his team unearthed in the Chadian desert. This remarkably complete cranium of Toumaï was complemented by additional artifacts the researchers found: two lower jaw segments and some individual teeth. Fragmentary as this evidence may seem, it actually is more extensive than some fossil finds. The claim for the primitive *Orrorin tugenensis* species seen in Figure 19.22 originally was based mostly on three thigh bones and several teeth.

So, what are paleoanthropologists looking for in such fossils? What features help them decide whether a given species should be placed in the hominid family tree or be put over with the apes? To Brunet, three features stood as evidence that Toumaï was a hominid. One was its canine teeth; they are smaller and less sharp than those of the apes. Another was the enamel on its teeth—it is thicker than the enamel apes have. A third was what might be called the slope of the face; the lower face doesn't jut out beyond the

eyes in the way ape faces do. Against this, Toumaï clearly has some ape-like features. Note its widely spaced eyes and massive brow, for example.

Brunet's views, however, are *interpretations* of evidence, and interpretations can vary. He may see, in Toumaï's teeth, the canines of a male hominid, but a French colleague of his, Brigitte Senut, sees in these teeth the canines of a female *ape*. It may not surprise you to learn that Senut has her own "earliest hominid" candidate—the *Orrorin tugenensis* specimen, which she and her colleagues unearthed in Kenya.

Tracing Human Evolution over Time

Bearing such considerations in mind, we can begin to trace the hominid lineage that leads to our own species. When we ask whether the ancient *S. tchadensis* belongs at the base of this lineage, there is a critical piece of evidence that is missing. Brunet needs to find some pelvic or leg fossils. Along with canine teeth structure, the most important criterion for placing a creature in *Hominidae* is evidence of *bipedalism*, meaning the tendency to walk on two limbs rather than four. But the evidence for *S. tchandensis* thus far only includes fossils from the head, so who knows how it walked?

Bipedalism is critical to hominid evidence because this trait eventually became characteristic of all hominids. By contrast, our closest non-hominid relatives—the chimpanzees and gorillas—are "knuckle walkers" that can rise up on two legs, but normally get around on four. We can trace our split with the apes by tracing the split between four-legged and two-legged walking. Senut and her colleagues claim to have good evidence that the six-million-year-old *O. tugenensis* walked upright, and we are fairly certain that the later *Australopithecus anamensis*—near the middle of Figure 19.22—was bipedal. By the time we get to the *Australopithecus afarensis* species, there is no doubt that the human line was bipedal.

The name of this last species, *Australopithecus afarensis*, is not likely to ring a bell but one particular *A. afarensis* is perhaps the most famous hominid ever found. She is "Lucy," who lived 3.18 million years ago in what is now Ethiopia. In her, we actually can see a transition to bipedalism. Lucy had the pelvis of a biped, but nevertheless possessed long arms, short legs, and feet that were built for grasping—features consistent with a species that came down from life in the trees, but that probably still spent considerable time in them. To get some idea of Lucy's stature compared with ours, see **Figure 19.25**.

The Australopithecines are generally agreed to be ancestral to our own genus, *Homo*; but which Australopithecines stand in this line of descent? If you

Figure 19.24
An Ancient Human Ancestor?
This cranium of *Sahelanthropus tchadensis*, or Toumaï, was discovered in the deserts of Chad, and has been determined to be 6 or 7 million years old. Toumaï's discoverers believe it is a very ancient hominid, but other researchers believe it should be grouped with apes.

Smaller
brain

Longer arms
(shorter legs)

Grasping
feet

Figure 19.25
"Lucy" and Modern Humans
Compared
What was the hominid Lucy like compared to a modern human female? The figure gives an idea. Lucy stood about three-foot-seven and had a much smaller brain than modern humans, even allowing for her smaller stature. Her brain size or "cranial volume" was about that of a modern chimpanzee—450 cubic centimeters, compared to 1,400 cubic centimeters for a modern *H. sapiens*. Lucy's hip and pelvic bones make clear that she was bipedal, but note the longer arms and grasping feet common to tree-dwelling primates. Lucy's combination of features have prompted some researchers to label her a "bipedal chimpanzee." Her species, *Australopithecus afarensis*, is important because our own species may be descended from it. (Adapted from Boyd, R. and Silk, J.B., *How Humans Evolved*. New York: W.W. Norton & Company, 2000, p. 329.)

look at Figure 19.22, you can see two candidate species, *A. africanus* and the more recently discovered 2.5-million-year-old *A. garhi* from Ethiopia. *A. garhi* has the right mix of physical characteristics and may also have been the first hominid to use tools to butcher animals. Stone tools—actually little more than rocks with sharpened edges—were found with the *A. garhi* fossils, along with fossil remains of animals that had cut marks consistent with butchering and extraction of bone marrow. Before this discovery, it was thought that the first toolmaker was *Homo habilis*.

Into the Genus *Homo: Habilis* and *Ergaster*

Homo habilis—"handy man" in honor of its toolmaking abilities—gets us to our own genus, *Homo*. But there is significant disagreement about whether *H. habilis* was *enough* like us that it deserves to be placed in our genus. The main reason that *H. habilis* gets the *Homo* designation is its use of tools; in physical form it is arguably an Australopithecine.

Changes to physical forms that are more like ours come at several steps in the hominid line, but the most dramatic change by far comes with the rise of *Homo ergaster*, whose best-preserved remains come from a boy who died 1.6 million years ago on the shores of Lake Turkana in Kenya. Experts estimate that, had this 9-year-old "Turkana Boy" grown to maturity, he would have reached a height of 2 meters (6 feet). His brain was 30 percent larger than that of *Homo habilis* and more than half the size of the average modern *Homo sapiens* brain. He had a much more modern face, long limbs typical of those humans who dwell today in arid climates in Africa, and advanced tool technology. If you look at **Figure 19.26**, you can see Turkana Boy's skeleton, which was found in amazingly complete form. Indeed, the only features missing from it were hands and feet. But what did Turkana Boy's species actually look like? **Figure 19.27** provides an artist's interpretation of it and several others.

Migration from Africa

All the hominid species we've reviewed so far lived solely in Africa. Then, about 2 Mya, the initial human migration out of Africa took place. Who were the first intercontinental travelers? As usual, we can pinpoint some individuals; what is more difficult is connecting the dots. There is no doubt that fossils from the same tall, modern-looking, brainy species, *Homo erectus*, have been found very far afield of Africa, on the Pacific island of Java and the Chinese mainland. There's also no doubt that these specimens are extremely old; some of the Javanese fossils seem to date from about 1.6 Mya. On the other hand, the *very* oldest non-African fossils we have are from a hominid found near the Black Sea who dates back to 1.75 Mya. We might expect this hominid to look like the *H. erectus* found in Java, but, alas for clarity's sake, its features sit somewhere between those of *H. erectus* and the much more primitive *Homo ha-*

bilis. To add to this confusion, a skull dating from 1 Mya was recently found in Ethiopia that has characteristics of both the Far East *H. erectus* and the earlier, purely African *H. ergaster*.

If you look at Figure 19.22 again, you can see what seems to be (just barely) the conventional wisdom about all this: That *Homo ergaster* gave rise not only to *Homo erectus*, but to our own line of descent. *Homo erectus* then went on to see the world, as it were, but was an evolutionary dead end; the last of its line died out about 40,000 years ago in Java. Note, however, that this species had a long run—almost 2 million years, which is a period of existence at least 10 times as long as the one our species has had so far. Also, keep your eye on the *H. erectus* extinction date of 40,000 years ago; it's interestingly close to another extinction date we'll be looking at later.

Into Europe

H. erectus was in the Far East more than 1.6 million years ago, but we have to come all the way up to 800,000 years ago to find evidence of hominids in Europe. The first European hominid we know of was a member of the species called *Homo antecessor*, whose remains were found at the Gran Dolina excavation site in northern Spain in 1994. Coming forward another 100,000 years, we find a second European hominid, *H. heidelbergensis*, first found at a town near Heidelberg, Germany. Then there is the best known of all the ancient hominids, the Neanderthals (*H. neanderthalensis*), whose earliest remains date from 200,000 years ago, and whose range was extremely broad—not only most of Europe, but parts of the Middle East and Asia as well. Coming very late to Europe was our own species, *Homo sapiens*, which arrived about 40,000 years ago.

Connecting the dots here is difficult. If you look at Figure 19.22, you can see the story as the discoverers of the Spanish *H. antecessor* fossil believe it unfolded. While still in Africa, *H. antecessor* gave rise to both *H. heidelbergensis* and to *Homo sapiens*. Then *H. heidelbergensis* went on to give rise to the Neanderthals. One piece of evidence that makes plausible the idea that *H. antecessor* gave rise to modern humans is that *H. antecessor* was in some ways strikingly like modern humans, particularly for a creature that was so ancient.

The Neanderthals

Of all the lost members of the hominid family, it is the Neanderthals that have most strongly captured the modern human imagination. This is so partly because the Neanderthals were the first extinct hominids to be discovered. When Neanderthal remains were uncov-

**Figure 19.26
Much More Like Us**
In the remarkably complete skeleton of "Turkana Boy," we can see the evolution of hominids to a form more like our own. This member of the species *Homo ergaster* was tall and had a much larger brain capacity than the earlier hominid "Lucy." His remains, dating from 1.6 million years ago, were found near Kenya's Lake Turkana.

ered in 1856, at a limestone quarry in Germany's Neander Valley, humanity got a wake-up call about human evolution. Though the notion was resisted at first, the Neanderthal bones made clear that there once had been a species on Earth that was very much like humans, but that was not *exactly* human. In the years that followed, the Neanderthals became the best known of the extinct hominids, simply because they left so many traces of themselves behind. In Europe alone, there are perhaps 20 major Neanderthal excavation sites, and others have been found as far away as Uzbekistan.

So, what were these near humans like? **Figure 19.27** shows you an artist's interpretation of their physical stature: short, stocky bodies—the average man was about five-foot-six—powerfully built, with a heavy "double arched" brow and a receding chin; big-boned, with large joints to match. It's easy to see how such features were turned into a *caricature* that has been with us since the nineteenth century: that of the caveman. It is the Neanderthals that provided us with the image of dumb, prehuman brutes, grunting their way through the Stone Age. But does this image fit with the reality? Well, consider that the Neanderthals had a cranial capacity as large as ours; that some put up shelters in their campsites; and that one reason we have so many artifacts from them is that they took the trouble to bury their dead.

This is not to say, however, that they were "just like us." Whenever direct comparisons are made, the Neanderthals do indeed look primitive in comparison with ancient *Homo sapiens*. As paleoanthropologist Ian Tattersall has pointed out, Neanderthals thrust spears at prey, but humans developed the valuable technique of *throwing* spears from a distance. The Neanderthals used nothing but stone for their relatively primitive tools, while *Homo sapiens* used bone and antler as well as stone in constructing their much finer implements. And the Neanderthals were "foragers" while ancient humans were "collectors." What's the difference? Humans monitored their environments and used "forward planning" by, for example, placing their campsites near animal migration paths. By contrast, Neanderthals do not appear to have timed their migrations in this way.

Given all this, it's not difficult to see why the Neanderthals died out: They encountered a species they could not compete with. They had been the sole hominids in Europe for nearly 200,000 years, but this isolation ended when modern humans arrived there about 40,000 years ago. Within another 13,000 years, all the Neanderthals were gone. There is a temptation, of course, to think that they died at the hands of the newly arrived *Homo sapiens*, but we have no evidence of violent conflict between the two species. What does seem clear is that modern humans could out-compete the Neanderthals. Humans knew where the antelope were going to be; they used better tools; they organized their campsites more efficiently. As a result, it's reasonable to assume that they got the lion's share of resources.

One fascinating idea stemming from this scenario is that it may have occurred elsewhere. Do you remember when it was that *Homo erectus* died out in the Far East? About 40,000 years ago. Perhaps, like the Neanderthals, they died because they could not compete with a newer, cleverer species that had moved into their territory.

Figure 19.27
Members of the Hominid Family
What did now-extinct members of the hominid family look like? Working from fossil and other evidence, artist Jay Matternes has produced drawings that provide some idea of their appearance.

(a) *Paranthropus boisei* lived about 2 million years ago. Though it was not a member of our genus (*Homo*), and not an ancestor of modern humans, it was a hominid.

(b) *Homo ergaster* is the species represented by Turkana boy. Its fossils date from a time only slightly later than *P. boisei*, but its physical form clearly is more human-like—not surprising since it probably was a human ancestor.

(c) *Homo neanderthalensis* lived in Europe and elsewhere in a period running from about 200,000 years ago to 27,000 years ago. These were the Neanderthals, a species that lived in proximity to modern humans for thousands of years before becoming extinct.

(a) *Paranthropus boisei*

(b) *Homo ergaster*

(c) *Homo neanderthalensis*

Modern *Homo Sapiens*

The newcomers to Europe and the rest of the world were us—modern human beings. Where had we come from? The short answer is Africa, though there is some question about the routes we took to get to Europe. Critically, we fully evolved *in Africa* before migrating to Europe and the rest of the world. This has been a contentious issue for years in anthropology, but it now seems to have been settled, mostly by the testing of ancient and modern DNA. This same kind of molecular testing has yielded approximate dates for the first appearance of modern human beings—between 100,000 and 200,000 years ago, with 130,000 years ago being a best estimate. If the Gran Dolina site researchers are correct, modern humans evolved in Africa during this time period as direct descendents of the *Homo antecessor* species. (The *H. antecessors* that came to Spain 800,000 years ago could be thought of as a hominid migratory expedition that didn't pan out.)

By the time modern humans arrived in Europe, they already possessed many of the capacities that set them apart from the Neanderthals. But there was more to come. The new Europeans de-veloped lamps to light caves; they made clay kilns; they dug pits in the permafrost that served as meat freezers. Most impressive of all, perhaps, they were artists. If you look at **Figure 19.28**, you can see a flowering of their creative minds: a portion of the 17,000-year-old cave paintings at Lascaux France—the product of a team of artists working by artificial light in the deep recesses of the cave.

These advances seem to have come about very rapidly. Almost none of them are seen before the arrival of *Homo sapiens* in Europe; but all of them are seen very soon after it. For years, researchers marveled that there was so little in the African record to indicate that African *H. sapiens* possessed the kind of mental capacities that European *H. sapiens* did. This lead to the idea that human beings may have undergone a genetic change that resulted in what has been termed the "creative explosion"— the flowering of human culture in Europe. Under this view, human mental capacity did not evolve in a slow, steady way. Instead, while still in Africa, our species went through a period of rapid evolution, perhaps 50,000 years ago, that made the European advances possible.

Figure 19.28
Flowering of Human Culture
Paintings done by a team of artists some 17,000 years ago on cave walls near Lascaux, France. Other cave paintings in France date from about 30,000 years ago.

Figure 19.29
The Earliest Art?
This piece of ocher, found in South Africa, has been dated to 77,000 years ago. The researchers who discovered it believe it represents the world's oldest known work of art. The date of the piece is important, as it predates the supposed creative explosion that began about 40,000 years ago, when modern humans migrated to Europe.

Against this, a more recent school of thought holds that there was no creative explosion. Instead, there was only the appearance of one, caused by the fact that modern human beings left so many well-preserved sites in Europe. When the full record from Africa and elsewhere is uncovered, these researchers believe, it will tell the story of a human mental evolution that was slow and steady.

Most scientists believe that the essence of what sets modern humans apart from other species is symbolic thinking. Human beings can design tools before they make them; they can plan for the future; they can represent three-dimensional animals on a two-dimensional cave surface. Until recently, however, almost all the earliest manifestations of symbolic thinking were found in Europe. But this may have begun to change. If you look at **Figure 19.29**, you can see a piece of red ocher stone found recently in South Africa and dated to 77,000 years ago. The researcher who uncovered this stone believes it represents the earliest-known example of human art. Even if it is not art, other researchers say, the geometric pattern on it provides clear evidence of symbolic thinking.

So, did we modern human beings become *fully* modern only in the last 50,000 years? Or did the last major event in human evolution occur 130,000 years ago, with our emergence as a species? Fortunately, our long evolution has given us the capacity not only to ask such questions, but to answer them.

On to the Diversity of Life

In reviewing the history of life in this chapter, you necessarily looked, in some small way, at almost all of Earth's major life-forms—bacteria, animals, plants, and so forth. In the three chapters coming up, you'll take a more detailed look at each of these life-forms. This is a tour that will make plain the astounding diversity that exists in the living world.

Chapter Review

Summary

19.1 The Geological Timescale: Life Marks Earth's Ages

- Earth's 4.6 billion years of history are measured in the geological timescale, which is divided into broad eras, shorter periods, and shorter-yet epochs. These time frames were defined in the nineteenth century, based in part on the different life-forms that existed within each of them, as reflected in the fossil record. Many of the major transitions in the fossil record have come about because of major extinction events.

- Life is thought to have begun on Earth about 3.8 billion years ago; from that time until perhaps 2 billion years ago, it was strictly microscopic and single-celled. According to the fossil record, all the animals and plants that exist today came about in the last 16 percent of this 3.8-billion-year period.

- Evolution can be conceptualized as a branching tree, with humans sitting on one ordinary branch. It is not shaped as a pyramid with humans at the apex. The story of evolution recounted in the chapter leads to human beings, but it could just as easily have led to any other modern organism.

- Every living thing on Earth belongs to one of three domains of life: Archaea, Bacteria, or Eukarya. Both bacteria and the archaea are single-celled, microscopic life-forms; the domain Eukarya is composed of four kingdoms: plants, animals, fungi, and protists.
  Web Tutorial 19.1: Evolutionary Timescales

19.2 How Did Life Begin?

- Life began with the origin of self-replicating molecules. There currently is a debate regarding not only the kind of environment in which life is likely to have arisen but also how this environment could have accumulated the necessary chemical raw materials to allow the construction of life's complex organic molecules. One hypothesis is that life began in a "prebiotic soup" of hot-water systems—in the deep-sea vents or the kind of hot-spring pools that exist in Yellowstone Park today. Other researchers feel, however, that early replicating molecules could not have withstood these temperatures, and that a temperate location near a shoreline is a more likely environment for life to have gotten started.

- A critical question for origin-of-life researchers had been to account for the existence in living things of both the worker molecules called enzymes and the information-bearing molecules DNA and RNA, since neither kind of molecule can be synthesized with-

out the other. The discovery of RNA molecules, called ribozymes, that have enzymatic capabilities helped solve this dilemma. Ribozymes provided evidence for an ancient "RNA world" in which the only living things were simple RNA molecules that could bring about their own replication.

- Replication is the step at which life could be said to begin. This is because, through mistakes, replicating molecules will begin to differ, meaning that some will leave more offspring than others, which is the beginning of Darwinian evolution and the diversification of living things.
  Web Tutorial 19.2: RNA-like Self Replication

19.3 The Tree of Life

- Life today can be traced to a universal ancestor that gave rise to the domains Archaea, Bacteria, and Eukarya. The earliest kingdom in Eukarya, the protist kingdom, went on to give rise to the other kingdoms in Eukarya: animals, plants, and fungi.

19.4 A Long First Period: The Precambrian

- The earliest evidence we have for life is a chemical signature of it, carbon utilization, found in rocks in Greenland dated to about 3.8 billion years ago. Carbon signatures indicating photosynthesis (and hence life) are abundant beginning 3.5 billion years ago. All of this life was either bacterial or archaeal, and all of it seems to have existed in the oceans.

- Oxygen came to exist in the Earth's atmosphere through the activity of photosynthesizing organisms, originally photosynthesizing bacteria. Photosynthesis meant an abundance of food on the Earth. However, atmospheric oxygen was toxic to many existing species, and its production set a strict condition for all life: Adapt to oxygen, stay separate from it, or perish. Some early eukaryotes adapted to oxygen by ingesting, and then continuing to live in symbiosis with, bacteria that were able to metabolize oxygen. Algal cells struck up a similar relationship with other bacterial cells that could perform photosynthesis.

19.5 The Cambrian Explosion

- The fossil record indicates a tremendous, rapid expansion in the number of animal forms in a "Cambrian Explosion" that began about 544 Mya, but this evidence has been challenged. It may be that the Cambrian Explosion was merely an explosion in the number of animal forms big and hard enough to leave fossils, and that the surge in animal diversity took place over a relatively long period of time beginning well back in the Precambrian era. Molecular evidence indicates that animals arose much earlier than the Cambrian Explosion, perhaps 1.5 billion years ago.

19.6 The Movement onto the Land: Plants First

- Plants, which evolved from green algae, made a gradual transition to land in tandem with their symbiotic partners, the fungi. Plant-fungi fossils exist from about 460 Mya, but molecular studies indicate they were on land 1.3 billion years ago. Major transitions in plant life came with the development of a water-retaining covering (the cuticle), embryos that matured internally, and a "vascular" or fluid-transport system.

- Later plants went on to develop seeds, which can be thought of as packages containing an embryo and food for it, encased in a tough outer covering. The living ancestors of the first seed plants are the gymnosperms, represented by today's conifers. The flowering plants, called angiosperms, developed about 165 Mya and eventually succeeded the gymnosperms as the most dominant plants on Earth. Today, angiosperms include many food crops, cactus, and tree varieties.

19.7 Animals Follow Plants onto the Land

- The first land animals were arthropods; a centipede-like creature laid down the oldest terrestrial animal tracks we know of. Insects soon followed in great abundance. The arthropods were the only land animals for millions of years thereafter.

- Four-limbed vertebrates (tetrapods) moved onto land in the form of lobe-finned fishes, which gave rise to amphibians (represented by today's frogs and salamanders). Reptiles later branched off from amphibians, and mammals branched off from reptiles. Birds are the living descendents of the reptile branch that included the dinosaurs.

- Amphibians inhabit two worlds, water and land, in keeping with their evolutionary transition from one to the other. Reptiles evolved a protective amniotic egg that allowed their offspring to develop away from water, freeing reptiles to migrate inland.

- Mammals appear as a group of small, insect-eating animals about 210 million years ago. They began to evolve into the varied forms seen today shortly before the reign of the dinosaurs was ended with an asteroid impact 65 million years ago; after this they radiated into many niches, becoming the dominant land animals.

- The order of mammals called primates, whose fossils date from 55 Mya, is characterized by large, front-facing eyes, limbs with an opposable first digit (thumbs in today's human beings), and a tree-dwelling existence (which some later-arriving primates lost).

19.8 The Evolution of Human Beings

- A common primate ancestor is believed to have given rise to both the chimpanzee and the human family trees between 6 and 7 million years ago. The structure of the human family tree is a matter of considerable debate among researchers. Human evolution is studied by several kinds of scientists, but the core evidence in the field is provided by fossils, which are found and interpreted by scientists called paleoanthropologists.

- Human evolution is the study of the family *Hominidae*—the family of man-like primates. Every member of this family is referred to as a hominid, including human beings. All the members of the hominid family tree are extinct except for *Homo sapiens*, the human species. All early and mid-period hominid evolution took place in Africa. Until recently, it was believed that all such hominid evolution took place in East Africa, but several fossil discoveries in Chad may have extended the range of early human evolution across much of the African continent. One of these fossils, dubbed *Sahelanthropus tchandensis*, may be as much as 7 million years old, meaning it may lie at the base of the hominid family tree. Conversely, it may belong to the primate line.

- Paleoanthropologists interpret features of fossils—such as characteristics of teeth and skulls—in order to make judgments about where a given fossil-form lies in the hominid family tree. Interpretations can differ, however. Two features critical to inclusion in the hominid tree are tooth structure and evidence of bipedalism or upright walking.

- Bipedalism is clearly seen in the hominid genus *Australopithecus*, which is thought to be ancestral to our own genus, *Homo*. The most famous Australopithicene, "Lucy," lived 3.18 million years ago. A change to a physical form and mental capacity much closer to ours comes with the evolution of *Homo ergaster*, exemplified by "Turkana Boy," who lived 1.6 Mya.

- Hominids are thought to have first migrated from Africa about 2 Mya. A species called *Homo erectus* has been found at sites dating from 1.6 Mya in Java and China. Hominid fossils in Europe date from 800,000 years ago in the form of *Homo antecessor*, believed by some researchers to be the direct ancestor to modern human beings.

- The best known of the extinct hominids are the Neanderthals (*Homo neanderthalensis*), who populated Europe as well as parts of Asia and North Africa for nearly 200,000 years. The last of them disappeared 27,000 years ago—13,000 years after *Homo sapiens* first migrated to Europe. It seems likely that the Neanderthals died out because they could not compete with the more advanced humans.

- Modern human beings fully evolved in Africa between 200,000 and 100,000 years ago, with a best-estimate date being 130,000 years ago. Their arrival in Europe 40,000 years ago coincides with a remarkable cultural flowering that occurred among them. There is a debate as to whether humans may have undergone a genetic change shortly before leaving Africa that made this "creative explosion" possible. Some researchers feel there was only the appearance of such an explosion, and that the African human record eventually will reveal a picture of slow, steady human evolution.

Key Terms

amniotic egg   384

angiosperm   382

Archaea   374

Bacteria   374

bryophytes   382

Cambrian Explosion   380

continental drift   373

Cretaceous Extinction   371

Eukarya   374

gymnosperm   382

hominid   388

Permian Extinction   371

phylum   380

ribozyme   377

seedless vascular plant   382

Understanding the Basics

Multiple-Choice Questions (answers in the back of the book)

1. Put the following in the proper temporal sequence, earliest first.
   a. first dinosaurs
   b. first bacteria
   c. first amphibians
   d. first primates
   e. free oxygen accumulation in the atmosphere
   f. first land plants
   g. first birds

2. The time frames in the geological timescale generally denote _____.
   a. 10,000-year increments
   b. 10-million-year increments
   c. the reappearance of certain life-forms
   d. transitions in life-forms
   e. the appearance of larger life-forms

3. The first life on Earth may have been (select all that apply)

   a. eukaryotic cells
   b. ribozyme-like molecules
   c. bacteria
   d. formed on land
   e. formed at extreme temperatures

4. Which of the following characteristics of animals and/or plants are adaptations to life on land? (Select all that apply.)
   a. multicellularity
   b. pollen and seeds
   c. amniotic egg
   d. muscles
   e. internal fertilization

5. What is the order of evolution among the following organisms, earliest first?
   a. amphibians
   b. lobe-finned fish
   c. mammals
   d. reptiles
   e. primates

6. True or False: Dinosaurs were often hunted by humans.

7. Photosynthesis was a huge innovation in the history of life because (select all that apply)
   a. It allowed RNA to replicate itself.
   b. It put huge quantities of oxygen into the atmosphere.
   c. It resulted in the production of more food than had been previously available.
   d. It resulted in blockage of UV light, increasing habitability of the land for terrestrial organisms.
   e. It helped the Earth to thaw out.

8. Mitochondria and chloroplasts (select all that apply)
   a. are thought to have arisen as symbiotes
   b. are very similar to bacteria
   c. are very similar to algae
   d. are organelles within cells
   e. were early protists

9. Which of the following organisms have an amniotic egg? (Select all that apply.)
   a. grasshopper
   b. lizard
   c. salamander
   d. fish
   e. bird
   f. turtle

10. The family tree of the hominids is rooted in _____ and is thought to extend back _____ years.
    a. Asia; 3 to 4 million
    b. Europe; 3 to 4 million
    c. Asia; 6 to 7 million
    d. Africa; 3 to 4 million
    e. Africa; 6 to 7 million

Brief Review

1. What are two differences between domain Bacteria and domain Eukarya?

2. What is the amniotic egg, and why was it a breakthrough for terrestrial animals? In which vertebrate class did the amniotic egg evolve?

3. What are two characteristics of primates that are not found in other mammals? Why are they important for the evolution of hominids?

4. Which two groups are more closely related, humans and chimps or humans and gibbons?

5. Were Neanderthals the direct ancestors of humans?

6. When did life begin, and how much time passed between the origin of the first bacterial cells and the colonization of land? What was the land like during that time?

7. Describe three characteristics that evolved in mammals that had not been present in earlier organisms.

Applying Your Knowledge

1. How would Earth be different if photosynthesis had never developed in any organism?

2. Why does it make sense that life started so small? Why does it make sense that it began in water?

3. Given what the text says about the characteristics of Neanderthals in comparison with human beings, what would the world be like if Neanderthals had survived into modern times?

20 *The Diversity of Life 1*

Creatures large and small.
(page 402)

2. Viral envelope fuses with T-cell membrane

cell membrane

3. Capsid disintegrates: viral RNA and enzymes are released

The cause of AIDS.
(Section 20.2, page 404)

One kind of bacteria.
(Section 20.3, page 409)

The smallest living thing discovered to date is a type of bacteria that measures about two-tenths of a micrometer in diameter—that is, two-tenths of one-millionth of a meter in diameter. When we turn to the *biggest* living thing, elephants or whales might come to mind, but it turns out that animals aren't even in the running for this title. At a maximum length of 27 meters (or about 89 feet), the blue whale is the largest animal that has ever existed, but it's small compared to California's coastal redwood trees, which might reach a height of 100 meters or about 330 feet. This is large indeed, but consider that a giant sea kelp once was found that was 274 meters in length, meaning it was about 900 feet long. It may be, though, that in terms of size, both kelp and redwoods have to take a back seat to a life-form normally thought of as quite small. In 1992, researchers reported finding a fungus growing in Washington State that runs underground through an area of 1,500 *acres* and that arguably is a single organism.

Now, how about the *deepest*-living things? The current record-holders are bacteria that were found in the early 1990s—in a combination of oil drilling and scientific exploration—living almost 3 kilometers beneath the Earth's surface, which is about 1.9 miles down. Food and water are so scarce at such depths that these bacterial cells may live in a kind of suspended animation, dividing perhaps once a year, or even once a *century*. Turning to the highest living things, 12 species of bacteria have been found to be living in the Himalayas at 8,300 meters or 27,000 feet above sea level, which is just a couple thousand feet lower than the peak of Mount Everest. A species of chickweed survives in the Himalayas at over 20,000 feet.

All kinds of life-forms—clams, tube worms, crabs—live kilometers beneath the surface of the oceans, near the "hot-water vents" that spew out water and minerals from the Earth's interior onto the ocean floor. Microbes called archaea, living at these deep-sea vents, set the pace for life in a hot environment. An average, midday temperature in the Sahara Desert would be so *cold* it would end the reproduction of the archaean *Pyrolobus fumarii*, which lives within hot-water vents at temperatures of up to 113° Celsius, which is hotter than the temperature at which water boils. At the other extreme, the well-named bacterium *Phormidium frigidum* carries out photosynthesis in Antarctic lakes whose temperatures sit right at the freezing point of water.

Finally, what about the oldest living things? Humans have been known to live to 120, but this is an eyeblink compared to the lives of some plants. In California there is a Sequoia tree that was growing 3,500 years ago, when the pharaohs ruled Egypt, and

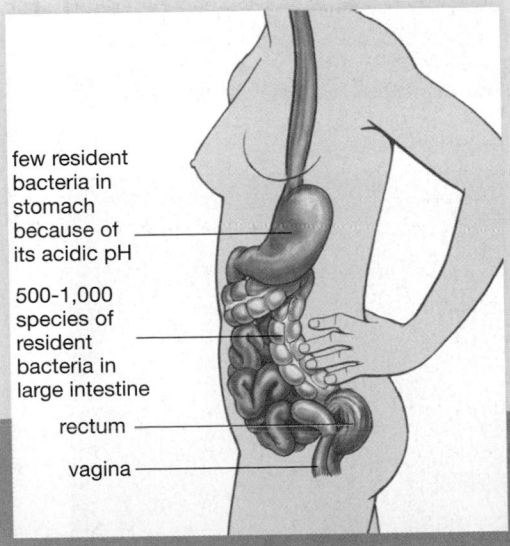

At home within us.
(Section 20.4, page 411)

few resident bacteria in stomach because of its acidic pH

500-1,000 species of resident bacteria in large intestine

rectum

vagina

Hot-water lover.
(Section 20.6, page 413)

An early version of male and female.
(Section 20.8, page 415)

+ cell

– cell

diploid

cell fusion

zygote (diploid)

there is a bristlecone pine tree (*Pinus longaeva*) that has been living in the dry slopes of eastern California for 4,900 years. These trees are mere youngsters, however, compared to some microbes, which can survive in a form called spores for immensely long periods of time. In the 1990s, bacterial spores were found living within a bee that had been encased in amber for 25 to 40 million years. Even this eye-popping number did not prepare scientists for what came next, however. In 2000, researchers announced that they had found, encased within salt crystals at the bottom of a New Mexico air shaft, archaean spores that date from 250 million years ago. These spores were revived and billions of their offspring now exist. This claim is controversial—one possibility is that the material encasing the spores wasn't really 250 million years old—but if borne out, it raises the question of whether some microbes are "effectively immortal," as one researcher has put it.

Looking at life like this—at its biggest or deepest or oldest extremes—is one way to get at its incredible diversity. But it does not begin to do justice to life's variety, because life is diverse in so many ways. Honeybees do a "dance" to let their hive-mates know the location of a food supply. Corn plants, when attacked by army worms, can call in an air force: the plants release an air-borne substance that attracts parasitic wasps, which then prey on the worms. Pacific salmon live years in the ocean only to make one arduous, upstream journey to spawn in the waters where they were born, after which they die. Look closely at almost any creature, and you are likely to find something only slightly less dramatic (**see Figure 20.1**).

20.1 Life's Categories and the Importance of Microbes

The purpose of this chapter and the two that follow is to introduce you to life as it exists across all its large-scale categories. Those readers who went through Chapter 19 know that all living things can be placed into one of three "domains." Two of these are Archaea and Bacteria, whose members are all single-celled and microscopic. The third domain, Eukarya, encompass-

(a) Mouse beneath the foot of an elephant

(b) Aquatic snails moving across kelp

(c) Fungus growing on a fallen log

(d) Water flea swimming near green algae

Figure 20.1
An Amazing Diversity in the Living World

es such incredible diversity that it is further divided into four separate "kingdoms." These are plants, animals, fungi, and a group of mostly microscopic organisms called protists. We will begin our tour of the living world by starting small, looking in this chapter at Domains Bacteria and Archaea and at the protists within Domain Eukarya. Then in Chapter 21, fungi and plants will be covered; in Chapter 22 animals will be reviewed. **Figure 20.2** shows you the evolutionary relationships between all these categories of life.

Because this chapter is devoted to mostly unfamiliar *microbes*—meaning living things so small they can't be seen with the naked eye—it might be helpful to say a word at the start about their significance. Microbes are something like the foundation of a house: seldom thought of but critically important. To the extent that they cross our minds at all, we are aware of them mostly for the diseases they cause. This is an important topic—one we'll go into extensively—but thinking of microbes strictly as disease-causing organisms is like thinking of cars strictly as wreck-causing machines. Where does the oxygen we breathe come from? If your answer is "plants," that's partly correct. But the photosynthesis carried out by plants supplies less than half our oxygen; the balance comes from microscopic algae and bacteria—mostly drifters on the ocean's surface. How about the nitrogen that is indispensable to all plants and animals? Among living things, only bacteria are capable of plucking nitrogen out of the air and turning it into a form that plants can use (see page 713). If there were no bacteria, there would be no plants—and consequently no animals. And how is it that dead tree branches or orange peels or the bones of animals are broken down and recycled into the Earth? Almost entirely through the work of bacteria and fungi. Without these organisms, Earth would long ago have become a garbage heap of dead, organic matter. Animals cannot decompose a dead tree branch, but bacteria and fungi can.

The upshot of all this is that life on Earth would grind to a halt without microbes; they are an essential underpinning to all forms of life. They come to this status in part because of the environments they live in, which is to say all environments on Earth that support life of any kind. It probably didn't escape your attention that the coldest- and hottest- and highest- and deepest-living things were all bacteria or archaea. Wherever a plant or animal can live, microbes can be found too. Just as impressive is the sheer number and tonnage of these tiny organisms. A common denominator for measuring the amount of living material is something called *biomass*, defined as the total dry weight of material produced by a given set of organisms. Each bacterium or microscopic alga has an infin-

itesimally small weight, of course—but then again, there are so many of them! It has been estimated that there are more bacteria living in your mouth now than the number of people who have ever lived, and there seem to be more bacterial cells in the human body than there are human cells (a topic we'll return to). A typical gram of fertile soil—an amount about the size of a sugar cube—has about 100 million bacteria living in it, and a mere drop of water near the ocean's surface contains thousands of the tiny algae called phytoplankton. All this adds up. When the calculations are done, we find that microbes probably make up more than half of Earth's biomass. Put another way, the microbes of the world outweigh all the plants and animals and visible fungi of the world combined.

In sum, microbes matter, and not just in ways that are harmful. We'll now start to look at the portion of the living world that is made up of them. Our first stop on this tour, however, will be a category of tiny replicating entities that most biologists would say lie just outside of life, though they have a great effect on living things.

20.2 Viruses: Making a Living by Hijacking Cells

If a living thing is too small to be seen and can cause disease, most people would put it in the vague category known as "germs." But there is a fundamental distinction to be made between *two* kinds of infectious organisms. On the one hand there are bacteria, which may be very small but nevertheless are *cells*, complete with a protein-producing apparatus, a mechanism for extracting energy from the environment, a means of getting rid of waste—in short, complete with everything it takes to be a self-contained living thing. On the other hand there are viruses, which by themselves possess

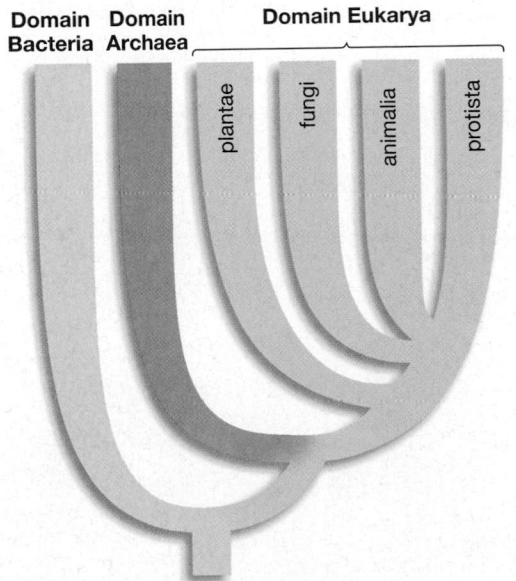

Figure 20.2
The Tree of Life
Life is presumed to have developed from a single common ancestor (the base of the tree), which gave rise to the three domains of the living world: Bacteria, Archaea, and Eukarya. Domain Eukarya is then further divided into four "kingdoms," plants, fungi, animals, and protists.

Figure 20.3
The Virus that Causes AIDS
The anatomy and life-cycle of HIV, the human immunodeficiency virus.

none of these features. Indeed, viruses can be likened to a thief who arrives at a factory he intends to rob possessing only two things: the tools to get inside and some software that will make the factory turn out items he can use. The factory being broken into is a living cell, and the software that the virus brings is its DNA or RNA, which it puts inside this "host" cell. Once this is accomplished, viruses employ different tactics, as you'll see, but in every case the result is that viruses make more copies of themselves. Viruses are an integral part of the living world, and not all of them cause harm. But

unlike the case with bacteria, it's right to think of them first and foremost in terms of the diseases they cause, not only in humans, but in all kinds of living things. **Viruses** are non-cellular replicating entities that must invade living cells to carry out their replication. To put this in the scientific terminology, they are obligate intracellular parasites.

HIV: The AIDS Virus

If you look at **Figure 20.3a**, you can see a simplified rendering of a particular virus, the human immuno-

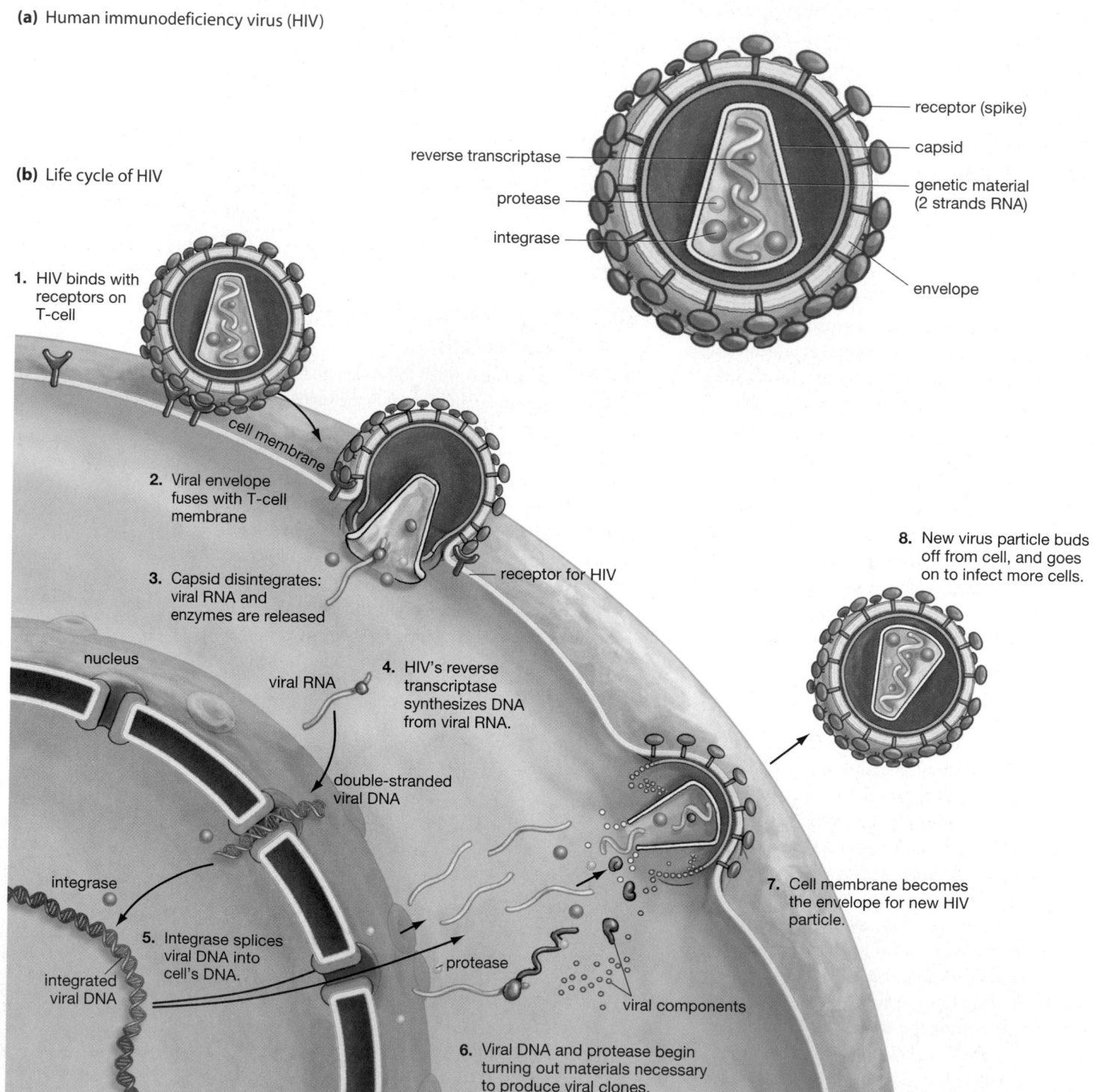

(a) Human immunodeficiency virus (HIV)

receptor (spike)

reverse transcriptase

capsid

protease

genetic material (2 strands RNA)

integrase

envelope

(b) Life cycle of HIV

1. HIV binds with receptors on T-cell

cell membrane

2. Viral envelope fuses with T-cell membrane

receptor for HIV

3. Capsid disintegrates: viral RNA and enzymes are released

nucleus

viral RNA

4. HIV's reverse transcriptase synthesizes DNA from viral RNA.

double-stranded viral DNA

integrase

5. Integrase splices viral DNA into cell's DNA.

integrated viral DNA

protease

viral components

6. Viral DNA and protease begin turning out materials necessary to produce viral clones.

7. Cell membrane becomes the envelope for new HIV particle.

8. New virus particle buds off from cell, and goes on to infect more cells.

deficiency virus (HIV), which is the cause of AIDS. Almost all viruses have two of the three large-scale structures you can see in HIV: the genetic material at the core (in HIV's case, two strands of RNA), and a protein coat, called a **capsid**, that surrounds the viral genetic material. Many viruses then go on to have a third major element—a fatty membrane, called an *envelope*, which you can see surrounding the HIV capsid. Protruding from the HIV envelope are a series of receptors, often referred to as spikes, which are proteins capped with carbohydrate chains. These serve the critical role of binding with receptors that protrude from the target cell, thus giving the virus a way to get in.

If you look at **Figure 20.3b**, you can see how the life cycle of HIV proceeds from this initial binding. The target cell in this case is the one most commonly invaded by HIV, an immune-system cell called a helper T-cell. As you can see, once HIV binds with two receptors on the T-cell's surface, the viral envelope fuses with the T-cell membrane. With this, HIV's capsid, with the genetic material enclosed, is inside the cell. Once there, the capsid disintegrates. Now two HIV enzymes that had been enclosed in the capsid get to work. If you look at Figure 20.3a, you can see these enzymes, integrase and reverse transcriptase. The reverse transcriptase gets busy first, turning HIV's RNA strands into double-stranded DNA. Then integrase does just what its name implies: It integrates the viral DNA into the *cell's* DNA through a cut-and-paste operation.

At this point, the viral DNA might simply stay integrated in the T-cell's DNA, causing no great harm but getting copied, along with the cell's DNA, each time the cell divides. The effect of this, however, is that every "daughter" cell of this infected cell will be infected too; each new cell will have viral DNA spliced into its own DNA. Each of these cells thus has a time bomb ticking within it, because at some point the HIV DNA will change course. It will no longer simply go on replicating within the cell's DNA. Instead, it will start turning out the materials necessary to make whole new copies of the virus. As you can see in the figure, virus construction takes place just inside the cell's outer membrane (helped along by a third enzyme that HIV brought with it, protease). This location is important, because the cell's membrane ends up serving as the final structural part of each new HIV "particle," as the viral clones are called. When the capsid is completed, it buds off from the cell, taking with it part of the cell's membrane, which now becomes the capsid's envelope. When enough viral particles have budded off from the cell in this way, it dies. The viral particles that emerge from the cell then go on to infect other cells.

Viral Diversity

In the HIV life cycle, you can see four steps that are common to almost all viruses: get genetic material inside the host cell, turn out viral component parts, construct new particles from these parts, and move these particles out of the cell. HIV uses RNA as its genetic material, but many viruses use DNA. Viruses that lack an envelope don't get their genetic material inside the cell by fusing with the cell's membrane in the way HIV does. If you look at **Figure 20.4**, you can see a spacecraft-shaped virus called T-4 that infects bacteria through an alternate means. T-4 keeps its capsid outside the target cell, but gets its DNA inside by injecting it through the bacterium's cell wall and membrane.

(a)

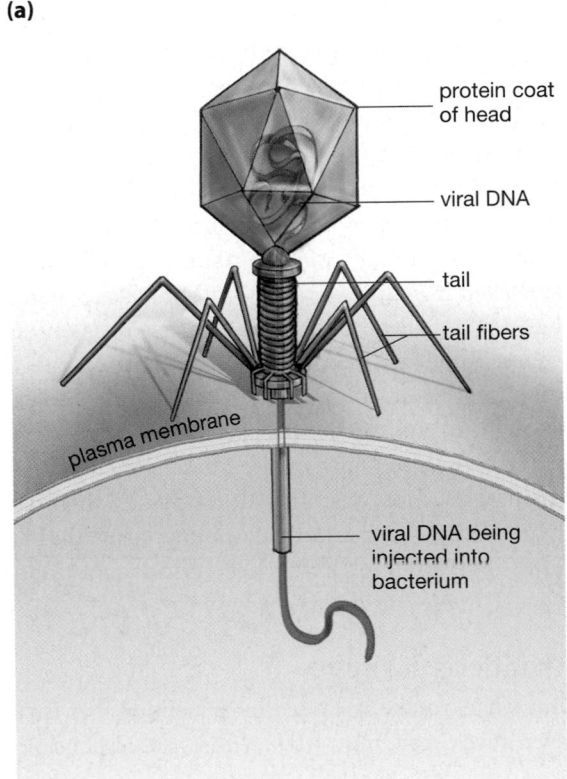

protein coat of head

viral DNA

tail

tail fibers

plasma membrane

viral DNA being injected into bacterium

(b)

Web Tutorial 20.1
Life Cycles of Viruses

Figure 20.4
Another Variety of Virus

(a) The T4 virus looks like a spacecraft that has landed on the surface of a bacterium.

(b) A viral invader lands. An artificially colored T4 virus injects its DNA into an *E. coli* bacterium (in blue).

As you might be able to tell from the size of T-4 compared to its target cell, viruses are very small things. Thousands of them can typically fit within a bacterial cell. Some amount to nothing but their genetic material and the capsid that surrounds it, and there are even virus-like entities, called *viroids*, that lack a capsid; they are simply small strands of infectious RNA. What viruses lack in size, however, they make up in numbers. One researcher has calculated that a typical milliliter—a thousandth of a liter—of ocean water has 10 million virus particles in it. If so, then ocean-going viruses contain as much as 270 million metric tons of carbon, which is more than 20 times the amount of carbon contained in all the whales in the world.

In every case, viruses are not only small, but *simple* things compared to the organisms they infect. First of all, they lack the usual machinery that cells have—a protein assembly line, a waste disposal system, and so forth. Even when we look at the one thing all of them do have, which is genetic material, they are still very simple entities. Human beings are thought to have about 30,000 genes, and even a primitive organism like baker's yeast has 6,000 genes. But the AIDS virus? It has nine genes. To be sure, some viruses are more complex than HIV, but in no case is a virus complex enough to replicate by itself. Because viruses can carry on scarcely any of life's basic functions by themselves, most scientists don't classify them as living things. (For a look at another agent that is infectious, but not living, see "Prions and 'Mad Cow' Disease" on the next page.)

The Effects of Viruses

But what trouble is caused by something that isn't even alive! Apart from AIDS, viruses are responsible for smallpox, chicken pox, measles, rabies, polio, herpes, rubella, and some forms of cancer, hepatitis, and pneumonia, to say nothing of common colds and flus. In 2003, parts of the world were thrown into turmoil by the appearance of a new disease dubbed SARS (severe acute respiratory syndrome) whose cause was quickly identified as a so-called corona virus (so named because its club-like spikes make it look as though it has a halo, as you can see in **Figure 20.5**). Normally corona viruses cause nothing more than colds, but the deadly SARS came about because of a common occurrence in viruses: an existing virus, which previously infected various animals, mutated and "jumped" to human beings. What's likely to have changed in such a virus? The spikes that bind with cells. Once those changed form through mutation, the virus had a way to get into human cells.

Viruses have no special affinity for human hosts, however. They invade every life-form, from protists to fungi to plants to bacteria, not to mention all varieties of animals. In early 2001, hundreds of thousands of cattle and sheep had to be destroyed in Europe because they had been exposed to a virus that causes an affliction known as foot and mouth disease. In humans, viruses are combated by the immune system and by vaccination. You can read about both things in Chapter 27.

20.3 Bacteria: Masters of Every Environment

Domain Bacteria is made up entirely of the microbes called bacteria. Keeping in mind that almost all the organisms we're looking at are microbes, what separates bacteria from any of the others? Readers who went through Chapter 4 will recall that if we set a bacterial cell and, say, a fungal cell side by side, anyone peering through a microscope could see a fundamental difference between the two. The fungal cell would have a large, circular-shaped structure near its center while the bacterial cell would not. The circular structure is the fungal cell's nucleus, which contains almost all of its DNA. But bacteria are **prokaryotes**: organisms whose DNA is not contained within a cell nucleus. Only bacteria and archaea lack a nucleus. All other organisms—all plants, animals, fungi, and protists—are composed of cells that have a nucleus, which makes them **eukaryotes**. The lack of a cell nucleus is, however, just one defining feature of bacteria. Here is a list of others.

Figure 20.5
From Annoyance to Killer
Pictured is a coronavirus, which for years was a cause of nothing more serious than the common cold. Then, in 2003, one strain of coronavirus underwent a mutation that made it the cause of a deadly human respiratory infection. The result was worldwide alarm over SARS—severe acute respiratory syndrome. The virus is named for the crown-like appearance of the spikes that extend from its envelope.

Not Alive, but Deadly: Prions and "Mad Cow" Disease

When we think of a disease that is transmissible, we normally assume that some sort of tiny living thing—a microorganism—is involved in transmitting it. We have, for example, salmonella, meningitis, and tuberculosis: three diseases, each caused by a different bacterium that can move from one living "host" to another. And this is the case with most transmissible diseases; at root, they are caused either by microscopic living things, or by viruses, which always have the DNA or RNA that living things possess.

But then there is the illness that has come to be called Mad Cow disease. Almost alone among transmissible human diseases, it appears to have a *component part* of a living thing as its cause—a protein. Recall from Chapter 3 that much of the scaffolding, or structure, of living things is made from proteins; that the chemical tools called enzymes are made from proteins; and that some hormones are made from them. Clearly, proteins have many functions in living things. But proteins themselves are not living.

So, how could a protein cause a transmissible disease? A variety of protein called a prion protein exists in living tissue in a normal, harmless form. Such prion proteins also can come to exist, however, as "rogue" proteins that are *misshapen*. In their normal form in humans, prion proteins reside in the outer or "plasma" membranes of various cells, including brain cells. For reasons not yet understood, a prion protein will become deformed and then go on to deform *more* prion proteins when it comes into contact with them. The result is a chain reaction in which more and more proteins become deformed. Collections of these deformed proteins destroy brain cells; the ultimate result is a brain with sponge-like holes in it—and death for the victim. Rogue prion proteins, referred to as just-plain prions (PREE-ons), are now thought to be the infectious agent in Mad Cow disease, though not all scientists are convinced of this.

A number of rare human illnesses are believed to be caused by prions, among them an affliction, identified in the 1920s, called Creutzfeldt-Jakob disease. However, even in its most common form, Creutzfeldt-Jakob disease is very rare, striking only about 1 in a million adults, for reasons that are still unknown. In contrast, the year 2000 saw a wave of prion-linked human illness spread in Western Europe. This was something new, and it was linked to a series of incidents involving farm animals.

In 1984, a single cow in England began behaving erratically and then dropped dead of a disease that affected its nervous system. This incident turned out to be the start of an epidemic of prion-caused disease in British cattle—the actual Mad Cow disease, officially known as bovine spongiform encephalopathy (BSE). Scientists now believe that Mad Cow disease spread among British cattle because *prions* were transmitted through a kind of recycling: Cattle may have originally been infected by eating the remains of sheep that had developed a prion-caused disease called scrapie. More cattle were infected when they were fed the remains of ground-up *cattle*.

Then came the jump to human beings. People who ate prion-contaminated beef products likewise ingested prions, and these prions seem to be active in human beings. How is this possible? Mad Cow disease has been transformed into a human variant, dubbed New Variant Creutzfeldt-Jakob disease or nvCJD, which thus far has claimed several hundred lives, the vast majority of them in Britain.

Distressingly little is known about nvCJD, and what is known is not reassuring. The prions that appear to cause it cannot be eliminated from beef products by any known means: neither heat, nor radiation, nor common chemical treatments get rid of them. Then again, it's not clear what proportion of humans will come down with nvCJD after eating infected meat. In America, not one domestic case of nvCJD has been reported; indeed, not one instance of Mad Cow disease has been reported among American cattle. U.S. health officials are taking no chances, however. In May 2003, Canadian officials announced that a single Canadian cow had came down with Mad Cow disease; one day later, the United States banned the import of all Canadian cattle and beef.

Figure 1
A Mad Cow Quarantine in Italy

Unwanted Guest:
The Persistence of Herpes

The first outbreak usually is the worst, but the real problem is that the first outbreak usually isn't the last. Herpes comes back, as herpes sufferers well know. A few weeks or months after the initial outbreak, everything seems fine, but then there may be a tingling—nothing that can be seen yet, but instead just a feeling. Not much later, however, it's back: the same unsightly "cold sore" on the mouth or lesions on the genitals, in the same place that the first outbreak occurred.

This series of events is familiar to lots of people. An estimated one in five Americans over the age of 12 is infected with the herpes virus, though this statistic overstates the trouble caused by it. The vast majority of herpes carriers do not even realize they harbor the disease, because such outbreaks as they have are so mild as to go unnoticed. This very thing facilitates the spread of herpes, however. People who have no symptoms can nevertheless be "silent shedders": they can pass herpes along to others, who may get the full-blown form of the affliction.

But why does herpes come back in the way it does? Where does it go between outbreaks and why can't we just get rid of it permanently? The term "herpes" actually is short-hand for *herpes simplex viruses*, a pair of viruses that belong to a group of 100 known viruses in the herpes family. (Others in the family cause chicken pox, shingles, and the Epstein-Barr disease.) Herpes simplex viruses come in "type 1" and "type 2" varieties. The type 1 variety supposedly is "oral," while the type 2 is "genital." But either variety can end up in either location, because of oral sex.

The herpes sores that can be so distressing are the result of newly formed virus particles breaking out of skin cells, thereby destroying them. Fever, swollen glands, and other symptoms often accompany these lesions, particularly in an initial infection. Within a couple of weeks or so, however, the immune system has killed all the virus particles in and around the skin cells and the symptoms are gone. The problem is that, by this time, the virus has also infected *nerve* cells in the area. Such nerve cells (or neurons) have long extensions of themselves called axons. With the initial infection, herpes virus particles start making a slow migration up these axons to the *body* of the nerve cells, specifically to the nucleus inside the cell body. In the case of genital herpes, this means a journey from the vagina or penis to cell bodies that sit right at the base of the spinal cord. And these cell bodies are where the virus stays—forever. Once there, it does next to nothing; it's not causing any nerve damage or replicating. The nerve cells it is in never divide, so it isn't passed on to a larger group of cells. But neither is it eliminated. It just resides in the nerve cell nuclei until one day—often a stressful day—it gets activated by an unknown mechanism and begins a journey back up the very axons it came in on. Once it reaches the original nerve-cell endings it spreads to skin cells, and the result is new lesions in the same old place.

As noted, some people with herpes can shed virus particles from time to time even when they have no lesions, meaning they are infectious during these periods. This, of course, puts these carriers at terrible risk of passing the virus on to their uninfected partners. The good news about herpes is that there is a drug, called Valacyclovir, that has shown significant ability to suppress the virus at all times. In a large clinical trial, herpes carriers who took one Valacyclovir tablet a day transmitted the virus to their partners at less than half the rate of carriers who took only a placebo.

Figure 20.6
Small Is a Relative Thing
The bacteria, protist, and viral clones shown in the figure are all microscopic. Nevertheless, they differ greatly among themselves in terms of size. A typical human cell might be about a third the size of the *Paramecium*.

- *No membrane-bound organelles*. A nucleus is an example of an *organelle*: a highly organized structure within a cell that carries out specific cellular functions. You may remember from Chapter 4 that, in addition to a nucleus, eukaryotic cells have such organelles as mitochondria and lysosomes, which are surrounded by a membrane. Bacteria have only a single kind of organelle, the ribosome, which differs from other organelles in that it is not surrounded by a membrane.

- *Single-celled organisms with small cell size*. Bacteria often come together in groupings that have an organization to them, but each bacterial cell is a self-contained living thing—each one can live and reproduce without the aid of other cells. Bacterial cells are also very small, relative to eukaryotic cells; thousands of them could typically fit into a single eukaryotic cell. (If you look at **Figure 20.6**, you can see a size comparison of bacteria, a T4 virus, and a protist you'll be looking at called a paramecium.)

bacteria (*E. coli*)
2 µm long

protist (*Paramecium*)
75 µm long

viral clones (T4)
0.2 µm long

- *Asexual reproduction.* Bacteria reproduce by a simple cell-splitting or **binary fission**: one cell splits into two, with both "daughter" cells being exact replicas of the parental cell. In contrast, most eukaryotes are capable of sexual reproduction, in which the genetic material of two separate organisms produces offspring, usually through the fusion of egg and sperm.

If you look at **Figure 20.7**, you can see micrographs of the three forms bacterial cells most often take: round, rod-shaped, and spiral-shaped. A round bacterium is known as a *coccus*; a rod-shaped bacterium is a *bacillus*; and a spiral-shaped bacterium goes under a variety of names, the best known of which is a *spirochete*. Different species of bacteria fit into all three groups.

Almost all bacteria have a structure called a cell wall at their periphery that is largely composed of a material called peptidoglycan. This may seem like a technical detail, but the fact that bacteria have cell walls is of great importance to humans because it represents a *difference* between bacterial cells and human cells. As you'll see, we humans have exploited this difference in our development of the medical drugs known as antibiotics.

Bacterial Diversity

Scientists have taken small soil samples, looked for DNA sequence differences among the bacteria in these samples, and concluded that about 10,000 different species of bacteria exist in such handfuls of earth. Extrapolating from these samples, it's safe to say that millions of species of bacteria exist. Surprisingly, perhaps, only 4,500 species of bacteria and archaea have been identified to date.

An incredible diversity exists among the various kinds of bacteria. It may seem strange to think of these tiny creatures as "diverse," given that they are all microscopic and single-celled. But physical form is only one kind of diversity. Imagine that only some human beings got their nutrition in the conventional way—by ingesting food—while others could *make* their own food by carrying out photosynthesis. Bacteria do things both ways. Imagine that only some human beings needed oxygen to live, while others could take it or leave it, and still others were poisoned by it. Bacteria fit into all three categories. Animals and plants have diverse forms, but bacteria have diverse metabolisms. If you look at "Modes of Nutrition" on the next page, you can see the various ways that life's creatures get the nutrition they need. Note that bacteria utilize every one of these modes, while humans utilize only one.

(a) Round bacteria (cocci)

(b) Rod-shaped bacteria (bacilli)

(c) Spiral-shaped bacterium (spirochete)

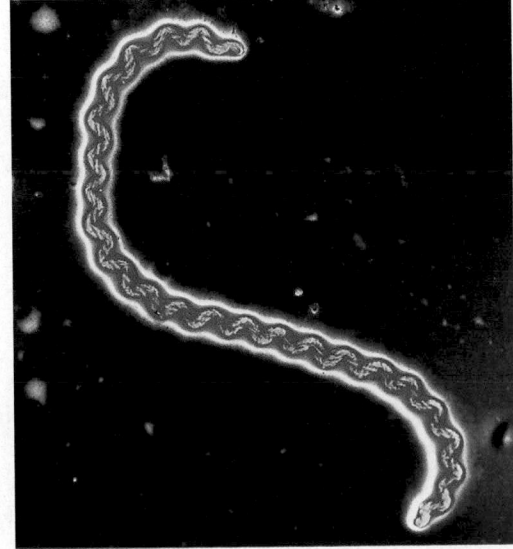

Figure 20.7
Different Shapes of Bacteria

(a) The round bacterium *Staphylococcus epidermis* is a normal part of the bacteria that cover our skin.

(b) The rod-shaped bacterium *Bacillus anthracis* is the cause of the deadly disease anthrax.

(c) The spiral-shaped bacterium *Leptospira interrogans* often infects rodents, sometimes infects dogs, and occasionally infects human beings.

Modes of Nutrition: How Organisms Get What They Need to Survive

All living things need energy and nutrients. The question is, how do they get them? What is their "nutritional mode," as biologists would put it?

The most fundamental distinction in nutritional mode separates groups known as autotrophs from those called heterotrophs. "Autotroph" means "self-feeding." **Autotrophs** are organisms that can manufacture their own food, defined as some form of organic (carbon-containing) molecule that can be broken down to yield energy. All organisms that are not autotrophs are **heterotrophs**, meaning "other feeders;" they cannot manufacture their own food, but must get it from elsewhere, as animals do.

The idea of heterotrophs is not strange to us—it's what we are, after all—but the notion of autotrophs may be a little more exotic. Those who have gone through Chapter 8 on photosynthesis will recall that almost all plants are autotrophs in that they manufacture their own food, initially a sugar. To do this, they need a carbon source, because carbon is the "backbone" of the organic molecules we know as food, and they need an energy source that can drive the complex process of photosynthesis. The carbon source for plants turns out to be carbon dioxide (CO_2), obtained from the atmosphere, while the energy source is sunlight. Here we see the *two-part* requirement for nutrition that holds for all organisms: a source of carbon on the one hand, and an energy source on the other.

Within this framework there are four nutritional modes, which you can review in **Table 1**. The two most important of these modes are *photoautotrophy*, which is the nutritional mode of plants, and *chemoheterotrophy*, in which organic materials (better known as food) act as both carbon supplier *and* energy source. This is another way of saying that the cereal you ate this morning supplied you, as a chemoheterotroph, with both carbon and high-energy electrons.

There is also *chemoautotrophy*, in which organisms—some bacteria and archaea—get their carbon from carbon dioxide, like plants do, but power the production of food from this carbon by oxidizing (pulling electrons from) such inorganic materials as hydrogen sulfide and ammonia. A small number of bacteria and archaea practice *photoheterotrophy*, in which the sun supplies the energy but the carbon comes from surrounding organic material.

Table 1

Nutritional mode	Carbon source	Energy source	Practiced by
Autotrophy			
Photoautotrophy	Carbon dioxide (CO_2)	The sun's rays	Almost all plants, some bacteria, and many protists
Chemoautotrophy	Carbon dioxide	Inorganic compounds such as hydrogen sulfide and ammonia	Some bacteria and archaea
Heterotrophy			
Photoheterotrophy	Organic material	The sun's rays	A few bacteria and archaea
Chemoheterotrophy	Organic material	Organic material	Almost all animals, all fungi, most bacteria, many protists, and a few plants

20.4 Intimate Strangers: Humans and Bacteria

In the chapter introduction, you saw how bacteria are indispensable to life in general because they can capture atmospheric nitrogen, decompose dead organic material, and so forth. As it turns out, however, bacteria may be indispensable to *human* life in an even more direct way. From the time we travel down our mother's birth canal, we enter into a lifelong interdependence with these microorganisms. If you look at **Figure 20.8**, you can see the places bacteria are found in quantity outside and inside the human body, along with a micrograph showing what one class of these bacteria looks like. Outside,

(a)

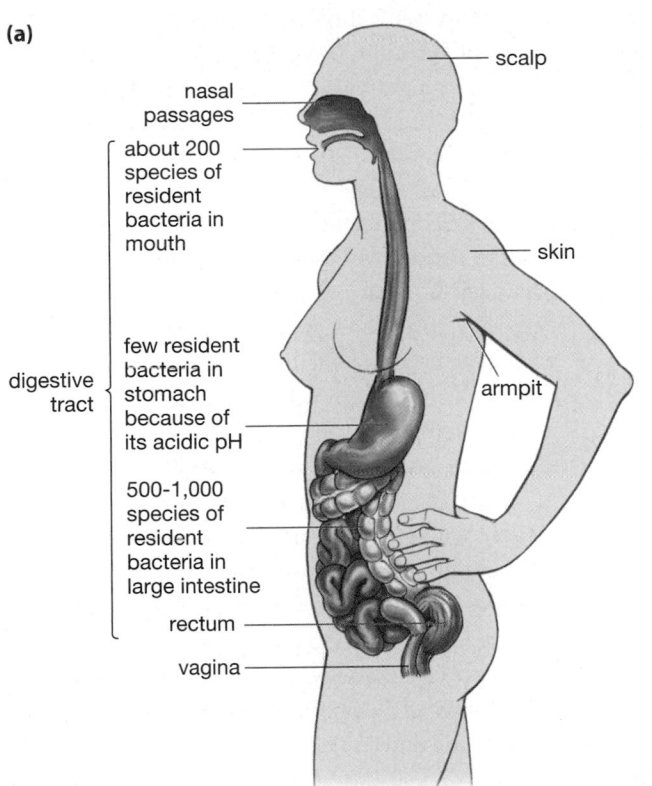

scalp

nasal passages

about 200 species of resident bacteria in mouth

skin

digestive tract

few resident bacteria in stomach because of its acidic pH

armpit

500–1,000 species of resident bacteria in large intestine

rectum

vagina

(b)

**Figure 20.8
At Home in Us**

(a) We human beings live with trillions of "resident" bacteria, meaning bacteria that are always present on us, or within us. (Bacteria on the scalp or skin might temporarily be washed away, but they quickly return.) The greatest concentration of these bacteria is found in the digestive tract, particularly the large intestine.

(b) An example of resident bacteria. Pictured is a kind of bacterium commonly found in the human nose. The little yellow balls are *Staphylococcus aureus*, seen here among the hair-like cilia that extend from the cells lining the nasal passages. Many of these bacteria can be seen adhering to mucus (in blue).

we are covered in bacteria from head to toe, with heavy concentrations in the armpits and scalp. Inside, they exist in nasal passages, in the vagina in females, and, most especially, in the digestive tract. Perhaps 100 trillion bacterial cells live within the length of the tract, from mouth to rectum. The number of *human* cells in a human body is thought to be about 100 trillion as well, so when we count bacterial cells not just in the digestive tract but elsewhere, we find that bacterial cells outnumber our own. (The reason we are not bloated with them is that they are such small cells.) This is not to say that bacteria are everywhere within us; most of our tissues are kept bacteria-free, except for occasional invaders. But about half the contents of our colon are bacteria, as are perhaps a quarter of our feces by weight. These are not transient bacteria who come for brief periods and then are gone. They are so-called "resident" bacteria whose permanent home is the human body.

This account may make you feel like you've been colonized, but the relationship between us and many of the bacteria we harbor actually is one of **mutualism**, which is to say a relationship between two organisms that benefits both of them. If we could shrink ourselves down to the size of a bacterium and enter, say, the human small intestine, we would see a community of

competing but *interdependent* organisms, most of which are bacteria, but one of which is us. What bacteria get from participating in this community is food and habitat. What humans get is a fully functional digestive system. How do bacteria help bring this about? Consider that rats whose bacteria have been wiped out through laboratory techniques require 30 percent more calories to maintain their body weight than do normal rats. Without bacteria, the structure of these rats' intestines is altered in a way that's unhealthy: they have low numbers of the cells that line the digestive tract and move nutrients from the tract to the bloodstream. Researchers have made mice "germ-free," then reintroduced bacteria into them, and then watched as mouse genes were turned on that help metabolize sugars and fats. Bacteria even metabolize some sugars that we cannot digest, and they produce some vitamins as well. The essential message here is that, within the digestive tract, mammals and bacteria have had such a long working relationship that each has become dependent on the other. We humans don't just tolerate the bacteria in our gut; we need them.

20.5 Bacteria and Human Disease

It goes without saying, of course, that not all bacteria are beneficial to human beings. Even within our digestive tract, there are bacteria that are "commensal" with us—they benefit from the relationship, while we are unaffected by it. And, of course, there are bacteria that are **pathogenic**, which is to say disease-causing. These are not bacteria that routinely inhabit any part of our body in large numbers. Instead, they are opportunists that invade specific tissues. Among the diseases they cause are tuberculosis, syphilis, gonorrhea, cholera, tetanus, botulism, leprosy, typhoid fever, and diphtheria, not to mention all manner of food poisonings and blood-borne infections. In the fourteenth century, the bacterially caused bubonic plague wiped out a *third* of Europe's population in just four years. Closer to home, you may recall a substance referred to as "anthrax" that was maliciously mailed to various offices after the September 11 attacks. Anthrax actually is a bacterium (*Bacillus anthracis*) that, when not in the hands of terrorists, occasionally infects farm animals.

How do pathogenic bacteria cause illness? A few invade human cells and reproduce there. More often, however, bacterial damage comes from substances bacteria either secrete or leave behind when they die. These compounds are *toxins*, which is to say substances that harmfully alter living tissue or interfere with biological processes. In the case of respiratory anthrax, *Bacillus anthracis* secretes a trio of toxins that cause blood vessels in the lungs and brain to "hemorrhage" or leak. The botulism bacterium, *Clostridium botulinum*, secretes a toxin that blocks the signals that go from nerves to muscles. The end result can be a paralysis of the muscles that control the diaphragm, in which case victims lose the ability to breathe. Of course, all pathogenic bacteria must have a way to get into the body in the first place. The bacterium that causes bubonic plague, *Yersinia pestis*, enters on the bite of a flea, while the tetanus bacterium, *Clostridium tetani*, may hitch a ride in on a rusty nail. Meanwhile, the tuberculosis bacterium, *Mycobacterium tuberculosis*, can simply be inhaled.

Killing Pathogenic Bacteria: Antibiotics

Prior to the 1930s, doctors were nearly powerless to stop any of these bacterial invaders. Some progress was made in the late 1930s with the development of the synthetic chemicals called sulfa drugs. But modern medicine was born in the 1940s with the development of **antibiotics**, meaning chemical compounds produced by one microorganism that are toxic to another microorganism. The first antibiotic, penicillin, was a substance produced by a fungus. Like all antibiotics, it had two critical qualities: it could kill microorganisms within human beings while leaving the humans themselves relatively unharmed. (For an account of penicillin's development, see "The Discovery of Penicillin" on page 419.)

How can antibiotics be toxic to bacteria but not to people? They exploit the differences between bacterial cells and human cells. Remember earlier when we noted that almost all bacteria have cell walls, while human cells don't? Penicillin and several other antibiotics work by blocking cell-wall construction, which bacteria have to undertake when they divide. Penicillin confiscates a construction tool; it binds with a bacterial enzyme that helps stitch the cell wall together. A bacterium without a cell wall is doomed: it ruptures, floods, and dies. But the *human* cells around it—lacking cell walls—are left unharmed.

It is hard to overstate how much of human health hinges today on antibiotic processes such as these. If you have grandparents who were alive in the 1930s, they may well have had friends or relatives who died of tuberculosis or blood poisoning or tetanus. But do you know of anyone who, during your lifetime, has died of such an illness? Probably not. Antibiotics have made all the difference.

The Threat of Antibiotic Resistance

This power of antibiotics ought to spark alarm in us about something that is happening today, which is that antibiotics are steadily *losing* their ability to kill bacteria. How could this happen? An estimated 30 percent of antibiotic prescriptions written today are thought to be needless, in the sense that the person taking the antibiotic doesn't even have a bacterial infection, but rather is suffering from a viral or other illness. (So why do people get such prescriptions? They ask their doctors for them and the doctors go along.) Even when people do have bacterial infections, they often take their antibiotics only until they start feeling better, rather than following through with the full course of recommended treatment, which can last weeks or even months.

Those of you who have read through the chapters on evolution may be able to see what this leads to. Normal bacteria may be wiped out by a needlessly short course of antibiotics. But a few bacteria will survive these inadequate treatments because they have sets of genes that allow them to do so. In the *absence* of antibiotics, these survivors might not have had anything special going for them, relative to others in their population. (They aren't *generally* superior bacteria; they just resist antibiotics better.) But with antibiotics these survivors have been left without bacterial competitors for food and habitat. As a result, they flourish, giving rise to antibiotic-resistant *lines* of bacteria. Moreover, they will do this rapidly, since one generation of bacteria can give rise to another in as little as 20 minutes.

Other factors also enter into this picture. It may surprise you to learn that nearly half the antibiotics used in the United States don't go into people at all; they are put into animal feeds because they serve as growth stimulants. In a similar vein, farmers spray huge tracts of fruit trees with antibiotics to ward off bacterial infections. Hand soaps now contain antimicrobial agents whose residues stay on bathroom and kitchen surfaces, wiping out some bacteria while leaving the resistant variety to multiply in the absence of competitors. (Such hand soaps are unnecessary in the first place because plain soap and water will work just as well to wash the germs down the drain instead of killing them.)

The upshot of this massive over-use of antibiotics is that bacterial infectious diseases are making a comeback. The problem is most pressing in hospitals, where physicians are seeing one formerly useful drug after another fail to cure infections. If we cannot stay ahead of bacterial evolution by developing new antibiotics—while cutting back on the needless use of existing antibiotics—we may find ourselves returning to the days of our grandparents, when a simple cut could be life-threatening.

20.6 Archaea: From Marginal Player to Center Stage

As little as 10 years ago, any biology textbook you picked up would likely have referred to the archaea as archae*bacteria*, and most would have mentioned the archaea as a kind of marginal life-form, existing in only a few extreme habitats, such as hot springs or salty lakes. Today, the archaea are recognized as constituting their own domain in life—standing alongside Domain Bacteria and Domain Eukarya—

and they have belatedly been recognized as existing in abundance in lots of environments. The importance of the archaea stretches beyond this, however, in that, of all the organisms living today, archaea may have been the first to exist. Whether this means that archaea are ancestral to all other existing life-forms remains to be seen—many researchers have their doubts—but it is certain that archaea lie near the trunk of life's family tree. In particular, the *thermophiles*, or heat-loving archaea, appear to be a very old branch on life's family tree, which is one piece of evidence leading many scientists to suspect that life began in or near hot-water vents of the type seen on the ocean floor today.

It took a long time to recognize the unique qualities of archaea because, superficially, they are very similar to bacteria. They are microscopic, single-celled, and their cells lack a nucleus (making them prokaryotes, along with the bacteria). In addition, it is hard to learn much about archaea because it is so difficult to "culture" them, meaning to grow populations of them in a laboratory. The lab environment is so different from the extreme environments inhabited by many archaea that cultures of them are quickly taken over by common bacteria.

Beyond these things, however, there was a long-term resistance among scientists to seeing archaea as anything but an odd type of bacteria. Indeed, a single individual, Carl Woese of the University of Illinois, had to wage a lonely battle lasting years before his claims about the uniqueness of the archaea were generally accepted. In 1996 there came a triumphant confirmation of his ideas about the archaea with the sequencing of the entire genome of an archaean species, *Methanococcus jannaschii*. This work revealed that an amazing 56 percent of *M. jannaschii*'s genes were completely unknown to science—they were unlike anything seen in either bacteria or in eukaryotes. As for the remaining 44 percent of the genome, some *M. jannaschii* genes worked like those

(a)

(b)

Figure 20.9
Life in Extreme Environments

(a) Deep-sea archaeans *Methanopyrus kandleri* is an archaean that lives in the ocean at temperatures near those of boiling water. It has been found in geothermal vents on the sea-floor at depths of 2,000 meters, or about 1.2 miles down. One of many archaeans that produce the gas methane as part of their metabolism, it can only live in environments in which there is no oxygen.

(b) Prospecting for extremeophiles Researchers looking for archaean extremeophiles in the Obsidian Pool in Yellowstone National Park.

of eukaryotes, while others worked like those of bacteria. It makes sense, then, that archaea lie between bacteria and eukaryotes on life's family tree, as you can see in Figure 20.2 (page 403).

All this speaks to the uniqueness and evolutionary place of the archaea, but what about the widespread distribution of them? In the 1980s, scientists developed a technique that allowed them to do a kind of census taking of archaea out in nature. This method revealed that archaeans live in extreme environments, such as the hot springs in Yellowstone National Park, in more numbers than had been thought. But the real surprise came when more expansive environments were tested; archaea turn out to account for almost a third of the microscopic organisms living in the surface waters off Antarctica, for example, and huge populations of them inhabit deeper-ocean waters.

Prospecting for "Extremophiles"

The species of archaea that inhabit extreme environments have in recent years become the target of a kind of new-age prospecting, with "miners" being scientists from chemical and biotechnology firms. The archaea they are looking for are **extremophiles**—archaea or bacteria that flourish in conditions that would kill most organisms, such as high heat, high pressure, high salt, or extreme pH (**see Figure 20.9**). One of the most extreme of the extremophiles was reported on in 2000, when researchers revealed the existence of an archaean they found thriving in the acidic wastes of an abandoned copper mine. Dubbed *Ferroplasma acidarmanus*, this hardy microbe can live in liquid that has a pH of zero—a habitat more acidic than battery acid. There are also archaea that not only live in, but seem to require, the crushing water pressure that comes with life at the bottom of the ocean; and there are archaeans that thrive in habitats so salty that no plant or animal could survive in them.

To live in such environments, extremophiles ("extreme-lovers") must produce *enzymes* that function in them. And, through modern biotechnology processes, enzymes can be isolated from an organism and then turned out in quantity in factories. These enzymes can then be put to use in *human-made* extreme environments, such as the inside of a washing machine or the confines of a laboratory container. One U.S. company has already introduced a clothing detergent containing a cleaning additive that is simply an enzyme from a heat-loving extremophile.

20.7 Protists: Pioneers in Diversifying Life

We've thus far looked at two of life's domains, Bacteria and Archaea. As noted, the third domain, Eukarya, is so diverse we will look at only one of its four kingdoms in this chapter, the mostly microscopic organisms known as protists.

What's a protist? No one can provide a satisfactory definition. They are something like the objects in a drawer marked "miscellaneous": the primary thing they have in common is that they don't belong in any other drawer. Domain Eukarya has within it three well-defined kingdoms—plants, animals, and fungi—but protists are defined in terms of what they are *not* relative to these life-forms: Protists are eukaryotic organisms that do not have all the defining characteristics of either a plant or an animal or a fungus.

You may recall from Chapter 19 that animals, plants, and fungi *evolved* from protists—animals from protists called choanoflagellates, plants from green-algae protists, and fungi from an unknown variety of protist. Not surprisingly, then, there are protists that are *like* plants, animals, and fungi. Some protists ingest food, as animals do; others make their own food, as plants do; and still others send out slender extensions of themselves and digest their food externally, as fungi do. These similarities will provide us with a way to conceptualize the protist kingdom, but the protists themselves don't actually stay confined within these categories. To give one well-known example of a category-breaker, there is a microscopic protist called *Euglena gracilis* that is bright green and, when at rest, takes on a cigar shape (see **Figure 20.10**). The green color of *Euglena* comes from the chloroplasts within it, which you might remember are the organelles that perform photosynthesis. So, when swimming around its home, which tends to be a freshwater pond, *Euglena* is making its own food through photosynthesis, which would presumably place it with the plant-like protists. Yet when sunlight becomes scarce, *Euglena* simply switches over to an animal-like nutritional mode—it ingests organic matter. Then, when sunlight returns, it goes back to photosynthesis.

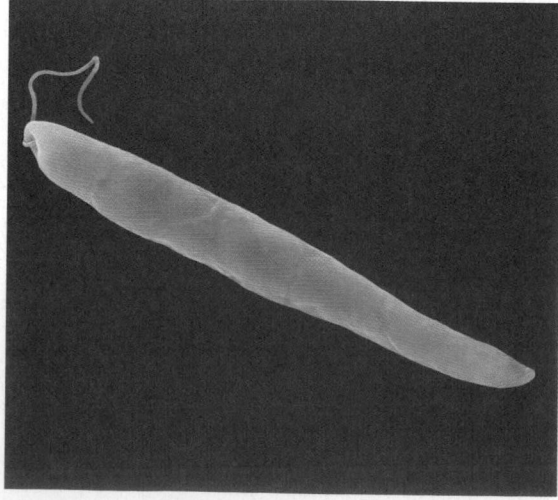

Figure 20.10
More Like a Plant or an Animal?
The protist *Euglena gracilis* switches back and forth between the plant-like behavior of making its own food and the animal-like behavior of capturing food from its external environment.

Protists, then, are difficult to categorize. The only things we can say about all of them is that they are eukaryotes and that they live in environments that are at least moist, if not fully aquatic—damp forest floors as well as oceans and lakes. Almost all are microscopic, though, as you'll see, some are very large. About 100,000 species are known to exist. Though only a small proportion are parasites that affect humans, the rogue's gallery of protists is a formidable one. A microscopic protist, *Plasmodium falciparum*, causes one of the world's most widespread diseases, malaria, by passing between human and mosquito hosts. Campers in the United States are aware of the intestinal parasite *Giardia*, which contaminates water. Other protists cause sleeping sickness and amoebic dysentery. Pathogenic protists also affect humans in less direct ways. The cause of the great Irish Potato Famine of the 1840s was a fungus-like protist, *Phytophthora infestans*, that devastated the Irish potato fields. A close relative of this pest, *Phytophthora ramorum*, is now wiping out stands of California oak trees and bay laurels.

20.8 Protists and Sexual Reproduction

When we look at the living world as a whole, the protists in it are fascinating because they are the organisms that made the break with prokaryotic life—with life as nothing but single-celled bacteria and archaea. After life first appeared on Earth, it consisted solely of bacteria and archaea for more than 2 billion years. The first life-forms to appear other than bacteria and archaea were the protists. And in these organisms, we can see how the living world branched out; we can see living things making transitions to life as we know it today.

One such transition has to do with reproduction. You may recall that bacteria reproduce through a simple splitting of one cell into two. As it turns out, most protists reproduce this way as well. But many protists can reproduce by mixing genetic material from *two* individuals; they give rise to offspring through *sexual* reproduction, in other words. This change was terrifically important to evolution because it meant that offspring would be different from their parents. Bacterial daughter cells are clones of their parent cell—they are genetically identical to it. But the offspring of sexually reproducing organisms have a mixture of genes from both parents, meaning these offspring will not be identical to *either* parent. Once variation started appearing simply as a consequence of reproduction, evolution was off to the races in terms of creating new life-forms, because so much variation was being produced.

This does not mean, however, that life went in one step from reproduction by simple cell splitting to reproduction as we now know it today in, say, human beings. Remember, the protists show us transitions. Let's look at what sexual reproduction is like in an ancient, early-evolving protist.

The protist in question is a type of single-celled algae called *Chlamydomonas*. Most of the time, *Chlamydomonas* reproduces through cell splitting. In times of little nutrition, however, *Chlamydomonas* switches over to sexual reproduction. This begins with two normal *Chlamydomonas* cells, which means two cells that are haploid—that contain only a single set of chromosomes. You may recall that bacteria and archaea are always haploid. It makes sense, then, that the usual state for *Chlamydomonas* is haploid, since, on life's family tree, it lies so close to the bacteria and archaea. Yet Chlamydomonas has made a switch, as you can tell by looking at **Figure 20.11**. Note that at one point, two haploid *Chlamydomonas* cells fuse to create a zygote—the same thing that takes place with human sperm and egg cells. The result is a cell with *two* sets of chromosomes, one set coming from each parent. This cell then undertakes the meiosis reviewed in Chapter 10. You may recall that meiosis always entails a swapping of pieces between the chromosomes that came from parent A and those that came from parent B. Further, these chromosomes then assort randomly, such that any "daughter" cell will get a different mix of chromosomes from each parent. In *Chlamydomonas*, four new offspring cells are produced from the fusion of the original two

Figure 20.11
Sexual Reproduction in a Protist
The simple alga *Chlamydomonas* normally is a haploid organism, meaning one that possesses a single set of chromosomes. In reproduction, however, *Chlamydomonas* cells of opposite mating types (+ and −) can fuse to create a zygote or fertilized egg that is diploid—that has a paired set of chromosomes. Meiosis then ensues in the zygote and the result is four haploid *Chlamydomonas* cells, each of which differs genetically from the others, thanks to the mixing of chromosomes that took place in meiosis.

+ mating type (haploid)

− mating type (haploid)

haploid

haploid

+ cell

− cell

pairing

diploid

cell fusion

zygote (diploid)

meiosis

cells. The critical thing is that, because of the shuffling done in meiosis, each of these cells has a unique mixture of chromosomes from each parent. The difference between bacteria and *Chlamydomonas* is the difference between clones and diverse offspring.

One more detail about this process is important. You may wonder about the little plus (+) and minus (−) signs next to the *Chlamydomonas* cells in Figure 20.11. This is an early protist version of what it means to be male and female. There are so-called + and − "mating types" of *Chlamydomonas*, and only these opposites can come together in sexual reproduction. (A + cell cannot fuse with another + cell.) The whip-like flagella that extend from + and − mating types differ in their micro-structure. As a result, only opposite types of flagella can adhere to one another—something that is necessary to get the fusion process going. What we think of as male-female differences are later-arriving variations on this theme.

With this as background, let's now look at a few representatives of the protists, within the categories of plant-like, animal-like, and fungus-like.

20.9 Plant-Like Protists

Plant-like protists are perhaps the only large group of protists known to the average person. The catchall name for them is **algae**, defined as protists that perform photosynthesis. If you look at Figure 20.13, you can look at three varieties we'll be reviewing.

Figure 20.12a shows a microscopic "golden" alga called *Synura scenedesmus* that can be found swimming in freshwater ponds in the United States. In this species, we can see a transition between the single-celled life carried out by bacteria and the multicelled life carried out by more complex organisms. All varieties of golden algae come in species that exhibit **colonial multicellularity**: a form of life in which individual cells form stable associations with one another but do not take on specialized roles. Each of the three

objects you see in the picture of *Synura* is a cluster of *Synura* cells—a colony of them. Each member of the colony keeps its two whip-like flagella pointed to the outside of the group, the flagella beat back and forth, and the colony literally rolls through the water. None of these cells, however, performs a function different from any other cell, which is why this *Synura* is referred to as colonial and not truly multicellular.

If you look at **Figure 20.12b**, you can see a form of *green* algae, called *Volvox*, that represents an evolutionary step beyond *Synura*. The beautiful, translucent circles that outline *Volvox* are a gelatinous material that initially encloses a single layer of anywhere from 500 to 60,000 *Volvox* cells, all of them spaced around the periphery of the sphere. Almost all of these cells have flagella that they move back and forth in unison, so that *Volvox* moves slowly through the water in a given direction, spinning along an axis as it goes (something like a torpedo). For our purposes, the key thing about *Volvox* is that not all of the cells in this colony will reproduce. Only a select group of cells without flagella, generally at the rear pole of the axis, will divide to produce new colonies. These colonies in turn give rise to new spheres that exist inside the original parent sphere. Eventually the gelatinous material around the parent sphere ruptures and the daughter spheres emerge, each of them then continuing the process. The important point is that *Volvox* has cells that specialize. As such, *Volvox* has arguably achieved **true multicellularity**: a form of life in which individual cells exist in stable groups, with different cells in a group specializing in different functions. In human beings, of course, we can see a great specialization in, for example, nerve and muscle cells. *Volvox* shows us specialization in a rudimentary form.

Finally, if you look at **Figure 20.12c**, you can see some representative *brown* algae—the giants of the protist world. One variety of brown algae, the sea kelp, has individuals that may be 100 meters long,

Figure 20.12
Transitions Visible in Algae

(a) Three colonies of the golden algae *Synura*, each of which is composed of a cluster of individual cells. *Synura* is a colonial protist, as none of the cells in a colony takes on any specialized function.

(b) Colonies of the green algae *Volvox* with daughter colonies growing inside. *Volvox* colonies can be regarded as truly multicellular organisms, in that they have specialized reproductive cells. The largest *Volvox* colonies can be seen with the naked eye.

(c) A frond of the brown algae known as sea kelp. These unusually large protists have assemblages of cells that conduct food throughout the organism.

(a) Golden algae

(b) Green algae

(c) Brown algae

and that often grow in enormous "kelp forests." For our purposes, brown algae are notable because their leaf-like "blades" and stem-like "stalks" represent another leap up in complexity: they contain organized assemblages of cells that conduct food throughout the organism.

One other thing is important about the algae. Note that the golden algae and *Volvox* share three characteristics: they are microscopic, aquatic, and carry out photosynthesis. If we were to go through all the algae, we would find these same qualities in countless species. Creatures in this category, including some bacteria, are known as **phytoplankton**: small photosynthesizing organisms that float near the surface of water. Such organisms are extremely important to life on Earth for two reasons. First, they produce most of the Earth's oxygen. Second, they sit right at the base of most aquatic food chains. All large life-forms on Earth ultimately depend on photosynthesizers for their food. On land, lions may eat zebras, but zebras eat grass. On the ocean, whales may eat the shrimp-like creatures called krill, but krill eat phytoplankton.

20.10 Animal-Like Protists

Once referred to as protozoa, the animal-like protists are alike in that they do not get their nutrients from photosynthesis, as algae do, but instead get them from consuming other organisms or bits of organic matter that they find. Furthermore, they digest this material internally, and they have evolved various means of moving toward their prey. If you look at Figure 20.13, you can see three varieties of animal-like protists.

Figure 20.13a shows a common animal-like protist, *Paramecium*, which is known as a ciliate because of all the hair-like cilia that cover its exterior. These cilia beat in unison, allowing paramecia to move forward or back in an exacting fashion—toward or away from objects in its environment. *Paramecium* may be single-celled, but it is complex. It takes food in through a mouth-like passageway called a gullet, digests it in a special organelle called a food vacuole, and then empties the resulting waste into the outside world through a special pore on its exterior. Some species even have tiny dart-like structures (called trichocysts) that they can shoot out when threatened.

Figure 20.13b shows a so-called ameboid protist, meaning a protist that gets around by means of a pseudopod or "false foot." The amoeba sends out a slender extension of itself (the foot) and then the rest of its body flows into this extension. It takes in bits of food by encircling them with extensions and then fusing these extensions together. What once had been outside the amoeba is now inside, being digested. The ameboid protists are where we get the idea of a life-form as a "blob," since many of them have no fixed shape, but instead are constantly changing form. Many ameboid protists are parasites, and one of them, *Entamoeba histolytica*, is a serious human parasite, causing an estimated 100,000 deaths per year, mostly in the tropics, by entering the human digestive system through contaminated water. When a parasite invades the human intestinal wall, the resulting condition is known as dysentery. When that parasite is an amoeba, the result is amoebic dysentery.

Figure 20.13c shows another human parasite that enters human beings through contaminated water. So widespread is this "camper's parasite," *Giardia lamblia,* that health authorities have advised Americans never to drink stream or lake water without both filtering and boiling it, or filtering and treating it (with iodine or chlorine). *Giardia* lives in the small intestines of humans and other animals, where it causes symptoms that include nausea, diarrhea, and vomiting. It gets around not by the false foot of the amoeba, nor by the cilia of *Paramecium*, but by pairs of whip-like flagella, as we saw in the algae protists.

**Figure 20.13
Animal-like Protists**

(a) A green *Paramecium*, whose many cilia both help it move and bring food to its gullet, visible in the center.

(b) An amoeba bends itself around food, which it will soon ingest.

(c) The parasite *Giardia lamblia* within the human small intestine. Seen here as the pear-shaped green and white objects, *Giardia* use sucking discs to attach themselves to finger-like extensions of the intestine's inner lining.

(a) A *Paramecium*

(b) An amoeba

(c) The *Giardia* parasite

20.11 Fungus-Like Protists

As you'll see next chapter, all fungi get nutrients through a two-step process: They send out slender filaments to a food source, and then release enzymes that digest the food externally. Once this is done, the food is taken back up into the fungus. One class of fungus-like protists, called the oomycetes, operates this same way—so much so that many of these protists can be mistaken for fungi, even by experts. The protist noted earlier that caused the Irish Potato Famine, *Phytophthora infestans*, is in this category. If you look at **Figure 20.14a**, you can see filaments of an oomycete called a water mold extending from a goldfish. In general, the water molds and their terrestrial relatives are **saprobes**, meaning organisms that obtain their nutrition from *dead* organic matter. Clearly, however, they attack living organisms as well.

Figure 20.14b shows another kind of fungus-like protist, this one known as a plasmodial slime mold. This organism assumes several forms during its life-cycle. In the form you see in the picture, its name is appropriate, because it is essentially moving slime. If you looked at it under a microscope, you would see lots of cell nuclei, but almost none of the *boundaries*—the plasma membranes—that normally separate one cell from another. The result is a free-flowing, but slowly moving mass of cytoplasm; the interior of a single cell spread out over a large area, with only one plasma membrane at its periphery. This material moves by the same "cytoplasmic streaming" we saw in the ameboids. As it rolls over rocks or forest floor, it consumes underlying bacteria, fungi, and bits of organic material. Should an object stand in its path, it simply flows around it, or even through it, if the object is porous enough. In short, this is life as a blob again, only this is a large blob. The plasmodial slime mold's similarity with fungi is that, when nutrition is scarce, it changes shape, forming a structure that releases fungus-like spores.

By now, you may be getting the impression that protists could be star contestants in a show called "Can You Top This for Strangeness?" If you look at **Figure 20.14c**, you can see another contestant. Pictured is a much-studied organism, *Dictyostelium discoideum*, a so-called cellular slime mold that has a multiple personality. At one point in its life cycle, it exists in the form of individual microscopic cells that crawl along the forest floor feeding on bacteria. Each "Dicty" is on its own at this stage, but if the bacterial food runs low, these individual cells begin "aggregating" or coming together in an organized group. Eventually, they develop into a migrating "slug" of up to 100,000 cells that has front and back ends and that migrates to a more fertile area of the forest. Then at a certain point, they change form again. They arrange themselves into a stalk-like reproductive structure that has, at its top, spores that will be dispersed and develop into new individual cells that once again crawl along the forest floor. The whole aggregation process will not take place unless starvation is imminent, however; without hunger as a motivator, the individual cells stay separate.

Now, once you get past the shock of realizing that such a thing could happen—that individual cells could just collect themselves and create a larger, moving organism—you can begin to see what interesting questions it raises. What's the signaling mechanism that brings 100,000 separate cells together? How do they begin to cooperate to form these various structures? (To put this another way, how does multicellularity begin to work?) And, perhaps most intriguingly, why should some cells sacrifice themselves by serving on the *stalk* of the reproductive structure—from which location they will not reproduce themselves—while others get to be at the top and disperse to a new life in better hunting grounds? If evolution is all about passing on genes, why should some cells give up the chance to pass on theirs? Scientists study Dicty in hopes of learning more about all these questions.

Figure 20.14
The Fungi-like Protists

(a) The wispy white outgrowths stemming from the goldfish are the filaments of a parasitic protist known as a water mold.

(b) This plasmodial slime mold, *Physarium polycephalum*, is growing on and around a tree trunk in Pennsylvania.

(c) A *Dictyostelium* in its slug stage, composed of tens of thousands of individual cells that have come together to produce an organism capable of moving across the forest floor.

(a) Water mold growing on fish

(b) Plasmodial slime mold

(c) *Dictyostelium* slug

How Did We Learn?
The Discovery of Penicillin

In wartime England, late in 1940, as the German bombings raged, a 43-year-old policeman lay dying in the Radcliffe Infirmary in Oxford. Albert Alexander was, however, not a victim of the German air raids. His enemy was smaller and more subtle. A few months earlier, he had scratched his cheek on a rosebush thorn. This minor wound had then become infected, and from that point on he steadily went downhill as bacteria worked away inside him. By December his face was a mess of festering wounds, one of which cost him an eye.

Incomprehensible as it may seem, in 1940 a scratch from a rosebush thorn could do this to a person. The notable thing about Albert Alexander was not that he became deathly ill from such a trivial injury, but that he came close to beating his tiny enemies. He happened to live near an Oxford University laboratory where a handful of researchers were hurriedly trying to extract, from a common fungus, a product that the world eventually came to know as penicillin. When Albert Alexander became the first human being to receive a therapeutic dose of penicillin in February 1941, the results were startling. His fever dropped, his infection began to clear; even his appetite returned. But there was to be no happy ending for him, for the researchers had only a five-day supply of the drug. Trying everything they could think of, they even extracted precious micrograms of penicillin from Alexander's own urine, to put back into him. But it was not enough; he died days later.

Nevertheless, Alexander's case had shown that penicillin could work in human beings, and clear-cut successes with the drug were not long in coming. A 15-year-old boy with an infected hip underwent a remarkable turn-around when injected with it; children had their eyesight saved when blindness would have been the expected outcome. These early trials made clear that, if ever there was a "miracle drug," penicillin was it. Prior to its advent, doctors could only watch and hope for the best as their patients were wracked by infections that ranged from pneumonia to meningitis to diphtheria to blood poisoning. With the advent of penicillin, at last doctors could do something.

How did it happen that a small band of researchers in wartime England ended up realizing the wondrous potential of this substance? The story begins not in the 1940s, but in 1928, when another scientist in England, Alexander Fleming, discovered the existence of penicillin through a combination of perceptiveness and luck. Returning to his hospital laboratory from a summer vacation, he noticed spot of mold (a type of fungus) in one of the petri dishes in which he was growing or "culturing" bacteria. Such bacterial cultures can easily become contaminated; this dish probably became tainted by means of fungal spores wafting in from another lab in the building. Something about this particular contamination caught Fleming's eye, however: the bacteria in the vicinity of the mold had clearly burst—they were dead. Realizing that chance had brought to him a substance that had the power to kill bacteria, Fleming grew more of the fungal mold, prepared a broth from it, tested its power against several kinds of deadly bacteria, and even went so far as to inject it into healthy mice to see if it had adverse effects (which it didn't). This latter finding was crucial. There are lots of substances that can kill bacteria; the trick is to find one that can kill bacteria while leaving human beings unharmed.

> *The team had to brew up liters of fungal fluid to get mere millionths of a gram of active penicillin*

Having advanced his work with penicillin to this point, however, Fleming then abandoned it. He had clearly recognized its therapeutic potential right from the start, but his subsequent research seemed to convince him that penicillin was just one bacteria killer among many that had no future in medicine. He found that it was unstable; that it appeared very difficult to purify from the stew of fungus chemicals it existed in; and that it quickly lost its power to kill bacteria, once they had been exposed to it. After 1931, Fleming didn't publish anything on penicillin nor did he encourage his students to work with it. He seemed to regard it as a substance that was useful mostly for killing off unwanted bacteria in petri dishes. A great deal of credit goes to him for being perceptive enough to recognize what had been laid in front of him. But had research on penicillin ended with him, there never would have been a drug called penicillin. By 1935, as Trevor Williams has written, "there was not one person in the world who believed in penicillin as a practical aid to medicine."

But this was soon to change, thanks to the work of two immigrants to Britain. One was Howard Florey, an Australian trained as a medical doctor who was then head of a school of pathology at Oxford University. The other was Ernst Chain, a refugee from Hitler's Germany who had been hired by Florey to develop a biochemistry unit in the school. The critical decision the two made in 1938 was to investigate substances in the same class as penicillin—antibiotics, which is to say substances made by one microorganism that are toxic to another. Critically, one of the compounds Florey and Chain decided to investigate was penicillin, whose existence they knew of from reading the earlier papers of Fleming and others.

continued on next page

From the beginning, the team's research on penicillin proceeded on two tracks. One was simply seeing if the substance worked. The other was finding out what the substance *was* and trying to get enough of it to work with. Remember that penicillin is the product of a living organism—originally the fungus *Penicillium notatum*—and as such it existed within a mixture of thousands of other compounds the fungus produces. The trick was to isolate and characterize the germ-killing substance within the fungal soup. This biochemical work was the job of Chain. While this was going on, the team had to brew up liters of fungal fluid to get mere millionths of a gram of active penicillin.

Finally armed with enough of the drug to put it to the test, the group carried out the critical experiment. On the morning of May 25, 1940 they injected eight mice with deadly doses of streptococcal bacteria, and an hour later they injected four of the mice with penicillin. Then a round-the-clock watch began. Normally, the dose given would have killed all the mice within 24 hours, and indeed by 3:30 a.m. the next day the four unprotected mice were dead. But the four mice given the penicillin were all fine! A long road lay ahead with human subjects such as Albert Alexander, but penicillin had done in mice what had so long been sought: It killed bacterial invaders while leaving their "host" unharmed.

This effort was being carried out against the backdrop of the outbreak of World War II. By the time the mouse experiments were started, much of Europe had fallen to Hitler and it was feared that England might be next. (The wartime importance of a drug such as penicillin was clear to the Oxford team, which had contingency plans to destroy all its lab equipment and notes in the case of a successful German invasion. Only the precious *P. notatum* spores would be retained, by means of the researchers rubbing them into their clothing.) In this chaotic environment, the scientists were forced to go outside England to get the help they needed to ramp up the production of penicillin to an industrial scale.

Howard Florey thus went to America to enlist aid there. Oxford researchers eventually found themselves working with chemical engineers from the U.S. Department of Agriculture in the unlikely location of Peoria, Illinois. Where once the English scientists had fermented penicillin in milk bottles, eventually they and their American colleagues were brewing it up in 25,000-gallon tanks.

Getting to this point meant coming up not only with better fermenting methods, but with better starting ingredients. To this end, military pilots collected soil samples from around the world in an effort to find a *Penicillium* species that would yield more of the precious drug. As luck would have it, a species that did the trick was found on the project's doorstep. In 1943, lab worker Mary Hunt bought a moldy cantaloupe at a Peoria market. The melon contained a fungus, *Penicillium chrysogenum*, that doubled the amount of penicillin produced; its daughter spores are the ones used to this day to produce penicillin.

Despite some detours, this crash program was a smashing success. The drug that once was restricted to mice, then to a few human subjects, was put into commercial production early in 1944. By the time of the allied invasion of Europe, in June 1944, enough was being produced that every soldier who needed it could have it. Not much later, all restrictions on it were lifted; penicillin was available by prescription from the corner drugstore.

In 1945, Alexander Fleming, Howard Florey, and Ernst Chain were awarded the Nobel Prize in Physiology or Medicine for their work in discovering this wonder drug. Bestowing the prize just after the war ended, the Nobel committee noted:

In a time when annihilation and destruction through the inventions of man have been greater than ever before in history, the introduction of penicillin is a brilliant demonstration that human genius is just as well able to save life and combat disease.

Penicillin's Discoverers
The three scientists who were awarded the Nobel Prize for their work on the development of penicillin. From left to right, Alexander Fleming, Howard Florey, and Ernst Chain.

How Did We Learn? Penicillin

Until the 1940s, human beings had few defenses against infections by the pathogenic bacteria we looked at earlier. What happened in the 1940s to change this? A group of researchers in England discovered the first antibiotic, penicillin. To learn more about how they did it, see "The Discovery of Penicillin" on page 419.

On to Fungi and Plants

The bacteria, archaea, and protists reviewed in this chapter represent only a portion of the living world. Coming up next are two life-forms that most people think of as related and similar, though in fact they are only distantly related and are quite dissimilar. These are fungi and plants.

Chapter Review

Summary

20.1 Life's Categories and the Importance of Microbes

- All living things on Earth can be classified as falling into one of three domains of life: Bacteria or Archaea, whose members are all single-celled and microscopic; or Eukarya, whose diversity is so broad it is further divided into four kingdoms: plants, animals, fungi, and protists.

- Microbes—living things so small they cannot be seen with the naked eye—are indispensable to all life on Earth. They produce more than half of Earth's atmospheric oxygen; the bacteria among them are responsible for putting nitrogen into a form plants can use; and bacteria and fungi are the most important "decomposers" of the natural world—they break down dead organic matter, such as tree branches, and recycle the resulting elements back into the Earth.

- Microbes live in all environments in which larger life-forms exist. They are present in numbers so immense that the weight or "biomass" of all microbes on Earth exceeds the biomass of all larger life-forms.

20.2 Viruses: Making a Living by Hijacking Cells

- Viruses are non-cellular replicating entities that invade living cells to carry out their replication. Because viruses cannot carry out replication by themselves, most scientists do not classify them as living things.

- The Human immunodeficiency virus (HIV), which causes AIDS, has two structures common to almost all viruses: genetic material and a protein coat, called a capsid, surrounding this material. HIV also has one other structural element that many viruses possess: a fatty membrane, called an envelope, which surrounds the capsid.

- Almost all viruses carry out four steps in their life cycle. They get their genetic material inside a "host" cell; turn out viral component parts, construct new virus clones or "particles" from these parts; and move the new particles out of the cell, at which point the particles go on to infect more cells.

- Viruses cause a host of human illness. New viruses harmful to human beings periodically come along by means of viruses that infect other animals mutating and then "jumping" to human hosts. All forms of life are vulnerable to viral infections.

Web Tutorial 20.1: Life Cycles of Viruses

20.3 Bacteria: Masters of Every Environment

- Bacteria are microscopic, single-celled organisms that are prokaryotes: organisms whose genetic material is not contained within a nucleus. Other defining features of bacteria are that they have only a single organelle (the ribosome) and reproduce asexually through a simple cell splitting called binary fission. Millions of species of bacteria exist. Bacteria are metabolically far more diverse than plants or animals.

20.4 Intimate Strangers: Humans and Bacteria

- Bacteria live on and in human beings in great numbers. In the digestive tract, the relationship between humans and many bacteria is one of mutualism: a relationship between two organisms that benefits both of them. Bacteria get food and habitat from this relationship; human beings get an efficiently functioning digestive system.

20.5 Bacteria and Human Disease

- Only a small number of bacteria are pathogenic or disease causing, but these bacteria are responsible for some of humanity's worst diseases. A few pathogenic bacteria cause harm by invading human cells, but bacteria generally do their damage by releasing or leaving behind harmful substances called toxins.

- The primary human defense against pathogenic bacteria is the class of drugs known as antibiotics, defined as substances produced by one microorganism that are toxic to another. The first antibiotic, penicillin, was developed in the 1940s. Antibiotics work by exploiting the differences between bacterial and human cells, such that they kill bacteria while leaving human cells relatively unharmed.

- The power of antibiotics is being threatened by the emergence of antibiotic-resistant strains of bacteria. These bacteria are evolving in greater numbers because of an overuse of antibiotics in medicine and agriculture.

20.6 Archaea: From Marginal Player to Center Stage

- Archaea were once thought to be a form of bacteria, but have been shown to differ greatly from bacteria in their genetic makeup and metabolic functioning. Like bacteria, they are single-celled, microscopic, and are prokaryotes (cells without nuclei). They appear to be among the earliest evolving organisms on Earth and exist in large numbers both in extreme environments, such as hot springs, and in the world's oceans.

- The extreme environments that so many archaea live in have prompted biotechnology firms to "prospect" for novel archaeans in their home environments, with the intent of developing commercial products from the enzymes these "extremophiles" produce.

20.7 Protists: Pioneers in Diversifying Life

- A protist is a eukaryotic organism that does not have all the defining features of a plant, an animal, or a fungus. Protists are mostly single-celled, and all of them live in environments that are at least moist, if not aquatic. Plants, animals, and fungi evolved from them. Thus there are protists that are plant-like, animal-like, and fungi-like, but many protists do not fit neatly into any of these categories.

20.8 Protists and Sexual Reproduction

- For the first two billion years after life appeared, it consisted solely of bacteria and archaea. Protists were the first life-form to evolve other than bacteria or archaea; they were the organisms that made transitions to many of the capabilities and forms seen in larger organisms today. Among these transitions was the change to sexual reproduction, which protists were the first to practice.

20.9 Plant-Like Protists

- Protists that get their nutrition by performing photosynthesis are known as algae. Some algal species provide examples of colonial multicellularity, defined as a form of life in which individual cells form stable associations with one another but do not take on specialized roles. Other algal protists provide examples of true multicellularity: a form of life in which individual cells exist in stable groups, with different cells specializing in different functions.

- Most algae are microscopic but some varieties, particularly the brown algae, grow to very large sizes. Microscopic algae are important members of the group of organisms known as phytoplankton: small photosynthesizing organisms that float near the surface of water. Phytoplankton are very important to life in general, because they produce most of the Earth's oxygen and form the base of so many aquatic food chains. All phytoplankton are either algae or bacteria.

20.10 Animal-Like Protists

- Once referred to as protozoa, the animal-like protists are alike in that they do not get their nutrients by performing photosynthesis, but instead get them from consuming either other organisms or bits of organic matter. They digest this material internally and have evolved various means of moving toward their prey. The so-called ciliate protists move through use of hair-like cilia surrounding their bodies; amoeboid protists move by means of extending pseudopodia or "false feet." Many amoeboid protists are parasites, and some of them are human parasites that live in the digestive system.

20.11 Fungus-Like Protists

- Some protists get their nutrients by extending slender filaments to a food source, after which they digest that food source externally, in

the way fungi do. Protists in this category include the oomycetes, one group of which is known as the water molds. Many oomycetes are saprobes, meaning organisms that obtain their nutrition from dead organic matter.

- Fungus-like protists exist in the strange forms known as plasmodial slime molds and cellular slime molds. The latter category includes the organism *Dictyostelium discoideum*, which exists for part of its life cycle as a collection of separate cells that crawl over the forest floor feeding on bacteria. In times of starvation, however, these cells collect into a single, mobile organism composed of up to 100,000 cells that moves to a more favorable location and distributes individual spores that begin the life cycle again.

Key Terms

algae 416
antibiotics 412
autotroph 410
binary fission 409
capsid 405
colonial multicellularity 416
eukaryote 406
extremophile 413

heterotroph 410
mutualism 411
pathogenic 411
phytoplankton 417
prokaryote 406
saprobe 418
true multicellularity 416
virus 404

Understanding the Basics

Multiple-Choice Questions (answers in the back of the book)

1. Microbes
   a. produce most of the world's oxygen
   b. make nitrogen available to plants
   c. recycle dead organic matter
   d. account for most of the world's biomass
   e. all of the above

2. Viruses
   a. are the smallest living things
   b. have only one organelle
   c. are beneficial to most organisms
   d. replicate only by invading living cells
   e. have circular chromosomes

3. All viruses possess _____ which they _____.
   a. toxins; kill cells with
   b. cell walls; protect themselves with
   c. DNA or RNA; copy inside themselves
   d. many cells; insert inside a host cell
   e. DNA or RNA; transfer into a host cell

4. Bacteria
   a. are single-celled eukaryotes
   b. live outside cells
   c. reproduce sexually or asexually

d. are multicelled prokaryotes

e. are single-celled prokaryotes

5. Within the human body, bacteria exist in greatest numbers in the _____, with many of these bacteria having a _____ relationship with their human host.

   a. lungs; commensal

   b. feet; antagonistic

   c. digestive tract; mutualistic

   d. digestive tract; antagonistic

   e. kidneys; mutualistic

6. Damage done by pathogenic bacteria most often comes from

   a. bacterial use of bodily resources

   b. bacterial invasion of human cells

   c. the access bacteria give to other microbes

   d. bacterial blockage of blood vessels

   e. bacterial release of toxins

7. Archaea are

   a. single-celled and often found in extreme environments

   b. multi-celled but restricted to marine environments

   c. multi-celled and found only at higher elevations

   d. superficially similar to fungi

   e. a later-evolving, single-celled life-form

8. Protists were the first life-forms to

   a. reproduce sexually

   b. exhibit true multicellularity

   c. exhibit colonial multicellularity

   d. evolve following the bacteria and archaea

   e. all of the above

9. Phytoplankton are important because they

   a. produce antibiotics

   b. purify water systems

   c. sit at the base of terrestrial food chains

   d. sit at the base of aquatic food chains

   e. fight viruses

10. The hallmark of true multicellularity is

    a. the number of cells involved

    b. the stability of the association between cells

    c. specialization among cells in the association

    d. the existence of nervous tissue

    e. sexual reproduction

Brief Review

1. What is an extremophile?

2. Why do most biologists classify viruses as nonliving?

3. List two reasons why phytoplankton are so important to life on Earth.

4. Antibiotics used in humans must have at least two qualities. What are they?

5. What is an amoeba? What class of diseases is associated with them?

6. What is the probable cause of Mad Cow disease? Why is it such an unusual infectious agent?

7. Which of the following classes of living things evolved from protists? Animals, fungi, plants.

8. How do plants get the nitrogen they need?

Applying Your Knowledge

1. What does it mean to be a "successful" organism? Bacteria are certainly the most numerous organisms on Earth, they live in nearly all environments, and they are the least susceptible to being eliminated through environmental catastrophe. Are they Earth's most successful organisms?

2. What does it mean to be an "organism"? The cellular slime mold *Dictyostelium discoideum* exists initially as a collection of separate cells moving over the forest floor. In times of starvation, these cells come together to form a single "slug" that moves to more fertile territory. Eventually it will change into a new structure that will throw off separate cells again. Is "Dicty" an organism or a group of temporarily cooperating cells?

3. What would life on Earth be like if there were no decomposers?

21 The Diversity of Life 2

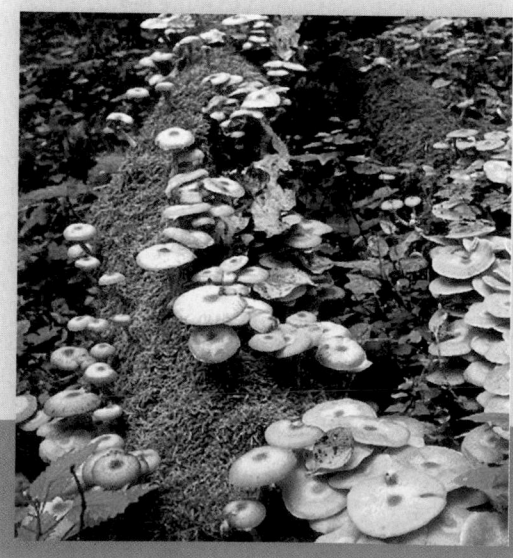

Breaking down what remains.
(Section 21.1, page 426)

dikaryotic

Life cycle of a fungus.
(Section 21.3, page 429)

Reproducing a club fungus.
(Section 21.4, page 431)

Common houseflies can suffer a hostile takeover by a fungus called *Entomophthora muscae*. It's not unusual for one organism to live off another, but in the case of *E. muscae*, the story has a bizarre twist. This fungus gets inside flies either by drilling through their tough outer skeleton or by squeezing between some cracks in it. The strange thing is that, upon entry, the first thing *E. muscae* does is send out extensions of itself to the fly's brain—specifically to parts of the brain that control crawling behavior. Eventually, the fly begins to crawl *upward*. This usually means upward on a plant stem or leaf, but it may mean upward on the wall of a house, toward the ceiling. Like any fungus, *E. muscae* lives by digesting organic material, and in this case the organic material is the fly's body. By the time the fly begins making its upward trek, it is nearly dead from the internal damage *E. muscae* has done.

If you look at **Figure 21.1**, you can see the end result of all this: a fly that has crawled up on a conifer needle, and, in one of its last acts, has put its mouthparts on the needle, to which they are now glued by the fungus. The white you see around the fly's abdomen are fungal spores. Soon they will be showered over everything *beneath* the fly—including, perhaps, some more flies, which then can be parasitized as well. Fungi have various ways of getting their spores up off the ground for dispersal. The structure we call a mushroom is essentially a spore-dispersal tower. But *Entomophthora muscae* has taken another tack. It gets its *prey* to lift it to higher ground; then it sticks its prey in place; then it uses the prey as a launching pad for a shower of fungal spores. *E. muscae* shows us once again that, while nature is certainly diverse, it is not always pretty.

Figure 21.1
Doing a Parasite's Bidding
Pictured is a root maggot fly (genus *Delia*) that has been killed by an *Entomophthora* fungus, whose white spores can be seen bursting out from the fly's abdomen. Just before death, the fly made its way up to the conifer needles pictured and stuck its feeding organ to them. From the height the fly reached, the *Entomophthora* spores shower down on any additional flies that may lie below. *Entomophthora* brings about a behavioral change in its prey that causes them to climb or fly to heights from which its spores can be dispersed.

rock

A mutually beneficial arrangement.
(Section 21.5, page 432)

cell wall
(made of lignin
and cellulose)

cell membrane

nucleus

An important type of cell.
(Section 21.6, page 433)

A bull's eye for bees.
(Section 21.8, page 439)

21.1 The Fungi: Life as a Web of Slender Threads

Entomophthora muscae is a member of one of the "kingdoms" of the living world, the fungi. There are lots of fungi that make their living as parasites, as *E. muscae* does, but then again there are fungi that live in a beneficial association with plants and fungi that do us the favor of decomposing fallen trees (**see Figure 21.2**). Fungi are a large and diverse kingdom, and hence the subject of the first half of this chapter. Once we've reviewed them, we'll look at a better-known kingdom, the plants.

At first glance, plants and fungi may seem to be alike. After all, they're fixed in one spot and tend to grow in the ground. But as you'll see, the main connection between plants and fungi is that many of them have struck up underground partnerships. When it comes to evolution, the surprising thing is that fungi and *animals* are more closely related than fungi and plants. There was a single evolutionary line of protists that gave rise to fungi, plants, and animals, but plants branched off from this line first.

So if a fungus is not a plant, what is it? As the fly example shows, fungi do not make their own food as plants do. Instead, fungi are *heterotrophs*—they consume existing organic material in order to live. They make a living by sending out webs of slender, tube-like threads to a food source. This food source could be a fly, as in *E. muscae*'s case, but it could just as easily be bits of organic matter below ground or a fallen log in a forest. Whatever the case, fungi cannot immediately take in or "ingest" their food in the way that animals do. Fungal cells have cell walls, which means that only relatively small molecules can pass into the fungal filaments. The fungus' solution to this problem is to digest its food *externally*, through digestive enzymes it releases. When the food has been broken down sufficiently by these enzymes, the resulting molecules are taken up into the filaments. Almost all fungi obtain nutrition in this manner. Whether we are talk-ing about a microscopic bread mold or extensive webs of fungi that spread underneath the forest floor, this is a defining characteristic of fungi. This characteristic and others can be stated in a more formal way.

- Fungi largely consist of slender, tube-like filaments called **hyphae**.
- Fungi get their nutrition by dissolving their food externally and then absorbing it into their hyphae.
- Collectively, the hyphae make up a branching web, called a **mycelium**. If you look at **Figure 21.3**, you can see the nature of this structure. You may have thought of a mushroom as the main part of a fungus, but in reality it is merely a reproductive structure, called a *fruiting body*, that sprouts up from the larger mycelium below. A fruiting body amounts to a large, folded up collection of hyphae.
- Fungi are **sessile** or fixed in one spot, but their hyphae grow. The fungal mycelium does not move, but its individual hyphae grow toward a food source. This growth comes, however, only at the tips of the hyphae, not throughout their length.
- Fungi are almost always multicellular. The exception to this is the yeasts, which are unicellular and thus do not form mycelia.

This last point leads to a more general concept about the living world. You may recall from last chapter that all bacteria and archaea are single-celled, and that protists are usually single-celled. But protists are the limit of single-celled life. With fungi, plants, and animals, life becomes almost completely multicellular. There is no such thing as a single-celled plant or animal, and the one group of single-celled fungi, the yeasts, seem to have evolved into this state from an earlier multi-celled form. This is not to say that all life becomes *big* once we get past the protists. As you'll see, there are plenty of microscopic fungi (and even some microscopic animals). But from here on out, all the life-forms we'll be looking at are made up of more than one cell.

**Figure 21.2
Fungal Diversity**

(a) Fungi serve with bacteria as the major "decomposers" in nature. Here a honey fungus, *Armillaria mellea*, is breaking down a dead tree in a forest in Poland.

(b) Fungi are also human pests. Pictured is a human nail with fungal spores on it that are the cause of athlete's foot.

(c) Fungi distribute their spores in various ways. Pictured are spores being expelled from some puffballs in Costa Rica. What brings about the expulsion? Drops of rain falling on the puffballs.

(a)

(b)

(c)

21.2 Roles of Fungi in Society and Nature

Like bacteria, fungi are mostly hidden from us—and mostly known to us by the trouble they cause. This trouble is considerable, as fungi are responsible for mildew, dry rot, vaginal yeast infections, bread molds, general food spoilage, toenail and fingernail infections, and a variety of related skin afflictions, among them athlete's foot, "jock itch," and ringworm. The agricultural blights of corn smut and wheat rust are fungal infections. Indeed, fungi probably are the single worst destroyers of crop plants. One survey in Ohio indicated that only 50 plant diseases there were caused by bacteria and 100 by viruses, but 1,000 by fungi. If you look at **Figure 21.4**, you can see an example of what happened to American elm trees in cities across the United States beginning in the 1930s because of a fungus called *Ophiostoma ulmi*—the cause of Dutch elm disease. In recent years, fungi called molds have caused great damage to housing in such states as Texas and California. In Texas alone, insurance companies paid more than $1 billion in mold insurance claims in 2001–2002. (To learn more about the strange effects of a fungus that infects rye, see "A Psychedelic Drug from an Ancient Source" on page 430.)

Even given all this fungal pestilence, we could say of the fungi what we said of bacteria: While we could do without some of them, we could not live without others. Mold in houses may be a huge problem, but there is another mold that is the source of penicillin. If you know someone who has high cholesterol, chances are he or she controls it with one of the so-called "statin" drugs (Pravastatin, Lovastatin, or Simvastatin). All these drugs contain a compound produced by the fungus *Aspergillus terreus*. In the realm of food production, brewer's yeast makes bread rise and beer ferment, and blue cheese is blue because of the veins of mold within it. Most soft drinks contain citric acid that is produced from a fungus, and we simply eat fungi outright in the form of mushrooms. Out in nature, fungi join bacteria as the major "decomposers" of the living world, breaking down organic material such as garbage and fallen logs and turning it into inorganic compounds that are recycled into the soil. In fact, the final breakdown of woody material is almost entirely the work of fungi. And, as noted, fungi are involved in a critical association with plants, about which you'll learn more later.

Some 77,000 species of fungi have been identified so far, but this is just a fraction of the number that actually exist. Because fungi tend to grow in inaccessible places, most of them are unknown to us. By one estimate, the total number of fungal species may be about 1.6 million.

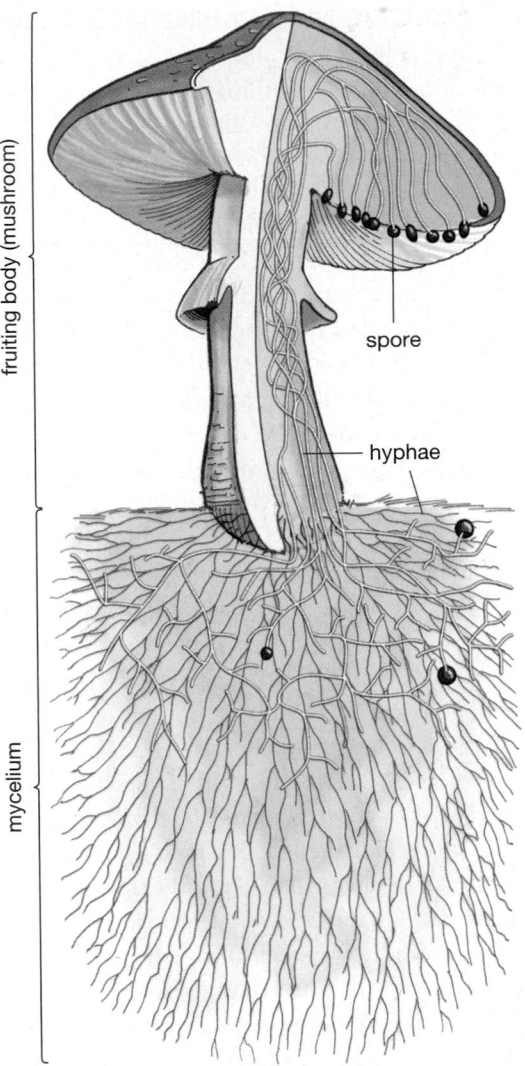

Figure 21.3
Structure of a Fungus
Fungi are composed of tiny slender tubes called *hyphae*. The hyphae form an elaborate network called a *mycelium*. The same hyphae also form a reproductive structure called a fruiting body, which in this case is the familiar mushroom.

(a) Gillet Avenue, Waukegan Illinois, 1962   **(b)** Gillet Avenue, Waukegan Illinois, 1972

Figure 21.4
The Effects of Dutch Elm Disease

21.3 Structure and Reproduction in Fungi

Let's now look at just one type of fungus as a means of learning something about fungi in general. In **Figure 21.5**, you can see a so-called club fungus that we know as the common mushroom. If you look down at the figure's lower-right, you can see that the mushroom's hyphae amount to thin lines of cells—something that is true of all hyphae. In many cases, individual cells in the hyphae are separated from one another by dividers called septa. But as it happens, septa are somewhat porous dividers; they have tiny openings that allow for a fairly free flow of cellular material between one cell and the next. This allows for rapid movement of cellular resources right to the tip of the hyphae—the site of hyphal growth. The result is that hyphae can grow very quickly, whether they are growing toward a food source or organizing themselves into a mushroom cap. Did it ever seem to you that a mushroom sprouted in your yard overnight? It probably did.

If you look at the upper left of the figure, you can see how the mushroom cap is structured. The underside of each cap is made up of a profusion of accordion-like folds called gills. Each gill is simply a collection of hyphae. And right at the tip of some of these hyphae is a reproductive structure called a basidium. Reproductive cells called spores are produced within the basidium and then ejected from it. Caught by the wind, these spores are then carried away to new ground on which they can "germinate" or sprout new hyphae. Fungal spores are, however, something like lottery tickets: a multitude are made, but only a few will be winners. Such a tiny fraction of spores end up germinating that huge numbers must be released to ensure that all nearby environments receive some. Tens of millions will be ejected each hour from the underside of a fairly small mushroom cap. We noted earlier that the cap's *height* allows spores to be caught by the wind, rather than just falling to the ground below. It turns out that the cap's *shape* allows them to be shielded from the rain. Water plays a part in the ejection of spores from the gills, but it wouldn't do for the spores simply to be rained on.

The mushroom cap is one example of a large fungal reproductive structure, but most fungi don't have this kind of size. Think of a flat circle of blue-gray mold on some spoiled bread. Reproductive structures are present, topped by spores, but magnification is necessary to make out any of this detail, as you can see in **Figure 21.6** on page 430. To a great extent, fungi can be regarded as microbes.

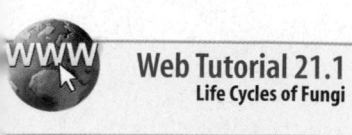

Web Tutorial 21.1
Life Cycles of Fungi

The Life Cycle of a Fungus

We've noted the role that fruiting bodies play in releasing mushroom spores, but how do these spores get produced in the first place? For that matter, what's a spore? These questions can best be understood within the context of the life cycle of a fungus, which is set forth in Figure 21.5. To understand it, we need to go over three tricky concepts related to fungal reproduction. One of these can be called the dikaryotic phase of life; the others are the nature of sex in fungi and the nature of spores.

The Dikaryotic Phase of Life

Taking the life cycle in Figure 21.5 from the beginning, over at step 1, you can see that it starts with spores that have been released from fruiting bodies. These spores germinate, generate hyphae and, in step 2, two of these hyphae fuse—two hyphal cells come together and become one cell, from which a single hypha grows. Note, however, that the cells in this new hypha have *two* nuclei each (symbolized by the little black and white dots within them). This is an unusual condition for a cell; in the normal case, one cell has one nucleus. This condition has come about because, while two cells fused in step 2, their nuclei remained separate. Thus begins a phase of life that is unique to fungi: the **dikaryotic phase**, in which cells in a fungal mycelium have two nuclei. And what is the nature of the genetic material in these nuclei? Each nucleus exists in what is known as a haploid state—there is but a *single* set of chromosomes in each one. This contrasts with the diploid state in almost all human cells. Our nuclei have *paired* sets of chromosomes within them. The haploid state of these nuclei may seem like a technical detail, but it's important for what's coming up. Once a mushroom mycelium enters dikaryotic phase it can stay there for a long time. The phase can go on for years, in fact, and ends only when the most visible manifestation of the mycelium, the mushroom cap, sprouts above ground as seen in step 3.

Sex in Fungi

The dikaryotic state initially exists in all the cells in the mushroom—even the cells that make up the spore-releasing basidia that line the gills. But in some of these cells, right at the tips of the basidia, this will change. The two nuclei in these cells will fuse into one nucleus as seen in step 4. This change means these cells have become diploid; they now have a single nucleus that contains *two* sets of chromosomes. Now think about where each of these sets of chromosomes came from. One of them came originally from

Figure 21.5
The Life Cycle of a Fungus

the black spore over at step 1, while the other came from the white spore. They existed separately in a single cell for a while, but now they have fused. With this, we have had a fusion of genetic material from two separate organisms—sex has taken place. It's not the merger of egg and sperm we're used to in human reproduction, but it's sex nevertheless.

Next, as you can see in step 5, each of the cells in which this fusion has taken place undergoes the meiosis that was reviewed in Chapter 10. This means a mixing of chromosomes from the two parents and two rounds of cell division. The result is four haploid spores attached like little bags to the tip of a basidium; these will be among the millions of spores released from the mushroom cap. Each of these spores will be of one "mating type" or another—symbolized by the black and white colors in the figure. Just as only opposite *sexes* can come to-

gether to create offspring in humans, so only opposite *mating types* can come together (in hyphae fusion) to create offspring in fungi when they reproduce sexually.

The Nature of Spores

This gets us to the nature of a **spore**, which can be defined as a reproductive cell that can develop into a new organism without fusing with another reproductive cell. Note the difference between the spores of the mushroom and the *gametes* of a human being—eggs or sperm. A human being cannot develop from an egg or a sperm; a fusion of both cells is required. Meanwhile, the spores that mushrooms develop from do not undergo fusion. A fungal spore is produced in meiosis and, once it comes into being, it is dispersed and can develop into a whole new mycelium by itself.

A Psychedelic Drug from an Ancient Source

In 1943, chemist Albert Hoffman of Switzerland's Sandoz pharmaceutical company found himself working with a substance that had a long history, most of it tragic. The substance came from a fungus in the genus *Claviceps*, which infects several grain crops, among them rye. The visible manifestation of a *Claviceps* infection is little sickle-shaped growths of black hyphae that pop out among the rye grains (**see Figure 1**). Centuries ago, the French perceived these growths to look like an *ergot*—a little spur that some birds have on their legs—and the name stuck.

In nature, when wild grasses get ergot infections, the effect is not all that notable. The fungus takes some plant nutrition away, the ergot growths fall to the ground in autumn, and spores from it infect the next generation of grass in the spring. The problem for humans comes when the fungus infects *food* crops such as rye, and the ergot are ground up along with the rye grains. The result is that ergot becomes a flour ingredient. This is serious because ergot contains a powerful alkaloid; its active ingredient is a member of the family of alkaline substances that also includes cocaine,

Figure 1
Damaging Intruder
Black ergots of the *Claviceps purpurea* fungus sprout from among the grains of a wheat plant.

Figure 21.6
Bread Mold Up Close
The dark spots on moldy bread are composed of a mycelium that forms stalks tipped by spores, visible in this micrograph as tiny black balls. The spores will be dispersed to produce new mycelia elsewhere—perhaps on more bread. These are spores of the mold *Rhizopus nigricans*, growing on the surface of some bread.

21.4 Categories of Fungi

Fungi are placed into different large categories or "phlya" based on the reproductive structures they have. As you've seen, mushroom fungi have a reproductive structure called a basidium; accordingly, mushrooms are in the fungal group known as basidiomycetes. Likewise, there is a phylum called the ascomycetes and one called the zygomycetes—both named for the reproductive structures they have. The basidiomycetes are often called *club fungi* (because of the club-like shape of the basidium); the ascomycetes are sometimes called *cup fungi* (because many of their fruiting bodies have cup shapes); and the zygomycetes are called *bread molds* (because they are commonly found growing on old bread).

To put a finer point on this system of categorizing, all three of these fungal phyla are named for their *sexual* reproductive structures. The problem with the system is that not all fungi have been observed to engage in sexual reproduction; some have only been observed reproducing asexually. As a result, there is then a fourth grouping of fungi that is not a phylum, but instead is a category that serves as a holding pen. Asexual reproducers are put in this category, called the mitosporic fungi, until such time as they are seen reproducing sexually; then they are moved to one of the three phyla. The mitosporic fungi are still sometimes referred to as the *imperfect* nicotine, and morphine, along with such poisons as hemlock. In numerous instances, recorded in Europe since the Middle Ages, ergot made its way into the bread that people ate, and the results were disastrous. France in particular had repeated instances of "ergotism," with two of these episodes alone resulting in 50,000 deaths. What did ergot do? Here is a description by Oswald Tippo and William Louis Stern. Ergot's effects included:

> Abortions in pregnant females; burning sensation in extremities; feelings of being consumed by fire; constriction of blood vessels leading to the blockage of circulation and resulting in the appearance of blue discolored areas on the body; onset of gangrene; shriveling and falling off of hands, arms, and legs; experiencing of hallucinations such as wild beasts in pursuit of the victim . . .

Horrible as these effects were, medical people hearing of them recognized that ergot had the ability to do good as well as harm. Unwanted abortions are a terrible thing, but labor sometimes needs to be *induced* when a fetus is overdue; likewise, the constriction of blood vessels has its uses when properly controlled. Alkaloids often have such double-edged capabilities. Cocaine was first isolated from the coca plant in 1860, but in the 1880s it became a miracle drug for eye surgery when it served as the first *local* anesthetic. Morphine, which is derived from poppy plants, is used in medicine as a pain-killer. Thus, it's not surprising that drugs were also isolated from ergot over time. In the 1930s, for example, a drug called ergonovine—still in use today—was developed that helps stop bleeding after childbirth.

Thus it was that Albert Hoffman found himself working with ergot in his Basel lab in 1943. He was looking for other useful alkaloids that the fungus might yield. Years before, he had isolated from ergot a chemical core—a compound called lysergic acid—and added to it a manufactured compound called diethylamide, but the results seemed uninteresting to him. This time, however, he apparently absorbed a tiny quantity of the substance through his skin. The outcome, as he later wrote, was that:

> I was seized by a peculiar sensation of vertigo and restlessness. Objects appeared to undergo optical changes and I was unable to concentrate on my work. . . . With my eyes closed, fantastic pictures of extraordinary plasticity and intensive color seemed to surge toward me.

Though he had not intended to, Albert Hoffman had discovered one of the world's most powerful psychoactive drugs: lysergic acid diethylamide, which the world would come to know by its initials, LSD.

fungi—not because there is something flawed about them, but because our knowledge of their reproduction is imperfect. Beyond these categories, you may recall that there are single-celled fungi, called yeasts. While yeasts are ascomycetes, they are often studied as a unified group. Figure 21.6 shows a representative bread mold. **Figure 21.7** shows representatives of all the other fungal types.

(a) Spores on the basidium of a club fungus

(b) One of the cup fungi, the edible morel mushroom

(c) An imperfect *Aspergillus* fungus, feeding on bread

(d) A daughter yeast cell, budding from a parent cell

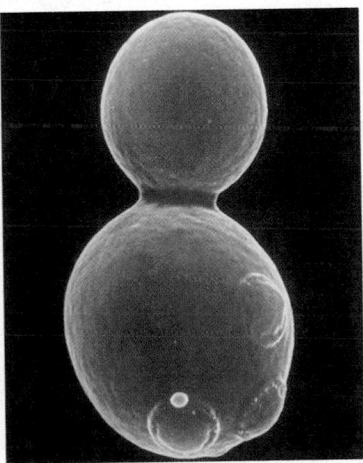

Figure 21.7

21.5 Fungal Associations: Lichens and Mycorrhizae

Lichens

Everyone has seen the thin, sometimes colorful coverings called *lichens* that seemingly can grow almost anywhere—on rocks as well as on trees; in Antarctica as well as in a lush forest (**see Figure 21.8**). As it turns out, lichens are not a single organism. A **lichen** is a composite organism composed of a fungus and either algae or photosynthesizing bacteria. If you look at **Figure 21.9**, you can see that this association is structured as a kind of sandwich: an upper layer of densely packed fungal hyphae on top; then a zone of less dense hyphae that includes a layer of algal or bacterial cells; then another layer of densely packed

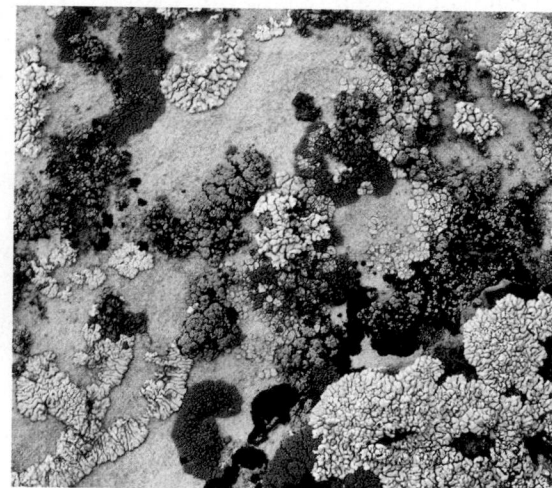

Figure 21.8
Life on the Rocks
Lichens growing on sandstone rocks, near the Montana-Wyoming border.

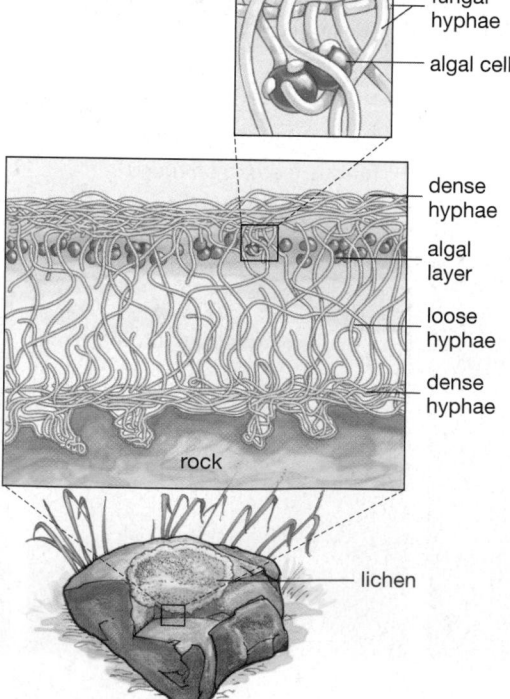

Figure 21.9
The Structure of a Lichen
A lichen is not a single organism. It is composed of a fungus and an alga (or sometimes a photosynthesizing bacterium) living in a mutually beneficial arrangement. The fungal hyphae form a dense layer on the top and the bottom and a loose layer in the middle, within which the alga is nestled. The fungus may provide a moist, protective environment for the alga, and the alga, which performs photosynthesis, provides food for the fungus.

fungal
hyphae

algal cell

dense
hyphae

algal
layer

loose
hyphae

dense
hyphae

rock

lichen

hyphae on the bottom that sprout extensions down into the material the lichen is growing on (such as a rock). The example here is an association between a fungus and an alga, which is the case in about 90 percent of lichens. In such a relationship, the fungal hyphae either wrap tightly around the algal cells or actually extend into them.

A lichen is mostly a fungus, then, but it is a fungus that could not grow without its algal partner. Why? Because the alga makes its own food through photosynthesis and then proceeds to supply the fungus with most of the nutrients it needs. For years, it was assumed that what fungi do for algae is keep them from drying out. Increasingly, however, scientists have come to believe that most fungi are doing nothing at all for the algae, in which case the fungi should be considered an algal parasite, rather than a partner.

In nature, the general significance of lichens comes from their role as pioneers at sites where life is just getting established, such as barren rocks. Because the algae in lichens make their own food, and because the fungi in them can dig into rock itself, lichens can make a living in such habitats, whereas most other organisms cannot. The lives of lichens, however, bear some comparison with French movies: they tend to be long and slow. Some lichens have been alive for thousands of years, but at most they spread out at a rate of about 3 centimeters a year, which is a little over an inch. Indeed, they have been observed to grow as little as 1 millimeter per year, at which rate they would grow 4 inches in a century.

Mycorrhizae

By some estimates, 90 percent of seed plants live in a cooperative relationship with fungi. The linkage here is one of plant roots and fungal hyphae, with both the plants and the fungi benefiting. What the fungus gets from the association is food, in the form of carbohydrates that come from the photosynthesizing plant; what the plant gets is minerals and water, absorbed by the fungal hyphae. So important is this relationship to plants that some species of trees, such as pine and oak, cannot grow without fungal partners. Other plants will have stunted growth without a fungal partner.

Fungal hyphae generally grow into the plant roots, but in some instances they wrap around the root without penetrating it. In either case, the root-hyphae associations of plants and fungi are known as **mycorrhizae** (**see Figure 21.10**). The mycorrhizal relationship is one of the oldest and most important in nature. It appears that at least 460 million years ago, when the very first plants made the transition to life on land, they did so with fungal partners.

21.6 Plants: The Foundation for Much of Life

In your review of the living world so far, you've seen that human beings have reason to feel ambivalent about bacteria, protists, and fungi. While there is much to appreciate in these organisms, there is a good deal to fear as well. When it comes to plants, however, it's hard to find much to fear—but easy to find much to appreciate. For starters, we humans are utterly dependent upon plants for food. Try naming something you eat that isn't a plant or that didn't itself eat plants, and you will end up with a very short list. Then there is the atmospheric oxygen that plants produce as a by-product of photosynthesis. Beyond this, plants stabilize soil, provide habitat for animals, and lock away the "greenhouse" gas carbon dioxide. They yield lumber, medicines, and certain varieties of them are so beautiful that human beings spend hours tending them. Against all this, what's the worst thing we could say of plants? That a few varieties grow a little too much for our satisfaction? What other form of life helps us so much and harms us so little?

The Characteristics of Plants

We all have an intuitive sense of what plants are, though not all plants match our intuitions. A few are parasites (on other plants) and some, like the Venus flytrap, consume animals. Allowing for such exceptions, plants share the following characteristics.

- *Plants are photosynthesizing organisms that are fixed in place, multi-celled, and mostly land-dwelling.* We

Figure 21.10
Underground Partners
Mycorrhizae are associations between plant roots and fungal hyphae that benefit both the plant and the fungus. Shown is an association between Aspen tree roots and thread-like mushroom hyphae that are wrapped around them. The hyphae help bring water and minerals to the trees, while the tree provides the fungus with food.

know that plants are fixed in one spot (sessile), and that they make their own food through photosynthesis. That they are multi-celled follows from the fact that they develop from embryos, which are multi-celled by definition. During the course of their evolution from green algae, plants made a transition from water to land, and land is where most of them are found today—though some have made the transition *back* to water, as with water lilies.

- *Plant cells have cell walls and organelles specialized for photosynthesis.* Both plant and animal cells are enclosed by a plasma membrane, but plant cells have something just outside the membrane: a **cell wall**, defined as a relatively thick layer of material that forms the periphery of plant, bacterial, and fungal cells (**see Figure 21.11**). The

cell wall
(made of lignin and cellulose)

cell membrane

nucleus

central vacuole
(contains mostly water)

chloroplast
(site of photosynthesis)

Figure 21.11
Characteristics of Plants
All cells have an outer membrane, but plant cells have a wall external to this membrane. The compounds cellulose and lignin, which help make up the cell wall, impart strength to it. Plant cells have a higher proportion of water in them than do animal cells, with much of this water located in an organelle called a central vacuole. The sites of photosynthesis in plants are the organelles called chloroplasts.

plant cell wall is composed in large part of a tough, complex compound called cellulose. In woody plants, cellulose is joined by a strengthening compound called lignin. Together, cellulose and lignin allow plant cells to support the massive weight of trees. Plant (and algae) cells also have organelles called **chloroplasts** that are the sites of photosynthesis. If there is one feature that has fundamentally shaped plant evolution, it is the chloroplast. Why are plants *able* to be fixed in one spot? Because they make their own food in chloroplasts and thus don't need to move toward food, as animals do. Given this, it makes sense that plants would evolve into relatively inflexible organisms with protective exteriors—the very thing provided by cell walls.

- *Successive generations of plants go through what is known as an alternation of generations.*

Figure 21.12
The Alternation of Generations in Plants, Compared to the Human Life Cycle

(a) Humans Almost all cells in human beings are diploid or 2n, meaning they have paired sets of chromosomes in them. The exception to this is human gametes (eggs and sperm), produced through meiosis, which are haploid or 1n, meaning they have a single set of chromosomes. In the moment of conception, a haploid sperm fuses with a haploid egg to produce a diploid zygote that grows into a complete human being through mitosis.

(b) Plants In plants, conversely, diploid (2n) plants—the multicellular sporophyte fern in the figure—go through meiosis and produce individual haploid (1n) spores that, without fusing with any other cells, develop into a separate generation of the plant. This is the multicellular gametophyte shown. This gametophyte-generation plant then produces its own gametes, which are eggs and sperm. Sperm from one plant fertilizes an egg from another, and the result is a diploid zygote that develops into the mature sporophyte generation. The alternation between the sporophyte and gametophyte forms is called the alternation of generations.

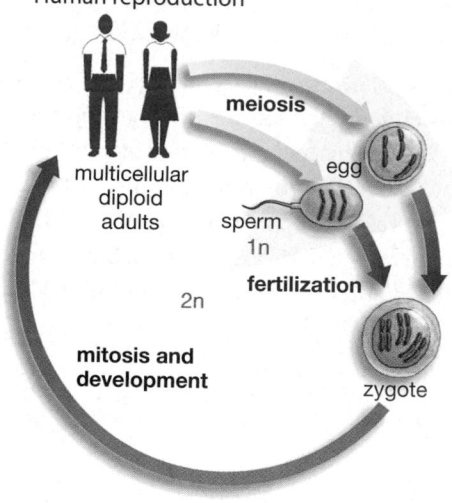

Human reproduction

multicellular diploid adults — **meiosis** — egg — sperm 1n — **fertilization** — 2n — **mitosis and development** — zygote

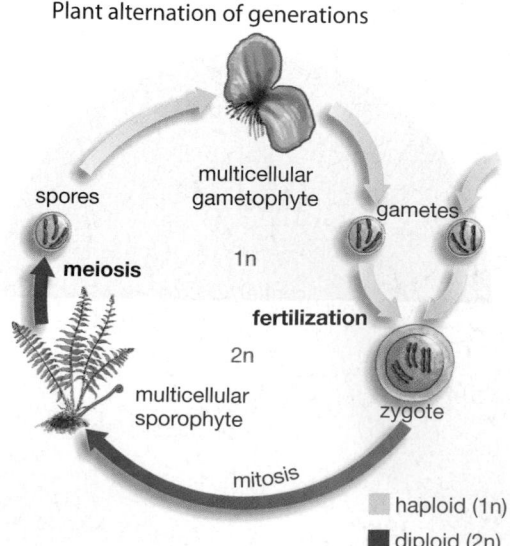

Plant alternation of generations

spores — **meiosis** — multicellular gametophyte — gametes — 1n — **fertilization** — 2n — multicellular sporophyte — zygote — mitosis

haploid (1n)
diploid (2n)

One way to conceptualize this characteristic is to compare plant reproduction with human reproduction. The eggs and sperm that human beings produce are so-called gametes that are *haploid* cells, meaning they have but a single set of chromosomes in them. When these haploid cells fuse in the moment of conception, what's produced is a *diploid* fertilized egg, meaning an egg with two sets of chromosomes—one set from the father and one from the mother. This egg gives rise to more diploid cells through cell division, and the result is a whole new human being (**see Figure 21.12a**).

A typical *plant* in its diploid phase will, like human beings, produce a specialized set of haploid reproductive cells. Instead of these cells being egg or sperm, however, what's produced is a *spore*: a reproductive cell that can develop into a new organism without fusing with another reproductive cell. Like the spores we saw in fungi, plant spores have the ability to grow into a new generation of plant all on their own. In some plants, this spore lands on the ground, starts dividing, and after a time a mature plant exists. When *this* plant reproduces, however, it does not do so through more spores. It produces gametes—eggs and sperm. These go on to fuse, and the result is a diploid plant just like the one we started with.

The upshot of all this, as you can see in **Figure 21.12b**, is that plants move back and forth between two different kinds of generations, one of them spore-producing, the other gamete-producing. In this cycle, the generation of plant that produces spores is known as the **sporophyte generation**, while the generation of plant that produces the gametes is the **gametophyte generation**. The fern shown in Figure 21.12b gives you some idea of how physically different these generations can be, but the disparities actually can be much greater than this. In a massive organism such as a redwood tree, the tree that is familiar to us is the sporophyte generation. But what do its spores develop into? On the male side, barely visible pollen grains. On the female side, small collections of cells, hidden deep within a redwood "pinecone." The fact that these gametophyte individuals are tiny, however, doesn't mean that they are unnecessary. The eggs and sperm they produce are required to bring about a whole new redwood tree. In sum, all plants go through an **alternation of generations**: a life cycle practiced by plants, in which successive plant generations alternate between the diploid sporophyte condition and the haploid gametophyte condition.

21.7 Types of Plants

For our purposes, it is convenient to separate the members of the plant kingdom into a mere four types (**see Figure 21.13**). These are the *bryophytes*, which include mosses; the *seedless vascular plants*, which include ferns; the *gymnosperms*, which include coniferous ("cone bearing") trees; and the *angiosperms*, a vast division of flowering plants—by far the most dominant on Earth today—that includes not only flowers such as orchids, but also oak trees, rice, and cactus. We'll look at all four types briefly here. Chapters 23 and 24 provide detailed descriptions of the workings of flowering plants.

Bryophytes: Amphibians of the Plant World

If you look in low-lying, wet terrain, you are likely to see a carpet-like covering of moss. In countries such as Ireland, whole fields of peat moss grow and are harvested to be used as fuel for heating and cooking. Mosses are the most familiar example of a primitive type of plant that falls under the classification of **bryophyte**, which can be defined as a type of plant lacking a true vascular system (**see Figure 21.14**).

Figure 21.13
Four Main Varieties of Plants
The most primitive type of plant **(a)** the bryophytes (moss in the figure), lack a fluid-transporting vascular system. **(b)** Ferns, representing the seedless vascular plants, have a vascular system but do not have seeds. **(c)** Gymnosperms (conifers in the picture) do utilize seeds. **(d)** Flowering plants (blossoming pear trees in the picture) produce seeds and are responsible for several other plant innovations, among them fruit.

(a) Moss

(b) Ferns

(c) Conifers

(d) Flowering plants

(a) Mosses

(b) Liverworts

(c) Hornworts

Figure 21.14
Three Kinds of Bryophytes
(a) Mosses, **(b)** liverworts, and **(c)** hornworts. These plants have no vascular tissue and thus tend to be small. The sperm of bryophytes must travel through water to get to eggs. For this reason bryophytes are found most often in moist environments.

What's a vascular system? A network of tubes within an organism that serves to transport fluids. We can get a good idea of what the bryophytes are like by looking at the mosses.

Mosses are representatives of some of the earliest plants that made the transition from water to land. As such, they can be conceptualized as plants that made only a partial break with the aquatic living of their evolutionary ancestors, the algae. In making this transition, they had to deal with something the algae didn't, which is the effect of gravity. Lacking a vascular system, mosses cannot transport water and other substances very *far* against the force of gravity; instead they must lie low, hugging the surface to which they are attached while spreading out horizontally to maximize their exposure to sunshine. Nevertheless, the mosses are hearty competitors in some tough environments, such as the arctic tundra and the cracks in sidewalks. In keeping with their aquatic origins, they have sperm that can get to eggs only by swimming through water. Not much water is necessary; a thin film left over from the morning dew will suffice. But some water must be present.

Not surprisingly, mosses and other bryophytes usually are found in moist environments. Bryophytes have no roots at all, but instead use single-celled extensions called *rhizoids* to anchor themselves to their underlying material, which may be soil or rock or wood. You might expect that rhizoids would serve to absorb water, as roots do, but this is true only to a very limited extent. Bryophytes take in water almost entirely through their above-ground exterior surface.

Seedless Vascular Plants: Ferns and Their Relatives

As noted, all plants except the bryophytes have a *vascular system*, or network of fluid-conducting tubes, which transport both food and water. When we begin to look at vascular plants, we find that the most primitive variety of them are the so-called **seedless vascular plants**: plants that have a vascular system, but that do not produce seeds as part of reproduction.

Easily the most familiar representatives of the seedless vascular plants are ferns, with their often beautifully shaped leaves, called fronds (**see Figure 21.15**).

Figure 21.15
Three Kinds of Seedless Vascular Plants
(a) Fall-colored ferns in New Hampshire, **(b)** horsetails, and **(c)** club mosses. Because these plants have vascular tissue, they are able to grow taller than most bryophytes. Like bryophytes, however, they do not produce seeds and are tied to moist environments.

(a) Ferns

(b) Horsetails

(c) Club mosses

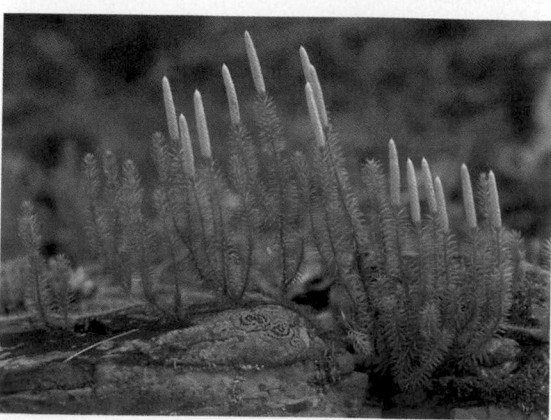

These plants have moved a step further in the direction of separation from an aquatic environment. Their vascular system allows them to grow *up* as well as *out*, and it allows for roots that extend into the ground, where they serve their absorptive function. Despite this evolutionary innovation, the sperm of the seedless vascular plants is like that of the bryophytes: it needs to move through water to fertilize eggs.

The First Seed Plants: The Gymnosperms

There are two kinds of seed plants, the gymnosperms and the angiosperms, but putting things this way makes it sound as though these plants are on a kind of equal footing with the bryophytes and seedless vascular plants. In reality, the gymnosperms replaced seedless vascular plants as the most dominant plants on Earth, though this event took place a long time ago—about the time the dinosaurs came to dominance. Then the gymnosperms lost this status to the angiosperms, which began flourishing about 80 million years ago. Today there are only about 700 gymnosperm species compared to 260,000 angiosperm species. Nevertheless, the gymnosperm presence is considerable, especially in the northern latitudes, where they exist as vast bands of coniferous trees, including pine, fir, and spruce. Conifers such as these provide most of the world's lumber (**see Figure 21.16**).

Reproduction through Pollen and Seeds

Why were the gymnosperms able to outcompete so many of the seedless vascular plants back in the dinosaur days? Part of the answer lies in what might be called sperm transport. In gymnosperms, sperm are contained in tiny spheres called pollen grains. Critically, these grains are transported to the female eggs through the *air*, rather than being limited to *swimming* to them, as is the case with the seedless plants. Given this innovation, the gymnosperms could propagate over great distances, which gave them a competitive advantage over the seedless plants.

Another advantage the gymnosperms had were their seeds, which can be thought of as tiny packages of food and protection. If you look at **Figure 21.17**, you can see one example of a gymnosperm seed, this

(a) Spruce tree

(b) *Ginkgo biloba*

Figure 21.16
Gymnosperms
(a) This spruce tree is a member of the grouping of gymnosperms known as conifers, which account for about three-quarters of all gymnosperm species. The conifers also include redwood, pine, juniper, and cypress trees.
(b) There are other types of gymnosperms as well. Pictured are the leaves and seeds of the maidenhair tree, *Ginkgo biloba*, which are used today in herbal preparations.

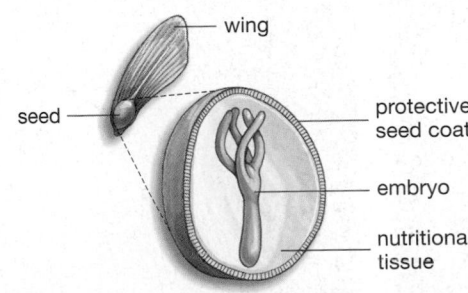

Figure 21.17
A Gymnosperm Seed
Seeds are tiny packages of food and protection. They come in many shapes and sizes, but they all contain an embryo, some food, and a protective seed coat.

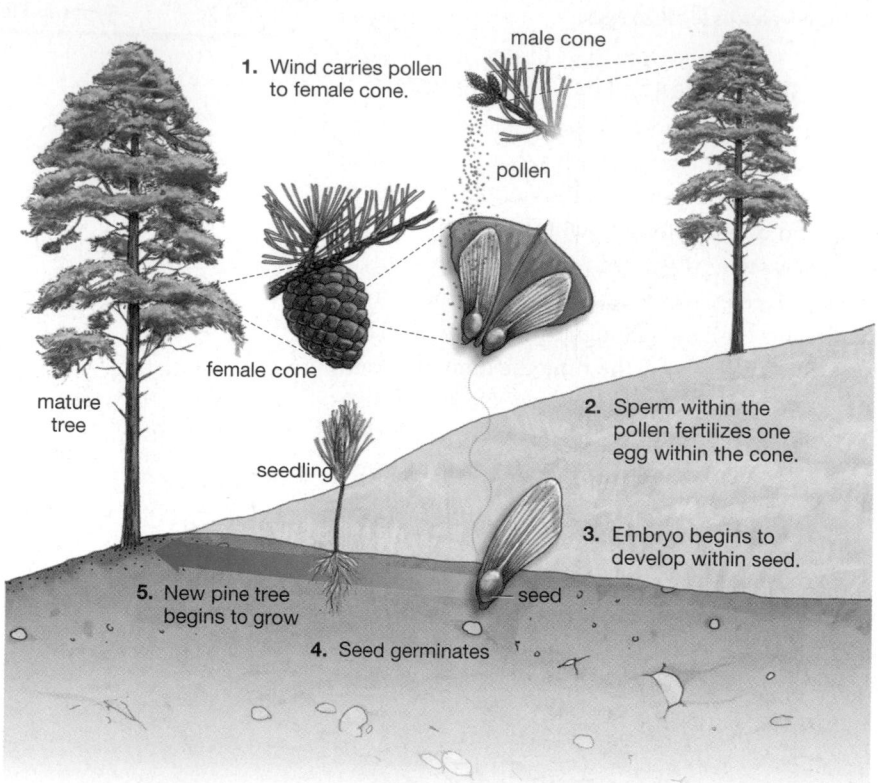

1. Wind carries pollen to female cone.

male cone

pollen

mature tree

female cone

seedling

2. Sperm within the pollen fertilizes one egg within the cone.

3. Embryo begins to develop within seed.

5. New pine tree begins to grow

seed

4. Seed germinates

Figure 21.18
The Life Cycle of a Gymnosperm
Pine trees have two kinds of cones. Pollen is produced within the smaller male cones, while eggs are produced within the larger female cones. When the wind carries pollen onto the female cone, the sperm within the pollen fertilizes one of the eggs within the cone. An embryo then begins to develop inside a seed, which falls to the ground. Once conditions are suitable, the seed germinates and a whole new pine tree begins to grow.

Figure 21.19
Angiosperm Variety

one from a pine tree. **Figure 21.18** then shows you how this seed fits into the life cycle of the pine. As you can see, pollen grains are carried on the wind to the female reproductive structure, which resides in the familiar pinecone. Then the sperm in the pollen grain comes together with an egg in the reproductive struc-

ture, and the result is a fertilized egg that begins to develop as an embryo. This is no different in principle than human egg and sperm coming together to create a human embryo. In the pine tree, however, the embryo is developing inside a seed, a structure that is unique to plants. Seeds have a tough coat, inside of which is not only the embryo but a food supply for it—a kind of sack lunch of stored carbohydrates, proteins, and fats. In sum, a **seed** is a plant structure that includes a plant embryo, its food supply, and a tough, protective casing. When seeds reach the ground, they contain all the starting materials necessary to bring about germination of a new generation of plant.

Gymnosperm seeds turn out to differ from the seeds produced by angiosperms. Angiosperm seeds come wrapped in a layer of tissue—called fruit—that gymnosperm seeds do not have. The details of this anatomical feature are presented in Chapter 24. For now, just be mindful that a **gymnosperm** can be defined as a seed plant whose seeds are not surrounded by fruit. The very name *gymnosperm* comes from the Greek words *gymnos*, meaning "naked," and *sperma*, meaning "seed."

Angiosperms: Nature's Grand Win-Win Invention

As noted, there are about 260,000 known species of the flowering plants known as angiosperms. The term *flowering plants* may bring to mind roses or tulips and, indeed, these flowers are angiosperms. But the angiosperm grouping includes all manner of other plants as well—almost all trees except for the conifers, all our important food crops, cactus, shrubs, common grass: the list is very long (**see Figure 21.19**). As noted, **angiosperms** are defined by an aspect of their anatomy; their seeds are surrounded by the tissue called fruit. The details of angiosperm anatomy and physiology

(a) Calla lilies on the California coast

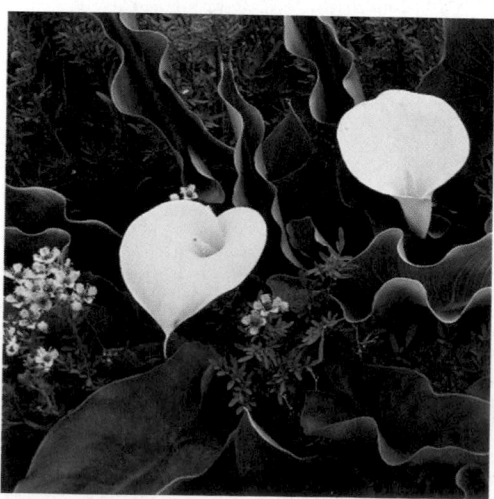

(b) Cholla cactus in Arizona

(c) Corn in a field

21.8 Angiosperm-Animal Interactions

For an angiosperm such as a new honeysuckle plant to come into existence, a two-part process must take place. First, sperm—developing once again inside a pollen grain—must get to an egg and fertilize it, which produces the embryo encased in a seed coat. Next, this seed must land on a patch of soil somewhere and begin to germinate or sprout.

Now, in the angiosperms, how is it that sperm gets to egg in the first place? Remember that with gymnosperms, pollen grains were carried by the *wind*. By contrast, the angiosperms have induced *animals* to carry pollen from one plant to another—to pollinate them. Not all angiosperms are pollinated in this way; some are pollinated by wind, and a few aquatic species rely on water currents. But most are pollinated with the help of animals, be they insects, birds, mammals, or even snails (**see Figure 21.20**).

Angiosperms use various attractants to encourage animal pollination. The most important of these is nectar, which is essentially sugar-water, but angiosperms don't stop there. So important is pollination to them that they have developed a host of pollination marketing strategies. How about a *fragrance* that, say, bees are sensitive to? How about *colors* that they're attracted to? Insect-pollinated flowers generally have both sweet fragrances and coloration patterns—nature's equivalent of homing signals and landing lights. They serve to get an animal to the flower in the first place and then into the right *position* for feeding and pollination (**see Figure 21.21**).

Why do plants spend so much energy attracting animal pollinators while gymnosperms let the wind do the work? Windborne pollination in gymnosperms can be thought of as a kind of scatter-shot approach: If the wind *happens* to blow a pollen grain onto the fe-

(a) Pollen-covered honeybee on a dandelion

(b) Carib martinique pollinating a flower

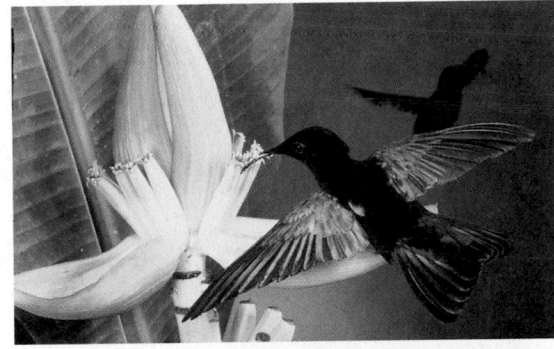

(c) Lesser long-nosed bat pollinating a cactus

male reproductive structure, then pollination occurs. Think how much more directed things are with animal pollination. It is essentially door-to-door service. Animal pollination is one of the reasons that angiosperms are by far the most dominant plants on Earth.

Figure 21.20
Animals Help Pollen Get from Here to There
Flowering plants were the first to take advantage of the mobility of animals to transport pollen from one plant to another. Relationships between flowers and pollinators often are species-specific, which helps to ensure that the pollen will be delivered to the right address.

(a) This is what we see (normal sunlight).

(b) This is what the bee sees (ultraviolet light).

(c) This is what the bee "thinks."

Figure 21.21
Food Lies This Way
Animals may be attracted to a particular flower by its fragrance, color, or pattern of visual elements. Insects are guided into the nutrients in the center of the flower by color patterns called nectar guides, visible to an insect—because it perceives ultraviolet light—but not to us.

Seed Endosperm: More Animal Food from Angiosperms

Once pollination has occurred, the resulting seed, with the embryo inside, has to reach the ground and then germinate in it. All seeds contain food reserves for the growing embryo, but angiosperm seeds develop a special kind of nutritive tissue, called **endosperm**, that often surrounds the embryo (**see Figure 21.22**). This endosperm supplies much of the food for human beings throughout the world. Rice and wheat grains are seeds, consisting in large part of the endosperm meant to sustain the plant embryo. It's worth noting that *whole-grain* wheat is wheat that still has its embryo (usually called "wheat germ") and its seed coat (usually called "bran"). By contrast, white bread, regular pasta, and so forth are made from wheat whose wheat germ and bran have been removed through processing.

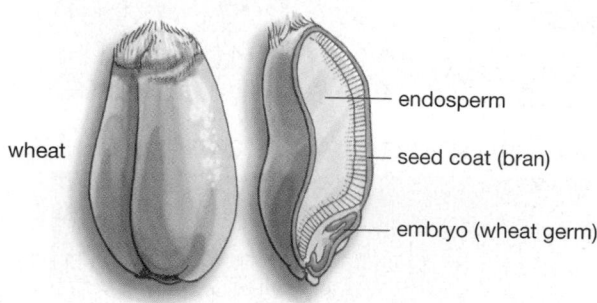

Figure 21.22
Food for the Seedling, Food for Humans
Endosperm is a food reserve in seeds. It feeds the embryo before it can make its own food. It is this same endosperm that nourishes humans throughout the world in the form of wheat, corn, rice, and even coconut.

Fruit: An Inducement for Seed Dispersal

Some flowering plants also add an inducement for the *dispersal* of their seeds: the tissue called fruit. This is not fruit in the technical sense, but fruit as that term is commonly understood—the flesh of an apricot or cherry, for example. As such, it represents one more piece of bounty that plants provide to animals. To understand how fruit benefits plants as well, imagine a bear who consumes a wild berry, which consists not only of the fruit flesh, but of the seeds inside this flesh. The fruit is digested by the bear as food, but the *seeds* are tough; they are passed through its system intact to be deposited, with bear feces as fertilizer, at a location that may be very remote from the place where the bear *ate* the berry. The result is seed dispersal at what may be a promising new location for a berry plant (**see Figure 21.23**).

Given pollination and the varieties of food that angiosperms produce, it's easy to see that, with the rise of the flowering plants, animals and plants entered into a much more interdependent relationship than had existed before, one that is still evolving today.

On to a Look at Animals

In this chapter and the one that preceded it, you've looked at bacteria and archaea, and at three of the kingdoms within the eukaryotic domain—protists, fungi, and plants. This leaves one more eukaryotic kingdom to go. It is a kingdom that is arguably the most familiar of all, because we human beings are part of it. Yet it is a kingdom so diverse that it holds a good many surprises as well. It is the kingdom of animals.

Figure 21.23
Seed Carriers
Angiosperms have taken advantage of the mobility of animals not only to transfer pollen, but also to disperse seeds.
(a) Some seeds are wrapped in tasty fruit that is consumed by animals, such as bears.
(b) Other seeds come wrapped in burrs and spines that stick to the fur of animals and are carried away.

(a) Wild berries induce seed dispersal

(b) Burrs help seeds travel

Chapter Review

Summary

21.1 The Fungi: Life as a Web of Slender Threads

- Fungi do not make their own food, as plants do, but instead are heterotrophs—they consume existing organic material in order to live. Fungi consist largely of webs of slender tubes, called hyphae, that grow toward food sources. Fungi cannot immediately ingest the food the hyphae reach, since only small molecules can pass through the cell walls of fungal cells. Fungi thus digest their food externally, through release of digestive enzymes, and then bring the resulting small molecules into the hyphae.

- Collectively, hyphae make up a branching web, called a mycelium, that forms the bulk of most fungi. Many fungi have a reproductive structure called a fruiting body that produces and releases reproductive cells called spores. All fruiting bodies are organized collections of hyphae.

- Fungi are sessile or fixed in one spot, though their hyphae grow toward food sources. Such growth comes only at the tips of the hyphae, not throughout their length.

- Almost all fungi are multicellular. The sole exception to this, the single-celled yeasts, are thought to have evolved to the single-celled state from an earlier multi-celled condition.

21.2 Roles of Fungi in Society and Nature

- Fungi are the cause of many crop diseases, human infections, and forms of damage to buildings and homes. They are also sources of medicines, and are used extensively in food processing. In nature, fungi join bacteria as major "decomposers" of the living world, breaking down organic material such as fallen trees and turning it into inorganic compounds that are recycled into the soil.

21.3 Structure and Reproduction in Fungi

- Individual cells that form hyphae often are separated from one another by dividers called septa. These septa are porous enough, however, that they allow for a fairly free flow of cellular material between one hyphal cell and the next—so much so that hyphae can bring resources very quickly to the point of growth at the hyphal tips. As a result, fungi can grow very quickly.

- The fruiting body of the mushroom fungi, the mushroom cap, is made up on its underside of accordion-like gills that both produce spores and release them into the wind, which carries them to new locations. Only a tiny fraction of fungal spores will successfully germinate, or sprout new mycelia. Because of this, fruiting bodies release huge quantities of spores as a means of ensuring new fungal growth.

- Within their life cycle, many fungi have a so-called dikaryotic phase of life, in which the fusion of cells from different hyphae produces a single hypha whose cells each have two nuclei. Each

of these nuclei is haploid, meaning each contains only a single set of chromosomes.

- When the below-ground mycelium in a mushroom fungus sprouts into the above-ground mushroom cap, all the cells in the cap initially are dikaryotic, including those in the reproductive structure called the basidium. The nuclei in certain cells of the basidia then undergo fusion, which is the first step in carrying out sexual reproduction. These cells are now diploid—they have a single nucleus that contains a paired set of chromosomes. These same cells then undergo meiosis, and the result is four haploid spores attached to tip of the basidium. These spores are then released and blown by the wind to new locations, where they may germinate and result in new mycelia.

- A spore is a reproductive cell that can develop into a new organism without fusing with another reproductive cell. Unlike human eggs and sperm, which fuse to make a fertilized egg, fungal spores do not need to fuse with any other cell to give rise to a new generation of fungi.

Web Tutorial 21.1: Life Cycles of Fungi

21.4 Categories of Fungi

- There are three major categories or "phyla" of fungi: basidiomycetes (also known as club fungi), ascomycetes (also known as cup fungi), and zygomycetes (also known as bread molds). Fungi are placed in these categories in accordance with the structures they use in sexual reproduction.

- Fungi that have not yet been observed to reproduce sexually are placed in a holding category, called the mitosporic (or imperfect) fungi, until such time as they are seen reproducing sexually; at that point they are placed in the appropriate phylum. The single-celled yeasts are ascomycetes, but often are studied as a unified group.

21.5 Fungal Associations: Lichens and Mycorrhizae

- Lichens are composite organisms, made up of both fungi and algae (or fungi and photosynthesizing bacteria). Within a lichen, the relationship between fungi and algae may be mutually beneficial to both kinds of organisms: Fungi derive food from the photosynthesizing algae, and the algae are shielded by the fungi from forces that would dry them out. Many scientists have concluded, however, that algae derive nothing from the relationship, in which case the fungi actually are parasites.

- Up to 90 percent of seed plants live in a cooperative association with fungi that links plant roots with fungal hyphae. In this relationship, plants supply fungi with food produced in photosynthesis, while the fungi supply plants with minerals and water, gathered by the web of fungal hyphae. Associations of plant roots and fungal hyphae are called mycorrhizae.

21.6 Plants: The Foundation for Much of Life

- Plants are the foundation for much of life on Earth, because they are responsible for much of the living world's production of food and oxygen. In addition, they stabilize soil, provide habitat for animals, and lock up carbon dioxide. All plants are multi-celled, and almost all are fixed in one spot and carry out photosynthesis. All plant cells have a cell wall and contain organelles called chloroplasts, which are the sites of photosynthesis. Plants reproduce through an alternation of generations: a life cycle in which successive plant generations produce either spores (the sporophyte generation) or gametes (the gametophyte generation). Within a given species, these two generations can differ greatly in size and structure.

21.7 Types of Plants

- The four principal categories of plants are bryophytes, seedless vascular plants, gymnosperms, and angiosperms. Bryophytes include mosses; seedless vascular plants include ferns; gymnosperms include coniferous trees; and angiosperms include a wide array of plants, such as orchids, oak trees, rice, and cactus.

- Bryophytes are representative of the earliest plants that made the transition from water to land. They lack a fluid-transport or vascular system and thus tend to be low-lying. Bryophyte sperm can get to eggs only by swimming through water. Thus, bryophytes are most commonly found in damp environments.

- Seedless vascular plants have a vascular system but do not produce seeds in reproduction. Their sperm must move through water to fertilize eggs.

- Gymnosperms are seed-bearing plants whose seeds are not encased in tissue called fruit. There are only about 700 gymnosperm species, but their presence is considerable, particularly in northern latitudes, where gymnosperm trees, such as pine and spruce, often dominate landscapes. The sperm of gymnosperms is encased in pollen grains that are carried to female reproductive structures by the wind. Gymnosperms produce seeds in carrying out reproduction. Seeds are structures that include a plant embryo, its food supply, and a tough, protective casing.

- Angiosperms, or flowering plants, are seed plants whose seeds are encased in tissue called fruit. Angiosperms are easily the most dominant group of plants on Earth, with some 260,000 species having been identified to date.

21.8 Angiosperm-Animal Interactions

- Angiosperm pollen grains generally are transferred from one plant to another by animals, such as insects and birds. Such animal-assisted pollination is unique to angiosperms. To induce animals to carry out this pollination, angiosperms produce nectar and have developed attractive colorations and fragrances.

- Angiosperm seeds contain tissue called endosperm, which functions as food for the growing embryo. Endosperm supplies much of the food that human beings eat. Rice and wheat grains consist largely of endosperm.

- Angiosperm seeds are unique in the plant world in being wrapped in a layer of tissue called fruit. Fruit that is edible functions in angiosperm seed dispersal, because animals will eat and digest the fruit but then excrete the tough seeds inside, often in a different location.

Key Terms

alternation of generations	434	hyphae	426
angiosperm	438	lichen	432
bryophyte	435	mycelium	426
cell wall	433	mycorrhizae	432
chloroplast	434	seed	438
dikaryotic	428	seedless vascular plant	436
endosperm	440	sessile	426
gametophyte generation	434	spore	429
gymnosperm	438	sporophyte generation	434

Understanding the Basics

Multiple-Choice Questions (answers in the back of the book)

1. Most fungi are composed almost entirely of
   a. ball-shaped objects called hypha
   b. leaves and stems
   c. reproductive cells called spores
   d. slender filaments called hyphae
   e. slender filaments called septa

2. With respect to food, animals _____ while fungi _____
   a. digest, then ingest . . . ingest, then digest
   b. consume existing organic material . . . make their own
   c. ingest only . . . digest only
   d. digest externally; digest internally
   e. ingest, then digest . . . digest, then ingest

3. Fungi reproduce through cells called spores, which
   a. have a single set of chromosomes
   b. can germinate without fusing with another cell
   c. often are released from structures called fruiting bodies
   d. usually are released in huge numbers
   e. all of the above

4. Only one of these organisms grows toward new sources of food. Which one is it?
   a. flowering plant
   b. bacterium
   c. fungus
   d. moss
   e. algae

5. Fungi cause (select all that apply)
   a. tetanus
   b. athlete's foot
   c. common colds
   d. dry rot
   e. wheat rust

6. Defining characteristics of plants include (select all that apply)
   a. alternation of generations
   b. hyphae
   c. cell walls
   d. reproduction through fruiting bodies
   e. nutrition from photosynthesis

7. You are walking through a botanical garden and you see a 6-meter-tall plant that shows no evidence of flowering, but seeds are present. To which group of plants does it belong?
   a. gymnosperms
   b. angiosperms
   c. mosses
   d. ferns
   e. cacti

8. Only angiosperms (select all that apply)
   a. are pollinated by animals
   b. produce seeds
   c. encase seeds in fruit
   d. have seeds containing endosperm
   e. have sperm encased in pollen grains

9. In the alternation of generations that plants employ (select all that apply)
   a. all generations produce eggs and sperm
   b. one generation produces spores, the next produces eggs and sperm
   c. succeeding generations tend to be about the same size
   d. succeeding generations tend to differ in size
   e. all generations produce spores

10. Plants (select all that apply)
    a. produce oxygen
    b. decompose organic matter
    c. destabilize soil
    d. lock up carbon dioxide
    e. usually form associations with underground fungi

Brief Review

1. Fungi could be said to take a "lottery" approach to reproduction. In what respect?

2. How does a spore differ from a gamete?

3. Animals have evolved various means of moving toward the food they eat. What is the approach that fungi take?

4. Describe two means by which angiosperm reproduction is aided by animals.

5. Describe two common associations that fungi make with other organisms. What does each party in each of these associations do for the other, and what do they gain themselves?

Applying Your Knowledge

1. Animals move because they need to—they have to get to prey and they must evade predators. These dual needs led to the evolution of the animal nervous system, which in turn led to the development of varying levels of intelligence in animals. Meanwhile plants never had a need to move, because they made their own food through photosynthesis. Do the separate evolutionary paths of animals and plants mean that there is an inherent value to struggle in the living world—in the animals' case, the struggle to obtain food?

2. Like all living things, fungi require water to begin growing. The recent scourge of mold fungi in American homes has primarily affected new homes. Why should they be affected more than old homes?

3. The *Entomophthora muscae* fungal parasite that invades flies has no consciousness, yet it manages to undertake actions that affect the behavior of the flies it attacks. (It sends hyphae into the flies' brains and, as a result, the flies crawl upward.) Almost all parasitism is disturbing to human sensibilities, but this brand is particularly unsettling. Why should this be so?

22 *The Diversity of Life 3*

The largest invertebrate.
(Section 22.7, page 458)

Shedding an old skeleton.
(Section 22.9, page 461)

notochord

pharyngeal slits

One of our chordate relatives.
(Section 22.11, page 467)

We human beings are, in a sense, intimate strangers with the bacteria and fungi that were reviewed in the last two chapters. We are intimate with these organisms in that we carry out our lives right along beside them: we walk through clouds of them, wash off layers of them, and have trillions of them living inside us. That said, except for the occasional outbreak of athlete's foot or stomach flu, they never cross our minds. So small are bacteria and most fungi that, while they may be everywhere, for us they are effectively nowhere. It's a different story with the animals that are the subject of this chapter. Our cats and dogs and neighborhood birds are part of our conscious lives. We pay attention to a new spider web on our porch or to the lizard on our hiking path. We wonder about the circling hawk overhead.

Animals come from the long evolutionary line of *other* feeders: the heterotrophs, who cannot manufacture their own food but must get their nutrition from outside themselves. Many bacteria fit into this category, as do lots of protists and all of the fungi. But animals, in their quest for food, added something that is unique to them: A nervous system; a system for transmitting complex messages rapidly over long pathways in the body. Once this happened, the living world was off to the races in terms of adding novel abilities. Think of sight, hearing, smell, flight, walking, singing, and reading. Then there are such things as the echo-location of bats and the waggle-dance of honey bees. For the average person, to be alive means to sense, to investigate, to respond, to move. In all these areas, animals reign supreme in the living world.

This chapter is about the broad diversity that exists in animals (**see Figure 22.1** on the next page). Given that animals are part of our daily lives, some of what follows will be familiar. But there are likely to be many surprises as well.

A human tail.
(Section 22.11, page 467)

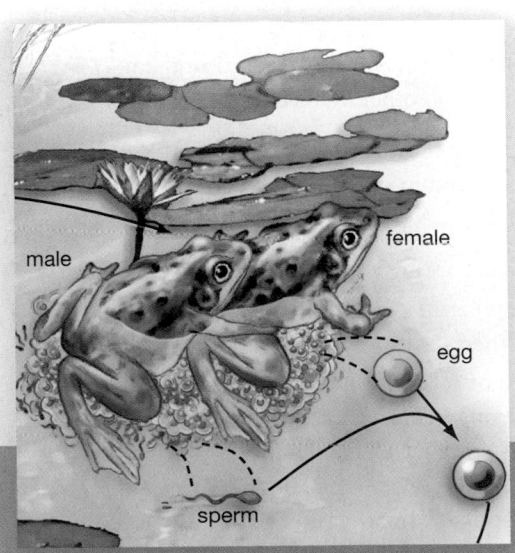

A double life.
(Section 22.11, page 470)

An evolutionary innovation.
(Section 22.11, page 470)

Figure 22.1
Animal Diversity
An octopus, a feather star, and a chimpanzee are very different creatures, yet all are members of the animal kingdom.

(a) Octopus

(b) Feather star

(c) Chimpanzee

(a) Octopuses often are found crawling over ocean rocks, but they swim as well, by expelling a jet of water from a hose-like siphon, often propelling themselves "backwards" as with this one.

(b) Though they look like plants, ocean-dwelling feather stars such as this one are animals that are part of the same phylum as sea stars. They extend their arms to catch bits of food drifting in the ocean currents.

(c) Chimpanzees are the closest living relatives of human beings.

22.1 What Is an Animal?

In defining animals, the question that needs to be answered is: What characteristics do *all* animals have that other organisms *don't* have? It turns out there is a single, rather technical feature that is sufficient to set animals apart from all other living things.

- Animals pass through something called a blastula stage in their embryonic development. A *blastula* is a hollow, fluid-filled ball of cells that forms soon after an egg is fertilized by sperm (see Chapter 29 for details). All animals go through a blastula stage, but no other living things do.

Three other characteristics are found in all animals, but they're found in other kinds of organisms as well. All animals:

- Are multicelled; there are no single-celled animals.
- Are heterotrophs; they must get their nutrition from outside themselves.
- Are composed of cells that do not have cell walls. (The outer lining of animal cells is the plasma membrane. By contrast, all plants and most other creatures have a relatively thick additional lining—the cell wall—outside their plasma membrane.)

Apart from these universals, animals *usually* go on to share other characteristics. Animals tend to move, though there are animals that, for at least

part of their lives, are as *sessile*, or fixed in one spot, as any plant. Except for the animal group that includes sponges, animal bodies are organized into **tissues**, each tissue being a collection of similar cells that serves a common function.

Then there are characteristics of animals that don't fit our preconceived notions. While it's true that animals generally are large relative to bacteria or protists, some animals are microscopic. We often think of animals as creatures with vertebral columns or "backbones," but there are far more **invertebrates**, or animals without vertebral columns, than animals with them. Indeed, 99 percent of all animal species are invertebrates. We generally think of animals as land creatures and, with a huge assist from insects, there certainly are a lot of land animals. However, in terms of animal *diversity*, as measured by basic body plans, there are more kinds of ocean-going animals than land animals, as you'll see. This makes sense because animals existed in the sea for at least 100 million years before any of them came onto land.

22.2 Animal Types: The Family Tree

Basic body plans turn out to provide a sensible way of dividing up the animal kingdom. Depending on who is counting, there are between 36 and 41 animal phyla, with each phylum being informally defined as a group of organisms that share a basic body plan. The classification scheme for the living world introduced in Chapter 18—that of kingdom, phylum, class, order, family, genus, and species—provides the basis for a more formal definition of phylum. A **phylum** is a category of living things, directly subordinate to the category of kingdom, whose members share traits as a result of shared ancestry. (For more on classification, see Chapter 18, page 359.)

So, in what ways are the various animal phyla related to one another? To put this another way, what does the animal family tree look like? At the moment, this question is a matter of great debate among **zoologists**, meaning biologists who study animals. By measuring similarities in DNA and RNA sequences among living animals, these scientists have come up with entirely new conceptions of who is more closely related to whom. A consensus seems to have emerged about this, however, and you can see it laid out for you in **Figure 22.2**. Not all the 36–41 animal phyla are shown; some of the phyla at the top represent groups of phyla. For more on how DNA and RNA evidence has changed our view of animal evolution, see "Redrawing the Animal Family Tree" on page 449.

One way to conceptualize this tree is that, over time, animals became more complex through a series of *additions* to the characteristics found in more primitive animals. The twist is that only some varieties of animals evolved to get these additions, while others retained the primitive, "ancestral" condition. Let's take a tour of the tree now, focusing on features that were added to the animal kingdom through evolution.

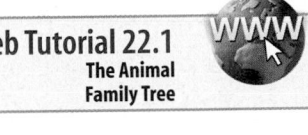

Web Tutorial 22.1
The Animal Family Tree

Figure 22.2
A Possible Family Tree for Animals
The animal kingdom is divided into groups called phyla. The members of each phylum have in common physical features that are evidence of shared ancestry. Nine of the estimated 36–41 animal phyla are shown here. All these phyla are regarded as having evolved from an ancestral species of protist, shown at lower left in the family tree. The red horizontal lines on the tree mark the points in animal evolution at which certain structural innovations appeared, such as tissues and bilateral symmetry. Human beings are members of phylum Chordata, at upper right.

Additions 1 and 2: Tissues and Symmetry

Looking down at the trunk of the tree in Figure 22.2, you can see that all animals have a common ancestor—probably a protist similar to the modern-day protists called choanoflagellates. Now notice that the tree splits above this common ancestor and yields, over to the left, a phylum called Porifera, which are sponges. Porifera are truly the outliers of the animal world in that, almost alone among animals, they lack tissues and a quality known as symmetry (which will be defined shortly). If you look again at the split above the common ancestor, this time going to the right, you can see that the animals on this branch did get the additions of tissues and symmetry. Note also that this right branch leads to all the other animal phyla. Thus, all the animals that stem from this branch will have tissues and symmetry (which is what makes Porifera the outlier).

But what is this other addition, symmetry? If you look at **Figure 22.3a**, you can see that the jellyfish that's pictured can be thought of as being divided by imaginary planes, thus yielding body sections. These sections are mirror images of one another; they have **symmetry**, meaning an equivalence of size, shape, and relative position of parts across a dividing line or around a central point. The jellyfish, part of phylum Cnidaria, actually has a particular kind of symmetry.

It has **radial symmetry**, meaning a symmetry in which body parts are distributed evenly around a central point. In simpler terms, the symmetry of jellyfish is the symmetry of pie sections.

To appreciate symmetry, consider what a lack of it is like. Look at the sponge in Figure 22.3b. Where is its symmetry? There isn't any, because there is no section of the sponge that is a mirror image of any other.

Symmetry can, however, come in several forms. Look at the dog in Figure 22.3c., divided by what is known as an imaginary "sagittal" plane. The dog obviously has symmetry, but it is a different kind of symmetry from that of the jellyfish. It has "bilateral" symmetry. We'll take a moment to consider this form of symmetry, since it constitutes the third addition to the animal kingdom.

Addition 3: Bilateral Symmetry

Animals usually are *different* front-to-back and top-to-bottom, but *symmetrical* side-to-side. Put another way, your head is different than your feet, and your chest is different than your back, but your left *side* is very similar to your right. This is what **bilateral symmetry** means: a bodily symmetry in which opposite sides of a sagittal plane are mirror images of one another.

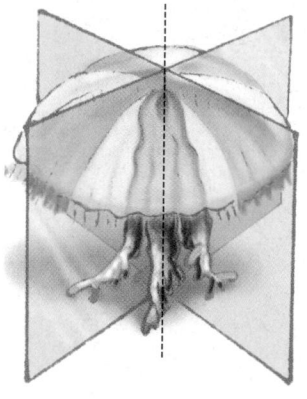

(a) Radial symmetry:
Symmetry around a central point

(b) Asymmetry:
No planes of symmetry

(c) Bilateral symmetry:
Symmetry across the sagittal plane

dorsal

sagittal plane

posterior

anterior

ventral

Figure 22.3
Symmetry Is an Equivalence in Body Sections
If an imaginary plane drawn through an animal can divide that animal into sections that are mirror images of one another, then that animal has symmetry.

(a) Radial symmetry The imaginary planes drawn through the jellyfish show that it has radial symmetry: a symmetry in which body sections are distributed evenly around a central point. Radial symmetry is characteristic of the phylum Cnidaria, which includes jellyfish.

(b) Asymmetry The sponge has no symmetry—no plane drawn through the sponge body would yield sections that are mirror images of one another.

(c) Bilateral symmetry The dog has a kind of symmetry common to most animals: bilateral symmetry, in which the sides of an animal are mirror images of one another. More formally, bilateral symmetry exists when body sections on opposite sides of a sagittal plane are symmetrical to one another. Notice also the terms for different parts of the dog—dorsal and ventral, meaning "back" side and "belly" sides; and anterior and posterior, meaning "head" end and "tail" end.

Redrawing the Animal Family Tree

When you look at the animal family tree in Figure 22.2, some of its groupings may seem strange at first. To take one example, the phylum Nematoda, which is made up of tiny roundworms, sits right next to the phylum Arthropoda, which includes insects and spiders. If you look down the evolutionary lines of the arthropods and roundworms, you can see that they both stem from a common line, which is another way of saying that arthropods and nematodes had a common ancestor. But what leads scientists to believe that these two very different kinds of animals are related in this way? One critical piece of evidence has long been recognized. It is that only the arthropods and roundworms are "molting animals." They all have an external skeleton that they shed before growing a new one. In the case of roundworms, this skeleton is a multi-layered "cuticle." In the case of arthropods, it is a tougher external skeleton, made of the material called chitin.

Even given this evidence, however, scientists for decades classed arthropods not with roundworms, but with the so-called *segmented worms*—the annelids that include the common earthworm. They did so primarily because the arthropods join the annelids in having a segmented body. (Think of how earthworms seem to be made up of a series of little "ring" segments.) So if this "segmentation" evidence argued for placing the arthropods with the earthworms, but the "molting" evidence argued for placing them with the roundworms, why did the roundworm argument win out? The deciding factor was a new kind of evidence: the sequencing of RNA and DNA from all the animals in question. When scientists looked for similarities in these DNA and RNA sequences, they found that arthropods and roundworms seem to be much more closely related than are arthropods and earthworms. This same kind of evidence has altered our understanding of the animal family tree in other ways. For example, molluscs are now placed with the earthworms, whereas once they were over with the arthropods.

None of this is to say that we are now certain of who evolved from whom among the animals. On the contrary, our understanding of the animal family tree is a work in progress. The tree you see in Figure 22.2 is based on the best evidence we have for now; but then again, new evidence keeps coming in.

In looking at the animal family tree, you can see that bilateral symmetry was an evolutionary innovation that affected all modern-day animals except for the sponges and the phylum Cnidaria, which includes the jellyfish. Thus, bilateral symmetry is the general rule in the animal world.

The bilateral symmetry/radial symmetry divergence is in one sense the divergence between having a head and not having one. Jellyfish and sponges don't have one, but most other animals have at least a "cephalization," or concentration of nerve cells at one end of their bodies. Animals more complex than the cnidarian jellyfish evolved to sense their world primarily at one end of themselves—their heads—which is the end with which they move into their worlds. This is understandable because it is more advantageous to know something about the future (where you're going) than the past (where you've been).

Addition 4: A Body Cavity

Your stomach expands when you've just had a big meal, but then contracts when you're busy for a few hours. Your heart expands and contracts perhaps 70 times a minute. You bend over to tie your shoes and, unbeknownst to you, many of your internal organs slide out of the way. What allows you to do all this? The answer is an internal space you have; a large, fluid-filled body cavity. We humans are not alone in having such a cavity, or coelom (pronounced "SEE-lome"). There are only three animal phyla in Figure 22.2 that *don't* have this cavity: the sponges, the cnidarians (jellyfish, etc.), and the members of phylum Platyhelminthes, which is made up of flatworms.

What's the value of such a cavity? Well first, an expandable stomach has the same value as a gas tank: It allows you to go for a while without refueling. It also allows reproductive organs to expand to accommodate eggs or offspring. Then there is the fact that if a heart couldn't expand and contract, it couldn't work at all. Finally, a body cavity protects organs from bodily blows and provides a large part of the body with flexibility.

In most instances the coelom surrounds another physical structure, the *digestive tract*—meaning the tube, functioning in digestion, that runs from the mouth to the anus. We can therefore think of the

449

coelom as one tube that encircles another; the coelom is generally tube-shaped, and it surrounds the tube that is the digestive tract. (There are, however, lots of variations on this general principle.) **Figure 22.4** displays what it means to have no coelom, as in flatworms; a *pseudocoel*, as in roundworms; and a *true coelom*, as in earthworms.

The concept of a coelom is intimately linked to that of tissue layers. Almost all animal embryos have what are known as germ layers, defined as layers of cells that *become* various types of tissue in adult ani-

flatworm

No coelom (acoelomate). Phylum Platyhelminthes, composed of flatworms, is one of the phyla that has no coelom. Note that from its gut to its exterior, the flatworm is composed of uninterrupted tissue—endoderm (inner tissue), mesoderm (middle tissue), and ectoderm (outer tissue).

ectoderm

mesoderm

endoderm (gut)

roundworm

Pseudocoel. Roundworms, by contrast, have an enclosed cavity, known as a "pseudocoel," that lies between their gut and mesodermal tissue layers. The pseudocoel develops as a continuation of the space that exists when an embryonic animal is in the blastula or hollow ball-of-cells stage.

ectoderm

mesoderm

pseudocoel (mesoderm on one side only)

endoderm (gut)

earthworm

Coelom. The earthworm is one of the many animals that has a true coelom (or just-plain coelom). Note that both the coelom and the gut of the earthworm are lined with mesodermal tissue layers (whereas in the roundworm, only the pseudocoel is lined by mesoderm). The true coelom develops from an animal's mesodermal tissue.

ectoderm

mesoderm

coelom (surrounded by mesoderm)

endoderm (gut)

Figure 22.4
An Important Space
Most animal bodies have an enclosed cavity or coelom—an internal space that surrounds their digestive tract or other internal structures. A coelom gives an animal flexibility, protects its organs from external blows, and provides space for the expansion of such organs as the stomach. Only three of the phyla covered in the chapter lack a coelom.

mals. Most animals have three types of germ layers: endoderm, mesoderm, and ectoderm. Endoderm is initially an inner layer of cells in the embryo, mesoderm a middle layer, and ectoderm an outer layer. The general importance of these tissue layers will be reviewed later. For now, just note the linkage, displayed in Figure 22.4, between mesoderm and a coelom. This linkage provides a way of formally defining a **coelom**. It is an enclosed body cavity in an animal, that is lined with cells of mesodermal origin. You may wonder why there are no red lines on Figure 22.2 showing where the coelom was added in animal evolution. So valuable is this internal space that it seems to have evolved independently several times among animals—at least once each among the two large groupings you can see toward the base of the tree, the protostomes and the deuterostomes. But what are these two large groupings? Let's see.

A Split in the Animal Kingdom: Protostomes and Deuterostomes

The protostome/deuterostome categories you can see toward the bottom of the animal family tree simply represent an early split among animals along two evolutionary paths. The difference between the two types of animals is grounded in how each type develops in its early embryonic stages. Remember how you saw earlier that the chief defining characteristic of animals is that they all go through something called the blastula stage in development? Well, in **Figure 22.5a**, you can see what happens to the hollow ball of cells called a blastula: It develops an invagination whose opening is called a blastopore. In protostomes, this blastopore becomes the mouth, but in deuterostomes it becomes the anus. (*Protostome* means "mouth first," while *deuterostome* means "mouth second.")

If you look at Figure 22.5b, you can see the effect that this developmental difference and others have on adult protostomes and deuterostomes. Note that the protostome has a dorsal heart and a ventral nerve cord, while in the deuterostome this arrangement is reversed.

Having reviewed the broad-scale features of the animal kingdom, we will now take a brief tour of it by walking through each of the nine phyla shown in Figure 22.2.

22.3 Phylum Porifera: The Sponges

Back in the 1780s, the United States was just that: a group of states that had just united into a single entity. The sponges that make up the phylum Porifera bear some comparison to this. Each sponge is a single, unified entity, but not by much. Sponges have no

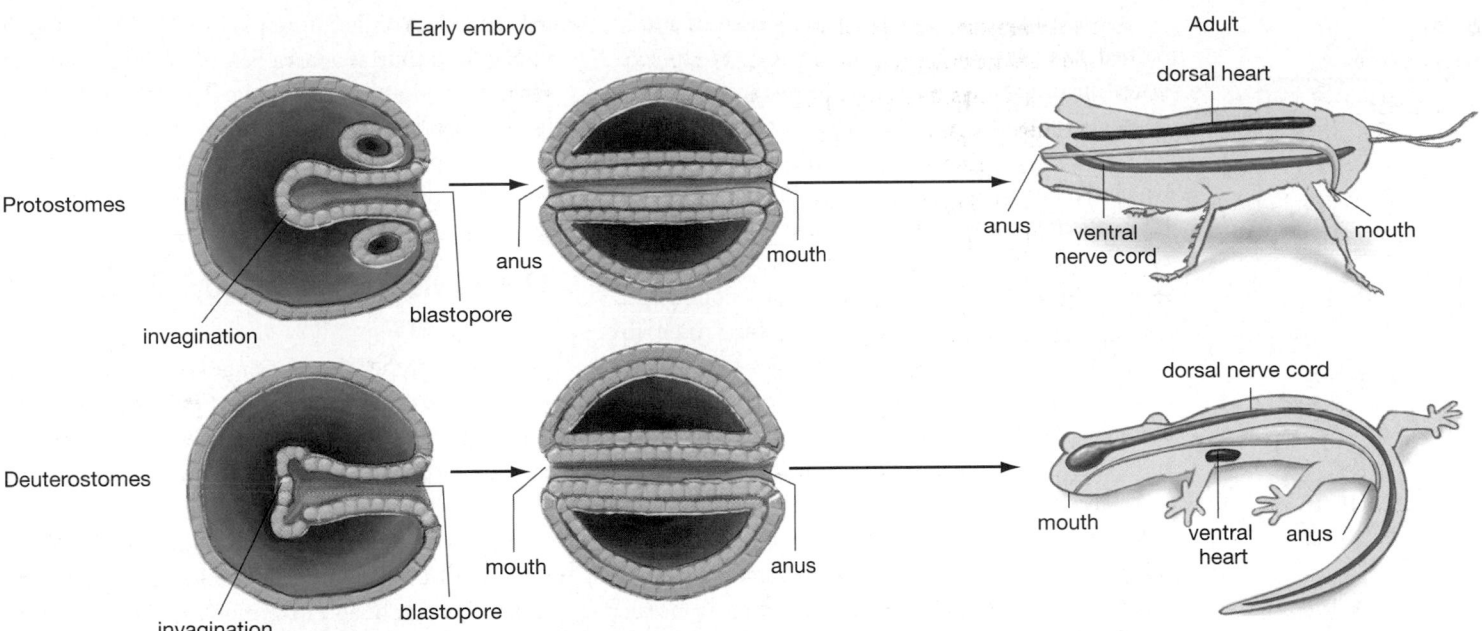

Early embryo

Adult

Protostomes

invagination

blastopore

anus

mouth

dorsal heart

anus   ventral   mouth
         nerve cord

Deuterostomes

invagination

blastopore

mouth

anus

dorsal nerve cord

mouth   ventral   anus
           heart

At one point in their embryonic lives, all animals pass through a so-called blastula stage of development, the blastula being a hollow ball of cells. In most animals, this blastula then invaginates to form a structure that develops into the animal's gut. The opening to this invagination is called a blastopore. In protostomes, the blastopore becomes the mouth. In deuterostomes, by contrast, the blastopore becomes the anus.

Developmental differences such as these have consequences in the adult. Protostomes, such as the insect shown, have their heart on their top or dorsal side and nerve cord on their bottom or ventral side. In deuterostomes, such as the reptile shown, this placement is reversed. The portions of the embryos colored yellow, red, and blue signify the endodermal, mesodermal, and ectodermal tissues noted in the discussion of the animal coelom.

Figure 22.5
The Protostome-Deuterostome Divide

organs; no stomach, no heart. They don't really even have tissues. Each of their cells acquires its own oxygen and eliminates its own wastes. In experiments, scientists have strained some sponge species through a filter, "disaggregating" them into the individual cells they are made of. The scientists then watched as these cells came back together to make up a single sponge once again. This is possible only in an organism in which each cell functions with a great deal of independence. If you were disaggregated into your individual cells, there is no chance they would come back together to re-form you. On the other hand, the cells in sponges clearly work together in a coordinated way. Sponges may not show much organization relative to fish, but they show a great deal of organization relative to, say, bacteria.

So, what manner of organism is a sponge? The simplest varieties have a layer of outer cells that is pockmarked with thousands of microscopic pores. Water flows in through these pores in the outer-layer cells and then is expelled out through a single large opening at the top of the sponge (**see Figure 22.6**). Because sponges are fixed in one spot (generally on the sea floor), everything they need in the way of food and oxygen must come *to* them, while everything they need to get rid of must be washed away *from* them. The water that flows through them takes care of both needs. Food and oxygen wash in through the micro-

scopic pores, and wastes wash out through the single large opening (called an *osculum*). Most sponges have elaborations on this theme, but the essential concept is the same: Move the water in, capture the food that comes with it, and move the water out, expelling wastes in the process. Millions of cells, called collar cells, wave tiny, whip-like flagella that keep the water flowing through.

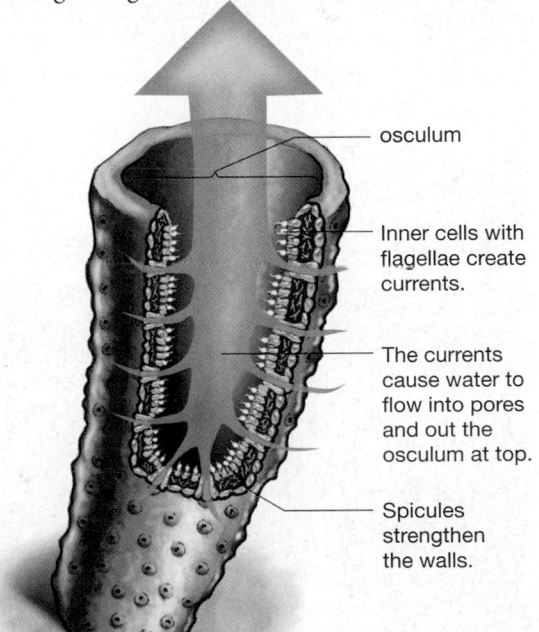

osculum

Inner cells with flagellae create currents.

The currents cause water to flow into pores and out the osculum at top.

Spicules strengthen the walls.

Figure 22.6
Sponges: A Body Plan for a Simple Lifestyle
Sponges filter water through themselves in order to live. Cells on their interior surface have hair-like extensions, called flagella, whose rapid back-and-forth movement draws water in through pores in the sponge's side walls. After filtering this water for nutrients, the sponge then expels it through a large opening at the top of its body, called an osculum. Sponges lack true tissue layers, but possess many specialized cell types. The cells are held together in a stable arrangement by tiny, hard structures called spicules and by the flexible protein called collagen.

Most sponges have skeletons composed of small, barbed structures called *spicules* that keep the sponge pores open and generally give the sponge structure. Some sponges have no spicules, but instead have skeletons made of a special variety of the protein collagen, which can be a soft, pliable material. (Think of the collagen *injections* that people sometimes get to improve their looks.) Sponges with collagen skeletons are the sponges from which we get our everyday notion of a sponge, meaning a soft, absorbent object used in cleaning. Put another way, the sponges that people once used were the skeletal remains of ocean-dwelling animals (which were harvested by divers). Today our sponges generally are made of synthetic materials.

Depending on whose count you accept, between 5,000 and 10,000 species of sponge have been recognized so far, with probably lots more remaining to be identified. Almost all these species dwell in ocean water, though there are a few freshwater varieties (**see Figure 22.7**).

Sponges can reproduce merely by budding. A group of cells breaks off from an existing sponge and then develops into a new sponge. Sexual reproduction exists too, however, and here again the sponge puts water currents to use. Sperm are released from one sponge and make their way via water currents to another sponge, where they are taken up and transported to egg cells. An offspring that comes from sex-

ual reproduction has a moving or "motile" stage. It swims for a time as a larva before landing on a solid surface—perhaps a rock or the body of a living animal—whereupon its outer layer of cells secretes a substance that will allow it to attach to the material beneath it. Then it begins its life of filtering water.

22.4 Phylum Cnidaria: Jellyfish and Others

If the signature activity of sponges is filtering water to get food, the signature activity of cnidarians is stinging prey to get it. In the main, cnidarians (knee-DAR-ee-uns) harpoon their prey with extensions that are not only barbed, but that may release poisons. These extensions are *tiny*, since each one springs from inside a single cell, but they are numerous enough that a single jellyfish may be able to immobilize and eat animals the size of small fish. Only a few species have a sting potent enough to cause real harm to human beings, but it makes sense to give all jellyfish a wide berth.

Jellyfish are undoubtedly the best-known cnidarians, but the phylum also includes corals, whose calcified remains make up coral reefs; the delicate sea anemones, whose petal-like tentacles close up when touched; and hydrozoans, which can look more like sea plants than animals (**see Figure 22.8**). One type of hydrozoan is the hydra that you may see in your biolo-

(a) A leaf sponge

(b) A yellow, warm-water tube sponge

Figure 22.7
Sponge Diversity
Sponges differ greatly in size and shape, as you can see from these examples.

(a) Jellyfish

(b) Sea anemone

(c) Coral polyps

Figure 22.8
Cnidarian Diversity
One characteristic that unifies cnidarians as diverse as jellyfish, sea anemones, and corals is their ability to immobilize prey with harpoon-like stinging cells.
(a) Pictured are some Pacific Ocean jellyfish, *Chrysaora fuscescens*, whose sting, while painful, generally is not harmful to human beings. One of its relatives, *Chrysaora quinquecirrha*, is a major irritant during the summer in the Chesapeake Bay.
(b) The large sea anemone *Urticina piscivora* is found off the shores of British Columbia in Canada. At about 20 centimeters or 8 inches across, it is so big it can eat small fish.
(c) What builds a coral reef? Coral polyps, such as these seen in a coral reef in Western Australia. Note the mouths and extended tentacles of the polyps, which help form the living outer layer of coral reefs.

gy lab. There are about 9,000 identified species of cnidarians, nearly all of them ocean dwellers, with a few living in freshwater.

The basic body plan of a cnidarian is that of a sack, though it often is a sack that is turned upside down. If you look at **Figure 22.9**, you can see how this plays out in connection with a hypothetical jellyfish. In the familiar adult or "medusa" stage of a jellyfish, the sack is upside down; note that the mouth is on the *underside* of the body in this stage. Conversely, look at this jellyfish's immature "polyp" stage, when it is fixed to the ocean floor; now the mouth is on top. Medusa and polyp stages are present in many cnidarians, though corals, sea anemones, and hydra have

only the polyp stage. The medusa stage predominates in jellyfish—misnamed, because they are not fish—while the polyp stage predominates in most hydrozoans. In all medusa and in many polyps, however, the basic body plan is the same: a single opening to the outside, serving as both mouth and anus, is surrounded by tentacles that both sting prey and bring the prey to the mouth. Note also the material that lies between the jellyfish's gastrovascular cavity and its exterior. This is the *mesoglea*, a secreted, gelatinous material that makes up most of the medusa-stage jellyfish. Its consistency accounts for the name jellyfish. The gastrovascular cavity functions in both digestion (*gastro–*) and in circulation (*vascular*).

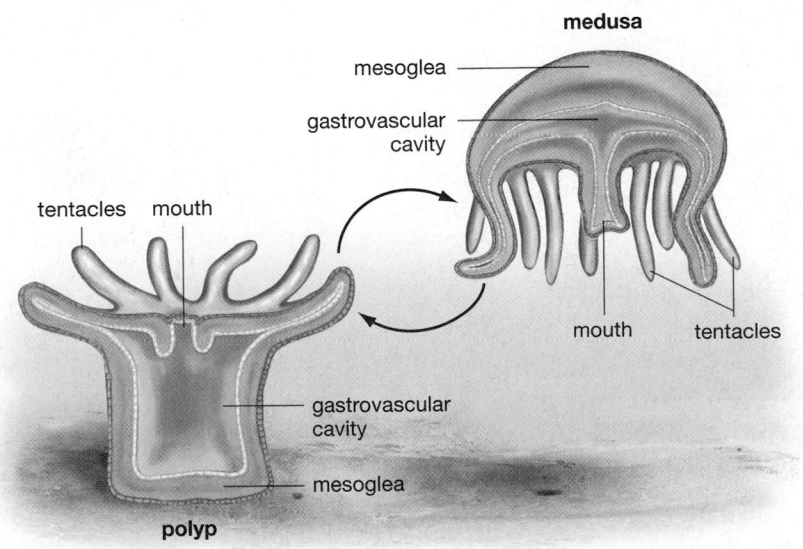

medusa

mesoglea

gastrovascular
cavity

tentacles   mouth

mouth   tentacles

gastrovascular
cavity

mesoglea

polyp

Figure 22.9
Two Stages of Life for Many Cnidarians
Many cnidarians go through both a polyp stage, in which they are attached to a solid surface beneath them, and a medusa stage, in which they swim freely through the water. Note that in the polyp stage, the cnidarian's mouth and tentacles face upward, while in the medusa stage, they face downward. The gastrovascular cavity of the cnidarian functions in both digestion and circulation. The mesoglea noted in the figure is a secreted, gelatinous material that makes up the bulk of the medusa stage in jellyfish cnidarians. All cnidarians use stinging tentacles to capture prey.

Figure 22.10 shows you the life cycle of a cnidarian, this one a hydrozoan known as *Obelia*. Medusa-stage male *Obelia* release sperm into the water while females release eggs; these unite, eventually producing a larval stage offspring that settles to the ocean-floor bottom, now becoming a polyp. This starting polyp can give rise to an entire colony of *Obelia* polyps through the process of *budding*: Groups of cells break off from one polyp and form another polyp. Note that in this polyp stage, some of the branch-like outgrowths are "feeding polyps" that have the familiar sack-like appearance of cnidaria (tentacles, mouth), while other outgrowths are entirely given over to reproduction, containing "medusa buds." These buds are immature medusa-stage *Obelia*, which eventually will be released to become free-swimming individual medusae. The *Obelia* life cycle is one among many that exist in cnidarians.

Cnidarians don't have any true organs, but they are a long way from sponges in that they have a nervous system, and cells that function like muscle cells. This gives medusa-stage cnidarians the ability to swim. (Polyp-stage cnidarians sometimes can slide slowly along the ocean floor.) The typical jellyfish medusa contracts cells that ring its mesoglea, thus expelling a jet of water from its underside. This action both moves the animal in the opposite direction from the jet and pushes in the mesoglea. Like a compressed cylinder of foam rubber, the mesoglea then snaps back into shape, ready for the next contraction.

Special mention should be made of the reef-building corals, which have no medusa stage but live almost entirely as polyp-stage cnidarians. The fantastic ocean cities known as coral reefs take their names from the coral animals, which actually are close relatives of sea anemones. Coral reefs have a rock-like appearance and, indeed, they are composed mostly of calcium carbonate, better known as limestone. But this limestone comes from living organisms. The corals secrete it, a practice they share with a type of red algae with whom they share their habitat. The limestone forms an external skeleton for the corals, and when each coral polyp dies, its limestone skeleton remains. Thus coral reefs are composed largely of the stacked-up remains of countless generations of coral polyps, along with the remains of their neighboring red algae. But the thin outer veneer of each reef is composed of *living* algae and the latest generation of pinhead-sized polyps. If you looked up close at any one of these coral animals, you would see the basic features of a cnidarian polyp: stinging tentacles pointed upward, surrounding a mouth.

The Protostomes

22.5 Phylum Platyhelminthes: Flatworms

With the flatworms, you've arrived at animals that fit our everyday notions of what animals look like, in that they have something like a head and have the same

Figure 22.10
Cnidarian Reproduction
This hydrozoan cnidarian, known as *Obelia*, reproduces through both sexual and asexual means. Sexual reproduction can be observed at the right of the figure, where male and female medusae release sperm and eggs, respectively, that fuse to form the new generation of *Obelia*. The polyp that results from this fusion, however, can reproduce by asexual means. Cells bud off from the first polyp (center) and grow into another polyp, shown at left, which may be the first of many that will develop this way. Polyps within these larger structures specialize. Some are involved in feeding, while others function in reproduction. The reproductive polyps have medusa developing inside them (the medusa buds), which are released to the surrounding water, starting the life cycle over again. The different stages of the life cycle are drawn at different scales.

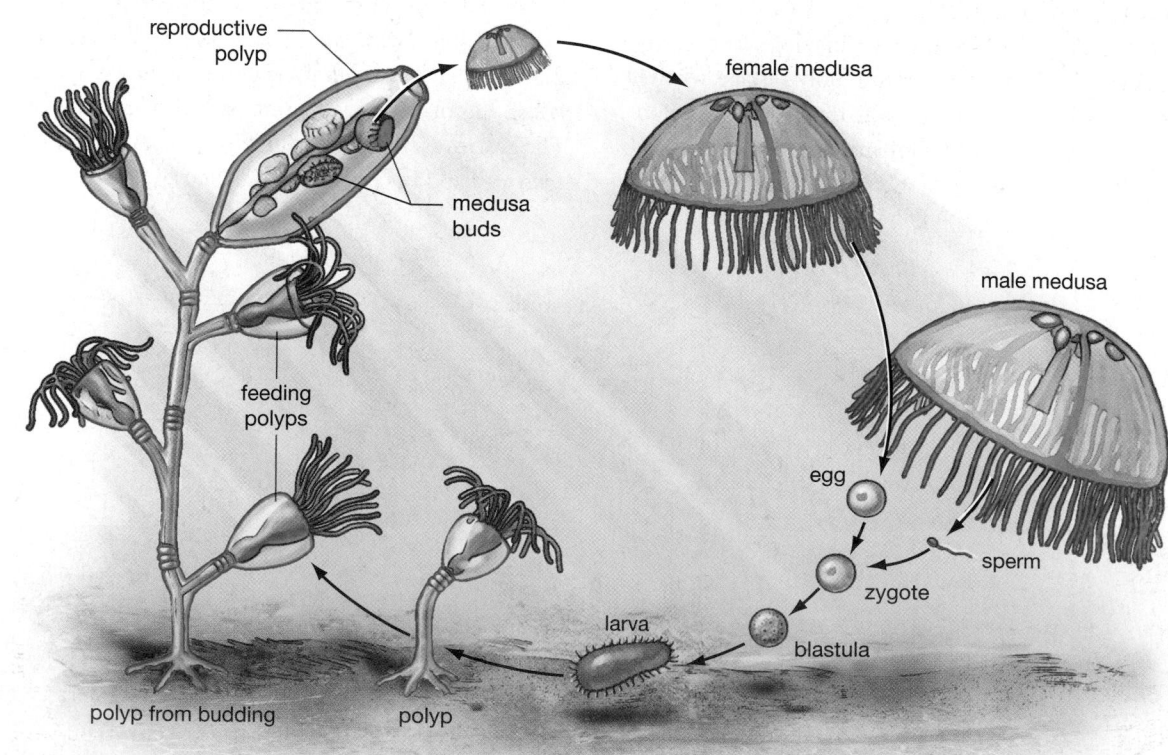

side-to-side (bilateral) symmetry as, say, a mouse. Further, flatworms go beyond the tissues of the cnidarians and have **organs**, meaning highly organized structures formed of several *kinds* of tissues. (Your stomach is an organ that includes nerve and muscle tissues.)

Despite this complexity, flatworms lack a good many features that exist in almost all the phyla further up the complexity ladder. They have no coelom, or enclosed internal cavity. Thus, except for the tube of their digestive tract, they have very little internal space in them. This may sound like a good thing, but it actually limits their flexibility. Further, they have no system of blood circulation. Therefore, every cell in a flatworm must get its oxygen directly from the environment around it, through diffusion from water or air outside the body. This is why flatworms are flat—they have to maximize the number of cells that are near an exterior surface, as opposed to being buried deep inside (**see Figure 22.11**). Those flatworms that are on land tend to be found under stones or rotting wood; many live at the bottom of the ocean, and a few live in freshwater. Some 25,000 species of flatworm have been identified.

Humans are unlikely to notice flatworms since, of the minority that live around us, most are very small. When they do come into our consciousness, it is often in the unpleasant role of parasites. Two of the three traditional classes of flatworms live strictly as **parasites**, defined as organisms that feed off their prey but do not kill them, at least immediately. Some of these worms can infect human beings. There are, for example, the tapeworms that can enter the human body in undercooked meat or fish. Tapeworms can be small, like most flatworms, but some reach up to

20 meters in length, which is about 66 feet. Then there are several species of another variety of flatworm, the flukes, that cause the disease schistosomiasis, which affects more than 200 million people in tropical areas around the world, often causing serious damage to the human bladder, liver, or spleen. With flukes, the means of entry is not food but unprotected human skin, as with people who are standing in fishing areas or flooded rice paddies.

The flukes are in one class of flatworms (Trematoda), while the tapeworms are in another (Cestoidea). There is then a third class of flatworms, the Turbellaria, whose members generally are not parasitic, but free-living. If you look at **Figure 22.12**, you can see something of the anatomy of one variety of turbellarian, the flatworm *Dugesia*, which is likely to

Figure 22.12
The Flatworm *Dugesia*

(a) Flatworm anatomy

Dugesia's nervous system includes primitive eyes and two collections of nerve cells, the cerebral ganglia, that connect to nerve cords that run the length of the animal. In reproduction, *Dugesia* is hermaphroditic, meaning it possesses male sex organs (testes and penis) as well as female sex organs (ovaries and other structures). When two *Dugesia* copulate, each projects its penis and inserts it in the genital pore of the other.

(b) Feeding and digestion

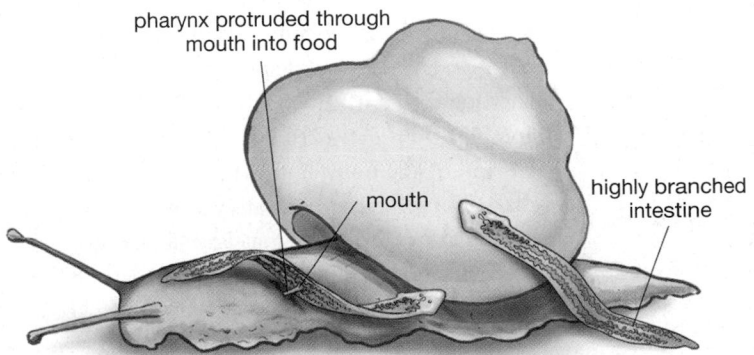

Dugesia feeds by turning its muscular pharynx inside out and projecting it into the food source. Food taken up through the pharynx is distributed through the body by *Dugesia's* highly branched intestine. Flatworms lack a true circulatory system and thus depend on their digestive system for the distribution of nutrients. Their digestive system lacks an anus, meaning *Dugesia* has only one digestive-tract opening, its mouth.

Figure 22.11
Flatworms
The flatworm in this picture, *Pseudoceros ferrugineus*, was photographed in the oceans off the coast of the Philippines. Most flatworms are free-living like this one, but there are also many parasitic flatworms that live for at least part of their lives inside a host.

be found crawling under rocks at the bottom of freshwater streams. About 1 centimeter or less than half an inch long, *Dugesia* has a "head," in that one end of it has not only a pair of primitive eyes (called ocelli) but also a concentration of nerve cells (the cerebral ganglia) that are connected to nerve trunks that run the length of the body.

Given this concentration of features in *Dugesia*'s head, the location of its mouth may come as a surprise. It's located midway down its body, on its ventral (bottom) side. To feed, it shoots a muscular structure called a pharynx outside its mouth, coats the prey with enzymes to break down its tissues, penetrates the prey with the pharynx, and then sucks the resulting semi-liquid material back in. (Your pharynx is the area at the back of your throat where your windpipe and digestive tract meet. Imagine being able to shoot it outside your mouth.) Food goes from the pharynx into an intestine, where it is digested and then simply diffuses into nearby tissues. Remember that flatworms have no blood circulation system. Thus, *Dugesia*'s intestine has to be highly branched because it is serving as both a food digestion and a food delivery system. Flatworms have no anus; their mouth is the single opening to their digestive tract, and waste material is expelled out of it.

Like most flatworms, each *Dugesia* has both ovaries and testes (the organs noted earlier). It is thus **hermaphroditic,** meaning a state in which one animal possesses both male and female sex organs. When two *Dugesia* copulate, each projects its penis and inserts it in the genital pore of the other. Most turbellarians can also reproduce asexually by a straightforward means: They break themselves in half. The posterior ("tail") part of the worm grasps the material beneath it while the anterior portion moves forward. The separated halves then grow whatever tissues they need to make themselves complete worms.

Members of phylum Platyhelminthes, such as *Dugesia*, have organs thanks to a critical embryonic addition found in flatworms, and in all animals more complex than flatworms. Recall from the earlier discussion of the body cavity (the coelom) that all animal embryos have what are known as germ layers, meaning layers of cells that *become* various types of tissue in adult animals. These layers are the endoderm, mesoderm, and ectoderm. If you looked at the embryos of jellyfish just past the blastula stage, you would see that they have only the endoderm and ectoderm. But Platyhelminthes and all the other more complex phyla also have a third layer, the mesoderm, literally in the middle of the other two. (Endoderm is initially an inner layer of cells and ectoderm an outer layer; mesoderm comes in the middle.) Animals with the three germ layers are said to be **triploblastic,** while the cnidarians, with two layers, are **diploblastic.** The addition of mesoderm was an important event in animal evolution because the interactions between germ layers in embryos allow for the development of more complex structures. (For details on germ layers, see Chapter 29 on animal development.)

22.6 Phylum Annelida: Segmented Worms

More worms? Actually, three of the nine phyla covered in this chapter are worms. (Still to come are the roundworms in Nematoda.) Evolution resulted in a lot of worm or worm-like phyla—perhaps a dozen altogether—but the reason so many are being covered here is that they occupy interesting places in the spectrum of animal diversity.

Annelid worms occupy such a position, in that they provide the clearest example of a feature that exists in a lot of animals, including ourselves: **body segmentation,** which can be simply defined as a repetition of body parts in an animal. Just as a set of identical Lego blocks can be snapped together to make a larger structure, so can a repeated set of segments be connected to make a larger body. Think of the vertebrae that make up your backbone; 24 of them run in a line from your neck to the base of your back, each of them having a similar basic structure and a similar function (support and protection).

Segmentation is so useful in animals that it evolved independently in them several times. It happened at least once in the protostome lineage that you've just been going over and then once again in the deuterostome lineage—more specifically in our own phylum, Chordata.

Though segmentation is widespread in the animal kingdom, it is most visible in the annelid worms. Indeed, the name Annelida comes from the Latin word *anellus,* or "little ring." That pretty much describes what we see in the best-known annelid, the common earthworm, whose body seems to be composed of a series of little rings that have been joined together (**see Figure 22.13**).

Segmentation is valuable in earthworms for the same reason that individual rooms are valuable in a house: The activities being carried out in one room can *differ* from those being carried out in another. Each of the earthworm's 100–150 segments is separated from adjoining segments by a partition, and each segment can function independently of the others to some degree. The muscles in individual segments (or groups of segments) can contract independently. This, in turn, makes for independent control of needle-like bristles that the worm can extend from each segment.

These features account for the mesmerizing way in which earthworms move. One set of muscles toward the rear of the earthworm contracts, making the worm thick and compact in the area, even as the bristles in these segments are being pushed into the ground like so many stakes. Now, with its hindquarters fixed in place, the worm uses a different set of muscles to make the mid-portion segments *lengthen*, thinning out as they do, meaning this part of the worm has moved forward. Then the worm plants bristles in the front, anchors itself, and literally brings up its rear. Note that this movement is possible only because of segmentation. If the *whole worm* lengthened, without part of it being compacted and fixed in one spot, it would get nowhere.

Segmentation is important in annelids, then, and is thought to have evolved in them precisely because of its power to help them move. (Earthworms use this power extensively, because they burrow in the dirt for hours at a time, swallowing soil for the nutrients it contains and eating leaves or other decaying vegetation.) In more general terms, segmentation is valuable to living things because it can confer flexibility while maintaining strength. We can see this in our own "backbones." Imagine how inflexible you would be if, instead of 24 moveable vertebrae, you had a single bone running from your skull to your posterior.

Earthworms generally are helpful to human beings—and not just as fish bait. They churn up soil, aerating it and depositing their cylindrical "worm casting" waste, which enriches the soil. Earthworms have no lungs; they take in oxygen right through their skin. Their skin needs to be moist for this to happen,

Figure 22.13
The Body Plan of an Earthworm
The segmentation of body parts—a widespread feature in the animal kingdom—is clearly seen in earthworms, whose segments are repeated hundreds of times. In general, such segmentation provides flexibility in combination with strength. In the earthworm, it also allows the actions being carried out in one segment to differ from those being carried out in another. Note, in the blowup of the earthworm's body, the muscular walls between segments; these give the earthworm independent control of the segments and the bristles that can be extended from them. The earthworm also expands our notion of what a "heart" amounts to. It has a dorsal blood vessel that contracts, as do our human hearts, giving the main impetus to the circulation of red blood that moves through the worm's system. But it also has five pulsating vessels on each side of its intestine that serve as accessory hearts.

however. The great threat to an earthworm is drying out, which is why these "nightcrawlers" generally stay underground during the daytime. Like the flatworms, earthworms are hermaphrodites. Each member of a copulating pair inseminates the other.

Though we've focused on earthworms, they actually represent only one small part of phylum Annelida, which contains about 17,000 named species. Most annelids actually are ocean-dwelling, and some of these colorful creatures do not fit in with our idea of drab worms (**see Figure 22.14**). There also are freshwater

(a) Hawaiian Christmas tree worm

(b) Medicinal leech

Figure 22.14
Annelid Diversity
Not all annelid worms are drab, and not all live underground.
(a) Polychaetes are ocean-dwelling worms. Pictured is a Hawaiian Christmas tree worm in the genus *Spirobranchus*. These polychaetes stay in one spot, burrowed into tubes they themselves have constructed, generally within a coral. The bushy "Christmas trees" that extend from the worm's head are structures called radioles that it uses to filter-feed from the water.
(b) Leeches are a smaller class of mostly parasitic annelid worms. Pictured is a leech that is feeding from a human arm. This particular leech, *Hirudo medicinalis*, serves a therapeutic function. These leeches are used today in connection with human reattachment and plastic surgery. Enzymes they secrete serve as anticoagulants—they keep blood from clotting—and help reduce pain at the site of surgery. A leech might be attached at the site of surgery for half an hour or so and then be removed, after which its enzymes will continue working for hours longer.

annelids, who are part of the same class as the earthworms but who tend to be much smaller. Then there is the smallest class of the annelids, which is composed entirely of leeches. Most leeches live up to their reputation of being blood-sucking parasites. Though most live in freshwater, some live in the ocean while others dwell in damp-land habitats.

22.7 Phylum Mollusca: Snails, Oysters, Squid, and More

With the molluscs, we reach a phylum that has lots of members who are familiar to us. Everyone has seen a snail, many of us have eaten clams or mussels, and squid and octopus are probably known to us from television or books. But molluscs are even more varied than these examples would suggest. Some molluscs are slugs and others worm-like; some have highly developed brains and others no brains at all; some are filter feeders and others fierce ocean predators. Some are very small, but one is a behemoth that is one of the enduring mysteries of the animal world. The giant squid, *Architeuthis dux*, reaches a length of about 20 meters or 60 feet and weighs up to a ton (**see Figure 22.15b**).

Depending on the expert consulted, there are between 50,000 and 100,000 described species of molluscs. They live in freshwater, saltwater, and on land. There actually are eight classes of molluscs, but here we will look only at the three most familiar classes, the **gastropods** (snails, slugs), the **bivalves** (oysters, clams, mussels), and the **cephalopods** (octopus, squid, nautilus).

What features unite this huge, diverse group as a single phylum? Outside the realm of technical anatomical details, there really is only one feature common to all molluscs. If you look at **Figure 22.16a**, you can see an aquatic snail that displays this feature along with others. Note a layer near the dorsal (top) surface of the snail called a *mantle*. This is a fold of skin-like tissue that surrounds the upper body of the mollusc and that usually secretes material that forms a shell (though there are lots of molluscs without shells).

Past this universal feature, the snail displays a number of structures that are common to *most* molluscs. The mantle generally drapes over part of the mollusc body like a tablecloth, meaning there is a mantle cavity—a space underneath the mantle. This cavity generally is the site of gills, by which all aquatic molluscs obtain oxygen, and by which the filter-feeding bivalves (clams, mussels, oysters) obtain not only oxygen but food. In land-dwelling molluscs, such as garden snails, much of the cavity is a primitive lung that evolved from the gill.

Then there is the single or "unitary" foot as shown on the snail's ventral (bottom) side. Through wave-like muscular contractions, this foot can propel the mollusc along the surface underneath it, be it a leaf or the ocean bottom. Some sessile bivalves, such as oysters, have lost the foot altogether, however; and as you'll see, in squid and octopus it has evolved into something else entirely. Note, in the blowup of the snail's mouth, there is a tooth-covered membrane called the *radula*. Present in most molluscs except the bivalves, this organ can be extended outside the mouth, where it serves as a kind of rasping file. Mol-

Figure 22.15
Mollusc Diversity
Pictured are species in three of the best-known classes of molluscs:

(a) Snails are gastropods. Pictured is a colorful terrestrial snail in the *Liguus* genus. These snails live in trees in southern Florida and through much of the Caribbean, though their numbers are dwindling in Florida.

(b) The largest cephalopod of all is the giant squid *Architeuthis dux*, shown here, which can reach a length of about 20 meters or 60 feet. This squid, prepared for an exhibit at New York's American Museum of Natural History, measured a mere 25 feet in length and weighed 250 pounds. It was netted off the coast of New Zealand in 1997.

(c) The bivalve *Argopecten irradians* is better known as the bay scallop—a part of many seafood dishes. Note the small blue dots around the edge of the scallop. These are a few of the animal's many primitive eyes.

(b) Cephalopod

(a) Gastropod

(c) Bivalve

luscs use it for scraping a surface or for cutting small prey; then they retract it back into the mouth, thus moving food into their digestive tracts.

The snail has some other features worth pointing to now (though we could have looked at variations on them in the annelids as well). These are a heart and a stomach. These organs obviously aren't unique to snails (or even molluscs), and that's just the point. Along with gills and lungs, these organs are signs of the molluscs' advanced position in terms of structural specialization.

Why does something like a heart exist? Because creatures as large as molluscs need a *delivery system* for food and oxygen. Simple diffusion of food from a gut won't work anymore, because some tissues are buried so deep they would never be served. The delivery system's vehicle is blood, but that blood must be propelled by some force so that it can make a set of rounds through the animal, picking up oxygen from the gills and food from the digestive tract. The propelling force for this work is the beating of the heart.

The circulation of the cephalopods (squid, octopus) is like ours in that it is a **closed circulation system**— a circulation system in which the blood *stays within* the blood vessels, while the oxygen and nutrients diffuse out of the vessels to the surrounding tissues. Most molluscs, however, have an **open circulation system**: a circulation system in which blood flows out of blood vessels altogether, into spaces or "sinuses" where it *bathes* the surrounding tissues. Veins collect the blood in these sinuses for a return trip to the gills and the heart. Gastropods such as snails can be either single-sex or hermaphroditic, and this is the case for the bivalves as well. All cephalopods, however, are single-sex.

Figure 22.16b gives you some idea of one set of variations evolution has wrought with the basic body plan of the mollusc. Remember how the unitary foot is a usual mollusc feature? Look at what has become of it in the squid; it has been divided into eight arms (with suckers) and two longer tentacles. The radula is still there, but now it lies next to a set of jaws that operate something like a parrot's beak. Meanwhile, the mantle cavity now has another function; the siphon you can see at one end of it acts like a jetting water hose that not only helps propel squid movement—they expel water out of it— but also directs this movement by being aimed first one direction and then another.

Cephalopods deserve mention for another reason, which is that they are not only the biggest invertebrates in the world, they are the smartest. One researcher who worked for decades with octopus said that they had the intelligence of dogs, which is very smart indeed in the animal world. Many researchers

(a) Aquatic snail

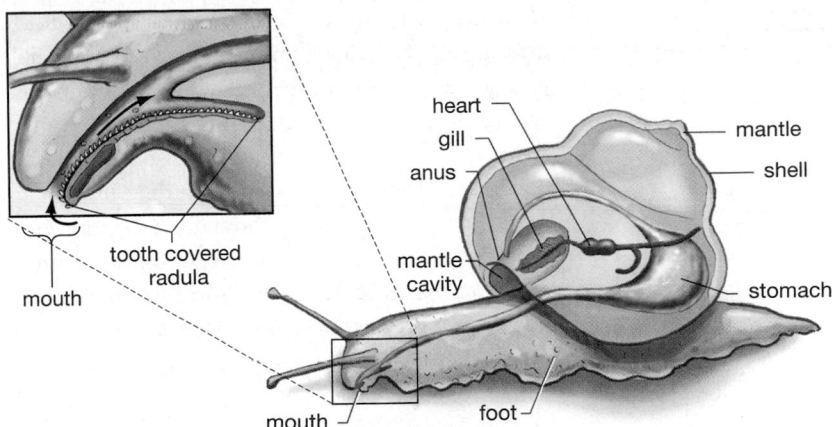

Aquatic snails such as this one have features that are common to many molluscs. All molluscs possess a skin-like tissue called a mantle, which secretes material that can form a shell, whether it is an external shell (as in the snail) or an internal shell (as in a squid). Snails also possess a tooth-covered rasping structure for feeding, called a radula, and they are complex enough to have evolved some specialized organs that are familiar to us—the heart and the stomach. The unitary "foot" of the snail, which works through wave-like contractions, is another common mollusc feature.

(b) Squid

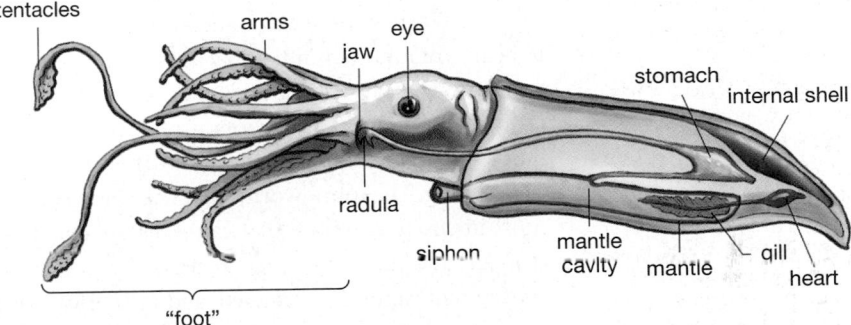

In the squid, the mollusc's unitary foot has evolved into a multisegmented appendage of eight arms and two tentacles. Note how other mollusc features have been modified in the squid. The mantle cavity houses not only gills, but a siphon the squid jets water out of, thus propelling itself. The radula now exists near jaws that function like a parrot's beak.

Figure 22.16
The Body Plans of Molluscs

would go further, however, saying that octopus and squid seem to plan and calculate in very sophisticated ways. These animals also are fast swimmers, have keen eyesight, can change color in an instant (to hide from predators), and as a last resort in defending themselves, have the ability to shoot out black "ink" from a special sac. Given their remarkable capabilities, the curious thing about these molluscs is that they live only a year or two; most animals this sophisticated live much longer lives.

22.8 Phylum Nematoda: Roundworms

Nematodes, commonly referred to as roundworms, exist in such enormous numbers that it is impossible to imagine life without them. They fit into numerous ecological roles, such as that of "detritivore," meaning an organism that feeds on dead or cast-off organic material. Nevertheless, many farmers in the United States would *like* to imagine life without them, because several species of these animals are a major cause of damage to such crops as soybeans and corn. Farmers and research scientists have been united for decades in an entrenched battle against them. In addition, some are human parasites. The disease trichinosis, usually brought on by eating undercooked pork, is caused by a roundworm; likewise there is hookworm, which affects hundreds of millions of people in warmer climates throughout the world (**see Figure 22.17**).

An acre of prime farmland might contain several hundred billion roundworms, but you don't have to go to farmland to find these animals. They exist in desert sands, polar ice, ocean bottoms, lakes—name the place where life is going on, and the nematode worms are likely to be among the living. Indeed, scientists have only the vaguest idea of how many *species* there are; about 15,000 have been catalogued, but 100,000 seems to be the minimum number that actually exist.

Most roundworm species are very small—the crop pests, which feed on roots, generally are microscopic—but some parasitic roundworms are several meters long. The roundworms that have been studied most intensely are those that cause disease and crop damage, and these have a characteristic appearance: transparent, smooth, C-shaped, and cylindrical with tapered ends (hence the term *roundworm*). Across the breadth of roundworm species, however, there is a great diversity in form.

Roundworms generally are of one sex or the other, meaning they are not hermaphroditic, as the flatworms are. Reproduction is always sexual; unlike flatworms, roundworms can't reproduce by pulling themselves apart. Roundworms are the first of two "molting" animal phyla we will look at; they have an external skeleton, called a cuticle, that they shed or "molt" four separate times during their lifetime. We'll take a more detailed look at molting, however, in the animals coming right up, the arthropods.

22.9 Phylum Arthropoda: Insects, Lobsters, Spiders, and More

Phylum Arthropoda is large and varied indeed. It is so large that there are more described species in one arthropod group, the insects, than there are in all the other animal phyla combined. It is so varied that its members range from legless barnacles to hundred-legged millipedes (**see Figure 22.18**). There are lots of ways to group the animals in this phylum, but for our purposes, it will be convenient to think about them batched into three "subphyla." These are:

- Subphylum Uniramia, which includes insects, millipedes, and centipedes, among other organisms
- Subphylum Crustacea, which includes shrimp, lobsters, crabs, and barnacles, among other organisms
- Subphylum Chelicerata (chel-is-er-AH-ta), which includes spiders, ticks, mites, and horseshoe crabs, among other organisms

Before getting to these subphyla, it will be useful to review the characteristics that all arthropods share. First, all arthropod animals have an **exoskeleton**, defined as an external material covering the body, providing support and protection. You can see an example of an exoskeleton in the grasshopper pictured in **Figure 22.19**. Second, all arthropods have what are known as **paired, jointed appendages**, which are just what they sound like: appendages, such as legs, that come in pairs and that have joints. (The word *arthropod* actually means "jointed leg.")

Taking the exoskeleton first, it is made of a tough carbohydrate called chitin that comes embedded in protein. The crustacean arthropods (crabs, lobsters, and so forth) have, in addition, a calcified component to their skeleton that makes it very hard, as anyone who has ever "cracked" a lobster knows. Such a skeleton is not only protective but also serves to anchor arthropod muscles very securely. Your own muscles work by pulling against your *endo*skeleton—your internal skeleton. Arthropod muscles pull against a skeleton too, but it's a skeleton that surrounds their bodies.

Strong though it may be, the exoskeleton only works because it is also flexible. Like a knight's armor, the exoskeleton has plates that overlap and thin, flexible sections between these plates that can bend as necessary. Even with this flexibility, however, the exoskeleton presents a problem: The arthropod body can only grow so much before it expands right into it.

Figure 22.17
Roundworms
The tiny worms called nematodes are a normal part of many ecosystems, including soil ecosystems. However, a small number of roundworm species are harmful to humans, either directly as parasites, or indirectly as crop pests. Pictured is an artificially colored micrograph of the nematode *Toxocara canis*, a parasite that infects dogs. Humans can become infected with *T. canis* eggs if they have contact with an infected dog or contaminated soil. The worm is magnified × 450.

(a) Subphylum Chelicerata

(b) Subphylum Crustacea

(c) Subphylum Uniramia

Figure 22.18
Big Numbers, Much Diversity
The arthropods represent the largest animal phylum, in sheer numbers as well as in diversity. Shown are representatives of the three arthropod subphyla:
(a) A web-building *Argiope* spider, this one found on the Snake River at the Idaho-Oregon border. The Chelicerata grouping to which it belongs is the only arthropod subphylum whose members do not have antennae.
(b) A flame lobster from Hawaii. Note the well-defined arthropod characteristics in this crustacean: an exoskeleton and the legs that exist as paired, jointed appendages.
(c) The arthropod subphylum Uniramia includes insects. Pictured is a short-horned grasshopper native to western North America.

So how does the arthropod solve this problem? Its solution is **molting**: a periodic shedding of an old skeleton followed by growth of a new one. A crustacean such as a crab will retreat to a relatively safe place and begin to slip out of its old exoskeleton, as if it were Houdini trying to get out of a straightjacket (**see Figure 22.20**). Through chemical processes, the old skeleton has begun to split by this time. Since the new, developing exoskeleton lies just underneath the old one, you might think this process would leave the crab just as hemmed in as before. But at this stage the new skeleton can be *stretched*, and the crab proceeds to do just that by ingesting a large amount of water, thus inflating both its body and the skeleton to a new size. The new skeleton then hardens in its inflated size, the crab loses the extra water, and shrinks to its previous size. The result? It now has room to grow. Insects pull off this same feat, but stretch themselves with air instead of water.

The jointed appendages that arthropods possess come in many forms. There are legs for walking, claws for predation and defense, and wings for flying. These appendages are flexible and often come with sensory attachments, such as sensory "hairs," that keep the arthropod in touch with its environment.

Figure 22.20
Old and New
Arthropods have an outer or exoskeleton of a fixed size. They are able to grow by periodically shedding, or molting, this stiff skeleton. The crab in the photograph has just finished molting; its old exoskeleton lies nearby.

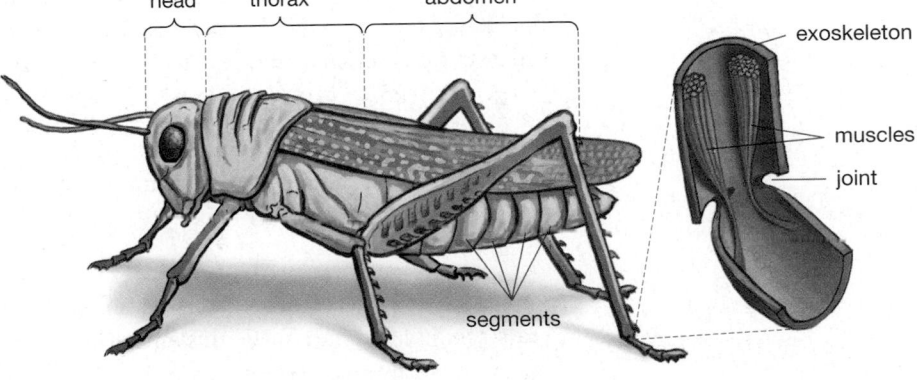

Figure 22.19
Arthropod Features
Arthropods have paired, jointed appendages, as with the legs of this grasshopper. The insects among the arthropods have bodies made up of three large-scale sections: head, thorax, and abdomen. Like the annelid worms, arthropods are segmented. This segmentation is clearly visible in the abdomen region of the grasshopper, but is less pronounced in the head and thorax because there the segments have fused. The entire arthropod body is covered in a rigid exoskeleton that is jointed to allow movement.

Together, jointed appendages and an exoskeleton make for an animal that is often nimble and well defended—a combination that is one of the reasons arthropods are so numerous. In addition, arthropods often have keen senses, such as sight and chemical perception (as with ants following a "pheromone" or chemical scent trail).

Subphylum Uniramia: Insects First

Recall that the arthropod phylum is divided into three subphyla. The first of these subphyla, Uniramia, has within it a group of animals we all have some familiarity with, the insects.

Who can comprehend how many insects there are in the world? There are more species of them—about a million have been counted so far—than there are species in all the other groupings of animals combined. If we could get an accurate count of their numbers, we would probably find that there are *tens* of millions of insect species. To look at their numbers another way, for every person on Earth, there may be 200 million insects. The vertebrates in the animal world have been the biggest creatures on land for the last 350 million years. But size counts for only so much in the face of the numbers the insects can put up. Here is the lead sentence from a September 2000 article in the Australian *Financial Review*:

> Extensive spraying could start as early as next week to try to control an impending locust plague which threatens to cause up to $500 million damage to Australia's forecast big grain harvest.

Had the *Financial Review* existed thousands of years ago, it could have made this same kind of report. Consider this passage on locusts from the Bible's Book of Joel, which dates from about 2,500 years ago:

> For a nation has invaded my land, powerful and innumerable, … It has laid waste my vines, and splintered my fig trees …

The battles that insects and human beings have been engaged in for so long have involved not only plagues of locusts, but the bubonic plague (carried by fleas), malaria (transmitted by mosquitoes), and the everyday predations of lice, termites, and ants. On the other hand, we have insects to *thank* for most of the plant growth we see in the world, in that insects pollinate flowering plants. In addition, insects provide us with honey, they help break down organic matter, and many of them are beneficial to humans in that they feed on the very insect pests that are so troublesome to humans.

If you look again at Figure 22.19, you can see the body parts of a typical insect. The three larger body regions featured in this grasshopper—head, thorax, and abdomen—are the rule in insects. In the abdomen, you can see a regular segmentation reminiscent of that you saw with the annelid worms.

The main cavities in the insect are the sinuses, or spaces, that its blood flows into. This blood bathes tissues in an "open" circulation system that almost all arthropods have. Sexes are separate in the insects, and reproduction is generally sexual.

Other Uniramians: Millipedes and Centipedes

In addition to insects, the uniramian subphylum also includes millipedes and centipedes (**see Figure 22.21**). Millipedes don't really have a thousand legs, despite their name. But hundreds of legs are possible, because these creatures have up to 100 body segments, each of

(a) Millipede

(b) Centipede

Figure 22.21
Millipedes and Centipedes
Insects constitute only one of the three classes of arthropods in the arthropod subphylum Uniramia. Millipedes and centipedes make up the other two classes.

(a) Millipedes have two pairs of legs per segment and live mostly on decaying plant matter.

(b) Centipedes have only one pair of legs per segment and are carnivores. Shown is the Texas giant centipede, *Scolopendra heros*.

which has two pairs of legs. This structure makes for movement that is slow but relatively powerful as millipedes make their way across the damp, dark environments they favor, which often means the forest floor.

Centipedes look much like millipedes, but are a different class of arthropod. They have only one pair of legs per segment and a pair of more prominent antennae extending from their head. Moreover, centipedes are carnivores, whereas millipedes feed largely on decaying plants. Centipedes come equipped for their predatory work, as their front two legs have become modified into venom-injecting fangs. This may sound ominous, but only a few tropical species pose a threat to human beings.

Subphylum Crustacea: Shrimp, Lobsters, Crabs, Barnacles and More

The second arthropod subphylum, Crustacea, includes several kinds of animals that don't seem to have much in common at first glance. How are a crab and a barnacle alike, for example? But remember that in putting living things together in a category, biologists are first and foremost concerned with shared *ancestry*, not with whether one creature has the same general appearance as another. At a crime scene, convincing evidence is likely to be found in small details, such as hair samples and fingerprints. The same thing holds true for evidence about the relatedness of groups of animals: the telling details are likely to involve small features.

This turns out to be the case with crustaceans. What all of them have in common is five pairs of appendages extending from their heads—two pairs of antennae and three pairs of feeding appendages. If you look at **Figure 22.22**, however, you can see the fantastic diversity that evolution wrought in crustaceans.

One of the crustaceans pictured in Figure 22.22, the water flea in the genus *Daphnia*, certainly is not familiar in the way that crabs or barnacles are. But it is representative of a variety of small, aquatic crustaceans that exist in huge numbers, mostly in the oceans, but also in freshwater bodies. As a whole, the crustaceans are mostly ocean-dwelling, but many live in freshwater, while a few live in damp-land environments. Crustaceans are known to humans mostly as a food source, such as shrimp and lobsters, or as a marine pest, such as the barnacles that attach themselves to ships. It is not just humans who use crustaceans as a food source, however. Closely related to shrimp are the crustaceans known as krill. Generally no more than an inch long, these animals feed on the plant life that floats in the icy ocean waters off Antarctica. Traveling in huge, dense swarms, they then become an important part of the diet of whales, seals, and penguins.

(a) Barnacles   **(b)** Water flea   **(c)** Shrimp

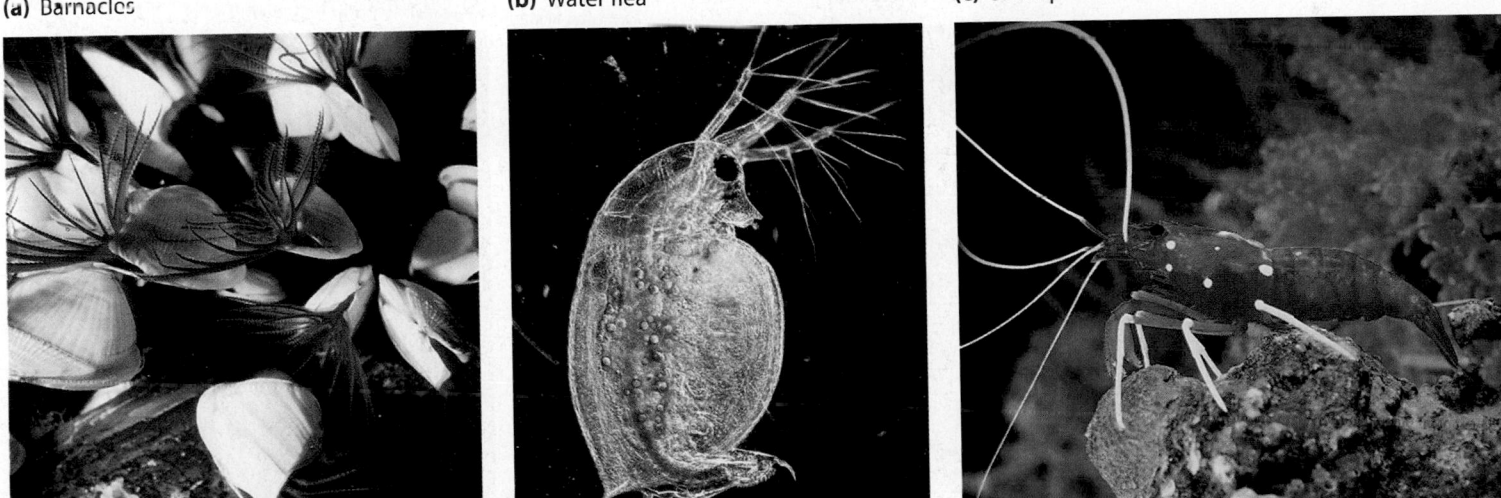

Figure 22.22
Crustacean Diversity
Diversity among the arthropod subphylum Crustacea is stunning.

(a) One class of crustaceans includes barnacles. When seen on a pier or ship, barnacles may seem lifeless to us, but notice the feathery extensions coming from these barnacles in the south Pacific. These are cirri, which barnacles extend from their shell and then use to catch drifting plankton.

(b) Water fleas in the genus *Daphnia*, such as the one shown here, live in huge numbers in ponds and lakes. Though barely visible with the naked eye, they are complex animals. Under microscopes, their tiny hearts can be seen beating a furious rate. As they are not insects, they are not really fleas. They get their name from the jumping, jerky motions they make in the water. Note the clearly visible digestive tract in this water flea.

(c) The crustacean class that includes shrimp also includes lobsters, crabs, and the pill bugs so often seen when we turn over rocks. Shown is the colorful fire shrimp, *Lysmata debelius*.

Subphylum Chelicerata: Spiders, Ticks, Mites, Horseshoe Crabs, and More

The third arthropod subphylum, Chelicerata, provides another example of small physical features yielding critical clues about relatedness. You might think that horseshoe crabs should be categorized as crustaceans, along with the other crabs, but it turns out that horseshoe crabs aren't really crabs at all. If you looked at the underside of a horseshoe crab, near its mouth, you would see two small appendages called *chelicerae*, which have pincers and which the crab uses to bring food to its mouth. If you looked near the mouth of a common spider, you would again see two chelicerae, only now each chelicera has become modified to become a venom-injecting *puncturing* appendage, rather than a grasping appendage. Ticks, mites, and all the other chelicerates likewise have paired chelicerae, from which this subphylum gets its name (**see Figure 22.23**).

Horseshoe crabs may be familiar to anyone who has spent time on the beaches of the Atlantic seaboard in May or June. Fearsome though they may look, they are harmless creatures that feed on worms, clams, or whatever else they can scavenge from the ocean bottom.

It is another grouping of chelicerates, however, that really inspires human fear: the arachnids, a class that includes mites, ticks, and scorpions, along with the more familiar spiders. Why "arachnophobia" should be so widespread in human beings is something of a mystery since, of the 34,000 identified species of spiders, only a handful cause any real harm to people. Part of the problem may be that spiders are blamed for wounds actually inflicted by other creatures. In one study of 600 suspected "spider bite" occurrences in southern California, 80 percent turned out to be the work of other arthropods—mostly ticks and some of the true bugs of the insect world (meaning bedbugs and other members of their order). Spiders evolved one of the world's great prey-snaring abilities, which is the spinning of their remarkable silk webs.

If we want to look for true causes of human misery, a better place to start would be with another arachnid, the microscopic dust mite, which is now known to be a major cause of asthma and other human allergic reactions. In the last decade, the mite's fellow arachnid, the *Ixodes* tick, has become feared because of its role as a carrier of the bacterium that spreads Lyme disease (named after the town of Lyme, Connecticut, where the disease was first identified).

(a) Horseshoe crabs

(b) Tarantula spider

(c) Dust mite

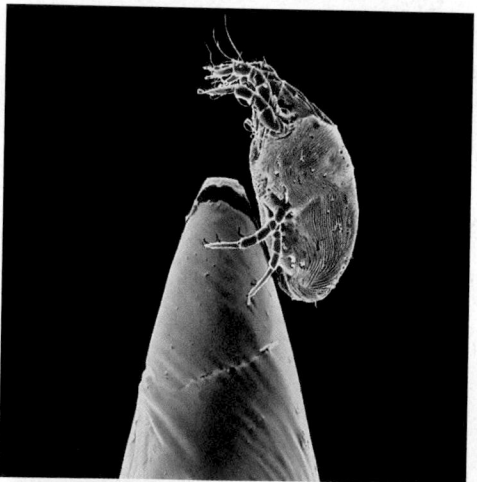

Figure 22.23
Chelicerate Diversity
All members of the arthropod subphylum Chelicerata possess paired chelicerae, which are pincer-like appendages used for feeding. These appendages stand in contrast to the mandibles used by the other two arthropod subphyla.

(a) In the springtime, East Coast beaches often have lots of horseshoe crabs such as these. In this picture, a group of males is competing for access to a female.

(b) The much-feared but generally harmless tarantula, this one a dry-weather Chilean rose tarantula, *Grammostola spatulata*, that is often kept as a pet. Like all spiders, the tarantula is a member of the Chelicerata class Arachnida, from which we get the term *arachnophobia*.

(c) Dust mites actually are eight-legged arachnids as well. The dust mite shown is standing on the head of a sewing needle. Such mites exist in almost all homes in the millions. Body fragments and excrement from them actually make up a large portion of the "dust" that is visible when sunlight shines into a room. This material sets off allergic reactions in many people.

(a) Sea star

(b) Sea cucumber

(c) Sea urchins

Figure 22.24
Echinoderm Diversity
There are five classes in the echinoderm phylum, three of which are represented here.

(a) Sea stars such as this one are fierce predators. Here a sea star is managing to open the shell of a bivalve known as a rock cockle.

(b) True to its name, this sea cucumber does look something like the vegetable, but sea cucumbers come in many shapes and colors. Like most echinoderms, sea cucumbers move slowly along the ocean floor.

(c) Kelp is a favorite food of many sea urchins. Here a group of sea urchins is shown foraging on some kelp.

The Deuterostomes

22.10 Phylum Echinodermata: Sea Stars, Sea Urchins, and More

With the echinoderms, we cross into the animal grouping noted earlier, the deuterostomes, that also includes our own phylum, Chordata. You might expect that, as our relatives, the echinoderms would have the kind of sophisticated features we've recently been seeing—brains, well-developed sense organs, strictly sexual reproduction—but none of this is true in the best-known echinoderm, the sea star (**see Figure 22.24a**). It has no brain, its only sensory or-

gans are the primitive eyespots found on the tips of its arms, and a whole new sea star can be regenerated from the arm and part of a central disk of an existing sea star. Even the bilateral symmetry that you've seen in every animal since the jellyfish is absent in the adult sea star: It has *radial* symmetry, like the jellyfish.

This is not to say, however, that the sea star and its echinoderm relatives are completely primitive. Most have a remarkable system for moving that involves forcing water into a series of suction-tipped tube feet that then extend, like so many inflated water balloons, from the underside of the sea star's arms (**see Figure 22.25**). Moreover, the

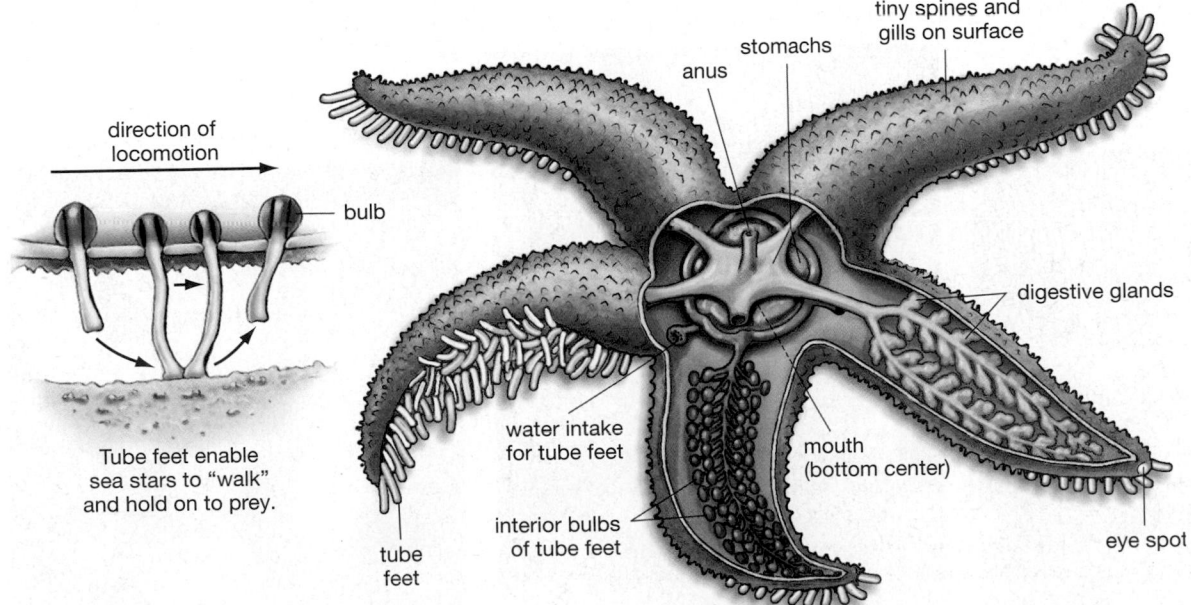

direction of locomotion

bulb

Tube feet enable sea stars to "walk" and hold on to prey.

tube feet

interior bulbs of tube feet

water intake for tube feet

anus

stomachs

tiny spines and gills on surface

digestive glands

mouth (bottom center)

eye spot

Figure 22.25
The Body Plan of a Sea Star
The sea star is radially symmetrical in its adult form, and it has no brain. Its only sensory organs are the primitive eyespots found on the tips of its arms. It has, however, evolved a remarkable system for moving along the sea floor and grasping prey. It first takes in water from the surrounding sea and then channels this water into a series of water bulbs. When inflated with the water, these bulbs lengthen, functioning as suction-tipped "tube feet."

sea star evolved into radial symmetry *from* bilateral symmetry. How do we know? Sea star larvae have bilateral symmetry, a quality that is lost when the larvae develop into adults. Looked at together, these echinoderm features add up to a phylum that is something of a mystery to zoologists—a mixture of characteristics from all over the animal map.

Sea stars aren't the only familiar echinoderms. Sea urchins, with their spine-covered spherical bodies, are echinoderms as well, as are sand dollars. Then there are the less familiar but well-named sea cucumbers (**see Figure 22.24b**). There are about 7,000 identified species of echinoderms, all of them ocean-dwelling and nearly all of them inhabiting the ocean floor, though "floor" in this case may just mean the bottom of a tide pool. Some are sessile, but most move across the ocean floor at a slow pace. Their shared habitat and measured pace make sense when we realize that the entire phylum evolved from a group of sessile filter feeders.

Despite their slow movement, echinoderms can be formidable predators. Sea stars often feed on molluscs, such as oysters and mussels. In some cases they use the suction tubes on their feet to pry open a mollusc's shell just a little. Then they "evert" their stomach—turn it inside out—and slide it in through the narrow gap they have created between shell halves. Juices secreted by their stomach then start to digest the prey's tissues. Sea urchins, meanwhile, are some of the animal kingdom's most voracious algae eaters.

22.11 Phylum Chordata: Mostly Animals with Backbones

Say the word "animal," and most people think of a *vertebrate* animal—be it tiger, elephant, deer, lizard, or some other large and probably toothy creature. One thing that ought to be clear by now, however, is what a small portion of the animal world vertebrates make up. Nevertheless, there are a lot of vertebrate species. The 50,000 or so that have been identified are nothing compared to the 1 million species of insects, but there are more species of vertebrates than there are of sponges, or cnidarians (jellyfish, etc.), or flatworms, and the vertebrate numbers may match those of molluscs.

In other ways, too, the vertebrates have been a big success. All the largest and swiftest animals are vertebrates, whether in water or in air or on land. And the sheer variety of sensory capabilities that vertebrates have—from echo-location to reading—is unrivaled anywhere in the living world.

Large and important as they are, the vertebrates don't even constitute a phylum; instead they make up only a subphylum, Vertebrata. The larger phylum into which vertebrates fit, called Chordata, actually has two additional subphyla in it. One of these (Cephalochordata) is made up of only a single kind of animal, a small, eel-like creature called a lancelet, represented by only 25 or so species (**see Figure 22.26a**). The other subphylum (Urochordata) has about 3,000 ocean-going species in it, but is represented by only three classes of animals. The largest of these classes is made up of the tunicates, whose practice of expelling water earns them their alternative name of sea squirt.

Figure 22.26
Chordate Diversity

(a) A single type of animal, the lancelet, is the sole representative of one of the three subphyla of chordates, Cephalochordata. Lancelets spend much of their time burrowed into the sand or mud of the shallow ocean floor, filter-feeding on small organisms or passing food particles. Only a few centimeters long, the diminutive lancelets are chordates, but not vertebrates.

(b) The African cheetah shown here is a vertebrate, and thus a representative of another of the chordate subphyla, Vertebrata.

(c) Urochordates, representing the third chordate subphylum Urochordata, come in about 3,000 species, most of them similar to the vase-like tunicates shown here. These animals are filter feeders who spend their adult lives attached to rocks. Their common name, sea squirts, comes from their practice of suddenly ejecting a spout of water from an opening near the top of their bodies. This group was photographed in the ocean off the coast of Indonesia.

(b) Subphylum Vertebrata

(a) Subphylum Cephalochordata

(c) Subphylum Urochordata

Figure 22.27
Four Universal Chordate Features
All chordates possess four structures at some point in their lives: pharyngeal slits, a support structure called a notochord, a dorsal nerve cord, and a post-anal tail. In the lancelet, all these features are present in the adult. In humans, only the dorsal nerve cord is clearly evident in adults.

What Is a Vertebrate?

What *distinguishes* vertebrates from these other chordates? Only the vertebrates have just what you'd expect: a **vertebral column**. Better known as a backbone, this flexible column of bones extends from the anterior to posterior end of an animal. Conversely, what *unites* all the chordates are four features, which you can see pictured in a lancelet in **Figure 22.27**. At some point in their lives, all chordates have

- A **notochord**: a stiff, rod-shaped support structure, composed of cells and fluid and surrounded by a lining of fibrous tissue, running from the chordate's head to its tail

- A **dorsal nerve cord**: a rod-shaped structure consisting of nerve cells, running from the chordate's head to its tail

- A series of **pharyngeal slits**: openings to the pharyngeal cavity

- A **post-anal tail**: a tail located posterior to the anus

At this point, as a chordate, you may be wondering where your *own* post-anal tail or pharyngeal slits went, so a little explanation of these features is in order. Although the word "notochord" sounds like "nerve cord," the notochord is a flexible but tough *support* structure, not a nervous-system feature. A lancelet retains its notochord throughout life, but most vertebrates lose theirs in embryonic life. (Its outer portion develops into the backbone.)

The dorsal nerve cord may not seem like a feature unique to chordates—you've seen nerve cords in lots of other phyla—but it is the qualifier *dorsal* that makes the difference. The nerve cords you saw in the annelids and arthropods were ventral, meaning they were on the underside of these animals. The vertebrates among the chordates get not only the dorsal nerve cord, but a protective structure that develops around it, the vertebral column. The anterior (top) part of the vertebrate nerve cord undergoes tremendous development, becoming the brain.

The pharyngeal slits you see in the lancelet in Figure 22.27 take on more meaning when you remember that, in both humans and lancelets, the pharynx is a passageway just behind the mouth that can be thought of as the first chamber of the digestive tract. Pharyngeal *slits*, then, are perforations of the pharynx, and these serve different functions in different chordates. In the filter-feeding lancelets, they serve to trap food. Meanwhile, in embryonic fish, the slits *develop into* gills, which fish use to obtain oxygen. And in people? If you look at a month-old human embryo, you can see a series of pharyngeal clefts that for a time have openings in them. These pharyngeal slits, however, develop not into gills but into various other structures, including the space inside the middle ear.

Finally, what about that tail? If you look at **Figure 22.28**, you can see an 8-week-old human embryo with a very clearly developed tail. By the

(a) Human embryo tail at eight weeks

tail

(b) Human embryo tail at ten weeks

Figure 22.28
The Human Tail
(a) Eight weeks after conception, the human embryo has a very clearly developed tail.
(b) Two weeks later, the tail has almost disappeared. In adult humans the only vestige of our embryonic tail is a small bone at the base of the vertebral column, the coccyx.

time the embryo is 10 weeks old, however, the tail has almost disappeared. All chordates have a tail at some point. In our oceangoing ancestors, it was used to help move them through the water, as is the case with modern fish. In human adults, though, all that remains of our embryonic tails is a small bone, called the coccyx, located at the base of our vertebral column.

Diversity among the Vertebrates

For the remainder of the chapter, we'll concentrate on the vertebrates among the chordates. The evolutionary relationships among these vertebrates were covered in Chapter 19. For a summary of which animals gave rise to which others, see Figure 19.17 on page 385.

A signal shift in vertebrate evolution came with the development of a very familiar feature: jaws. There is general agreement that ancient, jawless vertebrates gave rise to the jawed variety. The development of jaws is considered perhaps the single most important event in vertebrate history, for it gave the vertebrates a great power to capture prey, carry offspring, and generally interact with the world in more effective ways. So useful was this feature that today all true vertebrates have jaws—with one exception.

A Jawless Vertebrate

The lamprey is a long, thin animal that looks something like an eel, but it should not be confused with one. Eels are fish, complete with jaws; lampreys, by contrast, have a sucking disk at their anterior end with which they attach themselves to their prey, which are usually fish (**see Figure 22.29**). The lamprey's oral disk has numerous teeth around its edge. It combines these teeth with a rasping tongue to pierce the flesh of its prey. It then hangs on to the victim through suction, continuing to rasp away, ingesting the fluids and flesh that it obtains in this way.

Lampreys are best known in the United States as a destructive force in the Great Lakes. Once confined to the eastern Great Lakes, parasitic lampreys were able to move west by the mid-twentieth century thanks to human alteration of a canal around Niagara Falls. By the 1950s, they had decimated a once-thriving trout fishing industry in the western Great Lakes. Human efforts to kill off lampreys while reintroducing trout have had only limited success. The main culprit seems to be human pollution, which is keeping stocked trout from reproducing.

Fish: Cartilaginous and Bony

All the early jawed vertebrates were fish, which today are a big success story in the vertebrate world. Of the 50,000 vertebrate species, more than half are fish. And of the 25,000 or so fish species, more than 24,000 are so-called bony fishes, whose name tells their story: with a couple of exceptions, their skeletons are made of bone. Another 750 fish species are cartilaginous fishes, meaning their skeletons are made of the more pliable connective tissue, called cartilage, that also gives shape to human ears.

By far the best-known cartilaginous fish are sharks, but not far behind are the graceful rays that seem to fly through the ocean (**see Figure 22.30**). The sharks' reputation for being an ancient life-form is well deserved. Their lineage dates back more than 350 million years; hence, they had been around for 130 million years by the time the first dinosaurs ap-

Figure 22.29
No Jaws, Powerful Predator
Lampreys, such as the one shown here, are jawless fish. Note the lamprey's sucking oral disk, which it uses to latch onto and then parasitize prey. This sea lamprey, *Petromyzon marinus*, is the species that, thanks to human intervention, was able to invade the western Great Lakes in the mid-twentieth century. It remains there today, although in smaller numbers than before.

Figure 22.30
Cartilaginous Fish
Sharks and rays, such as the giant manta ray shown here, have cartilaginous, rather than bony skeletons. The ancient cartilaginous fishes represent only about 3 percent of all fish species. This ray and its accompanying diver were photographed off the coast of Mexico.

peared. Unlike most of their bony fish relatives, sharks have no **swim bladder**, which is an inflatable organ in a fish that the fish can fill with gas for optimum buoyancy. Fish that do have swim bladders can inflate them as needed to maintain a neutral buoyancy—that is, to float in the water at a given depth without expending any energy. By contrast, a shark must keep swimming or it will sink.

Sharks, rays, and their close kin aside, all the rest of the fish world is made up of bony fish, from goldfish to tuna to herring (**see Figure 22.31**). What accounts for their great numbers today? Their basic body plan seems to have allowed them to adapt to every kind of underwater environment. Some have evolved a slender shape (eels), others a fantastic camouflage (anglerfish), and still others a biological "antifreeze" for frigid waters (the Antarctic icefish).

Almost all bony fish are so-called "ray-finned" fishes, so named because their dorsal fins are supported by straight-line structures that look like rays (see Figure 22.31). Four surviving species of bony fishes belong to another category, however, the lobed-finned fishes. These fish are important because it is their ancestors who brought vertebrates onto the land by struggling out of the swamps some 375 million years ago, using their muscular, lobed fins to propel themselves. Their lobed *fins* evolved into the four *limbs* of the **tetrapods**, meaning the four-limbed vertebrates (see Figure 19.16 on page 384 for this transition). All land vertebrates are tetrapods: amphibians, reptiles, birds, and mammals. Even snakes and whales are tetrapods; these animals simply lost the limbs their ancestors had. If you look at **Figure 22.32**, you can see a picture of one of the rare, living lobe-finned fish, the coelacanth (SEE-la-kanth).

Figure 22.32
Lobe-finned Fish
One of the few living lobe-finned (rather than ray-finned) fish is the coelacanth, which was first discovered in modern times in the Indian Ocean near Madagascar. A fish similar to this one is thought to be the ancestor of all land vertebrates. Note its four fleshy, lobed fins. Fins such as these evolved, in the lobe-finned ancestors, into the four limbs of land vertebrates.

Amphibians: At Home in Two Worlds

Amphibians were the first truly terrestrial vertebrates, having evolved from lobe-finned fishes, but this statement needs qualification. Are amphibians really land animals? Most of them actually live in two worlds—land and water. (Their very name means "double life.") If you look at **Figure 22.33** on the next page, you can see the life cycle of the best-known amphibian, the frog.

Even adult frogs must live in environments that are at least moist, because water can evaporate right through their skin. But frog offspring are fully aquatic for a time. They hatch from eggs that must be laid in water lest they dry out, and most young frogs spend the first part of their lives as swimming tadpoles. There are exceptions to the rule that amphibians must remain near standing water. Some frogs have become fully terrestrial, but even they must inhabit moist environments.

Apart from frogs, there are two other varieties of amphibians: salamanders and newts, collectively known as the tailed amphibians; and some wormlike, tropical amphibians known as caecilians. Salamanders may look like lizards, but their watery amphibian heritage betrays them. With some exceptions, they must live where it is moist, a fact that often keeps them hidden from human view.

Amphibians once were the dominant land animals; indeed, they were the only land vertebrates for some 75 million years. But about 250 million years ago they ceded their dominant status to the very group that evolved from them, the reptiles.

Reptiles and Birds

It may seem strange to lump reptiles and birds together, but remember that scientific classification

Figure 22.31
Bony, Ray-finned Fish
About 97 percent of fish species have bony (rather than cartilaginous) skeletons, and of the bony fish, almost all are "ray-finned," meaning that their dorsal fins are supported by stiff rays such as the ones visible on this yellowtail parrotfish, *Sparisoma rubripinne.*

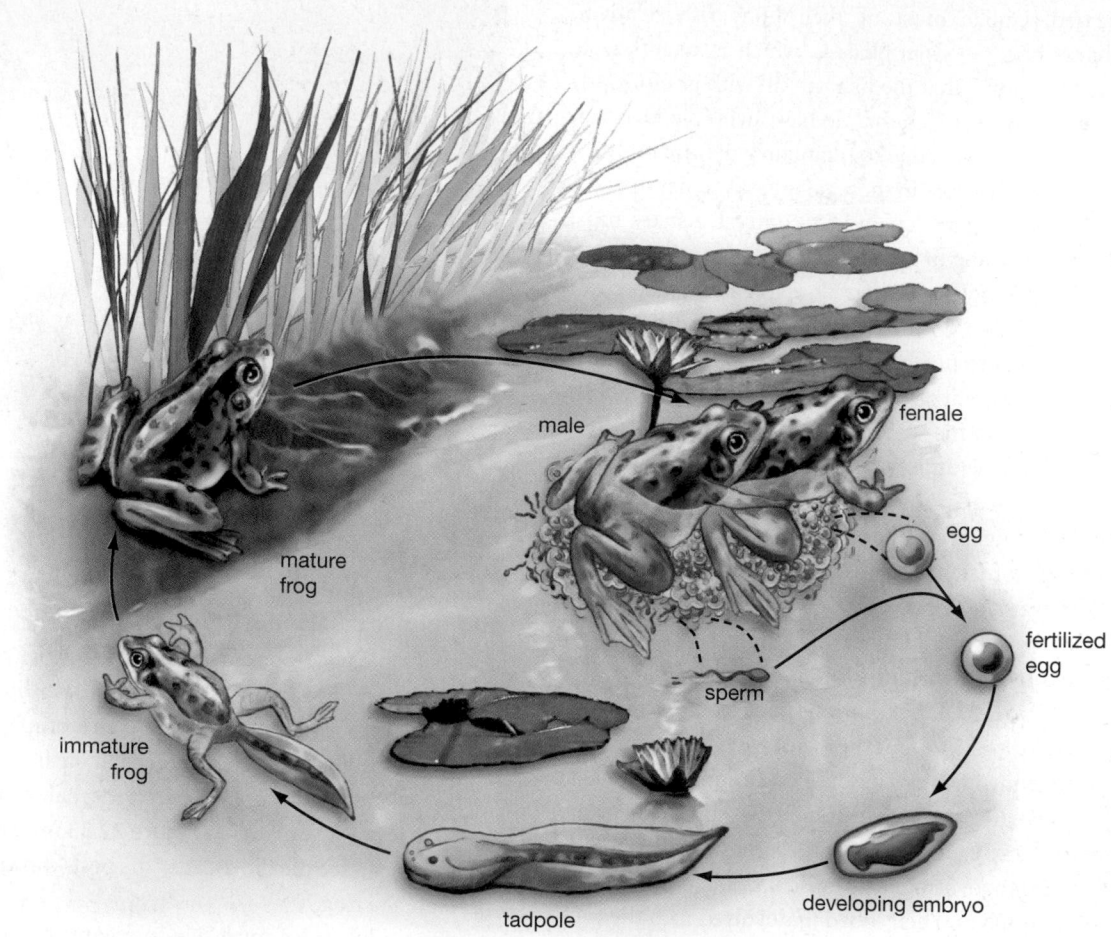

Figure 22.33
Amphibian Life Cycle
Amphibians (such as frogs, sala-manders, and newts) require an aquatic, or at least moist, environment for at least part of their life cycle. Note the female frog in the figure is laying her eggs into the water. The male then releases sperm that falls on the eggs, fertilizing them. Most frogs dwell solely in the water through much of their development, first as embryos, then as tadpoles.

has mostly to do with shared ancestry. There is general agreement that birds are the direct descendants of the reptiles we know as dinosaurs. If so, then the separate categories of "bird" and "reptile" make sense mostly in terms of describing *features* of the two kinds of animals.

One seemingly innocuous feature unites all reptiles and birds, but it is a feature that had far-reaching consequences. If you look at **Figure 22.34**, you can see an illustration of something known as the **amniotic egg**, named after a membrane (called an amnion) that aids the embryo inside of the egg. Recall that most amphibians must lay their eggs in water, lest the eggs dry out and the embryos inside them perish. The amniotic egg of reptiles and birds is different; it can be laid in environments ranging from moist forest floor to desert. Its tough shell keeps the egg from drying out, and the various membranes within it protect the embryo. The amniotic egg therefore gave reptiles a tremendous advantage over the amphibians in the kinds of locations the reptiles could call home; unlike the amphibians, reptiles could settle away from the water.

Characteristics of Reptiles

Several other things distinguish reptiles from amphibians. Looking back at the frog life cycle in Figure 22.33, you can see that the female frog lays her eggs in the water, after which the male spreads his sperm on top of them. This is external fertilization. By contrast, all reptiles employ internal fertil-

Figure 22.34
An Egg for Many Environments
The amniotic egg was an evolutionary development that allowed vertebrates to move inland from the water. The egg's features meant that, in dry environments, the embryo would not "desiccate" or perish through a loss of fluids. The egg's tough shell is the first line of defense; it limits evaporation of fluids. The amnion is one of several membranes that provide some cushioning protection for the embryo. The allantois serves as a repository site for the embryo's waste products. The chorion provides cushioning protection and works with the allantois in gas exchange, meaning the movement of oxygen to the embryo and the movement of carbon dioxide away from it. The yolk sac provides the nutrients the embryo will need as it develops.

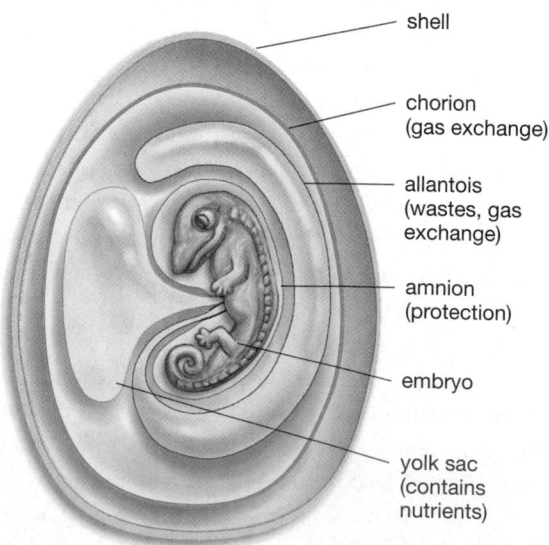

shell

chorion
(gas exchange)

allantois
(wastes, gas exchange)

amnion
(protection)

embryo

yolk sac
(contains nutrients)

(a) Green turtle

(b) Tree python

(c) American crocodile

Figure 22.35
Reptile Diversity
The three main groups of modern-day reptiles are the turtles, the lizards and snakes, and the crocodiles and alligators. Although some of these animals live in water, their scaly skin and amniotic eggs free them from dependency on it.

(a) This green turtle (*Chelonia mydas*) is swimming in the Red Sea.

(b) A newborn green tree python (*Chondropython viridis*) in New Guinea. It will change into its adult color in 6 to 8 months.

(c) American crocodiles such as this one (*Crocodylus acutus*) are found in far-southern Florida, through the Caribbean, Central America, and northern South America.

ization—eggs are fertilized inside the female's body. A requirement for this, of course, is that males possess a copulatory organ that allows sperm to be deposited inside the female. Another difference between amphibians and reptiles is that reptiles have a tough, scaly skin that conserves water, as opposed to the thin amphibian skin that allows water to escape. Reptiles also have a stronger skeleton than amphibians, more efficient lungs, and a better-developed nervous system.

There are three main varieties of modern-day reptiles: lizards and snakes; crocodiles and alligators; and turtles (**see Figure 22.35**). Then there is an ancient, extinct variety of reptiles that is as well known as the living examples. The dinosaurs first appeared about 220 million years ago and were certainly the most fearsome creatures ever to have walked on land. The last of them died out 65 million years ago.

Characteristics of Birds

Surprising as it may seem, one view is that "dinosaurs," properly defined, never did die out, but live on in their descendants, the birds. Indeed, many evolutionary specialists routinely think of birds as "avian dinosaurs." Two lines of evidence have convinced most scientists that birds descended from a line of bipedal (two-footed), meat-eating dinosaurs. One line concerns bone similarity. Long, S-shaped necks, types of hip bones, relative leg sizes. Only dinosaurs and birds share this list of characteristics. Second, there is the famous crow-sized fossil *Archaeopteryx*— a clear "transitional form" between dinosaurs and birds that had the dinosaur's teeth and claws, but the bird's feathers (**see Figure 22.36**). In the 1990s, scientists began filling in the transitional gaps on the other side, unearthing fossils of dinosaurs that were flightless but nevertheless had feathers.

Figure 22.36
Dinosaur and Bird
Scientists believe that this fossil, called *Archaeopteryx*, represents a transitional form between dinosaurs and birds. It has the teeth and claws of a dinosaur, but the feathers of a bird. The drawing at right is an artist's interpretation of the fossil at left.

Birds are a vertebrate success. They exist all over the globe in great numbers, and their 9,100 recognized species exceeds the number of reptile species (7,000) or amphibian species (4,300). Though there are obvious differences between an eagle and a hummingbird, all flying birds have a very similar appearance. By contrast, think how different snakes are from crocodiles among the reptiles, or frogs are from salamanders among the amphibians. The similarity among birds is a consequence of the strict requirements of vertebrate flight: light, hollow bones, wings, and powerful flight muscles that attach to a breastbone (**see Figure 22.37**). All birds use their own metabolism to maintain a relatively stable internal temperature—a quality called *endothermy* that we'll review shortly in connection with our last major grouping of animals.

Mammals: Small Numbers, Big Impact

The story of mammals could be titled "Big Effects from a Small Group." There are only about 4,400 species of mammals—not even half the number of bird species, and scarcely more than the number of amphibian species. The total number of *individual* mammals is infinitesimal compared to the number of insects or roundworms. Yet it's the mammals that are the biggest creatures not only on land (the elephants) but in the sea (the whales). It's the mammals that are the fiercest creatures from the savanna (lions) to the arctic ice (polar bears). And, of course, it's the mammals, in the form of humans, who control the fate of so much of the rest of the living world.

But what is a mammal? Here are two mammal universals and two near-universals. All mammals have mammary glands and maintain a near-constant internal temperature. Most mammals have hair and have eggs that develop inside their mother's body. Here's some detail on each of these characteristics.

Mammals are named for the **mammary glands** that all of them possess: a set of glands that, in females, provide milk for the young. Next, almost all mammals have hair, while no other animals have it. This feature is related to another universal mammal characteristic, which is that mammals are **endothermic**: their internal body temperature is relatively stable and their body heat is generated internally—by their own metabolism. Conversely, amphibians and reptiles are **ectothermic**, meaning their internal temperature is controlled largely by the temperature of their environment.

Endothermy, sometimes misleadingly called warm-bloodedness, is rare in the animal world. In fact, other than mammals, the only creatures to possess it are birds. Endothermy and ectothermy are very important in determining which creature will live where in the animal world. After a cold night in the desert, the muscles of a lizard cannot function at full capacity until that lizard has warmed itself in the sun. By contrast, a desert rat is as functional at sunrise as it is at sunset. But there is a price to be paid for its readiness, and that price is energy expenditure. It takes a great deal of energy to maintain the constant, relatively high body temperatures of mammals and birds. Pound per pound, the "basal" or resting metabolic rate of a rat may be four times that of a lizard. And it takes food to fuel this energy expenditure. The upshot is that, pound per pound, mammals and birds simply have to eat more than reptiles or amphibians.

The very quality of being able to maintain a stable body temperature has, however, allowed mammals to live where amphibians and reptiles

(a) Heron

(b) Bald eagle

Figure 22.37
Bird Similarity
Despite the obvious differences between the heron on the left and the bald eagle on the right, there are great similarities in the birds as well. Indeed, all flying birds display a similarity in body form. This is so because animals as large as birds must meet a strict set of requirements in order to fly. All birds have thin, hollow bones, tails to stabilize their flight, and powerful flight muscles that originate on their breastbone or sternum.

cannot—in cold climates. Consider the fact that there are arctic hares, arctic foxes, and arctic birds, but there are no arctic lizards or frogs. Past a certain point, north or south on the globe, there is no place a lizard can go to warm its body enough to live. Mammals have their limits as well, but the range of climates they can adapt to is greater. Their hair is a great aid in maintaining temperature, as is the thick layer of fat that lies just beneath the skin of such creatures as whales and seals.

With two important exceptions, mammals are **viviparous**: a condition in which fertilized eggs develop inside a mother's body. Contrast this with the **oviparous** condition, seen in all birds and many reptiles, in which fertilized eggs are laid outside the mother's body and then develop there. All embryos need nutrients and protection. In egg-laying (oviparous) animals, both things are provided by the egg itself (though parents also may provide protection). Conversely, a human egg (and then embryo) is protected by the mother's body and draws its nutrients directly from the mother in ways we'll look at shortly.

Reproduction turns out to be the defining feature of the three evolutionary lines of mammals: the monotremes, the marsupials, and the placental mammals (**see Figure 22.38**). **Monotremes** are egg-laying mammals, represented by the duck-billed platypus and spiny anteaters found in Australia. The monotremes do nourish their young on milk from mammary glands, but they have no nipples; thus the young must lap up the milk that diffuses onto the hair of the mother.

Marsupials are mammals in which the young develop within the mother to a limited extent, inside an egg that has a membranous shell. Marsupials are represented by several Australian animals, including the kangaroo, and by several animals in the Western Hemisphere, including the North American opossum. Early in development, the egg's membrane disappears, and in a few days time, a developmentally immature but active marsupial is delivered from the mother. In the case of a kangaroo, the tiny youngster has just enough capacity to climb up its mother's body, into her "pouch," and begin suckling from a nipple there. We can think of the kangaroo as developing partly inside its mother's reproductive tract, and partly inside her pouch.

All other mammals are known as **placental mammals**. They are mammals nurtured before birth by the **placenta**; a network of maternal and embryonic blood vessels and membranes that allows nutrients and oxygen to diffuse *to* the embryo from the mother while allowing embryonic wastes to diffuse *from* the embryo to the mother. (For more on the placenta, see Chapter 30, page 665.) Thus, in placental mammals, the embryonic young derive their nutrition not from food stored in an egg, but directly from the circulation of the mother. Further, the embryos of placental mammals can develop for a very long time inside the mother. The human gestation period—the time from conception to birth—is about nine months, and in elephants it is almost two years. By contrast, the gestation time for a kangaroo is about a month, after which its "pouch life" might last six months.

The diversity of the placental mammals is impressive. There are flying mammals (bats), swimming ocean behemoths (whales, dolphins, and so forth), all manner of large herbivores (horses, deer,

Figure 22.38
Mammal Diversity
All mammals have mammary glands that provide milk for their young. However, mammals differ in their reproductive strategies.

(a) This duck-billed platypus is a monotreme—a mammal that lays eggs.

(b) Kangaroos are marsupials—they give birth to physically immature young, which then develop further within the mother's pouch. Pictured are a mother and her fairly mature "joey" in eastern Australia.

(c) The young of placental mammals, such as this grizzly bear (*Ursus arctos*), develop to a relatively advanced state inside the mother, with nutrients supplied not by an egg, but by a network of blood vessels and membranes, the placenta.

(b) Marsupial

(a) Monotreme

(c) Placental mammal

Table 22.1 Animal Phyla

Phylum	Members include	Live in	Characteristics
Porifera	Sponges	Ocean water (marine), with a few living in fresh water	Sessile (fixed in one spot) as adults, no symmetry. System of pores through which water flows serves to capture nutrients. Bodies do not have organs or tissues. Sexual and asexual reproduction.
Cnidaria	Jellyfish, hydrozoans, sea anemones, coral animals	Almost all marine; a few in fresh water	Radial symmetry, medusa (swimming) and polyp (largely sessile) stages of life. Use stinging tentacles to capture prey. Have tissues. Can reproduce sexually or by budding.
Platyhelminthes	Flatworms (flukes, tapeworms, turbellarians)	Marine, fresh water, or moist terrestrial environments	Bilateral symmetry, hermaphroditic, possess organs, no central cavity, most primitive animals with triploblastic tissue structure. Many are parasites. Can reproduce by dividing themselves.
Annelida	Segmented worms	Most are marine, some fresh water and moist terrestrial	Distinct body segmentation in varieties such as earthworms. Leeches are annelids.
Mollusca	Gastropods (snails, slugs), bivalves (oysters, clams, mussels), cephalopods (octopus, squid, nautilus)	Marine, fresh water, moist terrestrial	Mantle that can secrete material that becomes shell; mantle cavity housing gills or lungs; unitary foot (lost in some sessile species, evolved into arms and tentacles in cephalopods).
Nematoda	Roundworms	Almost all environments	Small size in most, but some are several meters long. Many are crop pests, others animal parasites. Possess pseudocoelom. Reproduction always sexual.
Arthropoda	Vast group that includes insects, spiders, mites, crabs, shrimp, and centipedes	Many aquatic and terrestrial environments	External skeleton made of chitin; jointed, bilateral appendages; molting in many species; segmented bodies; generally an open circulation system.
Echinodermata	Sea stars, sea urchins, sea cucumbers	Always marine, most on ocean floor	Generally have radial symmetry as adults; tube feet in some species, slow ocean floor movement in most.
Chordata	Vertebrates, lancelets, sea squirts	Great variety of aquatic and terrestrial environments	At some point, all possess notochord, dorsal nerve cord, pharyngeal slits, post-anal tail. Vertebrates have vertebral column.

cows) and smaller herbivores (rodents, which make up more than half of all mammal species). Then, of course, there are the primates such as ourselves, defined by our forward-facing eyes, grasping hands, and arboreal or tree-dwelling habitat. Several species of primates, including our own, have come down from the trees to dwell on the ground (see Chapter 19, page 386). **Table 22.1** summarizes all of the animal phyla reviewed in this chapter.

On to Plants

In life's family tree, the animals you've just looked at are far removed from plants. Yet animals and plants are alike in one sense, in that they sit atop two great evolutionary lines. Plants occupy the higher branches of the line of "self-feeders": the *autotrophs* who make their own food by harnessing the power of the sun. The first creatures who performed this feat were bacteria; then came the algae (which are protists). And then, evolving from the algae, came the plants, moving onto land and constructing their green edifice wherever they took root, thereby providing food and shade for all animals that came after them. In a sense, this sequence of events describes the relationship that animals and plants have: Plants first, then animals. In a world without plants, there would be no land animals, but in a world without land animals, there would still be plants. The two chapters coming up describe the nature of the indispensable, green members of the living world, the plants.

Chapter Review

Summary

22.1 What Is an Animal?

- A single physical feature is sufficient to define animals. All animals pass through a blastula stage in embryonic development, but no other living things do. A blastula is a hollow, fluid-filled ball of cells that forms once an egg is fertilized by sperm.

- Three other features are characteristic of all animals, but also are shared, to varying degrees, by members of other kingdoms in the living world. All animals are multicelled, are heterotrophs (they cannot make their own food), and are composed of cells that do not have cell walls.

22.2 Animal Types: The Family Tree

- The animal kingdom is divided into large-scale categories called phyla. There are between 36 and 41 animal phyla, each phylum being a group of organisms that share a set of physical characteristics that result from shared ancestry.

- Animals can be thought of as having evolved from simpler to more complex forms through a series of additions to the characteristics found in more primitive animals. These additions are tissues, radial symmetry, bilateral symmetry, and an enclosed body cavity or coelom.

- A fundamental split in animal evolution came with the divergence of the protostome and deuterostome animal lines. Protostome animals include flatworms, roundworms, molluscs, annelid worms, and arthropods; deuterostome animals include echinoderms and chordates.

  Web Tutorial 22.1: The Animal Family Tree

22.3 Phylum Porifera: The Sponges

- Sponges are simple animals, lacking organs, tissues, or symmetry. Nearly all sponges live in marine environments, though there are a few fresh water varieties.

- Sponges live by drawing water into themselves through a series of tiny pores on their exterior, and then filtering this water for food.

- Sponges can reproduce sexually, with eggs and sperm carried from one sponge to another by water currents; or they can produce asexually, through budding.

22.4 Phylum Cnidaria: Jellyfish and Others

- The defining characteristic of members of phylum Cnidaria is their use of stinging tentacles to capture prey.

- Cnidarians include jellyfish, sea anemones, hydras, and the reef-building coral animals whose skeletons make up the bulk of coral reefs.

- Many cnidarians have both an adult, medusa stage of life, which swims in the water; and an immature, polyp stage of life, which generally remains fixed to rocks, animals, or other solid surfaces. Some cnidarians have only the polyp stage. Cnidarians have no organs, but they do have tissues.

- Cnidarians have radial symmetry, and reproduction can be sexual or asexual.

22.5 Phylum Platyhelminthes: Flatworms

- The flatworms of phylum Platyhelminthes are mostly small creatures, dwelling either in aquatic or moist terrestrial environments. Some parasitic flatworm species can, however, reach enormous lengths.

- Flatworms have bilateral symmetry, but have no coelom or system of blood circulation. They have no anus, meaning the flatworm's mouth is the single opening to its digestive system.

- Flatworms are the least complex animals to be triploblastic. They have three embryonic germ layers—endoderm, mesoderm, and ectoderm—whereas cnidarians lack a mesoderm and are therefore diploblastic.

- Most flatworms are hermaphroditic—a single flatworm is likely to possess both male and female sex organs. Many flatworms can reproduce asexually by breaking themselves in half.

- Parasitic tapeworms, which can infect human beings, are flatworms, as are the flukes that cause the disease schistosomiasis.

22.6 Phylum Annelida: Segmented Worms

- The worms of phylum Annelida provide a clear example of a physical feature that is widespread in the animal kingdom, body segmentation, meaning a repetition of body parts in an animal. Segmentation is generally valuable because it provides both flexibility and strength.

- Earthworms are representative of the annelid or segmented worms; earthworm bodies display a clear segmentation, allowing the worm to exercise a degree of independent control over each segment or group of segments.

- Most annelids are marine, and some dwell in freshwater. All annelids exist in environments that are at least moist. Leeches are parasitic annelid worms.

22.7 Phylum Mollusca: Snails, Oysters, Squid, and More

- Phylum Mollusca is an extremely varied group of animals whose members range from sessile, brainless mussels to agile, intelligent squid. Mollusc habitats range from marine and freshwater to moist terrestrial.

- Three important classes of molluscs are the gastropods, which include snails and slugs; the bivalves, which include oysters, clams, and mussels; and the cephalopods, which include octopus, squid, and nautilus.

- All molluscs possess a fold of skin-like tissue, called a mantle, that usually secretes material that forms a shell, though many molluscs do not have shells. Molluscs tend to have a mantle cavity that houses either gills (if the molluscs are aquatic) or lungs (if they are terrestrial); many have a unitary foot, whose wave-like contractions allow movement. Many molluscs have a tooth-lined membrane called a radula that can be extended outside the body for scraping and retrieving food.

- Cephalopods have a closed circulation system, in which blood stays within blood vessels, while oxygen and nutrients diffuse out of the vessels to the surrounding tissues. Most molluscs have an open circulation system, in which blood flows out of blood vessels into openings called sinuses, where the blood bathes tissues.

22.8 Phylum Nematoda: Roundworms

- The roundworms of phylum Nematoda exist in enormous numbers in all kinds of habitats on Earth. Most are microscopic, though some are large.

- A number of roundworms are agricultural pests, and some are human parasites. The disease trichinosis is caused by roundworms, and the parasites known as hookworms are roundworms.

- Roundworms are the least complex animals to possess an enclosed cavity—technically a pseudocoel instead of a true coelom. Their reproduction is always sexual, and they are not hermaphroditic.

22.9 Phylum Arthropoda: Insects, Lobsters, Spiders, and More

- Phylum Arthropoda is enormous and extremely varied. There are more species in one class of arthropods, the insects, than there are in all the other groupings of animals combined.

- Arthropods can be divided into three subphyla: Uniramia, which includes millipedes and centipedes along with insects; Chelicerata, which includes spiders, ticks, mites, and horseshoe crabs; and Crustacea, which includes shrimp, lobsters, crabs, and barnacles. All arthropods have an external skeleton or exoskeleton, and paired, jointed appendages. Arthropods go through molting, meaning the periodic shedding of an old exoskeleton.

- Members of the subphylum Uniramia include the insects, which have bodies divided into three sections: head, thorax, and abdomen. They have an open circulation system, sexes are separate, and reproduction is generally sexual. Centipedes and millipedes make up the two other classes of Uniramians.

- All members of subphylum Crustacea have five pairs of appendages extending from their heads—two pairs of antennae and three pairs of feeding appendages. Crustaceans range from large lobsters to microscopic water fleas.

- All members of subphylum Chelicerata have in common a pair of appendages, called chelicerae, that serve various feeding functions—grasping in horseshoe crabs, for example, and puncturing in spiders.

22.10 Phylum Echinodermata: Sea Stars, Sea Urchins, and More

- Echinoderms include sea stars, sea urchins, sand dollars, and sea cucumbers, among others. All members of phylum Echinodermata are marine, and most inhabit the ocean floor.

- Echinoderms have a radial symmetry as adults. The sea stars among them evolved to this condition from bilateral symmetry; sea star larvae have a bilateral symmetry that is lost as they develop into adults. Sea stars have no brain and only one sensory organ, the primitive eyespots on the tips of their arms. A new sea star can be generated asexually from the arm and part of the central disk of an existing sea star.

- Echinoderms tend to move slowly across the sea floor; but many are formidable predators, often feeding on such molluscs as oysters or mussels.

22.11 Phylum Chordata: Mostly Animals with Backbones

- Phylum Chordata is made up of three subphyla: Vertebrata, which includes all the vertebrates, including human beings; Cephalochordata, made up of creatures called lancelets; and Urochordata, made up of three classes of animals, including the tunicates or sea squirts. Only the vertebrates have a vertebral column, meaning a flexible column of bones running from the anterior to posterior ends of an animal.

- All chordates possess, at some point in their lives, a rod-shaped support structure called a notochord; a nerve cord on their dorsal side; a post-anal tail; and a series of pharyngeal slits that develop into various structures, depending on the type of chordate.

- With the exception of lampreys, all true vertebrates have jaws. Today's jawed vertebrates developed from ancient jawless vertebrates.

- Fish account for more than half the 50,000 species of vertebrates, with the vast majority of fish being bony fish, as opposed to the more ancient line of cartilaginous fishes, such as sharks, whose skeletons are made of the connective tissue cartilage.

- Most bony fish are ray-finned fishes, named after the ray-like structures in their dorsal fins. Four species of fish belong to another category of fish, the lobe-finned fishes. These fish are important because an ancient variety of them is thought to have given rise to all tetrapods, meaning four-limbed vertebrates. All land vertebrates are tetrapods: amphibians, reptiles, birds, and mammals.

- Amphibians were the first terrestrial vertebrates. Today amphibians include frogs; the tailed amphibians, salamanders and newts; and some wormlike amphibians known as caecilians. All amphibians must live in environments that are at least moist, most employ external fertilization of eggs, and most live in aquatic environments for part of their lives.

- Reptiles evolved from amphibians. An important feature in their evolution was the development of the amniotic egg, which can keep embryos moist even in dry environments. The amniotic egg allowed the reptiles to move inland from water sources. Reptiles employ internal fertilization and have a tough, scaly skin that conserves water. There are three main varieties of modern-day reptiles: turtles, lizards and snakes, and crocodiles and alligators. Dinosaurs were reptiles.

- Most scientists believe that birds are the direct descendants of dinosaurs. Birds exist all over the globe in great numbers. The similar appearance of all flying birds stems from the strict requirements of flight for creatures as large as vertebrates: light bones, wings, and powerful flight muscles that attach to a breastbone. All birds are endothermic: their internal body temperature is relatively stable and body heat is generated internally, by their own metabolism. Conversely, amphibians and reptiles are ectothermic: their internal temperature is controlled largely by the temperature of their environment. Birds and mammals are the only true endothermic animals.

- Though there are relatively few mammal species, mammals have had a great impact on the natural world. They account for the largest creatures on land and sea, and one species of mammal, human beings, controls the fate of much of the living world.

- All mammals have mammary glands, meaning glands that deliver milk to the young. Most mammals have hair, and their fertilized eggs develop inside the mother's body (making them viviparous). There are three evolutionary lines of mammals: the monotremes, which are egg-laying (or oviparous) mammals, represented by the platypus; marsupials, in which the young develop within the mother only to a limited extent, represented by kangaroos; and placentals, in which young are nourished within the mother through a placenta, represented by most of world's mammals.

Key Terms

amniotic egg 470

bilateral symmetry 448

bivalves 458

body segmentation 456

cephalopods 458

closed circulation system 459

coelom 450

diploblastic 456

dorsal nerve cord 467

ectothermic 472

endothermic 472

exoskeleton 460

gastropods 458

hermaphroditic 456

invertebrate 446

mammary glands 472

marsupial 473

molting 461

monotreme 473

notochord 467

organ 455

open circulation 459

oviparous 473

paired, jointed appendages 460

parasite 455

pharyngeal slits 467

phylum 447

placenta 473

placental mammal 473

post-anal tail 467

radial symmetry 448

swim bladder 469

symmetry 448

tetrapods 469

tissue 446

triploblastic 456

vertebral column 467

viviparous 473

zoologist 447

Understanding the Basics

Multiple-Choice Questions (answers in the back of the book)

1. All animals (select all that apply)
   a. go through a blastula stage in development
   b. have cells that lack cell walls
   c. are multicelled
   d. are heterotrophs
   e. all of the above

2. Bilateral symmetry is a condition in which
   a. no one animal species can overpower another
   b. the top and bottom halves of an animal are symmetrical
   c. two animal species evolve along parallel lines
   d. one side of an animal is symmetrical to the other
   e. one side of an animal is as strong as the other

3. A coelom is
   a. an enclosed body cavity, not found in sponges, cnidarians, or flatworms
   b. an enclosed body cavity, found only in deuterostomes
   c. a digestive organ, found in all animals except sponges
   d. an evolutionary offshoot of a species
   e. an offspring that arises from asexual reproduction

4. An animal has bilateral symmetry, but no coelom. What phylum is it in?
   a. Mollusca
   b. Cnidaria
   c. Chordata
   d. Porifera
   e. Platyhelminthes

5. Only _____ are endothermic, a physiological condition whose chief direct cost is _____.
   a. cephalopods and mammals; a short life-span
   b. cephalopods and echinoderms; smaller size
   c. mammals and birds; increased energy expenditure
   d. reptiles and amphibians; cold-induced lethargy
   e. mammals and birds; fewer offspring

6. A marine animal with radial symmetry goes through both medusa and polyp stages in its life cycle. Which of the following features is it certain not to have? (Select all that apply.)
   a. a brain
   b. a heart
   c. a coelom
   d. legs
   e. a mouth

7. The world's largest invertebrates, the _____, always _____.
   a. crustaceans; have exoskeletons
   b. echinoderms; have radial symmetry
   c. cephalopods; are single-sex
   d. chordates; have a post-anal tail
   e. cephalopods; are filter feeders

8. In earthworms, we can see a clear example of the widespread animal feature known as
   a. filter feeding
   b. body segmentation
   c. viviparous reproduction
   d. a post-anal tail
   e. a radula

9. Which of the following is not a physical feature of all vertebrates at some point in their lives? (Select all that apply.)
   a. pharyngeal slits
   b. a vertebral column
   c. a ventral nerve cord
   d. a post-anal tail
   e. a mantle cavity

10. If an animal has an exoskeleton, paired jointed appendages, and goes through the process of molting, it is:
    a. a bivalve
    b. a gastropod
    c. a tetrapod
    d. an arthropod
    e. a chordate

Brief Review

1. A coelom amounts to internal space in an animal. Why is such a feature valuable?

2. Do all animals have a single ancestor, or do the different phyla of animals have different ancestors? What evidence supports your answer?

3. What are the benefits and the costs of endothermy? What animals are endothermic?

4. Why is it fair to characterize sponges as "primitive" animals?

5. What is a coral reef chiefly composed of?

6. What feature common to molluscs was modified through evolution to become the arms and tentacles of the squid?

7. Which animal is a spider more closely related to, a dust mite or a grasshopper?

8. A mother provides milk for her offspring, and yet those offspring are hatched from eggs. What kind of animal is the mother?

Applying Your Knowledge

1. The text notes the tremendous number of insects in the world—both the number of insect species and the number of individual insects. One of the most spectacular examples of insect numbers can be seen in the so-called periodical cicadas, which emerge in the Eastern and Central United States in groups called "broods" after completing an underground larval stage that lasts either 13 or 17 years. One 17-year brood that emerged in 1956 near Chicago was found in densities of 1,500,000 per acre in lowland forests—about 533 tons of cicadas per square mile over their entire range. Biologists often talk of the reproductive "strategies" of various species. These are the traits of a species that help ensure its continued reproduction, generation after generation. What is the reproductive strategy of the periodical cicadas? Does their long underground immature stage aid in this strategy?

2. One of the distinguishing features of animals is that their cells do not have the thick outer lining known as a cell wall. Plant cells have a cell wall, as do fungi cells. Why would such a feature be advantageous for plants, but disadvantageous for animals?

3. Plants can have elaborate defense systems, and they can respond in sophisticated ways to their environment—for example, in preserving resources, they can go into a dormant state in winter. Given this, can plants have intelligence? Or is it only animals that have this trait, to one degree or another?

23 An Introduction to Flowering Plants

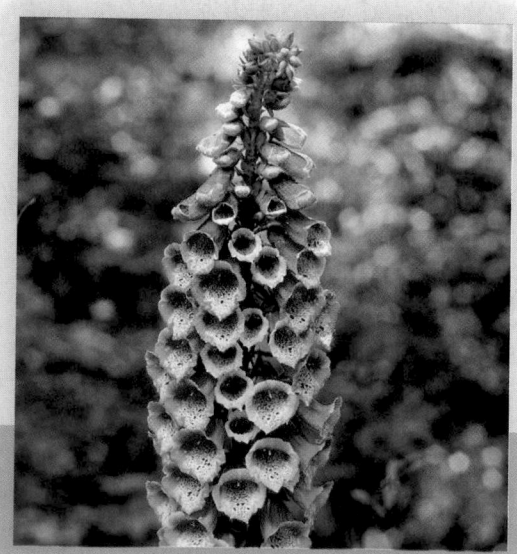

Heart medicine.
(Section 23.1, page 482)

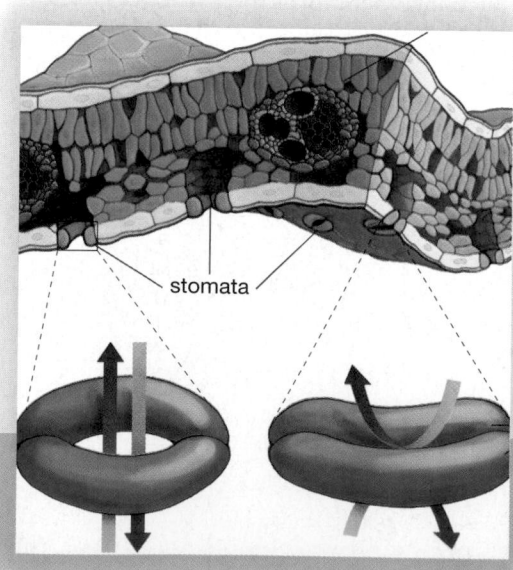

stomata

Guard duty.
(Section 23.2, page 485)

A stem for support, storage, and transport.
(Section 23.2, page 487)

The optometrist has almost completed the examination but would like a better look at the interior of the patient's eyes. Would she agree to have her pupils dilated with the application of a couple of drops to each eye? The patient tilts her head back, and in her pose, it's possible to imagine her as a lady of the Italian Renaissance, lifting her eyes upward and applying to them a few drops of a substance she believes will make her a *bella donna*—a beautiful lady. And what does this substance do? It dilates her eyes just slightly, making her pupils large and entrancing. Spin back further in time to the eleventh century in Scotland where, as legend has it, the Scottish leader Earl Macbeth poisons an invading army of Danish soldiers by lacing their drinks with juice from a plant known as sleepy nightshade. Only later will the English-speaking world call this plant by the name used today: *Atropa belladonna* (**Figure 23.1**). Skip forward to 1831, when scientists isolate from the belladonna plant one of its active ingredients, a compound called atropine. This is the substance that actually dilated the eyes of the Italian ladies and that, at one time, dilated eyes in optometry clinics. Come forward then to the fall of 2002. As the United States is getting ready for war with Iraq, it re-

ceives word that Iraq has ordered a million doses of atropine, along with "auto-injectors" that can be used to administer the drug into the legs. The U.S. is deeply suspicious of this move. Atropine works as an antidote to poison gases; why would Iraq be ordering an antidote to these gases unless it intended to use them as a weapon in the coming war? Doctors note that atropine is routinely employed in medicine, but not in connection with poison gas. In ambulances and emergency rooms, it is used to revive heart-attack victims. An injection of atropine can make an ailing heart beat faster.

Figure 23.1
A Plant that has Served Many Purposes
The flowering plant *Atropa belladonna*

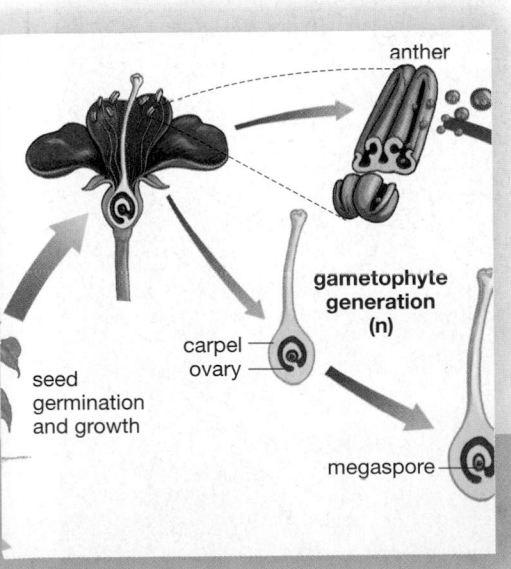

Part of a life cycle.
(Section 23.3, page 489)

The power of light.
(Section 23.4, page 496)

Climbing up by circling around.
(Section 23.4, page 497)

23.1 The Importance of Plants

Like a talented employee, belladonna keeps getting called back to work by human beings. If you were keeping track, we humans have derived, from just this one plant, a poison, an antidote to poison, a cosmetic, an aid to visual diagnosis, and a heart medicine. But that's the way with plants. The number of things they do for human beings is enormous. The best-known thing they do, of course, is provide us with food. But even in this role, their significance is not fully appreciated. In the world today, up to 90 percent of the calories that human beings consume come directly from plants. Indeed, as some botanists have noted, there are about a dozen plants that stand between humanity and starvation. (The most important of these plants is rice, with wheat coming in second.) Plants are able to serve this function because they make their own food through photosynthesis. The bounty they produce through this process has made Earth a planet of *surplus*—a planet of grains and leaves and roots that are available for the taking. Along these same lines, plants also produce much of the oxygen that most living things require. Then there are the products that human beings have learned to derive from plants, among them lumber, medicines, fabrics, fragrances, and dyes (**see Figure 23.2**).

Apart from these uses, plants are a kind of anchoring environmental force. Their roots prevent soil erosion, while their leaves absorb such pollutants as sulfur dioxide and ozone. One of the main greenhouse gases thought to be warming Earth is carbon dioxide, and plants absorb carbon dioxide when they perform photosynthesis. Thus, there is not only a *production* side to atmospheric carbon dioxide—in significant part the pollution human beings produce—there is also a *consumption* side to it, in the amount plants absorb. One proposed way to fight greenhouse warming, therefore, is to plant trees. A single mature maple tree will absorb about 450 kilograms (about 1,000 pounds) of carbon dioxide from the atmosphere over the course of a single summer.

A Focus on Flowering Plants

Though the plant kingdom is vast and varied, it turns out that there are just four principal types of plants in it. These are the bryophytes, represented by mosses; the seedless vascular plants, represented by ferns; the gymnosperms, represented by coniferous (evergreen) trees; and the flowering plants, also known as angiosperms. Chapter 21, which introduced plants, contained information on the bryophytes, the seedless vascular plants, and the gymnosperms. In this chapter, we will focus strictly on flowering plants. Why pay so much attention to just one type of plant? Because of the overwhelming dominance of flowering plants within the plant kingdom. There are about

Figure 23.2
Uses Galore
Plants are used by human beings in innumerable ways.

(a) Food, here in the form of Concord grapes.

(b) Wood, being harvested from a forest in British Columbia.

(c) A foxglove plant, which yields the heart medicine digitalis.

(a)

(b)

(c)

(a)

(b)

(c)

Figure 23.3
Angiosperm Variety
(a) A trumpet vine (*Clytostoma callistegiodes*) spreading on a bush.
(b) A Senita cactus, on the left, stands next to a Saguaro cactus in the Arizona desert.
(c) The cereal grain rye (*Secale*) growing in a field.

16,000 species of bryophytes, 13,000 species of seedless vascular plants, and 700 species of gymnosperms, but there are an estimated 260,000 species of flowering plant. The term "flowering plant" may bring to mind roses or orchids, and these plants are indeed angiosperms. But food crops such as rice and wheat are flowering plants, as are all cacti, almost all the leafy trees, innumerable bushes, pineapple plants, cotton plants and ice plant—the list is very long (**see Figure 23.3**). In this chapter, you'll get an overview of how flowering plants are structured, of how they function internally, and of how they respond to signals from the outside world. Chapter 24 will go into greater detail on angiosperm structure and function. A formal definition of angiosperms will be provided once you've learned a little about them.

23.2 The Structure of Flowering Plants

Let's begin our tour of the angiosperms by looking at their component parts.

The Basic Division: Roots and Shoots

We'll first look at the larger-scale structures of the angiosperms, starting with a simple, two-part division that rhymes: roots and shoots. Plants live in

two worlds, air and soil, with their root system below ground and their shoot system above (**see Figure 23.4**).

The function of the root system is straightforward: Grow to water and minerals and absorb them from the soil and then begin transporting them up

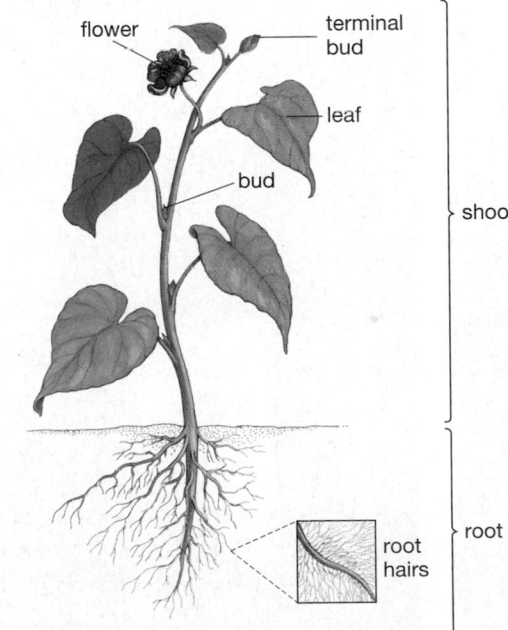

Figure 23.4
A Life-Form in Two Parts
Flowering plants live in two worlds, with their shoots in the air and their roots in the soil. Although flowering plants differ enormously in size and shape, they generally possess the external features shown.

through the rest of the plant. (For more on the minerals plants absorb, see "What Is Plant Food?" on page 486.) Most roots also serve as anchoring devices for plants, and some act as storage sites for food reserves.

The function of the shoot system is more complex. Photosynthesis takes place in this system, primarily in leaves, which means leaves must be positioned to absorb sunlight. Plants are in *competition* with one another for sunlight, which is a primary reason so many plants are tall. The food that is produced in photosynthesis must be distributed throughout the plant. It is not just food production that is centered in the shoot system, however; it is plant reproduction as well. Within flowers and their derivatives, we find all the components of reproduction—seeds, pollen, and so forth. Now let's look in more detail at the components of the root and shoot systems.

Roots: Absorbing the Vital Water

If you look at **Figure 23.5**, you can see pictures of the two basic types of plant root systems, one a **taproot system** consisting of a large central root and a number of smaller lateral roots, and the second a **fibrous root system** consisting of many roots that are all about the same size. **Figure 23.6** then shows you not only the taproot of a young sweetcorn plant but also another feature common to root systems. These are **root hairs**: threadlike extensions of roots that greatly increase their absorptive surface area. Each root hair actually is an elongation of a single outer cell of the root. Be-

tween roots and root hairs, the root structure of a given plant can be extensive. One famous analysis, conducted in the 1930s on a rye plant, concluded that its taproot and lateral roots alone, if laid end to end, would have totaled some 622 kilometers, which is about 386 miles. Meanwhile, the root hairs collectively were 10,620 kilometers long, meaning the plant had almost 6,600 miles of root hairs! This from a plant whose *shoot* stood 8 centimeters (about 3 inches) off the ground.

Why do plants lavish such resources on their roots? Essentially because plants have such a great need to take up water, and roots are the structures that allow them to do this. To perform photosynthesis, plants must have a constant supply of carbon dioxide, which enters the plants through microscopic pores, called *stomata*, that exist mostly on the underside of plant leaves. Open stomata, however, don't just let carbon dioxide in; they let the plant's water *out*, as water vapor. To accommodate this loss while still keeping vital tissues moist, plants continually pass water through themselves, from roots, up through the stem, and into the leaves (at which point it exits as water vapor). The evaporation of water from a plant's shoot is known as **transpiration**; through it, more than 90 percent of the water that enters a plant evaporates into the atmosphere. Because the roots of a single tall maple tree can absorb about 220 liters (or nearly 60 gallons) of water per *hour* on a hot summer day, the scale of transpiration is immense. Thus do we see the importance of root development.

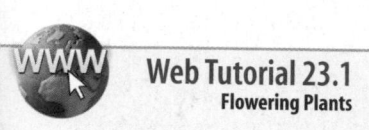

Web Tutorial 23.1
Flowering Plants

Figure 23.5
Two Root Strategies

(a) Dandelions such as this one employ a taproot system—a large central root and a number of smaller lateral roots.

(b) The French marigold employs a fibrous root system—a collection of roots that are all about the same size.

(a) Taproot system

(b) Fibrous root system

Figure 23.6
Root Hairs
Root hairs enormously increase the surface area of a root. The greater the surface area, the more fluid absorption can occur. Shown here are root hairs on the taproot of a sweetcorn plant.

The food storage aspect of roots has a meaning for human beings. Sweet potatoes and carrots, which are roots, can represent stored food for people as well as for plants.

Shoots: Leaves, Stems, and Flowers

Now let's turn to the shoot system, looking first at the leaves within it.

Leaves: Sites of Food Production

The primary business of leaves is to absorb the sunlight that drives photosynthesis, which is why most leaves are thin and flat. This leaf shape maximizes the surface area that can be devoted to absorbing sunlight while minimizing the number of cells in leaves that are irrelevant to photosynthesis. Beyond this, through their tiny stomata, leaves serve as the plant's primary entry and exit points for gases. As noted, the most important gas that's entering is carbon dioxide, which is one of the starting ingredients for photosynthesis. What's exiting is the by-product of photosynthesis, oxygen, and the water vapor.

The broad, flat leaves that are so common in nature have in essence a two-part structure—a **blade** (which we usually think of as the leaf itself) and a **petiole**, more commonly referred to as the leaf stem. If you look at the idealized cross section of this leaf in **Figure 23.7b**, you can see that the blade can be likened to a kind of cellular sandwich, with layers of cuticle, or waxy outer covering, on the outside, and a layer of epidermal cells just inside them. In the leaf's interior there are *vascular bundles*, which bear some relation to animal veins in that they are part of a transport system. Then there are several layers of mesophyll cells. It is these cells that are the sites of most photosynthesis.

Now note, on the underside of the blade, the openings called **stomata** (singular, *stoma*). These are the pores, noted earlier, that let water vapor out and carbon dioxide in—but for most plants only during the day. When the sun goes down photosynthesis can no longer be performed, and it is not cost-effective for a plant to lose water without gaining carbon dioxide. As such, the stomata close up until photosynthesis begins again the following day. If you look at **Figure 23.7c**, you can see how this opening and closing of stomata is achieved: Two "guard cells," juxtaposed like the sides of a coin purse, are arranged around the stomata. When sunlight strikes the leaf, these cells engorge with water, which makes them

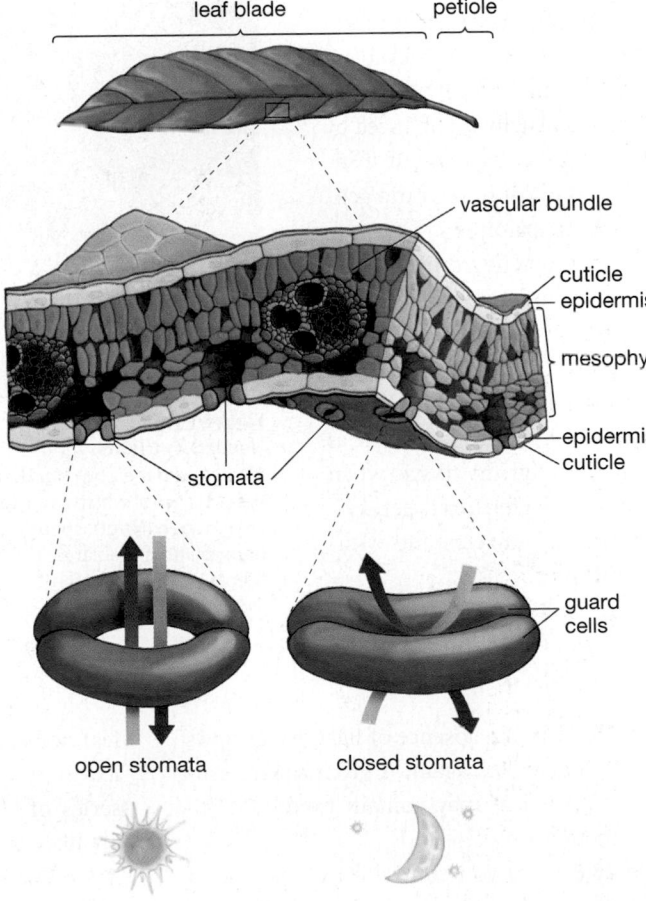

(a) Leaves tend to be broad and flat to increase the surface area exposed to sunlight.

leaf blade   petiole

(b) Photosynthesis occurs primarily within the mesophyll cells in the interior of the leaf. The vascular bundles carry water to the leaves and carry the product of photosynthesis, sugar, to other parts of the plant. Pores called stomata, mostly on the underside of leaves, allow for the passage of gases in and out of the leaf.

vascular bundle

cuticle
epidermis

mesophyll

epidermis
cuticle

stomata

(c) Guard cells of the stomata control the opening and closing of the stomata. When sunlight shines on the leaf during the day, the guard cells engorge with water that makes them bow apart, thus opening the stomata. When sunlight is reduced, water flows out of the guard cells, causing the stomata to close.

open stomata   closed stomata

guard cells

Figure 23.7
Site of Photosynthesis

What Is Plant Food?

Plants are able to make their own food through photosynthesis if they have just four things: water, sunlight, carbon dioxide, and a few nutrients. Water, sunlight, and probably even carbon dioxide are no mystery to you by now, but what exactly are these nutrients you've been reading about?

A **nutrient** is simply a chemical element that is used by living things to sustain life. Recall from Chapter 2 that "elements" are the most basic building blocks of the chemical world. Silver is an element, as is uranium, but these are not nutrients because living things do not need them to live. In the broadest sense, carbon, oxygen, and hydrogen are nutrients. And it turns out that almost 96 percent of the weight of the average plant is accounted for by these three elements, which come to plants primarily from water and air.

Plants need at least another 13 elements to live, however, and not all of these are supplied by water and air. When we think of common "plant food," we are generally referring to those nutrients that plants can *use up* in their soil and that thus must be replenished to assure continued growth and reproduction. Of these, the most important three are nitrogen, phosphorus, and potassium, whose chemical symbols are N, P, and K. When you look at a package of an average plant fertilizer, you will see three numbers in sequence on it (for example, 10-20-10). What these refer to are the percentage of the fertilizer's weight accounted for by these nutrients (see **Figure 1**). The growth of plants usually is enhanced by a fertilizer that has equal ratios of the three elements, but if increased *blooming* is your goal, an increased phosphorus ratio generally is recommended, as with the 10-20-10 example.

It is not just houseplants or lawns that benefit from fertilizer, but farm crops as well. Indeed, the planting of a crop on a parcel of land generally requires a large investment in fertilizer because a crop such as wheat removes a great deal of N, P, and K from the soil in a single season. Historically, fertilizers used on farms were *organic*, meaning they came from decayed living things, such as the fish that Native Americans taught the Pilgrims to use when planting corn. Nowadays, however, commercial fertilizers generally are *inorganic*, meaning they are mixtures of pure elements within binding materials, produced by chemical processes.

Nature is, of course, perfectly capable of producing a green bounty in such places as forests and marshes without the aid of any human-made fertilizer. Decaying plant and animal matter put nutrients back into the soil, and bacteria are able to fix nitrogen, meaning to absorb it from the air and transform it into a form that plants can take up. Looked at one way, however, houseplants and farm crops are *isolated* plants whose participation in this web of life is very limited, and thus they require a helping hand from humans in order to remain robust.

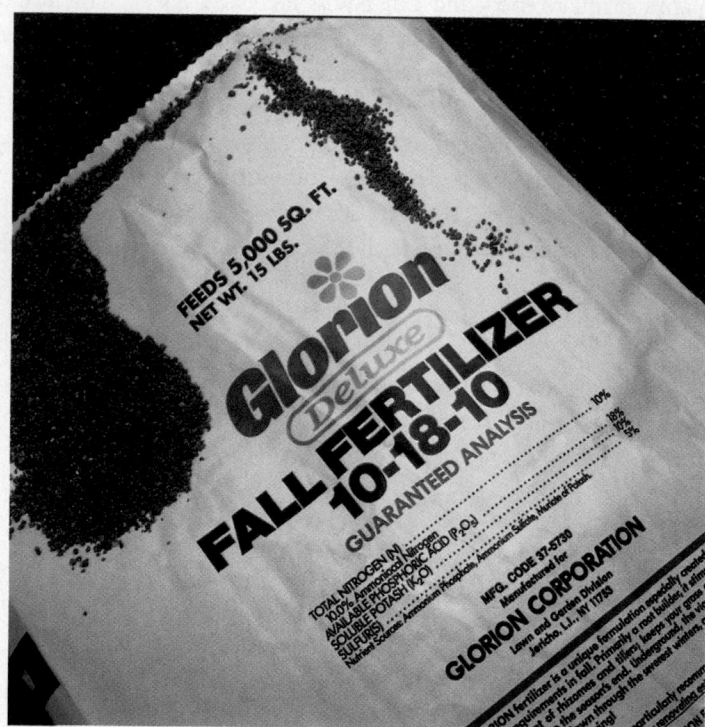

Figure 1
Needed Nutrients
Plants make their own food from sunlight, water, carbon dioxide, and a few nutrients, some of which come from the soil. The most important of these nutrients are nitrogen (N), phosphorus (P), and potassium (K). Because garden plants and houseplants are isolated from natural ecosystems, they must often get these nutrients in the form of fertilizer.

bow apart. Then, in the absence of light, water flows out and the door closes again. A given square centimeter of a plant leaf may contain from 1,000 to 100,000 stomata.

Figure 23.8 gives you some idea of the varied forms of leaves. In addition to the so-called simple leaf we've been looking at, there are compound leaves in which individual blades are divided into a series of "leaflets." Pine needles and cactus spines are likewise actually leaves. The cactus, in particular, has reduced the amount of leaf surface it has as a means of conserving water. So how does it perform enough photosynthesis to get along? It carries out most of its photosynthesis in its stem.

Stems: Structure and Storage

We all generally understand what the stem of a plant is, though it is less generally appreciated that the trunk of a tree is simply one kind of plant stem. The main functions of stems are to give structure to the plant as a whole and to act as storage sites for food reserves. In addition, water, minerals, hormones, and food are constantly shuttling through (and to) the stem, with water on its way up from the roots and food on its way down from the leaves to the rest of the plant.

If you look at **Figure 23.9**, you can see a cross section of one type of plant stem, showing the vascular bundles or veins you first saw in the leaves and the outer, or *epidermal, tissue* just as the leaves had. You can also see so-called *ground tissue* of two types: an outer cortex and an inner pith, both of which can play a part in food storage and wound repair and provide structural strength to the plant.

Flowers: Many Parts in Service of Reproduction

Flowers are the reproductive structures of plants. A single flower generally has both male and female reproductive structures on it, which might make you think that a given plant would fertilize *itself*. This is indeed the case with some plants, such as Gregor Mendel's pea plants, reviewed in Chapter 11. However, because the evolutionary benefit of sexual reproduction is to get the genetic diversity that comes with *mixing* genetic material from different individual organisms, natural selection has worked against self-fertilization by endowing many flowering plants

with ways to reduce the incidence of it. For example, the male pollen of a given plant might be genetically incompatible with that plant's female reproductive structures. Some of the illustrations you'll be seeing show a plant fertilizing itself, but this is done only for visual simplicity.

Figure 23.8
Leaves Come in Many Sizes, Shapes, and Colors
Simple leaves have just one blade. In compound leaves, the blade is divided into little leaflets. Some leaves are so modified that the average person can hardly recognize them as leaves—for example, the spines of a cactus.

compound leaves

simple leaves

leaves modified as spines

highly reduced leaves (needles)

leaves modified as tendrils

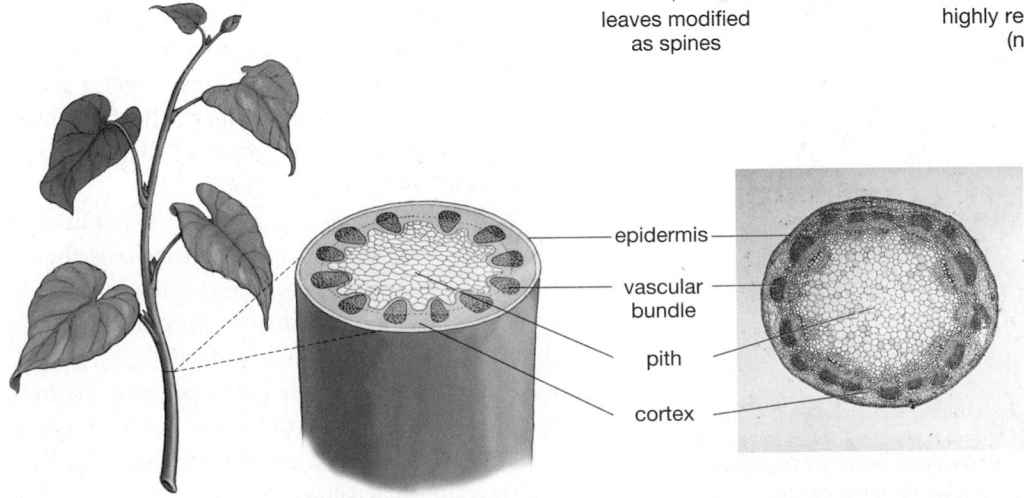

epidermis

vascular bundle

pith

cortex

Figure 23.9
The Stem and Its Parts
Stems provide support to the rest of the plant, act as storage sites, and conduct fluids. Vascular plants have a "plumbing" system that transports food, water, minerals, and hormones. The vascular bundles in the figure are groups of tubes, running in parallel, that serve this transport function.

If you look at **Figure 23.10**, you can see the components of a typical flower. Taking things from the bottom, there is a modified stem, called a pedicel, which widens into a base called a receptacle, from which the flowers emerge. Flowers themselves can be thought of as consisting of four parts: sepals, petals, stamens, and a carpel. The **sepals** are the leaf-like structures that protect the flower before it opens. (Drying out is a problem, as are hungry animals.) The function of the colorful **petals** is to announce "food here" to pollinating animals.

The heart of the flower's reproductive structures consists of the stamens and the carpel. If you look at Figure 23.10, you can see that the **stamens** consist of a long, slender **filament** topped by an **anther**. These anthers contain cells that ultimately will yield sperm-bearing pollen grains. At maturity, these pollen grains will consist of three cells surrounded by an outer coat.

It is these pollen grains that will be released and then carried—perhaps by a pollinating bee or bird—to the carpel of another plant (or perhaps of the same plant). As Figure 23.10 shows, a **carpel** is a composite structure, composed of three main parts: the **stigma**, which is the tip end of the carpel, on which pollen grains are deposited; the **style**, a slender tube that raises the stigma to such a prominent height that it can easily catch the pollen; and the **ovary**, the area in which fertilization of the female egg and then early development of the plant embryo take place.

Figure 23.10
Parts of the Flower
Flowers are composed of four main parts: the sepals, petals, stamens, and a carpel. The sepals protect the young bud until it is ready to bloom. The petals attract pollinators. The stamens are the reproductive structures that produce pollen grains (which contain sperm cells). The carpel is the female reproductive structure; it includes an ovary that contains one or more eggs.

23.3 Basic Functions in Flowering Plants

Having looked at the structure, or anatomy, of the angiosperms, let's now go over the activities of some of these components. We'll think in terms of systems here: the reproductive system, the transport system, the hormonal system, the communication system, and the defense system. In addition, you'll look briefly at the nature of plant growth. Because you've just reviewed the parts of a flower, let's start with reproduction.

Reproduction in Angiosperms

The function of a pollen grain is the fertilization of an egg. There are cells in the anthers of the original flower that undergo the type of cell division reviewed in Chapter 10, meiosis, thereby producing **microspores** that are haploid—that contain only a single set of chromosomes. As you can see in **Figure 23.11**, each pollen grain develops from one of the microspores inside the anther. In the type of plant pictured in the figure, the grain will consist, by the time it leaves the anther, of a tough outer coat and three cells: one **tube cell** and two **sperm cells**. Though the pollen grain never gets much more complex than this, it is not just a component of the original plant; it is its alternate generation on the male side. (For more on the alternation of generations in plants, see page 434 in Chapter 21.)

You can see in Figure 23.11 what the activities of the pollen grain's cells are in the context of the angiosperm life cycle. When the pollen grain leaves the anther, it is bound for the stigma of another plant (or its own plant). But for a grain to merely *land* on a stigma doesn't mean that anything has been fertilized. The tube cell in the grain must then begin to *germinate* on the stigma, forming a **pollen tube** that grows down through the style. Once this has taken place, one of the sperm cells in the grain travels through the tube, gets to the female egg, and only *then* is there fertilization. (The other sperm moves down along with the first, but then spurs the growth of food reserves for the growing embryo, about which you'll learn more in Chapter 24.)

And how does the egg arise that is fertilized by the sperm? Together with its supporting cells, the egg is the plant's alternate generation on the female side. Inside the plant's ovary, there is a cell that also goes through meiosis, thus producing a haploid **megaspore** (*mega*, because it's bigger than the male microspore). It in turn gives rise to several kinds of cells, one of which is the egg that the sperm from the pollen grain will fertilize.

Watch closely now, because once this happens—once sperm (from pollen grain) has fertilized egg (from megaspore)—it is the beginning of the kind of flowering plant we started with. We have alternated back to this generation of plant. Many a step remains before arriving at something that *looks* like the original plant; the fertilized egg (now called a zygote) must first have a tough covering develop around it. The combination of embryo, its food supply, and the covering is called a **seed**. This seed must be released and then land on a suitable patch of earth, there to germinate and grow to a full flowering plant. But the step at which this new generation appears is the point at which sperm fertilizes egg.

To put some terms to these generations, note that both the megaspore and pollen grain are haploid spores. Because *spores* are what the original, flowering plant produced, this flowering plant is the **sporophyte generation**. Meanwhile, the pollen and megaspore generation produced *gametes*—sperm or egg—and are thus the **gametophyte generation**. When the sperm and egg came together, they fused their haploid sets of chromosomes and thus produced a sporophyte embryo with a doubled, or diploid, set of chromosomes. A detailed account of angiosperm reproduction can be found in Chapter 24, beginning on page 520.

Recall that the angiosperm egg is fertilized and develops inside the structure called the ovary (see Figure 23.10). Also recall that as the fertilized egg develops into an embryo, it becomes enclosed within a seed. As this is taking place, the ovary that surrounds the seed is also developing into something: a tissue called fruit. We are all familiar with fruit, of course, and sometimes the tissue surrounding the seed is fruit as we commonly understand that term—the flesh of an apricot, for example. But ovaries can mature into fruit in other forms. The pod that surrounds peas is fruit in this scientific sense, as is the outer covering of a kernel of corn. A **fruit** is simply the mature ovary of a flowering plant. All angiosperms have fruit in this sense, and it provides us with our definition of the flowering plants. An **angiosperm** is a flowering seed plant whose seeds are enclosed within the tissue called fruit.

Asexual Reproduction in Angiosperms: Vegetative Reproduction

We are used to the human mode of reproduction, which—pending the arrival of cloned human beings—is always *sexual* reproduction: At some point, sperm must fertilize egg to produce a new embryo. But plants, including angiosperms, have another option—**vegetative reproduction**, which is *asexual* reproduction. This is familiar to us in the form of "cuttings" that can be taken from one houseplant to start another. A growing cutting represents a new plant that is an

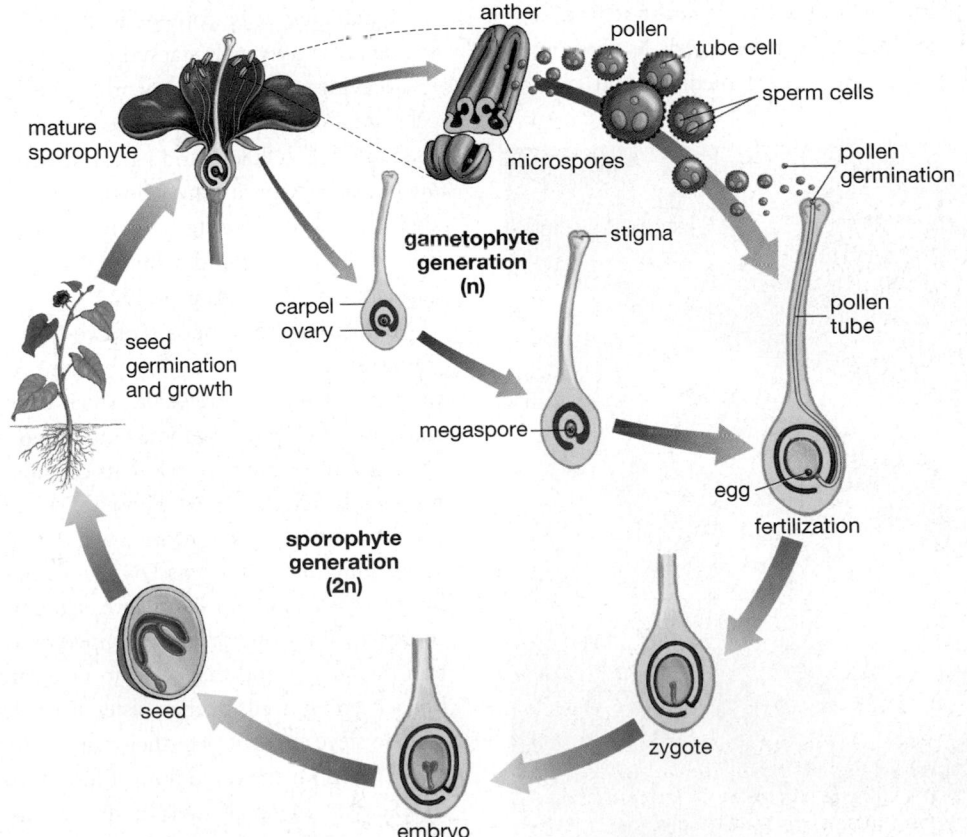

Figure 23.11
The Angiosperm Life Cycle
The mature sporophyte flower produces many male microspores within the anther, and a female megaspore within the ovary. The male microspores then develop into pollen grains that contain the male gamete, sperm. Meanwhile the female megaspore produces the female gamete, the egg. Pollen grains, with their sperm inside, move to the stigma of a plant. There the tube cell of the pollen grain sprouts a pollen tube that grows down toward the egg. The sperm cells then move down through the pollen tube, and one of them fertilizes the egg. This results in a zygote that develops into an embryo protected inside a seed. This seed leaves the parent plant and sprouts or "germinates" in the earth, growing eventually into the type of sporophyte plant that began the cycle.

exact genetic replica of the original plant; no alternate generation or fertilization is required. One sporophyte plant has been grown from another.

Human beings are motivated to put such vegetative reproduction to use when nature produces a particularly *valuable* plant, generally through mutation. Navel oranges, for example, seem to have arisen through mutation on a conventional orange tree that was grown in Brazil in the nineteenth century. If pollen from that tree had helped fertilize an egg from another tree, we may well have *lost* the advantage this unique tree provided—fat, seedless navel oranges—through the shuffling of genetic material that comes with sexual reproduction. The trick was to use cuttings (or "grafts") from the original tree to produce one *identical* generation of orange tree after another. Vegetative reproduction is also common in nature. The roots of aspen trees, for example, produce a form of shoot known as a sucker which, if physically separated from the parent plant, will grow into a new aspen tree. Oftentimes, then, a stand of aspen trees amounts to a group of clones of one another (**Figure 23.12**).

Plant Plumbing: The Transport System

In looking at leaves and stems earlier, you saw that they have something called *vascular bundles* running through them. This term refers to collections of tubes through which fluid materials move from one part of the plant to another. This transport system bears obvious similarities with the circulation systems of animals, but there are differences as well. Many animals employ blood as a transport medium, and animals

such as ourselves have a transport *pumping* device, called a heart. Plants do not have blood, and they have no pumping system. (In fact, plants have almost no "moving parts" at all.) Yet think of the transport job plants have to do. Water that is transpired from the top of a redwood tree may have made a journey of more than 100 meters straight up—more length than a football field! What kind of power is at work here?

There are two essential components to the plant transport system. First there is **xylem**, which can be defined as the tissue through which water and dissolved minerals flow in vascular plants. (**Tissue** means a group of cells that perform a common function.) Second there is **phloem**, the tissue through which the *food* produced in photosynthesis—mostly sucrose— is conducted, along with some hormones and other compounds. As noted before, water is making a directional journey from root through leaf, but the plant must be able to transport food and hormones everywhere within itself.

If you look at **Figure 23.13**, you can see an idealized view of a plant's transport system as it would appear within a stem. You'll also see that the vascular bundles noted earlier are composed of bundles of linked xylem and phloem tubes running in parallel.

Xylem is composed of two types of fluid-conducting cells, *vessel elements* and *tracheids*, which have different shapes as you can see. Upon reaching maturity, these cells do the rest of the plant the favor of dying. The cells' content is cleared out, leaving strands of empty cells stacked one on top of another—leaving tubes, in other words. The walls of these cells remain, however, and indeed are reinforced with the materials cellulose and lignin, which provide the *load-bearing* capacity that allows something as massive as a redwood tree to be so tall. (For more on the role of xylem in everyday houseplants, see "Keeping Cut Flowers Fresh," on page 492.)

Phloem is also composed of two types of cells, but the arrangement here is very different. One type of phloem cell—a *sieve element*, which does the actual nutrient conducting—doesn't undergo cell death upon maturity, but it does lose its cell nucleus, meaning nearly all its DNA. Those of you who went through the genetics unit may wonder how any cell could function without its DNA information center, but there is an answer. Each sieve element cell has associated with it one or more *companion cells* that retain their DNA and that seem to take care of all the housekeeping needs of their sister sieve elements. So, why do sieve elements lose their nuclei? Apparently to make room for the rapid flow of food through them. In Chapter 24 you'll look at the means by which phloem and xylem conduct their respective materials.

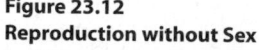

Figure 23.12
Reproduction without Sex
Individual aspen trees often are clones of one another, reproducing without the fusion of eggs and sperm from different individuals. This stand of aspen trees is in Colorado.

Communication: Hormones Affect Many Aspects of Plant Functioning

We're so used to associating hormones with *animal* functioning that it may come as a surprise to learn that plants also have hormones. Taken as a whole, plant hormones do many of the same things that animal hormones do. Their most important roles are to regulate growth and development and to integrate the functioning of the various plant parts. In less abstract terms, hormones help buds grow and leaves fall and fruit ripen. This goes hand in hand with helping plants respond to their environments—to heat and cold, munching goats, and voracious insects.

Though most people have an intuitive sense of what hormones are, a definition might be helpful. **Hormones** are chemical messengers; they are substances that, when released in one part of an organism, go on to prompt physiological activity in another part of that organism. In animals, hormones are generally synthesized in well-defined organs, called *glands*, whose main function is to produce hormones (for example, the thyroid or adrenal glands). In plants, however, hormone production is a more diffuse process, taking place not in glands, but in collections of cells that carry out a range of functions.

If you look at **Table 23.1** you can see a list of five of the most important hormones that function in plants. Three of these actually are *classes* of hormones, and two are individual hormones. You can read about the hormone ethylene in "Ripening Fruit Is a Gas." Let's go over just one other plant hormone, a member of the family of hormones known as *auxins*, to give you some idea of what plant hormones do.

vascular bundles

xylem
phloem

stem section

Fluids move through plants in sets of tubes called vascular bundles. Two types of tissue, running in parallel, can be found in each vascular bundle: xylem, the tissue through which water and dissolved minerals flow; and phloem, the tissue through which the food produced in photosynthesis flows.

water

water

vessel elements

tracheids

Xylem is composed of two kinds of fluid-conducting cells, vessel elements and tracheids.

sieve elements

companion cells

Phloem is composed of sieve elements and their companion cells.

food

**Figure 23.13
Fluid-Transport Structure of Plants**

Table 23.1 Plant Hormones		
Hormone	**Major functions**	**Where found or produced in plant**
Auxins	Suppression of lateral buds; elongation of stems; growth and abscission (falling off) of leaves; differentiation of xylem and phloem tissue	Root and shoot tips; young leaves
Cytokinins	Stimulate cell division; active in the development of plant tissues from undifferentiated cells	Roots
Gibberellins	Stem elongation, growth of fruit, promotion of seed germination	Seeds, apical meristem tissue, young leaves
Ethylene	Ripening of fruit, retardation of lateral bud growth, promotion of leaf abscission	Nearly all plant tissue
Abscisic acid	Induces closing of leaf pores (stomata) in drought; promotes dormancy in seeds; counteracts growth hormones	Young fruit; leaves, roots

Keeping Cut Flowers Fresh

As already noted, xylem is the plant tissue through which water moves *up*, from roots through leaves. The flowers we put in vases in our homes have lost their roots, of course, but they haven't lost their xylem, which continues to function long after the flower has been picked. Given this, many flowers can last a long time indoors; but we can maximize their stay if we follow a few simple rules.

First, realize that the liquid in the xylem is under negative pressure—its natural tendency is to move up *into* the stem, not to flow out of it. As such, if the stems are cut when they are out of water, *air* gets sucked up into the cut ends, creating air bubbles that can then get trapped in the xylem and keep water from rising up through it. When this happens, flowers can wilt, even when their stems are submerged in clean water. Recutting the stem under water (or under a steady stream from the faucet) can remove this blockage. Better yet, cut the stems under water the first time.

Beyond this, acidic sugar-water, such as can be found in citrus-flavored soft drinks, will prolong the life of some flowers by keeping bacterial growth down; changing water frequently is a good idea, particularly when it starts to look gummy or discolored. Keep your arrangement out of direct light or heat, and remove dead and dying flowers in the arrangement, because the hormone ethylene is given off by dying flowers and in many cases will hasten the demise of the healthy ones in the bunch. (For another role of ethylene, see "Ripening Fruit Is a Gas," page 494.)

Preserving Beauty
Following a few simple rules can prolong the life of cut flowers.

An Auxin Gives the "A" Shape to Trees

Why do Christmas trees have their characteristic "A" shape? (**See Figure 23.14**.) They develop in this way thanks in large part to the effects of an auxin known as IAA. Unlike animals, plants do not grow globally, over their whole surface, but instead confine most of their vertical growth to special regions, called *apical meristems*, that exist at the *tips* of the roots and shoots. **Figure 23.15** shows you how this works out with the shoots. The shoot apical meristem gives rise to a series of growth *modules*: more stem, one or more leaves, and a lateral bud that forms in tandem with each leaf. These lateral buds have meristem tissue in them and can grow into new branches, but they normally don't *when they lie close to the apical meristem*. Why? The apical meristem is producing IAA, which works in tandem with other hormones to suppress the growth of these buds. But, the farther away from the apical meristem, the *smaller* the concentration of IAA that is available to the lateral buds. The result is a greater budding of branches at the base of a tree, and a tapering of this growth going from the base up through the tree's apex. This phenomenon is called **apical dominance**: a suppression of the growth of lateral branches through the activity of apical meristems. It is most pronounced in certain conifers, such as the Douglas firs often used for Christmas trees. Meanwhile, trees that don't have such a strict IAA gradient don't get the strict "A" shape. This maintenance of apical dominance is just one of the many things that IAA does. To give you some idea of the complexity of its function, IAA may

Figure 23.14
Uniform "A" Shapes
The effects of apical dominance are clearly visible in this stand of blue spruce trees at a Michigan Christmas tree farm. The apical meristem tissue at the tip of the trees produces a hormone called IAA that inhibits the growth of lateral branches. Because the concentration of IAA is highest at the top near the apical meristem, and lowest at the bottom, the branches are very short near the top and longest at the bottom.

attests, this tree has carried out the *lateral* growth that botanists refer to as *secondary growth*, which you'll look at next chapter.

Beyond these things, it turns out that a plant's growth is indeterminate. In most plants it can go on indefinitely at the tips of roots and shoots. By contrast, animal growth is generally determinate: It comes to an end at a certain point in development. Imagine if, say, the tips of your fingers just kept growing long after your trunk and arms had reached their full extension.

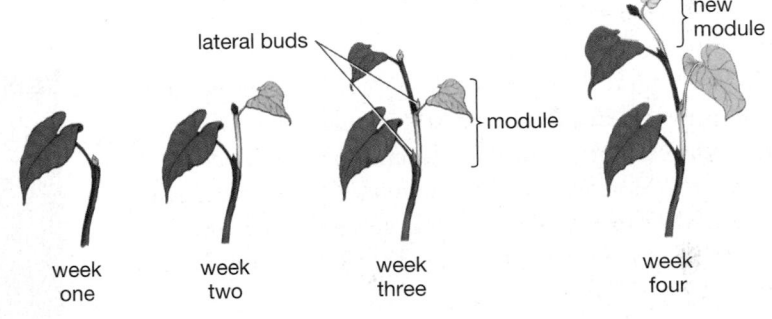

Figure 23.15
Modular Growth
Vertical growth in plants occurs in "modules." Each module includes a new portion of stem, at least one leaf, and a lateral bud that can give rise to a branch or a flower. Here alternating dark-green and light-green segments indicate modules.

serve to *suppress* the emergence of lateral buds, as noted, but it works to *promote* the cellular elongation that is important in plant growth.

Plant Growth: Indeterminate and at the Tips

Having looked a little at how plant growth is affected by hormones, we can note some basic characteristics of plant growth. To visualize how it works, imagine a boy of about 8 years old who decides to drive a long nail into the trunk of a secluded tree. He doesn't drive the nail in completely, but lets it stick out a bit. After 10 years pass, the boy happens to walk by the same tree; upon seeing it, a couple of things occur to him (**see Figure 23.16**). First, he has grown but the nail is in the same place; he would have to bend down now to pull the nail out, whereas when he drove it in he was standing up straight. Second, he would have a hard time actually pulling the nail out now because not much of it is visible; the tree has grown around it. Third, if the nail's height is any indication, the trunk of the tree may not have moved up, but the *top* certainly has; it's much taller than he remembered it.

The lessons here are that, in their vertical growth, plants do not grow the way people do—throughout their entire length—but instead grow only at their tips (of both shoots *and* roots, though the boy couldn't see the roots). In addition, as the half-buried nail

When Billy was eight ...   When Billy was eighteen ...

Figure 23.16
The Basic Characteristics of Plant Growth
If a young boy drives a long nail into a tree and returns 10 years later, two things will be apparent: The nail is at the same height it used to be despite the increased height of the tree, and it is almost completely buried in the tree. What does this say about tree growth? Trees do not elongate throughout their whole length, but only at their tips in "primary growth." Further, they widen laterally in "secondary growth."

Ripening Fruit Is a Gas

That banana you had? The one you put in that plastic bag, thinking you'd make it part of your lunch? It already had a few black spots on it by the time it went in the bag, but then you forgot about it for lunch and, by the time you looked at it again, it was more black than yellow and something you were no longer interested in eating. The question is: Why did it go downhill so *fast*?

The answer is that those little black spots on the banana result from concentrations of a gas called *ethylene*—a plant hormone that can ripen lots of fruits. The bag you put the banana in became a kind of gas chamber, with the ethylene concentrations inside being very high. Moreover, ethylene stimulates its own production; the more ethylene there is, the more that gets produced. Given this contagious quality to ethylene, you can see why it is true that one bad apple can spoil the bunch.

Ethylene doesn't work on all fruits; grapes, strawberries, and cherries, for example, are unaffected by it. But apples, avocados, and tomatoes join bananas in being very sensitive to it. If you wish to ripen one of these latter fruits fast, putting it in a plastic bag will give you an edible fruit faster than putting it on the window sill.

But what does it mean for a fruit to be ripe? Let's match up our intuitive sense of this with the underlying physical changes. Compared to unripened fruits, ripe fruits tend to be sweeter (starches are converted to sugars); softer (a secretion of enzymes softens cell walls); and more fragrant (ripening releases compounds that our nose detects as sweet-smelling). Ethylene helps bring about all these changes, basically by upping the tempo at which a plant carries out its metabolic processes. The reason a green banana turns to yellow is that ethylene hastens the breakdown of the green chlorophyll in the banana, which allows us to see yellow pigments that had been there all along.

For years, commercial fruit growers have employed ethylene, or test-tube compounds that help release it, in order to *time* the ripening of their fruit. This is why we can pick green tomatoes at the source and then ripen them when they get closer to market. It's also possible to *suppress* ethylene production by storing fruit in a room that has high concentrations of carbon dioxide and low concentrations of oxygen, a combination that suppresses ethylene synthesis. In this way, a fruit such as apples can be kept on hold for months before being brought to ripeness by simply being exposed to normal air. Ever wonder why you can have fresh apples in the spring when they generally are picked in the fall? Ethylene control is part of the answer.

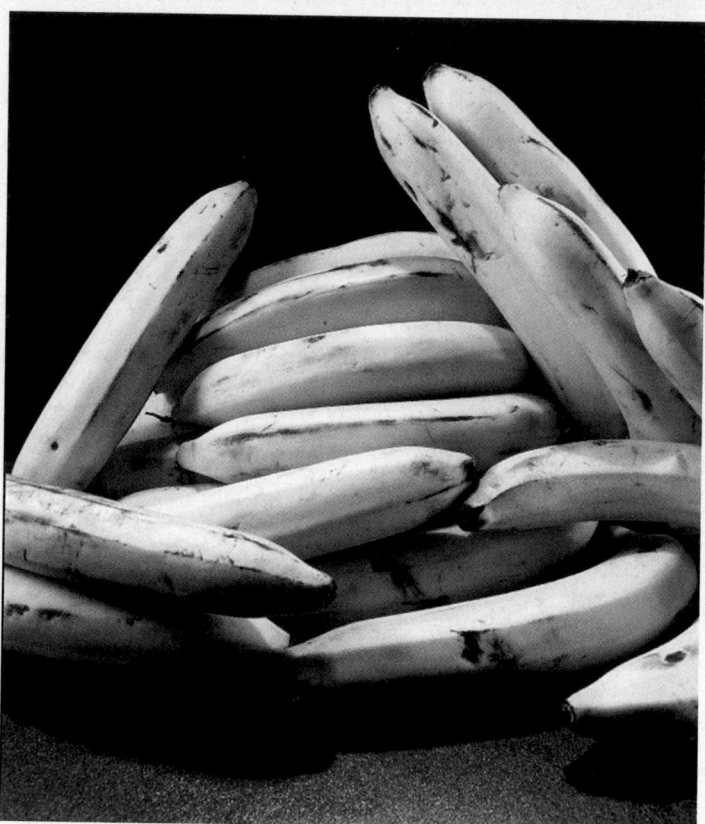

Spurring Their Own Ripening
These bananas ripen under the influence of a gas they produce, ethylene. Concentrations of ethylene produce the black spots on bananas.

Defense and Cooperation

Plants may be immobile and toothless, but they are not defenseless. Indeed, they have developed a formidable defense arsenal (**see Figure 23.17**). One variety of plant defenses, the structural defenses, are familiar to us because they're so visible—think, for example, of the spines on a cactus or the thorns on a rose. A second variety of defenses, the chemical defenses, are not so visible but are potent nevertheless. The chomping a beetle does on a potato plant induces the plant to produce substances (called *protease inhibitors*) that are believed to give the insect an ache in its gut that it won't forget. Other plants, when attacked by a fungus, release antifungal compounds that spread not only at the site of infection, but throughout the plant.

Beyond these self-defense mechanisms, plants can warn *other* plants of dangers in their midst. Airborne signaling compounds can be produced from the leaf surface of a plant under attack, waft to a neighboring plant, and prompt it to start producing compounds that are noxious or harmful to the would-be plant-eater. Some plants can even call in animal allies. Corn plants that are attacked by army worms can call in an air force: the plants release a substance that attracts parasitic wasps, which then devour the worms.

Plants also enter into cooperative relationships with other organisms. In Chapter 21 you saw that most plant roots are linked to the thin tubes, called *hyphae*, that extend from fungi. What the fungi get from this is nutrition from the photosynthesizing plant; what the plants get is a greatly expanded water and mineral absorption network. The combined root-hyphae associations are known as **mycorrhizae**. Other species, notably the legumes, such as soybeans, have developed partnerships with nitrogen-fixing bacteria, which is to say bacteria that are able to take nitrogen out of the atmosphere and put it into a form that living things can use. The bacterium infects the plant through a root hair, directs the construction of its own lodgings (called a *root nodule*), and then begins converting atmospheric nitrogen, while obtaining nutrition from the plant. This process must take place in the absence of oxygen, which the plant sees to by eliminating the available oxygen in the nodule. Lots of crops require applications of human-manufactured nitrogen, but legumes such as beans and alfalfa can do fine on their own (**see Figure 23.18**).

23.4 Responding to External Signals

Plants may lack a nervous system, but this doesn't mean they can't respond to their environment. They must do so, actually, because their life depends on it. They sense the march of the seasons by measuring available light and the surrounding temperature; they use internal clocks to synchronize their development and physical functioning; they respond to light, gravity, touch, heat, cold, and pH, among other things. Let's conclude the chapter by reviewing the plant's interactions with gravity, light, touch, and the seasons as examples of these environmental responses.

Responding to Gravity: Gravitropism

When a seed first starts to sprout, or "germinate," its roots and shoots must go in very specific directions: The root must go *down*, toward the water and minerals the plant needs, and the shoot must go *up* toward the sunlight. Imagine a seed that has simply fallen on the ground; it would not do for either root or shoot to grow *horizontally*; each must grow vertically. If you look at

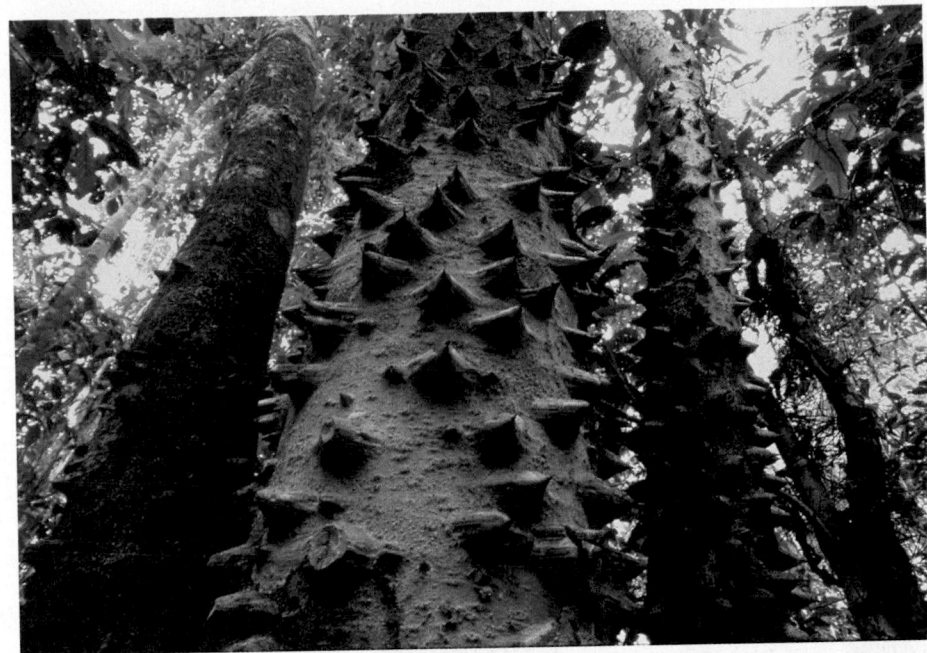

Figure 23.17
Silent and Fixed in One Spot, but Not Defenseless
The spiny bark of this Costa Rican tree, a member of the genus *Zanthoxylum*, protects it from plant predators.

Figure 23.18
Working Arrangement
Plants need nitrogen to grow. Some get it through a cooperative relationship with bacteria that are nitrogen-fixing, meaning they can convert atmospheric nitrogen into a form living things can use. Shown are the root nodules (the small spheres) on the roots of a soybean plant. Bacteria make a home in the nodules, where they fix nitrogen that is then used by the plant.

Web Tutorial 23.2
Response to External Signals

Figure 23.19, you can see dramatic evidence of a plant's ability to sense which way is up and which way down. The impatiens in Figure 23.19a was placed on its side and, within 16 hours, the shoot began curving upward, as you can see. Figure 23.19b shows the *root* of a germinating sweet-corn seed, likewise oriented horizontally (by researchers), but quickly beginning to bend down-

Figure 23.19
Plants Respond to Gravity

(a) Potted impatiens demonstrate the effects of gravitropism. The plant on the right was laid on its side 16 hours before the photo was taken, by which time the shoot had curved, beginning to grow upward.

(b) Similarly, the root of a germinating sweet-corn seed begins to curve downward only hours after being placed on its side. How do these plants sense which way is up and which way is down?

(c) One hint is that if the very tip, or "root cap" of the root is removed, the root no longer bends downward. Researchers believe that organelle "sedimentation"—the movement of certain organelles in response to gravity—is the sensing mechanism in gravitropism.

(a) When sunlight is overhead, the IAA molecules produced by the apical meristem are distributed evenly in the shoot.

(b) Once the sunlight shines on the shoot at an angle, the IAA molecules move to the far side and induce the elongation of cells on that side.

(c) Cell elongation results in the bending of the shoot toward the light.

Figure 23.20
Plants Respond to Light

ward. What's being exemplified here is **gravitropism**, meaning a bending of a plant's root or shoot in response to gravity. Figure 23.19c again shows the root of a sweet-corn plant, only this one has had its very tip, or *root cap*, snipped off. Here instead of bending in accordance with gravity, the root continues its straight, horizontal growth. Conclusion? Cells or substances in the root cap are essential for root gravitropism.

But how do roots "know" which way is down, and how do they orchestrate a course correction when they need one? Logically, there must be at least two elements at work here: first, a gravitational *sensing* mechanism; and then a means of *responding* to gravitational cues, such that corrective bending points the root toward the center of Earth.

The consensus among botanists today is that the sensing mechanism in gravitropism is the "sedimentation" that various plant cell organelles perform in response to gravity. Recall that organelles are small but highly organized structures inside cells. (Mitochondria and ribosomes are organelles, for example.) Like the bubble in a carpenter's level, some plant-cell organelles can be seen changing position in response to gravity. The most important of these organelles is a group of starch-storing structures called *amyloplasts* (though some plants seem to employ alternate organelles). When these organelles move in response to gravity, it sets in motion the responding mechanism in gravitropism. The organelles "land" on other structures inside the cell (such as the cytoskeleton), and the resulting impact triggers a redistribution of a substance you were recently introduced to: the hormone IAA. The result of this redistribution is differential growth within the plant—one *side* of the plant stem or root will grow more than the other side. With this growth, a root that is oriented horizontally will start bending toward the ground, while a stem that is oriented horizontally will start bending toward the sky.

Responding to Light: Phototropism

Many plants will bend toward a source of light, with the value of this perhaps being obvious: Plants produce their own food, and that production depends on light. Thus a plant needs to respond when its sunlight becomes *blocked* by another plant or some other physical object in its surroundings. As it turns out, it is once again IAA—this time produced in the shoot-tips of growing plants—that controls this **phototropism**, defined as a curvature of shoots in response to light. When light strikes one side of the shoot, it causes IAA to migrate to the other side, where the IAA acts to promote the *elongation* of cells on this far side. The effect is to make the shoot curve toward the light (**see Figure 23.20**).

Responding to Contact: Thigmotropism

We've all seen plants that manage to climb upward by encircling the stem of another plant. Whole stems can undertake such encircling, but it is often a thin, modified leaflet called a *tendril* that does so (see Figure 23.21). But how is a tendril able to wrap around another object? Once again through differential growth—more rapid growth on one side of a tendril than on the other. Contact with the object is perceived by outer, or epidermal, cells in the tendril. This sets into motion the differential growth, which probably is controlled by the hormones IAA and ethylene. This process is called **thigmotropism**, meaning growth of a plant in response to touch. Plants with this capability can piggyback on other plants in order to get more access to sunlight.

Responding to the Passage of the Seasons

The profusion of brightly colored leaves in the fall is one of the great seasonal markers in temperate climates such as those in the American Midwest and most of the East Coast. As green leaves turn red, gold, and purple, we know that autumn has arrived (see Figure 23.22).

Dormancy in Winter

Trees that exhibit a coordinated, seasonal loss of leaves are called **deciduous** trees. But why should these broad-

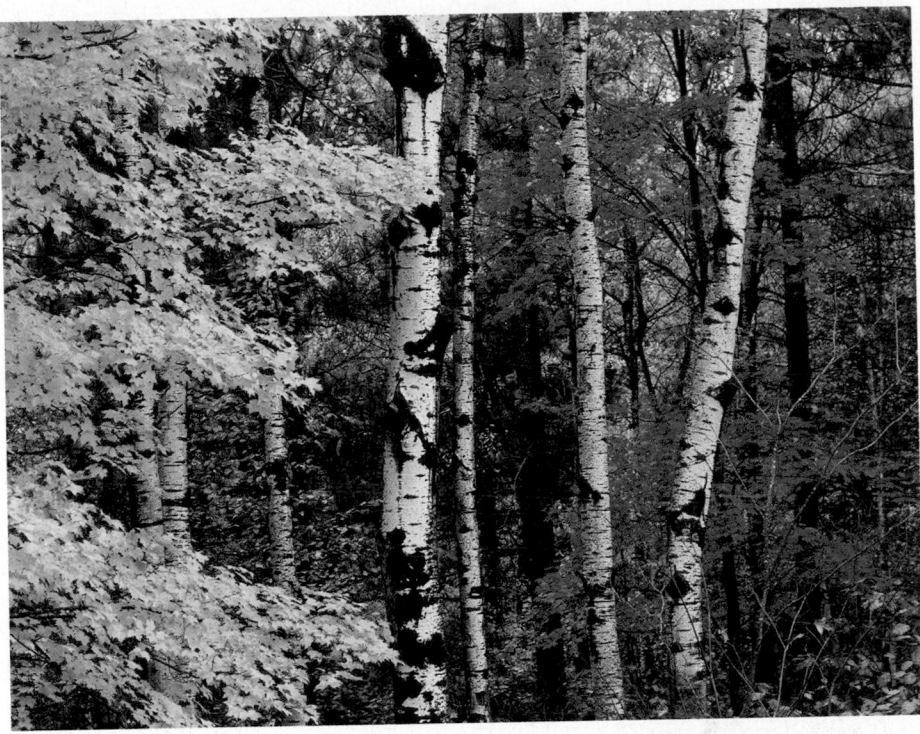

Figure 23.22
Seasonal Marker
Brightly colored fall leaves in Michigan's Ottawa National Forest. Plants have a number of mechanisms that allow them to respond to the passage of the seasons.

leafed trees lose their leaves, while the evergreen pines and firs keep the modified leaves known as needles?

First and foremost, there is relatively little water available in winter in cold climates (most of it being frozen in the ground), and flat-leafed trees transpire more than do evergreens. In addition, because of the way wind flows over flat leaves, they lose more *heat* than do pine needles. Thus, the deciduous trees have evolved a strategy that is a matter of straight economics. Such winter photosynthesis as they might perform would not be worth the water loss that would result. The strategy thus becomes to lose the leaves, grow new ones next spring, and in the meantime perform no photosynthesis but exist instead completely on food reserves. This state, in which growth is suspended and metabolic activity is low, is called **dormancy**. Evergreens exhibit dormancy too, in low temperatures, but deciduous trees are locked into it until the coming of spring.

Limitation of Loss in the Deciduous Strategy

The deciduous strategy, of first losing leaves and then growing them back, may at first seem very wasteful, akin to a company destroying much of its machinery each year, only to rebuild it months later. But consider how economical trees are about this. They *reclaim* the nutrients they have stored in their leaves. Proteins are broken down by enzymes and shipped, along with the nutrients, to storage cells in the stem and roots. By the time a leaf is ready for detachment from the tree, it is little more than an empty shell of cell walls.

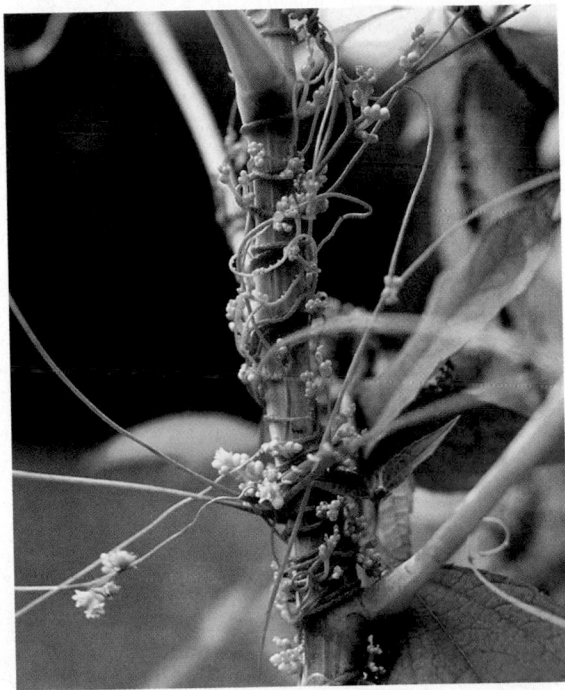

Figure 23.21
Moving Up by Curling Around
This dodder plant is able to curl around its host plant because of thigmotropism—a plant's ability to grow in response to touch.

Before this happens, however, the change in coloration takes place. It may surprise you to learn there is less adding of new colors here than an unmasking of colors that existed in the leaves all along. With the approach of fall, green chlorophyll, which is the main pigment in photosynthesis, begins to break down in the leaf. With it gone, the yellow and orange colors provided by the carotenoid pigments become visible. New colors are added as well; blue and red come with the synthesis of pigments called anthocyanins. (These pigments are largely responsible for the stunning red color of many maples in fall.) The combination of carotenoids and anthocyanins gives us the final result, which is multihued leaves.

Photoperiodism

So, how does a deciduous tree sense when it's time to begin preparing for cold weather? In general it is an interaction between two factors. First there is cold itself, which brings about changes in metabolism. In addition, there is a phenomenon known as **photoperiodism**, which is the ability of a plant to respond to changes it is experiencing in the daily duration of darkness, relative to light. This is another example of the plant's ability to respond to its environment, but it should not be confused with the "phototropism" or *bending* toward the light that was discussed earlier. In photoperiodism, plants are making seasonal adaptations based on the length of the nights they are experiencing. Most plants in the Earth's temperate regions and many in the subtropics exhibit photoperiodism, which can affect such processes as the timing of flowering as well as the onset of dormancy.

To get a feel for how photoperiodism works, consider ragweed, a plant that is the bane of many hayfever sufferers. After sprouting in the spring and reaching a certain level of maturity, ragweed flowers only when it is in darkness for 10 hours *or more* per day. When would this threshold be crossed? As the nights begin to get longer. Ragweed thus joins a group of plants, called long-night plants, whose flowering comes only with an *increased* amount of darkness. As you can imagine, most of these plants are like ragweed in that they flower only in late summer or early fall. Their counterparts are the so-called short-night plants, which flower only when the nights get short enough—that is to say, when nighttime hours are *decreasing* as a proportion of the day. Predictably, these plants tend to flower in early to midsummer.

The mechanism by which photoperiodism works is still something of a mystery. Long-night plants, as their name implies, need a certain uninterrupted period of darkness to be able to flower. Shine a light of a certain wavelength on many of these plants at night, even for a couple of minutes, during the time of year in which we would expect them to flower, and the flowering will be suppressed. Botanists have long known of a pigment family called *phytochrome* that provides the plant with information about the relative amounts of daylight or darkness, yet its role is clearly not controlling in the process. For us, the important point to note is that plants have a way of sensing the seasons and reacting to them.

On to a More Detailed Picture of Plants

This chapter has served to introduce you to the basic features of plants—their varieties, structures, and the most important systems that operate in them. There is more to say, however, about many of the topics that we haven't gone over (such as how trees grow *out* as well as up). Chapter 24 goes into more detail on plant structure and functioning, including the function of reproduction.

Chapter Review

Summary

23.1 The Importance of Plants

- Plants are vital to almost all life on Earth. The photosynthesis they carry out indirectly feeds many other life-forms. The oxygen they produce as a by-product of photosynthesis is vital to many organisms. The lumber and paper that trees provide is important to human beings. Plants act as an anchoring environmental force by preventing soil erosion and absorbing carbon dioxide and pollutants.

- There are four principal varieties of plants: bryophytes, represented by mosses; seedless vascular plants, represented by ferns; gymnosperms, represented by coniferous (evergreen) trees; and the flowering plants or angiosperms. Of the four varieties, angiosperms are by far the most dominant on Earth.

23.2 The Structure of Flowering Plants

- Plants live in two worlds, above the ground and below it. As such, their anatomy can be conceptualized as consisting of the above-ground shoots and the below-ground roots. Roots absorb water and nutrients, anchor the plant, and often act as nutrient storage sites. Shoots include the plant's leaves, stems, and flowers.

- Leaves serve as the primary sites of photosynthesis in most plants. Leaves have a profusion of tiny pores, called stomata, that open and close in response to the presence or absence of light. In this way, the stomata control the flow of carbon dioxide into the plant and the flow of oxygen and water vapor out of the plant.

- Stems give structure to plants and act as storage sites for food reserves.

- Flowers are the reproductive structures of plants, with most flowers containing both male and female reproductive parts. The male reproductive structure, called a stamen, consists of a slender filament topped by an anther. The anther's chambers contain the cells that will develop into sperm-containing pollen grains. The female reproductive structure, the carpel, is composed of a stigma, on which pollen grains are deposited; a tube called a style, which raises the stigma to such a height that it can catch pollen; and a structure called an ovary, where fertilization of the female egg and early development of the resulting embryo take place.
Web Tutorial 23.1: Flowering Plants

23.3 Basic Functions in Flowering Plants

- Pollen grains develop from cells called microspores inside the plant's anthers. At maturity, each pollen grain consists of two sperm cells, one tube cell, and an outer coat. When pollen grains from one plant land on the stigma of a second plant, they germinate, developing a pollen tube that grows down through the second plant's style. Sperm cells travel through the pollen tube, with one of the sperm cells reaching the egg in the ovary of the second plant and fertilizing it. Prior to this, the egg has developed from a cell called a megaspore within the ovary. Once it is fertilized by the sperm cell, the egg develops into an embryo that eventually will be surrounded by a tough outer covering. The combination of embryo, its food supply, and the outer covering is called a seed, which is capable of being implanted in the ground and growing into a new generation of plant. Angiosperms can be defined as plants whose seeds are surrounded by a layer of tissue called fruit. Fruit is the mature ovary of a flowering plant.

- Plants can reproduce asexually, through such means as grafting. This is known as vegetative reproduction.

- Fluid transport in plants is handled through two kinds of tissue: xylem, through which water and dissolved minerals flow; and phloem, through which the food the plant produces flows, along with hormones and other compounds. Xylem is composed of two types of fluid-conducting cells—vessel elements and tracheids—while phloem is composed of cells called sieve elements and their related companion cells.

- Plant hormones regulate plant growth and development and integrate the functioning of various plant structures. Many fruits ripen under the influence of the plant hormone ethylene, while the hormone IAA is important in controlling plant growth.

- Plants do not grow vertically throughout their length, but instead grow almost entirely at the tips of both their roots and shoots. Some plants, such as trees, thicken through lateral or "secondary" growth. The growth of most plants is indeterminate, meaning it can go on indefinitely.

- Plants have formidable defenses, both structural (such as cactus spines) and chemical (such as antifungal compounds).

- Plants enter into cooperative relationships with other organisms. Most plant roots are linked to fungal extensions called hyphae. This relationship brings added water and nutrients to the plant (from the hyphae) and food to the fungi (from the photosynthesis the plant performs). The combined root-hyphae associations are known as mycorrhizae. Some plants form cooperative relationships with nitrogen-fixing bacteria, the bacteria taking atmospheric nitrogen and transforming it into a form the plants can use, the plants providing the bacteria with nutrients.

23.4 Responding to External Signals

- Plants are able to sense their orientation with respect to the Earth and direct the growth of their roots and shoots accordingly—roots into the Earth, shoots toward the sky. This is called gravitropism.

- Plants will bend toward a source of light through the process of phototropism, meaning a curvature of shoots in response to light.

- Some plants can climb upward on other objects by making contact with them and then encircling them in growth. This is thigmotropism, defined as the growth of a plant in response to touch.

- Differential growth on one side of the root or stem makes possible phototropism, gravitropism, and thigmotropism.

- In temperate climates, deciduous trees exhibit a coordinated, seasonal loss of leaves and enter into a state of dormancy, existing on stored nutrient reserves in colder months.

- Plants can sense the passage of seasons and time their reproductive activities accordingly. One mechanism that assists in this process is photoperiodism, which is the ability of a plant to respond to changes it is experiencing in the daily duration of darkness, as opposed to light. Some plants that exhibit photoperiodism are long-night plants, meaning those whose flowering comes only with an increased amount of darkness—in late summer or early fall. Others are short-night plants, meaning those that flower only with a decreased amount of darkness—in early to midsummer.
Web Tutorial 23.2: Response to External Signals

Key Terms

angiosperm 489	**phloem** 490
anther 488	**photoperiodism** 498
apical dominance 492	**phototropism** 496
blade 485	**pollen tube** 488
carpel 488	**root hair** 484
deciduous 497	**seed** 489
dormancy 497	**sepal** 488
fibrous root system 484	**sperm cell** 488
filament 488	**sporophyte generation** 489
fruit 489	**stamen** 488
gametophyte generation 489	**stigma** 488
gravitropism 496	**stomata** 485
hormone 491	**style** 488
megaspore 488	**taproot system** 484
microspore 488	**thigmotropism** 497
mycorrhizae 495	**tissue** 490
nutrient 486	**transpiration** 484
ovary 488	**tube cell** 488
petal 488	**vegetative reproduction** 489
petiole 485	**xylem** 490

Understanding the Basics

Multiple-Choice Questions (answers in the back of the book)

1. Which of the following is not a benefit that plants provide to other living things?
   a. act to decompose dead organic material
   b. build up food supply
   c. lock up carbon dioxide from the atmosphere
   d. produce oxygen
   e. prevent soil erosion

2. Plants take in _____ and _____ through their roots, but take in _____ primarily through tiny pores on their leaves.
   a. minerals; carbon dioxide; water
   b. oxygen; carbon dioxide; water
   c. water; carbon dioxide; minerals
   d. oxygen; minerals; carbon dioxide
   e. minerals; water; carbon dioxide

3. Which of the following are not functions of roots? (Select all that apply.)
   a. nutrient storage
   b. loss of water through transpiration
   c. loss of oxygen in photosynthesis
   d. grow to water supplies
   e. absorption of water

4. You decide that you want your spruce tree in the front yard to be rounded instead of conical. What do you need to do to ensure that the plant no longer grows taller?
   a. Treat the top of the tree with growth hormones.
   b. Cut off the top of the tree.
   c. Trim the sides of the tree, but leave the top alone.
   d. Cover the top of the tree, so light cannot reach it.
   e. none of the above

5. Pollen grains are
   a. hormonal messengers that travel from one plant to another
   b. tiny food packets that move from one plant to another
   c. sperm-bearing sporophyte plants
   d. toxin-bearing packets that stunt the growth of other trees
   e. sperm-bearing gametophyte plants

6. Plant growth (select all that apply)
   a. occurs only in the midsection of any leaf, stem, or root
   b. serves almost solely to lengthen a plant, rather than widen it
   c. occurs, in vertical growth, only at the tips of roots or shoots
   d. must come to an end after a fixed number of months or years
   e. can go on as long as the plant is alive

7. The sucrose produced by photosynthesis is transported from the leaf to other parts of the plant through
   a. sieve elements
   b. vessel elements
   c. tracheids
   d. rhizoids
   e. guard cells

8. Fertilization in angiosperms occurs when
   a. a collection of seeds from a plant reaches the ground
   b. the megaspore in an ovary goes through meiosis
   c. pollen from one plant reaches the stigma of another
   d. a sperm cell from a pollen grain fuses with an egg cell in an ovary
   e. a seed begins to germinate in the ground

9. Phototropism and gravitropism lead to the bending of shoots or roots toward or away from a stimulus (light or gravity, respectively). Such bending is brought about by
   a. increased growth over the general surface of the root or shoot
   b. differential growth on opposite sides of the root or shoot
   c. decreased growth at the root or shoot apex, and increased growth at the base
   d. muscular contractions, leading to a curvature in the root or shoot
   e. all of the above

10. Photoperiodism allows some plants to respond to _____ by timing such things as _____ in accordance with the amount of _____ they are exposed to.
    a. predators; dormancy; moisture
    b. competition; growth; moisture
    c. the seasons; growth; toxins
    d. other plants; flowering; ethylene
    e. the seasons; flowering; darkness

Brief Review

1. The stomata that exist mostly on leaves allow important gas exchanges to take place in plants, but these exchanges also present plants with a problem they must solve. What gases are exchanged through the stomata, and in which direction? What problem must plants solve because of these exchanges, and how do they solve it?

2. What functions do roots perform? What are the main types of roots produced by flowering plants?

3. List the main parts of a flower, and describe the functions performed by each part.

4. Contrast the way people grow, and explain how plants grow and develop over their lifetimes.

5. Give examples of mutually beneficial relationships between plants and bacteria, and plants and fungi.

6. Distinguish between the gametophyte and sporophyte plant generations.

Applying Your Knowledge

1. Gardeners often "pinch off" the terminal shoot apex to stimulate bushiness in young plants. Explain the physiological basis for this common horticultural practice.

2. The text makes clear that plants respond to their environments in sophisticated ways, even to the point of signaling one another during attacks by predators. Given this, can plants be said to be conscious beings, or are animals the only conscious beings?

3. The "race for sunlight" in plants led to the evolution of the tallest living things in existence, trees. But sunlight is not the only thing that stands to make a tree successful or not in reproducing. Think about how plants function and then answer this question: What are the *costs* of being taller, as opposed to shorter?

24 Form and Function in Flowering Plants

Plant tubes.
(Section 24.3, page 509)

How woody plants grow wider.
(Section 24.5, page 513)

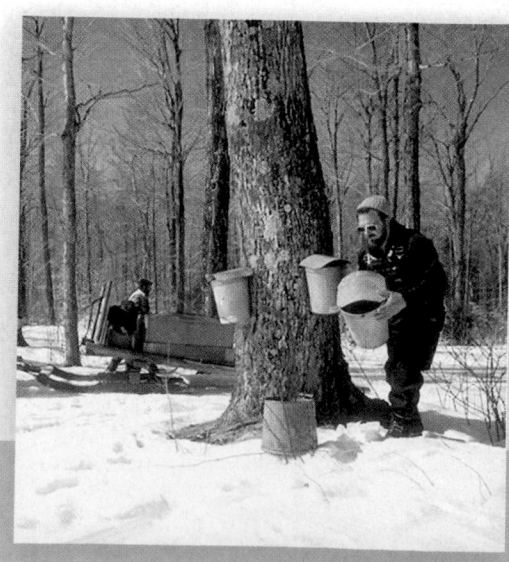

Pass the flapjacks.
(Essay, page 518)

Plants are fixed in one spot and have almost no moving parts, yet they manage to reproduce, transport fluids inside themselves, and keep growing for as long as they live.

Insects that eat plants are not much of a surprise, but plants that eat insects? About 500 species of flowering plants are carnivorous, with at least one variety, the tropical pitcher plant *Nepenthes*, able to capture animals up to the size of a small bird. But the most famous plant predator of them all undoubtedly is the Venus flytrap (*Dionaea muscipula*), which is native to the wetlands of North and South Carolina. So how does this plant, which has no muscles and is fixed in one spot, end up consuming insects?

Each trap is a single leaf folded in two, with the interlocking "fingers" of the two halves able to snap together in less than half a second, imprisoning any small wanderer (**see Figure 24.1**). But what keeps the leaf halves from wasting their energy by snapping together in pursuit of wind-borne blades of grass or other objects? The chemical reaction that puts the trap in motion is set off by a series of trigger hairs on the inside of each of the leaf's two sections. The trick is that *two* trigger hairs must be tripped in order for the halves of the leaf to snap shut. Insects wandering around inside the leaf are likely to trip two hairs, but blades of grass are not. And how does the plant slam its "jaws" shut without muscles? When the trigger hairs are tripped, they set off a chemical reaction that engorges cells at the base of the leaf with water. This rapid movement causes the leaf halves to come together. Enzymes are then released that begin to digest the struggling insect.

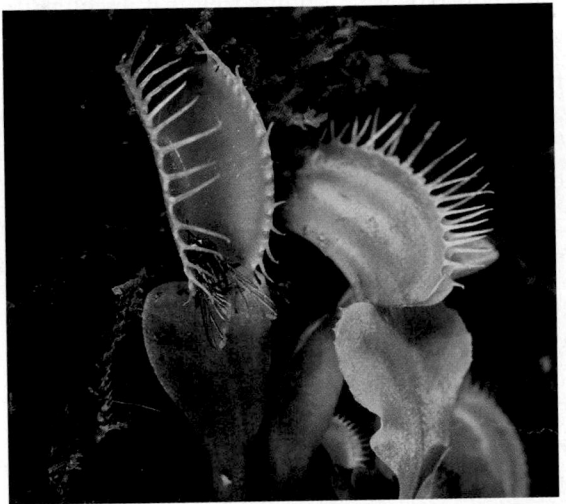

Figure 24.1
Fatal Entry
A fly enters the leaf of a Venus flytrap. Once the fly pulls on two trigger hairs within the leaf, its opposing halves will snap shut, trapping the fly. Then the plant will begin to digest its prey.

Food carriers.
(Section 24.6, page 519)

sink

sugar

water

root cell

vessel element

sieve element

Food and water take a trip.
(Section 24.6, page 520)

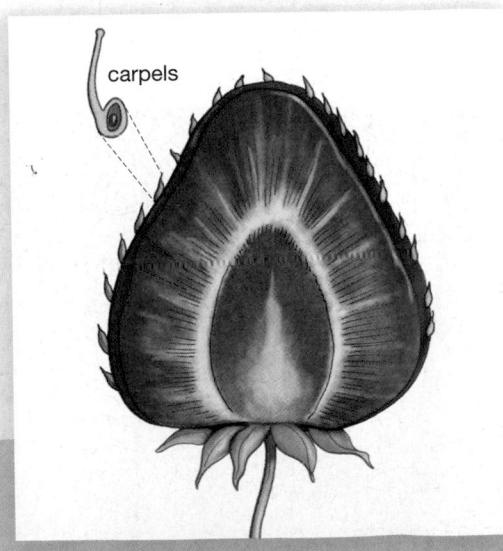

carpels

Where are the strawberry seeds?
(Section 24.8, page 526)

It may surprise you to learn that Venus flytraps make their own food through photosynthesis, just like any other plant. So why do they need these side orders of insects? For nutritional supplements. Like many other carnivorous plants, Venus flytraps grow naturally in mineral-poor soil, and the insects they catch are a good source of nitrogen and phosphate.

The world of plants is filled with species as unique in their own way as the Venus flytrap is. Queen Victoria water lilies (*Victoria regia*) have circular leaves that can be nearly 2 meters (about 6 feet) in diameter and that can serve as a floating platform for a person if pressed into service (**see Figure 24.2**). The seeds of orchids are so tiny that they resemble dust more than seeds, while the seeds of the double coconut come wrapped in a fruit that might be 0.6 meter (about 2 feet) across.

Yet there is a unity to plant life, particularly in the case of the flowering plants, or angiosperms, that you'll be looking at in this chapter. All angiosperms have a common set of cell types, for example, and all of them reproduce in a similar way. The goal in this chapter is to cover common angiosperm features in four areas: cell and tissue types, growth, fluid transport, and reproduction. Before we begin, it might be helpful to revisit the representation of the whole plant that you first saw in Chapter 23, so that you can "find your place" when reading about a plant's component parts. If you look at **Figure 24.3**, you can see a diagram of a typical plant, with its two-system division—roots and shoots—and the various parts of the plant that lie within these two systems. The function of each of these parts will become clear to you as you go through the details on them.

Figure 24.2
Floating Platforms
A woman plays a violin while standing atop a Victoria water lily at the Missouri Botanical Garden in St. Louis at the turn of the 20th century. The lilies are native to South America. Some South American Indians call the lilies *Yrupe*, which can be translated as "big water tray."

24.1 Two Ways of Categorizing Flowering Plants

The constituent parts of plants are often organized one way in a given kind of plant, but another way in a different type. So what are these types? Here are a couple of ways of *categorizing* plants, the significance of which will become apparent as you go along.

The Life Spans of Angiosperms: Annuals, Biennials, and Perennials

One important question that might be asked about any plant is: How long does it take for it to go through its entire life cycle—from being a seed germinating in the ground, through growth, flowering, seed dispersal, and then death? Plants that go through this cycle in one year or less are known as **annuals**. Some of these are food crops, such as tomatoes and the commercial grains. Plants that go through the cycle in about two years are **biennials**, which include carrots and cabbage. (Have you ever seen the flowers of a carrot plant? Probably not; we *pick* the taproots called carrots after one year, so their shoots don't get a chance to flower.) Plants that live for many years are known as **perennials**, a category that includes trees, woody shrubs such as roses, and many grasses. **Figure 24.4** shows some representative annuals, biennials, and perennials.

A Basic Difference among Flowering Plants: Monocotyledons and Dicotyledons

A second distinction among the flowering plants has to do with their anatomy, meaning the arrangement

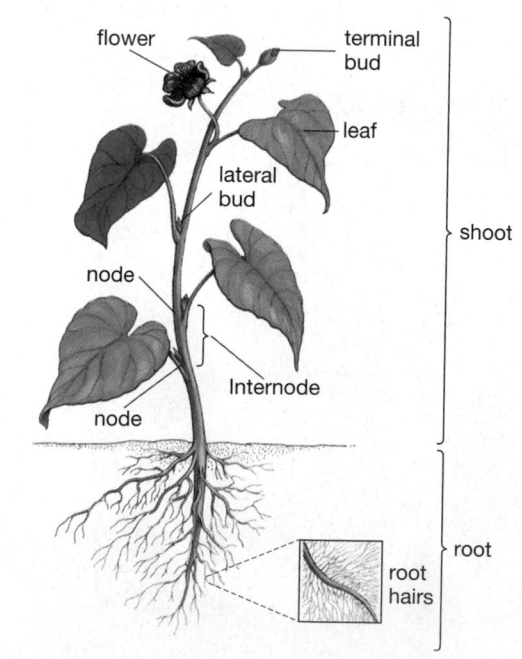

Figure 24.3
Anatomy of a Flowering Plant (An Angiosperm)

of the structures that make them up. With respect to anatomy, there are two broad classes of flowering plants: monocotyledons and dicotyledons, which are almost always referred to as monocots and dicots. A cotyledon is an embryonic leaf, present in the seed, as you can see in **Figure 24.5**. **Monocotyledons** are plants that have one embryonic leaf; **dicotyledons** are plants that have two.

This distinction in the embryos is only the start of how monocots and dicots differ. Their roots are different, their leaves are different, their transport tubes, or vascular bundles, are arranged differently (Figure 24.5). More than 75 percent of all flowering plants are the broad-leafed dicots. But given the

(a) One-year lifespan

(b) Two-year lifespan

(c) Variable lifespan

Figure 24.4
Categorizing Plants by Life Span

(a) Annuals such as tomato plants live for only one year.

(b) Biennials such as carrot plants have a two-year life span.

(c) Perennials such as this white oak tree live for many years, some for many hundreds of years. Plants with long life spans tend to be woody and larger than plants with short life spans.

	Monocots	Dicots
embryonic leaves	one cotyledon	two cotyledons
mature leaves	narrow leaves, parallel veins	broad leaves, branching veins
roots	fibrous root system	taproot system
vascular bundles	scattered throughout stem	arranged in ring in stem
type of growth	only primary growth	may have secondary woody growth
flower parts	multiples of three	multiples of four or five
examples	orchids, wheat, rice, bananas	oak and maple trees, cacti, sunflowers

Figure 24.5
A Cotyledon Is an Embryonic Leaf
Plants with one embryonic leaf (the monocots) are structured differently than plants with two embryonic leaves (the dicots), as shown in the figure.

260,000 known species of flowering plants, this still leaves more than 50,000 species of narrow-leafed monocots, which include most of the important food crops (corn, wheat, rice). **Figure 24.6** shows you an example of both a monocot and a dicot.

With these distinctions in mind, you're now ready to start looking at the basic elements that go into making up flowering plants.

24.2 There Are Three Fundamental Types of Plant Cells

You saw in Chapter 4 that all living things are made up of cells, and plants are no exception to this rule. As it happens, there are three fundamental types of plant cells that, alone or in combination with each other, go on to make up most of the plant's **tissues**, which are *groups* of cells that carry out a common function.

Parenchyma Cells

First, there are **parenchyma cells**, which have thin cell walls and are easily the most abundant type of cell in the plant, being found almost everywhere in it. Accordingly, these cells have a lot of different functions. They form the flesh of many fruits, the outer surface of most young plants, parts of leaves that are active in photosynthesis, and much of the "ground" tissue you'll be hearing about shortly. Further, parenchyma are alive at maturity, a quality that might hardly

seem worth mentioning except that some plant cells are dead in their mature, functioning state.

Sclerenchyma Cells

This dead-at-maturity condition characterizes a second type of plant cell, **sclerenchyma cells**, which have thick cell walls that help the plant return to its original shape when it has been deformed by some force, such as the push of wind or animals. Sclerenchyma cells are found in parts of the plant that are mature—that will not be growing further, and that need the support that sclerenchyma can provide. Like all plant cells, sclerenchyma have, running through their cell walls, a compound called **cellulose** that can be likened to the steel bars in reinforced concrete. Most sclerenchyma cell walls also are infused with a tough compound called *lignin*. The combination of lignin and cellulose results in cells that can bear the crushing weight of massive trees (**see Figure 24.7**).

Collenchyma Cells

The third type of plant cell, **collenchyma cells**, can be thought of as support cells, like sclerenchyma cells, but with the function of stretching or elongating in parts of the plant that are growing, such as young leaves and stems. Collenchyma cells combine the properties of parenchyma and sclerenchyma cells, performing some of the functions of each of these cell types. They provide mechanical strength in areas that are actively growing, and can also participate to some extent in photosynthesis and wound repair.

Parenchyma as Starting-State Cells

Both collenchyma and sclerenchyma are derived from parenchyma cells; that is, some parenchyma cells differentiate *into* collenchyma or sclerenchyma cells. Parenchyma are thus a kind of starting-state cell, but their capabilities are greater than this. They can be transformed "backward," in a sense, into the type of embryonic cells that give rise to the whole plant. You may have wondered in Chapter 23 how we can get a new plant by taking a cutting from an existing plant and placing it in the ground. The answer is that when a plant is cut, parenchyma cells lying close to the cut are transformed into *growth* cells of a type you'll look at shortly, and these can sprout a new root. This obviously gives plants a flexibility not possessed by animals such as ourselves. If one of our fingers is cut off, we do not grow a new finger, to say nothing of a whole new person.

(a) Monocot plant

(b) Dicot plant

Figure 24.6
Categorizing Plants by Physical Features

(a) Corn is one of several monocot plants that are food crops.

(b) Geraniums are an example of a dicot. See Figure 24.5 for a list of the anatomical differences between monocots and dicots.

24.3 The Plant Body and Its Tissue Types

You saw earlier that tissues are groups of cells that carry out a common function. So what kinds of tissues are there in angiosperms? The short answer is dermal, ground, vascular, and meristematic, with each of these four types of tissue generally being composed of one or more of the cell types you just looked at. Dermal tissue can be thought of as the plant's outer covering, vascular tissue as its transport or "plumbing" tissue, meristematic tissue as its growth tissue, and ground tissue as almost everything else in the plant.

First: A Distinction Between Primary and Secondary Growth Tissue

Before proceeding further with this topic, we need to take note of a basic distinction in plant tissue that has to do with the way plants grow. Some plants are capable only of what is called **primary growth**, meaning growth at the tips of their roots and shoots that principally increases their *length*. In contrast, other plants exhibit not only primary growth but also something known as **secondary growth**, which can be thought of as the *lateral* growth, or thickening, that occurs in **woody plants**. Secondary growth occurs in trees, for example, but not in orchids or strawberry plants. Non-woody plants such as an orchid are known as **herbaceous plants**, meaning those that never develop wood (or bark) and that thus contain only primary tissue. It is this *primary* tissue that you will look at first, with a review of secondary tissue to come shortly.

If you look at **Figure 24.8**, you can see the location of all four kinds of primary tissue in a dicot. Looking at the stem in cross section, you can see that ground tissue is well named, because visually it forms a kind of background against which you can see the tubes of the vascular tissue. Dermal tissue then is at the periphery of the plant, forming a "skin" layer around the ground tissue. The placement of the meristematic tissue is discussed shortly. First, let's look in a little more detail at dermal, ground, and vascular tissue.

Dermal Tissue Is the Plant's Interface with the Outside World

Plants can't move, they can't bite, and, as you saw in Chapter 23, they must carefully control their water supply. All this makes their **dermal tissue**, or *epidermis*, very important to them. This outer coat is generally only one layer of cells thick, but it serves to protect the plant and control its interaction with the outside world

Figure 24.7
Plant-Cell Walls Are Composed of Composite Materials, as Is Reinforced Concrete
The cellulose fibers of plant-cell walls are very strong in tension, as are the steel bars in reinforced concrete. Lignin is similar to the matrix of concrete in that it binds the fibers together and resists compression. Both plant-cell walls and reinforced concrete are important in providing support for structures that are tall and heavy.

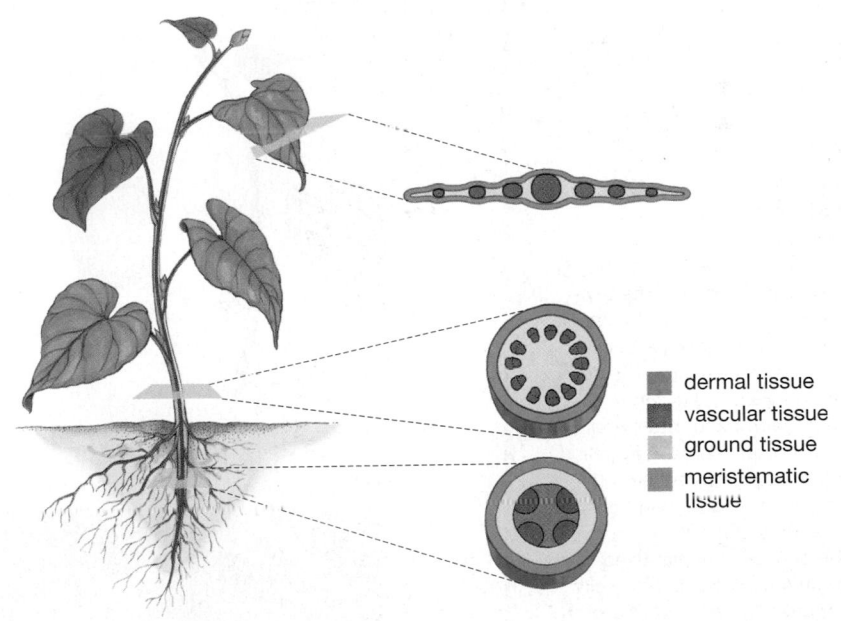

Figure 24.8
Four Types of Tissue in Primary Plant Growth
Dermal tissue (dark green) is found on the outside of the plant and is the interface between the plant and its environment. Ground tissue (pale green) is found throughout the plant and gives the plant its shape, stores food, and is active in photosynthesis. Vascular tissue (purple) transports water, nutrients, and sugar throughout the plant. Meristematic tissue (blue) occurs at the tips of shoots and roots and at leaf bases, and gives rise to the entire plant, through the production of cells that develop into the other three tissue types.

(**see Figure 24.9**). A plant's first line of defense against outside predators is a waxy coating called the *cuticle* that covers the epidermis of the plant's above-ground parts (its shoot). The cuticle is a kind of waterproofing, serving to keep water in, and an invader-proofing, helping to keep infecting bacteria and fungi out.

Plants need to exchange gases with their environments, however. They take in carbon dioxide and emit oxygen and water vapor through the microscopic pores called stomata, found mostly on the underside of their leaves. (You went over the functioning of stomata in Chapter 23, starting on page 485.) Stomata also represent a kind of weak point for plants, however, because they provide a passageway for microbial invaders and a conduit for excessive loss of moisture.

Dermal tissue also forms several kinds of extensions, called trichomes, that protrude from the plant's surface. You learned about one variety of them in Chapter 23: root hairs, meaning the thread-like outgrowths of individual epidermal root cells. As we noted there (page 484), these wispy outgrowths greatly increase the plant's ability to absorb water and minerals. Other types of trichomes serve not to absorb substances, but to secrete them. In some plants, trichomes secrete toxic chemicals that ward off plant-eating animals.

Ground Tissue Forms the Bulk of the Primary Plant

Most of the primary plant is ground tissue, which can play a role in photosynthesis, storage, and structure (**see Figure 24.10**). Large parts of ground tissue may be simple parenchyma, but other parts are combinations of cell types.

Vascular Tissue Forms the Plant's Transport System

As you saw Chapter 23, the plant's vascular system has two main functions. First, it must transport water and minerals; second, it must transport the food made in photosynthesis. In line with this, there are two main components to the plant vascular system. First there is **xylem**, the tissue through which water and dissolved minerals flow. Second there is **phloem**, the tissue that conducts the food produced in photosynthesis, along with some hormones and other compounds (**see Figure 24.11**). The movement of water through xylem is directional—from root up through stem and then out through leaves as water vapor. Meanwhile, the food made in photosynthesis must travel through phloem to every part of the plant, though, as a

Figure 24.9
Where Plant Meets Environment
Dermal tissue serves as the interface between a plant and the environment around it. The waxy cuticle and the single layer of cells in the epidermis work together to protect the plant and to control interactions with the outside world.
(a) Specialized epidermal cells called guard cells regulate the opening of the plant pores called stomata, thus controlling gas exchange between the plant and its environment. Here, guard cells have opened two stomata. In most plants, the majority of stomata are found on the leaves.
(b) Some epidermal cells have hair-like projections, called trichomes, that serve various functions. Two kinds of trichomes are visible in this rose plant. The larger of the two varieties, with the bulbous tips, help secrete chemicals that guard against plant-eating predators.

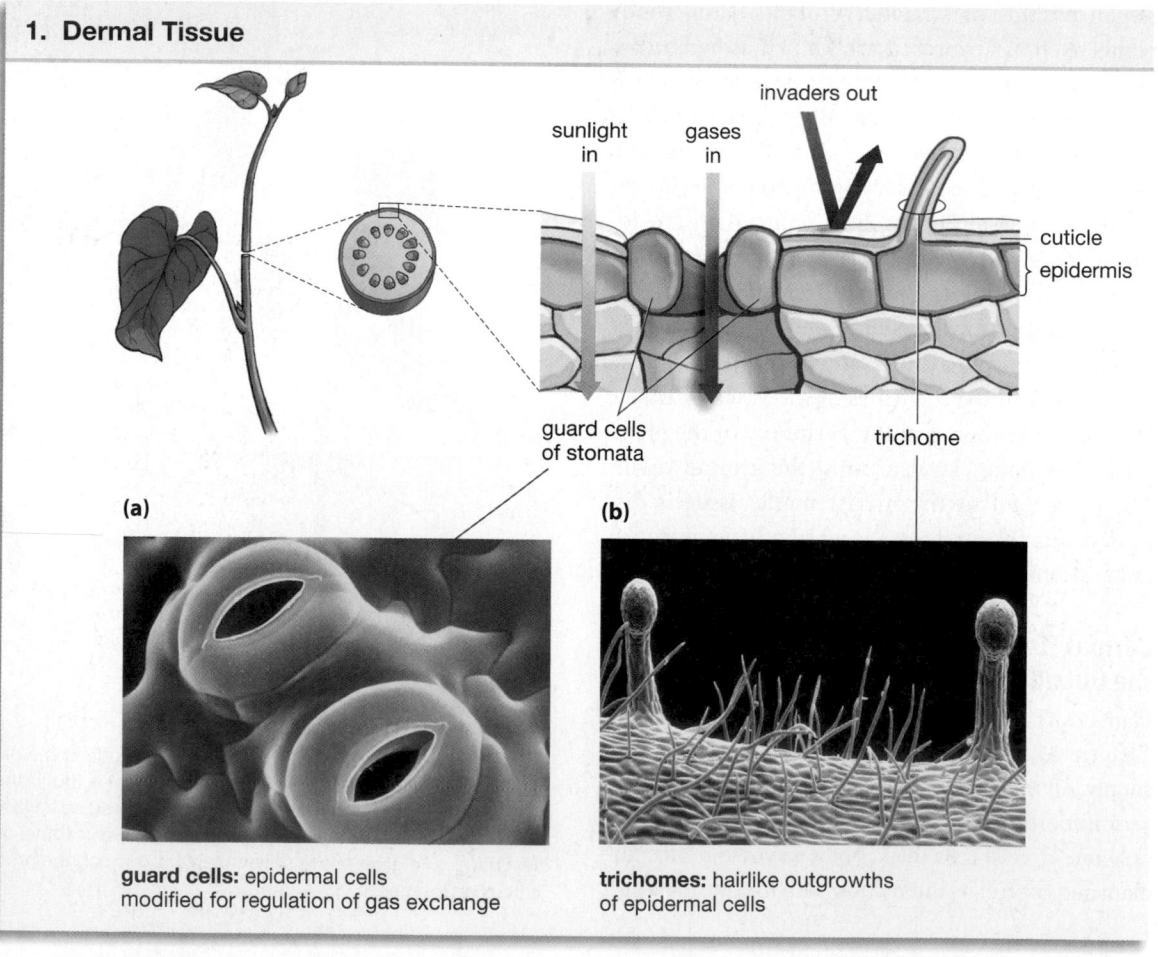

1. Dermal Tissue

invaders out

sunlight in   gases in

cuticle
epidermis

guard cells of stomata

trichome

(a)

(b)

guard cells: epidermal cells modified for regulation of gas exchange

trichomes: hairlike outgrowths of epidermal cells

2. Ground Tissue

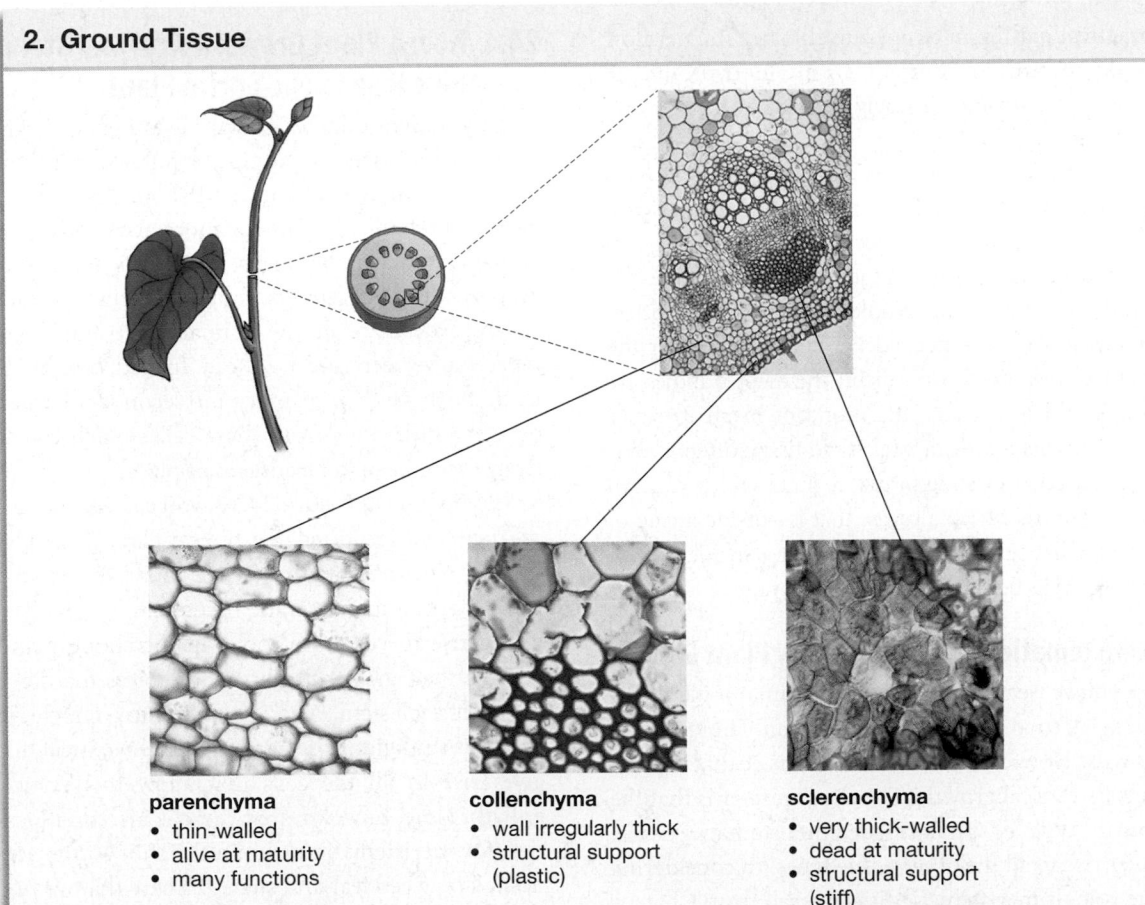

parenchyma
- thin-walled
- alive at maturity
- many functions

collenchyma
- wall irregularly thick
- structural support (plastic)

sclerenchyma
- very thick-walled
- dead at maturity
- structural support (stiff)

Figure 24.10
Ground Tissue
Most of a plant is made of ground tissue, which is composed of parenchyma, collenchyma, and sclerenchyma cells. Examples of these cell types shown here come from several different plants. In a cross section of a stem, thin-walled parenchyma can be found in most of the interior. Collenchyma—at the bottom of the collenchyma picture, surrounded by parenchyma—are support cells that can elongate in growing parts of the plant. Very thick-walled sclerenchyma, such as these from a pear, can provide strength to tissues.

3. Vascular Tissue

vascular bundle

xylem

phloem

tracheid

vessel element

sieve element

companion cell

Figure 24.11
Materials Movers
Vascular tissue transports fluids throughout the plant. Xylem is composed of cells called tracheids and vessel elements that transport water and dissolved minerals. Phloem is composed of sieve elements (and their companion cells), which transport the food produced during photosynthesis. These cell types are stacked upon one another to form long tubes.

practical matter, in temperate climates the net flow is downward in summer (from food-producing leaves) but upward in early spring (from root and stem storage sites).

Xylem and phloem are arranged in *vascular bundles*, which is to say collections of xylem and phloem tubes that run together in parallel in the stem—xylem tubes toward the inside of the stem, phloem tubes toward the outside. The bundles are arranged in different ways within a stem, depending on whether the plant is a monocot or a dicot; the dicot bundles are configured in a circle, the monocot in an irregular pattern. This is why dicot ground tissue often is conceptualized as existing in two regions, which you can see in **Figure 24.12**: a *cortex* that is outside a ring of the vascular bundles, and a *pith* that is inside it, with the pith cells being specialized for storage.

Meristematic Tissue and Primary Plant Growth

So you've seen three types of primary plant tissues—dermal, ground, and vascular. The question now is: How do these arise? How is it that a plant gets its vertical growth? The short answer is that the fourth type of plant tissue, meristematic tissue, gives rise to all the other tissue types. In considering the role of meristematic tissue, recall from Chapter 23 that, in their vertical growth, plants do not grow the way people do—throughout their entire length—but instead grow only at the tips of their roots and shoots. In addition, a plant's growth is *indeterminate*; in most plants, it can go on indefinitely at the tips of roots and shoots, as opposed to animal growth, which generally comes to an end when the animal matures.

Web Tutorial 24.1
Plant Tissue and Growth

24.4 How a Plant Grows: Apical Meristems Give Rise to the Entire Plant

Putting indeterminate growth together with the concept of growth at the tips, it follows that there must be plant cells at root and shoot tips that remain perpetually young—or more accurately, perpetually embryonic. That is, these cells are able to keep dividing, thereby giving rise to cells that then differentiate into all the primary cell and tissue types you've been reading about. Indeed, everything in plants (both their primary and secondary tissues) develops ultimately from these cells, which collectively form the **apical meristems** of plants.

If you look at **Figure 24.13**, you can see the apical meristem locations in a typical plant. Note that in this plant with a taproot, each lateral root tip has its own apical meristematic tissue that is capable of giving rise to yet more roots. In the shoot, plants confine their growth to the shoot apices that lie at the tip of each stem. Why? The better to compete for precious sunlight. It is the **shoot apical meristem** that gives rise to all the cells that allow this vertical growth. Note, however, that there is a second location for meristematic tissue in the shoot—the area nestled between leaf and stem. It's here that we find lateral buds (sometimes called *axillary buds*). Any **bud** is an undeveloped shoot, composed mostly of meristematic tissue. A **lateral bud** is meristematic tissue that may give rise to a branch or a flower (which obviously ends up growing laterally from the stem). Lateral buds also serve, however, as a kind of insurance policy for the plant in that they can switch roles. Should the plant's apical meristem be-

(a) Monocot stem

(b) Dicot stem

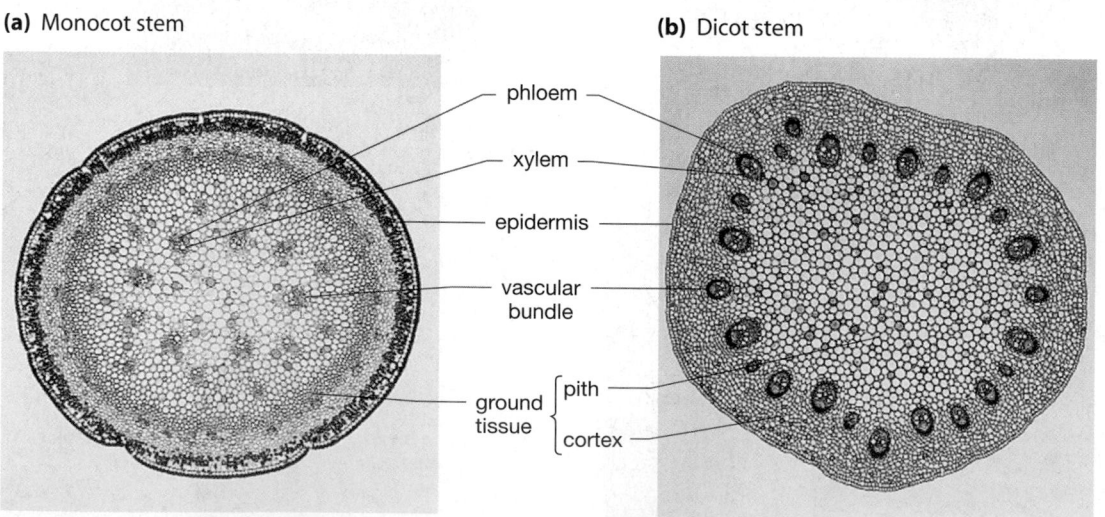

phloem
xylem
epidermis
vascular bundle
ground tissue
pith
cortex

Monocots (in this case an onion) have vascular bundles arranged in an irregular pattern within ground tissue.

Dicots (in this case a buttercup) have vascular bundles arranged in a ring that separates the ground tissue into pith on the inside of the bundles and cortex on the outside.

Figure 24.12
Two Types of Flowering Plants
These cross sections show the organization of primary tissues in a monocot and a dicot.

4. Meristematic Tissue

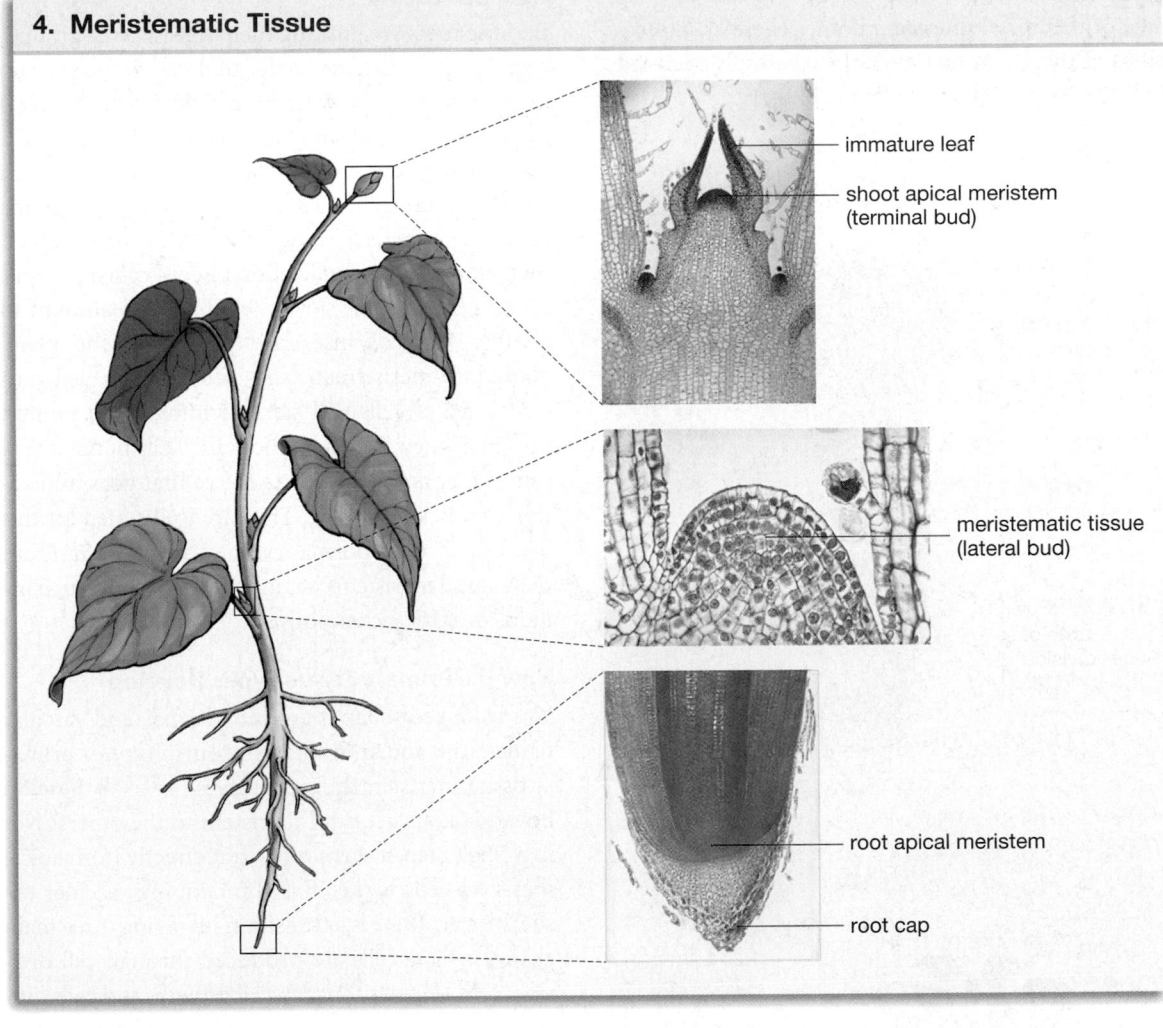

immature leaf

shoot apical meristem
(terminal bud)

meristematic tissue
(lateral bud)

root apical meristem

root cap

**Figure 24.13
Meristematic Tissue**
Growth originates from meristematic tissue. The shoot and root elongate at the apical meristems, while new branches originate at the lateral buds. Meristematic tissue gives rise to more dermal, ground, and vascular tissue, as well as more of itself.

come damaged, one of the lateral buds steps in to assume the role of the shoot apex, thus allowing the plant to maintain its vertical growth. As long as the original apical meristem is intact, however, it generally will produce hormones that *suppress* the growth of the lateral buds near it, leaving them dormant. The shoot apex is itself sometimes referred to as a **terminal bud**, particularly when *it* is dormant, as with trees in winter.

We can think of plant growth in terms of growth modules. Each module consists of an internode (the stem between leaves), a node (the area where a leaf attaches to stem), and one or more leaves (**see Figure 24.14**).

A Closer Look at Root and Shoot Apical Meristems
Now let's look a little closer at these important collections of cells from which all else comes, the shoot and root apical meristems. The right-hand pictures in Figure 24.13 show you what shoot apical meristem, lateral bud, and root apical meristem look like up close.

Shoot Meristems
As you can see in the topmost picture, the shoot apical meristem lies atop a dome-shaped collection of cells. Overlapping it are two budding leaves that serve a protective function. Next, in the middle picture, you can see a second shoot location for meristematic tissue—the lateral bud, nestled between leaf and stem. These buds are collections of meristematic tissue that are left behind, in a sense, by the apical meristem tissue as it continues its growth. (If you look again at the topmost picture, you can see

**Figure 24.14
Vertical Growth in Plants Occurs
in Modules**
Each growth module (indicated here by alternating dark green and light green segments) consists of an internode, a node, and one or more leaves. This plant progresses from one module in week one to four modules in week four.

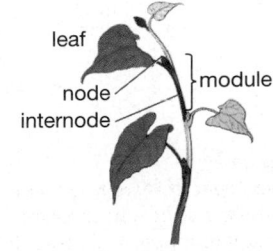

leaf

node

internode

module

week one   week two   week three   week four two small collections of darker-colored cells on each side of the apical meristem dome. These are collections of meristem tissue that have recently been left behind; they will become lateral buds.)

Figure 24.15
Tissue Development from Apical Meristems
Apical meristems give rise to the primary tissues. In development, cells first are mostly engaged in division, just above the apical meristem, then elongation, and finally differentiation. The result is three fully formed kinds of tissue.

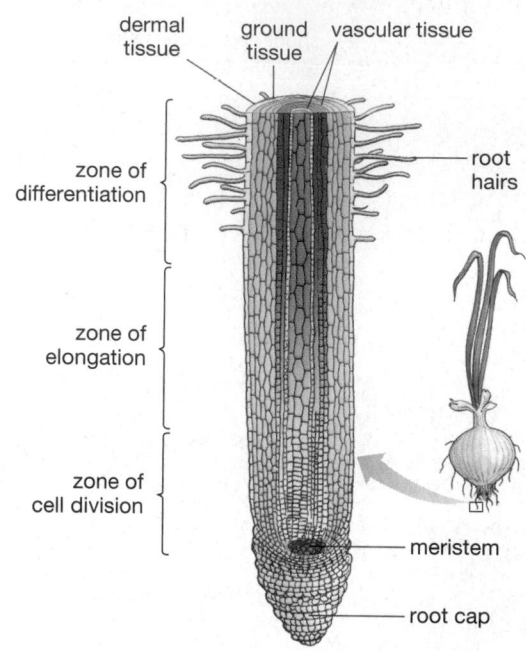

Figure 24.16
Growth by Cell Elongation
Much of the elongation of the shoot and root in a young plant results from cell elongation rather than from cell division. Thus it is cells just above the root tip, in the zone of elongation, that provide most of the root's growth, as shown here. The tip of the root (where cell division occurs) has elongated very little, and the cells in the upper root have completed most of their elongation. This same pattern holds true for the shoot.

Root Meristems

Because roots are pushing their way into the ground, root apical meristems are located not at the very tip of the root, but just up from the tip. The root apical meristems are adjacent to a collection of cells called a **root cap** that both protects the meristematic cells and secretes a lubricant that helps ease the way for the root in its progress. Toward the middle of the apical meristem, there is a collection of cells called the quiescent center. These slowly dividing cells amount to another kind of insurance policy for the plant. Should the meristematic cells become damaged, quiescent center cells will start dividing more rapidly, producing new meristematic cells. Cells in the quiescent center are, in short, a reserve that goes into action in times of trouble. They are well suited for this because, in their dormancy, they are more resistant than apical meristem cells are to injury from such influences as toxic chemicals.

How the Primary Tissue Types Develop

You've looked so far at ground, dermal, and vascular tissues. And you know that the fourth type of primary tissue, meristematic tissue, gives rise to all these. So how do plants get from meristem to the others? Not in a single step, it turns out—not directly from apical meristem cells to, say, fully functioning vascular tissue. Instead, there is a transition involving three main changes: *More* cells are produced through cell division; cells *elongate* through cell growth; and cells *differentiate* into the three kinds of tissue. These three changes are overlapping—cells are elongating even as they are differentiating—but events do take place in roughly this order. You can see this by looking at **Figure 24.15**. In a gradual transition with no sharp boundaries, the apical meristem gives way to a **zone of cell division**, then there is a **zone of elongation**, and finally a **zone of differentiation**, which is where the ground, dermal, and vascular tissues fully take shape. Note that root hairs don't appear until the zone of differentiation. Though the three kinds of tissues *finish* taking shape in the zone of differentiation, they actually begin this process just above the apical meristem (in the zone of cell division). It's accurate to think of the tissues in the zone of cell division as being precursors to the three tissue types.

If you look at **Figure 24.16**, you can see the practical effect of a zone of elongation: It is where most of the primary plant growth occurs. There is some growth with the addition of more cells down near the apical meristem, but most of the vertical expansion of the plant takes place because of cell elongation. Such elongation has the effect of extending the roots into the soil and the stem into the air.

513

24.5 Secondary Growth
Comes from a Thickening
of Two Types of Tissues

Intercalary Meristems Keep Grasses Growing

There is one important variation on primary growth through apical meristems. What about plants such as grasses that are constantly losing their tops through such means as grazing or mowing? Grasses get their growth from tissue known as **intercalary meristems**, which are found at the base of *each node*. There thus exists a series of vertical growth tissues that are intercalated, or interspersed, between regions of nondividing cells as we go up the plant. One practical effect of this structure is that when we mow the top half of a blade of grass, it grows back. A second is that, because these plants are growing at *many* points along their length (rather than just their apex), they can manifest very rapid growth. We can easily see nodes in the giant grass known as bamboo, which exhibits intercalary growth (**see Figure 24.17**).

24.5 Secondary Growth Comes from a Thickening of Two Types of Tissues

So far, you've been looking at a plant's vertical or primary growth. In the herbaceous plants that's all the growth there is. But you've seen that some plants—the woody plants—grow out as well as up and down; they have primary *and* secondary growth, in other words (**see Figure 24.18**). So how does this secondary growth come about? Once again, through cells that are meristematic. In essence, secondary growth yields three new kinds of tissue: a different type of xylem and phloem—secondary xylem and secondary phloem—and several layers of outer tissue that collectively go under the familiar name of *bark*.

At the start, it's worth noting that secondary growth in plants is related to two of the plant characteristics that we reviewed at the start of the chapter. First, secondary growth almost always takes place in perennials, rather than annuals (though plenty of perennials exhibit only primary growth, as with grasses). Second, with very few exceptions, the monocots described earlier have only primary growth. Meanwhile, dicots are more often woody, though many are herbaceous.

Secondary Growth through the Vascular Cambium: Secondary Xylem and Phloem

You saw earlier that the plant's vascular tissues are arranged into bundles of tube-like vessels, with the food-carrying phloem tubes toward the outside of the stem and the water-carrying xylem tubes toward the inside. In a cross section of a dicot plant stem, these tubes form concentric rings. If you look at the plant another way—through its entire *length*—you can see that these rings take the shape of cylinders that are nested, as if these layers of tissue were a series of open-ended cans, one inside the next (**see Figure 24.19**).

Figure 24.18
Growing Up versus Growing Out
Herbaceous plants grow at their tips, mostly vertically, through primary growth. Woody plants, however, grow not only vertically but also laterally, through what is called secondary growth. Dicots can be either woody or herbaceous, but almost all monocots are herbaceous.

Figure 24.17
Intercalary Meristems Keep Grasses Growing
One reason bamboo grows so rapidly is that growth occurs at several points along its length at once. The intercalary meristems responsible for this growth are located at the base of each internode.

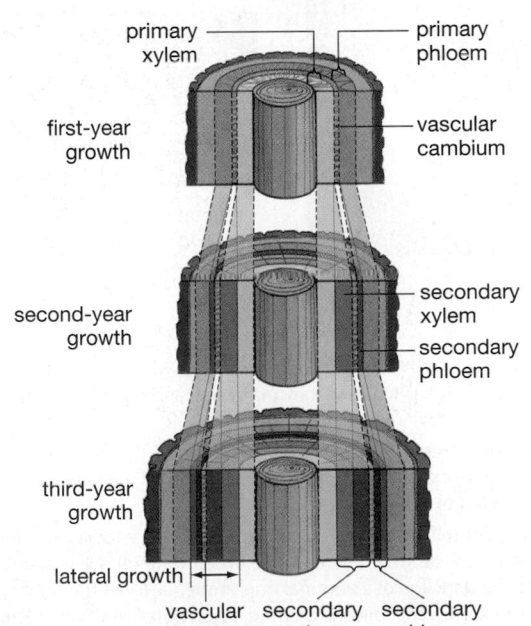

Figure 24.19
Vascular Cambium and Secondary Growth
Vascular cambium is meristematic tissue that produces secondary xylem tissue to its interior and secondary phloem tissue to its exterior. Over the years, the thickening of a tree comes about primarily because of the growth of secondary xylem.

Now notice that woody plants develop a thin layer of tissue *between* the primary xylem and primary phloem cylinders. This is the **vascular cambium**, one of the additional types of meristematic tissue that brings about secondary growth. The vascular cambium has one group of cells in it, called *ray initials*, that produce exactly what their name indicates:

rays of parenchyma cells that carry water and dissolved compounds through the *width* of the plant. (If you've ever looked at the stump of a tree, you've probably noticed fine lines that seem to radiate out, from near the center to the periphery of the trunk. These are the tree's transport rays, made up of parenchyma cells that form streaks of living cells in an expanse of dead xylem. You can see an example of them in Figure 24.22.)

More important for our purposes, the vascular cambium is something like a cell factory that is continually pushing out two different kinds of cells to either side of itself. The result is two new cylinders of tissue: **secondary xylem** to the inside of the vascular cambium, and **secondary phloem** to the outside. Secondary xylem and phloem initially do just what primary xylem and phloem do: transport, through the *length* of the plant, water through xylem and food through phloem. **Figure 24.20** shows you how the vascular cambium pulls off its feat of two-way xylem/phloem production. Note in the figure that the cells of the vascular cambium divide, producing one cell that differentiates into either xylem or phloem and another cell that remains vascular cambium. This process continues over and over again, causing the stem of the plant to thicken.

**Figure 24.20
How Vascular Cambium
Thickens the Plant**
The cells of the vascular cambium divide, producing one cell that differentiates into either xylem or phloem and another cell that remains vascular cambium. This process repeats, causing the stem of the plant to thicken.

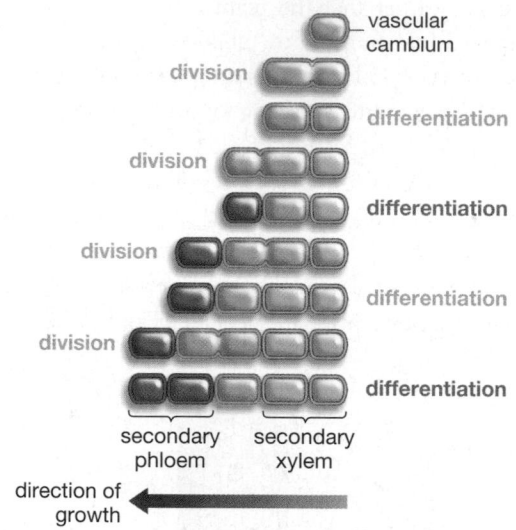

Secondary Xylem Is Responsible for Most of a Plant's Widening

It is the secondary xylem that is responsible for most of the widening of trees and other woody plants. Indeed, another term for secondary xylem is **wood**, a material that comprises about 90 percent of an average tree. After an initial period of carrying water, the secondary xylem cells will cease doing this, but are still valuable to the tree because of their strength.

Almost everyone is familiar with the annual rings of trees in temperate climates such as ours. But what is each visible ring? **Figure 24.21** tells the tale. Each ring represents the abrupt change between the secondary xylem of late summer and the secondary xylem of the following spring. In late summer, when plants are getting little water, they produce xylem cells with smaller interiors and proportionately thicker cell walls. Because cell walls are *darker* than the cell interiors, the summer xylem cells are relatively dark. Come next spring, with its plentiful water, the cells that are produced are much larger and thus have lighter color. Thus, the "line" of any given ring is made up of darker, late-summer cells. We can look just to the outside of any line and say "spring began here." To learn more about what we can tell by looking at a cross section of a felled tree, see "A Tree's History Can Be Seen in Its Wood."

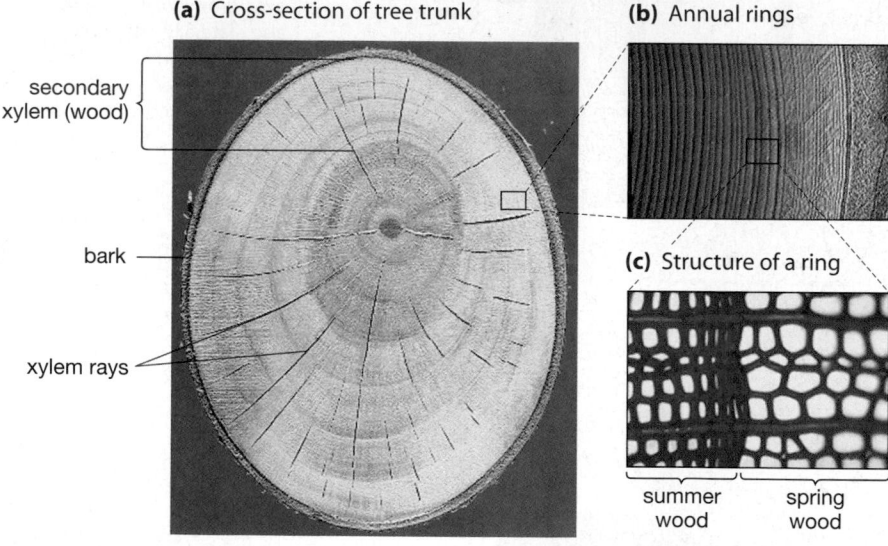

(a) Cross-section of tree trunk

(b) Annual rings

(c) Structure of a ring

**Figure 24.21
Annual Rings Tell Time and More**

(a) The thick secondary xylem (the wood) of a tree contains many concentric rings, with the dark line of each ring representing the end of one year's growth. The xylem rays transport water and nutrients laterally through the trunk.

(b) This close-up of the annual rings from an actual tree shows how growth can vary with environmental conditions. The earlier growth rings on the left are thicker than the rings on the right. The tree grew less in each of the later years because it was being affected by acid rain.

(c) This micrograph of a pine tree shows the structural basis for annual rings. On the left—toward the inside of the trunk—are smaller cells that grew in late summer and early fall, when water was less plentiful. The very narrow cells at left center create the dark line of an annual ring. Immediately to the right of these densely packed cells are the larger cells that grew the following spring, when water was again plentiful. These larger cells are visible as the lighter wood in the trunk.

A Tree's History Can Be Seen in Its Wood

Everyone knows about looking at the cross section of a felled tree trunk and counting its "rings" to gauge the age of the tree. But what other stories does this kind of tree wood have to tell?

First, are the rings wider in some years than others? To the extent that the tree grew more in a given year, it will have a wider ring. The wider the ring, the more likely it is that optimal conditions for growth existed during that year: plentiful rainfall, enough sun, a lack of pests. A series of unusually narrow rings probably means just the opposite (**see Figure 1**).

Next, are the rings perfectly concentric, or are they *eccentric* at some point in the tree's growth? Is a given set of circles wide on, say, the left as you look at the trunk, but narrower on the right, as in Figure 1? If so, it may be because some force—for example, pressure from another tree—was bending the tree trunk toward the left at that point in its history. Because trees prosper by being as tall as they can, they will resist being pushed over. They do so by growing extra wood on one *side* of themselves. The wider areas in a given set of circles represent this extra wood, known as *reaction wood*.

Look at the center of any large log, and the wood you see there is almost always darker than the surrounding wood. Why? The inner wood—which like all wood is secondary xylem—has long since closed down with respect to its water-transport function. The cells that make up the water columns were always dead in their mature, water-transporting state; but eventually each column was severed altogether, meaning it quit conducting water. The problem is that an *empty* xylem column is a *dangerous* column as far as the tree is concerned, because a fungus could grow right up through it. Therefore, trees have developed a plugging mechanism: Surrounding living cells push material into the columns, sealing them off. Over time, these cells produce oils, lignin, and microbe-fighting substances and then die themselves. The result is a center of a tree that is completely dead—and dark in coloration—but strong in its load-bearing strength and resistant to bacteria and fungi. This is the tree's *heartwood*. Its counterpart is the tree's *sapwood*—the lighter, outer wood whose xylem tubes are still conducting xylem sap.

reaction wood

heartwood (non-transporting, plugged-up xylem)

sapwood (functioning xylem)

phloem

annual rings

xylem ray

bark

Figure 1
The Anatomy of Wood

Secondary Growth through the Cork Cambium: The Plant's Periphery

With the secondary xylem cells pushing out from the interior of the tree or shrub, the plant's original outer covering (its epidermis) can't last. It splits apart, eventually to be shed altogether, usually within a year. Before it goes, however, the plant develops a new kind of outer covering, one that has the ability to renew itself constantly as the plant continues to grow. This quality may sound familiar by now, and indeed **cork cambium** represents the final type of meristematic tissue you'll be encountering—one that gives rise to the plant's outer tissues (**see Figure 24.22**).

The cork cambium itself is a product of other tissue in the stem—in a mature tree, the secondary phloem tissue you just looked at. Cork cambium is once again secondary meristematic tissue, which is like a cell factory that is continually pushing out different kinds of cells to either side of itself. The main product of this activity goes to the *outside* of the cambium in the form of **cork** cells. As these cells mature, they go on to infuse their cell walls with a waxy substance that acts as nature's own waterproofing and invader-proofing. But cork cells are born to die, in the sense that their genetic blueprint brings about a so-called programmed cell death. It is in this dead, mature state that they serve their protective function. In a single growing season, the cork cambium can produce layer upon layer of cork cells, the result being a well-protected tree. To its interior, the cork cambium can produce, in a few species, a layer of parenchyma cells called phelloderm.

What Is Bark?

So, woody plants have cork cambium and its two products (cork and phelloderm). Then *inside* this three-part structure, there is the secondary phloem. Put together, all four parts constitute a region of a woody plant that goes by a familiar name **bark**. Put another way, bark is everything outside the vascular cambium. Figure 24.22 shows all the layers of tissues in secondary growth.

Figure 24.23
Death from Lack of Nutrients
This tree has been girdled by someone who intends to kill it. The bark was removed all the way down to the secondary phloem, the tissue layer that transports food from one part of the plant to another.

If a tree is "ringed" by having a strip removed around its entire circumference—as hungry animals might do in winter—it might live without its cork, and the cork cambium interior to it, and the phelloderm inside that. But if this cutting continues into the younger, food-conducting secondary phloem, that would be the end of the tree, because it could no longer move its energy stores to where they're needed. Indeed, this kind of cutting describes the "girdling" that is a common way to kill unwanted trees (**see Figure 24.23**).

To conclude this section on plant growth, **Figure 24.24** shows you how the entire plant grows, with the starting point for both secondary and primary growth being apical meristem tissue.

24.6 How the Plant's Vascular System Functions

You have had ample opportunity already to look at the plant's vascular or "plumbing" system as it relates to plant growth, but now it's time to take a closer look at how the vascular system itself works, starting with the water-conducting xylem and then continuing to the food-conducting phloem.

How the Xylem Conducts Water

Remember the statement at the top of the chapter that a good many plant cells are dead in their mature, functioning state? You saw this once already with cork cells; here is another variety of these cells, which form most of the xylem. Two types of cells make up the water-conducting portions of

cork
cork cambium
phelloderm
}
bark
secondary phloem
}
vascular cambium
secondary xylem (wood)
xylem ray

Figure 24.22
Secondary Growth Tissues
The secondary xylem, the wood with which we are all familiar, is responsible for water transport and the structural support of the plant. Xylem rays are lateral conduits for water. Bark is composed of four layers of tissue: secondary phloem, phelloderm, cork cambium, and cork.

both the primary and secondary xylem. These are **tracheids** and **vessel elements**. Upon reaching maturity, these cells die, and their contents are then cleared out. What's left is a strand of empty, thick-walled cells stacked one on top of another—tubes, in other words (**Figure 24.25**). The walls of these xylem cells remain, however; indeed, *these* are some of the sclerenchyma cells noted earlier that have the strong lignin reinforcement in their cell walls. The upshot is not only a transport system but a *load-bearing* system, which is why something as massive as a tree can grow so tall. As noted earlier, this load-bearing function remains in a given group of xylem cells long after they have ceased to act as a conduit for the water and dissolved nutrients that are sometimes called **xylem sap**. (To get an idea of one of the uses human beings have for this sap, see "The Syrup for Your Pancakes Comes from Xylem" on the next page.)

A tube metaphor is more accurate for the vessel elements than for the slender, tapered tracheids, because the vessel elements not only lose their internal contents, but may also lose part or all of the cell-wall barriers between adjoining cells. The result is a great capacity to transport water relative to the tracheids, whose cell walls remain intact. Any two tracheid cells will have matched pairs of perforations that line up with one another, allowing water to move from one tracheid to another.

The Value of Having Tracheids and Vessel Elements

You may remember from Chapter 21 that, through evolutionary time, flowering plants took over as the dominant variety of plant from the gymnosperms (which include coniferous trees). One reason this happened was the development of vessel elements; almost all angiosperms have vessel elements *and* tracheids, while almost all woody gymnosperms possess only tracheids. As a result, angiosperms can simply transport more water than can gymnosperms. You may wonder, though: If vessel elements are so much more efficient than tracheids at transporting water, why has evolution preserved tracheids in angiosperms? As it turns out, compared with vessel elements, tracheids are less susceptible to trapping air bubbles that can arise in flowing water. Given this, tracheids may be another kind of insurance policy for plants as they face various environmental changes.

Suction Power Moves Water through Xylem

In some trees, water coming from the roots goes through a vertical journey of up to 100 meters, or about 300 feet, before it gets to the topmost leaves of the tree. What kind of force can move water such a long way? Plants spend no energy at all in this process. Instead, it is **transpiration** itself—the loss of water from a plant, mostly through the leaves—that moves water through xylem. As water vapor evaporates into the air, it creates a region of low pressure, and this pulls a continuous column of water upward

Web Tutorial 24.2
The Vascular System

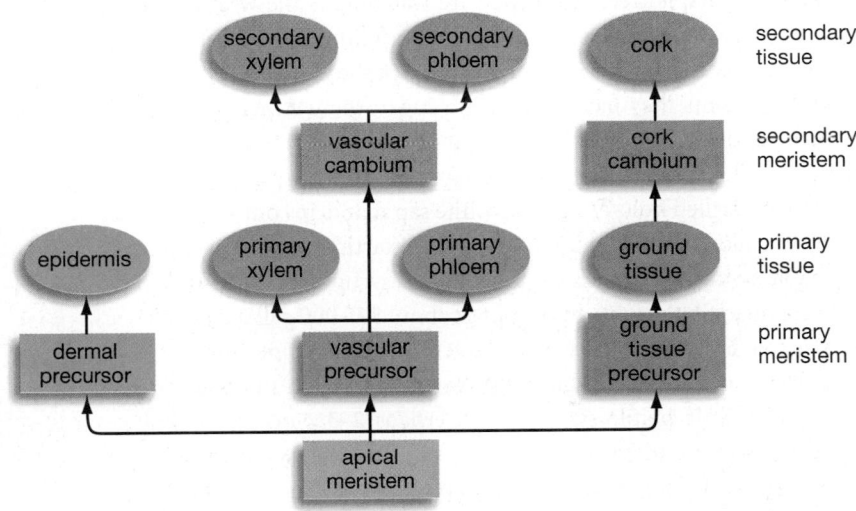

Figure 24.24
Summary of Primary and Secondary Growth in the Stem of a Vascular Plant
The "precursor" tissues that arise from the apical meristem are those that take shape in the zones of cell division, elongation, and differentiation noted earlier in the chapter.

Figure 24.25
Water Carriers
The fluid-conducting cells of the xylem are tracheids and vessel elements. Both kinds of cells stack up to form tubes.

The Syrup for Your Pancakes Comes from Xylem

In early March, when winter is winding down in New England and Eastern Canada, farmers who own sugar maple trees are kept busy in a game of drilling and watching. What they are drilling is a series of two-to-three-inch holes, about three of them per maple tree. What they are watching is the weather, because they need a series of freezing nights followed by warmer days to get what they want. Such nights prompt the maple trees to convert nutrients they have stored into sugar; the warmer days then bring about a flow of this sugar, upward in sap through the tree's xylem. This material can then be "tapped" through spigots inserted into the drilled holes. The clear white sap that drips out—as much as 40 gallons from a single tree—is the starting material for pure maple syrup. Vermont is the chief maple-syrup-producing state in the United States, with an output of about 275,000 gallons in 2001. Canada, however, is the world's largest maple syrup producer.

The "maple syrup" that most Americans buy in stores actually has very little maple syrup in it (perhaps 2–3 percent, the bulk being made up of corn syrup and syrup from regular sugar). This is understandable, because pure maple syrup is expensive; the best varieties cost anywhere between $30 and $45 per gallon. One reason for this expense is that harvesting the syrup is a labor-intensive business; each tap must be put in by hand, just as it was hundreds of years ago (**see Figure 1**). Beyond this, it takes about 50 gallons of sap to make a single gallon of maple syrup. The sap must be boiled down, until its sugar concentration reaches 66.5 percent.

Too many taps can kill a tree, but experienced syrup harvesters know how to tap the same tree year after year—potentially for hundreds of years—without harming it. The 40 gallons of sap a tree can yield up sounds like a lot, but it may account for only 10 percent of a tree's total supply of sugar.

In the text, you've read much about the plant's food supply flowing through *phloem*, not xylem. But in sugar maples and some other deciduous trees, the food produced in summer's photosynthesis is stored as starch in xylem cells, to be broken down into sugar and released to the growing upper portions of the tree in early spring.

Figure 1
Source of Maple Syrup
Maple trees in Vermont being tapped for their xylem sap, which will become the key ingredient in maple syrup.

Water Transport by Transpiration

H₂O   H₂O

1. Water evaporates from stomata on underside of leaves.

2. Water from stem is pulled up through xylem to replace water lost from leaves.

plant's energy *not* required

3. Water is pulled out of soil into roots to replace water lost from stem.

H₂O

(**see Figure 24.26**). Ultimately, the energy source for this movement is the sun, whose warm rays power the evaporation of water at the leaf surface.

Food the Plant Makes Is Conducted through Phloem

Now let's turn from water-and-nutrient transport to food transport. What is the nature of the food that flows through phloem? It's mostly sucrose—better known as table sugar—that is dissolved in water. Hormones, amino acids, and other compounds move through phloem as well, but sucrose and water are the main ingredients of this material, which is known as phloem sap.

Figure 24.26
Suction Moves Water through Xylem
When water evaporates from leaves, a low pressure is created that pulls more water up to fill the void. Water is so cohesive that it moves up in a continuous column. The sun's energy, rather than the plant's energy, fuels this process.

The phloem cells that this sap moves through are called **sieve elements**. Unlike xylem cells, sieve elements are alive at maturity, only in a curiously altered state. Each one has lost its nucleus, which you may remember is the DNA-containing information center of a cell. Sieve elements continue to function as living cells, however, because each one has associated with it one or more **companion cells** that retain their DNA and that seem to take care of all the housekeeping needs of their sister sieve elements (**see Figure 24.27**). The association between the two kinds of phloem cells is so intimate that when sieve elements die out, as they often do at the end of a growing season, their companion cells die as well. The reason sieve elements lose their nuclei seems to be to make room for the rapid flow of nutrients through them. The reason they are called *sieve* elements is that the ends of adjoining cells are studded with small holes, much like a sieve. Stacked on top of each other, these cells form the plant's food pipes, the **sieve tubes**.

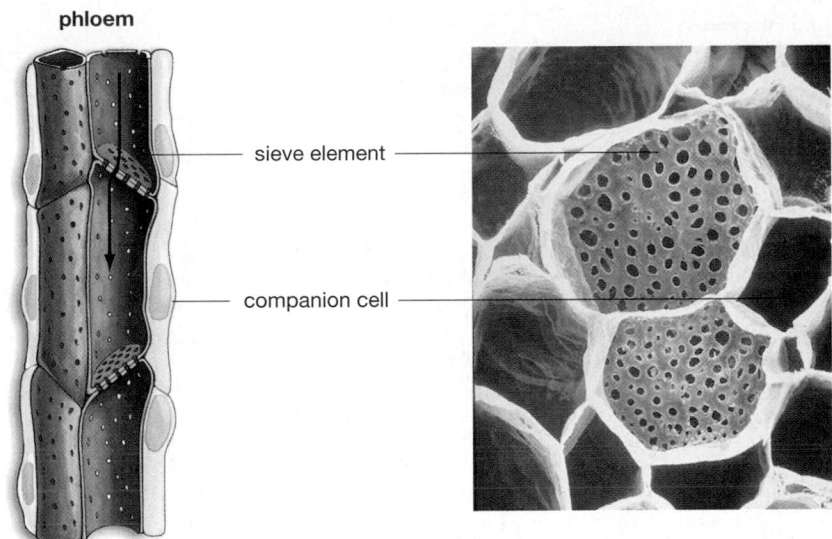

Figure 24.27
Food Carriers
The micrograph at right shows a cross section through some sieve elements (looking at them from above), surrounded by a number of companion cells. A plant's phloem sap moves from one sieve element to another through the perforations visible in the cells.

Sugar Pumping and Water Pressure Move Nutrients through the Phloem

The motive power for the movement of food through phloem is different from that of water through xylem; with food, the plant does not get a free ride on transportation (via transpiration). Instead, to load the sucrose it makes into the phloem, the plant must expend its own energy (**see Figure 24.28**). After this, a principal player in moving fluid through the phloem is a phenomenon you've encountered before—osmosis.

Osmosis and the Movement of Phloem Sap

You can review the process of osmosis in Chapter 5 (page 103), but here's a brief summary. Any time there is a membrane, such as the lining of a cell, that is immersed in water and is semipermeable—so that some molecules can pass through it but others can't—this creates the conditions for osmosis. There is a net movement of water across the membrane to the *side* in which there is a greater concentration of solutes, or substances that can be dissolved in liquid (**see Figure 24.29**, on the next page). In plants, the solute is sucrose, which arrives at the cell walls of the sieve elements and is then *pumped* into them through special membrane channels. (The pumping is what requires energy from the plant.) The result is a higher concentration of sucrose inside the cells than before, resulting in a net movement of *water* into the cells

Sugar Transport by Pressure Flow

source

1. Photosynthesis in leaves produces sugar, which is loaded into the phloem.

plant's energy required

2. Sugars are transported through phloem to fruits, stems, and roots.

3. Sugars are stored in parenchyma.

sink

Figure 24.28
How Food Moves through the Plant
Sucrose is produced in the leaves (source) by photosynthesis, after which the plant expends its own energy to load the sucrose into the phloem. Osmosis is then a key factor in transporting the sucrose through the plant for use and storage (sink).

because of osmosis. The effect is the same as water coming into a garden hose from a spigot: The water moves through its path of least resistance—through the hose and out the nozzle. Just so is this solution of water and sucrose moved through the sieve tubes under the power of this pressure flow

Figure 24.29
Osmosis in Action

(a) An aqueous solution divided by a semipermeable membrane has a solute—in this case salt—poured into its right chamber.

(b) As a result, though water continues to flow in both directions through the membrane, there is a net movement of water toward the side with the greater concentration of solutes in it.

1. Sugar is actively transported into phloem (requires ATP)

2. Water follows by osmosis.

3. Pressure gradient moves fluid down phloem.

4. Sugar moves by active or passive transport into root cell (may require ATP).

5. Water follows by osmosis.

(see **Figure 24.30**). The name given to this hypothesis about phloem sap movement is the **pressure-flow model**, first developed in the 1920s by German plant researcher Ernst Münch.

The loading site of this system is called a "source" and the unloading site is called a "sink," but these sites could also be called the "producer" and the "consumer," or perhaps "producer" and "bank." Sources tend to be sugar-producing leaves, while sink sites tend to be storage tissue such as roots, along with growing fruits and stems. At the sink, sucrose either moves passively or is actively pumped from sieve element cells to sink cells (the roots, for example). This movement triggers osmosis once again; only this time the net water flow is *out* of the sieve tube, because there has been an increase in the solute concentration outside the sieve tube. This flow creates a pull that, like the push at the source, helps move the phloem sap along.

Water Flows from Xylem to Phloem and Back Again

You saw earlier that phloem and xylem tubes are stacked together in bundles. These transport systems are not sealed off from each other, however; instead, they are closely interconnected. Remember the phloem sources, where water flowed into the sieve tube? Well, where did that water come from? From the adjacent xylem. And in the phloem sinks, when water flows out of the sieve tubes, most of it flows into adjacent xylem, where it joins water coming from the roots and moves on up with it (see Figure 24.30). With this, let's take our leave of transport in plants in order to cover another critical topic, reproduction and development.

24.7 Sexual Reproduction in Flowering Plants

To begin, it may be helpful to look again briefly at the reproductive parts of plants, their flowers, which you can see in **Figure 24.31**. You may recall from Chapter 23 that the heart of the flowers' re-

Figure 24.30
Phloem Sap Transport and Phloem-Xylem Linkage
In food transport, on the right, (1) sugar produced within leaves is actively pumped by the plant into the sieve elements of the phloem. (2) Water then "follows" the sugar in, under the power of osmosis. This creates (3) a pressure gradient that moves the sugar-water compound through the phloem. At the sink, (4) sugar moves either passively or through pumping, this time out of phloem cells, with (5) water following, again through osmosis. The phloem and xylem systems are linked. Water returns to the xylem from the phloem (bottom of the figure). Meanwhile, water is also transported to the *phloem* from the *xylem* (top left of the figure).

productive structures are the stamens and the carpel. A *stamen* consists of a long, slender filament that is topped by an *anther*, whose chambers contain cells that give rise to the male pollen. The carpel, meanwhile, is a composite structure, composed of three parts: the *stigma*, which is the tip end of the carpel, on which pollen grains are deposited; the *style*, a slender tube that raises the stigma to such a prominent height that it can easily catch the pollen; and the *ovary*, the area in which fertilization of the female egg and then development of the next generation of plant will take place.

Figure 24.31
Anatomy of a Flower: The Reproductive Structure of an Angiosperm

Flowering Plants Reproduce through an Alternation of Generations

If flowering plants reproduced the way people do, then maple trees, as an example, would produce gametes—eggs and sperm—that would come together and result in a new generation of maple trees. But flowering plants don't reproduce this way. What a generation of maple trees produces is not gametes but spores. A **spore** is a reproductive cell that can develop into a new organism without fusing with another reproductive cell. Maple tree spores do exactly this: they develop into an alternate generation of the maple tree plant. To say the least, however, this alternate generation does not look like a maple tree. On the male side, the alternate generation amounts to pollen grains, each one of which is microscopic and consists of three cells and an outer coat, at most. On the female side, the alternate generation is a small collection of cells, called an embryo sac, that is hidden away deep inside the reproductive parts of the maple tree. Though these entities are tiny, they have a critical role to play: *They* will produce the eggs and sperm that, once fused, will result in more maple trees.

As may be apparent from this account, plants exhibit a back-and-forth between generations. In their reproduction, they go through an *alternation of generations* (see page 434). Because the generation that is familiar to us—the maple tree—produces spores, it is known as the sporophyte generation. Because the generation that is less familiar to us produces gametes, it is called the gametophyte generation. Given how small the gametophyte generation is in angiosperms, most students have trouble seeing it *as* a generation. From a human perspective, pollen grains and embryo sacs look like small component parts of the sporophyte generation. Nevertheless, gametophytes are a separate generation of plant, with their own critical role to play in reproduction. For

a view of how gametophyte and sporophyte generations differ not just in angiosperms but in all types of plants, see **Figure 24.32**. In the more primitive plants, such as mosses, it is the gametophyte generation that is larger and more dominant, but the reverse is true with the later-evolving angiosperms.

Web Tutorial 24.3
Plant Reproduction

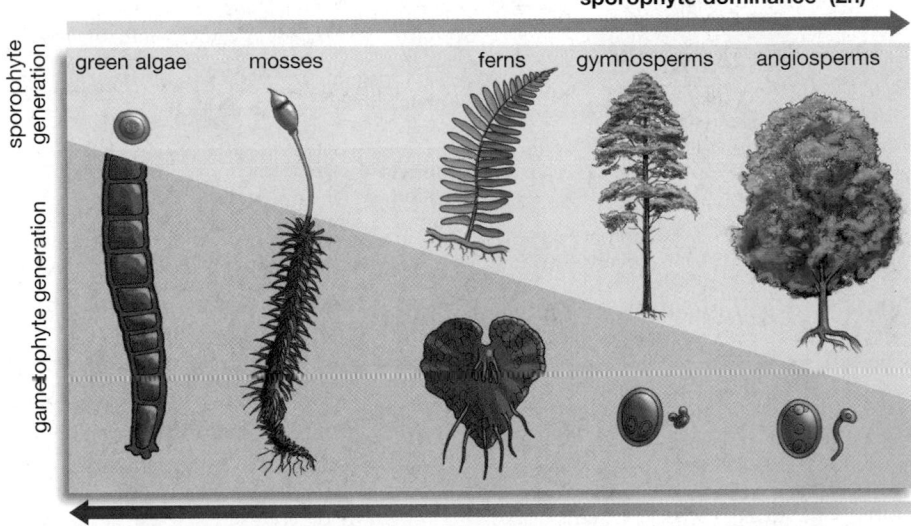

Figure 24.32
Generational Dominance Varies with the Type of Plant
In more primitive plants, the gametophyte generation is larger and more dominant. In mosses, for example, the gametophyte generation houses the sporophyte generation and supplies it with nutrition. By contrast, in the most recently evolved plants, the angiosperms, the gametophyte generation has been reduced to a microscopic entity that is almost wholly dependent on the sporophyte generation (in this example a tree). Though not plants, green algae are included for comparative purposes.

Look now at **Figure 24.33** to get an overview of angiosperm reproduction. One of the things you'll see in the figure is how the gametophyte generation starts out within the sporophyte generation. As you proceed through the story of angiosperm reproduction, you'll be looking in greater detail at each of the stages shown in this figure.

The Sporophyte and Gametophyte Generations Are Genetically Different

Apart from being different in size and appearance, the sporophyte and gametophyte generations are genetically very different. Let's look at this genetic difference first on the male side, starting with the sporophyte of a typical flowering plant (see the left side of **Figure 24.34**). Students who have been through the genetics section will recall that the normal state for the cells of most complex organisms is diploid, meaning that cells have chromosomes that come in matched *pairs*—a state sometimes referred to as $2n$. All the cells in the sporophyte generation are diploid, or $2n$. But special cells called **microspore mother cells**, which lie within the anthers of the sporophyte plant, will undergo the special kind of cell division called meiosis (reviewed in Chapter 10). Meiosis in the microspore mother cells will result in *microspores* that have only a single set of chromosomes each

(making them haploid or n). It is these microspores that will develop into pollen grains. Keeping an eye on the forest as well as the trees, the line between one generation and the next is crossed after the microspore mother cell has undergone meiosis. Once the microspores have been produced, the result is the gametophyte generation.

On the female side, both meiosis and development of the female gametophyte take place entirely inside the ovary lying at the base of the plant's carpel (see the right side of **Figure 24.34**). In this case, a single diploid cell—called a **megaspore mother cell**—undergoes meiosis, yielding female *megaspores* that are haploid. (Why is the female spore "mega" compared to the male's "micro"? Because the female spore is bigger.) Once the megaspores have been produced, the female gametophyte generation has come into existence.

Both the male and female gametophyte generations are multicelled structures (though just barely), with these cells arising by mitosis, or common cell division, from the original single haploid spores. Because mitosis makes exact copies of cells, this means that *every cell* in the gametophyte generation is haploid. In sum, the gametophyte generation is haploid (n), while the sporophyte generation is diploid ($2n$).

Development of the Male and Female Gametophyte Generation

The male and female gametophytes we've been talking about are going to produce the sperm and eggs that will come together and result in a new generation of the flowering plant we started with. But how do male and female gametophytes develop, such that they can do this? Let's see.

The Male Gametophyte

On the male side, things are pretty simple. As you can see on the left side of Figure 24.34, meiosis in each microspore mother cell yields four haploid microspores. Each spore develops into a pollen grain that initially consists of three things: an outer coat, a tube cell, and a generative cell. This pollen grain can be thought of as an *immature* male gametophyte plant. At some point, the generative cell divides once, resulting in two *sperm* cells. (In the type of plant you're looking at, this division comes before the pollen grain is released from the sporophyte plant, but in other species this division comes later.) Now having three cells, the pollen grain is released from the sporophyte plant and makes its way, by wind or bird or insect, to the stigma of another plant. This is what pollination is. More formally, **pollination** is the transfer of pollen from the anther of a flowering plant to the stigma of a flowering plant. You'll get to its story in a second.

Figure 24.33
Overview of Angiosperm Reproduction
1. The mature sporophyte flower produces many male microspores within the anther and female megaspore within the ovary. The male microspores then develop into pollen grains that contain the male gamete, sperm. **2.** Meanwhile, the female megaspore produces the female gamete, the egg. **3.** Pollen grains, with their sperm inside, move to the stigma of a plant. Moving through a pollen tube, the sperm reaches the egg and fertilizes it. **4.** This results in a zygote that develops into an embryo protected inside a seed. **5.** This seed leaves the parent plant and sprouts or "germinates" in the earth, growing eventually into the type of sporophyte plant that began the cycle. In this diagram, the plant is self-fertilizing: a sperm from the plant is fertilizing an egg in this same plant. This does occur in nature, but it is the exception rather than the rule. More often, pollen from one plant will fertilize one or more eggs in a different plant.

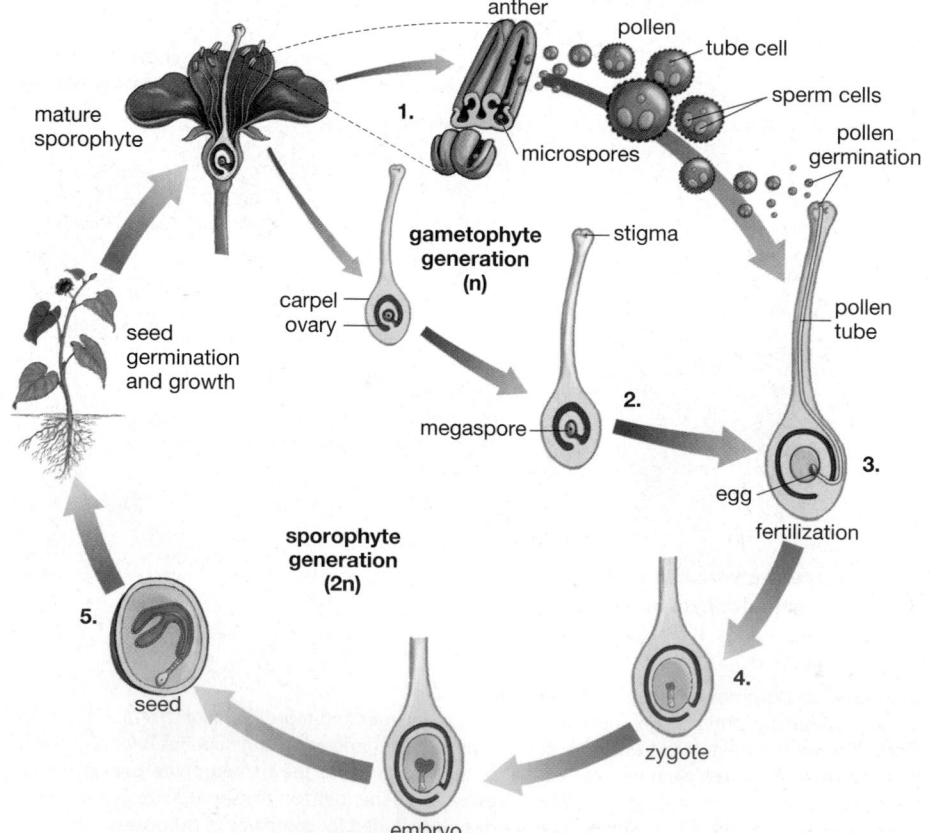

anther
pollen
tube cell
sperm cells
pollen germination
microspores
1.
mature sporophyte
gametophyte generation (n)
stigma
carpel ovary
pollen tube
megaspore
2.
3.
egg
fertilization
seed germination and growth
sporophyte generation (2n)
5.
seed
4.
embryo
zygote

Male Gametophyte Development

Female Gametophyte Development

anther

pollen
sac

ovary

ovule

microspore
mother cell
(2n)

megaspore
mother cell
(2n)

integument
micropyle

stalk

meiosis

4 microspores
(n)

4 megaspores
(n)

mitosis

mitosis

3 megaspores
degenerate

tube cell

generative
cell

mitosis

mitosis

mitosis

embryo
sac

8 haploid
nuclei

pollen grain

tube cell

outer coat

cytokinesis

egg

central cell

sperm cells

pollen
(male gametophyte)
is released from
sporophyte plant
it's housed in

mature female
gametophyte
within sporophyte

The male gametophyte generation takes shape inside
the chambers of the pollen sacs, where the diploid
microspore mother cells will undergo meiosis, each one
of them thereby giving rise to four haploid microspores.
These microspores represent the new, haploid
generation of the plant on the male side.

The single cell in each microspore goes through cell
division, thereby producing two cells, a tube cell and a
generative cell. Before or during this time, a protective
coat develops around the microspore. The combination
of the cells and protective coat is the pollen grain. At
some point, the generative cell in the grain divides into
two sperm cells. With this cell division, a mature male
gametophyte has developed. The pollen grain is then
released from the anthers to make its way to a stigma.

For the female gametophyte generation, development
begins in a structure inside the parent ovary called an
ovule. A single diploid megaspore mother cell in the ovule
undergoes meiosis, producing four haploid megaspores.
This marks the beginning of the female gametophyte
generation.

Three of the megaspores then die. The remaining
megaspore undergoes mitosis, eventually producing six
cells with a single nucleus each and one central cell with
two nuclei. These seven cells form the embryo sac, which
is the mature female gametophyte. One of the seven cells
in the embryo sac is the egg that will undergo fertilization
by one of the sperm in the pollen grain.

Figure 24.34
Development of the Male and Female Gametophyte Generation

The Female Gametophyte

On the female side, note in Figure 24.34 that there develops from the ovary wall a structure called an *ovule*—a part of the sporophyte plant—that will enclose the female gametophyte generation. The ovule consists of the protruding stalk, a central core of cells, and a couple layers of tissue called *integuments*. The integuments wrap around the central cells, almost coming together except for a tiny opening they leave (called a micropyle). From the ovule's central mass of diploid cells, a single cell—the megaspore mother cell—undergoes meiosis, thereby producing four megaspores. Then three of the megaspores will die, leaving the one that remains as an immature female gametophyte plant.

The surviving megaspore now undergoes three rounds of mitosis, but of a curious sort: There are several rounds of doubling of the cell's DNA (in the nucleus), but no subsequent cell division, as is usually the case. The result is a single cell that has eight haploid nuclei. This cell eventually does undergo cell division, but once again there is a twist. Six of the cells that result will each have a single nucleus, but one will have two nuclei. You can see, in Figure 24.34, the most common arrangement of these seven cells. Collectively, they form the **embryo sac**, which can be thought of as the mature female gametophyte plant. At one end is the cell of greatest importance, the egg, flanked by a couple of cells on either side. On the opposite end there are three other cells; and in the middle, a very large central cell, which is the cell that has two nuclei.

Fertilization of Two Sorts: A New Zygote and Food for It

The stage is now set for male to come into contact with female. The pollen grain, with its two sperm cells and one tube cell, now lands on the stigma of a plant with an egg and embryo sac matured down in the ovule (**see Figure 24.35**). The tube cell then sprouts something: a pollen tube, which tunnels its way down through the style, eventually gaining access to the female reproductive cells within the ovule. The two sperm cells travel down this tube to achieve fertilization. (Why *two* sperm cells? Stay tuned.) In sum, in its most mature state, the male gametophyte generation consists of three cells, one of which grows a tube and two of which are sperm cells—quite a different thing from the sporophyte generation with its billions of cells.

The pollen tube grows through the ovule's micropyle and ejects its two sperm cells into the embryo sac. One of these sperm fuses with the egg, yielding the zygote that is the beginning cell in the new generation of plant—another sporophyte generation like the flowering plant we started with. This is no different in principle than what takes place with *human* life, where egg and sperm fuse, producing a single-celled zygote that develops into a whole human being. And, as with human egg and sperm, the plant egg and sperm were both haploid, containing a single set of chromosomes each. So their fusion produces a diploid zygote—one with a *paired* set of chromosomes— that will divide over and over, resulting in a diploid sporophyte plant.

Figure 24.35
Double Fertilization in Angiosperms

When the male pollen (shown greatly enlarged) lands on the stigma, the tube cell within it sprouts a pollen tube, through which the two sperm pass in moving to the ovule. One sperm cell fertilizes the egg, forming a zygote—the new sporophyte plant. The other sperm cell fuses with the two nuclei of the central cell, forming the endosperm that will later nourish the embryonic plant.

pollination

pollen tube growth

double fertilization

And what of the other sperm? Here is one of the beauties of flowering plants. This sperm enters the central cell with its two nuclei, producing a cell with *three* nuclei (making it triploid or *3n*.) This too is a fertilization, only what it sets in motion is the development of *food* for the embryo—endosperm, which is tissue rich in nutrients that can be used by the embryo that will now develop from the zygote. Thus two fertilizations have taken place. This is known as **double fertilization** in angiosperms—a fusion of gametes and of nutritive cells at the same time. Double fertilization is an innovation that belongs almost solely to the flowering plants. As it happens, it has been a boon to all kinds of *animals*, including people. It is endosperm that supplies much of the food we human beings consume. The rice and wheat grains we're familiar with consist in large part of endosperm meant to sustain the plant embryo (**see Figure 24.36**).

Figure 24.36
Endosperm Is Food for the Embryo
In monocots such as corn, endosperm persists in the mature seed, providing nutrition for the embryo inside. The cotyledon in the figure is the corn plant's embryonic leaf.

24.8 Embryo, Seed, and Fruit: The Developing Plant

The Development of a Seed

Egg fertilization produces a single-celled zygote. The question is, how does the plant develop from this zygote into an embryo-containing *seed* that falls to the ground, eventually giving rise to a growing sporophyte plant? Many steps are involved here; what follows are only the highlights. First, recall that the female gametophyte, the embryo sac, was nearly surrounded by ovule tissue called *integuments*. These will now develop into the **seed coat** that will protect the embryonic plant until it germinates in the ground. What once was an ovule with a gametophyte inside is now a seed: a reproductive structure of a plant that includes an outer seed coat, an embryo, and nutritional tissue for the embryo (the endosperm). This seed is a reproductive structure that bears similarities to one employed by some animals, the egg (**see Figure 24.37**).

Figure 24.37
A Kernel of Corn and a Chicken Egg Are Similar in Some Ways
Both are home to an embryo, both contain plenty of food for development, and both offer protection for the embryo in dry, land environments.

The Development of Fruit

Something more will now develop *outside* the seed coat. Recall that the ovule was surrounded by the ovary of the flower. The ovary wall now develops into fruit. Strictly speaking, **fruit** is the mature ovary of any flowering plant. Given this, *all* flowering plants develop fruit, but it's clear that most of the 260,000 species of flowering plants are not fruits as we commonly understand that term. It follows that the botanical definition of fruit differs from the common definition; under the botanical definition, fruits can take on lots of forms. The pod of a pea plant is a fruit, for example, as is the outer covering of a kernel of corn (though here fruit has fused with the corn seed coat, leaving scarcely anything separate that can be recognized as fruit). On the other hand, fruits can take exactly the form we're used to, as with the flesh of an apricot or cherry. To add another twist, where is the fruit in a strawberry? The answer, shown in **Figure 24.38**, may surprise you. Fruit develops in all angiosperms, and it develops *only* in angiosperms. Thus, angiosperms can be defined by this anatomical feature. An **angiosperm** is a plant whose seeds develop inside the tissue called fruit.

Figure 24.38
Fruits Come in Many Forms
A fruit, the mature ovary of a flowering plant, surrounds a seed or seeds. Thus (a) the flesh of an apricot fits this definition of fruit, but so does (b) the pod of a pea, which has several seeds inside. The structure we commonly think of as (c) the strawberry fruit actually is the strawberry plant receptacle, with each receptacle having many fruits on its surface. What are commonly thought of as strawberry "seeds" are tiny strawberry plant carpels, each complete with its own fruit and seed. Fruits are important not only because they protect the seeds but also because they attract animals that disperse the seeds.

(a) Apricot

one carpel, one seed

(b) Pea

one carpel, many seeds

(c) Strawberry

carpels

many carpels, many seeds,
one receptacle

receptacle

Figure 24.39
Development of a Plant Embryo, Germination of a Plant Seed
Egg and sperm have come together in this dicot to produce a single-celled zygote, which divides repeatedly in developing as the plant embryo. The zygote is surrounded by the plant ovule, which develops into a seed.

seed coat   endosperm   cotyledons

ovule   zygote   embryo

1.   2.

zygote within ovule   embryogenesis and seed formation

1. The zygote divides into two cells, one of which is the embryo (green in the figure). The other cell (yellow in the figure) develops into a structure that will push the embryo into the endosperm.

2. The embryo starts to develop its cotyledons or embryonic leaves. Most of the endosperm nutrients eventually are taken up by these cotyledons. (Because this plant is a dicot, it has two cotyledons.)

Fruits Serve in Protection and in Seed Dispersal

What is common to many fruits is that they serve a protective function for the underlying seed, and many act as *attractants* for seed dispersal. As noted in Chapter 21 (page 439), the wild berry that a bear eats consists not only of the fruit flesh, but of the seeds it surrounds. The fruit is digested by the bear as food, but the seeds pass through the bear's digestive tract. Thus has this plant engineered seed dispersal at what may be a promising new location for a berry plant. Plants with such attractants *time* their fruit ripening, so that the fruit is not attractive before the seed is ready for dispersal.

Development of the Embryo and Germination of the Seed

While fruit and seed coat are maturing, the embryo inside them is also developing. **Figure 24.39** shows you the outline of the development of a plant embryo, this one a dicot plant. Recall that the process starts with a single cell, the zygote, encased within the structure that will become the seed, the ovule. The zygote divides, yielding two cells, one of which becomes the embryo. The other cell gives rise to a paddle-shaped structure that pushes the growing embryo into the endosperm.

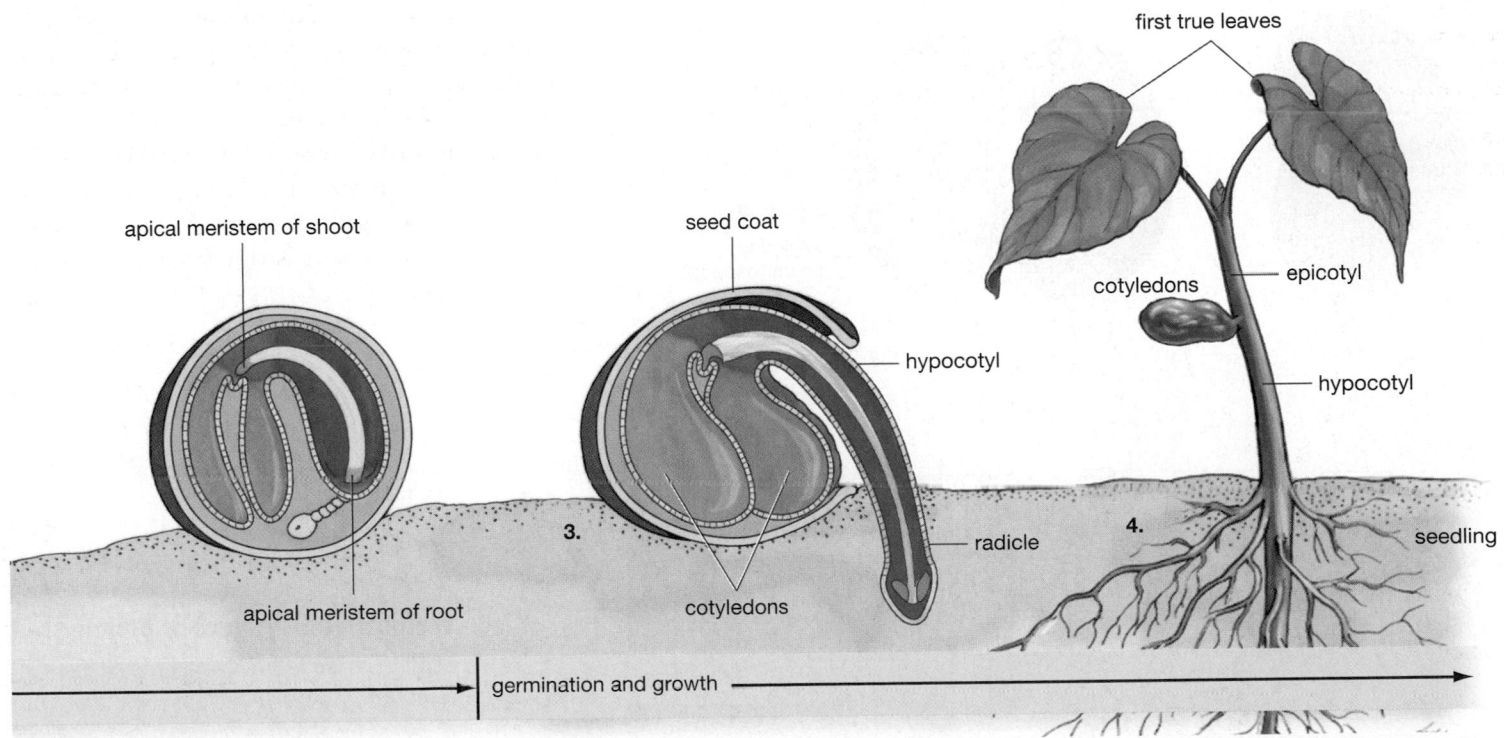

3. Having made its way to the ground, the seed is ready to "germinate" or start sprouting. The seed coat splits, allowing the emergence of the hypocotyl (tissue below the cotyledons), which includes the plant's radicle, or early root structure.

4. Root and shoot have both sprouted. The plant's cotyledons, having completed their function, will wither away. The plant sprouts its first true leaves and begins the process of photosynthesis. The reproductive cycle is ready to begin again.

Eventually, the embryonic tissue develops two **cotyledons**, or embryonic leaves. When the embryo is still tightly encased in the seed coat, the cotyledons can take on an important role you've seen before, which is to provide nutrients to the growing embryo. You may say: But isn't this the function of the endosperm? In most monocots (for example, the grains) the endosperm retains this function, but in most dicots the nutrients stored in endosperm tissue are *taken up* by the cotyledons as they develop. The foods we know as beans are comprised of embryos with large cotyledons (**see Figure 24.40**).

The seed that encases the embryo eventually separates from the sporophyte parent plant and makes its way into a suitable patch of earth, there to germinate, or to sprout both roots and shoots. First to emerge from the seed is the root structure or radicle, which is attached to **hypocotyl**, which can be thought of as all the plant tissue below the cotyledons. Then there emerges the **epicotyl**, meaning the tissue above the cotyledons. (In Figure 24.40, you can see the location of hypocotyl and epicotyl at an earlier stage within the bean seed.) The epicotyl gives rise to the first true leaves of the plant. The seed has sprouted into a new sporophyte plant.

Seed Dormancy Can Be Used to a Plant's Advantage

One of the survival strategies of plants is the use of dormancy, or a prolonged low metabolic level in seeds. Seeds can *postpone* germinating until they have favorable conditions around them, such as the proper temperature or amount of light. What generally sets seed germination in motion is an uptake of water from the surrounding environment. It is, however, the triggering mechanisms for this water uptake that tell the tale in dormancy. Some seeds require a scraping or abrasion before they will take up water; others simply need to dry out, once they've shed the fruit from around them; still others require the action of enzymes from an animal's gut, or even charring by fire.

Once the plant has germinated and matured a little, you could take a cross section of its stem and find concentric circles of the tissue types mentioned near the start of this chapter: dermal, vascular, and ground. Meanwhile, meristematic tissue could be found at the tips of the root and shoot, allowing the plant to grow further. With this, we have come full cycle: Another generation of plants is maturing.

On to Animals

In Chapters 23 and 24, you have looked at a group of living things, the plants, whose members are silent, fixed in one spot, and have almost no moving parts. Now it's time to shift gears. There are animals that are silent and animals that are fixed in place, but you'll also find with animals nature's only sound-makers and its supreme travelers. The next five chapters are concerned with the functioning of animals in general, but they focus on one animal that in some ways is very familiar to us—the human animal.

Figure 24.40
Cotyledons Serve a Nutritive Function
In a dicot such as this bean plant, the endosperm food reserves are taken up by the embryonic leaves or cotyledons of the embryo, which then serve as the mature seed's food reserves. The hypocotyl in the figure is tissue that eventually will lie below the cotyledons in the sprouting plant. Epicotyl is tissue that will lie above the cotyledons.

bean
(dicot)

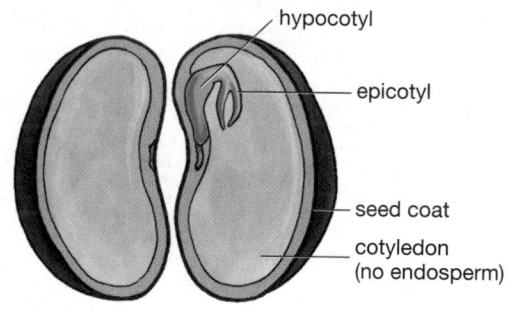

hypocotyl

epicotyl

seed coat

cotyledon
(no endosperm)

Chapter Review

Summary

24.1 Two Ways of Categorizing Flowering Plants

- Plants can be categorized by how long it takes them to go through a cycle from germination to death. Those that go through this cycle in a year or less are annuals; those that go through in about two years are biennials; those that live for many years are perennials.

- A cotyledon is an embryonic leaf, present in the seed. Angiosperms are classified according to how many cotyledons they have—one in the case of monocotyledons, two in the case of dicotyledons. Monocot and dicot plants are structured in different ways.

24.2 There are Three Fundamental Types of Plant Cells

- There are three fundamental types of cells in plants that, alone or in combination, make up most of the plant's tissues, meaning groups of cells that carry out a common function. These three cell types are parenchyma, sclerenchyma, and collenchyma.

24.3 The Plant Body and Its Tissue Types

- Some plants are capable only of primary growth, meaning growth at the tips of their roots and shoots that primarily increases their length. Plants that exhibit only primary growth are herbaceous plants, composed solely of primary tissue. Other plants exhibit both vertical growth and lateral, or secondary growth. These are the woody plants, composed of primary and secondary tissue.

- There are four tissue types in the primary plant body: dermal, vascular, meristematic, and ground. Dermal tissue can be thought of as the plant's outer covering, vascular tissue as its "plumbing," meristematic tissue as its growth tissue, and ground tissue as almost everything else in the plant.
  Web Tutorial 24.1: Plant Tissue and Growth

24.4 How a Plant Grows: Apical Meristems Give Rise to the Entire Plant

- The entire plant develops from meristematic cells in regions called apical meristems. Meristematic cells remain perpetually embryonic, able to give rise to cells that differentiate into all the plant's tissue types.

- Shoot apical meristems give rise to the entire shoot of the plant. In addition to providing for vertical growth, shoot apical meristems produce meristematic tissue called lateral buds at the base of leaves that can give rise to a branch or flower. Root apical meristems are located just behind a collection of cells at the very tip of the root, called the root cap.

- The plant's tissue types develop in stages from meristematic cells. This development takes place in a series of regions adjacent to the apical meristem. In a gradual transition, the apical meristem gives way to a zone of cell division, followed by a zone of elongation (in which developing cells lengthen) followed by a zone of differentiation (in which cells fully differentiate into different tissue types).

24.5 Secondary Growth Comes from a Thickening of Two Types of Tissues

- Secondary growth in plants takes place through the division of cells in two varieties of meristematic tissue: the vascular cambium, which gives rise to secondary phloem and xylem; and cork cambium, which gives rise to the outer tissues of woody plants. Secondary xylem, also known as wood, is responsible for most of a tree's widening.

- Looking at a tree from the secondary phloem outward to the tree's periphery, four tissues constitute the tree's bark: secondary phloem, phelloderm, cork cambium, and cork. The cork cells are dead in their mature state and provide layers of protection for the tree.

24.6 How the Plant's Vascular System Functions

- Two types of cells make up the water-conducting portions of xylem tissue. These are tracheids and vessel elements, both of which are dead in their mature, working state. Vessel elements, which exist almost solely in angiosperms, conduct more water than tracheids. Their existence in angiosperms is one of the reasons for the angiosperms' dominance in the plant world.

- Water movement through xylem is driven by transpiration, meaning the loss of water from a plant, mostly through the leaves. As water evaporates into the air, it pulls a continuous column of water upward through the plant.

- Sucrose is the main product that flows through phloem. The fluid-conducting cells in phloem are called sieve elements, which lack cell nuclei in maturity. Each sieve element has associated with it one or more companion cells, which retain their nuclei and seem to take care of the housekeeping needs of their related sieve elements.

- Plants must expend their own energy to load the sucrose they produce into the phloem. Dissolved sucrose then moves through the plant through the power of osmosis and the fluid pressure that results from it.
  Web Tutorial 24.2: The Vascular System

24.7 Sexual Reproduction in Flowering Plants

- All plants, including angiosperms, reproduce through an alternation of generations. A sporophyte generation (the familiar tree or flower) produces haploid spores that develop into their own generation of plant, the gametophyte generation. The male gametophyte is the pollen grain, consisting in maturity of an outer coat, two sperm cells, and one tube cell. The female gametophyte consists at maturity of an embryo sac composed of seven cells, one of which is the egg. The female gametophyte is housed inside a structure of the parent sporophyte plant called an ovule.

- Fertilization of the egg by sperm requires that a pollen grain land on the stigma of a plant. The tube cell of the pollen grain then germinates, sprouting a pollen tube that grows down through the sporophyte plant's stigma and style, eventually reaching the female reproductive cells inside the ovule. The sperm cells inside the pollen grain travel down through the pollen tube, and one of the sperm cells fertilizes the egg in the ovule, producing a zygote. With this, the new sporophyte generation of plant has come into being.

- The second sperm cell in the pollen grain enters the central cell in the embryo sac, setting in motion the development of food for the embryo, endosperm tissue. This second fertilization completes the process of double fertilization—a fusion of gametes and of cells producing nutritive tissue.

Web Tutorial 24.3: Plant Reproduction

24.8 Embryo, Seed, and Fruit: The Developing Plant

- With fertilization, the ovule integuments that surrounded the embryo sac begin to develop into the seed coat that will surround the growing sporophyte embryo. The ovary that surrounded the ovule then starts to develop into a layer of tissue that will surround the seed—fruit, which is defined as the mature ovary of a flowering plant. Under this definition the pod of a pea plant is fruit, as is the flesh of an apricot.

- The seed with its fruit covering eventually separates from the sporophyte parent plant and then germinates in the earth, sprouting both roots and shoots.

Key Terms

Understanding the Basics

Multiple-Choice Questions (answers in the back of the book)

1. Dermal tissue _____, while vascular tissue _____.
   a. protects the plant; conducts fluids
   b. provides strength; facilitates growth
   c. facilitates reproduction; protects the plant
   d. facilitates growth; provides strength
   e. protects the plant; facilitates reproduction

2. Biennials, like cauliflower, radishes, and beets,
   a. go through their entire life cycle in one season
   b. go through their entire life cycle in about two years
   c. grow and bloom each season, for many years
   d. have the shortest life span, among annuals, biennials, and perennials
   e. go through their entire life cycle twice each year

3. Sclerenchyma cells
   a. lack cellulose
   b. function in metabolic processes such as photosynthesis
   c. are generally dead at maturity
   d. are commonly found in rapidly growing parts of the plant
   e. are found exclusively in roots

4. Secondary growth
   a. leads to increased height of the plant
   b. is more widespread in herbaceous plants than in woody shrubs and trees
   c. leads to an increase in the girth of the plant
   d. is brought about through cell divisions in the cuticle
   e. is growth that occurs only in a plant's second year

5. Which of the following statements about the ascent of water in tall trees is true?
   a. Plants must expend metabolic energy to power the ascent of water into treetops.
   b. The evaporation of water from the leaf surface is required to lift water from the roots to the canopy of a tall tree.
   c. The ascent of water in the xylem is fastest when the stomata are closed.

d. The formation of embolisms, or air bubbles, in xylem elements increases the speed of ascent of water.

e. All of the above are true.

6. Phloem sieve tubes develop a positive pressure because
   a. Osmotic uptake of water occurs when sugars are loaded into the sieve elements.
   b. Sieve elements lack a nucleus.
   c. Sieve elements are dead at maturity.
   d. Sucrose is a bulky molecule that exerts a pressure against the sieve tube walls.
   e. All of the above are true.

7. Endosperm is formed when
   a. A sperm nucleus from the pollen fuses with one haploid nucleus from the embryo sac.
   b. Two nuclei from the embryo sac fuse with each other.
   c. A sperm nucleus from the pollen fuses with the egg nucleus in the embryo sac.
   d. An egg nucleus from the pollen fuses with a diploid nucleus in the embryo sac.
   e. A sperm nucleus from the pollen fuses with two central cell nuclei in the embryo sac.

8. Which of the following statements about spores is true?
   a. Spores are diploid structures that give rise to gametes.
   b. Spores give rise to the gametophyte generation of plants.
   c. Spores are part of the sporophyte generation.
   d. Spores give rise to multicellular haploid gametes.
   e. Spores give rise to single-celled diploid gametes.

9. Which of these is a gametophyte plant? (Select all that apply.)
   a. petal
   b. stigma
   c. embryo sac
   d. pollen grain
   e. sepal

10. The difference between a seed and a fruit is that
    a. Fruit is composed of triploid tissue; seeds are diploid.
    b. Seeds are always hard; fruits are always soft.
    c. Seeds develop from ovules while fruit tissue is derived from ovary walls.
    d. Annuals produce seeds while perennials produce fruits.
    e. Fruits are annuals while seeds are perennial.

Brief Review

1. Compare monocots and dicots with respect to their anatomy, morphology, and seed structure.

2. What are the three main cell types in a plant, and what distinct functions are performed by each?

3. What is meristematic tissue? Describe the organization of the meristem.

4. Compare the structure and function of the water-conducting (xylem) and food-conducting (phloem) cells in a plant.

5. What does a growth ring on a tree trunk represent? Why can you tell the age of a tree by counting its growth rings?

6. Describe the process of double fertilization in plants.

Applying Your Knowledge

1. If you were to regularly shear a lilac bush down to a stub, you would probably kill it. Yet, mowing after mowing, the grass in your lawn continues to grow. Is there a fundamental difference in the location of growing points in the lilac and the grass? Explain.

2. Beavers often kill young trees by girdling them—that is, removing a strip of bark from the circumference of a tree trunk. Why does this bark removal kill a tree?

3. Gardeners often speak of outdoor plants having become "established," meaning the plants have reached a point where they need less human care. What threshold does a plant have to cross in order to become established?

MediaLab

Why Do We Need Plants Anyway? The Importance of Plant Diversity

It is speculated that a meteorite struck the Earth near the Gulf of Mexico about 65 million years ago. After that event, there is no fossil record of any animal species over 65 pounds surviving. Most animals were probably not killed by rocks or tidal waves, but died when Earth's plant life could no longer support their needs. A significant meteor impact would send millions of tons of dust and debris into the atmosphere, blocking the sun's rays from reaching Earth's surface, significantly reducing photosynthesis, and ultimately leaving little food to support animal life. This event illustrates the essential role of plants in creating an environment that supports animal life. We simply couldn't survive without them. To learn more, the *Web Tutorial* will introduce you to the basics of plant structure and growth. In the *Web Investigation*, you will see how plants have adapted these basic structures to specific habitats and conditions. Finally, in the *Communicate Your Results* section, you will synthesize and apply your knowledge to the plant life around you.

This *MediaLab* can be found in Chapter 24 on your Companion Website (www.prenhall.com/krogh3).

WEB TUTORIAL

Plants, because of their ability to trap solar energy in a chemical form, are a food source for all other living organisms. They are pivotal members of every ecosystem and have adapted their basic body parts to suit these various environmental conditions. In this *Web Tutorial*, you will complete the following activity.

Activity

1. First, review the four primary plant tissues—dermal, vascular, meristematic, and ground.

2. Then, cover the process of by which plants transport water and nutrients.

3. Finally, explore plant reproduction through the life cycle of a typical sporophyte plant.

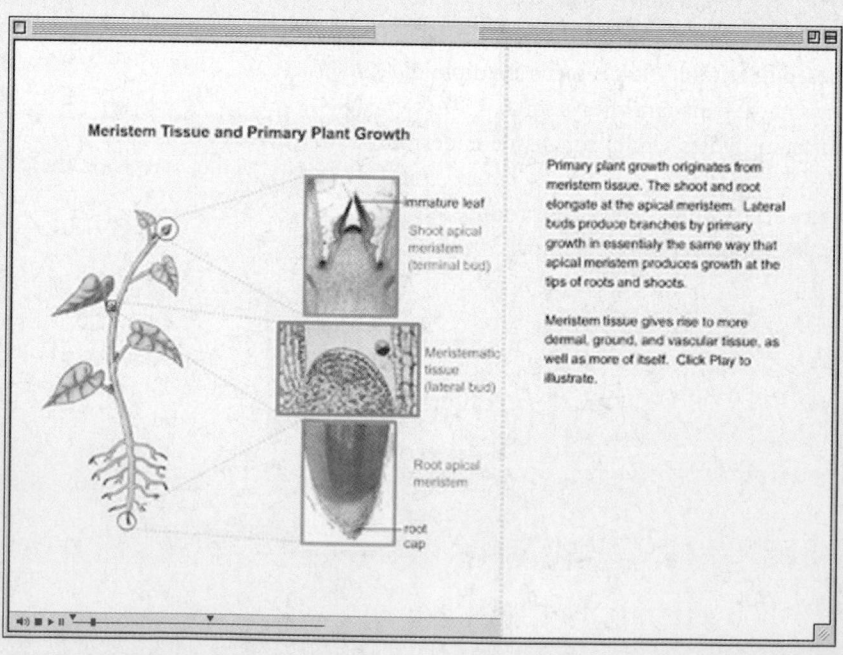

Investigation 1

Estimated time for completion = 15 minutes

There are two major groups of flowering plants, the monocots and the dicots, whose lineages diverged early in their evolutionary history. To contrast how these two groups of plants are constructed, select the keywords **DICOT** and **MONOCOT** on your Website for this *MediaLab*. Then compare the architecture and anatomy of the tomato plant, a dicot, and the rice plant, a monocot. How many differences can you observe in these two plants? Examine the roots, stems, leaves, and flowers.

Investigation 2

Estimated time for completion = 5 minutes

Flowering plants appeared on Earth about 150 million years ago. Since then, they have moved into an extraordinary number of habitats. Over genera-tions, plant species have altered their form and function to become better adapted to living in varying habitats. Select the keyword **SILVERSWORD** on your Website for this *MediaLab* to view a striking example of adaptation by a plant species found in Hawaii. How do the different forms of these plants suit their environment?

Investigation 3

Estimated time for completion = 5 minutes

The structures of flowering plants are the culmination of millions of years of plant evolution. Features such as vascular tissue and enclosed seeds have appeared in various plant groups at various times in the evolutionary history of plants. Select the keyword **FOSSIL PLANTS** on your Website for this *MediaLab* to determine when these plant features first appeared in the fossil record.

Now that you've gained some understanding of plant structures and functions by doing the preceding activities, consider these questions.

Exercise 1

Estimated time for completion = 30 minutes

Use your observations from *Web Investigation 1* to construct a chart illustrating the differences between the architecture and anatomy of dicot and monocot plants. You could start with something like **Table 22.1**, but you should be able to greatly expand on the differences. To do this exercise most efficiently, you may want to systematically work your way from flowers to roots, or follow any other order you would prefer.

Exercise 2

Estimated time for completion = 30 minutes

Using the adaptations you observed of the silversword species to environments in the Hawaiian Islands, answer this question: How would you construct a plant to be well adapted to the following environment?

- *Poor-quality soil, frequently disturbed by rock slides*
- *Growing season about 8 months long*
- *Annual rainfall of about 18 inches, most of it during the first third of the growing season*
- *About 8 hours of sunlight at the start of the growing season; about 16 hours by the last half*

After deciding how to construct this plant so that it will be adapted to its environment, draw your hypothetical plant. Then, list how its adaptations help the plant cope with its environmental hardships.

Exercise 3

Estimated time for completion = 30 minutes

Using the information you obtained from *Web Investigation 3*, construct a graph illustrating when the various plant features first appeared in the fossil record. Your chart should extend from the time when the first land plants appeared to the present day.

25 The Integumentary, Skeletal, and Muscular Systems

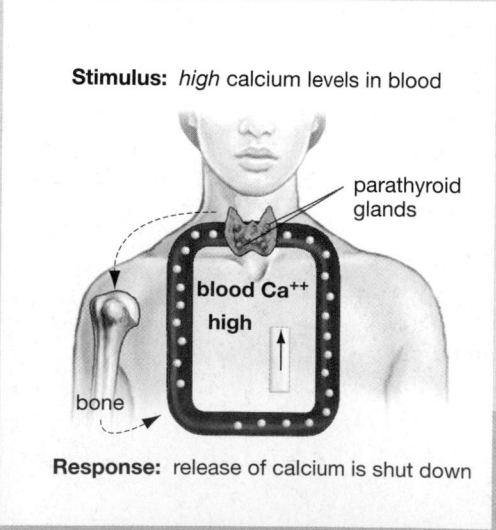

Stimulus: *high* calcium levels in blood

parathyroid glands

blood Ca⁺⁺ high

bone

Response: release of calcium is shut down

Negative feedback is key.
(Section 25.2, page 536)

Our outer wrap.
(Section 25.7, page 543)

Some of our 206 bones.
(Section 25.8, page 549)

Just as several individuals may make up an office, and several offices a department, so our bodies are organized into a number of small working units that go on to make up a functioning human being. Three of the larger units involve skin, bone, and muscle.

There is an old country saying that goes, "You don't miss your water until your well runs dry." Doesn't this seem applicable to the way we think of our bodies? We go along taking for granted our ability to eat or talk or run—until the day comes when we can't do one of these things. If you've ever, say, broken a leg, and ended up with a cast and crutches, you know that just walking around with ease can look like the most wonderful thing in the world. Broken bones heal, of course, and that reassures us—until we run up against a condition that won't heal. While still in his twenties, the actor Michael J. Fox woke up one morning and noticed, as he later remembered, that "the pinky in my left hand was twitching. It was a curiosity as much as anything because I couldn't stop it, no matter how I tried to." About a year later, after many doctor's visits, Fox got definitive word that he had Parkinson's disease, which is incurable. By then, it was not just his little finger that was twitching; it was both hands. Imagine if being able to hold your hands steady seemed as beautiful as the moon and just as far away.

We take our bodies for granted partly because they work so well most of the time, but partly because what goes on inside them is hidden from us and so complicated that our physical functioning just seems mysterious. The next six chapters of this book are aimed at clearing up some of this mystery. At their conclusion, you will have a basic understanding of how your heart beats, for example, and of how your immune system fights off invaders, and of how your eyes and brain provide you with a picture of the world.

If you think about just the first of these things—the workings of the heart—you can get a sense of what's in store. The human heart beats about 100,000 times *each day*, pumping about 8,800 quarts of blood through the body in the process. Moreover, it keeps this rhythmic contraction up without a second's rest from the third week of our embryonic life to the day we die. As if this weren't enough, it is carrying out this feat mostly with its original equipment. Very few of the muscle cells in the heart ever divide; as a result, the cells that are working for us at age 8 are pretty much the cells that are working for us at 80.

Comes with shock absorbers.
(Section 25.8, page 550)

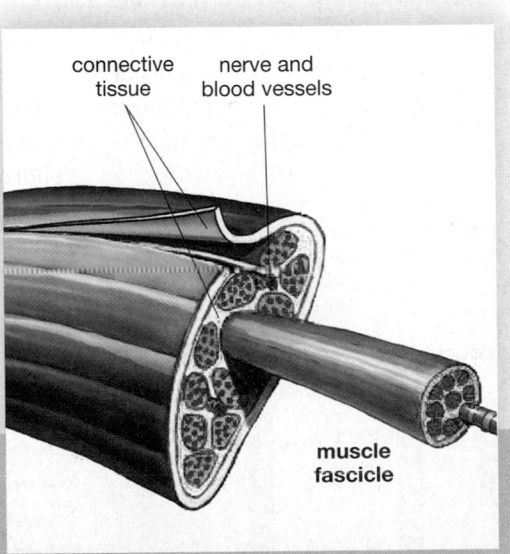

Muscles help us move.
(Section 25.9, page 550)

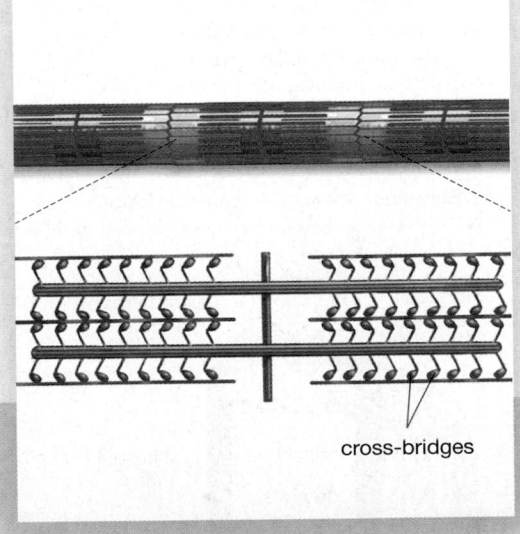

How does a muscle contract?
(Section 25.9, page 551)

An engineer who could invent such a machine would be considered a genius. But the truly remarkable thing is that there are lots of organs and systems in the body that are just as impressive as the heart. Once you've learned how these things work, it's hard to take your body for granted in the same way, because you've come to understand what an incredible machine the human body is.

25.1 The Disciplines of Anatomy and Physiology

When we study the makeup or functioning of any complex organism, we have entered the realms of two overlapping disciplines in biology: anatomy and physiology. All organisms have an anatomy and a physiology. But in these chapters, our primary concern is with human beings. Within this framework, human anatomy is the study of the body's structure and the relationships between the body's constituent parts. Human physiology is the study of how these parts work. Thus anatomy tells us where the heart is, for example, how it is structured, and how it is situated in relation to other organs. Physiology describes to us *how* the heart works.

25.2 How Does the Body Regulate Itself?

Before we get to specifics about the human body, it will be helpful to go over a couple of general concepts about its structure and functioning. One of these concepts concerns the question: Who's in charge here? We are in charge of our conscious actions, of course; human beings get to decide what they are going to do from one moment to the next. But what about the huge number of unconscious actions that the body undertakes each second—getting oxygen to cells, getting rid of waste, being prompted to breathe while asleep? You might think the brain would be in charge of all this, and indeed

messages from the brain do prompt a lot of physical activity. But there are plenty of physical processes that don't involve brain signals, and the brain *gets* lots of messages that say, in effect, "get this process going now." Human society is hierarchical to a great degree; we're used to bosses and employees who work in a straight line of authority. But the body doesn't work this way. Instead, it functions through a process of *circular* causation in which A prompts B and B prompts C, but in which C may then prompt A. It is a system of self-regulation in which all parts work together to influence each other.

In understanding self-regulation, it's useful to think about what kind of internal environment the body needs in order to function properly. The answer is a *stable* environment. The human body must guard against being too hot or too cold; too dehydrated or too hydrated; too stimulated or too relaxed. If it is to exist at all, it must avoid extremes. To put this another way, it must seek **homeostasis**, meaning the maintenance of a relatively stable internal environment. And it turns out that a single process is almost solely responsible for bringing about homeostasis. Let's look at this process by way of an analogy.

Most people are aware of how a home heating system works. Falling temperature causes a thermostat to turn on a furnace. To look at this another way, there is a stimulus (cold air) that brings about a response (furnace operation). The *product* of this response is hot air. When enough hot air circulates to raise the temperature, the thermostat senses this and shuts the furnace down.

Now let's think of your body which has, as an example, a certain amount of calcium circulating through it in the bloodstream. When levels of calcium in the blood fall too low (stimulus), organs called the parathyroid glands sense this and secrete a hormone that causes your bones to release calcium (response). Thus, the product of *this* stimulus-response chain is released calcium; when enough of it is circulating, the parathyroid glands sense this and stop releasing their calcium-liberating hormone (**see Figure 25.1**).

With both the thermostat and the parathyroid glands, we can see that their responses to a stimulus bring about a decrease in their own activity. In other words, their responses feed back on their activity in a negative way—they reduce it. This is **negative feedback**, which can be defined as a process in which the elements that bring about a response have their activity reduced by that response. The calcium example is

Figure 25.1
Calcium Levels: An Example of Negative Feedback
Calcium levels in the bloodstream are regulated in part by the parathyroid glands. These glands can sense when calcium levels are too low (the stimulus in the drawing at left). In response, the parathyroids secrete a hormone that causes the bones to release calcium. This brings about high calcium levels, which the glands also can sense (the stimulus in the drawing at right). High calcium levels cause the parathyroids to halt their production of the calcium-liberating hormone.

Stimulus: *low* calcium levels in blood

Response: release of calcium into blood

Stimulus: *high* calcium levels in blood

Response: release of calcium is shut down

only one of the countless negative feedback loops that exist in the body. In it, we can see not only how the body maintains homeostasis, but how the body is self-regulating. There was no central boss giving commands in this process. Instead two elements (calcium levels and the parathyroid glands) influenced each other to bring about stability. This is the way the body generally works.

Large-Scale Features of the Body

Many of the large-scale features of a human being—four limbs, one trunk, and so forth—are obvious, but a couple features are hiding in plain sight, we might say. The first of these is an internal body cavity. All animals more complex than a flatworm have such a cavity. Humans and other mammals actually have two primary body cavities. The first of these is a dorsal (back) cavity that is further divided into cranial and spinal cavities, into which our brain and spinal cord fit (**see Figure 25.2**). The second is a ventral (front) cavity that includes a thoracic or "chest" portion containing the lungs and heart as well as a lower abdominopelvic cavity containing such organs as the stomach, liver, and intestines. A muscular sheet called the diaphragm separates the thoracic and abdominopelvic cavities. Cavities provide flexibility and protection. With the space provided by a cavity, an organ like the stomach can expand as we eat and is protected from external blows to some extent.

Humans also have an internal skeleton that supports the body. We take for granted a skeleton that exists inside our skin, but it stands in contrast to what most animals have, which is an *external* skeleton (as with crabs and grasshoppers) or no skeleton at all (as with jellyfish).

25.3 Levels of Physical Organization

Features of the human body, such as a skeleton, fit into a larger organizational framework that is common to all living things. In our everyday world, several individuals may make up an office, several offices a department, and several departments a working company. In a similar fashion, each living thing is built up from a series of individual units that go on to make up a working organism. The organization of these units runs as follows. Recall from Chapter 4 that the basic unit of all life is the cell. Cells and cellular products that work together to perform a common function are known as **tissues**. There is, for example, muscle tissue—a group of cells that perform the common

function of contracting. Tissues in turn are arranged into various types of **organs**, meaning complexes of several kinds of tissues that perform a special bodily function. The stomach is an organ that has both muscle and nerve tissue within it. Organs then go on to form **organ systems**, which are groups of interrelated organs and tissues that serve a particular function. Contractions of the heart push blood into a network of blood vessels. The heart, blood, and blood vessels form the cardiovascular system, which is one of 11 systems in the human body.

Tissues, organs, and organ systems are three levels of organization within animals, but you may remember from Chapter 1 that the levels of organization in living things do not *start* with tissues (see page 12). Tissues are made of cells, cells have within them tiny working structures called organelles, and organelles are in turn made of the building blocks called molecules. At the bottom of this chain is the fundamental unit of matter, the atom. In this chapter, however, the focus is on the

Web Tutorial 25.1
Human Anatomy and Physiology

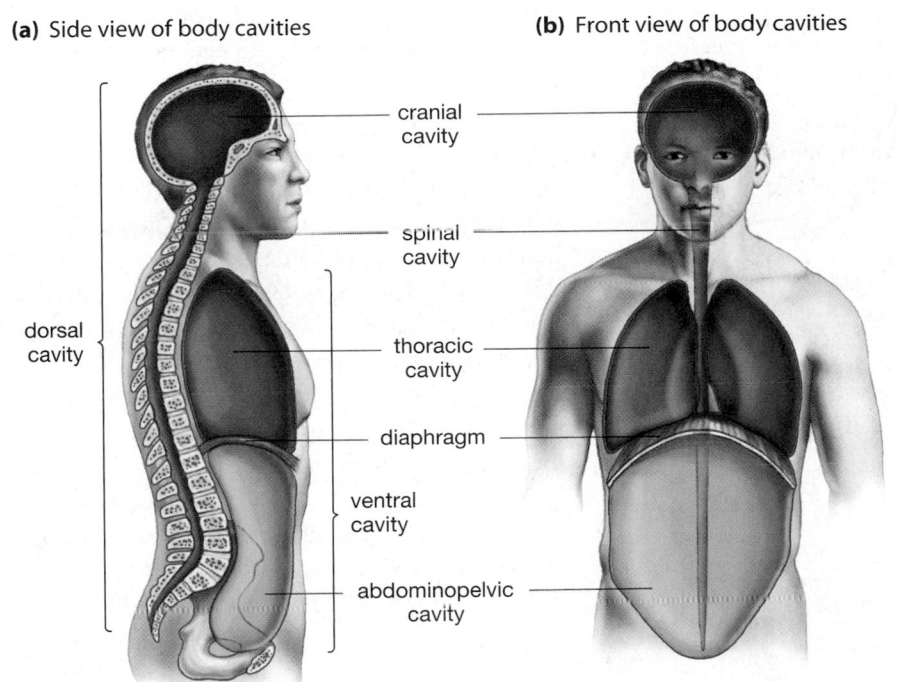

(a) Side view of body cavities

(b) Front view of body cavities

cranial cavity

spinal cavity

dorsal cavity

thoracic cavity

diaphragm

ventral cavity

abdominopelvic cavity

Figure 25.2
Body Cavities

(a) A side or "lateral" view of the two main cavities in the human body—the dorsal (back) and ventral (front) cavities—and the smaller cavities within them. The dorsal body cavity is bounded by the bones of the skull and vertebral column and includes both the cranial and spinal cavities. The ventral cavity includes a thoracic (chest) cavity and an abdominopelvic cavity, which is separated from the thoracic cavity by a muscular diaphragm.

(b) A front or "ventral" view of the body's cavities.

levels of organization that run from tissues through organ systems. **Figure 25.3** shows the various levels of structural organization within the human body, using the cardiovascular system as an example.

25.4 The Human Body Has Four Basic Tissue Types

Looking at the smallest level of organization we're interested in, the tissue, we can then ask: what kinds of tissues are there in humans and other animals? It turns out there are only four fundamental tissue types: epithelial, connective, muscle, and nervous. All other tissue varieties are subsets of these fundamental types. Let's look briefly at the characteristics of these four varieties.

Epithelial Tissue

The key word in epithelial tissue is *surfaces*, because **epithelial tissue** is tissue that *covers* surfaces exposed to an external environment. The outside of our body is exposed to the external environment, and as such, the outer layer of our skin is composed of epithelial tissue. But there are other surfaces as well. Think of a pipe; it has not only an external surface but also an internal surface that comes into contact with something that is external to it—the fluid that runs through it. Similarly, your body has arteries and veins that have the fluid called blood running through them and the tissues that line the internal blood-vessel surfaces are epithelial tissues. Likewise, the lining of your stomach and the lining of your lungs are surfaces that come into contact with something from outside you; once again, this contact is made by epithelial tissues. Given their location, epithelial tissues often serve as a barrier, as in the case of our skin; but many epithelial tissues are "transport" tissues that materials are moved across. (The food that enters your bloodstream does so by being transported across the epithelial tissue that lines your small intestines.) Epithelial tissues can be several layers of cells thick, or as thin as a single layer, depending on their function (**see Figure 25.4**).

Epithelial tissues often produce substances that aid in various bodily processes. The skin has epithelial tissue that produces the water-resistant protein keratin, for example, while the stomach has epithelial tissue that produces digestive juices. This substance-producing function can be carried out by isolated epithelial cells, but it is sometimes undertaken by concentrations of cells. Such concentrations are known as **glands**: organs or groups of cells specialized to secrete one or more substances. Later we'll look at two basic kinds of glands.

Connective Tissue

Connective tissue, defined as tissue that stabilizes and supports other tissue, is very different from epithelial tissue. Whereas epithelial tissue is always in contact with an external environment, connective tissue never is. Whereas epithelial tissue is almost completely composed of cells, connective tissue usually is composed of cells that are separated from each other by an extracellular material—a material that is secreted by the connective tissue cells themselves. Indeed, the prime function of many connective tissues is to produce this kind of material.

Bone and cartilage are clear examples of connective tissue. They are connecting something, after all (bodily structures), and their support and stabilization role is clear. They likewise display another hallmark of connective tissue, which is that their cells lie within a so-called *ground substance*. The ground substance of bone, which the bone cells themselves secrete, happens to be a mix of closely packed protein fibers and calcified material. These are the substances that largely make up the hard bones we're familiar with.

But ground substances need not be hard. Adipose or fat tissue is connective tissue, and its ground substance is soft. Indeed, a ground substance can even be fluid, as is the case with blood and a bodily fluid called lymph. How can a ground tissue be a fluid? Well, to take blood as an example, the ground substance that surrounds blood cells is mostly water, with electrolytes, proteins, and other materials in the mix.

Muscle Tissue

Muscle tissue is tissue that is specialized in its ability to contract, or shorten. There are three kinds of muscle tissue—skeletal, smooth, and cardiac—which differ in their structure and in the way they are prompted to contract. **Skeletal muscle** is the ordinary muscle that is attached to bone and is contained in, for example, our biceps. It is under our conscious control and has a striped or "striated" appearance when looked at under a microscope, owing to the parallel orientation of the

atom
(hydrogen)

molecule
(water)

organelle
(mitochondrion)

cell
(muscle)

tissue
(muscle)

organ
(heart)

organ system
(cardiovascular)

Figure 25.3
Levels of Organization in the Human Body
Atoms form molecules, which in turn combine to form organelles, which combine to form cells, such as heart muscle cells. A group of cells that performs a common function is a tissue; here cells have formed heart muscle tissue (whose common function is heart muscle contraction). Two or more tissues combine to form an organ such as the heart. The heart is one component of the cardiovascular system; other parts of the system are blood and blood vessels. All the organ systems combine to create an organism, in this case a human being.

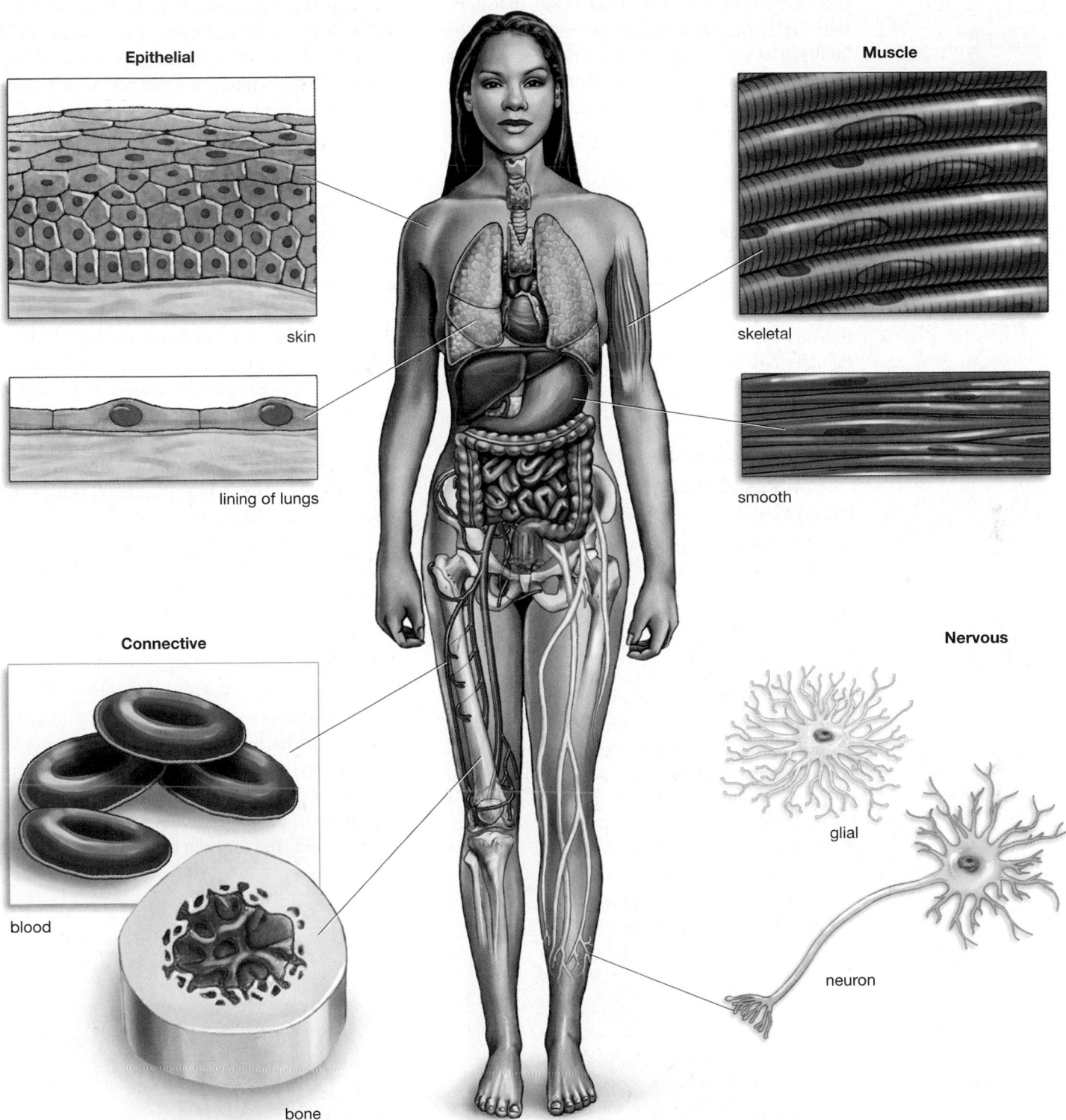

Figure 25.4
Four Types of Tissue
There are four basic tissue types in the human body: epithelial, connective, muscle, and nervous. Pictured are examples of each of the four types in some representative locations. Epithelial tissue, which always covers a surface exposed to an external environment, can take the form of many layers of cells (as with the skin) or a single layer of cells (as with the lining of lungs). Connective tissue, which supports and stabilizes other tissue, can take such diverse forms as bone and blood. Muscle tissue, which is specialized for contraction, comes in a striped or "striated" form (in both skeletal and cardiac muscle) and in a smooth form that lines the digestive tract, blood vessels, and other structures. Nervous tissue is specialized for electrical signal transmission. The two types of nerve cells are neurons, which conduct nervous system signals, and glial cells, which support the neurons.

cells that make it up. **Cardiac muscle** exists only in the heart and likewise is striated, but it contracts under the influence of its own pacemaker cells. **Smooth muscle**, which gets its name from its lack of striated appearance, is muscle responsible for contractions of blood vessels, the uterus, the passageways of the lungs, and other structures. As you might guess from this list of tasks, smooth muscle is not under voluntary control.

Nervous Tissue

Nervous tissue is tissue that is specialized for the rapid conduction of messages, which take the form of electrical impulses. There are two basic types of nervous-tissue cells: neurons, which actually carry the nervous-system messages; and glial cells, which perform support functions for the neurons.

25.5 Organs Are Made of Several Kinds of Tissues

Having looked at the four tissue types, let's now see how they combine to form an organ. **Figure 25.5** shows you the anatomy of the human stomach, with an emphasis on the kinds of tissues that go into making it up. The muscle tissue noted in the figure is one of several layers of smooth muscle that bring about contractions that help digest food and move it into the small intestines. Likewise, there is nervous tissue, which controls the release of digestive juices and the contractions of the stomach's muscles. Supportive connective tissue exists as well. And, of course, since the inner lining of the stomach is a sur-

face coming into contact with an external environment, there is epithelial tissue. True to what you saw earlier, some of this epithelial tissue is secretory—that is, it secretes substances that help with digestion.

25.6 Organs and Tissues Make Up Organ Systems

You've now seen how cells make up tissues, and how tissues make up organs. Let's take the final step up and see how tissues and organs together make up organ systems. What follows is a brief look at each of the body's eleven organ systems. Once you have finished reviewing them, the balance of this chapter will be devoted to a more detailed look at the first three of these systems. In Chapters 26 through 30, you'll be taking a look at the other eight.

Organ Systems 1: Body Support and Movement—The Integumentary, Skeletal, and Muscular Systems

- The **integumentary system** (**Figure 25.6a**) is sometimes thought of simply as skin. But a number of structures are associated with skin, including hair and nails and the glands we noted earlier. In addition to serving as an outer, protective wrapping, skin also helps keep body temperature stable.

- The **skeletal system** (**Figure 25.6b**) is composed not only of bones, but of cartilages and ligaments. This is a complex framework, as human beings have about 206 bones in their body, along with a large number of cartilages. Bones provide support and protection, and they can store fat and minerals.

Figure 25.5
Organs Are Composed of Tissues
The stomach is a typical organ in that it is composed of various tissue types. Nervous tissue controls the release of digestive juices into the stomach and also controls the contractions of stomach's digestive muscle tissues. Connective tissue helps support and stabilize the other tissues around it. Epithelial tissue lines the stomach's surface, which comes into contact with the food we eat. The individual epithelial cells pictured secrete digestive acids and enzymes.

epithelial tissue

connective tissue

muscle tissue

nervous tissue

The **muscular system** (**Figure 25.6c**) includes all the skeletal muscles of the body—about 700 of them. These muscles provide for movement, posture, and support. They are also vital players in homeostasis, in that our bodies are largely warmed by the heat given off from muscle contraction. The smooth and cardiac muscle tissues noted earlier are not part of the muscular system. Cardiac muscle is part of the cardiovascular system, and smooth muscle is part of several systems—in the stomach, for example, it is part of the digestive system.

Organ Systems 2: Coordination, Regulation, and Defense—The Nervous, Endocrine, and Lymphatic Systems

- The nervous tissue reviewed earlier goes on to make up the **nervous system** (**Figure 25.6d**), a rapid communication system in the body that includes the brain, spinal cord, all the nerves outside the brain and spinal cord, and sense organs such as the eye and ear.

- The endocrine system (**Figure 25.6e**) bears comparison with the nervous system, in that both systems are in the business of sending signals throughout the body. The **endocrine system**, however, is a communication system that works more slowly than the nervous system, through the chemical messengers called **hormones**. Many of these hormones are produced in specialized glands (such as the parathyroid gland we looked at). Remember the earlier remark that there are two basic varieties of glands in the body? One of these varieties is named for the endocrine system. **Endocrine glands** are glands that release their materials directly into surrounding extracellular fluid or into the bloodstream. This is what the thyroid gland does, for example. Endocrine glands stand in contrast to **exocrine glands**, which are glands that secrete their materials through tubes or "ducts." We'll see examples of these glands later.

- The **lymphatic system** (**Figure 25.6f**) consists of a widespread network of lymphatic vessels that collect extracellular fluid and deliver it to the blood vessels as a fluid called lymph. The lymphatic system is not just a fluid collection system, however; it is also an *inspection* system. The body's defenders—its immune cells—exist in heavy concentrations inside the organs that are part of the lymphatic system. These cells monitor lymph

(a) The integumentary system

hair

skin

nails

(b) The skeletal system

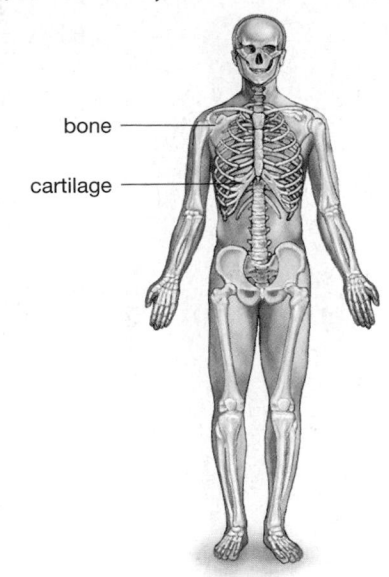

bone

cartilage

(c) The muscular system

skeletal muscles

(d) The nervous system

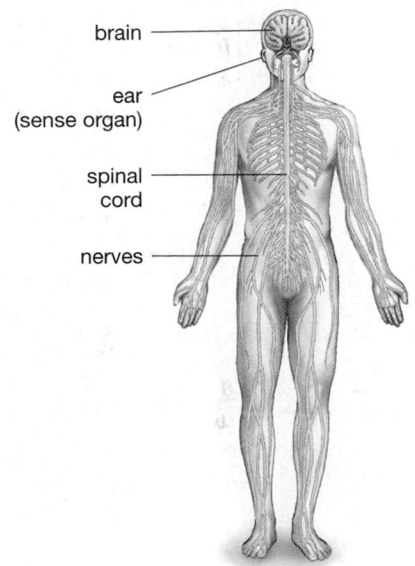

brain

ear (sense organ)

spinal cord

nerves

(e) The endocrine system

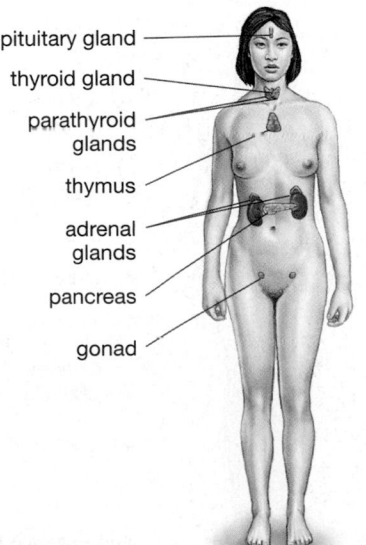

pituitary gland

thyroid gland

parathyroid glands

thymus

adrenal glands

pancreas

gonad

(f) The lymphatic system

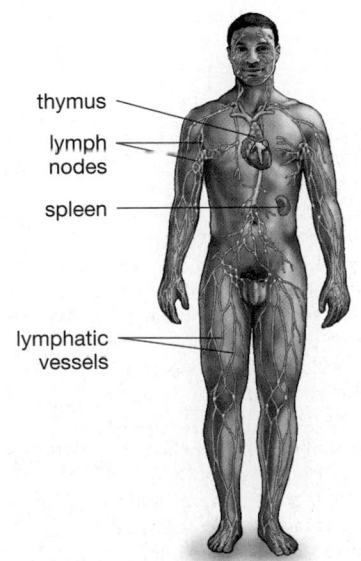

thymus

lymph nodes

spleen

lymphatic vessels

Figure 25.6a–f
The Organ Systems of the Human Body
(Continued on the next page.)

(g) The cardiovascular system

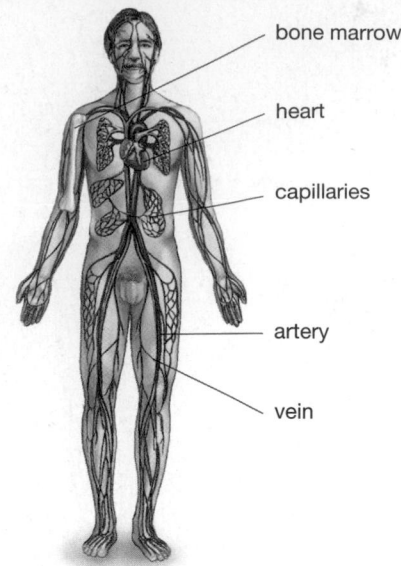

bone marrow

heart

capillaries

artery

vein

(h) The respiratory system

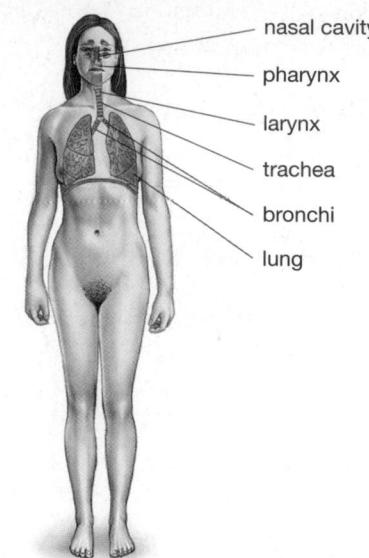

nasal cavity

pharynx

larynx

trachea

bronchi

lung

(i) The digestive system

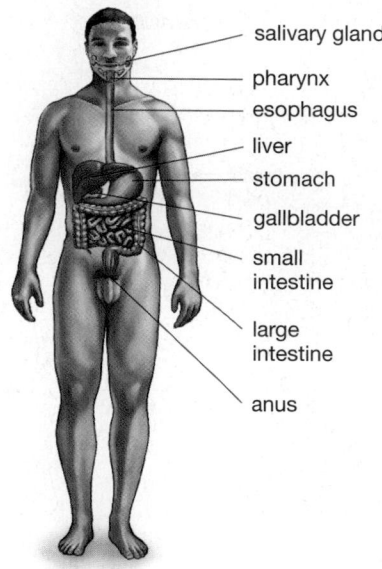

salivary gland

pharynx

esophagus

liver

stomach

gallbladder

small intestine

large intestine

anus

(j) The urinary system

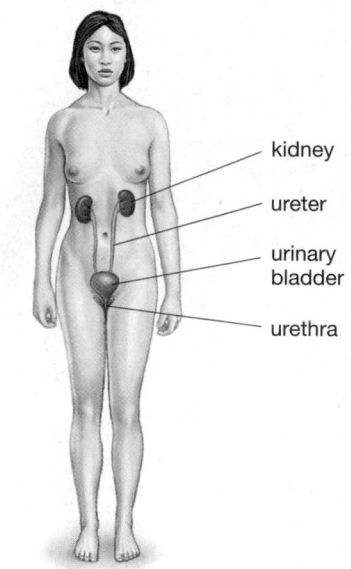

kidney

ureter

urinary bladder

urethra

(k) The male reproductive system

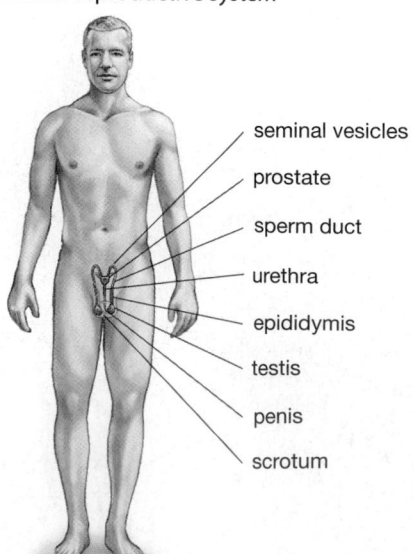

seminal vesicles

prostate

sperm duct

urethra

epididymis

testis

penis

scrotum

(l) The female reproductive system

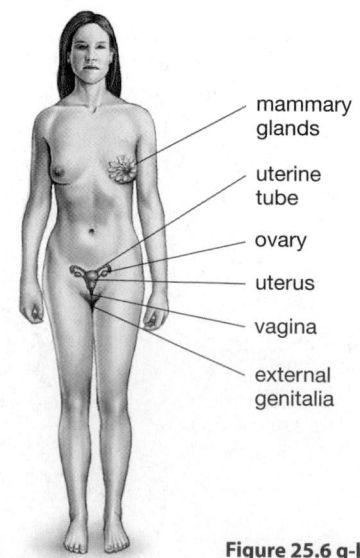

mammary glands

uterine tube

ovary

uterus

vagina

external genitalia

Figure 25.6 g-l

as it passes through the system in an effort to identify invading microorganisms. Lymphoid organs include the well-known lymph nodes located under the arms and elsewhere, along with the thymus gland, tonsils, and spleen.

Organ Systems 3: Transport and Exchange with the Environment—The Cardiovascular, Respiratory, Digestive, and Urinary Systems

- The **cardiovascular system** (**Figure 25.6g**) consists of the heart, blood, and blood vessels and an inner, "marrow" portion of bones where red blood cells are formed. The cardiovascular system is the body's mass transit system. It carries nutrients, dissolved gases, and hormones *to* tissues throughout the body, and it carries waste products *from* tissues to the sites where they are removed: the kidneys and lungs.

- The **respiratory system** (**Figure 25.6h**) includes the lungs and the passageways that carry air to and from the lungs. Through this system, oxygen comes into the body and carbon dioxide is expelled from it.

- The central feature of the **digestive system** (**Figure 25.6i**) is the digestive tract, a long tube that begins at the mouth and ends at the anus. Along its course, there are the digestive organs of the system—the stomach, small intestines, and large intestines—and accessory glands, such as the pancreas and liver.

- The **urinary system** (**Figure 25.6j**) has two major functions, one of them well known, the other not so much appreciated. The well-known function is the elimination of waste products from the blood through the production of urine. The underappreciated function is conservation. The system is very good at retaining what is useful to the body—water, proteins, and so forth—even as it eliminates what is useless. The primary organs that carry this selection process out are the kidneys, but the system also includes various other parts, such as the bladder.

- Males and females have different **reproductive systems** (**Figures 25.6k and 25.6l**). The two are linked, of course, in that together they produce offspring. Both systems are discussed in detail in Chapter 30.

With this brief review of the organ systems completed, you're ready to look in more detail at the first three organ systems noted earlier—the integumentary, skeletal, and muscular systems. They are batched together in this chapter because each of them has to do with body support and movement. We'll start with the integumentary system.

25.7 The Integumentary System: Skin and Its Accessories

The primary component of the integumentary system is the organ known as skin. It may seem strange to think of skin as an organ, since it is not a compact, clearly defined structure like the heart or the liver. But remember the definition of an organ: a complex of several kinds of tissues that performs a special bodily function. Clearly, that's what skin is. Joining skin to make up the integumentary system are the related structures of hair, nails, and a variety of exocrine glands.

The primary function of skin is easy to see: It covers the body and seals it off from the outside world. Skin also protects underlying tissues and organs, however, and helps regulate our temperature. In addition, it stores fat and makes vitamin D. Meanwhile, exocrine glands that are accessories to the skin excrete materials such as sweat, water, oils, and milk; and specialized nerve endings in the skin detect such sensations as pressure, pain, and temperature.

The Structure of Skin

Skin is an organ that is organized in two parts: a thin outer covering, the epidermis, and a thicker underlying layer, the dermis, that is composed mostly of connective tissue. Beneath the dermis—and not part of the skin proper—is another layer, called the hypodermis, made up of connective tissue that attaches the skin to deeper structures such as muscles or bones. You can see a cross section of human skin in **Figure 25.7**.

The Outermost Layer of Skin, the Epidermis

The outer layer of our skin, the epithelial tissue called the **epidermis**, would seem to be facing an impossible task. On the one hand, it has to serve as a permanent, protective barrier, keeping out everything from water to invading microorganisms; on the other it has to continually renew itself, given that it is cut, scraped, and simply worn away. How does it manage to do both things? The answer lies in the many *layers* of cells the epidermis is organized into. If we could take a micro-elevator down to the innermost layer of the epidermis, we would see a group of rounded cells rapidly dividing and, in the process, pushing the cells on top of them *up*, toward the surface of the skin. As we move toward the surface, we notice that the epidermal cells are flattening out. Furthermore, they're getting less active; at a certain point they cease dividing altogether. What is happening is that they are now so far from the underlying blood vessels (down in the dermis) that they are losing their blood supply. They are still carrying out a task, however, which is the production of **keratin**—a flexible, water-resistant protein, abundant in the outer layers of skin, that also makes up hair and fingernails. By the time epidermal cells

Figure 25.7
Our Outer Wrap: What Is Skin Made Of?

(a) A micrograph of human skin, showing the epidermal and dermal layers. Note how the cells of the epidermis flatten out about half-way toward the top.

(b) A cross-section of the skin's epidermis and dermis layers, and the hypodermis layer beneath them (which is not part of the skin).

epidermis
dermis
subcutaneous (hypodermis)
hair shaft
sebaceous gland
sweat gland duct
hair follicle
nerve fibers
sweat gland
artery
vein
fat
apocrine sweat gland
touch and pressure receptor
pore of sweat gland duct

reach the surface, they are scarcely cells at all any-more. They are dead and don't even have the remnants of internal organelles within them. Instead, they have become a series of tightly interlocked keratin sacs. In another two weeks they will be scraped or washed away, replaced by the next cells that have pushed up from the inner epidermis.

Beneath the Epidermis: The Dermis and Hypodermis

Whereas the epidermis is epithelial tissue, the inner layer of skin, the **dermis,** is mostly connective tissue. But if you look again at Figure 25.7, you can see that nerves and muscles exist in the dermis as well, along with sweat glands, hair follicles, and more. This is just another example of how all the various kinds of tissues tend to exist side by side in a typical organ.

Many of the structures in the dermis are serving the epidermis. For example, the nervous system touch and pressure receptors shown in Figure 25.7 allow us to know when something makes contact with our skin, and the blood vessels pictured provide a blood supply to the dividing lower cells of the epidermis. But the dermal blood supply takes on another role as well. It plays a big part in controlling our temperature. If you get too cold, the dermal blood vessels will constrict, thus moving blood away from your surface and retaining the heat that's in the blood. If you get too hot, the dermal blood vessels expand, thereby moving blood toward your surface so that the heat that's in blood can radiate to the outside world (making your skin feel "flushed"). One more thing to note about the dermis is that its cells are relatively fixed, unlike those of the outer epidermis. Ever wonder why a tattoo must be made with a needle sunk into the skin? The tattoo's pigment must be deposited into the fixed cells in the dermis, rather than the ever-changing cells of the epidermis.

As noted earlier, the "hypodermis," the layer beneath the dermis, is not actually part of the skin. But it deserves special mention here because of one of the aspects of it you can see in Figure 25.7—its abundant fat cells. The body has fat cells in other places, but when we talk about how much "fat" we have, what we basically mean is how much fat we have in the hypodermis. This is a layer of fat whose composition changes throughout the life span. It is relatively thick when we are infants, then gets thinner when we are children, and then expands steadily around our mid-sections and elsewhere as we age. The term "hypodermis" may ring a bell because it sounds like the more familiar term hypoder*mic*, as in needles. The fatty tissue of the hypodermis doesn't have much of a blood supply and thus is a good place to inject medicines that need a relatively slow, steady entry into circulation.

Here's one final thing about the skin. If you want to make it age fast, one sure way to do it is to spend a lot of time in the sun. You can read more about this in "There Is No Such Thing as a Fabulous Tan" on the next page.

Accessory Structures of the Integumentary System

As noted, skin has a number of accessory structures associated with it, including glands, nails, and hair.

Hair

Five million or so hairs exist on the human body, though only about 100,000 of them are on the human head. Hair clearly serves a major cosmetic role in modern society, but why does it exist on human beings in the first place? You might think that heat retention for our ancestors would have been its main function, but maybe not. Rub your hand with just the lightest stroke over the hair on your head and you can get a sense of how exquisitely sensitive hair is to our sense of *touch*. Like a cat's whiskers, hair may have served primarily to fine-tune our sense of contact with the world around us.

How can hair have this quality since it is not alive, but merely a shaft of the protein keratin, which is a product of underlying cells? If you look at Figure 25.7, you can see that each hair grows out of a tube-like structure called a hair follicle that begins fairly deep in the dermis. Each follicle is a tissue complex that has not only its own blood vessels and muscles, but its own nerve endings as well. Thus, when you touch a hair, you stimulate a hair follicle's nerve endings.

True to what we noted at the start of the chapter, the body's hair is perhaps more missed when it is gone than appreciated when it is here. Many men start losing the hair on their heads in their early twenties, a trend that accelerates as they get older. Women can lose hair too, though their loss tends to come later in life and usually involves a general thinning of the hair, rather than receding hairlines or bald spots. What causes hair loss?

Follicles go through growth and resting phases, with a given hair on our heads growing for anywhere from two to six years until a short resting phase is reached. At that point the hair drops out, and its follicle's growth phase starts again. Hair loss generally is a condition in which an ever-growing proportion of follicles start to shrink, resulting in a

There Is No Such Thing as a Fabulous Tan

The French clothing designer Gabriel Chanel once remarked that "fashion changes, but style remains." Decades ago, however, Chanel herself helped launch a fashion that seems stubbornly resistant to change. The fashion is that of getting a suntan, but this practice might as well be called the fashion of damaging your skin so that in a couple of decades it will be saggy, wrinkled, and spotted.

Throughout the early part of the twentieth century, it was chic to have pale skin, rather than a tan, as a tan was a sign of someone who *had* to be outdoors—working a job. According to one popular account, Gabriel Chanel (of Chanel No. 5 fame) got some sun on an ocean cruise in the 1920s, stepped off the boat tanned, and conveyed the message that it was chic to look that way. People in industrial countries were ready to hear this message because it came at a moment when their leisure time was increasing, meaning they had more opportunities to be out in the sun playing, rather than working.

These days, the constant message from health professionals is to *avoid* the sun, but this is a message society has not really taken to heart. Consider that in a British survey done in 2001, more than 70 percent of the respondents said that people who get tanned are taking a health risk. So far, so good; but this same percentage of respondents believed that "people with sun-tans look healthy." There are an estimated 15,000 businesses in the United States devoted solely to *giving* people tans through the same exposure to ultraviolet light that the sun delivers.

But in what ways does sun exposure harm the skin? The most serious thing it does is help cause skin cancer—three varieties of it, actually—but let's set this aside and focus here on what it does to the appearance of the skin.

The clearest way to get a sense of the cosmetic effects of the sun is to put your forearm up against that of a fair-skinned 50-year-old who has spent a lot of time outdoors. By some estimates, 90 percent of the difference you will see is attributable to sun damage. See

the brown marks commonly known as "liver spots?" They don't have anything at all to do with the liver; they're purely caused by sun exposure. How about the white spots that seem to be patches of skin where the pigment has just given up, leaving small splotches of pure white behind? Sun exposure again. Now what about the sagging that can be seen on the arm and the wrinkling on the hand? It turns out that just below the surface of the skin, in the layer called the dermis, there is a protein called elastin that does pretty much what it sounds like: It springs back to its original shape after having been bent or twisted in some way. Unfortunately, ultraviolet light breaks down elastin, so that after enough sun exposure, the skin loses that full, robust look—it sags and wrinkles. These aging effects are so well understood among dermatologists that they simply refer to sun-caused skin changes as "photo-aging."

But what about sunblocks? They are indeed recommended by dermatologists, with the understanding that they need to be SPF 15 or higher, applied in nice thick layers, and reapplied after activities such as swimming. And there is general agreement that they can block most of the harmful effects of the sun. There is a debate going on within the research community, however, about whether sun blocks are lulling people into a false sense of security about how much sun damage they are getting. The concern is that people will stay out in the sun until they get the general "flushed" feeling telling them they have had enough. It takes longer to get this feeling when sunscreen has been applied, but the critical thing is that sun damage has occurred *whenever* this point has been reached. What difference does it make if a person blocks the sun's rays for three hours before allowing them in? The general advice of dermatologists is simply to avoid lengthy exposure to direct sunlight, particularly between the hours of 10 a.m. and 2 p.m. Sunblocks and covering up help, but they have their limitations. If you avoid the sun, you may not end up with the most fashionable-looking skin over the next two weeks but over the next two decades, you will be the clear winner.

briefer growing phase and hair that comes out either short and fine (like a baby's) or doesn't come out at all. Genes clearly play a part in this process although, contrary to popular belief, it is not just genes from the mother's side of the family that are involved. Hormones called androgens clearly are involved as well; men have higher levels of androgens circulating in their bodies than women do, and thus experience more hair loss.

Glands

You may remember that when we went over the endocrine system, you saw that glands come in two varieties: those that secrete their substances directly into the bloodstream or surrounding tissue (endocrine glands) and those that secrete their substances through the tubes called ducts (exocrine glands). Skin contains two types of exocrine glands. The first of these are known as **sebaceous glands**, which produce an oily substance called sebum that is secreted into hair follicles and that then moves through them onto the skin (see Figure 25.7). Once on the skin, sebum lubricates the hair and inhibits bacterial growth in the surrounding area.

The problem with this process is that, under hormonal influence, sebaceous glands can be *too* active—they can produce too much sebum, particularly in teenagers. When this excess sebum mixes with skin cells that are being shed from the sebaceous follicle, the result can be a blocked follicle that swells with sebum—a whitehead. Once this blockage occurs, bacteria normally found on the skin begin to multiply in the follicle, producing irritating substances that can cause general inflammation and pimples. Taken together, these various skin afflictions are known as acne. No matter what you may have heard, acne is not caused by eating fatty foods, nor is it caused by stress, nor by a lack of face scrubbing. As with baldness, the hormones called androgens are the culprits. They prompt the increased sebaceous activity; since males at puberty have more androgens in them than females, it is males who suffer more from acne.

The second type of exocrine gland in the skin is the **sweat gland**, simply defined as a gland that produces the fluid sweat. This can mean a couple of different things, however, because sweat glands come in two varieties. One type is a *merocrine* (or eccrine) gland that produces the clear, saltwater-like fluid we normally think of as sweat. We have, at a minimum, 2 million merocrine sweat glands on our bodies. They exist on almost all skin surfaces, but we have an especially dense concentration of them on our feet, forehead, and palms (hence "sweaty palms"). The primary function of the merocrine sweat glands is to bring sweat to the surface of the skin, so that it can cool us by evaporating. These glands have their own ducts and follicles, which begin deep in the dermis.

The other sweat glands in the body, called *apocrine* glands, are very different from the merocrine glands. First, they only exist in a few places in the body—notably the groin, the anal area, and the armpits. As such, they have little effect on body cooling. Second, they secrete their products into hair follicles, not up through their own ducts. Most important, apocrine gland secretions contain not only regular sweat, but a fatty, milky fluid whose function in humans is unknown. The *effect* of this fluid is very well known, however. Bacteria feed on it, and the resulting bacterial byproducts are the cause of body odor. Apocrine glands only begin functioning at puberty, which is why children seldom have body odor.

Nails

Our final accessory structure of the integumentary system is the nails found on our fingers and toes. Like hair, nails are made of a variety of the protein keratin. They are clearly useful for protection and for prying, scratching, and picking up objects. Nails allow us to look, in a sense, at the blood vessels underlying the dermis, because it's the reddish color of these vessels that gives nails their pink hue.

25.8 The Skeletal System

We now shift gears, going from a consideration of our outer covering to a consideration of the framework that underlies it—our skeletal system. This system has only three structural elements to it: bone, ligaments, and cartilage. Most of us are quite familiar with **bone**, which can be defined as a connective tissue that provides support and storage capacity, and that is the site of blood cell production. Ligaments are fairly inaccessible to us; but if you look at **Figure 25.8**, you can see some typical ligaments carrying out a typical task—linking bones together. You can also see the third element of the skeletal system, cartilage. Note that cartilage is located *in between* bones in the foot, and this turns out to be one of its common functions. **Cartilage** is a connective tissue that serves as padding in most joints. It is more familiar to us, however, in other parts of the body. It forms our larynx (voice box), the C-shaped "rings" on our trachea (windpipe), our nose-tip and outer ears, and it links each of our ribs to our breastbone.

It's a good idea to look at Figure 25.8 to get a sense not only of the difference between bone, ligaments, and cartilage but also of the difference between all of these skeletal elements and another type

Three components of the skeletal system:

bone

ligaments

cartilage

Tendons are connective tissues that join bone to muscle.

Figure 25.8
Elements of the Skeletal System
Bones are the basic element of the skeletal system. Ligaments link one bone to another, and cartilage often serves as padding between bones. Tendons, while not part of the skeletal system, always link bone to muscle.

of tissue that is pictured, tendons. Though not part of the skeletal system, tendons are always associated with the bones of the system. Looking at all four elements in the figure, here's one way to think of them. Bones are the basic framework; cartilage often serves as padding between bones; **ligaments** are tissues that join bone to bone; and **tendons** are tissues that join bone to muscle.

Function and Structure of Bones

It's tempting to think of bones as being nothing more than support beams, but this conception is wide of the mark in two ways. First, support beams are not alive, but bone is very much a living, dynamic tissue, as you'll see. Second, bones do more than just support us. Once we are past infancy, all of our blood cells (both red and white) are created in the interior of our bones. Some bones store fat, in the form of yellow marrow, as a kind of energy reserve, and bones serve as the storage sites for important minerals such as calcium and phosphate. Beyond this, the only reason we can move at all is that our muscles are attached to bones. When we contract our bicep, for example, our forearm is raised by means of the bicep pulling on the bones of the forearm.

The Structure of Bone

Each bone in our body actually is considered a separate organ, because each bone is composed of several kinds of tissue. There is the calcified or "osseous" tissue we think of as bone, to be sure, but each bone also has its own blood vessels and nerves. (Cartilage, meanwhile, is composed of a single kind of protein fiber—a collagen that can be up to 80 percent water—and it has no nerves and no blood vessels.)

Bones are a great example of connective tissue, in that the *cells* in bones may account for as little as 2 percent of bone mass. What is the other 98 percent of bone made of? It is overwhelmingly a ground substance, secreted by bone cells, that is composed of hard, calcium-containing crystals and tough, yet flexible collagen fibers. This combination means that bones are hard without being brittle—they can support our weight and yet can bend or twist a little without breaking.

Large-Scale Features of Bone

The typical features of a long bone such as the humerus (in the arm) are shown in **Figure 25.9**. A long bone has a central shaft, or diaphysis, and expanded ends, or epiphyses (singular, epiphysis). There are two types of bone. **Compact bone**, which

Figure 25.9
Large- and Small-Scale Features of a Typical Bone
Note that in (c), the building units of compact bone, the osteons, run parallel to the long axis of the bone. Spongy bone does not contain osteons, but instead is composed of an open network of calcified rods or plates.

is relatively solid, forms the outer portion of the bone (all the way around it, as you can see in Figure 25.9b). **Spongy bone** then fills the epiphyses, and is well named. It is porous enough that it contains another type of tissue, called marrow, that comes in two forms: **red marrow**, which gives rise to blood cells; and **yellow marrow**, made up of energy-storing fat cells. Yellow marrow also exists in the so-called *marrow cavity* of a long bone, which you can see in Figure 25.9.

Small-Scale Features of Bone

Dropping down to the microscopic level and looking at bone *cells*, we find that three different types are involved in the growth and maintenance of bone. **Osteoblasts** are immature bone cells that are responsible for the production of new bone. They secrete the material that becomes the bone ground substance. Once osteoblasts are surrounded by this material, they reduce their production of it, and this marks their transition to osteocytes, the second type of bone cell. **Osteocytes** are mature bone cells; they *maintain* the structure and density of normal bone by continually recycling the calcium compounds around themselves. The third type of bone cell, the osteoclasts, could be thought of as the demolition team of bone tissue. **Osteoclasts** are cells that move along the outside of bones, releasing enzymes that eat away at bone tissue, thus liberating minerals stored in the bone. This may sound harmful, but it actually is essential for bone growth and for the regulation of blood levels of calcium. (This is the calcium-releasing function we reviewed at the start of the chapter.) The upshot of all this is that, at any given moment, osteoblasts are adding to bone, osteocytes are maintaining it, and osteoclasts are removing it.

Within compact bone, the basic functional unit is the osteon seen in Figure 25.9c (which is also known as the Haversian system). The essence of bone growth is that, within each osteon, osteoblasts produce layer after layer of concentric cylinders of bone—much like layers of insulation wrapped around a pipe. These layers surround what could be thought of as the hole in the pipe, which is a central canal (also known as a Haversian canal). These canals parallel the long axis of the bone and have blood vessels and nerves running through them—a kind of support system for the bone.

Unlike compact bone, spongy bone has no osteons. It consists of an open network of interconnecting calcified rods or plates. The red and yellow marrow fills the spaces within this network.

Practical Consequences of Bone Dynamics

Now, let's think about the practical consequences of this structure. Remember the earlier observation that bone is a living tissue? With its three kinds of cells constantly adding, maintaining, and breaking down the tissue, you can see the truth of this. But bone is more dynamic than even this would indicate, in that bones are responsive to our activities. As physiologist Frederic Martini has noted, when you undertake an exercise like jogging, which stresses your bones, the calcium-containing crystals of the affected bones create small electrical fields that apparently attract osteoblasts. Upon arrival, these osteoblasts begin producing bone. The result? If you take up jogging, you get denser leg bones. But there's a flip side to this coin: People who are using crutches to take the weight off a broken leg bone may temporarily lose up to a third of the mass in this bone because it is now scarcely being stressed at all.

Interestingly, though we develop almost all our height by late adolescence, we are still gaining in bone density up until about the age of 30. Then, beginning in middle age, the body may start removing more bone than it adds. This phenomenon particularly afflicts women, in the form of a condition known as *osteoporosis*, meaning a thinning of bone tissue that can result in bone breakage and deformation. One way we can guard against osteoporosis is to reach the age of 30 with as much bone density as we can muster—the equivalent of putting money in the bank as a hedge against a later withdrawal. And there are a couple of proven ways to get more bone density before 30: Take up moderate programs of "weight-bearing" exercise such as jogging or walking, and modestly increase calcium intake.

The Human Skeleton

Taking a step back from the microscopic world, you can see in **Figure 25.10** that there are a lot of bones in the skeletal system—206 of them in all. (Only the major bones are visible in the figure.) There are two main divisions to the skeletal system: the **axial skeleton**, whose 80 bones include the skull, the vertebral column, and the rib cage that attaches to it; and the **appendicular skeleton**, whose 126 bones include those of our paired appendages—the arms and the legs, along with the pelvic and pectoral "girdles" to which they are attached. Also note the blue-colored tissue joining ribs to our breastbone and lying in between each of the vertebrae. These are but a few of the cartilages in the body.

Axial skeleton

skull
- cranium
- facial bones
- mandible

thoracic cage
- sternum (breast bone)
- ribs (12 pairs)
- costal cartilages

vertebral column
- Intervertebral disks
- vertebrae (33 bones)
- sacrum

Appendicular skeleton

pectoral girdle
- clavicle (collarbone)
- scapula (shoulder blade)

upper limbs
- humerus
- radius
- ulna
- carpal bones
- metacarpal bones
- phalanges (finger, thumb bones)

os coxa (hip bone) **pelvic girdle**

lower limbs
- femur
- patella (knee bone)
- tibia
- fibula
- tarsal bones
- metatarsal bones
- phalanges (toe bones)

Figure 25.10
Solid Framework
A view of the human skeleton, which has two divisions, axial and appendicular. The major bones of the axial division are listed on the left, and the major bones of the appendicular division on the right.

Joints

Joints, or articulations, exist wherever two bones meet. What qualities are required of a joint? Well, some only need strength. We think of our skull as being a single bone; but in fact, it's composed of several bones that interlock with each other in joints that are immovable. For other joints, flexibility is the key requirement. The ball-and-socket joint at our shoulder permits a range of motion so extensive that movement of our upper arms is limited more by our shoulder muscles than by our bones.

Highly movable joints are typically found at the ends of long bones, such as those in the legs as well as the shoulder. You can see a view of such a joint—the human knee joint—in **Figure 25.11**. A joint such as this must serve two competing functions. On the one hand, it must keep the massive femur (thigh bone) and large tibia (shin bone) in a stable arrangement. On the other, it serves as a hinge that allows the tibia to swing as free as a screen door off the femur. How does it do both things? Well, the two bones are partly held in place by four main ligaments, some of which are visible in the figure. Recall that ligaments link bone to bone, but there are also tendons, which attach bone to muscle; the knee joint has these in place as well.

With respect to the motion that such a joint allows, a critical element is that one bone does not actually touch another. Instead, an extensive network of padding and lubricating tissues in between the bones performs the same function as the "gel" found in running shoes. Note that the top of the tibia and bottom of the femur are surrounded by cartilage, and that more cartilage—in the form of the meniscus tissue—lies on each side of the joint. The yellow tissue shown is fat padding that fills in spaces that are created when

the bones move, and the space in between the bones is filled with a thick, viscous fluid that not only lubricates joints, but aids in their metabolism.

Joints can get injured, of course, and as we age they can wear down altogether. If you follow sports, the name of one of the ligaments shown in Figure 25.11 may ring a bell. The anterior cruciate ligament (ACL), which runs from the back of the femur to the front of the tibia, is a frequent site of injury for athletes who participate in sports that involve rapid "cutting," such as volleyball, soccer, and basketball. An athlete will come to a quick stop, hear a pop, and be down with a torn or ruptured ACL that usually will have to be replaced by grafting tissue onto it from another part of the body. For older people, the usual problem is not a sudden injury, but rather a slow, steady degeneration of hip, knuckle, or knee joints in the disease known as osteoarthritis. Such "wear and tear" arthritis results in a breakdown of the cartilage in between bones, such that joints become swollen and misaligned, with bone sometimes grinding against bone.

25.9 The Muscular System

Bones may provide a scaffolding for the body, but how is it that this scaffolding is capable of movement? The answer is muscles, specifically the skeletal muscles that were introduced earlier, which are numerous and large enough that they account for about 40 percent of our body weight. (When we talk about the "meat" in, say, cattle, we are mostly talking about skeletal muscle.) Like bones, skeletal muscles are organs in that they contain a variety of tissues. At each end of a muscle, fibers of the outer muscle layer come together to form the tendons that attach muscle to bone.

Figure 25.11
A Highly Moveable Joint
A simplified view of the human knee joint. Note that the two bones never touch each other because they are covered with cartilage. The joint has shock-absorbing cartilage in the form of the menisci and a fat pad that protects the cartilage.

anterior
cruciate
ligament

articular
cartilage

ligament

patella

fat pad

joint cavity

articular
capsule

ligament

menisci

The Makeup of Muscle

As you can see in **Figure 25.12**, each muscle has within it a number of oval-shaped bundles called fascicles. Inside each fascicle there is a collection of muscle cells, but the term cell here may be misleading, because any one of these cells can be as long as the muscle itself—a gigantic length relative to the strictly microscopic dimensions of most cells. Because skeletal muscle cells are elongated, they are referred to as **muscle fibers**. Along their length, muscle fibers are divided into a set of about 10,000 repeating units, called **sarcomeres**, that are the fundamental units of muscle contraction. But what is it that's contracting in a muscle? A look inside a single muscle fiber reveals that it is composed of more strands—perhaps a thousand long, thin structures called myofibrils that run the length of the cell. Each myofibril, in turn, has a large collection of two kinds of strands inside it that alternate with one another; these are thin filaments made of the protein *actin* and thick filaments made of the protein *myosin*. It is these filaments that contract, as you'll now see.

How Muscles Work

To understand contraction, note first that the thick myosin filaments lie in the *center* of a given sarcomere. Meanwhile, the thin actin filaments are attached to either *end* of the sarcomere and extend toward the center, where they overlap with the thick filaments (**see Figure 25.13** on the next page). In contraction, the thin filaments slide toward the center, causing the unit to shorten, which is to say, causing the muscle to contract. To understand this, place just the tips of the fingers of your right hand in between the tips the fingers of your left hand. Now slide your right hand as far as it will go to the left. Note that neither set of *fingers* shortened in length, but that the total distance made up by both sets of fingers did shorten—exactly what happens within a sarcomere.

But what enables the thin filaments to slide? The thick myosin filaments have numerous club-shaped "heads" extending from them. These myosin heads are capable of alternately binding with or detaching from the adjacent thin filaments, creating so-called *cross-bridges*. The myosin heads pivot at their base, as if they were on a hinge. Here's the order of their activity: Attach to the actin filament, pull it toward the center of the sarcomere, detach from the actin, reattach to it, and pull again. In actual muscle contraction, this process happens many times in the blink of an eye; at any one point in a contraction, some myosin heads will be pulling an actin filament while others are detaching from it and still others binding to it.

This whole process gets going only when a signal arrives from a nerve telling a muscle to contract—often when a person has decided to move. This is why we speak of skeletal muscles as being under voluntary control, although it's easy to find exceptions to this rule. (The diaphragm that allows you to breathe is composed of skeletal muscles, but normally there is little that's voluntary in using them.)

When a nerve signal arrives, the actual message doesn't go directly from nerve to muscle. Instead, a kind of ferry-boat operation takes place in which the nerve end secretes a chemical, called a

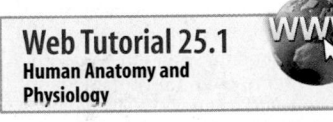

Web Tutorial 25.1
Human Anatomy and
Physiology

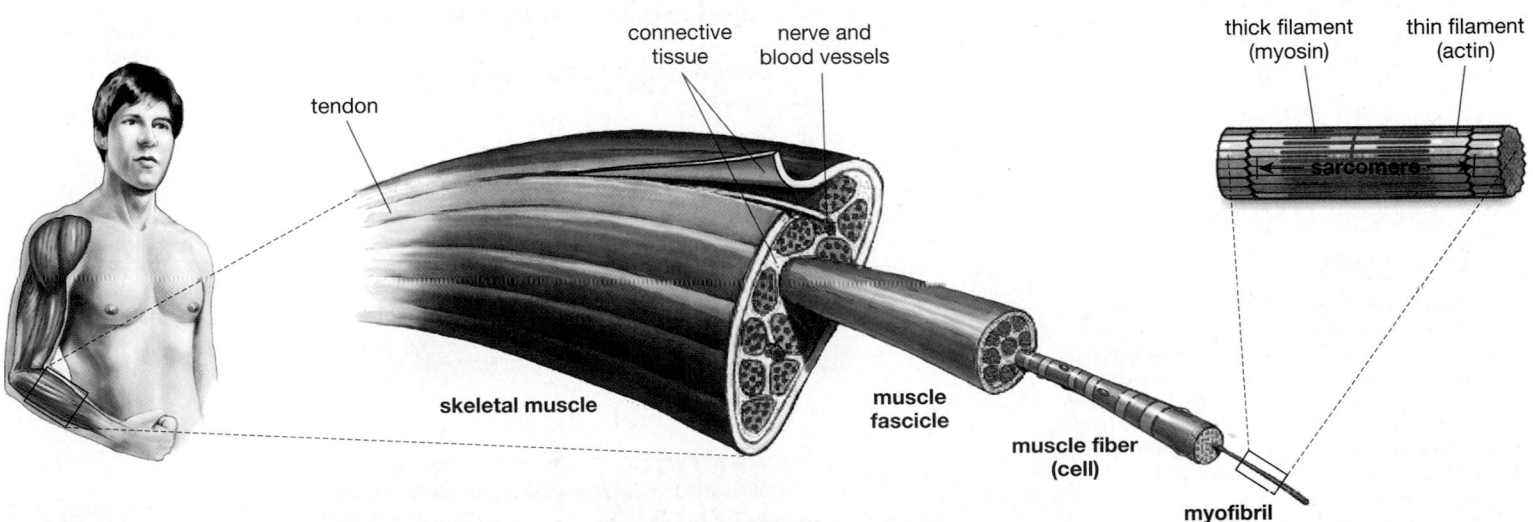

Figure 25.12
Structure of Skeletal Muscle
Skeletal muscles have oval-shaped bundles within them, called fascicles, that are composed of a number of muscle cells, each one of which is so elongated it is referred to as a "fiber." Each fiber is composed of many thin myofibrils, and each myofibril has within it a collection of alternating thick and thin protein strands called filaments. The thin filaments are made of the protein actin, the thick filaments of the protein myosin. Each myofibril is divided up lengthwise into a series of repeating functional units called sarcomeres.

neurotransmitter, that travels across a tiny gap that lies between nerve and muscle. Once the neurotransmitter arrives at the muscle, it binds with it, setting in motion a chemical reaction that results in calcium ions (Ca^{2+}) being released inside a sarcomere. These calcium ions have the effect of allowing the myosin heads to bind to the actin filaments, which of course has to happen before the myosin heads can *pull* the actin filaments.

Now, what about the practical consequences of this physiology? The cycle that runs from myosin binding, through pulling, and then detaching is known as a *twitch*. The muscle fibers that go through this cycle come in two varieties—fast-twitch and slow-twitch—whose names describe how long it takes them to complete a cycle. Fast-twitch fibers are not just faster than slow-twitch fibers, however; they also can generate more power. But there is a catch to this, in that fast-twitch fibers can generate power only for brief periods. In contrast, slow-twitch fibers generate less power but can do it over a sustained period of time. Thus, fast- and slow-twitch fibers are something like the hare and tortoise of muscle tissue.

Because slow-twitch fibers are infused with an oxygen-binding molecule called myoglobin, they have a red coloration that true fast-twitch fibers lack. The "dark meat" of a chicken leg is dark because it is primarily made of myoglobin-infused slow-twitch fibers. The chicken constantly uses its legs, but doesn't generate much power in doing so—the very thing that slow-twitch fibers are good at. The chicken will occasionally engage its breast muscles in a flurry of contraction so that it can flap its wings. Not surprisingly, chicken breasts are white-meat, which is to say muscle that is primarily composed of fast-twitch fibers. Most muscles contain a mixture of fast- and slow-twitch fibers. We simply utilize different proportions of each kind of fiber, depending on what we are doing. As you might guess, a long-distance runner primarily utilizes slow-twitch fibers while a sprinter primarily uses fast-twitch.

Finally, recall that any muscle contraction begins with a nerve ending sending a chemical packet called a

Figure 25.13
How a Skeletal Muscle Contracts

(a) Muscle at rest

The myofibril contains several sarcomeres, one of which is shown at rest. The thin filaments within the sarcomere, made of actin, overlap with adjacent thick filaments, made of myosin. The thick filaments have club-shaped outgrowths, called heads. The myofibril is also shown in cross section, at a location where thick and thin filaments overlap.

(b) Muscle contraction

Muscle contraction is a matter of the thin actin filaments sliding together within a sarcomere. This comes about when the myosin heads attach to the actin filaments and pull them toward the center of the sarcomere. The myosin heads pivot at their base and are capable of alternately binding with, or detaching from, the thin filaments.

neurotransmitter over to a muscle. It turns out that the only neurotransmitter that operates in muscle contraction is one called acetylcholine. Now imagine what would happen if something *interfered* with acetylcholine's release: Muscles could no longer get a message telling them to contract. This would be bad enough in the case of an arm muscle, but disastrous in the case of the muscles that allow us to breathe. This kind of muscle paralysis does take place, however, in connection with the puncture-related infection tetanus, and with a kind of food poisoning that's not so well known, botulism. In both cases, bacteria that enter the body release toxins that impede acetylcholine release, and in both cases the result can be death from suffocation. Thanks to vaccines and good hygiene, both afflictions are very rare in the United States—50 cases a year of tetanus, 110 of botulism—but they do point up that our survival depends on all these microscopic processes remaining in working order.

Given all this, it may seem strange that one of the best-selling drugs in the United States in recent years has been a form of ... botulism toxin! In 2002, the U.S. Food and Drug Administration (FDA) approved the cosmetic use of Botulinum Toxin Type A—better known as Botox—which is intended to temporarily get rid of forehead creases and "frown lines." Botox is sterile, purified, and stays localized in the area where a doctor injects it, which is the forehead. Nevertheless, like germ-borne botulism toxin, its effect is to paralyze muscles.

On to the Nervous and Endocrine Systems

Having looked at the basic characteristics of the body and at three of its organ systems, we're now ready to move on to two other systems, both of which function in communication. These are the nervous and endocrine systems.

Chapter Review

Summary

25.1 The Disciplines of Anatomy and Physiology

- Anatomy is the study of the body's internal and external structure and the physical relationships between the body's constituent parts. Physiology is the study of how these parts work.

25.2 How Does the Body Regulate Itself?

- The body regulates itself not through a hierarchical command structure, but rather through a system of circular control, in which A prompts B and B prompts C, but in which C may then prompt A. By self-regulating in this way, the body seeks homeostasis or the maintenance of a relatively stable internal environment. A single mechanism is almost singly responsible for bringing about homeostasis. This mechanism is negative feedback: a process in which the elements that bring about a response have their activity reduced by that response.

- Humans have two primary body cavities: a dorsal cavity that is further divided into cranial and spinal cavities; and a ventral cavity that is further divided into a thoracic cavity that contains the lungs and heart, and an abdominopelvic cavity that contains such organs as the stomach and liver.

25.3 Levels of Physical Organization

- Animal bodies function through a series of smaller-to-larger working units whose order runs as follows: cells, tissues, organs, and organ systems. Tissues are groups of cells that have a common function. Organs are complexes of several kinds of tissues that perform a special bodily function. Organ systems are groups of organs and tissues that perform a given function.
  Web Tutorial 25.1: Human Anatomy and Physiology

25.4 The Human Body Has Four Basic Tissue Types

- There are four fundamental tissue types in the human body: epithelial, connective, muscle, and nervous. Epithelial tissue covers all body surfaces exposed to an external environment and forms glands, which are organs that secrete one or more substances.

- Connective tissue supports and protects other tissues. Connective-tissue cells are embedded in a "ground" material, which they themselves generally secrete. A prime function of most connective-tissue cells is to produce this extracellular material, which varies in consistency from a fluid to a solid. For example, bone cells secrete a connective ground material that largely forms the solid bones we are familiar with.

- Muscle tissue is specialized in its ability to contract. There are three primary types of muscle tissue: skeletal, cardiac, and smooth. Skeletal muscle is always attached to bone and is under voluntary control. Cardiac muscle exists only in the heart and beats under the control of its own pacemaker cells. Smooth muscle is "smooth" because it lacks the striations that skeletal muscle has; it is not under voluntary control and is responsible for contractions in blood vessels, air passages, and hollow organs such as the uterus.

- Nervous tissue is specialized for the rapid conduction of electrical impulses. It is made up of two basic types of cells: neurons, which actually transmit the impulses; and glial cells, which are support cells for neurons.

25.5 Organs Are Made of Several Kinds of Tissues

- The stomach provides a case in point for how various tissue types come together to form a working organ. A typical cross section of the stomach is made up of muscle, nervous, connective, and epithelial tissue.

25.6 Organs and Tissues Make Up Organ Systems

- There are 11 organ systems in the body. The first three of these—the integumentary, skeletal, and muscular systems—function in body support and movement. The integumentary system is made up of skin and such associated structures as glands, hair, and nails. The skeletal system is made up of bones, ligaments, and cartilages. The muscular system includes all the skeletal muscles of the body, but not smooth or cardiac muscles.

- The nervous, endocrine, and lymphatic systems function in communication, regulation, and defense of the body. The nervous system is a rapid communication system that includes the brain, spinal cord, all the nerves, and sense organs such as the eye and ear. The endocrine system is a communication system that works more slowly, through the substances called hormones, many of which are produced in specialized glands. (Glands that release their substances directly into the bloodstream or extracellular fluid are endocrine glands. Glands that release their substances through the tubes known as ducts are exocrine glands.) The lymphatic system overlaps with the immune functions of the body. It consists of a network of lymphatic vessels that collect extracellular fluid and deliver it to the blood vessels as a fluid called lymph. Lymphatic system organs include the lymph nodes, thymus gland, tonsils, and spleen. Cells within lymph glands inspect lymph as it passes through the system to identify invading microorganisms.

- The cardiovascular, respiratory, digestive, and urinary organ systems function in transport and in exchange with the environment. The cardiovascular system consists of the heart, blood, blood vessels, and the inner "marrow" portion of the bones where red blood cells are formed. The respiratory system includes the lungs and the passageways that carry air to them. The central feature of the digestive system is the digestive tract, a tube that begins at the mouth and ends at the anus. Along its course, there are digestive organs of the system: the stomach, small intestines, and large intestines and such accessory glands as the liver and pancreas. The urinary system functions to eliminate waste products from the blood through the formation of urine and to retain substances that are useful to the body. It is made up of the kidneys and various other structures, such as the bladder.

- Humans have separate reproductive systems for females and males.

25.7 The Integumentary System: Skin and Its Accessories

- The primary component of the integumentary system is the organ called skin. Integumentary structures associated with skin are hair, nails, and a variety of exocrine glands.

- In addition to covering the body, skin protects underlying tissues and organs, controls the evaporation of body fluids, regulates heat loss, stores fat, and makes vitamin D. Exocrine glands associated with skin excrete such materials as water, oils, and milk. Specialized nerve endings in the skin detect touch, pressure, pain, and temperature.

- Skin has a thin outer epithelial covering, the epidermis; and a thicker underlying dermis, composed mostly of connective tissue. Beneath the dermis—and not part of the skin—is a third layer of tissues, the hypodermis. Epidermal skin cells are constantly worn away and replaced by new epidermal cells being pushed up from the inner epidermis. As they move toward the surface, these cells are transformed into a series of dead, tightly linked sacs made of the protein keratin. The dermis is filled with accessory structures, such as hair follicles and sweat glands, and contains blood vessels and nerves that support the surface of the skin. The blood supply of the dermis is important in controlling body temperature.

- The hypodermis, beneath the dermis, contains the layer of fat cells that largely determine how much "fat" we have on our bodies.

- Hairs originate in tiny organs called hair follicles and may have been important for our evolutionary ancestors in both heat retention and touch sensitivity.

- The skin contains two types of exocrine glands: sebaceous glands, that produce sebum, which lubricates hair and limits bacterial growth on the skin; and sweat glands, which produce sweat that cools the body by evaporating. Overactive sebaceous glands are the cause of acne. Sweat glands come in two varieties: the more-numerous merocrine glands, which produce the perspiration; and the less-numerous apocrine glands, which produce sweat mixed with a thick, cloudy secretion that moves through hair follicles onto the skin. Bacteria feed on this secretion, and the resulting bacterial by-products are the cause of body odor.

- Nails are made of the protein keratin and form over the tips of the fingers and toes, where they are useful in protection and in prying, scratching, and picking up objects.

25.8 The Skeletal System

- The human skeletal system is composed of bone, ligaments, and cartilage. Bone is a connective tissue that provides support and storage capacity, and that is the site of blood-cell production. Cartilage serves as padding in most joints, forms our larynx (voice box) and trachea (windpipe), and links each rib to the breastbone. Ligaments are tissues that join bone to bone. Tendons link bone to muscle but are not part of the skeletal system.

- Each bone of the skeleton is an organ that contains not only connective tissue—mostly the supporting connective tissue called osseous tissue—but blood vessels and nervous tissue as well.

- The typical bone features a long central shaft, called a diaphysis, and expanded ends, called epiphyses. There are two types of bone: compact bone, which is relatively solid and forms the outer portion of the bone; and spongy bone, which is less dense and fills the epiphyses. Spongy bone is filled with marrow, which comes in two forms: red marrow, which gives rise to blood cells; and yellow marrow, which is composed of energy-storing fat cells. Long bones have a central marrow cavity that is filled with yellow marrow.

- Three different types of cells are involved in bone growth and maintenance. Osteoblasts are responsible for the production of new bone; osteocytes are mature bone cells that maintain the structure and density of normal bone; and osteoclasts release enzymes that breaks down bone, thus releasing stored substances, such as calcium.

- In compact bone, the basic functional unit is the osteon. Osteoblasts produce layers of concentric cylinders of bone around a central canal of the osteon. The central canal, which parallels the long axis of the bone, has blood vessels and nerves running through it.

- Bone is responsive to our activities. The density of a bone will decrease to the extent that the bone is not used and will increase to the extent that the bone is stressed, as in some forms of exercise.

- The human skeleton has 206 bones in all, in two main divisions: an axial skeleton, whose 80 bones include the skull, the vertebral column, and the rib cage; and the appendicular skeleton, whose 126 bones include those of the arms and legs and the pelvic and pectoral girdles to which they are attached.

- Joints or articulations exist wherever two bones meet. Some joints provide a strong linkage between bones, while others provide great flexibility. Ligaments (joining bone to bone) and tendons (joining bone to muscle) help provide the stability that large-bone joints need. Normally, the bony surfaces of highly movable joints do not meet directly, but are instead covered with special cartilages and pads that provide shock absorption and lubrication.

25.9 The Muscular System

- A given skeletal muscle cell can be as long as the muscle itself; because of their elongation, these cells are called muscle fibers. Along their length, muscle fibers are divided into a set of repeating units called sarcomeres, which are the basic units of muscle contraction. Each muscle fiber is composed of thin structures, called myofibrils, that are in turn composed of assemblies of two kinds of protein strands that alternate with one another: thin filaments made of the protein actin, and thick filaments made of the protein myosin.

- Actin filaments attached to the end of each sarcomere overlap with the myosin filaments that lie in the center of each sarcomere. The myosin filaments bring about contraction by attaching to the actin filaments, pulling them toward the center of the sarcomeres, detaching, and then pulling again. As the actin filaments slide toward the center of the sarcomere, the sarcomere shortens.

- Skeletal muscles contract only when prompted to by the arrival of a signal from a nerve. Nerve signals can be blocked by, for example, bacterial toxins, in which case skeletal muscles can become paralyzed.

- Muscle fibers differ in how long it takes them to go through the cycle of myosin binding, pulling, and detaching—a cycle referred to as a twitch. Muscle fibers can be categorized as slow-twitch or fast-twitch. Slow-twitch fibers contract with less force, but can do so in a sustained manner; fast-twitch fibers contract with relatively more force, but can do so only for brief periods of time.
Web Tutorial 25.1: Human Anatomy and Physiology

Key Terms

appendicular skeleton 548	**muscular system** 541
axial skeleton 548	**negative feedback** 536
bone 546	**nervous system** 541
cardiac muscle 540	**nervous tissue** 540
cardiovascular system 542	**organ** 537
cartilage 546	**organ system** 537
compact bone 547	**osteoblast** 548
connective tissue 538	**osteoclast** 548
dermis 544	**osteocyte** 548
digestive system 542	**red marrow** 548
endocrine gland 541	**reproductive system** 542
endocrine system 541	**respiratory system** 542
epidermis 543	**sarcomere** 551
epithelial tissue 538	**sebaceous glands** 545
exocrine gland 541	**skeletal muscle** 538
gland 538	**skeletal system** 540
homeostasis 536	**skin** 543
hormone 541	**smooth muscle** 540
integumentary system 540	**spongy bone** 548
keratin 543	**sweat gland** 546
ligaments 547	**tendons** 547
lymphatic system 541	**tissue** 537
muscle fiber 551	**urinary system** 542
muscle tissue 538	**yellow marrow** 548

Understanding the Basics

Multiple-Choice Questions (answers in the back of the book)

1. To survive, the human body needs to maintain _____ and does so primarily through the means of self-regulation known as _____.
   a. high-energy output, positive feedback
   b. adequate fat layers, exocrine secretion
   c. bone density, muscle contraction
   d. homeostasis, negative feedback
   e. nerve signal transmission, hormonal secretion

2. The four basic types of tissue in the human body are
   a. epithelial, connective, muscle, nervous
   b. epithelial, blood, muscle, nervous
   c. skin, bone, muscle, nervous
   d. skin, connective, heart, nervous
   e. epithelial, bone, connective, muscle

3. Endocrine glands differ from exocrine glands in that endocrine glands
   a. have ducts
   b. are ductless
   c. produce only perspiration
   d. consist of epithelia and muscle tissue
   e. are found only in the liver

4. Muscle fibers that are striated and voluntary are found in
   a. cardiac muscle
   b. skeletal muscle
   c. smooth muscle
   d. rough muscle
   e. all four types of muscle

5. Which of the following drugs would seem most likely to cause muscle spasms (uncontrolled contractions)?
   a. one that prevents attachment of myosin heads to actin
   b. one that prevents the use of ATP
   c. one that blocks the detachment of myosin heads from actin
   d. one that elongates the sarcomere

6. Surface epidermal cells of the skin
   a. rapidly divide and are filled mostly with keratin
   b. never divide and remain in place through adult life
   c. rapidly divide and are in place only a short time
   d. are dead and filled with keratin
   e. rapidly divide and are filled with fat

7. Body odor comes primarily from
   a. the tightly linked nature of epidermal cells
   b. the odor of sweat
   c. bacteria that exist in the blood servicing the dermis
   d. byproducts of the bacteria that feed on apocrine sweat
   e. the layer of fat in the hypodermis

8. Cells called _____ build bone tissue _____ maintain it, and _____ break it down.
   a. osteoblasts, osteoclasts, osteocytes
   b. osteoclasts, osteons, osteoblasts
   c. osteoblasts, osteocytes, osteoclasts
   d. osteons, osteocytes, osteoclasts
   e. osteocytes, osteoblasts, octeoclasts

9. The essence of muscle contraction is that thick and thin muscle proteins
   a. slide past each other
   b. link irreversibly with each other
   c. are short enough to respond quickly
   d. stay completely separate
   e. pull in opposite directions

10. No skeletal muscle can contract without first
    a. receiving a hormone signal
    b. checking on the status of nearby skeletal muscles
    c. lining up its actin and myosin filaments
    d. receiving a nervous system signal
    e. linking to a bone

11. Which type of bone cell would you expect would be most active in a female with osteoporosis:
    a. osteocytes
    b. osteoclasts
    c. osteoblasts
    d. cartilage

Brief Review

1. Beginning with the cell, list in correct sequence the four levels of organization of the human body, from the simplest to the most complex.

2. What role does the lymphatic system play in immune function?

3. Why is our skin water-resistant?

4. List three functions of the skeletal system.

5. What is the general mechanism at work in hair loss?

6. A sample of bone shows an interconnecting network of calcified rods and plates filled in with both red and yellow marrow. Is this sample from the shaft (diaphysis) or the end (epiphysis) of a long bone?

7. People who have torn their anterior cruciate ligament report that their knee feels "wobbly" until they get it repaired. Why would this be?

8. Why does skeletal muscle appear striated when viewed under a microscope?

Applying Your Knowledge

1. Cells called melanocytes that lie deep in the epidermis produce a pigment, called melanin, that gives skin its color. Exposure to ultraviolet light—from the sun or a tanning lamp—causes melanocytes to produce more melanin, which they pass along to the skin cells above them, yielding a suntan. But why would sun exposure prompt this increased melanin production? What is the function of a tan, in other words?

2. The text notes that bone density increases in response to the stresses on bone that are provided by exercises such as running. Imagine two fairly inactive people who decide to start exercising. One becomes a runner, the other becomes a swimmer. Who experiences the greater increase in bone density: the swimmer (in the arm bones) or the runner (in the leg bones)?

3. If Botox works by temporarily paralyzing muscles, what does this say about the cause of age lines on the forehead?

26 The Nervous and Endocrine Systems

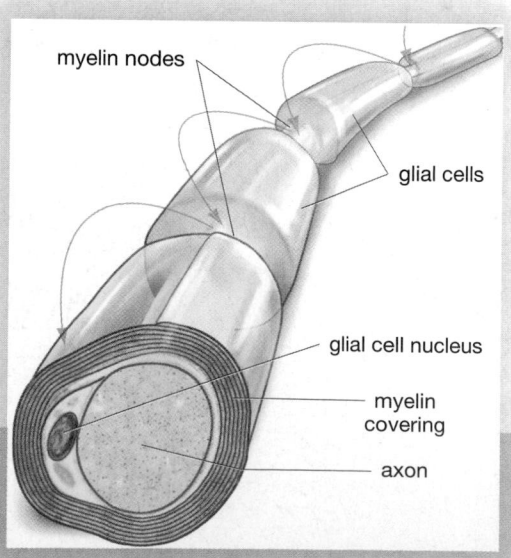

The nature of a nerve.
(Section 26.2, page 563)

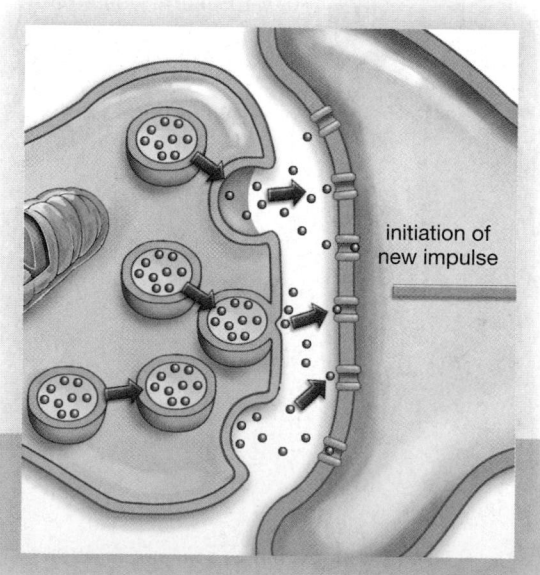

A nerve impulse is transmitted.
(Section 26.3, page 566)

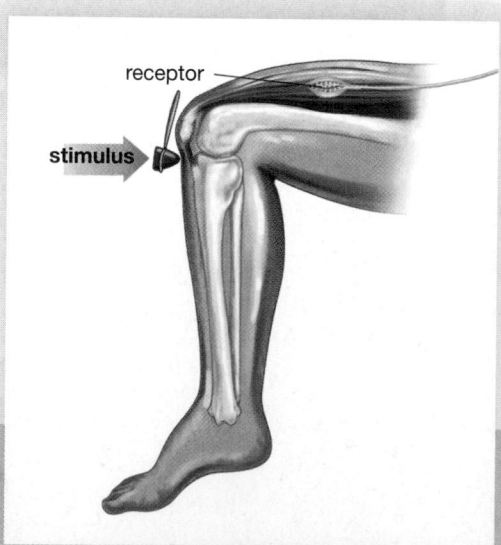

A knee-jerk reaction.
(Section 26.4, page 568)

To get through a day, our bodies must undertake a huge number of tasks each second, many of them coordinated with each other. How do we control such an enormous set of activities? Through our nervous and endocrine systems.

With its depiction of a man who can neither remember his present nor forget his past, the film *Memento* was a big hit in 2001. In it, we watch as the fictional Leonard Shelby relentlessly tracks down the murderer of his wife. He does so, however, while taking Polaroid pictures and scribbling notes to himself anywhere he can—some on his own body as tattoos. He does this because he has a big handicap to deal with. Having sustained a head injury in the same break-in in which his wife was killed, he can remember everything in his life up through the moment of his injury, but has lost the ability to create *new* long-term memories. Now, anything that happens more than 15 minutes in the past is lost to him. Hence the constant notes and Polaroids: Where am I staying? Who did I talk to this morning? What did he look like?

Though Leonard Shelby is a movie character, the condition he has actually exists in some people. A version of it was brilliantly described by the physician-writer Oliver Sacks in his book *The Man Who Mistook His Wife for a Hat*. Sacks introduces us to "Jimmy G.," who was admitted to Sacks's care in the mid-1970s. Though Jimmy G. is a gray-haired, 49-year-old ex-sailor, he perpetually believes himself to be the 19-year-old sailor he was back in 1945. About 1970, he apparently drank so heavily that he damaged his brain, losing not only his memory back to 1945, but his ability to make new memories as well. Hence, in his mind he is always a young man and it is always the end of World War II. This can lead to brief, horrible moments of disorientation, as Sacks describes.

The Importance of Memory
In the film *Memento*, the actor Guy Pearce played Leonard Shelby, a man who has lost his ability to create new long-term memories.

Stretch receptors and touch.
(Section 26.8, page 572)

Seeing in color; seeing in black and white.
(Section 26.12, page 579)

Controlling hormones.
(Section 26.15, page 583)

"Here," I said, and thrust a mirror toward him. "Look in the mirror and tell me what you see. Is that a nineteen-year-old looking out from the mirror?" He suddenly turned ashen and gripped the sides of the chair. "Jesus Christ," he whispered. "Christ, what's going on? What's happened to me?"

Sacks would not have done this but for his certainty about what would happen next. Two minutes later, Jimmy G. has no memory of the mirror or of Sacks. When Sacks briefly leaves the room and then reenters it, Jimmy G. greets him as a total stranger.

As Jimmy G. shows, the "self" that we take for granted largely amounts to a set of memories, which exist in the small physical space of the brain. We can think of memory as an agent of communication and control—one that allows us to act in the present based on our experience of the past. The human nervous system, which includes the brain, can be thought of as a wider-yet communication and control operation—one that constantly monitors our present, along with our past, and issues commands that allow us to function. Only some of these commands are conscious orders, however; most are actions that the brain takes without our knowledge.

Beyond the nervous system, the body has an additional communication and control operation in its hormonal or "endocrine" system. This system works ceaselessly, mostly outside our conscious awareness, to handle such things as our growth when we are children and our bodies' water-balance when we are adults.

Our goal in this chapter is to review both these communication and control operations: the nervous and endocrine systems. We'll start with the nervous system, which is such a wonder when healthy and, as Jimmy G. shows, such a heart-breaker when not.

26.1 Structure of the Nervous System

Taking the broadest view, the nervous system includes all the cells in the body that can be defined as nervous tissue, plus the sense organs we have, such as the eye and ear. Recall from Chapter 25 that two types of cells make up nervous tissue. These are neurons, which actually transmit nervous system messages; and glial cells, which support the neurons.

One helpful way to think about the nervous system is to consider three essential tasks it has to perform. It first has to *receive* information, both from outside and inside our bodies. (For example, what taste sensations are coming in?) It next has to *process* this information. (Do I like this?) Then it has to *send*

information out that allows our body to deal with this input. ("Lift your hand for another spoonful.")

The nervous system in which these activities take place can be divided into two fundamental parts. The first of these is the **central nervous system**: that portion of the nervous system consisting of the brain and the spinal cord. The second is the **peripheral nervous system**: that portion of the nervous system outside the brain and spinal cord, plus the sensory organs (**see Figure 26.1a**).

The central nervous system's brain and spinal cord are not physically separate entities; the spinal cord simply expands greatly at its top, and we call this flowering the brain. Because the brain and spinal cord are so different in terms of structure and function, however, they are thought of as individual units.

Meanwhile, the peripheral nervous system, or PNS, can be pictured as a group of nerves and related nerve cells that fan out from either the brain or spinal cord. One way to think about these peripheral nerves and related cells is to consider the direction of the messages they carry. Any nerves that help carry messages *to* the brain or spinal cord are said to be part of the **afferent division** of the peripheral nervous system. Any nerves that help carry messages *from* the brain or spinal cord are said to be part of the **efferent division** of the PNS. An easy way to remember the difference between these two terms is to remember that "efferent" sounds like "effect." And the efferent division *effects change* in various organs in the body.

What kinds of change? Many of the activities the nervous system controls are voluntary activities, which often means movement. You decide to lift your finger; you decide to stand up, and so forth. You may remember from Chapter 25 that all movement is handled by skeletal muscles—muscles, like the biceps, that are attached to bones and that are under voluntary control. So, one part of the PNS's efferent division is the **somatic nervous system**: that portion of the peripheral nervous system's efferent division that provides voluntary control over skeletal muscle.

But, there are lots of processes in the body that are not under voluntary control. When you walk from bright sunshine into a darkened movie theater, your pupils dilate, to let in more light, but you have no control over this dilation. Certain muscles allow our pupils to open up, but these are not skeletal muscles; they are the involuntary "smooth muscles." Likewise, the cardiac muscle of your heart beats in a rhythm that is largely out of your conscious control. And your glands release hormones in a way you have little control over. It is a *second* part of the PNS's efferent division that controls these operations, the

(a) The nervous system has two components

Central nervous system
— brain
— spinal cord

Peripheral
nervous system

(b) How these two components interact

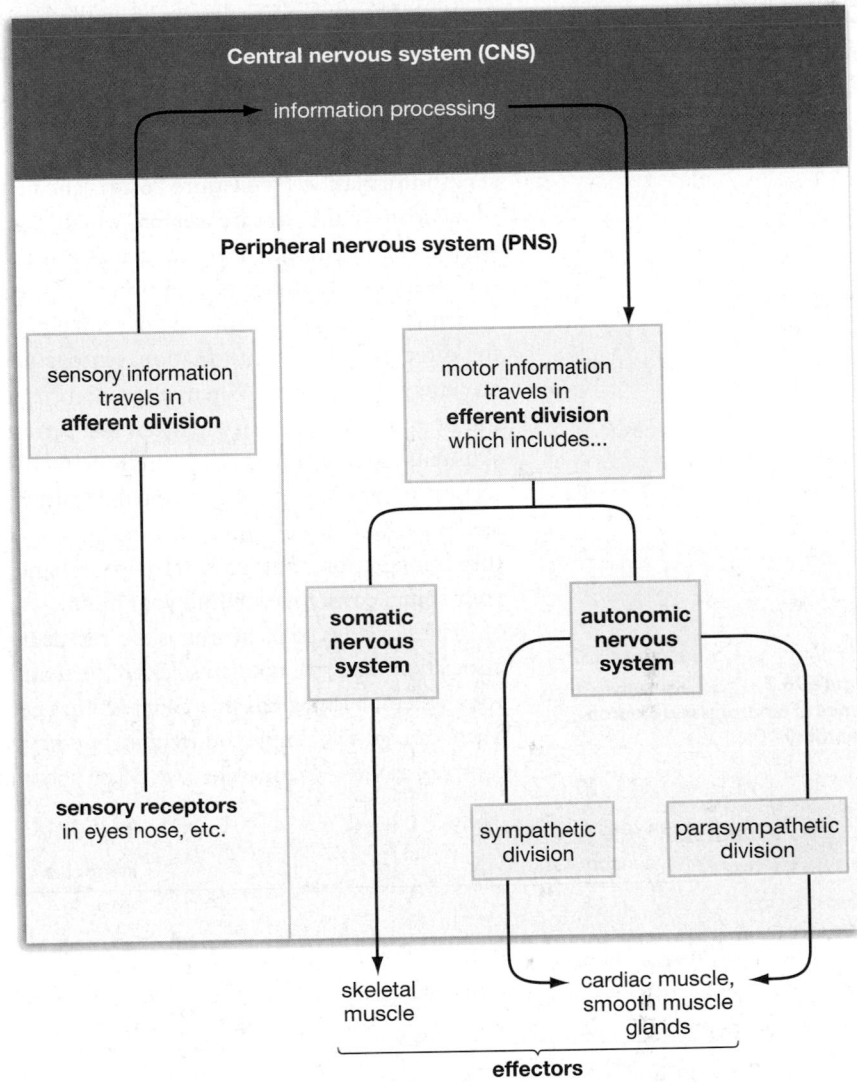

Central nervous system (CNS)

information processing

Peripheral nervous system (PNS)

sensory information
travels in
afferent division

motor information
travels in
efferent division
which includes...

**somatic
nervous
system**

**autonomic
nervous
system**

sensory receptors
in eyes nose, etc.

sympathetic
division

parasympathetic
division

skeletal
muscle

cardiac muscle,
smooth muscle
glands

effectors

Figure 26.1
Divisions of the Nervous System
(a) The two central branches of the nervous system are the central nervous system (CNS), which consists of the brain and the spinal cord; and the peripheral nervous system (PNS), which consists of all the nervous tissue outside the brain and spinal cord, plus the sensory organs.

(b) Information about the body and its environment comes to the nervous system from its sensory receptors—for example, cells in the eyes—which are part of the peripheral nervous system. This information then goes through the afferent division of the peripheral nervous system to the brain and spinal cord. After processing this information, the brain and spinal cord issue motor commands through the peripheral nervous system's efferent division. These commands go to "effectors" such as skeletal muscles and glands. The peripheral nervous system's efferent division has two systems within it: The somatic nervous system, which provides voluntary control over skeletal muscles; and the autonomic system, which provides involuntary regulation of smooth muscle, cardiac muscle, and glands. The autonomic system is further divided into sympathetic ("fight-or-flight") and parasympathetic ("rest-and-digest") divisions.

autonomic nervous system: that part of the peripheral nervous system's efferent division that provides involuntary regulation of smooth muscle, cardiac muscle, and glands (**see Figure 26.1b**).

Now let's go down just one more level, this time strictly within the autonomic system. It turns out that the autonomic system is divided into two divisions, the *sympathetic* and the *parasympathetic*. These terms

will be formally defined later; for now, just be aware of two characteristics they have. First, these divisions differ in that the nerves that make them up stem from different locations in the brain and spinal cord. Second, the sympathetic division generally has stimulatory effects on us—we get adrenaline going through this division, for example—while the parasympathetic division generally has relaxing effects.

26.2 Cells of the Nervous System

So, what about the cells that make up these systems? Remember first that the nervous-system cells that transmit signals are called neurons. These cells come in three varieties that neatly parallel the idea of a nervous system that receives, processes, and sends information (**see Figure 26.2a**). The first type of neuron is the **sensory neuron**, which does just what its name implies: It senses conditions both inside and outside the body and brings this received information to the central nervous system. (Given the direction of this information, sensory neurons are afferent neurons.) When someone brushes the top of your hand, sensory neurons just beneath the skin sense lots of things about this touch—what direction it came from, what shape the touching object was—and then convey a message containing this information that goes from your hand, into your spinal cord, then up into your brain.

The second type of neuron is the interneuron (or association neuron). Located solely in the central nervous system, **interneurons** interconnect other neurons. These can be very simple connections, but they can be complex as well. The memory we talked about at the start of the chapter amounts to a massive mobilization of interneurons. How do we remember? We process information in complex webs of interneurons.

The third type of neuron is the **motor neuron**: a peripheral-system neuron that sends instructions from the central nervous system (CNS) to such structures as muscles or glands. (Given the direction of this transmission, these are efferent neurons.) The key to understanding motor neurons is to think of them as neurons that transmit messages to organs or tissues *outside* the nervous system, thus prompting some kind of action. If you look at the right side of **Figure 26.2a**, you can see how this works. A message comes from the cell body of a motor neuron, travels down an extension of it, and then gets transferred to a muscle—causing the muscle to contract. Any organ or group of cells that responds to this kind of nervous-system signal is called an *effector*. Thus, a gland prompted to release hormones through a motor neuron signal is also an effector.

To sharpen the point about the difference between sensory and motor neurons, consider the newly popular drug Botox. Physicians inject this drug into the foreheads of older people who want to get rid of the "age lines" there. Botox works by

Figure 26.2
Types of Neurons and Neuron Anatomy

(a) Three types of neurons

sensory neuron   interneuron   motor neuron

afferent neuron   neuron within central nervous system   efferent neuron   effector (muscle)

(b) Anatomy of a neuron

direction of nerve signal

axon

synaptic terminals

dendrites

cell body

blocking the signal between motor neurons and the muscles they stimulate. The linkage works as follows: Botox blocks the nerve signal going to forehead muscles; this means there will be no forehead muscle contraction; and this means there will be no age lines. Now, one of the frequently asked questions about Botox is: Will it make my forehead numb? The answer is no, because Botox is blocking *motor* neuron transmission, not sensory neuron transmission. The motor signals are going out, the sensory signals are coming in, and only the motor neurons are responsive to Botox.

Anatomy of a Neuron

Now let's look at how a neuron is structured. Like any other cell, a neuron has a nucleus, it makes proteins, it gets rid of waste, and so forth. If you look at Figure **26.2b**, you can see, however, that the neuron has some extensions sprouting from it that clearly separate it from other cells. Projecting from the cell body are a variable number of **dendrites**: extensions of neurons that carry signals *toward* the neuronal cell body. There is also a single, large **axon**: an extension of the neuron that carries signals *away* from the neuronal cell body. Though you can't see it, the other thing that separates the neuron from other cells is its outer or "plasma" membrane, which has an amazing ability to respond to various kinds of stimulation, as you'll see.

The Nature of Glial Cells

Now, what about the second kind of nervous-system cell, the glial cells (also known as glia)? Found in both the CNS and PNS, glia have no signal-processing ability of their own, but they provide all kinds of support to neurons. For example, some glia wrap their cell membranes around the axons of neurons in the CNS and PNS. The membranous covering that glia provide to neurons is called **myelin**, and an axon wrapped in this way is said to be myelinated. The importance of this is that axons that are myelinated carry nerve impulses faster than those that are not. (The impulse skips from one gap or "node" in the myelin covering to the next.) If this sounds like some technical detail, consider that the disease multiple sclerosis results from a dismantling of the myelin covering in the brain and spinal cord by the body's own immune system. Because myelin is fat-rich, areas of the brain and spinal cord containing myelinated axons are glossy white. Thus do we get the term *white matter* of the CNS, which contains mostly axons. By contrast, areas containing mostly neuron cell bodies are *gray matter*. If you look at **Figure 26.3a**, you can see what a myelinated axon looks like.

(a) A myelinated axon

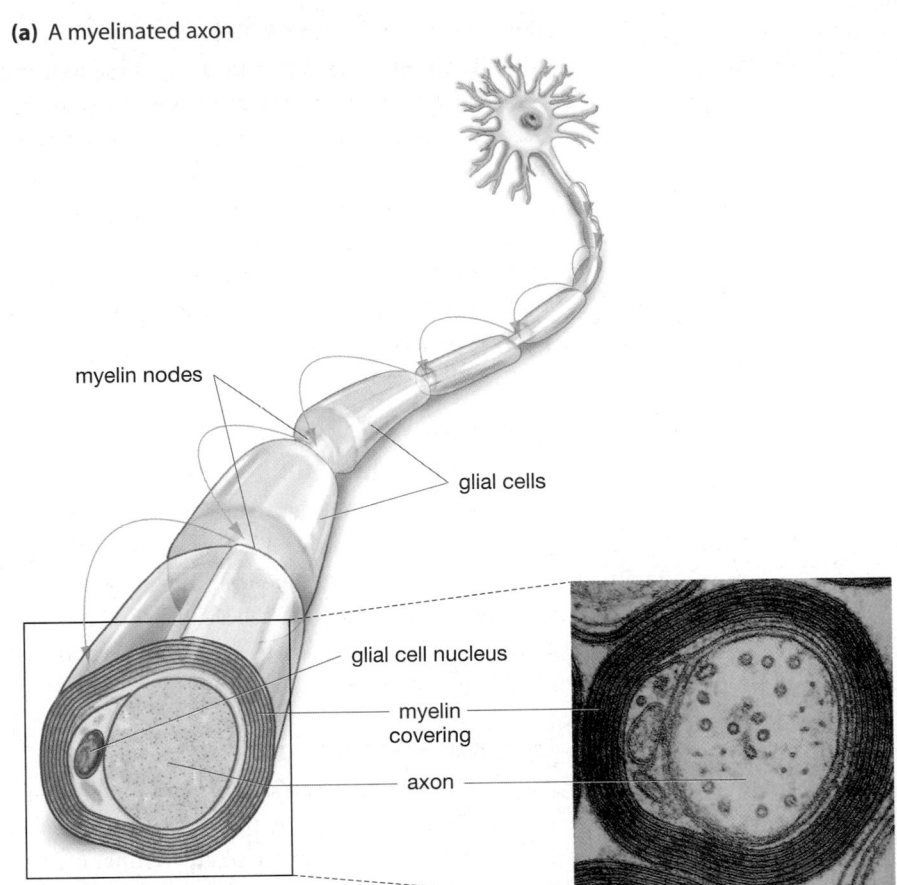

myelin nodes
glial cells
glial cell nucleus
myelin covering
axon

(b) Anatomy of a nerve

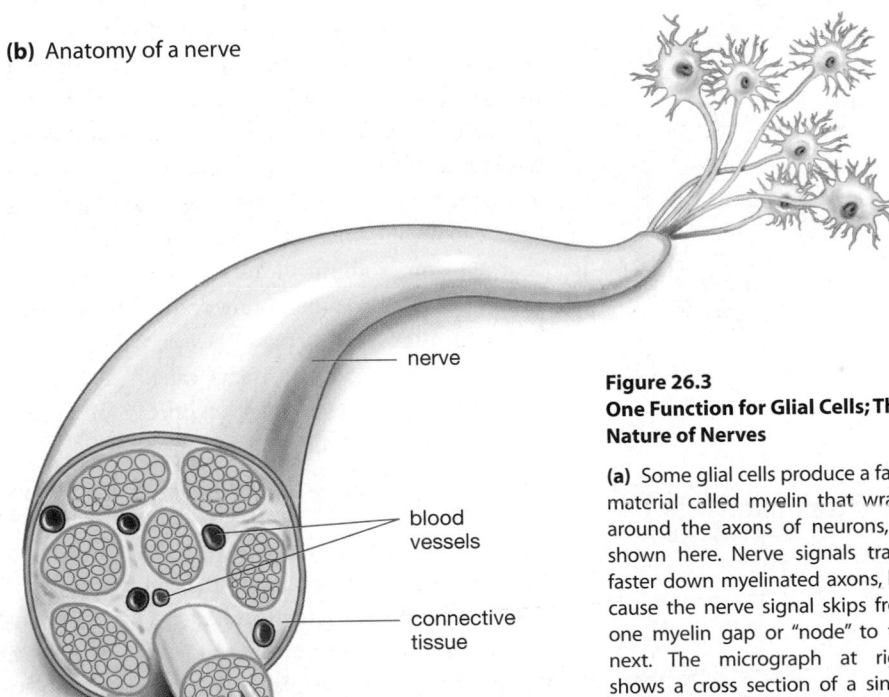

nerve
blood vessels
connective tissue
axons

Figure 26.3
One Function for Glial Cells; The Nature of Nerves

(a) Some glial cells produce a fatty material called myelin that wraps around the axons of neurons, as shown here. Nerve signals travel faster down myelinated axons, because the nerve signal skips from one myelin gap or "node" to the next. The micrograph at right shows a cross section of a single vertebrate axon that is wrapped in multiple layers of myelin covering.

(b) A nerve is a bundle of axons in the peripheral nervous system. It includes not only axons themselves, but supporting blood vessels and connective tissue.

Nerves

All this information about neurons and systems provides a way to understand a term that's been used extensively thus far, but that has not been defined. What is a **nerve**? It is a bundle of axons in the PNS that transmits information to or from the CNS. If you look at **Figure 26.3b**, you can see a representation of a nerve. Note that nerves have support tissue in the form of blood vessels and connective tissue.

26.3 How Nervous-System Communication Works

With this anatomy under your belt, you're ready to see how nervous-system signaling works. We'll look at a two-step process, which we can think of as (1) signal movement down a cell's axon and (2) signal movement from this axon over to a second cell, across what is known as a synapse.

Communication within an Axon

All the action in this first step is going to take place on either side of the thin plasma membrane that constitutes the outer border of any animal cell. Inside the plasma membrane is the cell and all its contents; outside is extracellular fluid (**see Figure 26.4**). Those of you who read Chapter 5 will recall that the plasma membrane regulates the passage of substances in and out of the cell. You may remember that some of these substances are the electrically charged particles called ions, meaning atoms that have gained or lost one or more electrons. Because ions are charged, they get the little + or − signs after their chemical names, as with Na^+ for the positively charged ion sodium. Ions cannot simply pass through the plasma membrane; rather, they need to move through special passageways, called protein channels. Some of these are so-called "leak" channels that are always open, but others are "gated" channels that can open or close.

It turns out that a "resting" neural cell—one not transmitting a signal—has a greater positive charge outside itself than inside. This is so mostly because there are more proteins inside the cell than outside, and proteins carry a *negative* charge. The charge difference also exists, however, because there are more of the positively charged Na^+ ions outside the membrane than there are positively charged potassium ions (K^+) inside, as you can see in Figure 26.4. As you know, in electricity, opposites attract, meaning the positively charged Na^+ ions outside the plasma membrane are attracted to the negatively charged interior of the cell. This amounts to a form of potential energy, in the same way that a rock perched at the top of a hill does. The rock would roll down the hill (releasing energy) if given a push, and the Na^+ ions would rush into the cell (releasing energy) if the proper channels were opened to them. The charge difference that exists from one side of the neuronal plasma membrane to the other is known as the **membrane potential**.

This potential exists in part because of what you've already seen: the greater abundance of Na^+ ions outside the cell. It's important to note that this abundance doesn't exist by accident. Every cell keeps this imbalance in place by constantly pumping three Na^+ ions out for every two (K^+) ions it pumps in. It takes a lot of energy to maintain this "sodium-potassium pump," but the cell does it for the same reason that you charge your cell-phone battery: in order to have ready access to a capability. In your case, the capability is talking on the phone; in the cell's case, the capability is that of having Na^+ ions available to rush into it. These ions can get the electrical impulse called a nerve signal going, as you'll now see.

When a neuron is stimulated by getting a chemical signal from another neuron, the effect of this stimulation is that, up near where the neuron's axon meets its cell body, Na^+ ion gates open up. Now the Na^+ ions can act on their attraction, and they do so, rushing into the cell. After a very brief time, this influx is great enough that the inside of the cell is more positive than the outside. This very state causes the *potassium* gates to open up more fully, however. Recall that potassium (K^+) ions exist in more abundance inside the cell than outside it. With the opening of their gates, they rush out of the cell, and the positive charge that has briefly existed on the inside of the cell begins to decline. Eventually, enough K^+ ions have moved out that the cell returns to its resting state, with a negative charge inside the membrane. This entire process takes place in a few milliseconds, or thousandths of a second.

Movement Down the Axon

All this alters the membrane potential at *one spot* along the neuron's axon. But how does a nerve signal get transmitted down the entire length of the axon? The key to this transmission is that an influx of Na^+ ions at an initial location on the membrane triggers reactions that cause the *neighboring* portion of the membrane to begin an Na^+ influx (see Figure 26.4). What occurs, in other words, is a chain reaction that moves down the entire length of the axon membrane. This is

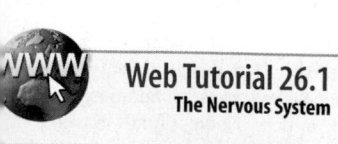

Web Tutorial 26.1
The Nervous System

Figure 26.4
Nerve Signal Transmission within a Neuron

(a) Resting potential

Electrical energy is stored across the plasma membrane of a resting neuron. There are more negatively charged compounds just inside the membrane than outside of it. As a result, the inside of the cell is negatively charged relative to the outside. The charge difference creates a form of stored energy called a membrane potential. Protein channels (shown in green) that can allow the movement of electrically charged ions across the membrane remain closed in a resting cell, thus maintaining the membrane potential.

(b) Action potential

1. Nerve signal transmission begins when, upon stimulation, some protein channels open up, allowing a movement of positively charged sodium ions (Na^+) into the cell. For a brief time, the inside of the cell becomes positively charged.

2. The Na^+ gates close and the gates for positively charged potassium ions (K^+) open up, allowing a movement of K^+ out of the cell. With this, there is once again a net positive charge outside the membrane. The influx of Na^+ at one point in the cell membrane then triggers the same sequence of events in an adjacent portion of the membrane—note the influx of Na^+ next to the outflow of K^+.

3. The nerve signal continues to be propagated one way along the axon by means of this action potential.

an **action potential**: a temporary reversal of cell-membrane potential that results in a conducted nerve impulse down an axon. (Temporary reversal? Remember the inside of the cell goes from negative to briefly positive, then back.) Action potentials have been compared to what happens to a lighted fuse: The heat of the spark causes the neighboring section of the fuse to catch fire, thus moving the spark along.

All action potentials are of the same strength. Once the original signal on the cell-body/axon border reaches sufficient strength to allow Na^+ ions to rush in, the action potential will get going. Thanks to its fuse-like quality, this potential will be the same strength all the way down the axon. How fast can this signal go? At best, about 120 meters per second—very fast indeed, but much slower than the electricity that comes from a wall socket.

Communication between Cells: The Synapse

Once it has traveled the length of an axon, an action potential then reaches a tip of the axon. How does the signal then get to the *next* neuron (or muscle, or gland cell)? This question was once very intriguing to biologists, because it was clear that, with a few exceptions, an axon does not touch the downstream cell. It comes extremely close, but there is almost always a small intervening space between the two cells. There are thus three entities involved in cell-to-cell transmission: the sending neuron, the receiving cell, and the gap between them. The area where all three come together is called a **synapse** (**see Figure 26.5**).

The action potential arrives at a branch of the axon, called a *synaptic terminal*, which has stored within it small sacs (or vesicles) containing a chemical called a neurotransmitter. The arrival of the action potential causes the synaptic terminal to release neurotransmitter molecules into the gap in the synapse, which is called a **synaptic cleft**. With this, the molecules diffuse over to the receiving cell and bind to receptors in that cell's outer membrane. This binding stimulates the opening of sodium gates there, allowing the now-familiar influx of Na^+ ions in the *receiving* neuron, and this keeps the signal transmission going.

But why doesn't the released neurotransmitter just keep on stimulating the receiving cell? Serving as one means of control are the proteins called enzymes. Released into the synaptic cleft, they break down the neurotransmitter, thus inactivating it. The sending cell may also be capable of taking the neurotransmitter back into itself, by a process known as "reuptake." In a given nerve impulse, a sending cell typically releases tens of thousands of neurotransmitter molecules, which are stored in hundreds of sacs. With all this in mind, you can understand the definition of a **neurotransmitter**: a chemical, secreted into a synaptic cleft by a neuron, that affects another neuron or an effector by binding with receptors on it.

The Importance of Neurotransmitters

It is difficult to overstate the importance of neurotransmitters. You may recall from Chapter 25 that the neurotransmitter acetylcholine must travel from nerve-cell terminals to muscles for any skeletal muscle to work. If acetylcholine doesn't make it out of a motor neuron, we can't contract the muscles that allow us to breathe. Likewise, the shaking and stiffness of Parkinson's disease are caused by a lack of the neurotransmitter dopamine, which in turn is brought on by the death of dopamine-producing cells in the brain.

On a different level, remember the reuptake process we talked about, whereby a releasing cell will take back a neurotransmitter that it has secreted into a synaptic cleft? Well, the antidepressant drugs Prozac, Zoloft, and Paxil are all called SSRIs, which stands for selective serotonin reuptake inhibitors. Serotonin is a neurotransmitter found in the brain, and SSRIs are aimed at reducing serotonin reuptake. The result is an increased amount of serotonin in synaptic clefts—and perhaps less depression. By the same token, drugs of abuse such as cocaine and the amphetamine-like ecstasy work by altering neurotransmitter release or reuptake. What makes us feel bad, or OK, or ecstatic? A big part of the answer is: the levels of neurotransmitters in our brains.

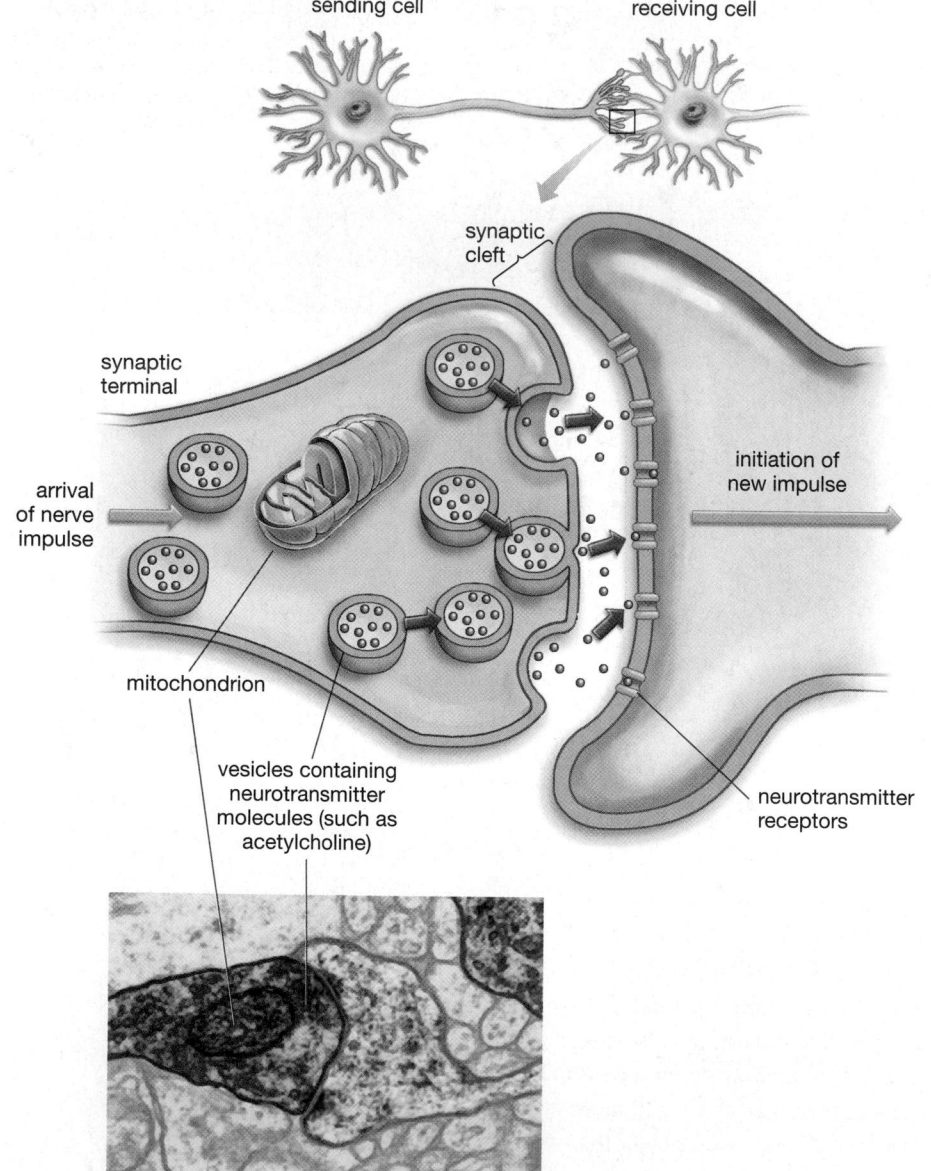

sending cell

receiving cell

synaptic cleft

synaptic terminal

arrival of nerve impulse

initiation of new impulse

mitochondrion

vesicles containing neurotransmitter molecules (such as acetylcholine)

neurotransmitter receptors

26.4 The Spinal Cord

Now that you've looked at how nerve impulses are transmitted at the cellular level, it's a good time to take a step back and look at the nervous system in its larger dimensions. Let's start by examining the spinal cord, which serves two key functions. First, it can act as a communication center on its own, receiving input from sensory neurons and directing motor neurons in response, with no input from the brain. This is what a reflex amounts to. Second, most sensory impulses that go to the brain don't go *directly* to the brain; they are channeled first through the spinal cord.

Extending from the base of the brain to an area just below the lowest rib, the spinal cord is about 14mm or a half-inch wide and consists of 31 segments, each having both a left and right spinal nerve stemming from it (**see Figure 26.6a**). These nerves are grouped into the classes you see named in the figure, which correspond to the region of the body they serve. ("Thoracic" is the chest area; "lumbar" the lower back, and so forth.) Remember how we noted that the peripheral nervous system could be thought of as a group of nerves and related nerve cells that fan out from the brain and spinal cord? In Figure 26.6a, you can see the start of a lot of this fanning, in the form of the spinal nerves. (The other major set of nerves that do this are the so-called cranial nerves, which fan out from the brain.)

The most striking feature of a cross section of the spinal cord, seen in **Figure 26.6b**, is a rough H- or butterfly-shaped area around the narrow central canal. This H is the gray matter of the spinal cord, composed mostly of the cell bodies of neurons. Surrounding the spinal cord's gray matter is its white matter which, as you've seen, is largely myelin-coated axons. The central canal of the spinal cord is a space filled with **cerebrospinal fluid**, a fluid that circulates both in the spine and the brain, supplying nutrients, hormones, and immune-system cells and providing protection against any jarring motion.

The Spinal Cord and the Processing of Information

Sensory input comes *to* the spinal cord from various sensory receptors in the body, while motor commands must go *from* the spinal cord to effectors such as muscles. Where are the spinal cord cells that take care of this business? The motor neurons that send the motor commands lie in the spinal cord's gray matter (as do the interneurons discussed earlier). The axons of these motor neurons leave the spinal cord through the ventral roots you can see in Figure 26.6b. Meanwhile, the cell bodies of *sensory* neurons lie outside the spinal

cord in the *dorsal-root ganglia* you can see in Figure 26.6b. (A **ganglion** is any collection of nerve-cell bodies in the PNS.) These sensory neurons have dendrites whose endings lie in, say, the hand. When we touch something, these dendrites' terminals sense it and send a message back to the cell body in the dorsal-root ganglion. From there, this signal proceeds via the cell's axon into the spinal cord. In sum, sensory information

(a)

brain

cervical spinal nerves

thoracic spinal nerves

lumbar spinal nerves

sacral spinal nerves

tip of spinal cord

(b) white matter   ventral root
gray matter   spinal nerve
dorsal root ganglion   central canal   dorsal root

Figure 26.6
Structure of the Spinal Cord

(a) Thirty-one pairs of spinal nerves extend from the spinal cord. These nerves are grouped according to the body part they control. Eight cervical nerves control the head, neck, diaphragm and arms; 12 thoracic nerves control the chest and abdominal muscles; five lumbar nerves control the legs; and five sacral nerves control the bladder, bowels, sexual organs, and feet.

(b) A cross-section through the lower thoracic region of the spinal cord, showing the arrangement of gray and white matter, the central canal, the ventral roots, the dorsal roots, and the dorsal root ganglia.

comes to the spinal cord through a dorsal root, while motor commands leave the spinal cord through a ventral root. Note that both dorsal and ventral roots come together, like fibers being joined in a single cable, to form a given spinal nerve.

Quick, Unconscious Action: Reflexes

The sensory/motor division of labor is clearly reflected in simple body **reflexes**, which can be defined as automatic nervous-system responses that help us avoid danger or preserve a stable physical state. If you accidentally touch a hot stove, you automatically pull back your hand. No conscious thought of "Oh, I've touched a hot stove; I'd better pull my hand back," is necessary; the reaction is automatic. The neural wiring of a single reflex is called a *reflex arc*. A reflex arc begins at a sensory receptor, runs through the spinal cord, and ends at an effector, such as a muscle or gland. **Figure 26.7** shows one of the best-known examples, the knee jerk, or patellar reflex, in which a properly placed sharp rap on the knee produces a noticeable kick. Note what's at work: A sensory receptor is stimulated, thus prompt-

ing a signal to move into the spinal cord. There the sensory neuron is linked via a synapse to a motor neuron, which issues a command that is carried out by an effector—in this case a skeletal muscle. This is an example of the simplest possible reflex arc, in that the sensory neuron is linked directly to the motor neuron. Because only one synapse is involved, this kind of simple reflex controls the most rapid motor responses of the nervous system. Many other reflexes have at least one interneuron placed between the sensory receptor and the motor neuron.

26.5 The Autonomic Nervous System

As noted earlier, the part of the peripheral nervous system's efferent or "outgoing" division over which we have no conscious control is called the autonomic nervous system. You can grasp its importance by imagining having to consciously control the beating of your heart. Recall that this system controls the involuntary regulation of smooth muscle, cardiac muscle, and glands.

1. Stimulus (tapping) arrives and receptor is activated.

afferent signal

receptor

stimulus

2. The signal from the receptor reaches a sensory neuron cell body in the dorsal root ganglion.

spinal cord

reflex arc

motor neuron

efferent signal

effector

3. The signal arrives at a sensory neuron/motor neuron synapse in the spinal cord. Information processing takes place prompting a signal to be sent through the motor neuron.

4. The motor neuron signal stimulates the effector (the quadriceps muscle) to contract. Note that CNS processing for this reaction was handled entirely in the spinal cord; the brain was not involved.

response

Figure 26.7
Steps in a Reflex Arc

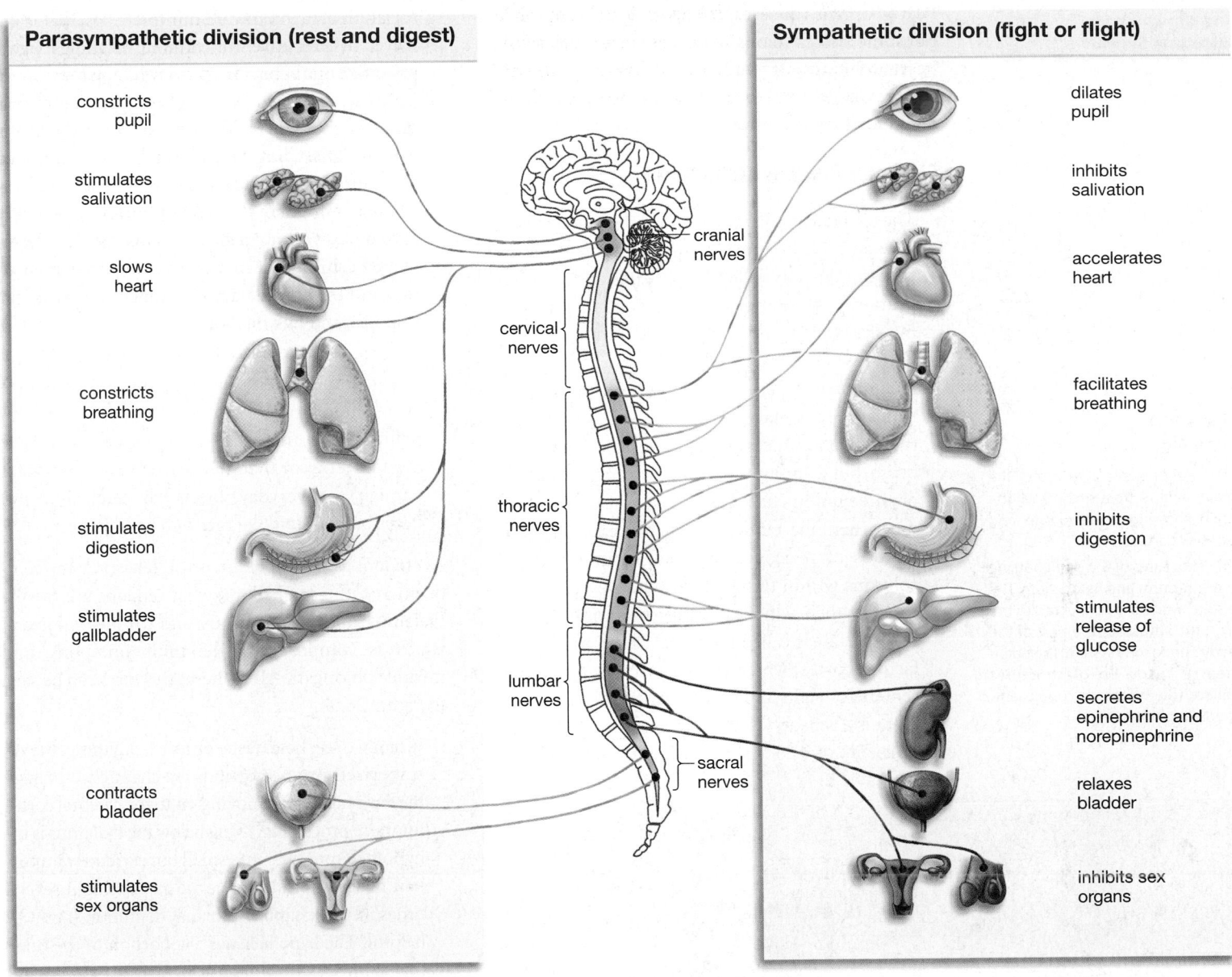

Parasympathetic division (rest and digest)

constricts pupil

stimulates salivation

slows heart

constricts breathing

stimulates digestion

stimulates gallbladder

contracts bladder

stimulates sex organs

Sympathetic division (fight or flight)

dilates pupil

inhibits salivation

accelerates heart

facilitates breathing

inhibits digestion

stimulates release of glucose

secretes epinephrine and norepinephrine

relaxes bladder

inhibits sex organs

cranial nerves

cervical nerves

thoracic nerves

lumbar nerves

sacral nerves

Sympathetic and Parasympathetic Divisions

Also recall that, within the autonomic nervous system, there are two "divisions," the sympathetic and parasympathetic. The **sympathetic division**, often called the *fight-or-flight* division of the autonomic nervous system, usually stimulates tissue metabolism, increases alertness, and generally prepares the body to deal with emergencies. The **parasympathetic division**, often regarded as the *rest-and-digest* division of the autonomic nervous system, conserves energy and promotes activities such as digestion. In **Figure 26.8**, you can see which spinal and cranial nerves are part of these two divisions. You can also see the effects each division has on various bodily functions. Although some organs are connected to only one division or the other, most vital organs receive both sympathetic and parasympathetic sig-

nals. Where such dual signaling exists, the two divisions often have opposing effects, keeping the body's stability mechanisms working in balance.

26.6 The Human Brain

Now that we've reviewed the spinal cord, it's time to look at the second major part of the central nervous system. The adult human brain is far larger and more complex than the spinal cord. Its 100 billion neurons constitute about 98 percent of the neural tissue in the body. An average adult brain weighs 1.4 kg (a little over 3 pounds). Like the spinal cord with its spinal nerves, the brain has nerves extending from it that allow it to communicate directly with other body tissues and organs. These are the cranial nerves and, as you might expect, some of them go to

Figure 26.8
Involuntary Control of Bodily Functions
The autonomic nervous system has two divisions, the sympathetic and the parasympathetic, which exercise automatic control over the body's organs, generally in opposing ways. Note how the parasympathetic aids in digestion, while the sympathetic controls "fight or flight" responses, such as an increase in heart rate. Axons of the parasympathetic division emerge not only from the spinal cord, but from the brain as well.

nearby organs (the eyes, the nose, the face muscles); but some also go to organs that are farther away (the heart and lungs). If you look at **Figure 26.9**, you can see the major structures that make up the brain. Let's look briefly now at each of them.

Six Major Regions of the Brain

- The **cerebrum**, the largest region of the human brain, is responsible for much of our higher mental functioning. With its valley-like fissures and fatty appearance, the roundish cerebrum fills up most of our skulls and is effectively draped over many other portions of the brain. It is divided into left and right *cerebral hemispheres*. The outer layer of the cerebrum is the **cerebral cortex**, the site of our highest thinking and processing. It covers the entire cerebrum, but it amounts to a *thin* covering—only two or three millimeters thick, which means it is little more than one-tenth of an inch deep at most. Its billions of neurons are arranged in functional columns within this area, and they are extremely varied in their activities. The cerebral cortex has, for example, areas called the visual cortex and the olfactory cortex, which are the primary processing centers for sight and smell, respectively. Likewise, there is a sensory cortex that gets touch information from our skin. Then there is a "prefrontal" as-sociation area, up toward our foreheads, that is involved in "executive" functioning, meaning it helps prioritize our behaviors. As may be apparent, these cortex areas are regions of higher processing. Out in the body, there are neurons that sense various forms of stimulation, but the cerebral cortex *makes* sense of the information these neurons provide. The cerebrum is more than the cerebral cortex, however. It also contains an area called the hippocampus, which plays a critical role in forming long-term memories; and the amygdala, which functions in the fear response and our memory of it.

- The *cerebellum* is a portion of the brain that refines our movements based on our "sense memory" of them. People who have damaged their cerebellum may find that their movements have become jerky, or that they reach too far (or not far enough) for everyday objects. The cerebellum also helps us maintain balance and equilibrium.

In looking at the brain, if you take away the cerebrum and the cerebellum, what remains are (a) the thalamus and hypothalamus; and (b) the brainstem, which is composed of the midbrain, pons, and medulla oblongata. All of these structures can be seen in Figure 26.9b.

- When we see, hear, taste, or touch anything, the resulting sensory perceptions are channeled through the **thalamus** before moving on to the cerebral cortex for more processing. Lying below the thalamus is the hypothalamus, which is small but extremely important in several ways. Since we'll be seeing it several times in this chapter, a formal definition might be helpful. The **hypothalamus** is a portion of the brain that is important in regulating drives and in maintaining homeostasis in the body. With respect to drives, cells in the hypothalamus are critical in telling us whether we are hungry or thirsty, for example. Likewise, the hypothalamus helps control our sleep-wake cycle, or "circadian rhythms." The hypothalamus is important in preserving homeostasis—the maintenance of a stable internal environment—because it controls a good number of the hormones that are released from our glands, as you'll see later.

- The *midbrain* helps us maintain muscle tone and posture through control of involuntary motor responses. With the amygdala, the midbrain is involved in our fear responses. Also located in the midbrain are the dopamine-producing cells noted earlier that keep our hands steady and our movements fluid.

- The Latin term *pons* refers to a bridge, and the pons serves as one. Its primary function is to relay

Figure 26.9
The Brain

(a) View of the left surface of the brain and a cross-section of the brain showing its cerebrum and cerebral cortex.

(b) Structures of the brain outside the cerebrum and cerebellum. The pituitary gland is connected to the hypothalamus, but is a part of the body's endocrine system. The brainstem is made up of structures called the midbrain, pons, and medulla oblongata.

(a)

(b)

cerebral cortex

cerebrum

cerebellum

thalamus

hypothalamus

pituitary gland

midbrain

pons

brainstem

medulla oblongata

messages between the cerebrum and the cerebellum. It also helps control involuntary breathing.

- Located next to the spinal cord, the *medulla oblongata* contains major centers concerned with the regulation of unconscious functions such as breathing, blood pressure, and digestion. The medulla oblongata actually has a connection to a well-known term. What does it mean to be "brain dead"? Under one definition, it means that all the centers of the brain *except* the medulla oblongata have permanently ceased to function. As long as the medulla is still working, a person continues to breathe, despite the loss of all conscious ability.

The brain and spinal cord contain internal cavities filled with the cerebrospinal fluid noted in connection with the spinal cord. In the brain, this fluid provides cushioning for delicate neural structures—the brain essentially floats in the cerebrospinal fluid.

26.7 The Nervous System in Action: Our Senses

Having learned some of the basics of the nervous system, we can see how it works in one of its most interesting areas, sensory perception.

It may come as a surprise to learn that we actually have more sensory capabilities than the famous "five senses" of vision, touch, smell, taste, and hearing. We have a sense of balance, for example, but it isn't one of these five senses. We have another little-recognized sensory capability, related to touch, that helps us do such things as dance and simply sit up straight. To demonstrate this capability to yourself, extend one arm out, parallel to the ground, and close your eyes. Now, use the same arm and touch your index finger to the tip of your nose. How were you able to do this? You have sensory neurons that monitor such things as the position of your joints and the tension of the tendons in your body. These neurons provide a sense, called *proprioception*, that in this instance helped guide your finger to your nose. (It sent out signals that said "on the right course" or "correction needed.") How do you know if you're sitting up straight? Proprioception is part of the answer.

Taking these and other sensory capabilities into account, it becomes apparent that our "five senses" really amount to the senses we are consciously aware of. It is understandable that these senses command our attention, however, because they alone make us not just sensory beings, but sensual beings. (If you wanted to evoke the richness of life in as short a space as possible, you could do worse than to write down just five words: seeing, touching, hearing, smelling,

and tasting.) As such, we'll briefly review how each of these senses works. But first, it's worth noting what all the senses have in common.

Each of our senses employs the sensory receptor cells noted earlier—cells that can respond to stimulation, such as vibration (for sound) or reflected light (for vision). In addition, all sensory receptor cells *transform* their responses into the language of the nervous system, meaning electrical signals that work through action potentials. Think of this task as being similar to the one undertaken by a so-called "transducer" clipped across the sound hole of an acoustic guitar. It has to turn the vibration of the guitar strings into an electric signal that goes to an amplifier. In a similar way, sensory receptors in your ear must turn the vibrations of your eardrum into an electric signal that goes to your brain. Fittingly enough, sensory receptors are sometimes called *transducers*. All the senses except one also have another commonality to them. If you look at **Figure 26.10**, you can see that except for smell, all sensory perceptions are routed through the brain structure noted earlier called the thalamus and

Figure 26.10
The Routing of Sensory Information
Nerve signals for all the senses except smell get routed through the brain's thalamus and then continue on to differing parts of the cerebral cortex for further processing. Signals for smell are routed to the olfactory cortex, the amygdala, and the hypothalamus.

that all these signals then go on to various parts of the cerebral cortex for additional processing. Now, let's look at the five best-known senses, taking touch first.

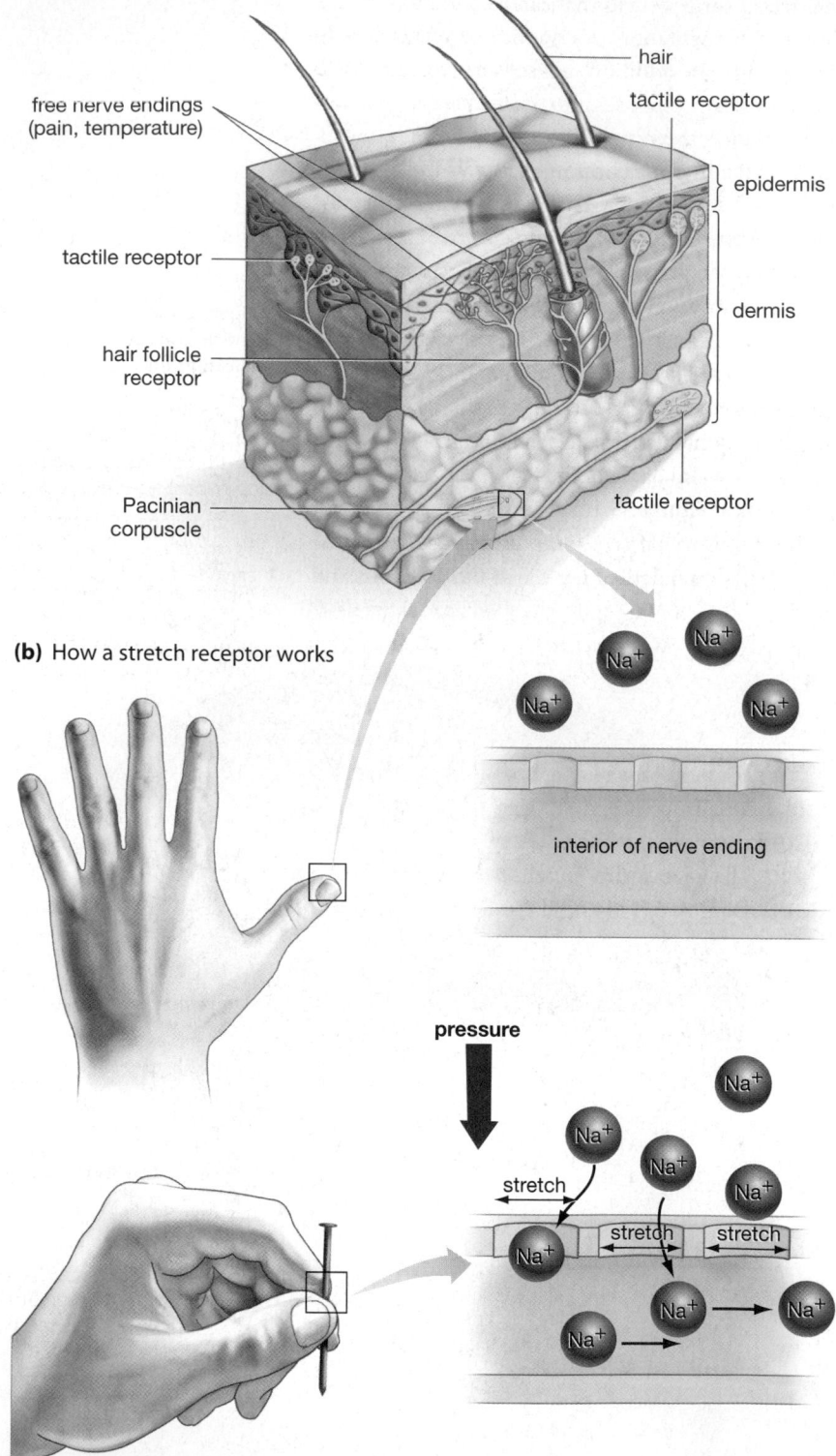

(a) Touch receptors in the skin

hair

tactile receptor

free nerve endings (pain, temperature)

epidermis

tactile receptor

dermis

hair follicle receptor

Pacinian corpuscle

tactile receptor

(b) How a stretch receptor works

Na⁺

Na⁺

Na⁺

Na⁺

Na⁺

interior of nerve ending

pressure

stretch

Na⁺

Na⁺

Na⁺

Na⁺

Na⁺

stretch   stretch

Na⁺

Na⁺

Na⁺

Na⁺

Figure 26.11
Our Senses of Touch

(a) Free nerve endings near the surface of the skin sense pain and temperature while five different types of sensory receptors in the skin sense other sorts of tactile sensations.

(b) One of the skin's sensory receptors is the Pacinian corpuscle, which is a stretch receptor. When the dendrite within the corpuscle is distorted by touch, its ion channels open in such a way as to allow an influx of sodium ions (Na^+). This instigates a nerve signal conveying the message "touch has occurred here."

26.8 Our Senses of Touch

Humans actually have several senses of touch. One of these is *thermal reception*, which means sensing hot and cold. Another is *tactile reception*, which includes our senses of pressure and the proprioception we talked about. A third is *pain reception*, which means just what it sounds like.

If you look at **Figure 26.11a**, you can see that, within our skin, we have several kinds of sensory receptors that contribute to these senses. Thermal and pain sensing operate through simple nerve endings near the surface of the skin. But the tactile sense has five special types of receptors in the skin alone. Why so many? Well, pressure can be light or heavy, and we want to know the difference. Likewise, contact can be brief or ongoing, and we need to assess the difference in a sophisticated way. We want the message "your elbows have reached the table" to come to our attention front and center; but we want the message "your elbows are still on the table" to be a *low-level* message, so that we can focus on other things. These various receptors allow for all this and much more.

So, how does a given touch receptor work? One of the receptors pictured, the Pacinian corpuscle receptor, consists of a single dendrite that is wrapped within onion-like layers of fluid and supportive tissue (which make up the corpuscle). As a result, this receptor is not likely to respond to gentle pressure. Instead, it responds to somewhat deeper pressure, usually involving vibrations (like pulling your finger across a page). The Pacinian is a so-called "stretch" receptor, meaning that the stretching of its outer membrane prompts a nerve signal from it. If you look at Figure 26.11b, you can see how this works. Undisturbed by touch, the ion channels in the receptor's membrane are not shaped correctly to let through the sodium (Na^+) ions that get a nerve signal going. When stretched, however, the ion channels open in such a way that the Na^+ ions rush in, and a touch message gets going. Note that the Pacinian receptor does the double duty of first responding to a stimulus (pressure) and then transforming this stimulus into the language of the nervous system.

Once the Pacinian's nerve signal is on its way, it comes into the spinal cord through one of the spinal nerves. It then moves up through the spinal cord and brainstem and into the brain's thalamus, from which point it is sent to the brain's somatosensory cortex. It's worth noting that sensory messages such as these always cross over a midpoint in the spinal cord, so that anything we feel on the left side of our body is processed on the right side of our brain, and vice versa.

26.9 Our Sense of Smell

As noted earlier, our sense of smell stands alone in *not* routing its messages up through the thalamus. If you look at **Figure 26.10** you can see where these messages go: to a part of the cerebral cortex (called the olfactory cortex), and to the amygdala and hypothalamus. These latter two structures are active in both emotion and memory. Some scientists believe this linkage is the reason that our sense of smell—or **olfaction**, as it is properly known—is able to evoke such strong memories. People, places, and events can all come back to us in a rush if we happen to encounter the right smell. Olfaction is also thought to be our "oldest" sense, in that some of the olfaction mechanisms at work in us are also at work in fruit flies, even though our evolutionary line diverged from theirs about 500 million years ago.

If you look at **Figure 26.12**, you can see how olfaction works. Air that bears fragrant molecules comes into our nasal passages. Right up at the top of these passages, back behind the plane of our forehead and just beneath the level of our eyes, we have a group of neurons, called olfactory receptor cells, whose dendrites extend down into the passages. These dendrites

have some hair-like extensions, called cilia, sprouting from their tips. Each of these cilia is covered with receptors capable of binding with the fragrance molecules. These fragrance molecules, which are called "odorants" come in, get trapped in a mucus layer that lines the nasal passages, and soon bind with receptors on the cilia. This binding puts into motion a complicated set of reactions inside the dendrite that results in Na^+ channels being opened up in the dendrite membrane. The result is a neural signal that goes up through the dendrite and then the cell as a whole, which synapses with neurons in the olfactory bulb—a nerve tract that is part of the brain. From there, the signal gets distributed in the pattern we talked about (to the amygdala, hypothalamus, etc.).

The receptors lying on the surface of the olfactory receptor cilia seem to come in about 350 different varieties—at most, there may be a thousand varieties. This sounds like a lot, but consider that human beings are thought to be capable of discriminating among about 10,000 different smells. How can 350 to 1,000 receptor types yield 10,000 smells? Well, as researcher Richard Axel has noted, a mere 26 letters in the English language yield a huge number of words

Figure 26.12
Our Sense of Smell
Smell or "olfaction" begins when fragrance molecules, called odorants, bind with receptors that cover cilia extending from olfactory receptor cells. This binding causes an influx of Na^+ ions into the cells, resulting in a nerve signal that moves from the cells to the olfactory bulb—a part of the brain.

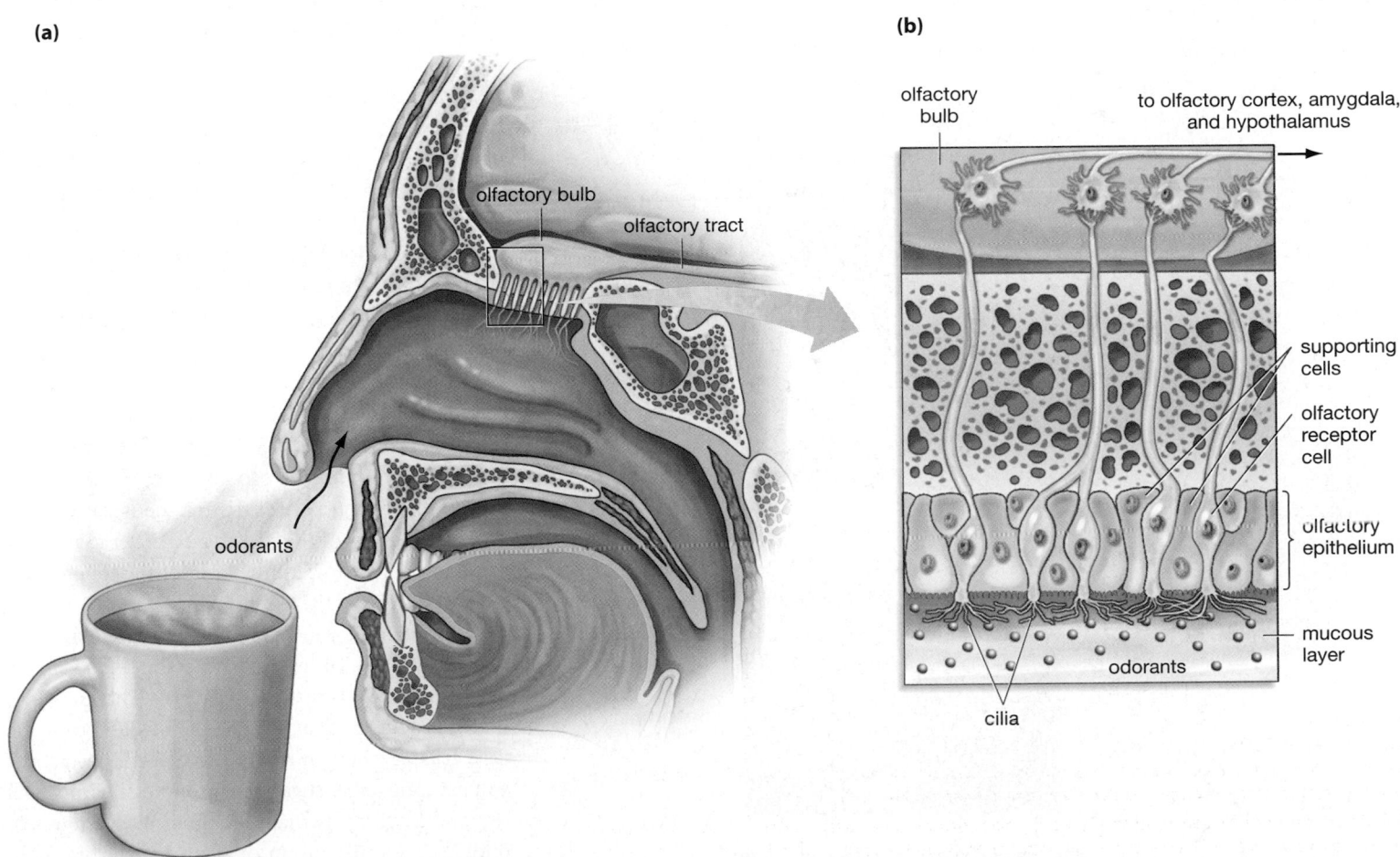

(a)

(b)

because the letters can be *combined* in different ways. In olfaction, each receptor adds nothing more than a message saying "receptor here stimulated"—one letter in a word. But the brain is receiving input from all these receptors. When a given combination of receptor signals comes in, the brain senses a "word," meaning the smell of, say, chocolate or lemon. The brain is essentially saying, "When receptors 4, 32, 87, and 220 fire together, that's chocolate."

26.10 Our Sense of Taste

Pity the person who eats a piece of chocolate while also having a stuffed-up nose. The flavor of the chocolate may be lost entirely, because a large part of what we call "flavor" comes not from our sense of taste, but from our sense of smell. Earlier, we pictured smells as coming in from the nose to the nasal passages, but remember that these same nasal passages empty out into the top of the throat. Every bite of food you take sends a huge concentration of odorant molecules wafting up the *other* direction—from the throat into the nasal passages.

When we consider pure "taste," as opposed to "flavor," the action does take place on our tongues, within several kinds of bumps that lie on the tongue's surface (some of which are visible after you drink milk). If you look at **Figure 26.13**, you can see the lo-

cations of some of these "papillae," and some detail on one of the larger varieties, which exist toward the back of the tongue. As you can see, if you go about halfway down these papillae, you get to something that sounds familiar: the taste bud, so named because each one actually looks something like a plant bud. Each taste bud is a collection of 50 to 100 cells, some of these being touch receptors and some supporting cells. But taste buds also contain *taste cells*, which is what we are interested in. Taste cells are not neurons, but they do have the ability to convey signals. Like the olfactory receptors we looked at, they have tiny hair-like projections extending from them—in this case, projecting out into the cavity that surrounds each papilla. These projections are capable of interacting with "tastants," meaning food molecules that elicit different tastes.

With all this in mind, here's how taste works. You eat some food and the resulting tastants dissolve in your saliva. Molecules or ions from the tastants then make contact with the projections (called microvilli) sprouting from the taste cells. Through one of several chemical-reaction routes, this contact results in a change in the membrane potential of the taste cells, and this change prompts them to release a neurotransmitter. Waiting to receive the neurotransmitter are the dendrites of nearby neurons, and our nerve signal is on its way.

You may have heard that humans have four basic taste sensations: sweet, sour, salty, and bitter. What makes these "basic" is that each one works through a different chemical reaction route in the taste cell. Salty foods spur neurotransmitter release through one set of reactions; sweet foods spur release through another. In recent years, some scientists have become persuaded that there is a fifth basic taste a "meaty" one called *umami* that is close to the taste of monosodium glutamate (MSG)—but this is still a matter of contention. What is clear is that every taste cell is capable of responding to any of the basic taste sensations. And, contrary to any "tongue maps" you may have seen, no part of the tongue is particularly responsive to any of the basic tastes. Bitter taste is not sensed primarily toward the back of the tongue, nor sweet taste toward the front.

At this point you may be wondering: How can there be just four or five *basic* tastes, but a huge number of tastes we actually experience? The answer is that the neurons that receive the signals from the taste cells vary in their response to specific tastants. If you eat some table sugar, one group of neurons will respond by firing perhaps 10 times over a few seconds, but another group of neurons will fire more than 100 times. Most researchers now agree that it is

Figure 26.13
Our Sense of Taste
Small bumps in the tongue called papillae contain taste buds—collections of tissues and various cells, including taste cells. Microvilli extending from taste cells are capable of binding with food molecules or "tastants," which they come in contact with through taste pores. This contact causes the taste cells to release a neurotransmitter that stimulates the dendrites of adjacent nerve cells. With this, a nerve signal regarding taste is on its way to the brain.

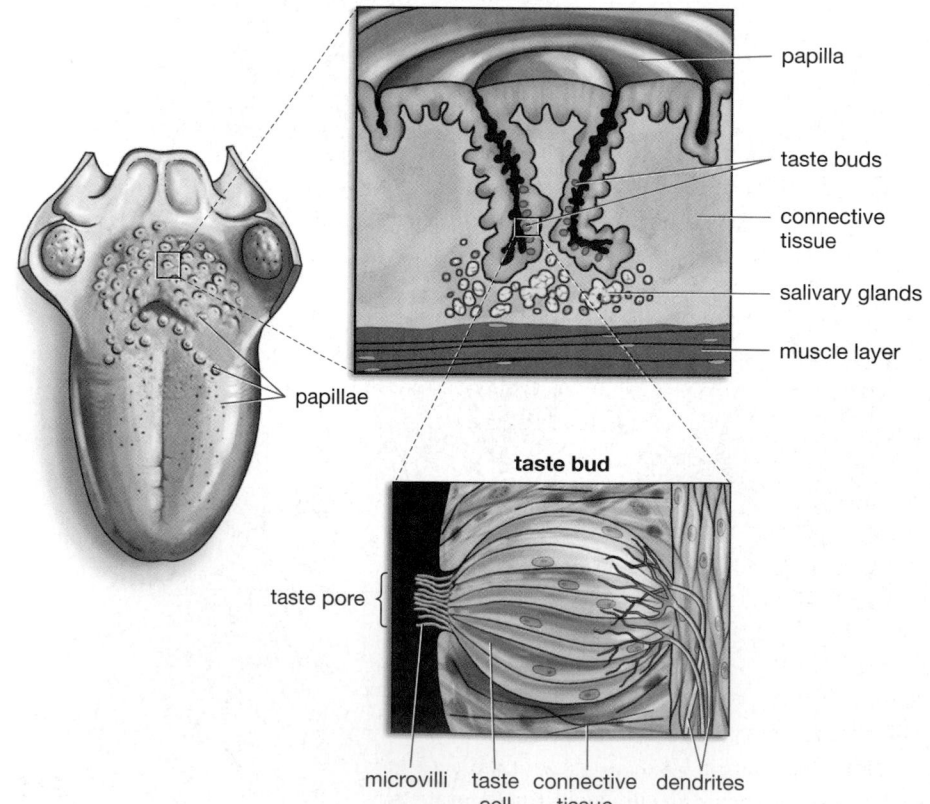

papilla

taste buds

connective tissue

salivary glands

muscle layer

papillae

taste bud

taste pore

microvilli   taste   connective   dendrites
cell   tissue

Too Loud

Our sense of hearing can easily be damaged. Eighty percent of the hearing loss in the United States—affecting 22 million people—involves damage to either the auditory hair cells referred to in the main text, or to the large nerve into which these cells feed. This type of hearing loss often comes as a consequence of old age, but it can come as a consequence of *young* age, which is to say the tendency of young people to listen to loud music. Damage caused by loud noise may be limited only to the hair cell's cilia—their roots may break off or the links between them may be destroyed—and in most of these instances, the hair cells can recover. When noise is loud or long-lasting enough, however, it can kill hair cells outright and once this happens, they are gone. There is no way to grow new ones (though scientists are trying awfully hard to figure out how to coax the body into doing this). The lack of hearing that results from this damage is bad enough, but some people also get a so-called tinnitus, meaning a permanent ringing in the ears.

So, how loud is too loud? The rule of thumb is, if you have to shout to be heard, you're in the danger zone. The amount of time a person is exposed to loud noise matters, however. You could be around a typical lawn mower for several hours without harm, but after 15 minutes at a loud rock concert, you are damaging your hair cells.

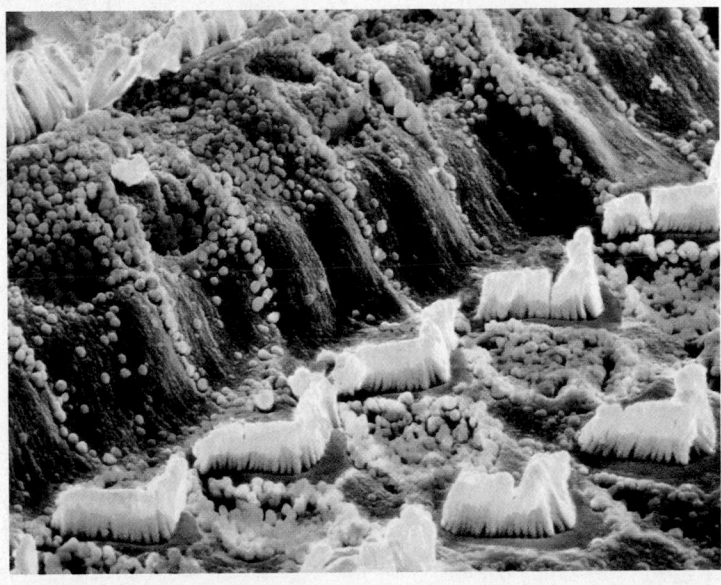

Figure 1
Vulnerable to Damage by Loud Noise
This color-enhanced micrograph shows the ear's hair cells, in yellow. Loud noise can damage the hair-like cilia visible on the cells, or can even kill the cells. Two types of hair cells are shown: "outer" cells, with a v-shape at right, and inner cells at left.

the *pattern* of firing activity across all taste neurons that the brain uses to tell us whether it is just basil in the soup or a particularly sharp basil. You've seen this pattern processing before, with smell, and it is at work elsewhere. We might say that in pattern processing, the brain is something like a talented news writer: It gets input from lots of individuals and turns these reports into a coherent, highly detailed story—in this instance, our sense of what we are tasting.

26.11 Our Sense of Hearing

Sound is always depicted as coming in "waves," but it does not physically exist as a series of tiny, invisible lines that run in peaks and troughs. Pluck a single string on a harp and then slow the video tape of this action way down. The first thing that happens is that the string moves in the opposite direction from the way it was pulled. This movement *compresses the air molecules* ahead of the string, making this air more dense than that of the ambient air around it. Now the string swings back the other way, and this *lowers* the air pressure ahead of the string—below

that of atmospheric air pressure. So what we perceive in hearing are "waves" of moving air molecules that are, by turns, more and less compressed than those of ambient air. This cycle of high and low compression happens very rapidly. When you hit the A above middle C on a piano, the waves of high and low compression are bumping up against your ear drum 440 times per second—meaning the piano string is going back and forth 440 times per second. It is these cycles that give sound its frequency. The faster the frequency, the higher the sound. The best human ears (usually children's ears) can perceive sounds ranging from about 20 to 20,000 cycles per second.

So, how do we go from a vibrating eardrum to the perception of a sound? If you look at **Figure 26.14a** on the next page, you can see the basic anatomy of the ear, and in Figure 26.14b, you can track the steps involved in hearing. (The elongated structure on the right of Figure 26.14b is the cochlea of the ear, uncoiled for illustrative purposes.)

Note that hearing begins when vibrations of the eardrum or *tympanic membrane* in turn vibrate the

(a) Anatomy of the ear

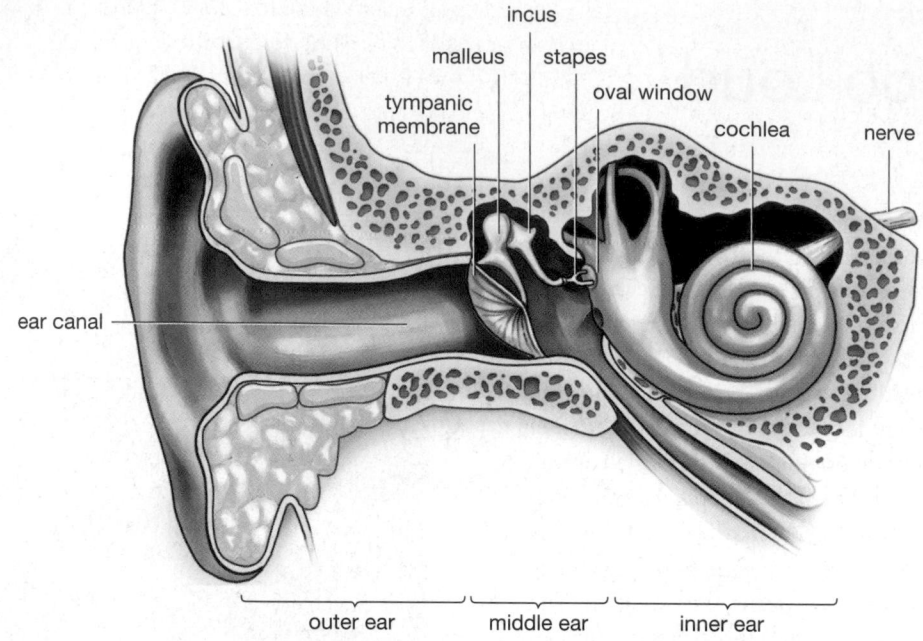

incus

malleus stapes

tympanic membrane

oval window

cochlea

nerve

ear canal

outer ear   middle ear   inner ear

(b) From air vibration to nerve signal

2. The tympanic membrane vibrates the three bones of the middle ear; the malleus, incus and stapes.

1. Sound waves enter through the ear canal and vibrate the tympanic membrane.

sound

3. The vibration of the stapes focuses the sound-wave vibration on the membrane of the oval window.

perception of sound

4. The oval window's vibrations cause fluid vibrations within the coiled, tubular cochlea (shown elongated here for illustrative purposes).

5. These fluid vibrations cause cells within the cochlea to release a neurotransmitter which triggers a nerve signal to the brain.

(c) How fluid triggers nerve signal

vestibular duct

cochlear duct

tympanic duct

nerve

1. Seen in cross-section, the cochlea has vestibular and tympanic ducts, in which fluid is vibrating.

tectorial membrane

hair cells

basilar membrane

2. This vibration shakes the basilar membrane, pushing hair cells on it up against the overlying tectorial membrane.

tectorial membrane

K^+

nucleus

Ca^{2+} Ca^{2+}

3. As the hair cells contact the tectorial membrane, cilia on them bend. This change in position causes "trap door" channels in the hair cells to open, which allows potassium ions (K^+) to flow into them.

4. This influx triggers an influx of calcium ions (Ca^{2+}) at the base of the hair cells, which in turn causes the cells to release a neurotransmitter.

5. The neurotransmitter is received by adjacent dendrites and a nerve signal is sent to the brain.

Figure 26.14
Our Sense of Hearing

three smallest bones in the body, the malleus, incus, and stapes (or "hammer, anvil, and stirrup"), which lie in the middle ear. In the same way that a lens serves to take light coming from a large area and focus it on a small one, these three bones take the vibrations coming from the relatively large tympanic membrane and focus them on the smaller oval window. This is important, because it *amplifies* the vibration signal for the next step. The oval window's vibrations now shake fluid that lies within the pea-sized structure called the **cochlea**: the coiled, membranous portion of the inner ear in which vibrations are transformed into the nervous system signals perceived as sound.

In the cross-section of the cochlea pictured in **Figure 26.14c**, you can see how vibrations of fluid in the cochlea are transformed into the sensation of sound. The cochlea can be seen to have a couple of ducts (the vestibular and tympanic) which are filled with fluid. In the middle, there is the cochlear duct, likewise filled with fluid, which has at its bottom a "basilar" membrane on which sit the elements that will produce sound. Note that, supported by the basilar membrane, there are a group of so-called "hair cells," so-named because each of them sprouts a group of hair-like cilia that come close to touching the tectorial membrane that folds over them in the cochlea.

Now, how does all of this yield sound? Think of it this way: If you rested your left hand on a water balloon and then pushed rhythmically on this same balloon with your right hand, your left hand would move up and down slightly. If there were something directly above your left hand, then your hand might make contact with it. In the same way, the vibrations of the fluid in the cochlea move the basilar membrane up and down, and this movement can push the hair cells up against the tectorial membrane that lies above them. If you look at the blow-up of Figure 26.14c, you can see what happens next. The cilia on the hair cells have microscopic "trap door" channels on them, and when these cilia bend from touching the tectorial membrane, the trap doors open. With this, potassium (K^+) ions flow in, leading to an influx of calcium (Ca^{2+}) ions at the base of the hair cell; and this leads the hair cells to release a neurotransmitter. Waiting to receive the neurotransmitter are adjacent dendrites, and, with this, vibration has been turned into a nerve signal.

The details of the hearing process actually are much more complicated than this account would indicate. While we need not go over these details, it's worthwhile to note just one of the ways this system is able to discriminate one sound from another. To lo-

cate where a sound is *coming from*, the brain in effect calculates the difference between how intense a sound is in one ear as opposed to the other, and what the time difference is between when sound arrives at one ear and then the other.

Finally, it is easy for hearing to be damaged, and this damage often is to the hair cells we've been looking at, as you can see in "Too Loud" on page 575.

26.12 Our Sense of Vision

Our visual system has to accomplish three central tasks. First, it has to capture light from the outside world and focus it at a very precise location within our eyes. Second, it has to take this focused light and convert it into a nervous-system signal. Third, it has to make sense of the visual information it receives. If you look at **Figure 26.15**, you can see some of the structures of the eye that function in the first two steps. Light comes into our eyes through the transparent cornea and passes through the opening known as the pupil. Surrounding the pupil is the iris, which is composed partly of smooth muscle and thus is capable of contracting or dilating, meaning it can let in less light in a bright environment, or more light in a darkened one. The incoming light is bound for the layer of cells at the back of the eye called the **retina**: an inner layer of tissue in the eye containing cells that transform light into nervous-system signals. But as the light rays come in, they are bent or "refracted"—first by the cornea

Figure 26.15
Anatomy of the Human Eye

cornea
iris
pupil
lens
vitreous body
retina
optic nerve

Figure 26.16
Focused and Unfocused

Sharp vision requires that incoming light rays converge just as they reach the retina.

(a) In normal vision, the eye's cornea and lens bring about this convergence; they refract the incoming light at an angle that matches the length of the eye.

(b) People who are farsighted have a mismatch between the length of their eye and the amount of refraction provided by their cornea and lens: Their eye is too short for the amount of refraction provided. Thus, light rays converge behind their retina. As a result, these people cannot see nearby objects clearly.

(c) People who are nearsighted have the opposite problem: Their eye is too long for the amount of refraction provided, with the result that light rays converge in front of their retina. These people cannot see distant objects clearly. Both nearsighted and farsighted vision can be corrected.

and then by the lens that lies behind it—such that they converge on a small area of the retina, as you can see in **Figure 26.16**. This is no different in principle than what happens with a camera. We take a picture of a large object (such as a statue) that ends up as a small image on a frame of film. In a similar way, thanks to refraction, large objects we view with our eyes end up as *very* small images on our retina. How small? At fractions of a millimeter, some of them are microscopic. The eyes do not always focus light rays in such a way that they converge properly on the retina, however. You can see what it means to be nearsighted or farsighted in Figure 26.16.

Now, how do retinal cells convert rays of light into electrical signals? If you look at **Figure 26.17**, you can see that there are three layers of cells in the retina: ganglion cells, connecting cells, and photoreceptors. The **photoreceptors** are the sensory receptors for vision, and they come in two varieties: rods and cones. **Rods** are photoreceptors that function in low-light situations, but that provide only black-and-white vision. **Cones** are photoreceptors that respond best to bright light, and that provide color vision.

(a) Normal vision

light rays converge on the retina

(b) Farsighted vision

light rays converge behind the retina

(c) Nearsighted vision

light rays converge in front of the retina

The blow-up of these cells shows that their posterior ends—the ends toward the back of the head—are filled with pigments, which lie embedded in a series of flattened, membranous discs. A pigment is simply a chemical compound that absorbs light. So, our light comes in and moves to, say, a rod in the retina. There it is absorbed by a pigment, and this absorption causes a normally bent part of the pigment molecule to . . . straighten out. That's it. Our entire sense of vision hinges on this tiny initial effect. Yet, as a shouted "hello" might cause an avalanche, so this small step puts big things in motion. In his book *What Makes You Tick?* vision researcher Thomas Czerner puts it this way:

> The infinitesimal energy of a photon [of light] changes the shape of a *single* molecule of pigment, which causes the release of *dozens* of molecules of an enzyme, which cause the rapid breakdown of *hundreds* of molecules of a chemical messenger, which cause the gates of *thousands* of ion channels in the cell membrane to slam shut, which blocks *millions* of sodium ions from entering the cell, which produces the grand finale, a local change in the resting membrane potential.

You might expect that this change in photoreceptor membrane potential would, like the others you've seen, result in the release of a neurotransmitter to an adjacent neuron. The twist in vision, however, is that in their *resting* state rods and cones are releasing neurotransmitter molecules in abundance to their connecting cells. When light strikes the rods and cones it has the effect of reducing this neurotransmitter release. Thus, the lack of neurotransmitter release from a rod or cone transmits the message "light stimulation here."

The signal that begins with a rod or cone goes first to connecting neurons, and then to the ganglion cells you can see in Figure 26.17. These cells have axons that are like tributaries coming together to form a river; only this river is the optic nerve, composed of about a million axons (see Figure 26.15). Because we have two eyes, we thus have a pair of million-fiber optic nerves carrying visual information from the eyes to the brain. The optic nerve takes the visual information to the thalamus, and from there it is transmitted, on other nerve fibers, to an area at the very back surface of the brain, the *primary visual cortex*, where most vision processing is done.

The details of this processing are much too complicated to go into here. But a central lesson of this complexity is that the human visual system does not work like a camera; it does not passively record bits of light and register a collection of these

(a)

direction of nerve signal

light

cone

synaptic ending   nucleus   flattened membranes   red, green and blue pigments

pigment

rod

ganglion cells   connecting cells   photoreceptors (rods and cones)

Figure 26.17
Turning Light into Neural Signals
Photoreceptor cells called rods and cones convert incoming light into neural signals.

(a) Incoming light moves to the retina at the back of the eye. The blow-up of the retina shows its three layers of cells: ganglion cells, connecting cells and rods and cones. Light reaches the rods and cones and stimulates a molecular change in them that results in a signal being sent back out the other direction—through the connecting cells and then the ganglion cells. With this series of events, a light signal has been converted to a neural signal that will go, via ganglion cell axons, to the optic nerve. The anatomy of both rods and cones can be seen at right. Light is absorbed by millions of pigment molecules embedded in the flattened membranes of rods and cones. Only the cones have pigments that respond to color.

(b) A color-enhanced micrograph of rods and cones. The light blue structure is a cone.

(b)

rod

cone

bits as images. Rather, the brain *constructs* images as much as it records them. To get an idea of this, look at **Figure 26.18**. In it, you see a V, formed out of bumps and a dot-like indentation. Now turn the book upside down and look again. The bumps have become indentations, and vice versa. Why? Note that when the book is right side up, most dots in the V are shaded in such a way that light seems to be coming from above them—there are "shadows" on the lower part of the dots. Light generally comes from above us, whether from a lamp or from the sun. This is so common that evolution has produced a genetically based "rule" in our visual system that says: "When shadows are in the lower part of an object, that object is raised above a surface."

Why would evolution produce rules such as these? After all, this rule is yielding an *inaccurate* interpretation of the dots on the page—they aren't really raised above the surface at all. Our visual system has such rules because what mattered in the evolution of our ancestors was not whether they perceived objects "correctly." What mattered was whether they perceived objects in ways that helped them survive and reproduce. Over the ages, individuals who could perceive, say, a

snake more quickly than other individuals survived longer and thus left more offspring. The many visual rules we have amount to rules for survival. They provide a series of "best bets" for quickly telling us what we are looking at. (If an object's lower half is shaded,

Web Tutorial 26.2
The Vertebrate Eye

Figure 26.18
Seeing Is Believing
Look at the figure and then turn the book upside down and look at it again. With the shift, dots that once appeared to be raised above the surface of the drawing now appear to be indented, and vice versa. Our visual system has a rule that causes us to perceive objects that are shaded at the bottom as protruding from a surface, while objects that are shaded at the top appear to be indented. This is but one example of how our visual system creates visual images, rather than simply recording them.

the best bet is that it's raised above a surface.) The idea that our visual system is often creating perceptions, rather than simply recording them, may seem strange, but that's the reality of visual perception.

26.13 The Endocrine System

We now leave the nervous system to focus on a different system in the body, the endocrine system. Like the nervous system, the endocrine system is in the communication and control business. And, like the nervous system with its neurotransmitters, the endocrine system works through a group of chemical messengers. The endocrine messengers are not neurotransmitters, however, but instead are substances called hormones. In this text, we will define **hormones** as substances secreted by one set of cells that travel through the bloodstream and affect the activities of other cells. Such a definition sets hormones apart from other kinds of signaling molecules in the body. There are signaling molecules, called *paracrines*, that do not travel through the bloodstream, but instead diffuse from one or more cells to a nearby group of cells, causing a metabolic change in them. Likewise, a cell can be affected by its own secreted chemical messenger, called an *autocrine*. Note that both paracrines and autocrines carry out strictly *local* communication between cells. The endocrine hormones we'll be looking at can have their effects over short distances, but they also have the ability to carry chemical signals throughout the body, given their transportation through the bloodstream.

This very means of distribution provides a key for getting to the heart of what separates the endocrine and nervous systems. In the nervous system, signals go from neurons A to B to C, in well-defined lines of transmission—rather like a telephone call going through relay stations. By contrast, a typical hormone is "broadcast," in a sense, as it moves through the bloodstream. Like a television signal, it can be "picked up" by any cell that has the proper "receiver." What are these receivers? They are receptors that are shaped in such a way that they can latch onto the hormone. With this, we get to the concept of **target cells**: those cell types that can be affected by a given hormone (see **Figure 26.19**). The target cells for a hormone called anti-diuretic hormone are located primarily in the kidneys, while the target cells for the hormone insulin are located throughout the body. Thus, hormones differ greatly with respect to the number of target cells they affect and the location of these cells.

Hormonal production takes place to a significant extent within specialized organs called endocrine glands, and this represents another contrast with the nervous system. You may remember that a gland is any localized group of cells that work together to secrete a substance. **Endocrine glands** are glands that release their materials directly into the bloodstream or into surrounding tissues, without using ducts. Thus, the endocrine system has a set of large organs whose primary function is to secrete chemical messengers. In contrast, the nervous system has no such organs—only its individual neurons, secreting neurotransmitters. The major endocrine glands are shown in **Figure 26.20**. While most hormones are secreted by these glands, it's important to note that not *all* hormones are. The heart, kidneys, stomach, liver, small intestine, placenta, and fatty tissue secrete hormones related to their functioning, yet they are not glands.

In a final point of comparison, the endocrine system tends to work more slowly than the nervous system, but its effects tend to be more long-lasting. The fastest-acting hormones take several seconds to work, while the slowest-acting ones may take several hours. Contrast this with the almost instantaneous effects of nervous-system messages. The opposite side of this coin is that the longest-lasting hormones can keep exerting their effects for hours after they have been released. In contrast, nervous-system signals disappear as fast as they arise. Given the time scales in which hormones act, it's not surprising that they tend to regulate processes that unfold over minutes,

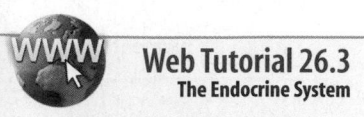

Web Tutorial 26.3
The Endocrine System

Figure 26.19
Hormones and Their Target Cells
For a hormone to affect a target cell, that cell must have receptors that can bind the hormone. The binding of hormone to receptor then initiates a change in the target cell's activity. The figure shows a peptide hormone that affects skeletal muscle tissue. The hormone does not affect the nerve cell, also shown in the figure, because this cell does not have the appropriate receptors to bind with the hormone.

Hormones and Target Cells

1. Endocrine cells release hormone.

2. Hormone enters circulation.

3. Hormone is carried throughout the body.

Hormone will not bind to cells that are not target cells

4. Binding occurs, hormonal effects take place.

receptor

target cell
(skeletal muscle)

hours, or even years: whether we have enough water in our systems, how we grow, and so forth. If you need to swerve to avoid a collision, look to the nervous system for a response; for the maintenance of water balance and bone density, look to the endocrine system.

Despite these various differences, modern research actually is blurring the distinction between the endocrine and nervous systems. The control of the two systems is tightly linked, as you will see, but this has been known for years. What's new is that scientists have a growing list of substances that once were thought to work strictly as hormones, but that now turn out to be both hormones and neurotransmitters. Several of these substances function as hormones outside the brain and as neurotransmitters within it.

26.14 Types of Hormones

Hormones come in three primary classes. The first of these is the **amino-acid-based hormones**: hormones that are derived from a single amino acid. You may remember that amino acids are the building blocks of proteins. String a number of amino acids together and the result is a polypeptide. String a large number of amino acids together—usually several hundred—and the result is a polypeptide that then folds up into a protein. It turns out that several hormones have individual amino acids as their chemical starting points. For example, the hormone epinephrine—better known as adrenaline—is produced from a chemical modification of the amino acid tyrosine. Likewise, the hormone melatonin is produced through a modification of the amino acid tryptophan.

The second class of hormones, the **peptide hormones**, are hormones composed of *chains* amino acids. These chains are polypetides of varying lengths—some of them long and complex enough that they constitute proteins, but some of them very short. The antidiuretic hormone noted earlier (which targets kidney cells) is a polypeptide that is a mere nine amino acids in length. Meanwhile, human growth hormone is a protein that is composed of 191 amino acids. But both antidiuretic and growth hormone are peptide hormones. Insulin is another peptide hormone, as are most of the hormones secreted by an important endocrine gland we'll be looking at, the pituitary.

With a few exceptions, peptide and amino-acid-based hormones have target cells whose hormone receptors are located on their outer membranes. These receptors are the "broadcast receivers" that stand ready to bind with these hormones when they pass by, as depicted in Figure 26.19. The effects of this binding are very diverse. Ion channels may be opened in a target cell as a result, or enzymes may be activated. In all cases, the cell will change its activities as a result of the binding.

The third major class of hormones, the **steroid hormones**, are all constructed around the chemical framework of the cholesterol molecule. Most of the steroid hormones are released from just a few glands—notably the male and female reproductive glands and the adrenal glands (which sit atop the kidneys). Like amino-acid-based and peptide hormones, some steroid hormones can latch onto receptors on the outside of a target cell. But most steroid hormones pass *through* a cell's plasma membrane, and then bind with a receptor protein inside the cell. This combined hormone/receptor molecule then enters the nucleus of the cell and binds with the cell's DNA there. This binding turns on one or more of the cell's genes, thus bringing about the production of one or more proteins. Two of the best-known steroid hormones are testosterone and estrogen.

Figure 26.20
The Major Hormone-Secreting Glands of the Body
Though it is part of the brain (and not an endocrine gland), the hypothalamus is shown because it plays a central role in hormonal regulation.

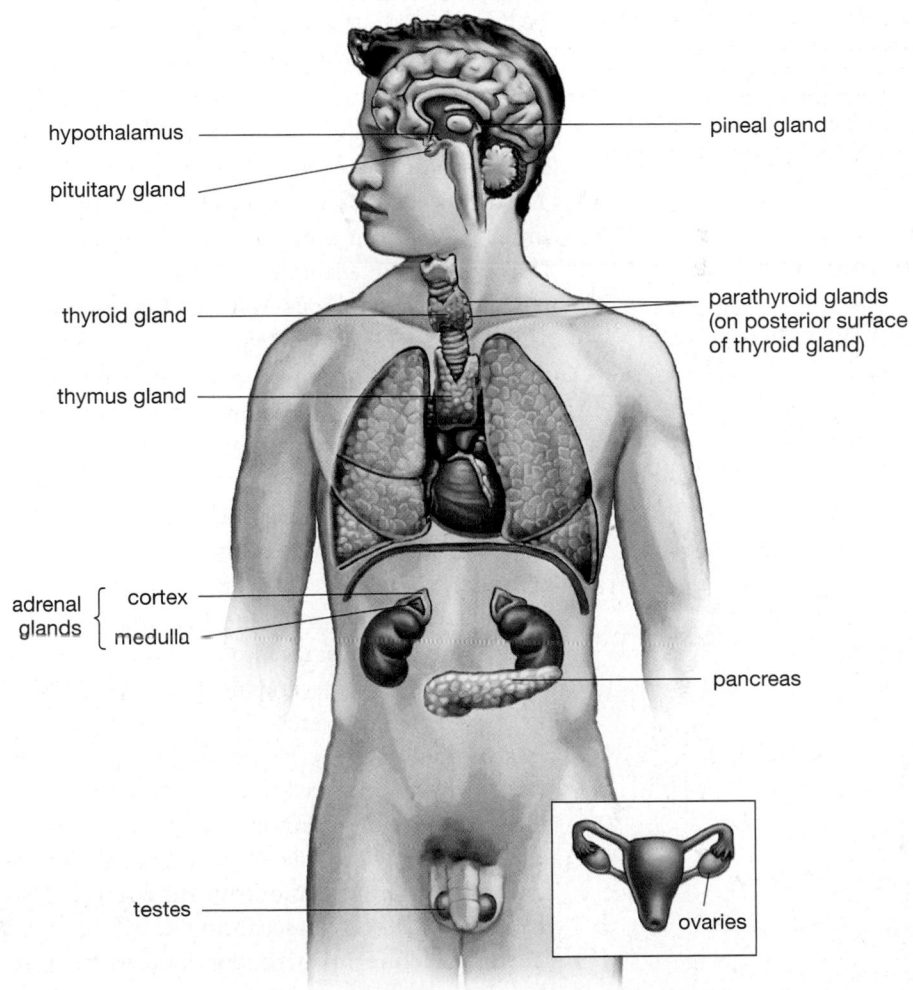

26.15 How Is Hormone Secretion Controlled?

Almost all hormone secretion is controlled by the negative feedback mechanism that was reviewed in Chapter 25 (see page 536). As a reminder, this is the same mechanism that operates in a home heating system. A thermostat senses that the home temperature is too cold and thus switches on a furnace. The product of this action is hot air, and this very product then feeds back on the themostat's activity in a negative way—it shuts it down. In hormone secretion, a given gland or set of neurons will sense that more of a certain hormone is needed and then send a signal out, prompting release of that hormone. The hormonal product that results then feeds back on the sensing mechanisms in a negative way, causing it to reduce or shut down production of the hormone. When we consider all the negative feedback loops in operation in the endocrine system, we find that they are big players in helping to preserve **homeostasis**: an organism's tendency to maintain a relatively stable internal environment.

Hormonal Hierarchy: The Hypothalamus

Though negative feedback ultimately controls most hormone secretion, it's accurate to view a good part of the endocrine system as a hierarchy that has, sitting on top of it, one of the brain structures we looked at earlier, the hypothalamus. The hypothalamus is prompted to act based on input it gets from other sources—sensory nerves feed into it, for example—so it is part of larger negative feedback loops. Nevertheless, as you can see in **Figure 26.21**, the hypothalamus controls a lot of the body's hormone secretion. Note all that it does. First, it acts as an endocrine organ itself, releasing, through one part of the pituitary gland—the posterior pituitary—two hormones that it produces itself. Second, it exercises control over the endocrine cells of the inner portion (or medulla) of the adrenal glands. Upon nervous-system stimulation from the hypothalamus, the adrenal medulla releases into the bloodstream the hormones adrenaline and noradrenaline. Third, the hypothalamus exercises control over a second part of the pituitary gland—the anterior pituitary—which is referred to as a "master gland" in that several of the hormones it releases go on to control *other* endocrine glands. Though lots of hormones are produced outside the control of the hypothalamus, you can see from this list that it is a central structure in the endocrine system. Note that the hypothalamus is a part of the brain, yet it is releasing some hormones and controlling the release of others. This is an example of how extensive the overlap is between the nervous and endocrine systems.

The Pituitary Gland

Let's look a little closer now at one of the prime links in the hypothalamic hierarchy, the pituitary gland. This structure is a small, lima-bean-sized organ that looks something like a punching bag. Suspended from the hypothalamus by a slender stalk (see Figure 26.21), the pituitary is a single entity in a sense. Yet it has anterior and posterior regions that differ greatly in function—so greatly that it's tempting to think of these regions as two neighbors who happen to live in the same apartment building. The posterior pituitary is really an extension of the hypothalamus and as such simply acts as a storage-and-release site for two hormones produced by the hypothalamus. Meanwhile, the anterior pituitary synthesizes its *own* hormones—six of them in all—though it releases them under control of the hypothalamus. Here are a couple of more formal definitions of these regions. The **posterior pituitary** is a region of the pituitary gland that stores and releases two hormones, oxytocin and antidiuretic hormone, that are produced by the brain's hypothalamus. The **anterior pituitary** is a region of the pituitary gland that, under control of the brain's hypothalamus, produces and releases hormones that work directly on target cells or on other endocrine glands.

The hypothalamus exercises its control over the anterior pituitary in an interesting way. The anterior pituitary's endocrine cells are surrounded by a network of the tiny blood vessels called capillaries. Move up to the hypothalamus, and it too has a capillary bed in its lower portion. Running between these two capillary beds are a small number of blood vessels. Nerve cells in the hypothalamus synthesize extremely small amounts of hormones that travel down their axons and are released into the hypothalamic capillaries. From there, they travel down the linking blood vessels to the anterior pituitary capillaries; and from there, they move into the pituitary gland itself. These can be so-called *releasing hormones* that stimulate pituitary cells to produce their own hormones. Conversely, they may be *inhibiting hormones* that serve to *reduce* the production of given hormones by the pituitary. The anterior pituitary itself is composed of five types of cells that release the gland's six different hormones. Once these hormones are made, they move out into the bloodstream for distribution throughout the body.

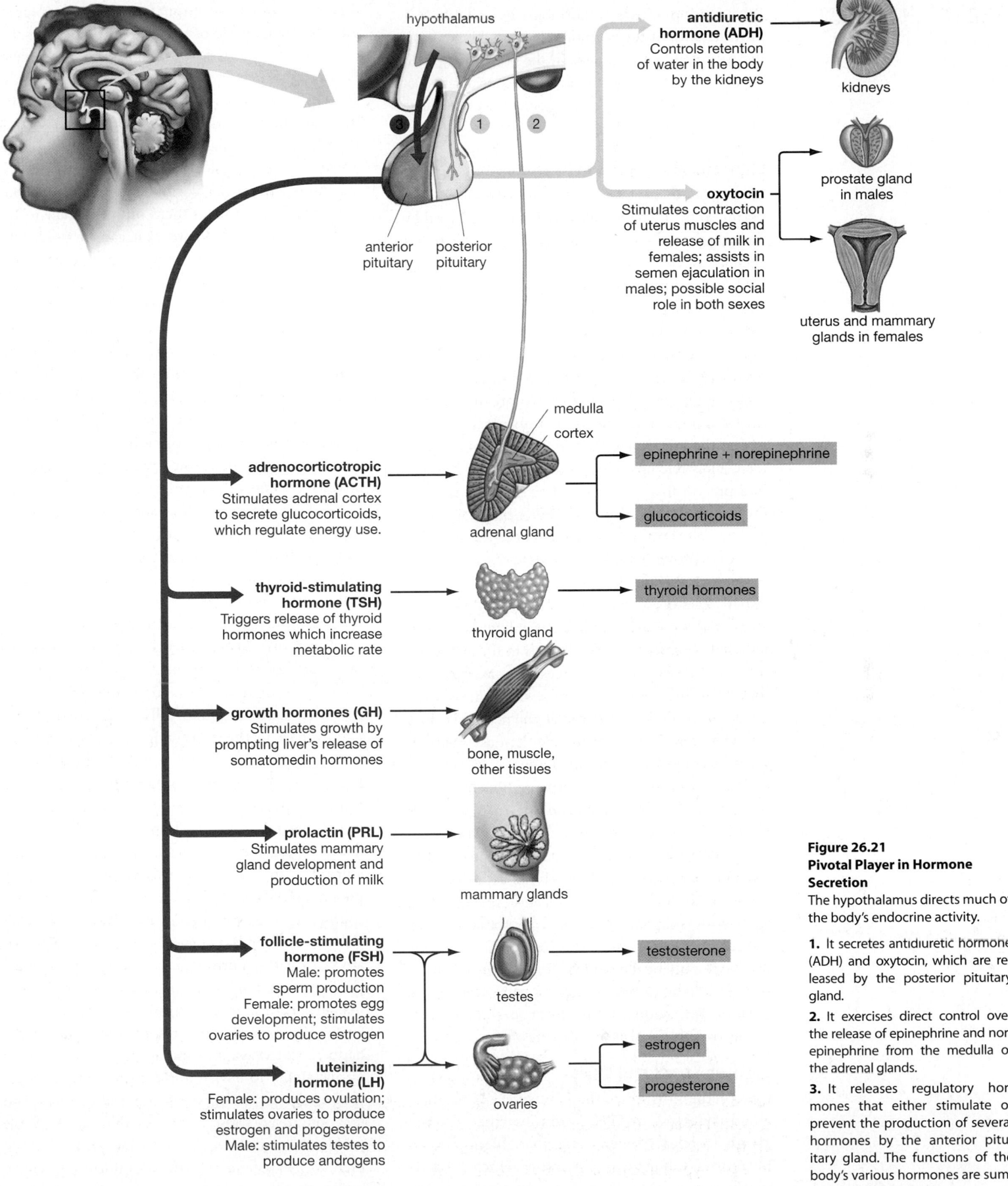

hypothalamus

antidiuretic hormone (ADH)
Controls retention of water in the body by the kidneys

kidneys

anterior pituitary   posterior pituitary

oxytocin
Stimulates contraction of uterus muscles and release of milk in females; assists in semen ejaculation in males; possible social role in both sexes

prostate gland in males

uterus and mammary glands in females

medulla
cortex

adrenocorticotropic hormone (ACTH)
Stimulates adrenal cortex to secrete glucocorticoids, which regulate energy use.

epinephrine + norepinephrine

glucocorticoids

adrenal gland

thyroid-stimulating hormone (TSH)
Triggers release of thyroid hormones which increase metabolic rate

thyroid hormones

thyroid gland

growth hormones (GH)
Stimulates growth by prompting liver's release of somatomedin hormones

bone, muscle, other tissues

prolactin (PRL)
Stimulates mammary gland development and production of milk

mammary glands

follicle-stimulating hormone (FSH)
Male: promotes sperm production
Female: promotes egg development; stimulates ovaries to produce estrogen

testosterone

testes

luteinizing hormone (LH)
Female: produces ovulation; stimulates ovaries to produce estrogen and progesterone
Male: stimulates testes to produce androgens

estrogen

progesterone

ovaries

**Figure 26.21
Pivotal Player in Hormone Secretion**
The hypothalamus directs much of the body's endocrine activity.

1. It secretes antidiuretic hormone (ADH) and oxytocin, which are released by the posterior pituitary gland.

2. It exercises direct control over the release of epinephrine and norepinephrine from the medulla of the adrenal glands.

3. It releases regulatory hormones that either stimulate or prevent the production of several hormones by the anterior pituitary gland. The functions of the body's various hormones are summarized in Table 26.1.

26.16 Hormones in Action: Two Examples

What kinds of effects do hormones have? **Table 26.1** provides a list of the hormones produced by most of the major endocrine glands in the body, along with the effects of these hormones. Let's consider two of them in some detail to give you some idea of the range of the endocrine system.

Oxytocin: Many Roles in Reproduction

We start with oxytocin, one of the two hormones produced by the hypothalamus and then released by the posterior pituitary. For decades, oxytocin has been known to have two clear-cut roles regarding the birth and nurturing of babies. When childbirth begins, oxytocin is released (from the pituitary and elsewhere) and stimulates muscle contractions in the mother that push the fetus down into the uterus, thus stretching it. This stretching then stimulates more oxytocin release, which stimulates more muscle contractions and stretching. What is in process here is one of the body's few *positive* feedback loops. Oxytocin and stretching both prompt *more* of each other in a process that ends only when the baby is born. Oxytocin's role then continues after birth, as it triggers the release of milk from the mother's breasts.

You might think that functions as diverse as these two would be plenty for any one hormone, but in the last 10 years or so, researchers have found that oxytocin's role is much broader yet. We might say that it is involved in reproduction from start to finish, though most of the evidence in this regard comes from animals other than humans. In mice, oxytocin seems to enhance the desire for physical contact, while in a mammal called the prairie vole, it makes females more receptive to sex. In human males, it facilitates ejaculations of some of the substances that help make up semen. And in both men and women, blood levels of oxytocin rise during sex and surge following orgasm, leading to speculations that it may be linked to making sex pleasurable. Research has generally indicated that oxytocin plays an "affiliative" role in several species—it stimulates all kinds of social contact, whereas its absence lessens this contact. If so, imagine how wide-ranging the roles are for this one hormone: Its effects range from something as mechanical as muscle contractions in childbirth to something as deeply psychological as the pleasure of sex.

Cortisol: Stress and Illness

One of the hormones that the *anterior* pituitary gland releases, ACTH, prompts the adrenal glands to release several so-called glucocorticoid hormones, the most important of which is cortisol. In our everyday lives, cortisol is critical in energy management. It helps bring about the production of our most important energy molecule, glucose, in a couple of ways—it provides the raw materials for glucose by facilitating the breakdown of muscle proteins, and it promotes the synthesis of glucose in the liver. Along similar lines, it promotes the breakdown of fats so that their component-part fatty acids can be used to power our activities.

In the main, then, cortisol helps transform energy molecules; it takes them out of storage forms and puts them into forms that can be used. Like oxytocin, however, cortisol plays more exotic roles as well. Cortisol is a stress hormone. It is part of a group of hormones that are released as part of the body's general "stress response." When you feel the pressure building in the days before a big exam and you feel yourself being uncomfortably tense and stimulated, that's cortisol at work. (Its role overlaps that of the more famous stress hormone adrenaline, which can be thought of as functioning more in times of panic, rather than ongoing stress.) During prolonged stress, cortisol carries out its normal function, in a sense, in that it's helping to provide energy. But it is also having more sinister effects during these times: It is making you vulnerable to illnesses and temporarily destroying cell connections in the part of the brain called the hippocampus, which is critical in making long-term memories. These effects stem partly from the fact that cortisol weakens the immune system. (Among other things, it actually brings about the death of some immune cells.) But cortisol also plays a part in the narrowing of the arteries that leads to heart attacks, and it makes cells less sensitive to insulin, leaving people more at risk for developing adult-onset diabetes.

All this raises the question: Why should the endocrine system work to make stressed people more vulnerable to illness? Isn't this a kind of "poor get poorer" syndrome? In his fine book on the stress response, *Why Zebras Don't Get Ulcers*, researcher Robert Sapolsky has suggested that human beings are stuck with a hormonal stress response that was built by evolution for beings, such as our mammalian ancestors, whose stresses were all *short term*. Such ancestors were not stressed about what would happen next week, but human beings are. Because of our ability to envision the future, our stress responses can go on for weeks, months, or years. And it is long-term stress responses that cause all the problems noted above. In cortisol, as with oxytocin, then, we can see that the effects of hormones can be both far-reaching and not at all straightforward.

Table 26.1 Hormones of the endocrine system: Their sources and effects

Gland/Hormone	Effects
Hypothalamus Releasing hormones	Stimulate hormone production in anterior pituitary
Inhibiting hormones	Reduce hormone production in anterior pituitary
Anterior pituitary Thyroid-stimulating hormone (TSH)	Triggers release of thyroid hormones
Adrenocorticotropic hormone (ACTH)	Stimulates adrenal cortex cells to secrete glucocorticoids
Follicle-stimulating hormone	Female: promotes egg development: stimulates ovaries to produce estrogen Male: promotes sperm production
Luteinizing hormone (LH)	Female: produces ovulation (egg release); stimulates ovaries to produce estrogen and progesterone Male: stimulates testes to produce androgens (e.g., testosterone)
Prolactin (PRL)	Stimulates mammary gland development and production of milk
Growth hormone (GH)	Stimulates growth by prompting liver's release of somatomedin hormones
Posterior pituitary Antidiuretic hormone (ADH)	Controls retention of water in the body by the kidneys
Oxytocin	Stimulates contraction of uterus muscles and release of milk in females; assists in semen ejaculation in males; possible social role in both sexes
Thyroid Thyroxine	Increases general rate of body metabolism
Calcitonin	Reduces calcium ion levels in blood
Parathyroid Parathyroid hormone (PTH)	Increases calcium ion levels in blood
Thymus Thymosins	Stimulate development of white blood cells (lymphocytes) in early life
Adrenal cortex Glucocorticoids	Includes cortisol, which stimulates glucose production and breakdown of fats. A stress-response hormone.
Mineralocorticoids	Cause the kidneys to retain sodium ions and water and excrete potassium ions
Adrenal medulla Epinephrine	Also known as adrenaline; stimulates release of energy stores; increases heart rate and blood pressure
Norepinephrine	Also known as noradrenaline; effects similar to epinephrine
Pancreas Insulin	Decreases glucose levels in blood
Glucagon	Increases glucose levels in blood
Testes Testosterone	Promotes production of sperm and development of male sex characteristics
Ovaries Estrogens	Support egg development, growth of uterine lining, and development of female sex characteristics
Progesterones	Prepare uterus for arrival of developing embryo and support of further embryonic development
Pineal gland Melatonin	Establishes day/night cycle

On to the Immune System

Having looked at the capabilities of the nervous and endocrine systems, it's time to move on to another of the body's systems. This system is not involved in communication and control, but instead has the job of defense. Indeed, we might say it is involved in a never-ending war of defense. On one side in this combat are all kinds of microscopic organisms—bacteria, viruses, fungi—that use every opportunity to enter the body and start reproducing in it. On the other side is the body's chief defender, the immune system, whose story is the subject of Chapter 27.

Chapter Review

Summary

26.1 Structure of the Nervous System

- The nervous system includes all the nervous tissue in the body, plus the body's sensory organs, such as the eyes and ears. Nervous tissue is composed of neurons, which transmit nervous system messages; and glial cells, which support neurons.

- The two major divisions of the human nervous system are the central nervous system (CNS), consisting of the brain and spinal cord; and the peripheral nervous system (PNS), which includes all the neural tissue outside the CNS, plus the sensory organs.

- The PNS has an afferent division, which brings sensory information to the CNS; and an efferent division, which carries action (motor) commands to the body's "effectors"—muscles and glands. Within the PNS efferent division are two subsystems: the somatic nervous system, which provides voluntary control over skeletal muscles; and the autonomic nervous system, which provides involuntary regulation of smooth muscle, cardiac muscle, and glands.

- The autonomic system is further divided into the sympathetic division, which generally has stimulatory effects; and the parasympathetic division, which generally has relaxing effects.

26.2 Cells of the Nervous System

- There are three types of neurons: Sensory neurons, which sense conditions inside and outside the body and convey information about these conditions to neurons inside the CNS; motor neurons, which carry instructions from the CNS to such structures as muscles or glands; and interneurons, which are located entirely within the CNS and which interconnect other neurons.

- Each neuron has extensions called dendrites that receive signals coming to the neuron cell body, and a single large extension, called an axon, that carries signals from the cell body. Glial cells serve to protect neurons and to facilitate communication by them. A nerve is a bundle of axons in the PNS that transmits information to or from the CNS.

26.3 How Nervous-System Communication Works

- Nervous-system communication can be conceptualized as working through a two-step process: signal movement down a neuron's axon, and signal movement from this axon to a second cell across a structure known as a synapse.

- An electrical charge difference, called a membrane potential, exists across the plasma membrane of neurons because the inside of the neuron is negatively charged relative to the outside. This represents a form of potential energy that is put to use when special protein channels in the neuron's membrane open up upon stimulation, thereby allowing charged particles called ions to flow into the neuron. This influx of ions at an initial point on the axon triggers reactions that cause the adjacent portion of the axonal membrane to initiate the same influx of ions. Thus, a conducted nerve impulse, called an action potential, moves down the entire axon in a set of linked reactions.

- A nerve signal moves from one neuron to another (or to a muscle or gland cell) across a synapse, which includes a "sending" neuron, a "receiving" cell, and a tiny gap between the two cells, called a synaptic cleft. A chemical called a neurotransmitter diffuses across the synaptic cleft from the sending neuron to the receiving neuron. It then binds with receptors on the receiving neuron, thus keeping the signal going. Neurotransmitters can be degraded in synaptic clefts by enzymes, or taken back into a sending cell in the process called reuptake.
Web Tutorial 26.1: The Nervous System

26.4 The Spinal Cord

- The spinal cord can act as a nervous-system communication center, receiving input from sensory neurons and directing motor neurons with no input from the brain. It also channels sensory impulses to the brain. In cross section, the spinal cord has a darker, H-shaped central area, composed mostly of the cell bodies of neurons; and a lighter peripheral area, composed mostly of axons. These two areas are the gray matter and white matter of the spinal cord. The central canal of the spinal cord is filled with cerebrospinal fluid, which provides the spinal cord with nutrients and protection. Spinal nerves extend from the spinal cord to most areas of the body.

- Spinal cord motor neurons, which are sending motor commands to muscles and other effectors, have cell bodies that lie within the gray matter of the spinal cord. The axons of these neurons leave the spinal cord through its ventral roots. Sensory neurons, which transmit information to the spinal cord, have their cell bodies outside the spinal cord, in the dorsal-root ganglia. Thus, sensory information comes to the spinal cord through a dorsal root, while motor commands leave the spinal cord through a ventral root. Dorsal and ventral roots come together, like fibers being joined in a single cable, to form a given spinal nerve.

- Reflexes are automatic nervous-system responses, triggered by specific stimuli, that help us avoid danger or preserve a stable physical state. The neural wiring of a single reflex, called a reflex arc, begins with a sensory receptor, runs through the spinal cord, and proceeds back out to an effector such as a muscle or gland.

26.5 The Autonomic Nervous System

- The sympathetic division of the autonomic nervous system is often called the fight-or-flight system, because it generally activates bodily functions. The parasympathetic division is often called the rest-and-digest system, because it conserves energy and promotes digestive activities. Most organs receive input from both systems.

26.6 The Human Brain

- The brain contains almost 98 percent of the human body's neural tissue. There are six major regions in the adult brain: the cerebrum, thalamus and hypothalamus, midbrain, pons, cerebellum, and medulla oblongata. The cerebrum is divided into right and left cerebral hemispheres and is the seat of our higher thinking and processing. The cerebrum also has a thin outer layer, the cerebral cortex, that is the site of our highest thinking. The brainstem is a collective term for three brain areas—the midbrain, pons, and medulla oblongata. These brainstem structures are active in controlling involuntary bodily activities (such as breathing and digesting), in relaying information, and in processing sensory information. Most of the body's sensory perceptions are channeled through the thalamus before going to the cerebral cortex. The hypothalamus is important in sensing internal conditions and in maintaining stability or homeostasis in the body, largely through its control of many of the body's hormones.

26.7 The Nervous System in Action: Our Senses

- Human beings have more sensory capabilities than the famous five of vision, touch, smell, taste, and hearing. Each sense employs cells called sensory receptors that do two things: respond to stimuli (such as vibration in sound) and transform these responses into the language of the nervous system—electrical signals that travel through action potentials. Signals from every sense except smell are routed through the brain's thalamus and then to specific areas of the cerebral cortex.

26.8 Our Senses of Touch

- Touch works through a variety of sensory receptors that distinguish among such qualities as light or heavy pressure and new or ongoing contact. In some sensory cells known as stretch receptors, the stretching of their outer membrane prompts an influx of ions that results in the initiation of a nerve signal.

26.9 Our Sense of Smell

- Our sense of smell, or olfaction, works through a set of sensory receptors whose dendrites extend into the nasal passages. "Odorants," which are molecules that have identifiable smells, bind with hair-like extensions of these dendrites, resulting in a nerve signal to the brain. The higher processing centers of the brain distinguish one odorant from another by sensing unique groups of neurons that fire in connection with given odorants.

26.10 Our Sense of Taste

- Our sense of taste works through a group of taste cells, located in taste buds near the surface of the tongue, which have receptors that bind to "tastants," or molecules of food that elicit different tastes. A given taste cell can respond through any of four (or perhaps five) chemical signaling routes that correspond to the four or five basic tastes of sweet, sour, salty, and bitter, and a possible fifth taste of umami. The neurons that receive input from taste cells vary in their response to different tastants. The brain makes sense of the pattern of input it gets from these neurons, thus yielding the large number of tastes we experience.

26.11 Our Sense of Hearing

- Our sense of hearing is based on the fact that vibrations result in "waves" of air molecules that are, by turns, more and less compressed than the ambient air around them. These waves of compression bump up against our eardrums (or tympanic membranes), which in turn vibrate, initiating a chain of vibration that ends in the fluid-filled cochlea of the inner ear. "Hair cells" in the cochlea have ion channels that open and close in response to this vibration, resulting in a nerve signal to the brain.

26.12 Our Sense of Vision

- The human visual system must accomplish three central tasks. It has to gather and focus light reflected by objects in the outside world; it must convert light signals into nervous-system signals; and it must make sense of the visual information it has received. Light first enters the eye through the cornea and then passes through the lens and various materials on its way to a layer of tissue called the retina at the back of the eye. Light is bent or refracted by the cornea and the lens in such a way that it ends up as a tiny, sharply focused image on the retina.

- Light signals are converted to nervous-system signals by cells in the retina called photoreceptors, which come in two varieties: rods and cones. Rods function in dim light but are not sensitive to color; cones function best in bright light but are sensitive to color. These photoreceptors have pigments, or light-absorbing molecules, embedded in membranes within them. When light strikes a pigment, it prompts a cascade of chemical reactions that results in neurotransmitter release being inhibited between the rod or cone and its adjoining connecting cell. This lack of release sends the signal, "photoreceptor stimulated here." Vision signals travel from photoreceptors through two sets of adjoining cells, the latter of which have axons that come together to form the body's optic nerves.

- The brain does not passively record visual information. Rather, it constructs images as much as it records them. The visual system operates through a series of genetically based "rules" that allow us to quickly make sense of what we perceive. Evolution shaped our vision in this way, to be maximally useful to us in survival and reproduction.

Web Tutorial 26.2: The Vertebrate Eye

26.13 The Endocrine System

- The endocrine system functions in the control and regulation of bodily processes. It works through a group of chemical messengers called hormones: substances secreted by one group of cells that travel through the bloodstream and affect the activities of other cells. Hormones stand in distinction to other signaling molecules the body uses that do not travel through the bloodstream. Molecules called paracrines diffuse from one or more cells to a nearby group of cells, causing a metabolic change in them. Likewise, a cell can be affected by its own secreted chemical messenger, called an autocrine.

- Each hormone works only on specific cells—the hormone's target cells. Hormones bind to their target cells via receptors on or in the target cells. This binding then spurs chemical reactions within the target cells.

- Hormonal production and secretion takes place to a significant extent within endocrine glands, meaning glands that secrete materials directly into the bloodstream or into surrounding tissues. Some hormones are secreted, however, not by specialized glands, but by organs such as the heart or kidneys.

- Once secreted, hormones can take from several seconds to several hours to work, but then can continue to have effects for extended periods of time. Given these time frames, hormones tend to regulate processes that unfold over minutes, hours, or even years.
  Web Tutorial 26.3: The Endocrine System

26.14 Types of Hormones

- There are three principal classes of hormones: amino-acid-based hormones, peptide hormones, and steroid hormones. Each amino-acid-based hormone is derived from a chemical modification of a single amino acid. Peptide hormones are composed of chains of amino acids. These chains exist in a range from short polypeptides to longer chains that constitute proteins. Steroid hormones are all constructed around the chemical framework of the cholesterol molecule. Amino-acid-based and peptide hormones generally link to their target cells via receptors that protrude from the target cells' outer membranes. Some steroid hormones can bind in this manner, but most pass through a cell's plasma membrane and bind with a receptor protein inside the cell. The combined steroid hormone/receptor molecule then binds with the cell's DNA, thus turning on one or more cell genes, which results in the production of one or more proteins.

26.15 How Is Hormone Secretion Controlled?

- Almost all hormone secretion is controlled by negative feedback. With its many negative feedback loops, the endocrine system is important in preserving homeostasis, meaning an organism's tendency to maintain a relatively stable internal environment.

- A part of the endocrine system can be viewed as a hierarchy that has the brain's hypothalamus at the top. Though it ultimately is prompted to act via negative feedback, the hypothalamus (1) acts as an endocrine organ, producing two hormones that are released by the posterior pituitary gland; (2) exercises control, via the nervous system, over the release of two hormones—adrenaline and noradrenaline—that are produced by the adrenal glands; and (3) controls release of six hormones secreted by the anterior pituitary gland. The anterior pituitary is known as the body's "master gland" because four of the hormones it releases go on to affect the release of hormones in other endocrine glands.

- The hypothalamus exercises control over the anterior pituitary via a set of releasing and inhibiting hormones that the hypothalamus sends to the anterior pituitary via a tiny set of blood vessels.

26.16 Hormones in Action: Two Examples

- The effects of a given hormone can be extremely diverse. The hormone oxytocin, released by the posterior pituitary, prompts labor contractions in childbirth and the release of milk from nursing mothers. It may also stimulate all kinds of social contact in various mammals, perhaps including humans. The hormone cortisol, released by the adrenal glands, helps bring energy stores into use, but also is a "stress" hormone that can have negative effects if stress goes on for extended periods.

Key Terms

action potential 564	**myelin** 563
afferent division 560	**nerve** 564
amino-acid-based hormones 581	**neurotransmitter** 566
anterior pituitary 582	**olfaction** 573
autonomic nervous system 562	**parasympathetic division** 569
axon 563	**peptide hormones** 581
central nervous system (CNS) 560	**peripheral nervous system (PNS)** 560
cerebral cortex 570	
cerebrospinal fluid 567	**photoreceptor** 578
cerebrum 570	**posterior pituitary** 582
cochlea 575	**reflex** 568
cones 578	**retina** 577
dendrites 563	**rods** 578
efferent division 560	**sensory neuron** 562
endocrine gland 580	**somatic nervous system** 560
ganglion 567	**steroid hormones** 581
homeostasis 582	**sympathetic division** 569
hormones 580	**synapse** 566
hypothalamus 570	**synaptic cleft** 566
interneuron 562	**target cells** 580
membrane potential 564	**thalamus** 570
motor neuron 562	

Understanding the Basics

Multiple-Choice Questions (answers in the back of the book)

1. The peripheral nervous system (PNS) is made up of
   a. the brain and spinal cord
   b. the brain and cranial nerves
   c. sensory organs and all of the nervous system outside the brain and spinal cord
   d. all of the nervous system inside the CNS plus the sensory organs
   e. all of the above

2. A nervous-system cell capable of responding to a sound and sending a message about that sound to the brain would be both a _____ and _____.

a. glial cell; an interneuron

b. glial cell; a motor neuron

c. sensory neuron; an afferent neuron

d. motor neuron; an afferent neuron

e. motor neuron; an efferent neuron

3. An action potential is possible because

a. Neurons are not affected by substances outside their outer membranes

b. The CNS and PNS are separate

c. Only the spinal cord has to be involved

d. There is no charge difference across the outer membranes of resting neurons

e. There is a charge difference across the outer membranes of resting neurons

4. A neurotransmitter

a. is stored in vesicles in the sending cell

b. diffuses across the synaptic cleft

c. binds with receptors on a receiving cell

d. can sometimes be taken back up by a sending cell

e. all of the above

5. In the brain, the site of our higher thought processes is the

a. cerebellum

b. cerebrum

c. thalamus

d. medulla oblongata

e. hypothalamus

6. All sensory receptors _____ and _____.

a. respond to sensory stimulation; transform that stimulation into a neural signal

b. respond to all forms of stimulation except smell; send messages through the spinal cord

c. are located in the spinal cord; send messages through the thalamus

d. are located in the brain; interconnect with neurons

e. respond to neurotransmitter stimulation; turn that stimulation into a neural signal

7. Several of the senses work by means of

a. the brain distributing portions of its processing to the spinal cord

b. the brain analyzing the pattern of input from many sensory receptors

c. the brain receiving messages from sensory receptors and then sending messages back to them

d. sensory receptors communicating first with each other, then with the brain

e. sensory receptors responding to light

8. Cells in different tissues and organs respond to the same hormone if these cells have the same kind of _____ molecules.

a. receptor

b. neurotransmitter

c. DNA

d. lipid

e. all of the above

9. What is the ultimate source of control over the release of most hormones?

a. the hypothalamus

b. genes

c. the pituitary gland

d. positive feedback

e. negative feedback

10. The hypothalamus directly controls hormone release through

a. the adrenal glands, the ovaries, and the testes

b. the adrenal glands and the posterior pituitary, but not the anterior pituitary

c. the adrenal glands, the anterior pituitary, and the posterior pituitary

d. both parts of the pituitary and such hormone-secreting organs as the stomach and the liver

e. the adrenal glands and the anterior pituitary, but not the posterior pituitary

Brief Review

1. Three functional types of neurons are found in the nervous system. What are they, and what role does each fill?

2. In what way is the neuron a cell that is specialized for rapid communication?

3. Describe how a simple reflex arc works.

4. Most of the senses reviewed in the book had these things in common: sensory receptor stimulation, transduction, neurotransmitters, receiving neurons, thalamus, and cerebral cortex processing. Describe what happened in general at each of these steps.

5. Why is the endocrine system better at controlling something like fluid levels in the body than our ability to shoot a basketball?

6. Do hormones choose their target cells?

7. What are the differences between amino-acid-based, peptide, and steroid hormones?

Applying Your Knowledge

1. In the section on the senses, you saw that the body can respond to many different kinds of stimulation—vibrations, smells, pressure, light, and taste among them. Can you think of any other kinds of stimulation that our bodies did not evolve to respond to, but might have? Could the senses we have be extended in any way? (Hint: Think of the olfactory abilities of dogs.)

2. It is often said that seeing is believing. Is it reasonable to put this much faith in the human visual system?

3. When most of us hear the word *hormones*, we think of substances that cause us to act in unusual ways. Is this the normal function of most hormones? Why do they have this reputation?

27 *The Immune System*

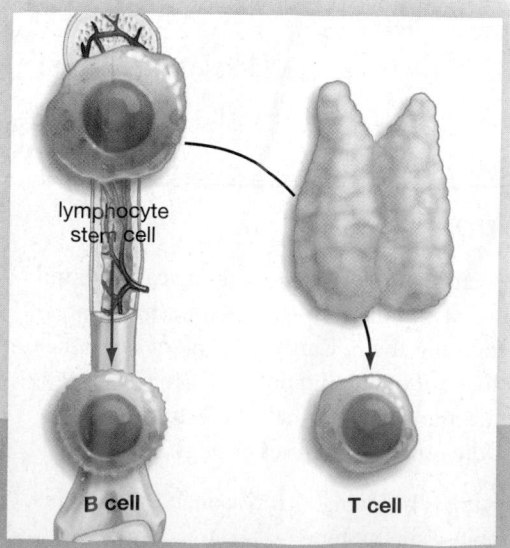

Where B and T cells develop.
(Section 27.3, page 595)

Moving in for inspection.
(Section 27.3 page 596)

Sending antibodies into battle.
(Section 27.4, page 597)

Infectious microbes enter the human body every day. Waiting to meet them is a highly organized network of human cells and proteins. Collectively, these defenders of the body are known as the immune system.

The word "vaccine" comes from the word "vacca," which is Latin for "cow." What do cows have to do with vaccines? In 1796, an English country doctor, Edward Jenner, decided to test a bit of folk wisdom, which held that farm laborers who caught the mild disease cowpox from cattle could never catch the dreaded disease smallpox from humans. Accordingly, Jenner took cowpox pus from a sore on the hand of a dairymaid and rubbed it into scratches he made on the arms of an eight-year-old boy, James Phipps. The next step—a chilling one from a modern perspective—was that Jenner applied pus from *smallpox* sores onto Phipps. The boy sailed through this and several subsequent smallpox applications, however, and Jenner's belief was proved correct: A person could be made immune to smallpox by being exposed to cowpox.

With Jenner's demonstration, a revolution was launched—the vaccine revolution. Because of it, polio, diphtheria, whooping cough, and tetanus have been nearly eradicated from developed countries. And the smallpox that Jenner worked against has been eliminated from the face of the Earth as a natural disease. (The last naturally transmitted case of it occurred in 1977.)

Defenders and Invaders
The large, spherical cells on the left are immune-system macrophages that are in the process of attacking invading *E. coli* bacterial cells, at the bottom of the photo. The macrophages will engulf the bacterial cells, ingest them, and dissolve them. (Micrograph X 2150)

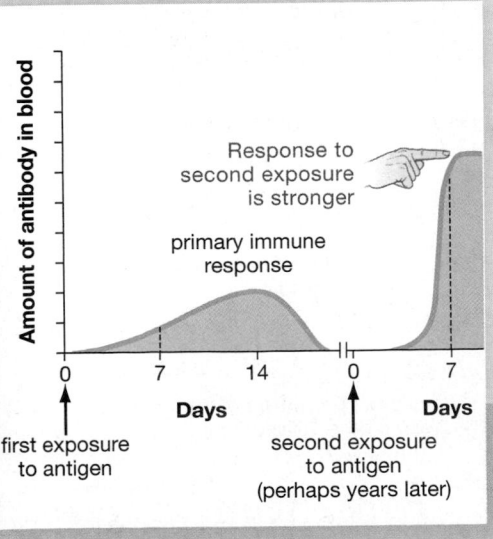

A faster response the second time.
(Section 27.4, page 598)

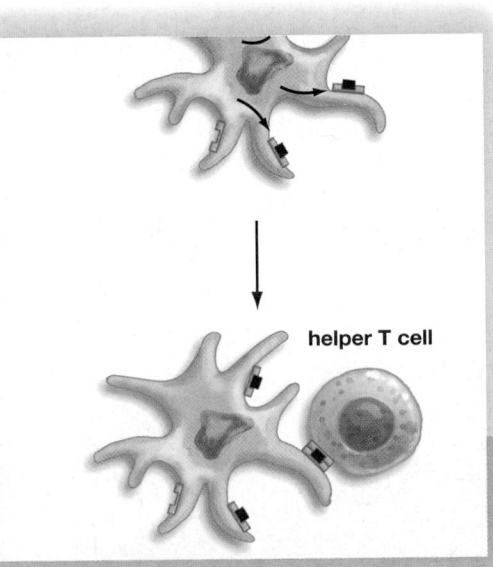

When the body's own cells are infected.
(Section 27.5, page 599)

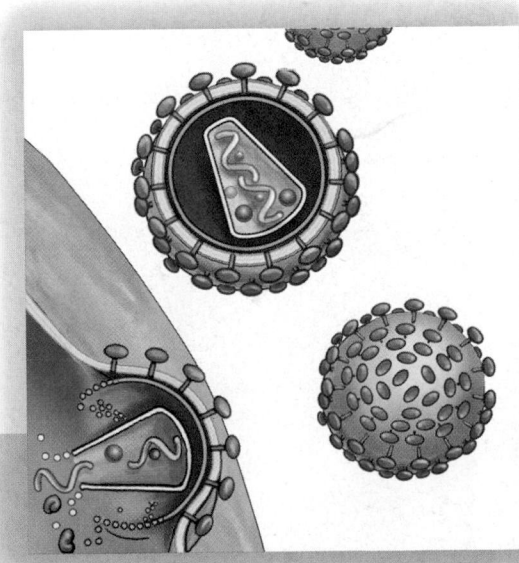

Budding killers.
(Section 27.6, page 601)

But how does vaccination work? To take James Phipps as an example, why should his exposure to cowpox have protected him from smallpox? Two centuries of hard-won scientific advances since Jenner's time have provided the answer. Vaccination activates one part of the *immune system*, a complex network of cells and proteins whose most important job is finding invading microbes and killing them. The immune system is tenacious and has an arsenal of weapons at its disposal. Then again, it needs these very qualities because it faces such a formidable line-up of invaders. In the chapter that follows, you'll learn how the immune system rises to the challenge of protecting the human body.

27.1 Two Types of Immune Defense

The immune system has two basic defensive strategies. First, it employs something called **nonspecific defenses**: immune-system defenses that do not discriminate between one invader and the next. Skin

cells do not discriminate between bacteria and fungi, for example; they keep both kinds of invaders out in the same way. Likewise, some immune cells will attack any cell perceived to be foreign.

The immune system's second main strategy, its **specific defenses**, provides protection against *particular* invaders. You have immune cells in your body that will latch onto bacterium A, but not to bacterium B. In a sense, these specific defenses *remember* invaders they have faced, which enables them to generate a rapid response to any subsequent invasion by the same microorganism. The result is **immunity**: a state of long-lasting protection that the immune system develops against specific microorganisms. (Here you can begin to see what was at work with smallpox.)

Before going into details about nonspecific and specific defenses, you need to be introduced to a term you'll be seeing repeatedly. An **antigen** is any foreign substance that elicits an immune-system response. A bacterial cell in the lining of our lungs is, of course, foreign to our bodies. But it is certain proteins or carbohydrates on the surface of the bacterial cell that are likely to set off the human immune response. In general, antigens are component parts of living things, but an inorganic material such as asbestos can serve as an antigen (in that it can trigger an immune response).

Table 27.1 lists just a few of the many players that take part in the immune process. All the entities on the lists do one of three things: They destroy antigens, they mark antigens for destruction, or they act as communication molecules. Note that all of the immune cells listed in Table 27.1a are different kinds of white blood cells.

Table 27.1a Selected Immune-System Cells

Phagocytes (cells that can ingest other cells)

Neutrophils ⎤
            ⎬ Microphages ("small eaters")
Eosinophils ⎦

Macrophages ("large eaters"), which can become antigen-presenting cells (APCs)

Mast cells (release histamine)

Dendritic cells (antigen-presenting cells)

Lymphocytes

Natural killer cells

B cells, which differentiate into:
  Plasma cells
  Memory cells

T cells, which differentiate into:
  Helper T (CD4) cells
  Cytotoxic (killer) T cells

Table 27.1b Selected Immune-System Proteins

Lysozymes (protective enzymes found in tears and saliva)

Complement proteins (kill some invaders, bind with others to aid phagocytes)

Antibodies (receptors on surface of B cells; later released by plasma cells derived from B cells)

Interleukins (diverse group of signaling molecules)

27.2 Nonspecific Defenses

The body's first line of defense actually is not a part of the immune system per se, but instead is a set of barriers. To cause trouble, a disease-causing organism—known as a *pathogen*—must enter the body's tissues; and that often means crossing an *epithelium*, or tissue that covers an exposed body surface. The epithelial covering of the skin, described in Chapter 25, has multiple layers, a waterproof keratin coating, and a network of tight seams that lock adjacent cells together. These specializations create a very effective barrier that protects underlying tissues.

The exterior surface of the body is also protected by hairs and glandular secretions. Secretions from sebaceous and sweat glands flush the surface of the skin, washing away microorganisms and chemical agents. Some secretions also contain bacteria-killing chemicals and protective enzymes, called *lysozymes*, which can be found in tears and saliva.

Those of you who read Chapter 25 will recall that some of our epithelial tissue lines *interior* surfaces that are exposed to an *exterior* environment. For example, our lungs are interior to us, but they come into contact with air from the outside world. Interior epithelial tissue is delicate, but it is well defended. The lungs have a set of hair-like cilia that sweep their passageways clean like so many tiny brooms. The stomach contains a powerful acid that can destroy pathogens. Urine, which has a pathogen-killing low pH, flushes the urinary passageways. And the female reproductive tract has a low pH thanks to lactic acid produced by *helpful* resident bacteria, the lactobacilli.

Nonspecific Cells and Proteins

But what happens if invaders get past these barriers? We have a line of nonspecific defense waiting to meet them. Let's look at some of the members of this team of defenders.

There is a type of white blood cell, called the **phagocyte**, that can be defined as a cell capable of ingesting another cell, parts of cells, or other materials. As you might guess from this description, phagocytes can take on a warrior role—they essentially surround invading microorganisms with cellular extensions, take them in, and then dissolve them in a set of acid baths. But phagocytes also take on a less-exalted role, which is that of janitor. They engulf and haul away the body's *own* cells and tissue fragments when they have become worn out or damaged. As you can see in Table 27.1a, phagocytes come in several varieties, two of them smaller (the neutrophils and eosinophils) and one larger (the macrophages). All three have the capacity to kill foreign invaders outright. Later, you'll be seeing the macrophage in a different role: It not only kills invaders, but then presents fragments of these invaders to other immune cells, something like a soldier who is holding an enemy's uniform out for the rest of the troops to see.

When an invader is a virus, rather than a bacterium, another key player in nonspecific defense is the natural killer cell, so named because it will attack any cell that it perceives as "foreign" in the sense of having unusual surface proteins. Cells infected by viruses often are altered this way; when an "NK" cell encounters one of these infected cells, it can kill them in one of two ways. First, it can use proteins to create so many pores in the membranes of infected cells that these cells break up, like a ship that's been riddled with holes. Second, it can cause these cells to commit suicide, through a process called apoptosis.

Table 27.1a also lists an immune-system cell called the mast cell. This cell releases a substance called histamine, whose role we'll get to shortly. Finally, it is not just cells that are involved in nonspecific defense; it is proteins as well. A group of them listed in Table 27.1b, the complement proteins, will make an appearance soon. Let's now see how all the players work together to mount a type of well-orchestrated nonspecific defense, the *inflammatory response*.

Nonspecific Defense and the Inflammatory Response

Let's say you accidentally puncture your skin with a nail that's been sitting outdoors. This means you not only have a puncture, you have lots of microscopic invaders that have gotten past the barrier of your skin. How does the immune system deal with the bacteria among them? In outline, three types of responses take place. First, blood vessels near the site of injury dilate and become more permeable—they increase in diameter and they undergo a change that allows cells and proteins to pass out of them. Second, these cells and proteins leave the blood vessels and move to the site of injury, where they kill the bacteria. Third, various compounds are released that wall off the site of injury, thus limiting the spread of the infection.

The mast cells noted earlier help get the first step going by releasing a substance called **histamine**: a compound that, in the inflammatory response, brings about blood-vessel dilation and increased blood-vessel permeability. Mast cells have significant quantities of histamine to release because they store it inside themselves in tiny granules. The blood-vessel dilation that histamine prompts is important because it results in increased blood flow near the injury site—an efficient means of bringing in more immune-system cells and proteins. The increased permeability histamine

Web Tutorial 27.1
The Immune System
www

causes is important because it allows these cells and proteins to move out of the blood-vessels so that they can get to the site of the infection. Normally, blood-vessel cells are locked tightly together; histamine has the effect of opening up spaces between them.

The first immune-system cells to squeeze through these spaces probably will be one of the smaller phagocytes noted earlier, the neutrophils. Slower in arriving, but longer-lived, are the macrophages. Both varieties of cells are guided to the site of injury by a form of chemical signaling: injured cells release compounds that produce a kind of trail that leads to them. Once the neutrophils and macrophages arrive, they begin ingesting bacterial invaders; later the macrophages will clean up the debris.

Flowing through the bloodstream at this time, and also activated by the attack, are the complement proteins noted earlier—about 20 of them in all. They are called complement proteins because their actions are complementary to those taken by other parts of the immune system. In this instance, one of their roles is to cut holes in the cell membranes of the bacteria. The site of infection is likewise being limited in size at this time. The area is sealed off partly through creation of a network of fibers composed of a blood protein that, appropriately enough, is called fibrin.

In looking at this simplified account of the inflammatory response, you can see that it brings more blood near a site of injury and more cells and proteins to the site. Blood is warm and red, of course, and this explains why the area around an injury site

takes on these same qualities. Meanwhile, the added cells and proteins at the site cause the swelling and pain that we associate with injuries.

It's important to note that all these responses are nonspecific: any group of invaders that entered through this route would get pretty much this same treatment by this same lineup of immune-system players. But what about instances in which the body's nonspecific defenses can't contain an infection? What happens when, say, a chicken pox virus comes into the nasal passages and starts to spread from there throughout the body? If this invader can't be defeated by nonspecific defenses, the body has another line of defense at the ready—the specific defenses, which have a marvelous ability to target specific invaders.

27.3 Specific Defenses

You may have heard the phrase *acquired immunity*; this means the immunity we acquire by virtue of what we come into contact with during our lifetimes. Acquired immunity comes in two types. **Passively acquired immunity** is immunity gained by the administration of disease-fighting substances, called antibodies, that have been produced by another individual. Our mother passes some of her antibodies to us while we are still in the womb. As an adult, you might receive them in the form of a gamma globulin shot, which people sometimes get prior to taking a trip abroad (**see Figure 27.1**). Importantly, antibodies administered in this way provide only short- or

Figure 27.1
Types of Acquired Immunity

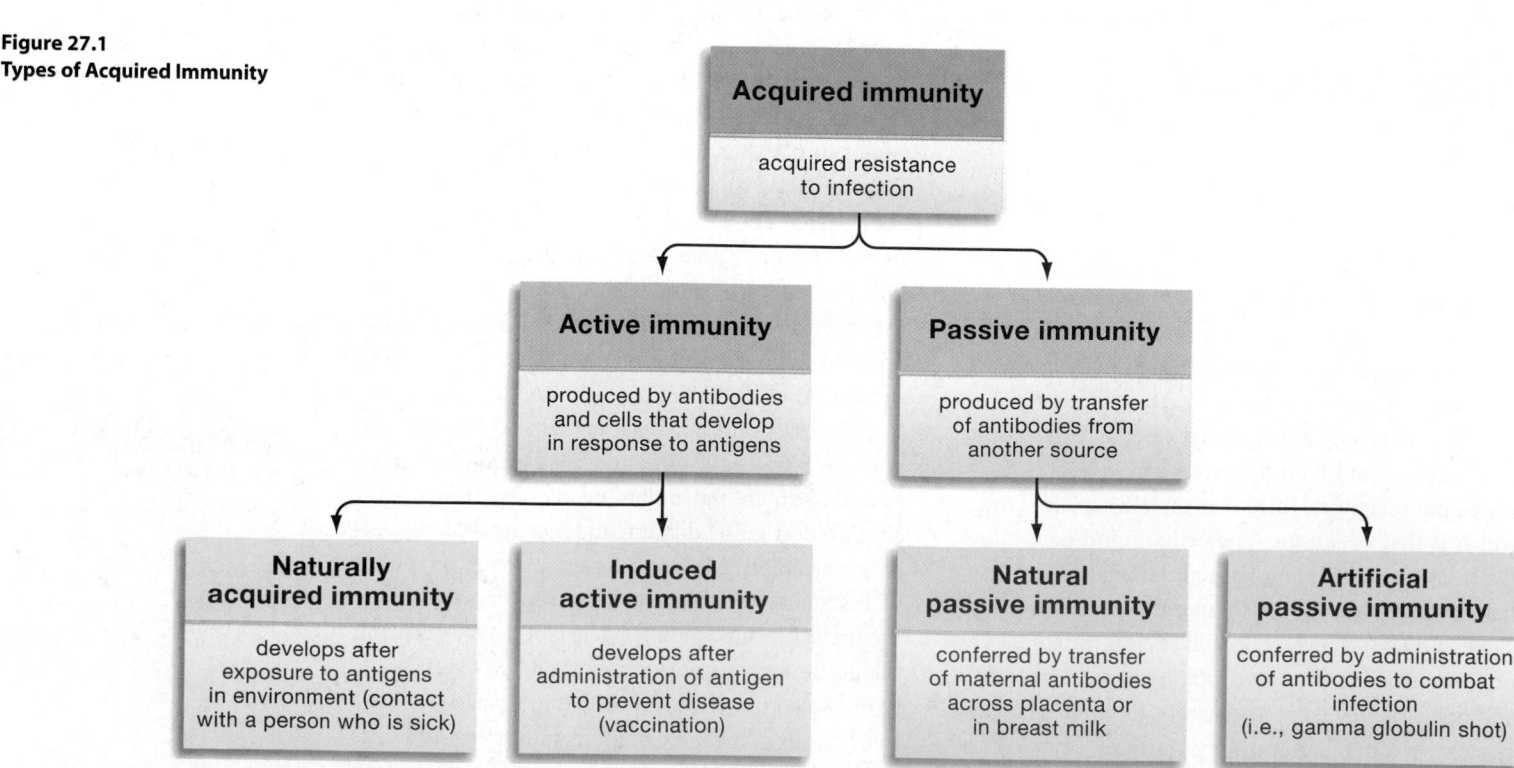

medium-term resistance to harm, because invader-fighting antibodies made outside our bodies are eventually degraded in our system. Truly long-lasting immunity is something that our bodies develop within themselves. This is **actively acquired immunity**: immunity developed as a result of accidental or deliberate exposure to an antigen.

Note the critical term there: exposure to an *antigen*—a substance the body recognizes as foreign. Think about this in relation to one well-known form of actively acquired immunity, the vaccinations mentioned at the start of the chapter. In vaccinations, a person is not being treated with a substance that kills an invader. Rather, the person is being injected with at least a part of the invader itself. This is deliberate exposure to an antigen, and it results in our body mounting an attack on the antigen in ways that we'll review shortly. Of course this "invader" has been made harmless back in the laboratory. It may be a poliovirus, for example, that has been killed, so that it can no longer cause disease. But the immune system's attack on it is full-blown; and having mounted it, the system enters a high state of readiness for any subsequent attack by the *real* invader—the live poliovirus. What vaccines do, then, is elicit readiness on the part of the immune system. Getting a disease like chicken pox does this as well—it elicits protection that keeps us from getting chicken pox again. But how does this trick of "invader memory" work? For that matter, how does the immune system defeat specific invaders the first time they attack? These are the subjects to which we now turn.

Antibody-Mediated and Cell-Mediated Immunity

Actively acquired immunity has two major arms. The first arm is called **antibody-mediated immunity**: an immune-system capability that works through the production of proteins called antibodies. The second arm is called **cell-mediated immunity**: an immune-system capability that works through the production of cells that destroy *other* cells in the body—those that have been infected by an invader. Cells that are central to both arms originate in the same place, which is the marrow of our bones. It is there that all white blood cells begin development in adults. The white blood cells that are key to specific immunity are called *lymphocytes*. Some lymphocytes go on to migrate to the body's thymus (located at the base of the throat), and there they specialize. They develop into the main cells of cell-mediated immunity, the **T-lymphocyte cells** or just **T cells** (with the *T* standing for "thymus" cell). Meanwhile, lymphocytes that remain in the bone marrow can de-

velop into the central cells of *antibody*-mediated immunity, the **B-lymphocyte cells** or **B cells** (for "bone marrow" cells). The development of T and B cells is tracked in **Figure 27.2**.

Eventually, both types of cells will migrate to the body's lymphatic system organs—the spleen and the lymph nodes, for example—where they are prepared to fight invaders. The lymphatic system is laid out for you in **Figure 27.3** on the next page. Think of it as a system of vessels that picks up fluids (called interstitial fluids) that have leaked from blood vessels. Eventually, these fluids are channeled back into the circulatory system, but while they are in the lymphatic system, they pass through the lymphoid organs, which are packed with immune-system cells. This is why, when you get sick, your "lymph glands" are swollen—they are filled with an abnormally large number of cells that are busy fighting off the infection. If you look back at Table 27.1, you can see the various types of lymphocytes listed.

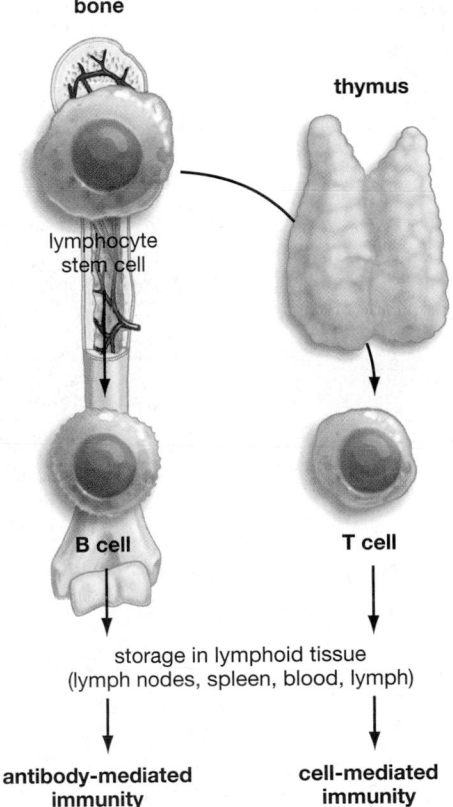

Figure 27.2
Development of T Cells and B Cells
Key players in the body's specific defense system are T cells and B cells, both of which start out as a type of white blood cell, called a lymphocyte stem cell, in the bone marrow. Some of these lymphocytes migrate to the thymus gland, where they differentiate into T cells (thymus cells). Others that remain in the bone marrow develop into B cells. Most T and B cells then migrate to lymphoid tissues, such as lymph nodes and the spleen, where they will serve their immune function.

(a) Lymphatic system

(b) Lymphatic vessels collect interstitial fluid from tissue

tissue cells

lymphatic vessel

blood capillary

lymphatic vessels

thymus

spleen

bone marrow

lymph node

(c) The fluid, now called lymph, is inspected by immune-system cells in lymph nodes.

fluid moves into lymph node

aggregates of immune system cells

fluid passes out of node, later to be returned to blood vessels

Figure 27.3
The Human Lymphatic System
(a) Fluid moving through lymphatic vessels passes through lymphatic organs, such as lymph nodes or the spleen, where the fluid is inspected by an array of immune-system cells.

(b) Detail of interstitial fluid moving into lymphatic vessels.

(c) Detail of fluid moving through a lymph node.

From this point forward, the antibody-mediated and cell-mediated immune operations will be treated separately. The two systems work together, but for now we'll look at them in isolation, starting with antibody-mediated immunity.

27.4 Antibody-Mediated Immunity

As you might imagine, a key player in antibody-mediated immunity is the **antibody**, which can be defined as a circulating immune-system protein that binds to a particular antigen. From this definition, it may be apparent that antibodies and antigens are closely linked. (They are so closely linked, in fact, that one is named for the other; the word *antigen* is short for "antibody generating.") In general, a given antibody will bind to a specific antigen and to no other antigen. In their binding capacity, you will see antibodies in two roles: first as *receptors* for antigens on the surface of B cells, extending in a generalized Y-shape from the cells' outer membranes; second as *free-standing* molecules that are produced by B cells and then stream away from them in great numbers, moving through the bloodstream.

The Fantastic Diversity of Antibodies

It's common knowledge that it's not just one virus that causes the common cold; rather, there are hundreds of viruses that bring on the general set of symptoms we call a cold. Then there are all the other potential invaders, such as bacteria, fungi, and so forth. How can the immune system cope with such a variety of foes? One of its key strengths is that it produces B cells that differ from each other with respect to the type of antigen receptors they have on their surfaces. Look at one B cell and it will have receptors that latch only onto an antigen on *this* virus; look at a *different* B cell and its receptors bind with an antigen of a different virus. This mind-boggling complexity is made possible by DNA arranging that takes place back in the bone marrow, when the precursors of B cells are being formed. The result is B cells with millions of variations in antigen receptors (or antibodies, to look at them another way). Now, how do these B cells do their job?

The Cloning and Differentiation of B Cells

Lying in readiness in the lymph nodes or circulating through the bloodstream, a B cell encounters, say, a bacterium—one that has an antigen that can be bound by this B cell's antigen receptors. If you look at **Figure 27.4**, you can see what happens next. This very binding causes the B cell to start dividing very

rapidly. Each new B cell of this type gives rise to more identical B cells, creating a selected "clone," or a huge number of identical cells of this type. Such numbers are necessary because the *bacteria* will be multiplying rapidly as well.

After a time, these B cells then differentiate into two types of cells. One variety is called a **plasma cell**: an immune-system B cell that is specialized to produce antibodies. These antibodies are not the cell-surface receptors you've been looking at, however.

**Figure 27.4
B Cells and Antibody-Mediated Immunity**

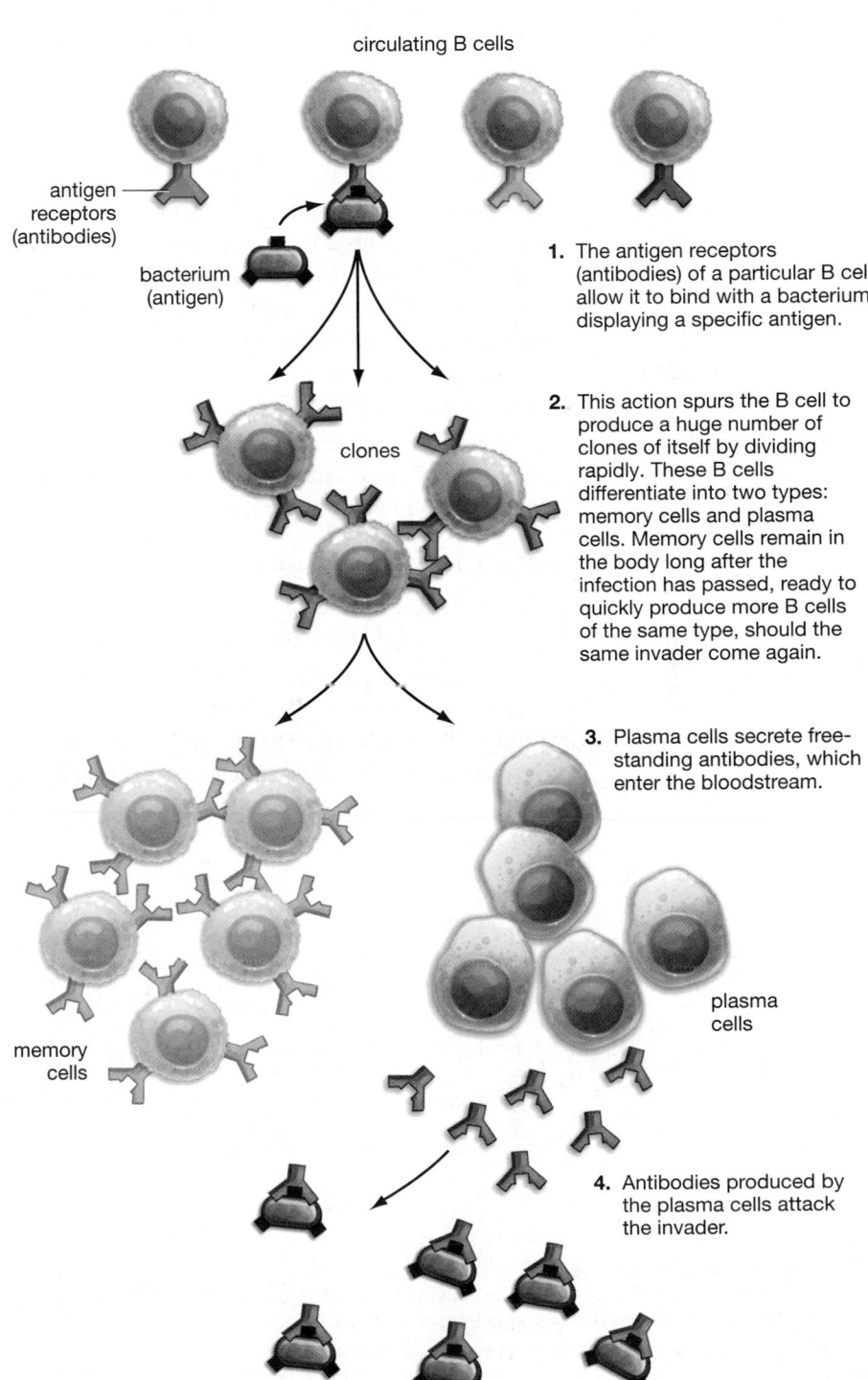

circulating B cells

antigen receptors (antibodies)

bacterium (antigen)

clones

memory cells

plasma cells

1. The antigen receptors (antibodies) of a particular B cell allow it to bind with a bacterium displaying a specific antigen.

2. This action spurs the B cell to produce a huge number of clones of itself by dividing rapidly. These B cells differentiate into two types: memory cells and plasma cells. Memory cells remain in the body long after the infection has passed, ready to quickly produce more B cells of the same type, should the same invader come again.

3. Plasma cells secrete free-standing antibodies, which enter the bloodstream.

4. Antibodies produced by the plasma cells attack the invader.

They are free-standing antibodies that leave the plasma cells by the millions—they are *exported* from the plasma cells—after which they move through the bloodstream and fight the invader directly.

The other type of B cell is called the **memory B cell**, and it is the body's permanent sentry. This is one part of the long-lasting invader readiness noted earlier. After the initial war with an invader is over, this specific variety of memory B cell remains in the body. Should this invader come in a *second* time, these memory cells will be ready to divide and produce more plasma cells to mount a very quick defense. This is why being inoculated with poliovirus antigens protects us permanently from this crippler. (And this is why cowpox antigens protected Edward Jenner's patients from smallpox; the antigens of the two viruses were similar enough that exposure to cowpox put the body in a state of readiness for smallpox.) If you look at **Figure 27.5**, you can see the typical time-course of exposure to antigen and production of antibodies. What is known as the "primary immune response" has reached a substantial level 14 days out from first exposure. Look at the second exposure, however, to see what a difference this first exposure has made. Now there is a much greater response in a much shorter time.

The Action of the Antibodies

But what is it that the circulating antibodies do to combat the invader? First, because they are binding to the invader's antigens, the antibodies can sometimes prevent the invader from attaching to anything *else*, which stops its spread. Antibodies can also come together with antigens in a clumping or

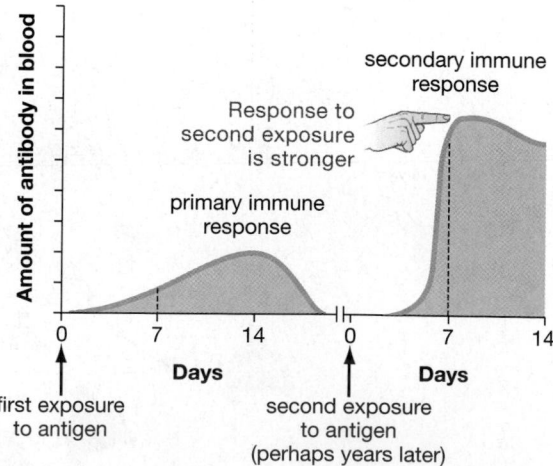

Figure 27.5
Prepared for an Invasion
The memory cells produced by the body during a first attack by an invader allow it to mount a faster, more vigorous defense should the same invader attack a second time.

"agglutination" that renders the invaders inactive. Third, antigens work in concert with an arm of the immune system you've already reviewed—the nonspecific defenses. Remember the cell-ingesting phagocytes and the complement proteins that you saw in nonspecific defense? Many invading bacterial cells have a slick outer coating that keeps phagocytes from latching onto them. Working together, antibodies and complement proteins often *can* bind to many of these invaders, and this gives the phagocytes something to hold onto, so that they can begin ingesting the enemy.

27.5 Cell-Mediated Immunity

Though antibody-mediated immunity is quite spectacular, it also turns out to be limited in that it works strictly on free-standing foreign organisms. The problem with this is that many viruses (and some bacteria) are successful in invading the body's *own cells*—they exist and multiply inside these cells, which makes the viruses inaccessible to antibodies. To deal with this threat, the body has developed another arm of acquired immunity, the cell-mediated immunity mentioned earlier.

You may recall that the central player in cell-mediated immunity is the *T*-lymphocyte or T cell, which comes in two main varieties. Let's now go through the actions of the cell-mediated immune system, taking as a starting point a body that has been infected with a virus.

Cells Bearing Invaders: Antigen-Presenting Cells

Lying in wait for invaders that enter the body are a class of white blood cells called dendritic cells (so-named because their spiky extensions look something like the dendrites that extend from nervous system cells). Dendritic cells begin their work by engulfing and killing free-standing microorganisms and then displaying fragments of these invaders on their surface. It won't surprise you to hear that these fragments then serve as antigens. Since dendritic cells are displaying or "presenting" antigens, they are referred to as **antigen-presenting cells**, or **APCs**. There actually are three classes of APCs in the immune system. Besides dendritic cells, the macrophages we looked at earlier play this role, as do B cells. Dendritic cells are the most efficient APCs, however, and there is some evidence that they alone can get the APC process going.

Outfitted with antigens on display, dendritic cells migrate to lymph nodes or the spleen where, you'll recall, immune-system cells exist in abundance. There, the dendritic cells encounter many helper T cells, a tiny fraction of which will have receptors specific to this antigen. If you look at **Figure 27.6**, you can see how the next interaction plays out. Helper T cells now lock onto these APCs, but there is great specificity in this action. The dendritic cell is displaying the invader's protein fragment within one of its own membrane proteins, meaning the helper T cell's binding is specific to both the dendritic and the invader proteins. Once this interaction has taken place, the helper T cell has been "activated," and this initiates the creation of a helper T cell clone. The first activated helper T cell divides into two cells, these two cells divide into four, and so forth. Critically, each cell in this clone is specific to this invader. These T cells then leave the lymph nodes or spleen and begin circulating throughout the body.

Helper T Cells and Cytotoxic T Cells

The helper T cells that have been activated now take on a central role in specific immunity. Beyond creating a helper T cell clone, they produce a signaling molecule, called interleukin-2, that activates another variety of T cell, the cytotoxic T cell. This activation brings about the creation of a cytotoxic T cell clone. Critically, both this clone and the helper T cell clone are being produced not only in active types, but in "memory" types for use in future invasions. Beyond this, other interleukins secreted by helper T cells are activating *B-cell* immunity by promoting the production and differentiation of B cells. Indeed, the entire process of B-cell development is dependent on signals that come from helper T cells.

Despite all this activity, by now you may be saying: So how are T cells actually getting rid of invaders? The answer is in the clone of **cytotoxic T cells**, which are also called "killer" T cells for a good reason. Using their own special receptors, they latch onto infected cells and kill them in one of two ways. First, they puncture the outer membranes of infected cells, causing them to "lyse" or burst—the same kind of lethal action that natural killer cells carry out, but now carried out by a huge number of cells that are targeting this specific invader. Second, they secrete signaling molecules that cause the infected cells to commit suicide through apoptosis.

Note that cytotoxic T cells are binding with the body's own infected cells. From this, it may be apparent why this is called *cell-mediated* immunity. In the end, it is an attack involving not the antibodies described before, but several sets of cells.

dendritic cell

1. Dendritic cell ingests virus

antigen-presenting cell (APC)

2. Now an APC, dendritic cell presents viral fragments as antigens

helper T cell

APC

3. Helper T cell binds to APC

APC

4. This binding activates helper T cell, stimulating production of more helper T cells and other immune cells

B cell
antibody-mediated immunity

cytotoxic T cell
cell-mediated immunity

**Figure 27.6
T Cells and Cell-Mediated Immunity**

Taking a step back from cell- and antibody-mediated immunity, in **Figure 27.7** you can see how the two systems work together, along with nonspecific defenses. In specific defense, however, note the central role of the **helper T cell**. We can define it as an immune-system cell that helps activate both cell- and antibody-mediated immunity, since it is necessary for the production of both T and B cells. This diverse set of helper-T functions is important in what's coming up.

**Figure 27.7
An Overview of the Immune-System Process**

27.6 AIDS: Attacking the Defenders

The picture of the immune system just painted is one of a sophisticated operation capable of dealing with all kinds of invaders. Yet everyone knows of at least one invader that the system seems powerless to deal with: the virus that causes AIDS.

The virus in question is **HIV**, the human immunodeficiency virus, and it is devastating for three reasons. First, it attacks the very system that is supposed to protect us from disease—the immune system we've just been reviewing. Second, its infection process gives it an immediate foothold in the body, as you'll see. Third, this virus is literally a shape-shifter: Its genetic material mutates rapidly and this brings about a rapid change in HIV's structure—in particular, a change in the proteins that protrude from its surface. As you've seen the antibodies and cells of the immune system work by binding to such proteins. But with HIV, these binding sites are changing all the time. Thus, HIV particles are like soldiers who are constantly "morphing" into shapes that the immune system's soldiers cannot recognize.

HIV works by attaching itself, most importantly, to helper T cells—specifically to so-called CD4 and CCR5 receptors on the surface of helper T cells. Once this binding is complete, the outer HIV envelope then fuses with the helper T cell membrane, much as two soap bubbles might fuse together to become one (**see Figure 27.8**). With this, HIV's proteins and its RNA genetic material are inside the T cell. Next, the virus uses these materials to create a double strand of DNA that it inserts into the infected cell's own length of DNA. Thus situated within a cell, the viral DNA may remain inactive or "latent" for years, during which time it is hidden from immune surveillance carried out by the body. But every time the T cell copies its own DNA in cell division, the inserted viral DNA is copied along with it and is passed along to the resulting "daughter cells."

In many infected helper T cells, however, the virus is far from latent. Remember, it now amounts to a length of DNA inserted into the cell's own DNA. In this form, it uses the T cell's metabolic machinery to begin turning out its *own* proteins and genetic material—the building blocks of new virus particles. These viral materials are brought together just inside the T cell's outer membrane and assembled into complete HIV particles, which then "bud off" from the T cell and go on to infect other cells. Repeated again and again, this process eventually depletes the T cell of energy and materials, and it dies.

Now, keep in mind the central immune role of the helper T cells that are dying here. They stimulate both T- and B-cell activation. Physicians refer to helper T cells as CD4 cells (from the name of one of their receptors). Not surprisingly, a critical question for any physician treating an AIDS patient is: What is the patient's CD4 count? Put another way, how many CD4 cells does this patient have left to help fight off disease? Not just the disease AIDS, mind you—*any* disease caused by a microorganism. A fungal infection that most people wouldn't even realize they had

can become life-threatening to an AIDS patient because the patient's immune system is so weakened.

Even given this power of HIV, you may wonder: Why is there no vaccine for it? Polio is caused by a virus, after all, and we have a vaccine for it. A big part of the answer stems from the difference between the way the polio and HIV viruses progress from infection through damage. The poliovirus multiplies initially in the blood but does its crippling damage when

Web Tutorial 27.2
HIV Replication

Figure 27.8
**How the AIDS Virus Attacks the
Immune System**

(a) HIV, the AIDS virus

reverse transcriptase
(viral enzyme)

protease
(viral enzyme)

envelope

genetic material (RNA)

receptor

(b) HIV replication cycle

1. Virus binds to helper
T cell receptors

cell membrane

CCR5 receptor   CD4 receptor

helper T cell

2. Virus enters into the
cell via membrane fusion

new virus
particles

genetic material
(RNA)

reverse
transcriptase

3. Using its reverse transcriptase,
virus turns its RNA into DNA that
is inserted into T-cell's genome

double stranded
viral DNA

nucleus

protease

viral components
being synthesized

integrated
viral DNA

5. Completed viral
particles bud
from cell

4. Using its protease,
virus assembles new
viral particles

helper T
cell DNA

it reaches the spinal cord. The polio *vaccine*, then, doesn't have to stop the first part of this process—the replication in the blood. It merely has to slow down this replication enough that the virus never reaches the spinal cord. Now think of the AIDS virus. It can have devastating consequences simply by virtue of having infected an initial group of T cells. Once this is done, the damage will follow. As AIDS researcher Norman Letvin has noted, any AIDS-eradicating vaccine would have to be a "sterilizing" vaccine that kept all cells from becoming infected in the first place, which is a very tall order. Then there is the fact, noted earlier, of HIV's rapid mutation rates and resulting shape changes. Vaccines depend on shapes, and HIV is a shape-shifter.

None of this is to say that scientists have given up on developing an AIDS vaccine. Indeed, this is a very active area of medical research. But it may be that the vaccine ultimately produced will be one that merely slows replication of HIV. This would be quite an accomplishment in itself, in that it could lengthen the period between infection and health consequences, giving HIV-positive persons years of disease-free life.

27.7 The Immune System Can Cause Trouble

In the account you've read so far, the immune system has been portrayed as a kind of multipart weapons system that the body uses to protect itself. The problem with weapons, however, is that they can get pointed in the wrong direction—toward their owners, rather than their targets. And this is what happens with the immune system: The price we pay for having it is that it sometimes attacks *us*, rather than the organisms that invade us.

A critical factor in the immune response is the system's ability to distinguish "self" (the body's own uninfected cells) from "non-self" (infected cells or antigens). The problem is that the immune system makes mistakes; it sometimes regards "self" as "non-self." The result is an **autoimmune disorder**: an attack by the immune system on the body's own tissues.

T cells learn to distinguish self from non-self during the embryonic or newborn phases of life. Developing in the thymus during this period, some T cells may never "learn" to distinguish correctly between self and non-self. Conversely, activated B cells can make antibodies against the body's own tissues. Why would such a thing happen? Well, suppose an invading organism had protein antigens whose building-block amino acid sequences were similar to those found in the body's own proteins. Antibodies meant to defeat a virus might end up targeting the body's own tissues instead. The upshot is that the body can attack itself with devastating consequences. If you look at **Figure 27.9**, you can see the results of the disease known as *rheumatoid arthritis*, which seems to be a result of antibodies attacking connective tissue around joints. There is also multiple sclerosis, in which the immune system starts attacking the nerve-covering myelin noted in Chapter 26. And there is insulin-dependent diabetes, an autoimmune disorder in which antibodies destroy the pancreatic cells that produce insulin.

Scientists have known about the immune system's role in all these diseases for some time. In the last few years, however, they have come to recognize its role in the biggest killer of them all, heart disease. It turns out that a heart attack—a complete blockage of one or more arteries in the heart—is, in significant part, a problem of the body reacting to its tissues as if they were foreign. Indeed, the inflammatory response you looked at earlier helps bring about most coronary blockages. For an account of this disease process, see "What Is a Heart Attack?" on page 613 of Chapter 28.

Allergies are immune-system overreactions to antigens. Any immune-system attack is triggered by substances that the body perceives as foreign. The foreign substances that trigger allergic reactions are called **allergens**. These substances cause the body to start releasing the histamine noted earlier, and this leads to inflammatory responses that can range from small and harmless (sneezing and sniffling) to large and life-threatening (asthma or anaphylactic shock). Allergens need not be living things, but they are almost always at

Figure 27.9
When the Body Attacks Itself
Rheumatoid arthritis has so disfigured this person's hands that simply signing a greeting card has become a difficult act. Rheumatoid arthritis is an autoimmune disorder.

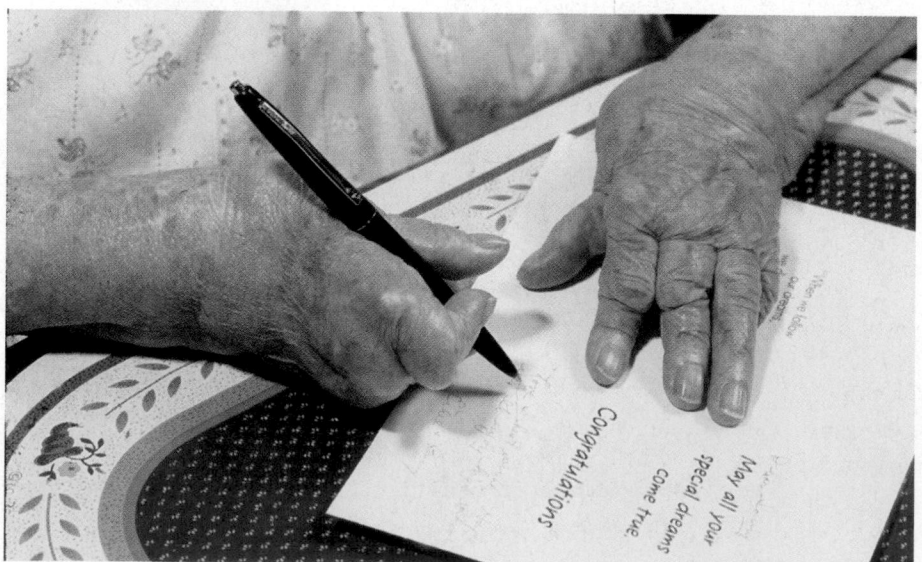

least derived from living things. Thus pollen, foods, fur, and dust mite excrement are common allergens. The dust mite actually is a major villain: An estimated half of all asthma attacks are thought to be caused by its droppings, which are found within couches, pillows, and rugs in almost every home.

Finally, the immune system is the single most important problem in organ transplantation. Imagine a person who receives, say, a kidney via transplantation. That person's immune system will regard the new kidney as non-self and immediately begin an attack upon it. The only exception to this rule comes when donor and recipient are identical twins.

The challenge for modern medicine has been to walk a fine line: to dampen the recipient's immune response somewhat, but not to dampen it so much that the recipient is made vulnerable to serious attacks by microbes.

On to Transport and Exchange

Having looked at the amazing capabilities of the immune system, it's time to move on to reviews of four other systems that keep the body functioning. Chapter 28 is concerned with blood, breathing, digestion, and elimination.

Chapter Review

Summary

27.1 Two Types of Immune Defense

- The immune system has two primary defensive strategies: non-specific defenses, which do not discriminate between one invader and the next; and specific defenses, which provide protection against particular invaders.

- An antigen is any foreign substance that elicits an immune-system response. These substances generally are proteins or carbohydrates that are part of an invading organism. Most of the cells active in immune responses are different varieties of white blood cells.

27.2   Nonspecific Defenses

- The body's first line of nonspecific defense is a set of barriers, such as tightly locked skin cells, and the secretions that protect these barriers, such as the acid secretions of the stomach and the low pH of urine.

- Nonspecific defenses mount a coordinated action called the inflammatory response. It involves not only cells and proteins that kill invaders, but substances that increase blood flow and blood-vessel permeability near the site of an injury.
  Web Tutorial 27.1: The Immune System

27.3 Specific Defenses

- Acquired immunity is the immunity that results from what humans come into contact with during their lifetimes. It exists in two forms. Passively acquired immunity is achieved through the administration of disease-fighting antibodies produced by another individual—for example, manufactured gamma globulins. Actively acquired immunity develops as a result of natural or deliberate exposure to an antigen. Actively acquired immunity can be produced by getting an immunization shot or by catching a disease such as chickenpox.

- Actively acquired immunity has two major arms. The first arm is antibody-mediated immunity, which works through the production of proteins called antibodies. The second arm is cell-mediated immunity, which works through the production of cells that destroy infected cells in the body.

- White blood cells called lymphocytes are fundamental to both antibody-mediated and cell-mediated immunity. One variety of lymphocyte, the B-lymphocyte cell (or B cell) is central to antibody-mediated immunity. Another type of lymphocyte, the T-lymphocyte (or T cell) is central to cell-mediated immunity and helps initiate antibody-mediated immunity.

- Mature B and T cells are most often found in organs of the body's lymphatic system, which is a system of vessels that captures fluids leaked from the bloodstream; that then subjects these fluids to scrutiny by immune-system cells; and that then returns the fluids to the circulatory system.

27.4 Antibody-Mediated Immunity

- An antibody is a circulating immune-system protein that binds to a particular antigen. Antibodies exist (1) as receptors on the surface of B cells that bind to specific antigens, and (2) as free-standing invader-fighting proteins that are secreted by B cells and move through the bloodstream.

- Antibody-mediated immunity begins with the binding of a B-cell antigen receptor to an antigen. This binding produces a cascade of effects, including the production of a B-cell clone—a huge number of identical copies of the B cell that bound originally to the antigen. Some of these cells are plasma B cells that export free-standing antibodies that fight the invader; others are memory B cells that stay in the body to provide a quick response to a subsequent attack by the same invader.

- Antibodies limit infectious attacks in several ways. Their binding with antigens may keep the antigen from binding with anything else, and in concert with complement proteins, antibodies bind to invaders in such a way that macrophages can bind with the invaders and kill them.

27.5 Cell-Mediated Immunity

- Cell-mediated immunity provides protection in instances in which the body's own cells have become infected by an invader. Viruses and some bacteria can infect the body's cells and remain inside them, in which case antibodies will have no access to these invaders. The central player in cell-mediated immunity is the T cell, which comes in two main varieties, helper T cells and cytotoxic (or killer) T cells.

- Cell-mediated immunity begins with several classes of white blood cells killing invaders and displaying protein fragments from them on their cell surfaces. These fragments now serve as antigens. Any cell that plays this role is known as an antigen-presenting cell, or APC. Dendritic cells, macrophages, and B cells all serve as APCs. Once dendritic cells display, on their surface, fragments from an invader, they migrate to lymphatic organs and bind with helper T cells that have receptors specific to this invader. This "activation" of helper T cells prompts the production of a helper T cell clone: An activated helper T cell divides into two, these two into four, and so forth. Critically, all the members of this clone are specific to this invader.

- Helper T cells from the clone then migrate out of the lymphatic organs to encounter infected cells wherever they may be in the body. Substances secreted by helper T cells activate cytotoxic T cells, which prompts the creation of a cytotoxic T cell clone. Both this clone, and the helper T cell clone are being produced in active and "memory" varieties. In addition, helper T cell activity stimulates B-cell clone development. Cytotoxic T cells bind with infected cells and bring about their destruction in two ways: They lyse or puncture the cells' membranes, and they initiate suicide or apoptosis in the infected cells.

27.6 AIDS: Attacking the Defenders

- AIDS, or acquired immune deficiency syndrome, is caused by HIV, the human immunodeficiency virus. This virus is devastating for three reasons: It attacks the immune system itself; its invasion process leads to a harmful infection very quickly; and its genetic material mutates rapidly, meaning the virus itself changes shape at a rapid rate, which allows it to evade immune-system antibodies.

- HIV attaches itself, most importantly, to helper T cells and thus gains entry to the cell. Once inside, the virus can insert its own genetic material into the T cell's DNA and remain inactive for extended periods of time, hidden from the immune system. Conversely, it can use the infected cell's metabolic machinery to turn out its own proteins and genetic material—the building blocks of new virus particles. These complete viruses then leave the cell to infect more cells; when this cycle is repeated often enough, the cell dies. Because helper T cells are central to immunity, the result can be a great vulnerability to common microorganisms.

- It will be very difficult to develop a vaccine that can prevent AIDS, because any such vaccine would have to prevent the infection of all T cells. Perhaps an AIDS vaccine will only be able to slow the replication of HIV, which in itself could be of great practical value. **Web Tutorial 27.2: HIV Replication**

27.7 The Immune System Can Cause Trouble

- The immune system can attack the body's own healthy tissues, essentially mistaking the body's own tissues ("self") for foreign substances ("non-self"). These attacks produce such autoimmune disorders as rheumatoid arthritis, multiple sclerosis, and Type I or insulin-dependent diabetes.

- An allergy is an immune-system overreaction to a foreign substance (an allergen) that causes the body to release infection-fighting histamine. The result is an inflammatory response that can range from small and harmless (sneezing and sniffling) to large and life-threatening (asthma or anaphylactic shock).

- The immune system is the most important problem in organ transplantation. The immune system regards any transplanted organ as "non-self" and thus initiates an attack on it.

Key Terms

actively acquired immunity 595	helper T cell 600
allergen 602	histamine 593
allergy 602	HIV 600
antibody 597	immunity 592
antibody-mediated immunity 595	memory B cell 598
antigen 592	nonspecific defenses 592
antigen-presenting cell (APC) 598	passively acquired immunity 594
autoimmune disorder 602	phagocyte 593
B-lymphocyte cell (B cell) 595	plasma cell 597
cell-mediated immunity 595	specific defenses 592
cytotoxic T cell (killer T cell) 599	T-lymphocyte cell (T cell) 595

Understanding the Basics

Multiple-Choice Questions (answers in the back of the book)

1. An antigen is
   a. any immune system protein
   b. any foreign substance that elicits an immune-system response
   c. any cell that functions in the immune-system response
   d. the ultimate product of a vaccination
   e. a particular kind of lymphocyte

2. Most of the cells active in the immune system are varieties of _____, one type of which are _____, which kill invading cells by ingesting them.
   a. mast cells; red blood cells

b. white blood cell; phagocytes

c. neurons; red blood cells

d. B cells; mast cells

e. white blood cell; mast cells

3. All T and B cells of the immune system begin development in
   a. the thymus
   b. the spleen
   c. the pancreas
   d. the hypothalamus
   e. the bone marrow

4. What is the body's first line of defense against infectious microbes?
   a. T cells
   b. antiseptics
   c. B cells
   d. physical barriers
   e. phagocytes

5. Once vaccinated, you have had a primary exposure to a specific antigen. If you ever encounter this antigen again, you will mount a more rapid immune response due to:
   a. cytotoxic T cells
   b. antigen presenting cells
   c. antibodies
   d. B and T memory cells
   e. complement proteins

6. The body's specific defenses _____ and work through two major arms: _____ and _____.
   a. operate against bacteria alone; mast cells; phagocytes
   b. operate against fungi alone; inflammation; acquired immunity
   c. operate against viruses alone; antibody-mediated; acquired immunity
   d. operate against particular invaders; antibody-mediated; cell-mediated immunity
   e. will not work against worms; inflammation; acquired immunity

7. An antibody is seen in two forms in immune-system functioning: as _____ and as _____.
   a. a stretch of DNA in a macrophage; a hormone
   b. an antigen receptor on a B cell; a free-standing protein produced by a B cell
   c. an antigen receptor on a T cell; a fragment of an invader on a T cell
   d. a stretch of DNA in a T cell; a protein produced by a T cell
   e. a communication molecule produced by T cells; an antigen receptor on a T cell

8. Cell-mediated immunity works primarily against _____ and primarily through _____.
   a. viruses that have just entered the bloodstream; mast cells
   b. bacterial cells; B cells
   c. bacterial and fungal cells; B cells
   d. all invading cells; T cells
   e. the body's own infected cells; T cells

9. Human immunodeficiency virus (HIV) infects _____, causing them to _____.
   a. neurons; lose their myelin
   b. T cells; turn out more HIV copies
   c. T cells and macrophages; attack each other
   d. many types of cells in the body; start dividing wildly
   e. B cells and their antibodies; attack the body's own tissues

10. In autoimmune disorders, the immune system
    a. attacks some microbes, but not others
    b. uses only its nonspecific defenses
    c. attacks the body, rather than invading microbes
    d. works too slowly to be effective
    e. fails to create memory cells

Brief Review

1. Name the main actions that take place in the inflammatory response.

2. What primary immune function does a dendritic cell carry out?

3. HIV infection can lead to several forms of cancer, including Kaposi's sarcoma and a type of lymphoma; it can lead to a kind of dementia and a physical wasting; it makes its victims prone to several kinds of fungal infections that are rarely seen in the general population. How can one virus have this many effects?

4. Why is the immune system an obstacle to organ transplantation?

5. In what way does the rapid mutation of HIV make the development of an AIDS vaccine more difficult?

Applying Your Knowledge

1. When smallpox raged in England in the eighteenth century, most of its victims were young children. Meanwhile, the people least likely to die from it were senior citizens. Why should this have been so?

2. The immune system is a particularly complex biological system. Why do you think it evolved to have so many different subsystems and component parts?

MediaLab

How Does Your Body Fight the Flu? Understanding the Immune System

In 1972, a child named David Vetter was born, and then spent his 12 short years encased in a plastic bubble. The bubble protected him from the millions of microbes we all battle daily. David had a disease called SCID (severe combined immune deficiency, found in 1 in 100,000 people born each year), which affects the body's ability to produce a functional immune system. This *Web Tutorial* will help you explore how a normal immune system functions to spare us a similar fate. In the *Web Investigation*, you'll gather information concerning the actions of antibodies and their success in fighting two of these biological battles, against influenza and HIV. In the *Communicate Your Results* section, you will discuss and analyze how well our bodies may be fighting these battles.

This *MediaLab* can be found in Chapter 27 on your Companion Website (www.prenhall.com/krogh3).

WEB TUTORIAL

There are two main defensive mechanisms of our immune system, the antibody-mediated and cell-mediated immune responses. This *Web Tutorial* will illustrate the actions of the two types of white blood cells, B- and T-lymphocytes, which coordinate the responses.

Activity

1. *First, you'll learn how the immune system is activated during the inflammatory response and how this stimulates B-lymphocytes to produce antibodies.*

2. *Then, you'll compare the primary and secondary immune response and see why we develop immunity only after a primary infection.*

3. *Finally, you'll learn the role of the T-lymphocytes and cell-mediated immunity that allows our bodies to destroy cells that may be harboring a foreign invader.*

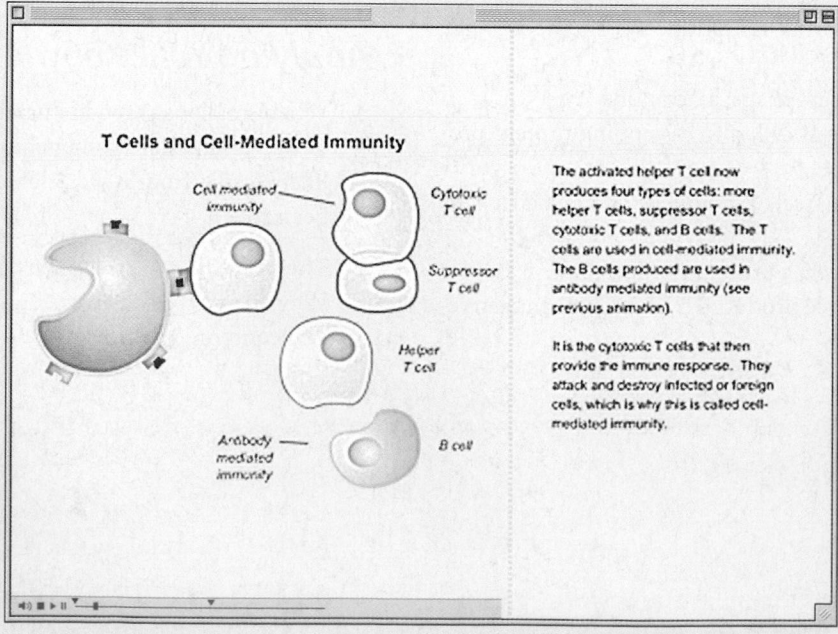

Investigation 1

Estimated time to complete = 15 minutes

In your everyday experiences, you know that getting the flu is at least an inconvenience, but you may not be aware that influenza can be deadly. Select the keyword **PANDEMIC** on your Website to read an article describing the 1918 influenza outbreak that killed over 20 million people. Then, click the keyword **FLUNET** to visualize the development and extent of flu outbreaks in the United States and around the world. Click on "Epidemic Activity" on the left side of the screen; you can select the geographic area you want data from, the specific type of virus (leave this at "Epidemiological Activity" for now), the format for presenting the data, and the time period for the data. Go back in time and try to find any patterns that indicate a worldwide flu outbreak like the pandemic of 1918.

Investigation 2

Estimated time to complete = 10 minutes

Select the keyword **ANTIBODIES** on your Website for this *MediaLab* to read an article describing the general structure and activities of antibodies. Pay particular attention to how the structure of antibodies helps them recognize a huge number of different antigens, and what functions are associated with the five different classes of antibodies.

Investigation 3

Estimated time to complete = 20 minutes

By this time you've probably heard at least a little about the HIV virus that causes AIDS. Select the keyword **CDC** on your Website for this *MediaLab* to access data for HIV and AIDS. To see a report of cumulative AIDS cases in the United States, click on "Cumulative Cases." How many have there been in the United States? How are these cases distributed through different age groups, or races in the United States? Go to "Exposure Categories" for the data on how the virus has been spread. What is the most frequent mode of transmission in the United States? Is it the same for all age groups? Races? Now click on the keyword **WORLD** to compare the U.S. data with data from other parts of the world.

Exercise 1

Estimated time to complete = 30 minutes

Going back through the years, can you find a pattern (from the Websites in *Web Investigation 1*) that indicates a worldwide flu season? Are there flu seasons within regions of the world? Is the outbreak of flu as widespread from year to year? Recently, which years have had the worst flu outbreak? Fast-forward now, about 10 years. You are working for a government agency that has been charged with creating policy to stem the spread of a new influenza strain, which has been rapidly spreading to pandemic proportions during the past four months. What is your plan?

Exercise 2

Estimated time to complete = 20 minutes

Use the description of antibody function from *Web Investigation 2* to compose a 100-word description of the immune system's response when presented with an antigen such as a particular influenza strain the first time, or a second or third time. What types of antibodies are produced at each exposure? What antibodies regulate the robust response to the second exposure? Why does influenza repeatedly attack human populations, frustrating our immune systems?

Exercise 3

Estimated time to complete = 45 minutes

Construct bar graphs illustrating differences in the occurrence of HIV/AIDS in the United States with its occurrence in 10 other countries around the world. Use the bar graphs to answer the following questions: Are the differences you find as striking between two developed countries versus a developed country and an undeveloped country? How about between Western countries and countries in Asia? Where is the occurrence of HIV/AIDS the highest? How likely are you to meet someone with HIV/AIDS in your own age group in the United States versus one of the other countries?

28 Blood, Breath, Digestion, and Elimination

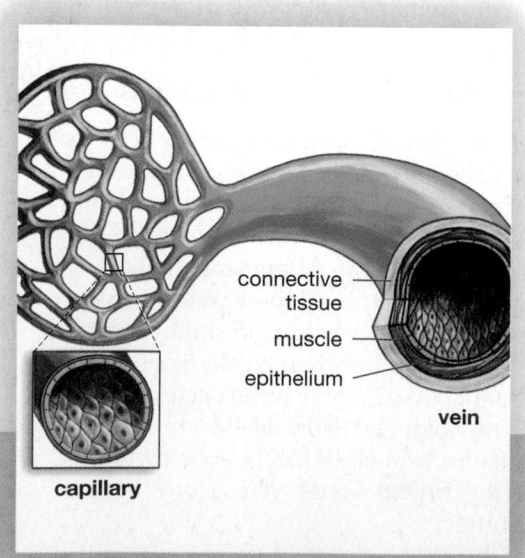

Body pipes.
(Section 28.2, page 611)

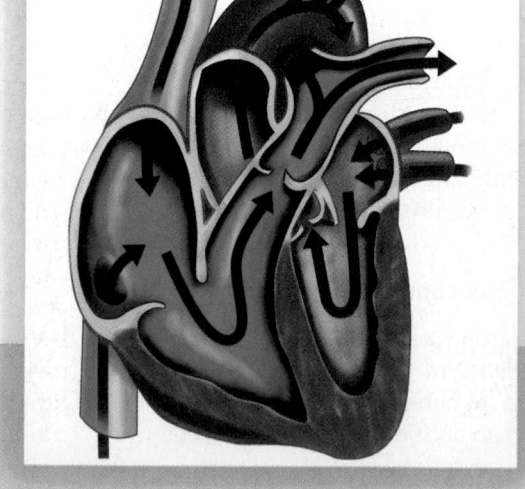

A hearty pumper.
(Section 28.3, page 612)

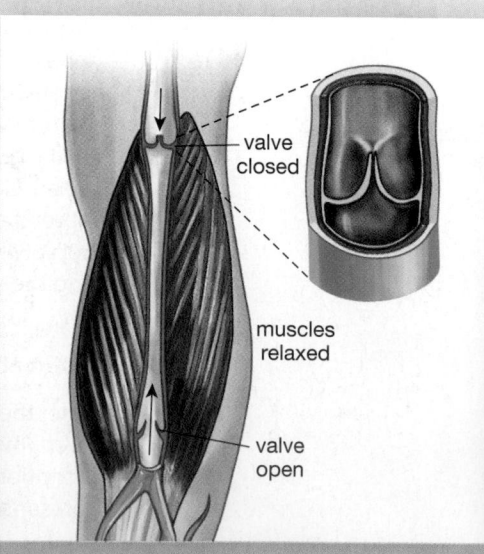

One-way street.
(Section 28.5, page 615)

Our bodies have a respiratory system that acquires oxygen and gets rid of carbon dioxide, a digestive system that breaks down food, and a urinary system that gets rid of some materials while recycling others. Tying all these systems together is another system, the circulatory system.

The cells that make up our bodies may be tiny things, but they are still living things, which means they have their own ongoing set of needs. They have to obtain energy and get rid of wastes; they have to obtain oxygen; they have to obtain nutrients such as nitrogen and phosphorus. When life consisted of nothing but single-celled creatures, every cell had access to the world outside itself, which meant that food could enter, waste could be expelled, and gases could be "exchanged" in a fairly simple manner. In a human being, conversely, many of our 100 trillion cells spend their entire existence wrapped deep inside layers of tissue.

During the course of evolution, this access problem, as it might be termed, was solved by the development of physiological *systems*: a special bodily apparatus for extracting nutrients from food, another for delivering oxygen, and another for removing waste. We call the system that extracts nutrients the digestive system, the one that delivers oxygen the respiratory system, and the one that removes waste the urinary system. If you think about it, what all these systems have in common is that they carry out various exchanges of materials between us and our surroundings. They do this, however, only with the help

of one additional system that links them together. This is the cardiovascular system, which uses the fluid called blood to pick up gases, nutrients, and wastes from one location in the body and transport them to another. The essential subject of this chapter is how the cardiovascular system works together with the digestive, respiratory, and urinary systems to create a coordinated life-support mechanism. If you look at **Figure 28.1** on page 610, you can see a representation of how these systems are linked. We'll start our review with the cardiovascular system.

28.1 The Cardiovascular System

The human **cardiovascular system** is a fluid transport system that consists of the heart, all the blood vessels in the body, the blood that flows through these vessels, and the bone marrow tissue in which red blood cells are formed. This system bears a rough comparison with a car's cooling system. A car uses antifreeze and water as its circulating fluids; the cardiovascular system uses blood. A car may use a water pump to circulate its fluids; the cardiovascular system uses a pump called the heart. A car has an assortment of conducting pipes; the cardiovascular system has blood vessels.

Breathe deeply.
(Section 28.6, page 616)

An absorbing story.
(Section 28.9, page 620)

Preserving what's useful.
(Section 28.13, page 625)

609

The similarities end there, however, because, while a car's cooling system transports only a couple of things, the cardiovascular system transports lots of things. It moves nutrients, vitamins, waste products, hormones, and immune-system cells and proteins, not to mention the oxygen we breathe in and the carbon dioxide we breathe out. All these materials are transported in the substance we'll look at first within the cardiovascular system—blood.

The Composition of Blood: Formed Elements and Plasma

Collect a sample of blood from a human being, prevent it from clotting, and spin it in a centrifuge, and it will separate into two layers. The lower layer, accounting for some 45 percent of its volume, consists of blood *cells* and cell fragments, which collectively are known as the **formed elements** of blood (**see Figure 28.2**). The yellowish, upper layer, accounting for the rest of the volume, is called **plasma**, meaning the fluid portion of blood. Within an actual blood vessel, the formed elements are suspended in the flowing plasma, just as tiny bits of sediment might be suspended within a moving stream.

Formed Elements

It turns out there are three kinds of formed elements in the plasma. The most numerous by far are the **red blood cells**, which transport oxygen to, and carbon dioxide from, every part of the body. Then there are **white blood cells**, which are critical players in the immune system reviewed last chapter. Finally, there are **platelets**—small fragments of cells that are important in the blood-clotting process. Let's now look at each of these elements in more detail.

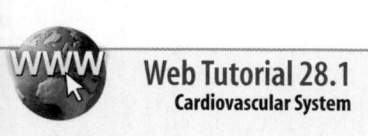

Web Tutorial 28.1
Cardiovascular System

Figure 28.1
The Transport and Exchange Systems of the Body
The human body has four systems that are active in transport and exchange: the cardiovascular, digestive, urinary, and respiratory systems. The cardiovascular system is central to all the others, in that it transports materials to and from them.

Red blood cells, or *erythrocytes*, are red because within them is the iron-containing protein **hemoglobin**. Molecules of hemoglobin that lie within a red blood cell (RBC) bind with oxygen as comes in from the lungs and then hold onto it, releasing it only when the cell reaches a part of the body whose oxygen concentration is relatively low. RBCs then work with blood plasma in picking up the carbon dioxide that cells have produced through their metabolism; they carry this CO_2 back to the lungs, where it will be exhaled. Blood is deep red because RBCs constitute 99.9 percent of all the formed elements in it. Indeed, the *number* of RBCs in an average person staggers the imagination. One cubic millimeter of blood—an amount that might scarcely be visible—contains 4.8 to 5.4 million RBCs. So numerous are these cells that they make up about a third of all the cells in the human body.

Apart from their numbers, RBCs are also notable for another quality, which is their odd structure. In their mature state, they essentially consist of a cell membrane that surrounds a mass of hemoglobin. Viewed another way, an RBC has almost none of the standard cellular equipment—a nucleus, other organelles, and so forth. This lack of cellular machinery means that the average RBC life span is only 120 days, and this means that about 180 million new RBCs have to enter the circulation *each minute* for us to have enough of them in our system.

The second formed element in blood, the white blood cells or *leukocytes*, have a completely different function from red blood cells. They have standard cellular equipment, but they are not in the oxygen or CO_2 transport business. Instead, in their many varieties, they are central to the body's immune-system operation. A typical cubic millimeter of blood contains 6,000 to 9,000 white blood cells. This is a tiny number relative to the millions of red blood cells in such a volume, but the comparison is somewhat misleading because most white blood cells (WBCs) are found in the body's tissues, rather than in the bloodstream. WBCs use the bloodstream primarily to *get to* sites of invasion or injury.

The third formed element, platelets, can be thought of as enzyme-bearing packets. They are not cells, but fragments of cells that have broken away from a set of unusually large cells that exist in the bone marrow. The enzymes in them aid in blood clotting at sites of injury. Apart from releasing these enzymes, the platelets clump together at the site of an injury, forming a temporary plug that slows bleeding while the process of clotting continues.

Blood's Other Major Component: Plasma

The formed elements you've just read about are suspended in blood's other major component, plasma,

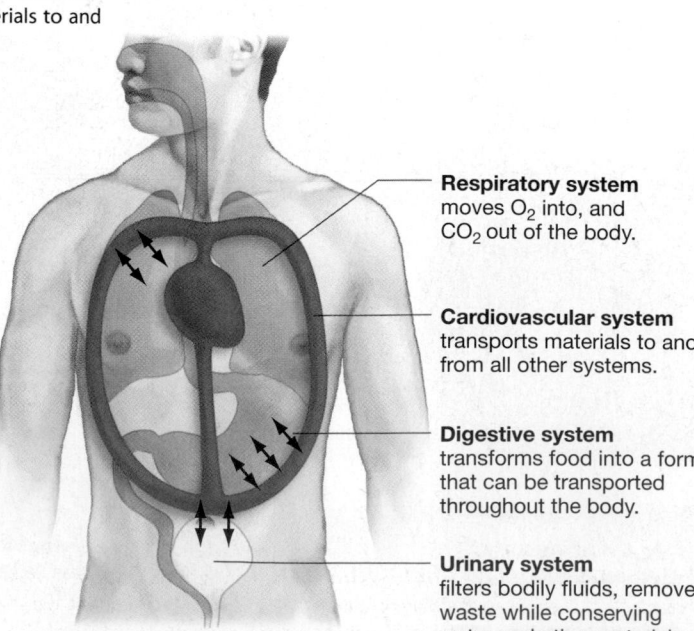

Respiratory system
moves O_2 into, and CO_2 out of the body.

Cardiovascular system
transports materials to and from all other systems.

Digestive system
transforms food into a form that can be transported throughout the body.

Urinary system
filters bodily fluids, removes waste while conserving water and other materials.

which is 92 percent water. Proteins and a mixture of other materials are dissolved in this fluid as well. Why aren't these proteins and other materials "formed elements"? Well, note that they are not cells, nor even cell fragments, but are instead much smaller molecules that go into making up a living thing.

There are three primary kinds of proteins in the plasma. First, there are the albumins, made in the liver, which function in the transport of both hormones and the components of fats known as fatty acids. Second, there is fibrinogen, also made in the liver, which aids in blood clotting. Third, there are globulins, which come in two forms. One is the immunoglobulins or antibodies that you saw so much of in Chapter 27, which attack foreign proteins and disease-causing organisms. The other is the transport proteins that carry small ions, hormones, or other compounds.

Looking strictly at transport proteins, we find that one variety of them has a real importance to our hearts. These *lipoproteins* essentially are capsules of protein that surround globules of fatty material—usually cholesterol. Lipoproteins are best known by the names of their two varieties: **low-density lipoproteins** (or **LDLs**), which carry cholesterol *to* outlying tissues from the liver and small intestine; and **high-density lipoproteins** (or **HDLs**), which carry lipids *from* these tissues to the liver. Keep both LDLs and HDLs in mind, because you'll be reading about them later in connection with heart attacks.

Taken together, the plasma proteins plus water make up 99 percent of blood plasma. The other 1 percent is a mixture of hormones, nutrients, wastes, and ions (which are better known as electrolytes). As you can imagine, wastes that are dissolved in the plasma are on their way out of the body altogether. For example, a substance called urea, produced by the liver's breakdown of proteins, is carried within the plasma to the kidneys, is filtered out by them, and is then urinated out of the body.

28.2 Blood Vessels

Having looked at what moves through the cardiovascular system, let's now look at the plumbing that carries these materials—our network of blood vessels.

Blood vessels are tubes, in a sense. To get a real idea of them, however, imagine a regular tube, such as a straw, that could change its internal diameter from second to second, that could take in some materials along its length while keeping others out, and that could repair itself when damaged. Because blood vessels are composed mostly of cells, they are dynamic entities that change their activities in accordance with the body's needs. Blood vessels carrying blood *away* from the heart are the **arteries**, while the vessels carry-

ing blood back *to* the heart are the **veins**. The farther from the heart these vessels are, the smaller they tend to be. Connecting the arteries with the veins are the smallest blood vessels of all, the **capillaries**.

Arteries and veins are always are made up of three distinct layers of tissue (**see Figure 28.3**). The

Figure 28.2
The Composition of Blood
Blood that is spun in a centrifuge separates into its two primary constituent parts: formed elements and plasma. Formed elements are cells and cell fragments that help make up the blood—red blood cells, white blood cells, and platelets. Blood plasma, the liquid in which the formed elements are suspended, is composed mostly of water, but also contains proteins and other materials.

blood sample

plasma

formed elements

55%

45%

Formed elements

Red blood cells 99.9%
White blood cells } 0.1%
Platelets

Plasma

Water 92%
Plasma proteins 7%
Other solutes 1%

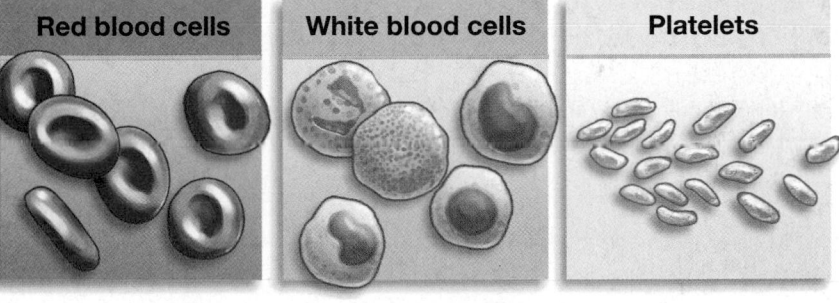

Red blood cells

White blood cells

Platelets

connective tissue

muscle

epithelium

artery

connective tissue

muscle

epithelium

vein

capillary

Figure 28.3
The Structure of Blood Vessels
Both arteries and veins have three layers to them: an inner epithelium, a layer of smooth muscle, and a layer of connective tissue. By contracting or relaxing, the smooth muscle can change the diameter of the vessels. Arteries and veins are linked by intervening capillary beds. Each capillary consists of a single layer of cells.

innermost layer is composed of a group of flat cells, which you may remember from Chapter 25 are *epithelial cells*—cells that come into contact with materials from outside the body, such as oxygen and nutrients. The middle layer of arteries and veins contains smooth muscle. These are muscles that allow the blood vessel to shrink or expand in diameter. This very ability has health consequences, because the dangerous condition called hypertension or high blood pressure is brought about by blood vessels that are *persistently* constricted by muscle contraction. (As the vessels' diameter decreases, the pressure within them increases.) The outer layer of arteries and veins is a stabilizing sheath of connective tissue. Taken as a whole, these three layers give arteries and veins a great dual capability: strength combined with flexibility. The largest arteries have diameters of up to 2.5 centimeters or about an inch, but farther out from the heart, the smallest arteries, the arterioles, have diameters that average 30 micrometers (μm), which is about a thousandth of an inch.

Tiny as this diameter is, things get a lot smaller yet with the body's other main variety of blood vessel, the capillaries. Their diameters average about three *ten*-thousandths of an inch. Why so minuscule? Their central function is to have substances pass into them and out of them along their length. As such,

their walls need to be very thin. Accordingly, each capillary is made of a *single* layer of cells. So small are capillaries that tiny red blood cells must move through them in single file.

28.3 The Heart and Blood Circulation

What makes blood flow through these vessels? The answer is the muscular pump we call the heart. A small organ, roughly the size of a clenched fist, the heart actually is shaped something like a valentine heart in its major outline. It lies near the back of the chest wall, directly behind the bone known as the sternum.

The heart sends blood out, and then gets it back, through two circulation loops. As noted earlier, one major task of the blood-transport system is to get oxygen to all the various bodily tissues. For blood to carry oxygen to tissues, it first has to *take up* the oxygen that is brought into the body through the lungs. So imposing is this task of oxygenating blood that one of the heart's circulation loops is devoted solely to getting blood to the lungs and then back to the heart. The oxygenated blood that comes to the heart in this loop is then pumped out to the rest of the body in the heart's second major loop (**see Figure 28.4a**).

To put these things more formally, there are two general networks of blood vessels in the cardiovascular system. One of these is the **pulmonary circulation**, in

Figure 28.4
Two Circulatory Networks and How the Heart Supports Them

(a) Veins in the systemic circulation bring blood into the right side of the heart; it is pumped out via the pulmonary circulation to the lungs, where it is oxygenated, and then returns to the left side of the heart. It is then pumped out from the left side of the heart, through the systemic circulation, to the rest of the body.

(b) The path of the blood's circulation through the four chambers of the heart.

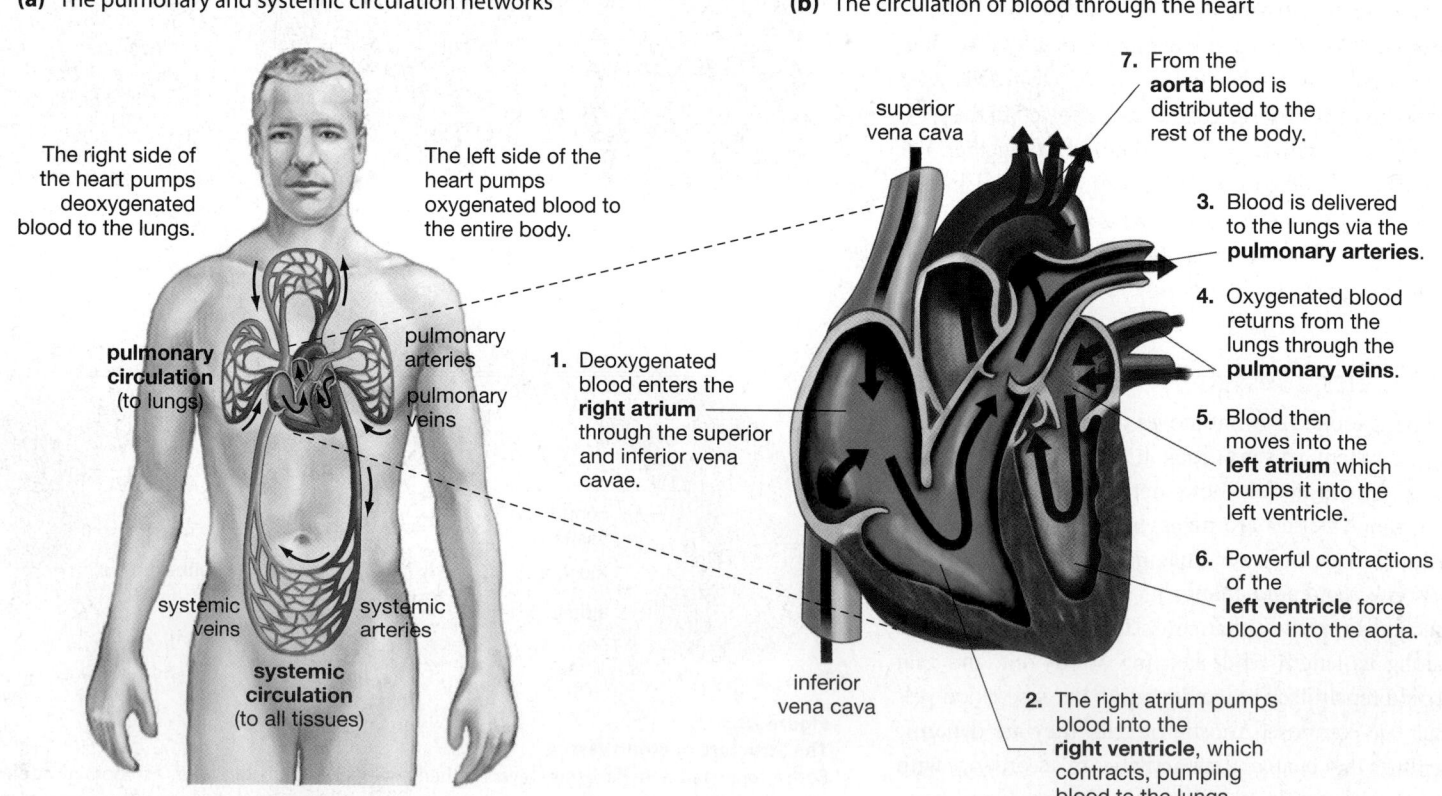

(a) The pulmonary and systemic circulation networks

The right side of the heart pumps deoxygenated blood to the lungs.

The left side of the heart pumps oxygenated blood to the entire body.

pulmonary circulation (to lungs)

pulmonary arteries

pulmonary veins

systemic veins

systemic arteries

systemic circulation (to all tissues)

(b) The circulation of blood through the heart

superior vena cava

inferior vena cava

7. From the **aorta** blood is distributed to the rest of the body.

3. Blood is delivered to the lungs via the **pulmonary arteries**.

4. Oxygenated blood returns from the lungs through the **pulmonary veins**.

5. Blood then moves into the **left atrium** which pumps it into the left ventricle.

6. Powerful contractions of the **left ventricle** force blood into the aorta.

1. Deoxygenated blood enters the **right atrium** through the superior and inferior vena cavae.

2. The right atrium pumps blood into the **right ventricle**, which contracts, pumping blood to the lungs.

which the blood flows between the heart and the lungs. Then there is the **systemic circulation**, in which the blood is moved between the heart and the rest of the body. Let's see how this two-network system works.

Following the Path of Circulation

The human heart contains four muscular chambers, two associated with the pulmonary circulation and two associated with the systemic circulation. These are the right atrium and right ventricle (pulmonary circulation) and the left atrium and left ventricle (systemic circulation). Let's take as the starting point the blood entering the right atrium from the veins called the superior and inferior venae cavae (on the *left* side of **Figure 28.4b**). These veins are returning blood to the heart from the upper and lower portions of the body, respectively. This is blood that is coming back after distributing oxygen and other blood-borne materials throughout the body—to our legs, our hands, our trunk, and so forth. As such it is deoxygenated blood, which actually is dark red in color, but which is indicated by the blue color of the veins it flows through. After the right atrium receives this blood, it pumps it the short distance to the right ventricle, which contracts, pushing the blood into the pulmonary arteries. (These vessels are arteries instead of veins, because blood moves *away* from the heart through them.) This blood is now bound for the lungs, where it will pick up oxygen. Once it does this, it returns to the heart through the two pulmonary veins, which empty into the left atrium. The blood then is pumped down into the left ventricle, which contracts and sends the blood coursing up into the enormous artery called the **aorta**. This vessel has branches stemming from it that will carry the blood to all the tissues of the body.

Taking a step back from this, you can see that the right side of the heart pumps blood only to the lungs, while the left side of the heart pumps blood to all the body's tissues, as shown in Figure 28.4a. All four chambers of the heart pump blood, but the right and left *atria* pump blood only into another portion of the heart—their adjacent ventricles. The right ventricle is pumping blood to the lungs, so there is some greater contraction power needed there. But the *left* ventricle is pumping to the whole body, and its contractions are by far the most powerful. When we "take our pulse," what we are feeling is the surge of blood produced by the contraction of the left ventricle.

Valves Control the Flow of Blood

Because both ventricles contract with such force, you may wonder why blood doesn't go back up into their respective atria with each beat. The answer is that there are valves between the atria and ventricles that allow the blood to flow only one way—from atrium to ventricle. Occasionally, because of disease or genetic predisposition, people do have this kind of backflow into the atria. The fluid turbulence that results can be heard as a kind of gurgling sound, known as a "heart murmur" (which is not necessarily a sign of a serious heart problem). Valves also exist to prevent backflow between the ventricles and the arteries they pump blood into. The heart's two sets of valves are responsible for the familiar "lub-dub" sound of the heartbeat. The "lub" is the sound of the valves closing between the atria and ventricles, while the "dub" is the sound of the valves closing between the ventricles and the arteries.

28.4 What Is a Heart Attack?

The heart is a unique organ, but like any other organ, it needs a supply of blood and the oxygen and nutrients that come with it. Indeed, the heart is a voracious user of these materials because it essentially is a set of muscles that never stops working. Blood does not come to the muscles of the heart through any of the chambers you've been reviewing. (Think about the two ventricles; one is sending blood to the lungs, the other to the rest of the body, but not directly to the heart itself.) The way blood does come to the heart is through two arteries that branch off from the aorta just after it emerges from the left ventricle. Because these arteries encircle or "crown" the heart before they start branching, they are known as the **coronary arteries** (**see Figure 28.5**).

Figure 28.5
Critical Vessels
The coronary arteries begin with a right and left coronary artery that branch off from the aorta. These arteries then undergo branching themselves, thus supplying blood to the whole heart. Blockage of the left anterior descending coronary artery figures in almost half of all heart attacks. The magnification of this artery shows the factors that lead to most heart attacks. A buildup of oxidized LDL molecules within the inner artery tissue layer and a resulting blood clot together bring about a complete blockage of the artery.

aorta

pulmonary artery

left main coronary artery

superior vena cava

right coronary artery

site of blockage

left anterior descending coronary artery

damaged heart muscle

blood clot   core of oxidized LDL molecules

It is difficult to overstate the importance of the coronary arteries, because about half of all deaths in the United States today are caused by a blockage of one or more of them. Such blockages generally have, as their starting point, the LDLs or low-density lipoproteins, noted earlier, that carry cholesterol molecules away from the liver and small intestine to varying locations in the body. One place these LDLs go is the coronary arteries. There they can lodge within one of the three layers of tissue that make these arteries up—the innermost layer that comes into contact with the flowing blood. Once present in large numbers, these LDLs can become damaged through oxidation (the same process that causes metal to rust), and this is where the real trouble starts. The immune system now regards these damaged LDLs as *foreign invaders* and thus initiates a complex attack against them. What follows is the "inflammatory response" that readers of Chapter 27 are familiar with. Inflammation that would take place with, say, a puncture wound causes tissue to become flushed and swollen. The same thing is happening here, only this tissue is swelling into the space through which blood flows in a coronary artery, thus beginning a blockage of it.

Even so, this swelling is rarely extensive enough to completely block an artery. Eighty-five percent of all heart attacks are set off by what happens next. The "cap" of swollen tissue ruptures, letting in some of the circulating blood, and the immune cells react with this blood to make it clot. Now there is a blood clot combined with a swollen cap, and the result can be a *complete* blockage of a coronary artery—a **heart attack**. The effect of this blockage is that groups of heart-muscle cells no longer have a blood supply, which kills them if it goes on for long. This can bring death to the heart-attack victim in several ways. The heart muscles may no longer be able to contract with sufficient force to pump blood through the body; or a wild, irregular rhythm, called a *ventricular fibrillation*, can be set off. Even if the victim survives, the damaged heart-muscle tissue will not regenerate; this person will have a weakened heart for life.

The good news about all this is that there are things we can do to lessen the likelihood that this sequence of events will get started. A key concept is to lower the number of LDLs we have circulating within us while raising the number of the HDLs or high-density lipoproteins mentioned earlier. The LDLs, as you've seen, lodge in the coronary arteries, setting off the immune response. The HDLs, conversely, not only remove these LDLs (bringing them back to the liver) but may also carry enzymes that break down the LDLs that have become damaged through oxida-

tion—the LDLs that set off the immune response. So, how do we lower LDLs and raise HDLs? Exercise does both things, and losing excess weight does both things. Meanwhile, eating saturated (animal) fat raises LDL levels, and smoking may damage the LDLs in ways that set off the immune response. It's worth noting that fatty LDL deposits can begin forming in coronary arteries from childhood forward. Heart attacks may be an affliction of the elderly and middle-aged, but heart-disease prevention can be practiced at any age.

28.5 Distributing the Goods: The Capillary Beds

Having looked at the players involved, you're now ready to see how the cardiovascular system actually carries out its central functions of bringing materials to tissues and taking materials away from them. Propelled by the heart through the aorta, blood flows through the tube-like arteries. These large-diameter arteries fork repeatedly, gradually decreasing in size until they become the smaller-diameter arterioles. These then branch into the delivery vehicles of the cardiovascular system, the capillary beds. If you look at **Figure 28.6a**, you can see a representation of one of these beds. Note that at one end, the bed extends from the body's arterial system, but that at the other it feeds into the body's system of veins—the venous system that brings blood *back* to the heart. Looking at the venous system as it begins with the capillaries, you can see that it consists of its smallest vessels, the tiny venules, which then merge into veins. Smaller veins eventually merge into larger ones that finally come together into the largest veins of all, the two vena cavae that feed directly into the heart.

Thus we can see that blood comes "out" through the arteries and "back" through the veins, but the real action in the circulatory system takes place in the capillaries that lie *between* the arteries and the veins. As you've seen, capillaries are very thin. Think now about a line of oxygenated red blood cells, suspended in plasma and moving in single file through a capillary along with hormones, glucose, ions, and other materials needed by the cells *outside* the capillary (**see Figure 28.6c**). The oxygen, glucose, and all the rest move out through the capillary wall and into the interstitial fluid—the liquid in which both the capillary and the cells around it are immersed. Once within this fluid, these needed materials will make their way to nearby cells. The distance they must travel to the cells is not far, however. So extensive is the body's capillary network that no cell is farther than two or three cells away from a capillary.

Forces That Work on Exchange through Capillaries

Red blood cells themselves are too big to pass out of the capillaries, but the oxygen within them diffuses across the capillary lining into the interstitial fluid. Nutrients such as glucose and small ions such as sodium likewise are distributed in this manner. Meanwhile, carbon dioxide and wastes are diffusing *into* the capillaries. The movement of all these substances is aided by concentration gradients, meaning these substances are moving from an area of their higher concentration to an area of their lower concentration. If you take oxygen, for example, there is more of it inside a capillary than outside of it. As a result, it will move "down" its concentration gradient and leave the capillary. (For more on concentration gradients and diffusion, see Chapter 5, page 103.)

Water flows in and out of capillaries as well, propelled by a couple of forces that oppose each other. It tends to flow out of capillary beds at their arterial end, but into beds at their venous end. The force at work at the arterial end is blood pressure, which results from the heart's contractions. This pressure is relatively strong at the arterial end—strong enough to push water out of the capillary, in a flow that brings with it some suspended materials. But the narrowness of the capillaries means that blood pressure is largely spent by the time blood approaches the venous end of a capillary bed. At that point another factor, osmotic pressure, tends to move materials into the capillary. (Proteins too big to leave the capillary result in an osmotic pressure that "pulls" on fluids. You can read more about osmosis in Chapter 5, on page 104.) At the venous end of a capillary, then, osmosis overcomes the force of blood pressure. Most of the water that leaves the capillary beds at the arterial end is returned to them at the venous end. Some remains as interstitial fluid, however, to be picked up by the body's other group of fluid vessels, the lymphatic vessels.

Muscles and Valves Work to Return Blood to the Heart

Because blood pressure has dropped to such low levels by the time the blood gets to the venous system, you may wonder how it can get back to the heart. The answer is that our skeletal muscles do double duty. In contracting, they squeeze the veins in a way that moves the venous blood along. Blood can move only *toward* the heart in this system, because the veins have a series of valves in them that block movement of blood away from the heart (**see Figure 28.7**).

Figure 28.6
Cardiovascular System Delivery Vehicle
Capillary beds are the sites of the exchange of materials between blood vessels and the body's tissues.

(a) An idealized view of how blood flows from arteries to arterioles, through capillary beds, and then into the venules and veins that return it to the heart.

(b) Blood pressure moves materials out of the capillaries near the arterial end of capillary beds, while osmosis moves materials into the capillaries near the venous end of the beds.

(c) Micrograph of red blood cells moving in single file through a capillary.

Figure 28.7
One-Way Flow to the Heart
Skeletal muscle contraction is the primary force that drives blood back to the heart through the venous circulation. A system of valves guards against the backflow of this blood.

Figure 28.8
Anatomy of the Respiratory System

(a) The large-scale components of the human respiratory system.

(b) In this magnification of the alveoli, the capillary network that all alveoli are surrounded by has been cut away, on the right, to reveal the structure of the alveolar sacs.

(c) A micrograph of single bronchiole surrounded by many alveoli—essentially the "cut-away" view of this tissue as seen in the illustration above.

28.6 The Respiratory System

As you've seen, one of the things the cardiovascular system transports is oxygen and another is carbon dioxide. Now it's time to look at the bigger picture of how these substances are exchanged between our cells and the air around us.

People can live perhaps a couple of months without food, and generally a few days without water. But if they go 5 or 6 minutes without breathing, death is usually the result. This is because oxygen is in the energy transfer business; without oxygen, our cells simply don't have enough energy to function. When oxygen is present, however, cells carry out their work and *generate* carbon dioxide as a result, and this CO_2 has to be disposed of. Thus do we see the two central functions of breathing: The first is capturing and distributing oxygen; the second is disposing of carbon dioxide. Apart from these tasks, breathing also helps balance the pH level in our bloodstream and allows us to talk by providing the air that passes over the vocal cords. All of these tasks are technically part of **respiration**, meaning the exchange of gases between the atmosphere outside the body and the cells within

it. What has to happen for this exchange to occur? Here's the sequence of events.

1. Oxygen-rich air has to be brought into the lungs in the process known as *ventilation*.

2. The oxygen in the air has to move from the lungs into the bloodstream, and then through the bloodstream to sites where it is needed. When it reaches one of these sites, it moves out of the bloodstream, diffusing toward the cells that will use it.

3. These cells take up the oxygen, carry out their work with it, and produce the waste product CO_2 as a result. This CO_2 then reverses the trip taken by the oxygen: It moves *out* of the cells, *into* the capillaries, back to the lungs, diffuses into them, and then is expelled from the body through ventilation.

Now let's see how this whole process works in greater detail. We'll begin by looking at the parts of the body that are involved.

Structure of the Respiratory System

The lungs are but one part of the respiratory system, which you can see in **Figure 28.8a**. This system

(a) Anatomy of the lungs

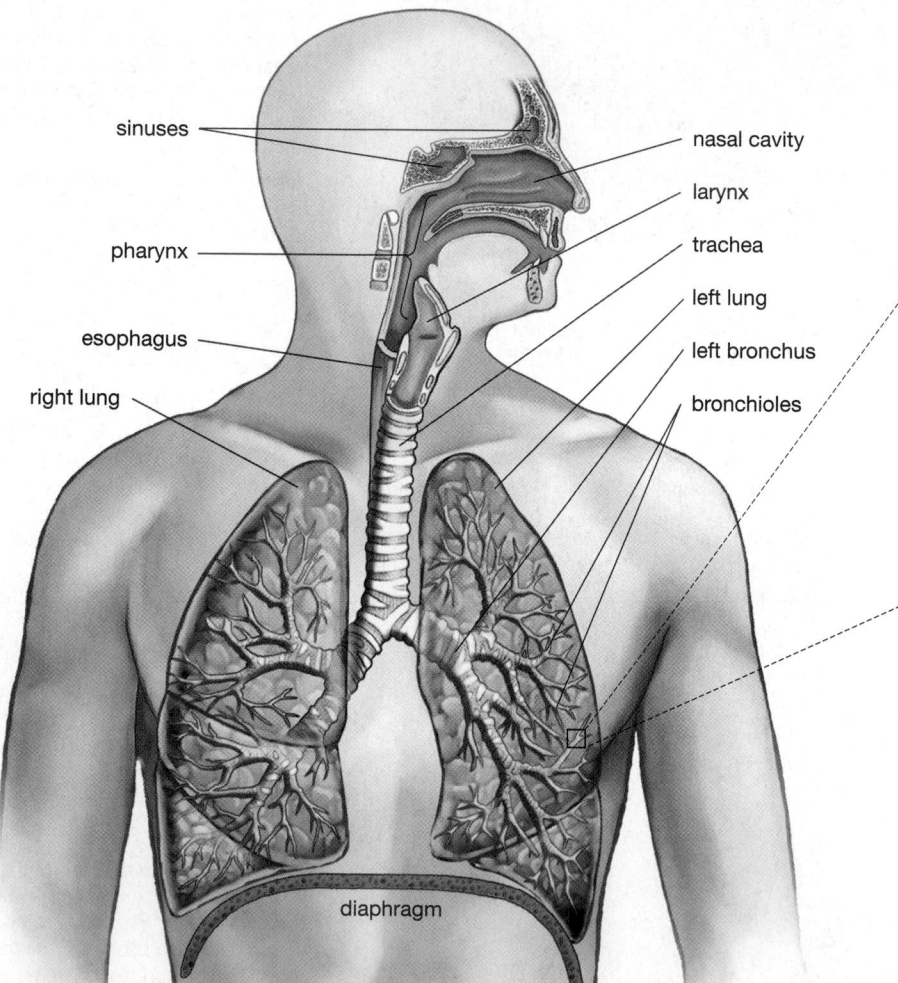

sinuses
nasal cavity
larynx
pharynx
trachea
esophagus
left lung
right lung
left bronchus
bronchioles
diaphragm

(b) The structure of alveoli

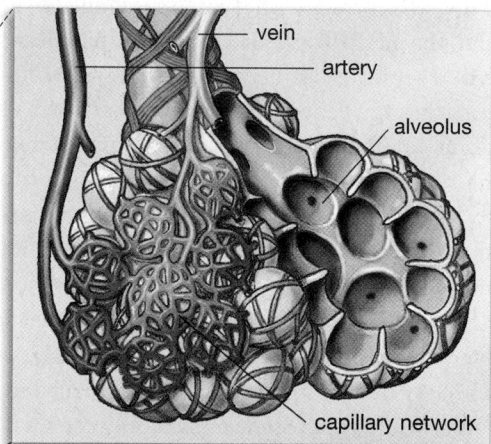

vein
artery
alveolus
capillary network

(c) A bronchiole and its alveoli

also includes the nose, nasal cavity, and sinuses, along with the pharynx (throat), the larynx (voice box) and the trachea (windpipe). In addition, there are air-conducting passageways: the left bronchus and right bronchus, and the many small air passageways they branch into, the **bronchioles**, which deliver air to the lungs.

If we ask what the lungs themselves are, they are made up mostly of tiny, hollow sacs that sprout in grape-like clusters from the end of each bronchiole. These sacs are the **alveoli**, the air-exchange chambers of the lungs. There are about 300 million of them in a typical set of lungs—a number that gives you an idea of just how tiny these sacs must be. The dual quality of being small and numerous gives alveoli what they need to get their job done, which is *surface area*. What does being small and numerous have to do with surface area? Imagine a cube of Jell-O, one inch on each side. Its surface area is 6 square inches. Divide this cube in half, however, and the Jell-O's surface area goes to *8* square inches, even though its volume—the amount of space it takes up—stays the same. Repeat this kind of dividing millions of times, as with our alveoli, and the results are startling. The alveoli in a typical set of lungs have a surface area about the size of a tennis court. If you look at Figure 28.8b, you can see how this surface area is used: to give the alveoli and the capillaries that cover them a huge area in which to exchange oxygen and carbon dioxide.

28.7 Steps in Respiration

First Step: Ventilation

As noted, respiration first involves **ventilation**, meaning the physical movement of air into and out of the lungs. To understand ventilation, look at the drawing, in **Figure 28.9**, of the old-fashioned "accordion bellows" that can be used to get a fire going. Pull the bellows handles apart, and the volume inside the bellows increases. This lowers the air pressure inside the bellows. Because gases always flow from areas of higher to lower pressure, the air flows into the bellows from the outside. Reverse this process—squeeze the bellows handles together—and the air pressure inside becomes higher than the pressure outside, meaning the air flows out of the bellows. Similarly, we have a space inside our chests (called the thoracic cavity) whose volume can increase or decrease. The contraction of a muscular sheet called the diaphragm causes the ribs to rise and, with this, the thoracic cavity expands like the inside of the bellows. Air then rushes in. Exhaling in this kind of "quiet" ventilation is a more passive process. When the diaphragm relaxes, the ribs drop due to the combined force of gravity and natural elasticity of the lungs. As a result, the thoracic cavity shrinks, and air is expelled. During the heavy breathing that takes place in exercise, exhalation is aided by a second set of chest muscles whose contractions help shrink the thoracic cavity.

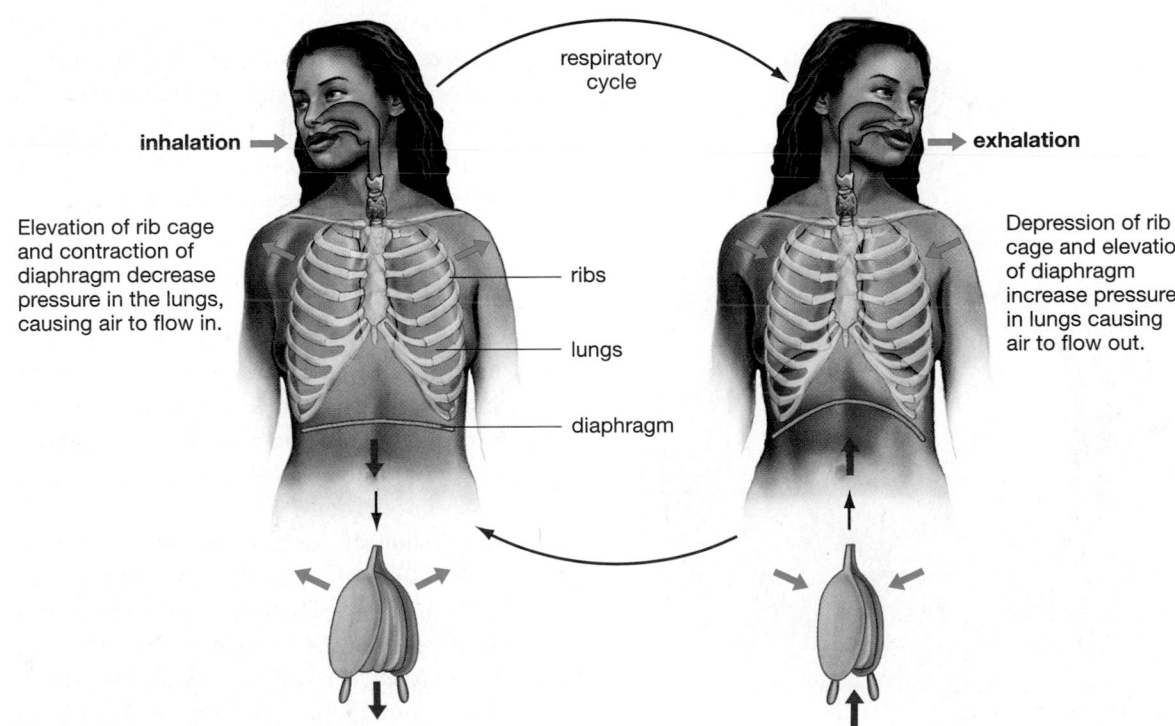

respiratory cycle

inhalation

Elevation of rib cage and contraction of diaphragm decrease pressure in the lungs, causing air to flow in.

exhalation

Depression of rib cage and elevation of diaphragm increase pressure in lungs causing air to flow out.

ribs

lungs

diaphragm

Figure 28.9
Ventilation—How Air Is Moved In and Out

Next Steps: Exchange of Gases

Having gotten into our lungs, oxygen now moves into the bloodstream. How does it get there? Remember that the sac-like alveoli have capillaries covering them. Think of the interface between a capillary and an alveolus as a border that can be easily crossed. An oxygen molecule is inhaled into an alveolus and then diffuses across the thin alveolar tissue into an adjacent capillary. Upon entry, this oxygen molecule encounters a passing red blood cell, which it diffuses into, binding with one of the hemoglobin molecules inside it. Locked up by this binding, the oxygen molecule moves with the red blood cell to the heart. In its ceaseless pumping, the heart is taking oxygenated blood cells like this one and sending them up through the aorta and from there out to the rest of the body. Moving through this route to a tissue somewhere in the body, the red blood cell drops off the oxygen molecule to be used.

This drop-off occurs once again by way of diffusion: the oxygen flows out of a capillary and into the interstitial fluid that surrounds it. Other body cells are immersed nearby in this interstitial fluid, of course, and they can now receive the oxygen. These same cells are, as noted, producing carbon dioxide, which now diffuses from them into the interstitial fluid, and then diffuses again into a capillary. This CO_2 is returned to the lungs via the venous system. Then, at the same capillary-alveoli interface noted

earlier, the CO_2 moves into the alveoli, from which it is expelled into the environment outside the body (**see Figure 28.10**).

As noted, all the oxygen that is loaded into red blood cells binds initially with hemoglobin molecules that exist in these cells. In contrast to this simplicity, the carbon dioxide that is being transferred to the lungs is transported by the blood in three different ways. We need only note here that, in a kind of chemical packing and unpacking, some CO_2 ends up traveling within the hemoglobin in red blood cells, while most of it travels outside of red blood cells, in the blood plasma.

28.8 The Digestive System

Now we shift gears again, moving this time from respiration to digestion. The digestive system is in one sense very simple. Its central structure is a muscular tube called the **digestive tract** that passes through the body from the mouth to the anus. Along its length, this tube receives input from various accessory organs that help with digestion, such as the salivary glands, gallbladder, liver, and pancreas. The central function of the digestive system is to get the foods the body ingests into a form the body can use. The system must also rid the body of the waste that remains once the useful material has been removed from the food.

You've seen already that nutrients are delivered to tissues throughout the body by the circulatory system. So the real question for the digestive system is: What does it need to do to get food into a form that can *move into* the circulatory system? For carbohydrates and proteins, the pathway is straightforward. Partway through a portion of the digestive tract called the small intestine, carbohydrates and proteins have been broken down enough that they move out from the inner lining of the intestine into adjacent capillaries. This network of capillaries then feeds into a common vein that goes to the liver. Most nutrients, then, are carried straight from the small intestine to the liver. In a controlled release, the liver then sends these nutrients out (through another vein) to the heart, which pumps them out to all the tissues of the body.

The digestion of fats takes a somewhat more complicated route. But the principle remains the same. Fats must be broken down to such a point that they can leave the digestive tract for the rest of the body. For all foods, "breakdown" means just what it sounds like: a transition from large to small. The transition goes from big, visible bites of food to smaller bits, and eventually from big *molecules* of

air in
air out
alveolus in lung
O$_2$
CO$_2$
capillary
CO$_2$ O$_2$
tissue cell

Figure 28.10
Gas Exchange in the Body

food to the building blocks that make them up. It is only these smaller molecules—simple sugars, amino acids, and fatty acids—that can leave the digestive tract for the rest of the body. Now let's take a look at the components of the digestive system, after which you'll follow the path of digestion.

28.9 Structure of the Digestive System

Figure 28.11 shows the locations and functions of the accessory glands and different subdivisions of the digestive tract. The digestive tract begins with the mouth (or oral cavity) and continues through the pharynx, esophagus, stomach, small intestine, and large intestine before ending at the rectum and anus. The digestive tract is sometimes called the alimentary canal, or the gastrointestinal tract.

The Digestive Tract in Cross Section

Thinking again of the digestive tract as a muscular tube, let's look at a cross section of it as it would appear within the small intestine. As you can see in

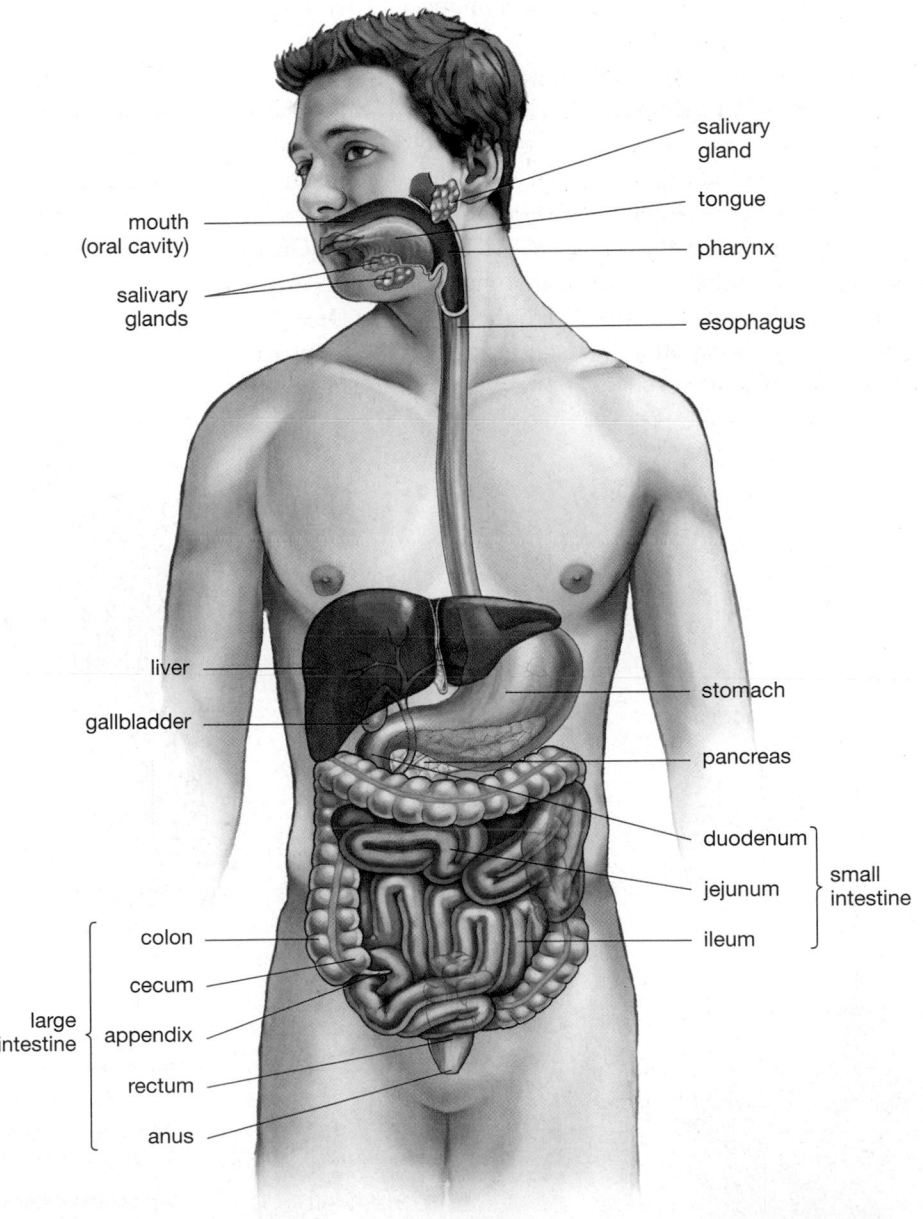

Figure 28.11
Components of the Digestive System

Figure 28.12, the digestive tract is a four-layered tube. The outermost layer is connective tissue known as the serosa. Inside of it there is muscle: two sets of smooth muscles, actually, which together are known as the muscularis externa. In a process called **peristalsis**, these muscles take turns contracting, which produces waves of contraction that push materials along the length of the digestive tract. Inside the muscularis externa there is the submucosa, a layer of tissue that contains large blood vessels and a network of nerve tissue that both coordinates the contractions of the smooth muscle layers and regulates the secretions of digestive juices. Finally, there is the epithelial layer that makes up the internal lining of the tract. It is called the mucosa, because it is constantly bathed in mucous secretions.

Along most of the length of the digestive tract, the mucosa has a large number of folds that increase the surface area available for absorption of digested food; these folds also work like accordion folds, in that they permit expansion, which is helpful after a large meal. The mucosa also has on it fingerlike projections called villi that further increase the area for absorption. These villi are the place where most of our digested food actually makes the transition out of the digestive system. If you look at

the blow-up of the villus in Figure 28.12, you can see where nutrients leave the system. Just outside it, they enter either an adjacent capillary or, in the case of fats, a lymphatic vessel whose connecting vessels will put the nutrients into the bloodstream.

28.10 Steps in Digestion

Let's now look at the process of digestion from start to finish, which means taking it from the top, so to speak. Our mouths are the entry place for food, of course, and we immediately start breaking food down in them by the mechanical means of chewing. Food starts to get digested there by chemical means as well, because enzymes in the saliva have the ability to break down carbohydrates.

The Pharynx and Esophagus

Food begins to move out of the mouth when the tongue pushes it back toward the pharynx, which we might think of as the upper throat (see Figure 28.11). This action is tricky, because the **pharynx** is a passageway that links the mouth with both the food-transporting esophagus and the *air*-transporting trachea. Once the tongue begins pushing food back, the esophagus opens while tissue called the epiglottis folds down over the larynx to keep the food from

Figure 28.12
Structure of the Digestive Tract
The digestive tract is a tube formed of several layers of tissue, each performing a different function. Note that the absorption of nutrients takes place when food that has been sufficiently digested moves across the epithelium and is taken up by either a capillary or a lymphatic vessel inside a villus.

absorption of
nutrients

microvilli

epithelium

lymphatic
vessel

villus

capillary
network

small
intestine

mucosa: highly folded lining of intestine where absorption occurs

submucosa: connective tissue containing blood vessels and nerves

muscularis externa: circular and longitudinal muscle layers used for peristalsis

serosa: connective tissue

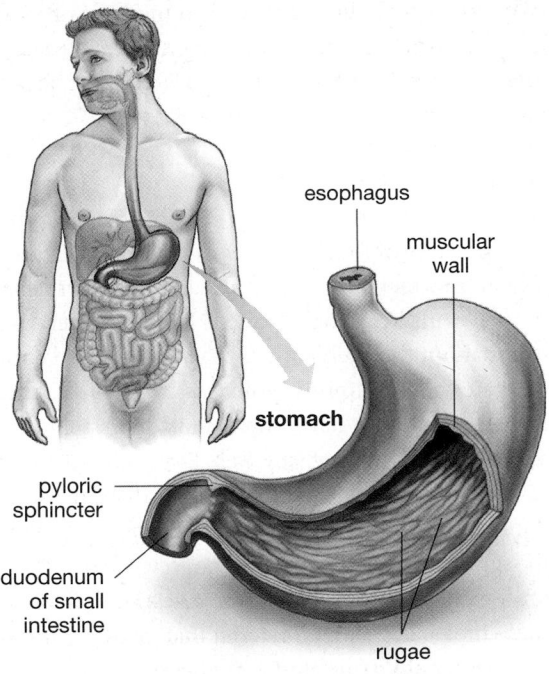

Figure 28.13
External and Internal Views of the Stomach

hydrochloric acid that the contents of the stomach have a pH that lies between that of lemon juice and battery acid. Why is such an extreme environment needed? It serves not only to break down food but also to kill bacteria and other invaders that ride in on the food. You may wonder why the stomach itself wouldn't be eaten away in this kind of environment. The answer is that the cells lining it produce a protective mucus.

A few substances, such as alcohol and some drugs, can pass directly from the stomach into circulation, but in general the stomach is only preparing food for transfer within the digestive system. Food stays in the stomach for two to four hours, but upon exiting it is no longer just plain food; it is now a soupy mixture of food and gastric juices known as **chyme**. A circular or "sphincter" muscle—the pyloric sphincter—regulates the flow of chyme between the stomach and the next structure in the digestive system.

The Small Intestine

The only thing small about the small intestine is its diameter, which is about 4 centimeters or 1.6 inches up where it starts (at the stomach) and about 2.5 centimeters, or an inch, where it ends (at the large intestine). In between these two points, the "small" intestine winds on for about 6 meters, or almost 20 feet. Eighty percent of our nutrients make the transition out of the digestive system along the length of the **small intestine**, which can be defined as the portion of the digestive tract that runs between the stomach, and the large intestine. (About 10 percent of our nutrients are transferred from the stomach and the remaining 10 percent are transferred from the large intestine.)

As you can see in **Figure 28.14**, the small intestine is made up of three regions. The first of these, the

blocking it. (Sometimes food does go down this "wrong way," of course, at which point we may simply start coughing or, in the worst case, need the Heimlich maneuver to keep us from choking.) The pharynx has a trio of muscles wrapping partway around it that get activated in a 1-2-3 sequence to push the food into the esophagus. The esophagus in turn has its own muscles, which work with gravity to send food on a 6-second trip to the next stop in the digestive tract.

The Stomach

The stomach digests food partly by the mechanical means of churning it, thus breaking it into small bits. It also carries out some chemical breakdown of foods, with proteins being the primary target of its digestive juices. In addition to performing digestive work, the **stomach** is an organ that has a less-appreciated second role: It serves as a temporary, expandable storage site for food. This capacity is the reason we can go several hours without eating. When empty, the stomach resembles a tube with a narrow cavity, but it can expand to contain up to 1.5 liters or almost half a gallon of material. This expansion is possible because the stomach contains numerous folds, called *rugae* (**see Figure 28.13**).

Glands feed into the stomach by way of millions of small depressions, called gastric pits, that open onto its interior. Each day, about 1,500 milliliters or 45 ounces of gastric juice pour into the stomach through these pits. This gastric juice is *caustic*—a mixture of hydrochloric acid and the enzyme pepsin. So acidic is the

Figure 28.14
Structure of the Small Intestine

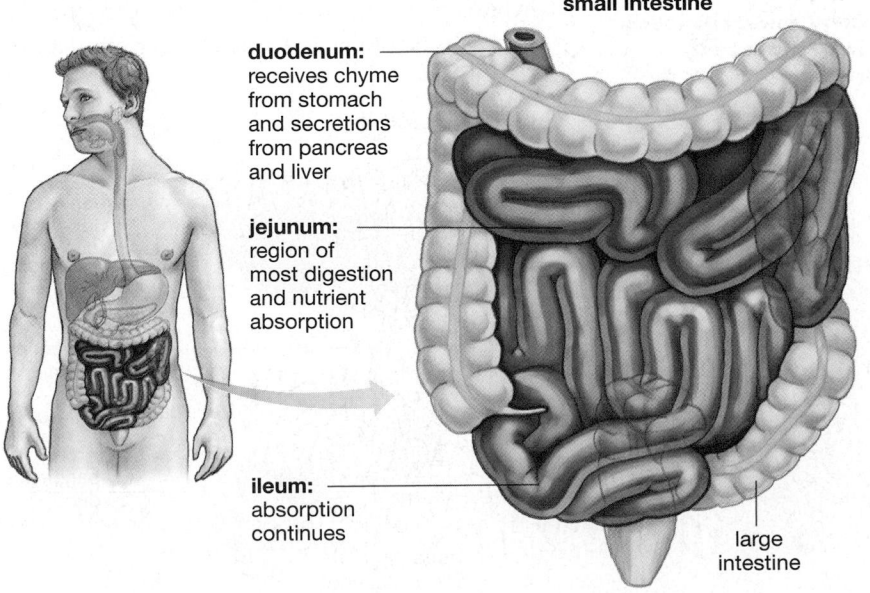

small intestine

duodenum: receives chyme from stomach and secretions from pancreas and liver

jejunum: region of most digestion and nutrient absorption

ileum: absorption continues

large intestine

duodenum, is the 25 centimeters or 10 inches that are closest to the stomach. Think of the duodenum as that portion of the small intestine that receives not only chyme from the stomach, but digestive secretions from three of the specialized digestive organs noted earlier: the pancreas, the liver, and the gallbladder. Next there is the *jejunum*, which goes on for about 2.5 meters or eight feet. This is the site within the small intestine where most chemical digestion and nutrient absorption occurs. Absorption continues to some extent in the third segment, the *ileum*, which is the longest, averaging 3.5 meters or 12 feet in length. The ileum ends at a sphincter muscle that controls the flow of chyme into the large intestine. On average it takes about 5 hours for chyme to pass through the small intestine. Thus, material that began its digestive journey in the mouth takes perhaps 9 hours to reach the end of the small intestine. Now let's look at what happens at the start of the small intestine, where juices from the digestive glands come into the picture.

The Pancreas

Feeding into the small intestine is the pancreas, which lies behind the stomach and is an elongated, pinkish-gray organ about 15 centimeters or 6 inches long. The pancreas is best known as the organ that produces insulin, which it secretes directly into the bloodstream. But our concern is with materials the pancreas secretes through a tube or duct. The duct in question, as you can see in **Figure 28.15**, is the pancreatic duct, which empties into the small intestine's duodenum alongside the common bile duct that stems from the liver and gallbladder. In digestion, the **pancreas** can be defined as a gland that secretes, into the small intestine, digestive enzymes and chemical buffers that help raise the pH of the chyme coming from the stomach. (Remember, this chyme is very acidic; when its pH is being "raised," that means it is becoming less acidic.) Pancreatic digestive

enzymes are classified according to the kind of food they work on. *Lipases* break down lipids, *proteases* break proteins apart, and *carbohydrases* digest sugars and starches.

The Gallbladder and the Liver

As Figure 28.15 shows, lodged within a recess under the right lobe of the liver is a muscular sac called the **gallbladder**: an organ that stores and concentrates a digestive material called bile. Note the operative terms about the gallbladder's role: it stores and concentrates bile. But bile is *produced* by the liver. This is why people can have their gallbladders removed and still function perfectly well. **Bile** can be defined as a substance produced by the liver that facilitates the digestion of fats. It does two things that allow the digestive lipase enzymes to go to work on fats: it breaks up clusters of fat molecules, and it coats these molecules with a material that gives the lipases a greater ability to bind with them.

Bile comes to the small intestine through either of two routes. It always travels through passageways within the liver called *hepatic ducts*, and then leaves the liver through the common hepatic duct. This bile may then (1) flow into the small intestine's duodenum through the common bile duct, or (2) enter the cystic duct that leads to the gallbladder. If it goes to the gallbladder, only later will it flow into the duodenum through the common bile duct. Why would it take one course or the other? A sphincter at the intestinal end of the common bile duct opens only at mealtimes. At other times, bile backs up through the cystic duct for storage and concentration within the gallbladder before moving to the small intestine.

Bile can become *too* concentrated and harden into the troublesome crystals known as gallstones. Most gallstones are small enough to be flushed away into the duodenum, but they can reach 2 centimeters or more in diameter—about three-quarters of an inch, which is large enough to block either the common bile duct or the cystic duct. The pain that results is so excruciating that gallstones have to be taken care of in one way or another. One modern way of getting rid of them is to pulverize them with high-energy sound waves.

The Liver

What about the organ that lies in front of the gallbladder, the liver? If we don't count the skin, the liver is the largest organ in the body. It weighs about 1.5 kilograms or 3.3 pounds (see Figure 28.15). The **liver** is a reddish-brown organ that is central to the

Figure 28.15
Accessory Glands in Digestion: The Liver, Pancreas, and Gallbladder

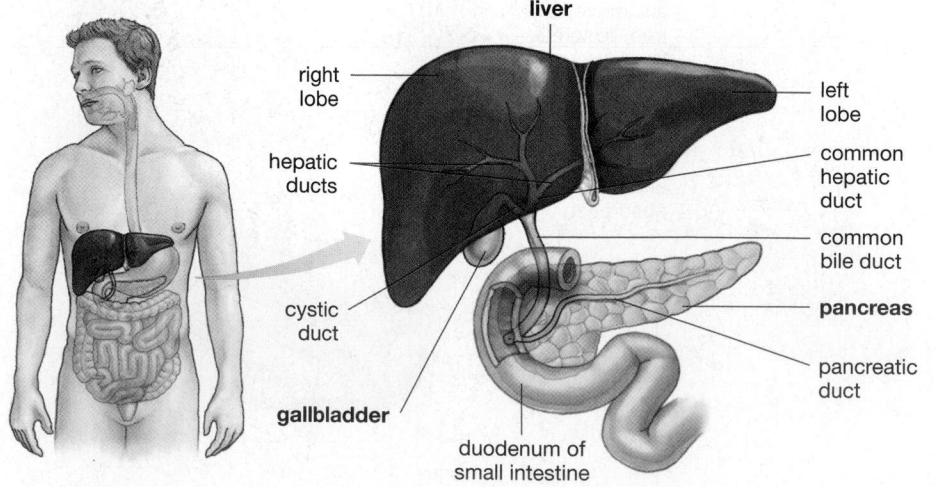

liver

right lobe

hepatic ducts

cystic duct

gallbladder

left lobe

common hepatic duct

common bile duct

pancreas

pancreatic duct

duodenum of small intestine

body's metabolism of nutrients and that serves as a major storage site for blood. This organ actually does hundreds of things for us, but here we will concentrate on a few of its digestive functions.

The liver clearly plays a central role in digestion because, as you may recall, all blood carrying nutrients from the digestive tract is channeled into a single blood vessel, called the hepatic portal vein, that flows into the liver. We could thus think of a series of blood vessel "streams"—stemming from the stomach, the small intestine, and so forth—all of them carrying digested nutrients and all of them flowing like tributaries into the common river of the hepatic portal vein that goes to the liver. This arrangement makes the liver a first stop for most nutrients. From this position, the liver *controls* which nutrients it will send to the rest of the body and which nutrients it will store. The liver is, however, not only the first stop for nutrients, but the first stop for *toxins* such as alcohol. This is why people who have abused their bodies by drinking too much can end up with damaged livers. In addition to transferring and storing nutrients, the liver produces the bile noted earlier, and it packages waste products for removal by the kidneys.

The Large Intestine

If most nutrients have been transferred out of the digestive system by the time the small intestine ends, what is there left for the large intestine to do? Its main task is to serve as a kind of trash compactor: It holds and compacts material that by now is largely refuse, turning it in to the solid waste we know as feces.

If you look at the upper drawing in **Figure 28.16**, you can see that the large intestine neatly frames the small intestine. The small intestine's last section, the ileum, feeds into the large intestine's first section by means of a sphincter (called the ileocecal valve) that you can see at about 7 o'-clock in the lower drawing. This sphincter can relax or contract, thus controlling movement of chyme into the large intestine. The large intestine continues for about 1.5 meters or 5 feet from this point before ending at the anus. Compared to the 20-foot small intestine, the large intestine is large only in diameter.

The **large intestine** can be defined as that part of the digestive tract that begins at the small intestine and ends at the anus. It is divided into three major regions: the cecum, the colon, and the rectum. Note that the cecum has a pouch called the *appendix* attached to it; the walls of this pouch can become infected, resulting in appendicitis. (When

healthy, the appendix is an arm of the immune system, though obviously not an essential one, as it can be removed.) The colon is the large intestine's second section, and by far its longest. The individual pouches in it that you can see in the figure result from bands of muscle that periodically encircle it. The colon then empties into the expandable rectum, which serves as a storage site for feces. The rectal chamber is usually empty except when peristaltic contractions force fecal materials into it from the lower part of the colon. Stretching of the rectal wall then triggers the urge to defecate. Material takes anywhere from 12 to 24 hours to move through the large intestine. Adding this to the other transport times, you can see that a complete trip through the digestive system takes anywhere from 19 to 33 hours.

Apart from waste disposal, the large colon also functions in water conservation. Roughly 1,500 milliliters or 45 ounces of watery material arrives in the colon each day, but some 40.5 ounces move back out, leaving very little to be ejected with the feces. The large intestine also absorbs vitamins produced by bacteria that live within the colon.

Figure 28.16
The Large Intestine

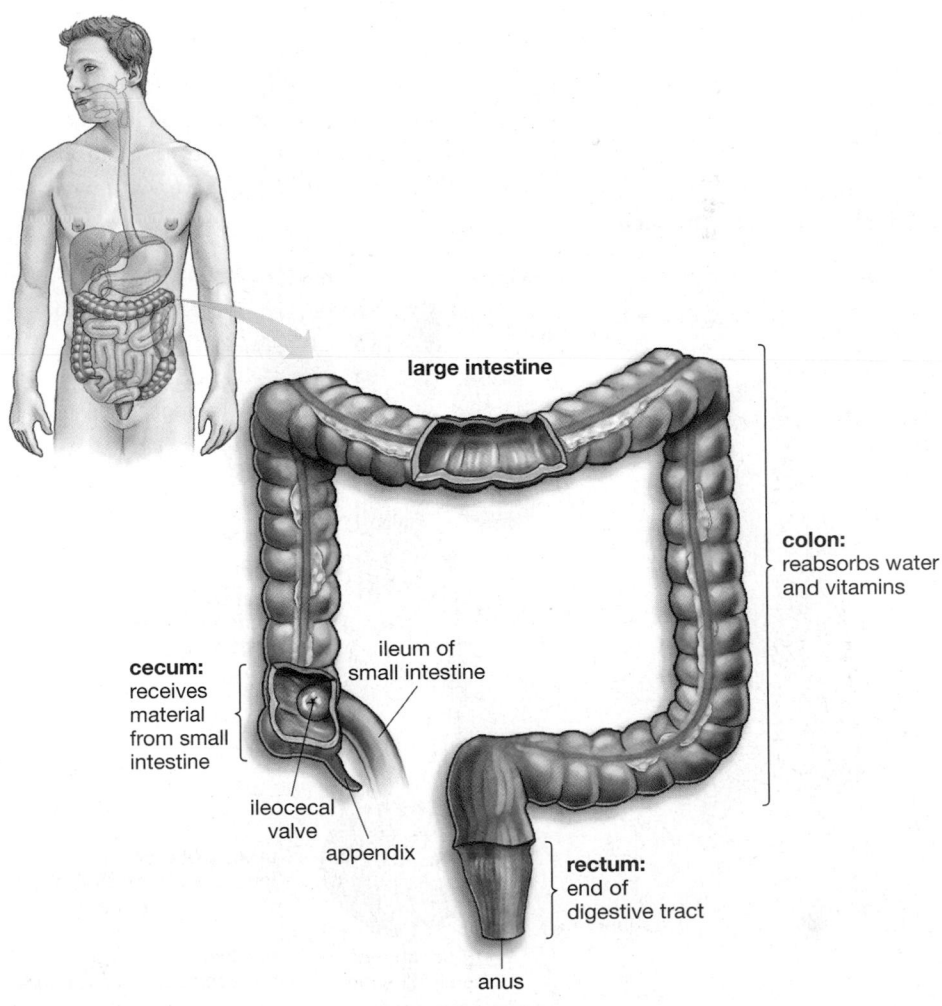

large intestine

colon:
reabsorbs water
and vitamins

cecum:
receives
material
from small
intestine

ileum of
small intestine

ileocecal
valve

appendix

rectum:
end of
digestive tract

anus

Carbohydrates that cannot be digested arrive in the colon intact and serve as a nutrient source for these bacteria. Their resulting metabolic activities are responsible for intestinal gas. Why do beans often trigger such gas? Because they contain a high concentration of carbohydrates that we cannot digest but that the bacteria can.

28.11 The Urinary System in Overview

Here our subject changes once again (for the last time in this chapter), as our tour of the body's systems moves from digestion to the elimination of liquid wastes. At this point, you may be thinking: Didn't we just look at waste removal in the digestive system? We did, but the urinary waste removal coming up is fundamentally different. Think of it this way. The digestive system simply had to *retain* the waste from food, with this waste never leaving the confines of the digestive tract until it was eliminated from the body. As you'll see, the urinary system has to get rid of waste that is produced by cellular activity throughout the body. As such, it works by *filtering* waste from the blood and then passing this waste on to the bladder for elimination.

Such waste removal obviously is important, but it turns out to be only one of several critical functions the urinary system undertakes. Equally important is the system's regulation of blood volume—how much blood we have within us—a task whose necessity becomes obvious when we think about consuming lots of liquids. Suppose the body simply incorporated all the water in these liquids into circulating blood? We would eventually swell and burst like a water balloon. Instead, the urinary system *regulates* how much water the body retains and how much it excretes, with the kidneys being a critical player in this process. The urinary system also controls ion concentration and maintains pH balance in the body. In short, it is important in preserving the stable state known as homeostasis. We almost never think of the urinary system in this regard, essentially because it works so well. But a person who suffers kidney failure and must rely on a kidney "dialysis" machine to filter wastes knows the value of the urinary system in a personal way.

In carrying out these activities, the urinary system is very much involved in the *conservation* of bodily resources. Indeed, the kidneys are as much in the conservation business as the waste removal business. They conserve water, amino acids, ions, sugars—all kinds of things that the body needs. Consider that the kidneys process about 180 liters (or almost 48 gallons) of fluid every day. Yet our urination is only about 1.8 liters, or about *half* a gallon daily. More than 47 gallons cycled back into the body each day! Conservation indeed. Now let's see how the kidneys and the larger urination system manage this feat.

28.12 Structure of the Urinary System

The pivotal structures in the urinary system, shown in **Figure 28.17**, are its two filtering organs, the **kidneys**, which produce urine while conserving useful blood-borne materials. Urine leaving the kidneys travels along two tubes, the left and right **ureters**, to the **urinary bladder**, the hollow, muscular organ that acts as a temporary, expandable storage site for urine. When urination occurs, contraction of the muscular bladder forces the urine through the conducting tube called the **urethra** and out of the body.

The kidneys are located on either side of the vertebral column, at about the level of the eleventh and twelfth ribs. They are shaped like kidney beans, but since they are each about 10 centimeters or 4 inches long, their size is more like that of a small pear.

In considering how the kidneys work, it's helpful to think first in terms of input and output. What comes into the kidney in the way of fluids? Blood from the circulatory system arrives by way

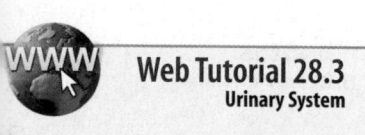

Web Tutorial 28.3
Urinary System

Figure 28.17
The Urinary System in Overview

aorta
vena cava   renal artery
renal vein

kidney:
produces urine

ureter:
transports urine toward
urinary bladder

urinary bladder:
temporarily stores urine

urethra:
transports urine out of body

of the renal arteries. As you can see in Figure 28.17, these branch off from the aorta, one renal artery going to the left kidney, one going to the right. (The word *renal* comes from *renes*, which means "kidneys"; you'll be seeing a lot of "renal" this and that.) Now, what comes *out* of the kidney? Two things: Blood flows out of the kidneys through the renal *veins* that are pictured, and urine exits each kidney through its ureter. Thus, each kidney has one input (the renal artery) but *two* outputs. This is a clue to what's happening inside. Some of the material coming into the kidney through the renal arteries is being channeled out of the blood vessels and into a *separate* system of vessels whose output tubes are the ureters. Now let's look more closely at the kidneys.

Seen in cross section in **Figure 28.18a**, each kidney can be divided into an outer renal cortex, an inner renal medulla, and a chamber called the renal pelvis whose numerous branches collect the urine produced by the kidneys and channel it into the ureter. The work of the kidney begins in its outer portion, or cortex. If you look at **Figure 28.18b**, you can see the kidney's basic working unit, called a *nephron*. Each kidney has within it about 1.25 million nephrons, each serviced by a single renal arteriole that has branched off from the entering renal artery.

In the figure you can see how a nephron begins: An arteriole branching off the renal artery enters a hollow chamber, called the *Bowman's capsule*, and then promptly expands into a knotted network of capillaries, called the glomerulus, that is enclosed by the capsule. *Emerging* from this network, there is again a single arteriole; but it once again branches into a network of capillaries that surrounds something called a nephron tubule. Thus, we have two sets of tubes—the capillaries and the nephron tubule—and these will become the two *outputs* just mentioned: The nephron tubule will transmit what the body doesn't need (waste sent to the bladder), while the capillaries will first lose, and then take back, what the body does need (nutrients, etc.). Note that nephron tubule has portions referred to as proximal ("near") and distal ("distant"). Then notice that, in between these two areas, the tubule takes on a shape that is as uniform as a paperclip: the structure called the loop of Henle.

All this put together adds up to a **nephron**: the functional unit of the kidneys, composed of a nephron tubule, its associated blood vessels, and the fluid in which both are immersed, the interstitial fluid. At the "output" end of the nephron, you can see that its tubule is only one of several that are emptying into a common *collecting duct*. Eventually, many of these ducts will themselves merge to feed into the renal pelvis, which feeds into the ureter. Now let's look at what takes place within a nephron.

28.13 How the Kidneys Function

First Kidney Function: Filtration in Bowman's Capsule

Imagine holding a washcloth, bag-like, underneath a running kitchen faucet. What happens? The water slowly flows out of the washcloth. What if this is a faucet that hasn't been turned on in a while, however, and the water thus contains some sediment? Now the washcloth acts to retain these larger particles while letting smaller substances (the water molecules) flow through. In short, the washcloth acts as a filter. The knotted network of nephron capillaries called the **glomerulus** takes on this same filtering role. Receiving blood that is under pressure, it is porous

Figure 28.18
Structure of the Kidney and Its Working Unit, the Nephron

(a) A kidney in cross section.

(b) A nephron in the kidney, composed of a nephron tubule and its associated blood vessels, which are immersed in interstitial fluid.

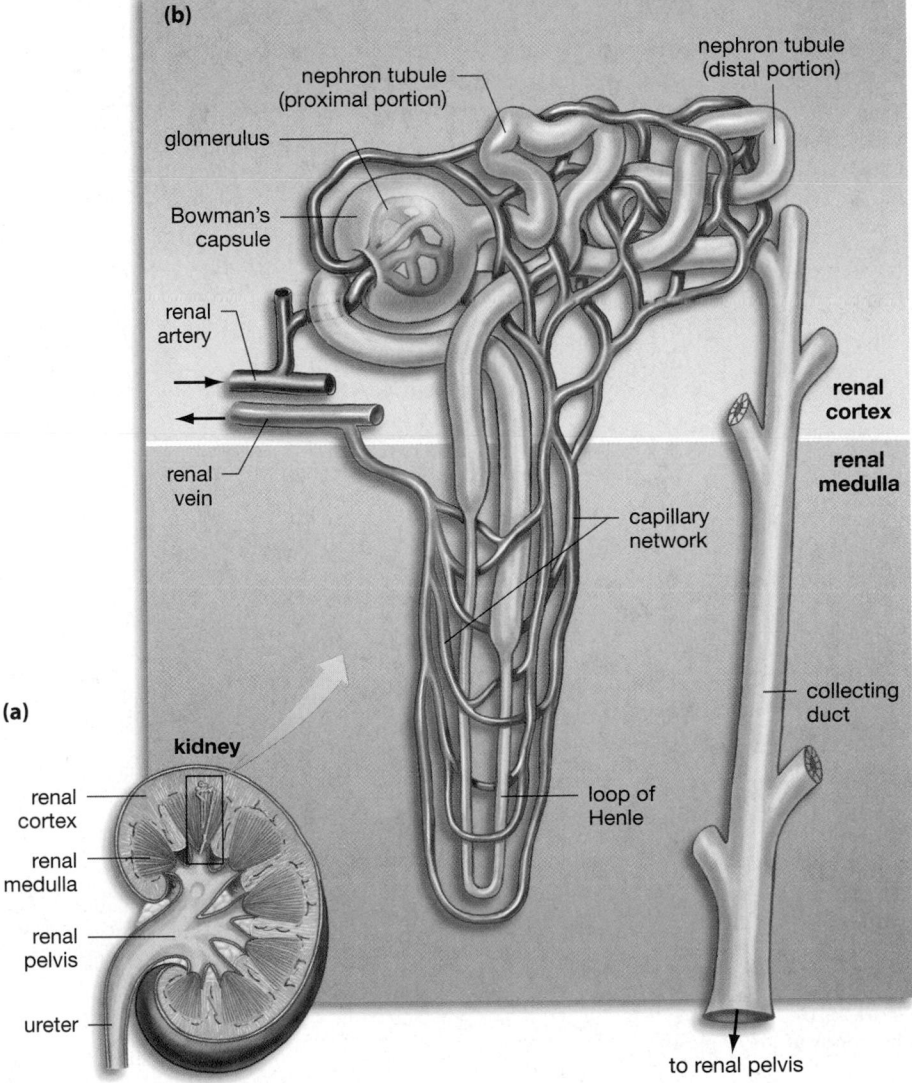

enough to let some smaller blood-borne materials pass *out* of it—and into the surrounding Bowman's capsule (see Figure 28.18b.) Remember that the fluid portion of blood is called blood plasma. This plasma is mostly water, but it has suspended within it small molecules such as vitamins, nutrients such as glucose, and so forth, along with waste materials. All these small substances now pass with the water out of the glomerulus. What stays in the glomerulus (and hence in the bloodstream) are plasma proteins and blood cells, which are too big to pass out.

We should note at this point the nature of the waste products that are moving out of the glomerulus. The body produces several kinds of waste. Every time you use a muscle, for example, you produce a waste product called creatinine

that has to be eliminated from the body. Likewise, proteins are broken down mostly in the liver, and a by-product of this breakdown is a substance called urea. Both urea and creatinine are picked up by the bloodstream and move to a glomerulus, where they flow out, along with the water, etc.

All the materials that have entered the Bowman's capsule from the glomerulus constitute a fluid, called *filtrate*, that is funneled from the Bowman's capsule into the nephron's next structure, its proximal tubule. If you look at **Figure 28.19**, you can see the structure of this proximal tubule in a simplified form (along with the rest of a nephron). Before we leave the glomerulus, however, note that its essential task is to filter blood. Hence, the function it carries out is called *filtration*, the first of four essential tasks undertaken by the kidneys.

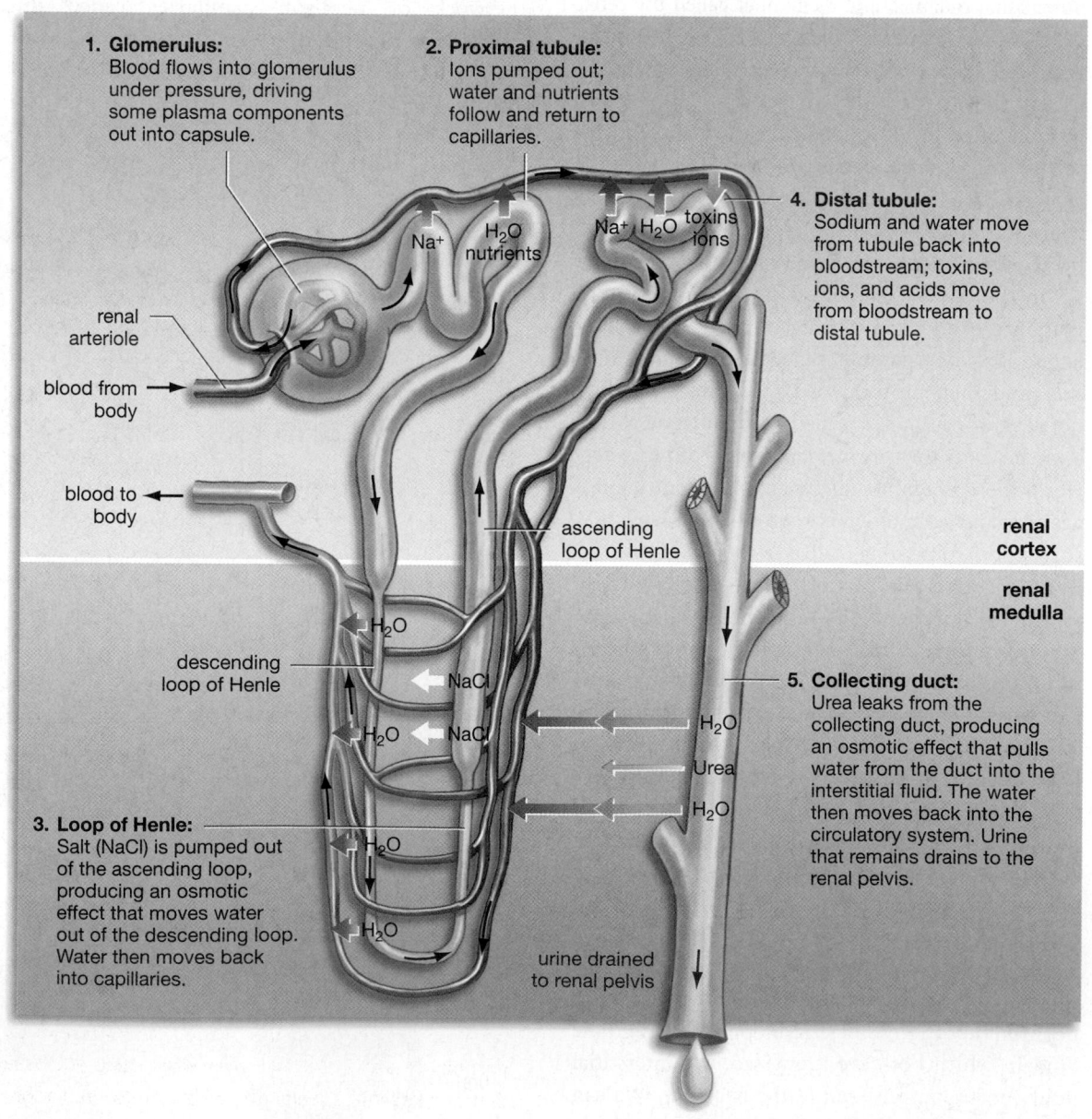

1. Glomerulus:
Blood flows into glomerulus under pressure, driving some plasma components out into capsule.

2. Proximal tubule:
Ions pumped out; water and nutrients follow and return to capillaries.

4. Distal tubule:
Sodium and water move from tubule back into bloodstream; toxins, ions, and acids move from bloodstream to distal tubule.

renal arteriole

blood from body

blood to body

ascending loop of Henle

renal cortex

renal medulla

descending loop of Henle

3. Loop of Henle:
Salt (NaCl) is pumped out of the ascending loop, producing an osmotic effect that moves water out of the descending loop. Water then moves back into capillaries.

5. Collecting duct:
Urea leaks from the collecting duct, producing an osmotic effect that pulls water from the duct into the interstitial fluid. The water then moves back into the circulatory system. Urine that remains drains to the renal pelvis.

urine drained to renal pelvis

Figure 28.19
Physiology of the Nephron

Second Kidney Function: Reabsorption from the Proximal Tubule

Recall that the kidneys are as much in the conservation business as the waste removal business. The process of getting useful materials back to the bloodstream begins immediately after the filtrate moves into the proximal tubule. Cells in the tubule actively pump sodium (Na^+) and several other ions suspended in the filtrate into the interstitial fluid surrounding the tubule. This means there are more "solutes"—materials dissolved in solution—outside the tubule than inside it. This, in turn, brings into play a process that you'll see at work several times in what's coming up: osmosis, meaning the tendency of water to move across a membrane from an area where solute concentration is lower to an area where it is higher. (For more on osmosis, see Chapter 5, page 103.) Thanks to osmosis, the solutes that are pumped out of the tubule will "pull" with them about two-thirds of the water lost in filtration, as well as almost all the nutrients lost there. The amount of water moved in this way is impressive. Our proximal tubules transfer 108 liters or about 29 gallons of water each day.

Once this water and the other substances have moved out of the tubule and into the interstitial fluid, they then move back into the capillaries. With this, the urinary system has completed a great deal of its second major task, the *reabsorption* of valuable materials back into the bloodstream. While this is going on, however, the urea and other waste products have been retained in the nephron tubule because, thanks to their chemical makeup, they cannot easily pass out of it. Reabsorption occurs in other parts of the nephron, but it takes place most significantly at the proximal tubule.

Third Kidney Function: Secretion into the Nephron Tubule

If you now jump ahead in Figure 28.19 (past the loop of Henle) to the *distal* tubule, you can see a similar movement of salt and water out of the tubule and into the bloodstream. Notice, however, that substances are also moving into the tubule at this point. Hydrogen ions (H^+) and potassium ions (K^+) are among the compounds that move from the capillaries into the tubule in a process known as *secretion*. Some poisons and medicines such as penicillin also move into the tubules through this process, to be excreted in the urine. (Secretion also takes place in the proximal tubule, but is illustrated here only in the distal tubule.) In short, secretion functions as a second system for removing substances from the bloodstream.

Fourth Kidney Function: Concentration in the Loop of Henle and the Collecting Duct

As noted earlier, at the proximal tubule about two-thirds of the water in the filtrate moved back to the circulatory system. But what about the other third of the water? This is where the loop of Henle and the collecting duct come into play: They allow the body to move more water back into circulation, thus conserving it. What you will see along the loop and the collecting duct is water being pulled out of the tubule system and moved back into the bloodstream. Fluid in the loop first moves down one of the loop's lengths—the left one in the figure—and then up the other. As such, these are referred to as the descending and ascending "arms" of the loop.

The tricky thing about the loop of Henle is that what happens in the descending arm is dependent on what happens *downstream*—in the ascending arm and the collecting duct. Here's a simplified version of what takes place. Sodium ions (Na^+) are pumped out of the thick portion of the ascending arm you can see in Figure 28.19, and attached to these ions by electrical charge are chloride ions (Cl^-). When linked together like this, sodium chloride is better known as salt, so salt is effectively being pumped out of the thick part of the ascending arm. This sets up a mechanism you've seen before: osmosis. The pumping puts more of a solute (salt) in the interstitial fluid than inside the loop tubule, and this means that *fluid* in the tubule will follow the solute out to the interstitial fluid. This fluid is water. It does not flow out from the ascending loop, however, because this part of the loop is impermeable to water. Instead it flows out of the *descending* loop, which does allow a fairly free flow of water. This water then moves back into the circulatory system and is thus conserved.

This same osmotic process is active not only in the loop of Henle, but in the distal tubule and in the collecting duct. In the lower portion of the duct, a small amount of the urea that has made it through the tubule system leaks out, because of a concentration gradient, and it serves the same function as the salt: It raises the solute concentration in the interstitial fluid. With this, water flows out of the *duct* and back into circulation. When the filtrate reaches the collecting duct, it has such a high concentration of waste in it that it goes by another name: urine. By the time this urine is transported to the bladder, an average of 99 percent of the fluid that originally came into the nephron system has been moved back into circulation.

To recap, the kidneys function by undertaking four main processes:

- **Filtration:** The process by which blood plasma materials move from the glomerulus capillaries into the nephron tubule.
- **Reabsorption:** The process by which filtered materials move from the nephron tubule back to the blood vessels, while waste is retained within the tubule. Occurs primarily in the proximal tubule.
- **Secretion:** The process by which hydrogen ions and various compounds (for example, toxins) move from capillaries into the nephron's tubules.
- **Concentration:** The process by which the final solute concentration of tubule fluid is increased through removal of water from the filtrate in the loop of Henle and the collecting duct—actions that conserve the water.

28.14 Hormonal Control of Water Retention

The kidneys don't just go along producing the same amount of urine in simple accordance with the amount of filtrate that flows into the Bowman's capsule. Rather, through a substance called **antidiuretic hormone (ADH)**, the body is able to *control* how much water is either sent to the bladder (in urine) or retained in circulation.

To understand why this is important, imagine a group of people who are lost in the desert. In such a situation, the body needs to *retain* as much water as possible. How does it do it? The heart has receptors in it that sense blood volume, while the brain's hypothalamus has receptors that sense the solute concentration in the blood. The concentration of solutes in our desert travelers' blood is likely to rise, while their blood volume will fall, because they have been steadily losing water (in breathing, perspiring, and so forth). When these things happen, the hypothalamus orders the release of ADH from the pituitary gland. ADH works on the distal nephron tubule and the collecting duct, having the same effect on both: It increases their permeability to water. This change means that more water moves out of the tubule and collecting duct and thus back *into* circulation. ADH has thus acted to reduce the amount of water lost by the kidney. Looked at another way, it means that the urine becomes more concentrated because it has less water in it. Should our travelers be saved, however, and then not be able to resist a fourth glass of lemonade, the pituitary's production of ADH will be shut

down. The tubule and collecting duct will *retain* more water, meaning that more of it will be urinated. Along these lines, if you've ever wondered why 12 ounces of beer makes a person have to urinate more than does 12 ounces of lemonade, it's because the alcohol in the beer suppresses the production of ADH.

28.15 Urine Storage and Excretion

Having seen how the kidneys produce urine, let's now look at the steps by which urine is then excreted from the body. Recall that urine is transported to the urinary bladder by the pair of tubes called the ureters—one stemming from each kidney. The ureters are muscular tubes that extend for a distance of about 30 centimeters, or 12 inches. Starting at the kidney, about every 30 seconds a peristaltic wave of muscle contraction squeezes urine out of the renal pelvis, along the ureter, and into the urinary bladder. Occasionally, solids develop within the collecting tubules, collecting ducts, or ureters. These are kidney stones, and they can be very painful; in addition to obstructing the flow of urine, they may also reduce or eliminate filtration in the affected kidney.

The Urinary Bladder

The urinary bladder, shown in **Figure 28.20**, is a hollow muscular organ that stores urine. Its dimensions vary with the volume of stored urine, but a full urinary bladder can contain up to 800 milliliters of urine, which is about 27 ounces. The area surrounding the urethral entrance, called the neck of the urinary bladder, contains an internal sphincter muscle that provides involuntary control over the discharge of urine from the bladder.

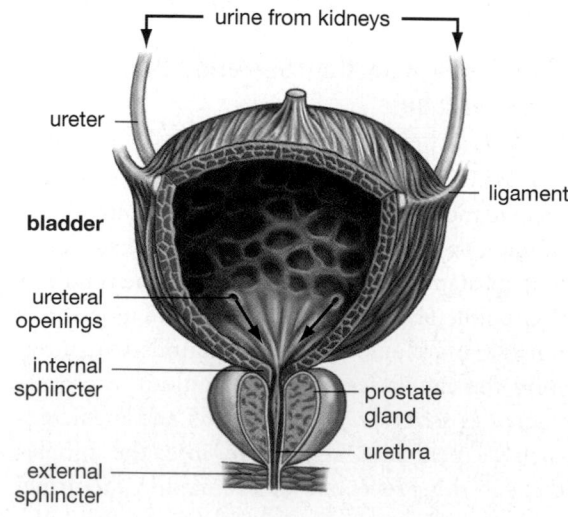

Figure 28.20
The Urinary Bladder in a Male

The Urethra

The urethra extends from the urinary bladder to the exterior of the body. Its length and functions differ in males and females. In the male (shown in Figure 28.20), the urethra extends to the tip of the penis and is about 18 to 20 centimeters (7 to 8 inches) in length. The initial portion of the male urethra is surrounded by the prostate gland. In contrast, the female urethra is very short, extending 2.5 to 3.0 centimeters (about 1 inch). In both sexes, the urethra contains a circular band of skeletal muscle that forms an external sphincter. Unlike the internal sphincter, the external sphincter is under *voluntary* control.

Urine Excretion

The urge to urinate usually appears when the bladder contains about 200 milliliters, or about 7 ounces, of urine. We become aware of this need through nerve impulses sent to the brain from stretch receptors in the wall of the urinary bladder. The stimulation of these receptors also results in involuntary contractions of the urinary bladder that increase the fluid pressure inside the bladder (which is why we "have to go" to the bathroom). Urine ejection cannot occur, however, unless both the internal and external sphincters are relaxed. We control the time and place of urination by voluntarily relaxing the external sphincter. When this sphincter relaxes, so does the internal

sphincter. If the external sphincter does not relax, the internal sphincter remains closed, and the bladder gradually relaxes. A further increase in bladder volume begins the cycle again, usually within an hour. Once the volume of the urinary bladder gets large enough, sufficient pressure is generated to force open the internal sphincter. This leads to an uncontrollable relaxation in the external sphincter, and urination occurs despite voluntary opposition. Normally, less than 10 milliliters (about a third of an ounce) of urine remain in the bladder after urination. As noted earlier, an average of about 1.8 liters (half a gallon) of urine is excreted daily.

On to Development and Reproduction

Animals breathe and digest and move in ways that have been reviewed over the last three chapters. Each generation of animals gives rise to another, of course, through the workings of a specialized system, the reproductive system. Between the moment of conception and the moment of birth, an animal must also go through an amazing transformation— in the case of humans, from a single cell to a baby in full cry. How do single sets of male and female cells interact to form a new living thing? How does this new life then make the transition from one-celled existence to trillion-celled existence? These are the subjects of the next two chapters.

Chapter Review

Summary

28.1 The Cardiovascular System

- The human cardiovascular system is a fluid transport system that consists of the heart, all the body's blood vessels, the blood, and the bone marrow tissue in which red blood cells are formed. This system transports substances both to and from the body's cells. Such substances include oxygen, carbon dioxide, nutrients, vitamins, hormones, waste products, and immune-system cells and proteins.

- Blood has two primary components: formed elements and blood plasma. Formed elements are blood cells and cell fragments; blood plasma is the fluid portion of blood in which the formed elements are suspended. There are three kinds of formed elements: red blood cells, white blood cells, and platelets. Red blood

cells carry oxygen to, and carbon dioxide from, every part of the body; white blood cells are central to the immune system; and platelets are small fragments of cells that are important in the blood-clotting process.

- Blood plasma is 92 percent water, but it also contains dissolved materials, including proteins. There are three primary classes of plasma proteins: albumins, which transport hormones and fatty acids; fibrinogen, which aids in blood clotting; and globulins, which aid the immune system and serve as transport proteins. Two transport proteins are important in the health of the heart. Low-density lipoproteins (LDLs) carry lipids to bodily tissues from the liver and small intestines; high-density lipoproteins (HDLs) carry lipids from these tissues to the liver. Other plasma compounds include nutrients, wastes, hormones, and electrolytes.

Web Tutorial 28.1: Cardiovascular System

28.2 Blood Vessels

- Blood vessels carrying blood away from the heart are arteries; blood vessels returning blood to the heart are veins. The smallest blood vessels, the capillaries, connect the arteries with the veins.

- Arteries and veins are always made of three distinct layers of tissue, the middle layer of which is muscle that allows arteries and veins to widen or constrict in diameter. Capillaries, conversely, are composed of only a single layer of cells; this allows the movement of blood-borne materials into and out of them along their length.

28.3 The Heart and Blood Circulation

- The heart's contractions propel blood out to the various tissues of the body. Two blood-circulation loops exist in the body. The first loop is the pulmonary circulation, in which blood circulates between the heart and the lungs (with the result that blood is oxygenated). The second loop is the systemic circulation, in which blood circulates between the heart and the rest of the body (with the result that needed materials are transported to and from all parts of the body).

- The human heart contains four muscular chambers—two for pulmonary circulation (the right atrium and right ventricle) and two for systemic circulation (the left atrium and left ventricle). A series of valves that open and close ensures that blood flows only one way through the heart.

28.4 What Is a Heart Attack?

- About half of all deaths in the United States today are caused by the blockage of one or more of the coronary arteries that supply heart tissue with blood. Such blockages generally are caused by a build-up of low-density lipoprotein (LDL) molecules in a coronary artery, followed by an immune-system reaction to these LDLs and formation of a blood clot in the artery. A heart attack occurs when this process results in the complete blockage of a coronary artery, which cuts off the blood supply to groups of cells within the heart, thus killing them.

28.5 Distributing the Goods: The Capillary Beds

- Arteries near the heart branch into smaller arterioles, which feed into the delivery vehicles of the cardiovascular system, the capillary beds. The capillary beds then feed back into the body's system of veins that returns blood to the heart.

- Materials needed by the body's tissues move out of the capillaries and into the interstitial fluid that surrounds both the capillaries and nearby cells. Meanwhile, carbon dioxide and wastes from these cells flow into capillaries from the interstitial fluid. The movement of all these substances is aided by their concentration gradients—they are moving from areas of their higher concentration to areas of their lower concentration. The movement of water is driven in two directions by two opposing forces. At the arterial end of the capillary beds, blood pressure tends to drive water out

of the capillaries, but at the venous end of the beds, osmosis overcomes the force of blood pressure and pulls most of this water back into the capillaries.

- Blood pressure is at low levels by the time blood has moved through the capillaries. Blood returns to the heart by the contraction of skeletal muscles, which squeeze the veins in a way that moves the venous blood toward the heart. A system of valves in the veins ensures that this movement is one-way—toward the heart.

28.6 The Respiratory System

- The central function of the respiratory system is to capture oxygen and to dispose of carbon dioxide. It also aids in controlling pH balance in the bloodstream and in producing sounds for speaking. Respiration can be defined as the exchange of gases between the atmosphere outside the body and the cells within it.

- The respiratory system includes the lungs; the nose, nasal cavity, and sinuses; the pharynx (upper throat); the larynx (voice box); the trachea (windpipe); and the conducting passageways, called bronchi and bronchioles, that lead to the lungs. The lungs themselves are largely composed of the tiny hollow sacs, called alveoli, that lie at the end of each bronchiole and that are the air-exchange chambers of the body. The enormous surface area of the alveoli and their associated capillaries is used for the exchange of oxygen and carbon dioxide.

Web Tutorial 28.2: Respiratory System

28.7 Steps in Respiration

- The first step in respiration is breathing or ventilation, meaning the physical movement of air into and out of the lungs.

- Once in the lungs, oxygen diffuses across the thin wall of an alveolus into an adjacent capillary and binds with hemoglobin protein in red blood cells. Oxygen then moves with the blood cells to the heart, which pumps the blood to body tissues, where the oxygen diffuses into the interstitial fluid and then into nearby cells. The carbon dioxide produced in the body cells moves into nearby capillaries, to be carried to the lungs. All the oxygen loaded into red blood cells binds initially with the hemoglobin in them. Carbon dioxide, however, is transported both within red blood cells and in blood plasma.

28.8 The Digestive System

- The central functions of the digestive system are (1) to get the foods the body ingests into a form the body can use and (2) to rid the body of the waste that remains after nutrients from the food have been absorbed. The central structure of the digestive system is a muscular tube called the digestive tract that passes through the body from the mouth to the anus and that receives input along its length from accessory digestive organs such as the gallbladder, liver, and pancreas.

- Digestion is a process of breaking down foods—first into small pieces, and then into small molecules. These small molecules leave the digestive system for transport through the rest of the body.

28.9 Structure of the Digestive System

- The digestive tract begins with the mouth (or oral cavity) and continues through the pharynx, esophagus, stomach, small intestine, and large intestine before ending at the rectum and anus. Through most of its length, the digestive tract is a tube composed of four layers: the serosa, or outermost layer; the muscularis externa, whose two sets of muscles produce the waves of contraction, called peristalsis, that move food along; the submucosa, which contains blood vessels and nerve tissue that control digestion; and the mucosa, which absorbs digested food. Absorbed food is taken up by an adjacent capillary (in the case of carbohydrates and proteins) or a lymphatic vessel (in the case of fats).

28.10   Steps in Digestion

- Digestion begins in the mouth through both mechanical means (chewing) and chemical means (enzymes breaking down carbohydrates). Food is pushed by the tongue into the pharynx (or throat), and moves by muscle contraction from there to the esophagus, whose own muscle contractions work with gravity to push food into the stomach.

- The stomach digests food partly by the mechanical means of churning it and partly by chemical means, with proteins being a primary target of the stomach's digestive juices. The stomach's contents are very acidic—a quality that is valuable both for breaking food down and for killing microorganisms that come in with the food. The material that leaves the stomach is a mixture of food and digestive juices called chyme.

- Eighty percent of the digestive tract's absorption of nutrients takes place within the small intestine—the portion of the digestive tract that begins at the stomach and ends at the large intestine.

- In digestion, the pancreas is an organ that secretes, into the small intestine, three classes of digestive enzymes that help break down fats, proteins, and carbohydrates. It also secretes "buffers" that raise the pH of the acidic chyme coming from the stomach.

- The gallbladder stores and concentrates bile, a substance produced by the liver that aids in the digestion of fats. The liver is a large organ that plays a central role in digestion. All blood carrying nutrients from the digestive tract is channeled through the hepatic portal vein to the liver, making the liver a first stop for much digested material. The liver controls which nutrients it will store and which nutrients it will send to the rest of the body. The liver is also the first stop in the body for ingested toxins such as alcohol, making it vulnerable to damage.

- The large intestine holds and compacts material left over from digestion, turning it into feces. It also returns water to general circulation and absorbs vitamins produced by resident bacteria. One of the large intestine's regions, the rectum, is usually empty except when peristaltic contractions force fecal materials into it. The resulting stretching triggers the urge to defecate.

28.11   The Urinary System in Overview

- The urinary system filters waste materials from the blood, regulates blood volume, and conserves useful materials, such as water, nutrients, and ions.
Web Tutorial 28.3: Urinary System

28.12   Structure of the Urinary System

- The urinary system consists of two kidneys that produce urine; the left and right ureters that the urine travels through upon leaving the kidneys; the muscular urinary bladder, which receives the urine from the ureters and temporarily stores it; and the tube called the urethra, through which urine passes from the bladder out of the body.

- The working unit of the kidneys is the nephron, composed of a nephron tubule, its associated blood vessels, and the interstitial fluid in which both are immersed. Several nephron tubules empty into a common collecting duct, which will merge with other such ducts to feed into the renal pelvis, which feeds into the ureter.

28.13   How the Kidneys Function

- The kidneys undertake four principal processes: (1) filtration, in which portions of the blood plasma move from the bloodstream to the kidney's nephron tubules; (2) reabsorption, in which water and nutrients move back into the blood vessels while waste is retained within the tubules; (3) secretion, in which hydrogen ions, toxins, and other compounds move from the capillaries into the tubules; and (4) concentration, in which the final solute concentration of the urine is increased through the removal of water from the loop of Henle and the collecting duct, thus conserving water.

- The filtration process occurs primarily at the knotted network of capillaries called the glomerulus, which retains some large materials in the blood while letting smaller materials, such as water, nutrients, and waste move, as a fluid called filtrate, into a surrounding nephron structure called the Bowman's capsule. Reabsorption of valuable products back into the bloodstream occurs to a significant extent immediately after filtration at a structure called the proximal tubule. Secretion occurs to a significant extent at the distal tubule, and serves to clear the body of toxins such as poisons or drugs. Concentration is a process by which the filtrate that moves forward from the proximal tubule becomes increasingly concentrated waste by means of water moving out of the tubule and collecting duct through osmosis.

28.14 Hormonal Control of Water Retention

- The body is able to control how much water the kidneys send to the bladder (in urine) or retain in circulation. Retention of water by the kidneys is regulated by the brain structure called the hypothalamus, which controls the secretion of antidiuretic hormone (ADH). An increased secretion of ADH means that more water will move out of the kidney's tubules and collecting ducts and back into circulation.

28.15 Urine Storage and Excretion

- Waves of muscle contraction squeeze urine out of the renal pelvis, thus moving it through the ureters and into temporary storage in the urinary bladder. The tube called the urethra then carries the urine from the urinary bladder to the exterior of the body. An internal sphincter muscle provides involuntary control over the discharge of urine. The urethra also contains an external sphincter that is under voluntary control. We become aware of the need to urinate when the bladder is stretched beyond a certain threshold. We then relax the voluntary, external sphincter, which relaxes the involuntary internal sphincter, and the urine moves out of the bladder and body.

Key Terms

alveoli 617

antidiuretic hormone
  (ADH) 628

aorta 613

artery 611

bile 622

bronchiole 617

capillary 611

cardiovascular system 609

chyme 621

concentration 628

coronary artery 613

digestive tract 618

filtration 628

formed elements 610

gallbladder 622

glomerulus 625

heart attack 614

hemoglobin 610

high-density lipoprotein
  (HDL) 611

kidneys 624

large intestine 623

liver 622

low-density lipoprotein
  (LDL) 611

nephron 625

pancreas 622

peristalsis 620

pharynx 620

plasma 610

platelet 610

pulmonary circulation 612

reabsorption 628

red blood cell (RBC) 610

respiration 616

secretion 628

small intestine 621

stomach 621

systemic circulation 613

ureters 624

urethra 624

urinary bladder 624

vein 611

ventilation 617

white blood cell (WBC) 610

Understanding the Basics

Multiple-Choice Questions (answers in the back of the book)

1. Many poor college students get paid to donate plasma. Which of the following substances is not donated when the plasma is removed?
   a. antibodies
   b. electrolytes
   c. water
   d. lipoproteins
   e. red blood cells

2. What transports oxygen within the blood?
   a. cholesterol in lipoproteins
   b. albumin in plasma
   c. white blood cells moving through capillaries
   d. enzymes in platelets
   e. hemoglobin in red blood cells

3. Which of the following would have the same oxygen content? (Select all that apply.)
   a. blood entering the lungs, blood leaving the lungs
   b. blood entering the right side of the heart, blood entering the left side of the heart
   c. blood entering the right side of the heart, blood leaving the right side of the heart
   d. blood entering the tissue capillary beds, blood leaving the tissue capillary beds
   e. blood entering the left side of the heart, blood leaving the left side of the heart

4. A heart attack can best be described as
   a. a sudden, harmful contraction of the heart muscles
   b. an invasion of heart tissue by pathogens such as bacteria
   c. a death of cells in the heart brought about by blockage of a coronary artery
   d. a failure of the nervous system to bring about heart contractions
   e. a rapid, harmful expansion of blood volume supplied by the heart

5. The small size of alveoli, coupled with their large numbers, provide the lungs with what critical quality for gas exchange?
   a. a resistance to damage caused by pollutants
   b. an affinity for oxygen and lack of affinity for carbon dioxide
   c. an affinity for carbon dioxide and lack of affinity for oxygen
   d. a large surface area
   e. a small surface area

6. The movement of oxygen into capillaries at the lungs and the movement of carbon dioxide into capillaries from the interstitial fluid is driven by
   a. ventilation
   b. hemoglobin binding
   c. the pumping of them
   d. osmotic gradients
   e. concentration gradients

7. The essential function of the digestive system is to
   a. get food into a form that can move into the circulatory system
   b. add nutrients to food
   c. ensure that not too many fats are put into circulation
   d. remove microorganisms from the digestive tract
   e. guard against the release of waste from the digestive tract

8. Most of the nutrients in the food we eat make the transition out of the digestive system in
   a. the stomach
   b. the liver
   c. the small intestine
   d. the large intestine
   e. the pancreas

9. In addition to filtering waste from the body, what are two other critical functions of the kidneys?
   a. storage of blood, distribution of nutrients
   b. production of urea, production of hemoglobin
   c. regulation of blood volume, conservation of useful materials
   d. production of hemoglobin, channeling of lymphatic fluid
   e. storage of nutrients, regulation of digestive system

10. In the loop of Henle and the collecting duct, _____ is/are returned to circulation primarily through the force of _____.
    a. nutrients, gravity
    b. ions, muscle contraction
    c. nutrients, osmosis
    d. vitamins, nerve signals
    e. water, osmosis

Brief Review

1. What are the primary functions of the three formed elements found in blood?

2. Describe the essential difference between the heart's atrial chambers and its ventricular chambers.

3. Why can substances diffuse in and out of capillaries, but not arteries or veins?

4. What arteries in the body carry deoxygenated blood?

5. What do eating animal fats, smoking, and exercise have to do with heart attacks?

6. Where, specifically, does oxygen enter the bloodstream?

7. Why are most nutrients ready to enter the bloodstream from the small intestine, but not ready to enter from the stomach?

8. Apart from waste storage and compaction, what does the large intestine do?

9. Why don't blood cells and protein molecules get passed into the filtrate that moves through the kidneys' nephrons?

10. What is the small signal of discomfort that tells us when we need to urinate?

Applying Your Knowledge

1. Heart attacks have sometimes been called a disease of modern civilization, because their incidence is much higher in affluent, developed societies than in poorer, less developed ones. Why should this be so?

2. Suppose that instead of returning nearly all nutrients and 98 percent of fluids back into circulation, the kidneys could return only half these proportions. Could human beings function? How would it change the way they live?

3. Species of an animal called the desert kangaroo rat (genus *Dipodomys*) do not need to drink any liquid water. They get the water they need through their metabolism of the dry seeds they eat. Can you guess what special adaptations their loops of Henle might have undergone to allow them to get by on such a small amount of water? (Hint: Water moves back into circulation along the length of the loop of Henle.)

29 *Animal Development*

Sixteen cells, future frog.
(Section 29.1, page 636)

Cells take their places.
(Section 29.1, page 637)

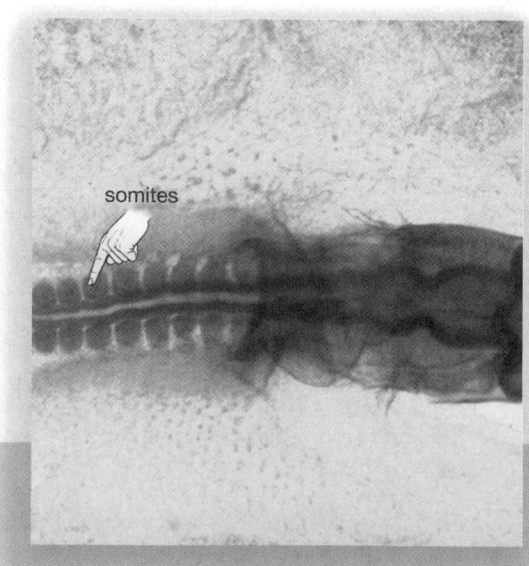

somites

The segments in animal bodies.
(Section 29.1, page 639)

> **How can a living thing start out as a single cell and end up as a fully formed animal? It goes through a process called development.**

Of all the marvels in the natural world, the most spectacular may be a complex process that goes under a simple name: development. The set of steps by which, for example, a human embryo goes from being a speck of microscopic cells to a newborn cradled in its mother's arms is so remarkable that even the old adage about "seeing is believing" is turned on its head. People who view pictures of such a work in progress can scarcely believe what they're seeing. It's not uncommon, months after the birth of a child, for parents to find themselves looking at the baby and then at each other in amazement, still wondering how such a thing is possible.

This process is all the more notable because it takes place through self-assembly. There is no outside hand here; no master artisan watching over each step and intervening where necessary. There is instead a starting set of instructions supplied by maternal and paternal DNA, and a starting set of proteins and other molecules that come in the maternal egg. From these elements, an embryo fashions itself, aided only by the nurturing environment of egg or womb.

How can such an event take place? As you'll see, in species as diverse as frogs, insects, and human beings a common, core set of steps is followed in development. Moreover, nature has provided a number of "tools" that are employed in development, and these likewise tend to be utilized across the different species.

Because nature can fashion an entire organism from the instructions contained in a single egg, scientists long wondered: Would it be possible to regenerate *parts* of the human organism by harnessing the power of development? Could we grow new knee joints for arthritis sufferers, for example, or new cardiac tissue for heart attack victims? In just the past few years, researchers have taken some giant steps toward this goal. As you'll see, the key to this progress has been a deepened understanding of the developmental tools known as stem cells.

Double digit growth.
(Section 29.2, page 640)

Sculpting through cell death.
(Section 29.4, page 643)

What are stem cells?
(Section 29.5, page 644)

29.1 General Processes in Development

Let's now begin by looking at the developmental progression that is common to much of the animal world, noting first what happens in development, and then going over *how* these things happen. We'll be looking at several species, rather than just humans, as this will provide a clearer picture of what takes place.

Two Cells Become One: Fertilization

When a sperm encounters an egg, these two cells fuse in the moment generally referred to as **fertilization**, but more poetically known as conception. The fertilized egg brought about by the fusion of egg and sperm, a **zygote**, is itself a cell, although a very special one in that an entire living thing will develop from it. Development at its simplest level is a process by which this single, original cell divides to become two cells, after which the two become four, the four eight, and so on. Once the zygote starts dividing, we call it an **embryo**.

Three Phases of Early Embryonic Development

Early embryonic development in animals can be divided into three phases.

- *Cleavage.* Cellular division results in a ball of cells with an interior cavity.
- *Gastrulation.* These cells rearrange themselves into three layers that will give rise to specific organs and tissues.
- *Organogenesis.* Organs begin to form.

First Phase: Cleavage

Cleavage is a developmental process in which a zygote is repeatedly divided into smaller individual cells through cell division. The reason the cells get progressively smaller is that none of the usual cell growth occurs between these cell divisions.

The product of this process of cleavage is a **morula** (from the Latin for "mulberry"), a tightly packed ball of early embryonic cells. This configuration soon changes, however, as the cells arrange themselves into a **blastula**: an early embryonic structure composed of one or more layers of cells surrounding a liquid-filled cavity. Several hundred to several thousand cells make up the blastula, whose cavity is known as a **blastocoel** (see Figure 29.1a).

The original egg contains a quantity of yolk, which helps give the zygotes of many species a *polarity*, meaning a difference between one end and the other. In many zygotes, one end contains a relatively greater proportion of yolk, and this end is called the **vegetal pole**. Meanwhile, the other end has relatively less yolk and lies closer to the cell's nucleus, and this end is called the **animal pole**. As you'll see, this polarity helps define the way the embryo develops.

Second Phase: Gastrulation

Anyone who has ever watched a play in rehearsal probably has witnessed a phenomenon that bears some comparison with the second phase in embryonic development, gastrulation. It's the moment in which the director says to the assembled cast, "Take your places." What happens then is a carefully directed movement of actors; some move only a little, whereas others go from one side of the stage to the other. After all this movement is done, the actors—having assumed their places—are ready to take on their assigned roles.

Gastrulation is likewise a process of directed movement, in this case of groups of cells that move to particular places in the developing embryo. Once this movement is completed, the cells will have formed themselves into three different layers that are ready to take on their assigned roles. These layers—the endoderm, mesoderm, and ectoderm—are "germ" layers

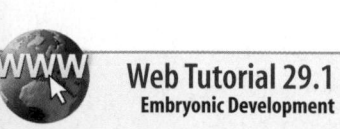

Web Tutorial 29.1
Embryonic Development

Figure 29.1
Cleavage of a Frog Egg

(a) 1. Like all animals, the frog starts out as a single-celled zygote. 2. Cell division begins and the zygote is now called an embryo. 3. Repeated cell division of the embryo results in a tightly packed ball of smaller cells, called a morula. 4. This configuration gives way to a blastula, in which the cells are arranged around a liquid-filled cavity, the blastocoel. The yolk at the vegetal end of the zygote impedes cleavage, so that fewer but larger cells result at the vegetal pole than at the animal pole of both the morula and blastula. The drawing at far right shows a cross-section of the blastula, with its blastocoel visible.

(b) An artificially colored micrograph of a frog embryo at the 16-cell stage of development.

(a)

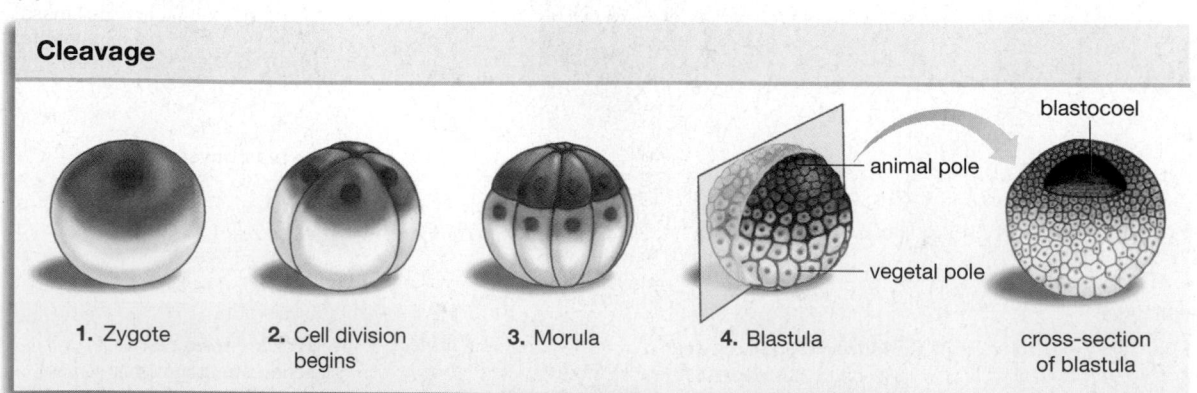

Cleavage

1. Zygote   2. Cell division begins   3. Morula   4. Blastula   cross-section of blastula

blastocoel
animal pole
vegetal pole

(b)

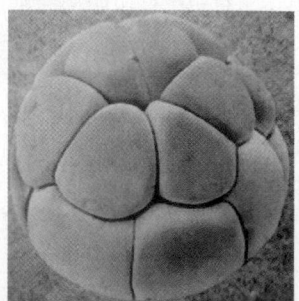

of cells, meaning layers that *lead to* other kinds of structures (**see Table 29.1**). As it turns out, endoderm, mesoderm, and ectoderm have a kind of "inside/middle/outside" quality to them, and this is reflected in the organs and tissues that develop from them. In gastrulation, endoderm takes its place as the innermost layer, mesoderm as the middle layer, and ectoderm as the outer layer. In line with this, endoderm gives rise to interior tissues (the liver and bladder, for example), mesoderm to tissues exterior to these (muscle and skeletal systems), and ectoderm to tissues that are more exterior yet (the skin and nervous system, which first appear in the embryo's outermost layer.) **Gastrulation** can thus be defined as a process in early development in which an embryo's cells migrate to form three layers of tissue: the endoderm, the mesoderm, and the ectoderm.

One Example of Gastrulation: The Sea Urchin   Let's now look at the process of gastrulation in one organism, the sea urchin, chosen because its gastrulation is so easy to visualize (**see Figure 29.2**). By the time it is ready for gastrulation, the sea urchin blastula amounts to a single layer of about a thousand cells arranged in a hollow ball, the interior of which is the liquid-filled blastocoel. Gastrulation begins at the blastula's vegetal pole. Some cells at the pole, called *mesenchyme* cells, detach from the ring of blastula cells and move into the blastocoel, and with their loss, the vegetal pole begins to pinch

Table 29.1 Three Layers of Cells That Are Assembled in Gastrulation and Some of the Structures They Give Rise to in Mammals	
Cell layer	**Organs or types of tissue it gives rise to**
Endoderm	Lungs, liver, pancreas, lining of digestive tract, lining of bladder, and several glands
Mesoderm	Much of the body mass of more complex animals, including most of the muscle and skeletal systems; blood, blood vessels, and bone marrow; the uterus and the sperm- and egg- producing gonads; the kidneys; and the cortex of the adrenal gland
Ectoderm	Entire nervous system; lenses of eyes, tooth enamel, and the outer or epidermal layer of skin

inward. This process, called *invagination*, eventually will carry the vegetal pole as much as halfway toward the blastula's animal pole. A primitive gut, called the *archenteron*, starts forming around this indentation. Cells growing at the tip of the archenteron begin to send out slender extensions of themselves that adhere to selected cells that lie "above" them on the rim of the blastocoel. These extensions then contract, effectively pulling the archenteron toward the animal pole, and eventually moving the archenteron all the way to the pole itself.

Now, how does all of this yield the three layers of cells we just talked about? When the archenteron reaches the rim of the blastocoel, a fusion of the two

Gastrulation

Figure 29.2
Gastrulation in the Sea Urchin

1. The sea urchin blastula amounts to a few thousand cells, arranged in a single layer around the liquid-filled blastocoel.

2. Mesenchyme cells at the blastula's vegetal pole move into the blastocoel, prompting the vegetal pole to pinch inward, moving toward the animal pole. The structure that starts forming from this indentation is the archenteron, or primitive gut.

3. Mesenchyme cells, growing at the tip of the elongating archenteron, send out slender extensions of themselves that adhere to cells on the rim of the blastocoel. These extensions contract, moving the archenteron to the animal pole.

4. The mouth of the sea urchin forms where the archenteron contacts the blastocoel lining. A digestive tube then runs from this mouth to the rim of the vegetal pole, which develops into an anus. These cells constitute the inner layer or endoderm of the sea urchin. Mesenchyme cells move back down into the blastocoel, forming the middle layer or mesoderm of the sea urchin. The outer cells of the blastula form the sea urchin's outer layer or ectoderm.

638

Organogenesis

1. Start with embryo near end of gastrulation.

2. Notochord induces development and infolding of neural plate.

3. Neural folds deepen from anterior to posterior, giving rise to neural tube.

4. Neural tube complete; will give rise to brain and spinal cord.

Figure 29.3
Body Planes in a Frog and Formation of the Frog Central Nervous System

Figure 29.4
Neural Crest Migration in a Frog Embryo
This cross-section through a frog embryo shows some of the pathways of neural crest cells as they migrate to various locations, prompting the development of different tissues and organs.

structures takes place that initiates formation of the mouth of the sea urchin. A tube then develops from the mouth that runs the length of the sea urchin, right down to the original vegetal pole. There, the rim of the invagination you saw earlier will develop into an anus. As you might guess, this entire feeding and digestive apparatus is the inner cell layer or endoderm of the sea urchin. The cells whose slender extensions reached the blastocoel are also mesenchyme cells; once they get the archenteron to the top of the blastocoel, they break away from the tip of the archenteron and then move back down into the blastocoel cavity. There they will form the mesoderm, or middle layer, of the sea urchin—eventually its skeleton and muscles. Finally, the outer cells of the blastula form the outer cell layer or ectoderm of the organism, eventually becoming its skin and related organs.

Third Phase: Organogenesis

In vertebrates, an interplay of two of these three germ layers marks the first steps on the path to the development of organs—in this case, organs of the nervous system.

In talking about development in any organism, an important concept is *body planes*—imagined divisions that pass through the center of an animal, dividing it into two parts of roughly equal size. In **Figure 29.3**, step 1, you can see that a frog embryo has been divided with two such planes. The first yields dorsal and ventral portions of the embryo; the second yields anterior and posterior ends. In the case of a frog, dorsal eventually will mean its back, ventral its belly; anterior will mean its head, and posterior its hindquarters.

Looking at steps 2 and 3 in Figure 29.3, you can see what takes place toward the frog embryo's dorsal surface as gastrulation is nearing completion. First, there is the development of a rod-shaped support organ found in all embryonic vertebrates, the **notochord**. In addition to support, one of the notochord's functions is to *induce*, or bring about, development in the ectodermal tissue that lies above it, toward the dorsal surface. This development begins with an elongation of the ectodermal cells to form a flattened surface called the *neural plate*, which curls up and eventually folds all the way over on itself to form an enclosed, hollow tube that will lie below the dorsal surface. Developing from anterior to posterior, this **neural tube** is a dorsal, ectodermal structure that gives rise in vertebrates to both the brain and spinal cord.

Equally important are **neural crest cells**: cells that break away from the top of the vertebrate neural tube as it folds together and then migrate to varying parts of the embryo, giving rise to various tissues and organs. For example, the medulla or inner portion of the adrenal glands (which in humans sit atop the kidneys) is derived from neural crest cells. You can see the routes of these migrations and some of their outcomes in **Figure 29.4**. One consequence of a failure of neural crest-derived tissue to develop properly is a gap that occasionally occurs between the nose and mouth in humans, which is known as a cleft lip.

As this ectodermal movement is taking place, mesodermal tissue on both sides of the notochord is developing into repeating blocks of tissue, called **somites** (**see Figure 29.5**). A good part of the human body is built of repeating units—think of each of the vertebra that make up our spinal column, the muscles that attach to each of these vertebrae, and the ribs that extend from the vertebrae. All these structures develop at least in part from the somites.

Themes in Development: From General to Specific; Retention of Structures and Processes

As complicated as all this may seem, it amounts to a brief look at important, but early periods of development in animals. Looking at the larger picture, notice that in the early stages of development, there is a movement from the general to the specific. The animal goes from a small group of superficially similar cells, to three *layers* of cells, to tissues that proceed from these layers (notochord, somites), to actual organs formed from these tissues. To put a little finer point on this, think of the somites. They arise from undifferentiated mesodermal tissue on each side of the notochord and they take shape as about 40 blocks of mesodermal tissue. These blocks then go on to give rise to several structures that re-

Figure 29.5
Somites
These regular, repeating blocks of mesodermal tissue, visible in this case on either side of the notochord of a chick embryo, will give rise to muscles and the vertebrae that enclose the spinal cord.

tain the somites' repeating nature, but that are much more specialized (vertebrae, ribs).

It's also worth noting that the three most basic developmental processes we looked at—cleavage, gastrulation, and organogenesis—are processes that take place in all animals, not just a selected few. In a similar vein, if we were to look in detail at nervous-system development in vertebrates as different as frogs, chickens, and human beings, we would see the same sequence of events taking place: the supportive notochord inducing development of a neural plate that folds over on itself, eventually becoming both spinal cord and brain. It is often said that evolution is a "tinkerer" that retains what has worked for one species and then modifies it only slightly for later-evolving species. In development, we can see clear examples of just how much is retained from one species to the next (**see Figure 29.6**).

snake   chicken   possum   cat   bat   human

Figure 29.6
Embryonic Development in Six Vertebrates
Pictured are six vertebrates in early, middle, and late stages of their development. Note the general similarly in vertebrate shape in the early stage of development, which roughly corresponds to the period following somite formation. The embryos are not to scale—in reality some are bigger than others. Photo courtesy of Michael K. Richardson. Human embryo from R. O'Rahilly.

Figure 29.7
Cells Can Induce Development in Other Cells
Transplantation experiments with chick embryos revealed that a group of cells on the posterior portion of the chick's limb bud give out positional information for the development of digits in the chick wing.

(a) When cells from a zone of polarizing activity (ZPA) were left in their normal posterior location, the chick wing developed as usual.

(b) When limb bud ZPA cells were transplanted to the anterior portion of a second limb bud, the result was mirror images of two sets of developing posterior wing digits, much like two sets of human fingers extending from a joined hand.

chick embryo

(a) Normal limb bud

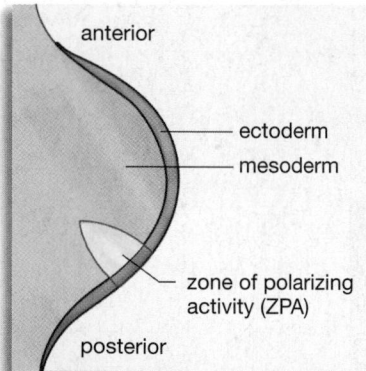

anterior

ectoderm
mesoderm

zone of polarizing activity (ZPA)

posterior

Normal wing

(b) Grafted limb bud

transplanted ZPA

ZPA

Second set of digits induced

29.2 What Factors Underlie Development?

Now that you've taken a brief look at what happens in early development, the next question is: *How* do these things happen? How do vegetal pole cells "know" they are vegetal pole cells? How do neural crest cells take different routes through an embryo and end up serving as different kinds of cells?

The Process of Induction

As noted, the notochord *induces* or prompts the development of the ectodermal tissue that lies above it. Such **induction** is an important process in development in general. It can be defined as the capacity of some embryonic cells to direct the development of other embryonic cells. If you look at **Figure 29.7**, you can see how induction works in the well-studied example of chick wings. In essence, there is a relatively small group of cells that gives out positional information for the development of a portion of the wing. Researchers learned this by working with the "limb bud" that is transformed into the chick wing.

They took cells from a posterior "zone of polarizing activity" (ZPA) in one limb bud and transplanted them to the *anterior* portion of a second limb bud. The result was activity in this bud by both the natural and transplanted ZPA; this resulted in *two* sets of developing digits in wings, spreading out like two sets of human fingers developing from joined hands. In short, the cells in the ZPA induced the development of other cells, sending out a message that said, in effect, "begin digit development here."

The Interaction of Genes and Proteins

This induction process raises the question of what lies at the root of development. There are lots of cells in an embryo. How can some of them (such as the ZPA cells) control the development of others? It turns out that, at its most basic level, development is controlled by the interaction of genes and proteins—the genetic regulation reviewed in Chapter 14. Biologists' understanding of how this interaction works in development has grown dramatically in the period from the early 1980s to the present. Though there have been several important "model" organisms in this research, the most important of them has been the tiny fruit fly, *Drosophila melanogaster*. Let's look at a little of what the *Drosophila* research has uncovered.

Three Lessons in One Gene

There is a *Drosophila* gene, called *bicoid*, that codes for a protein that is also called bicoid. This single gene offers a clear example of three principles that operate in development:

- A critical early step in development is the establishment of positional information in the embryo.
- Substances called *morphogens* are important in establishing this positional information.
- Development operates from the general to the specific through a genetic cascade.

Look at the unfertilized *Drosophila* egg pictured in **Figure 29.8** to see how these principles play out with respect to the bicoid protein. Recall first, the body planes described earlier. In Figure 29.8a, the top of the egg is its dorsal portion and the bottom its ventral portion, while the left side corresponds to its anterior portion and the right side to its posterior. Eventually, the anterior portion will be the head of the fly, the posterior its hindquarters, the dorsal portion its back, and the ventral portion its belly.

While the egg is still in the mother, a group of "nurse cells" surrounds its anterior portion and pumps molecular products into it. These products include bicoid messenger RNAs (mRNAs)—genetic instructions copied from the *bicoid* gene. Eventually, these mRNA instructions will lead to the bicoid protein. Looking at the figure, you can see that the *bicoid* mRNAs are found at the anterior end of the egg. These mRNAs eventually start to diffuse through the egg, but because they are deposited only at the anterior end, they will exist in a *concentration gradient*, with the greatest concentration being at the anterior end, a lesser concentration toward the center, and none at the posterior end. This leads to the concentration gradient of the bicoid protein you can see in Figure 29.8b.

Positional Information

With this general background, you can now see how *bicoid* exemplifies one of the principles of development noted earlier. What does the bicoid protein do? It imparts positional information to the embryo and is critical in setting in motion the development of structures in the anterior and center portions of the embryo. Recall that the far-anterior portion of the egg eventually becomes the head of the *Drosophila* fly. In experiments, however, scientists have taken bicoid-laden cytoplasm from the anterior portion of one egg, placed it at the *center* of an egg with no bicoid in it, and watched as the head and related structures developed at the center. Meanwhile, an egg with no bicoid protein gives rise to a fly that never develops a head, though its posterior structures start to develop normally.

Morphogens

The bicoid protein is a **morphogen**: a diffusable substance whose local concentration affects the course of local development in an organism. Several other morphogens are operating in *Drosophila* in early development. Indeed, several positional "systems" are at work in the fly. What's important to note is that, with these systems, a three-dimensional *grid* is set up in which the destiny of various cells is determined by their position within this grid. How? Their exposure to different morphogens varies according to their position.

But what is it that morphogens are doing to affect cells? You may remember learning in Chapter 14 about proteins that feed back on DNA, binding with it and thus controlling its transcription, which is to say turning its genes on or off. These DNA-regulating proteins are called **transcription factors**. Morphogens are cell-signaling molecules that bring about the production of transcription factors. Diffusing out from one group of cells, morphogens provide a signal to other cells to start producing transcription factors.

We can see an example of this effect in the chick wing development noted earlier. Recall that ZPA cells in the limb buds were able to induce the development of digits in the chick wing. ZPA cells can play their controlling role because they produce a morphogen, called sonic hedgehog, that acts on surrounding cells: it diffuses to them and prompts them to begin producing transcription factors. Moreover, like all morphogens, sonic hedgehog is having its effects through a concentration gradient. The order of the digits in the chick wing—the equivalent of the order of our digits from thumb to little finger—is specified by how much sonic hedgehog the receiving cells are exposed to. The chick's posterior digit (the equivalent of our little finger) forms from cells closest to the ZPA—the cells exposed to the greatest amount of sonic hedgehog. Farther out from the ZPA the concentration of sonic hedgehog lessens and the result is cells that become the chick's *anterior* digit (our thumb). In a similar way, the placement of the head and center structures of *Drosophila* is determined by the concentration gradient of the bicoid morphogen. Bicoid exists in greatest concentration at the anterior portion of the embryo, and this is where the fly's head develops; it exists in lesser concentration in the middle of the fly, and this is where its center-portion structures develop.

The Genetic Cascade

The developmental effects we've been reviewing work through what is sometimes called a genetic cascade. Like water flowing from one level to the next, gene products flow from one developmental

Figure 29.8
***Drosophila* Egg and Bicoid Gradient**
A fly begins to develop. **(a)** Nurse cells surround the anterior portion of an unfertilized *Drosophila* egg. The cells pump messenger RNA molecules for the bicoid protein into the egg. **(b)** The messenger RNAs are translated into bicoid proteins that diffuse through the now-fertilized egg. These proteins exist, however, in a concentration gradient—in high concentration at the anterior end of the embryo, but in low to undetectable concentration at the posterior end. The bicoid protein is a morphogen that imparts information regarding development of anterior and center-position structures in the fly. An egg without bicoid in it gives rise to a fly that never develops a head.

(a) Bicoid mRNAs are deposited in unfertilized egg.

(b) Bicoid proteins diffuse through embryo.

level to the next. An initial set of genes is turned on, perhaps by getting a signal from a morphogen, and in time these genes regulate *other* genes, which in turn may regulate still more genes. This explains how development moves from the general to the specific. In *Drosophila*, for example, the first level of genes specifies broad positional patterns across the embryo—anterior and posterior, dorsal and ventral. Then, through the cascade, this positioning gets finer-grained; now other genes are switched on, and development is being specified *within* sections of the embryo. Finally, control is exercised over the development of specific body *structures*, such as wings or antennae. It's worth noting that the genetic cascade turns genes off as well as on. To take one example, once somites have given rise to ribs, vertebrae, and so forth, the genes for building somites will be turned off permanently.

29.3 Unity in Development: Homeobox Genes

Recall how you saw earlier that species as diverse as fruit flies, frogs, and human beings have similar processes going on in their development. Now that you have some sense of how genes control development, you won't be surprised to learn that it is similar developmental genes that underlie these similar processes. The remarkable thing, however, is *how* similar these genes are across species, how widely they are distributed across the living world, and how long they have existed. As scientists would put it, these genes have been *highly conserved*—portions of them have been passed on intact, like prized bits of knowledge, down long evolutionary lines.

The best example of this conservation comes with a group of genes whose similarity was discovered in *Drosophila* in the 1980s. Scientists were then tracing development in *Drosophila* by mutating the developmental genes of one generation of flies and then watching to see what effect this had on the next generation. Some of the changes they got by doing this were dramatic. One mutation resulted in flies that had legs where their eyes were supposed to be. What the scientists learned from this exercise was that gene X had developmental effect Y.

In carrying out this work, the scientists were sequencing these genes—they were learning the order of their building-block A's, T's, C's, and G's. As they did this, they found that every one of these developmental genes had within it an identical sequence of about 180 letters (or base pairs). The real shock came, however, when this so-called *homeobox se-*

quence was found to exist in all animals studied—in frogs, and humans, and mice, for example, as well as flies. This was surprising because mice and flies went down separate evolutionary paths about 550 million years ago. The implication was that a common ancestor of both animals (probably a variety of worm) possessed homeobox genes at least 550 million years ago. The "at least" comes because versions of homeobox-containing genes have now been found in fungi and in *plants*, which diverged from animals about 1.2 billion years ago.

Not surprisingly, homeobox genes produce transcription factors. One well-studied group of homeobox genes, named *Hox* genes in vertebrates and *HOM* genes in flies, gives out anterior-posterior positioning information—these genes specify where different structures should go along the anterior-posterior axis. (Remember the *Drosophila* flies that got legs where their eyes were supposed to be? This came about because scientists mutated one of their *HOM* genes, thus altering their legs' positioning.) So conserved are the *HOM/Hox* genes that they not only have the same general function in humans and in flies, but are arranged in the same order along their respective chromosomes. Even more surprising, some homeobox-containing genes are partly interchangeable across species. Scientists have spliced into the *Drosophila* genome a mouse gene that codes for eye development in the mouse. They then watched as this gene brought about normal eye development in the *fly*. Not mouse eyes in the fly, mind you—fly eyes.

What all this means is that there is a general set of genetic instructions for development that are so important they have changed very little over time and across species. Fly eyes and mouse eyes are structurally quite different, but there is a general set of genetic instructions for "eyes" that seems to trigger the development of *specific* kinds of eyes in specific animals.

Spurred on by these kinds of findings, scientists today are busy studying how homeobox genes and their proteins differ among the species. This is important work because it stands to tell us a great deal not only about development, but about evolution. How does one species evolve from another—how does it branch off? Developmental genes often are involved, for the simple reason that one organism will not physically differ much from another without a change in these genes. Insects have six legs, rather than the multitude that many of their fellow arthropods have, because a homeobox gene in one of their ancestors underwent a mutation. In its mutated state, this gene produced a protein that turned *off* another gene—a gene that brings about multiple leg formation. By tracking developmental gene differences in modern animals, scientists can learn how these various animals evolved in the first place.

29.4 Developmental Tools: Sculpting the Body

Genes may lie at the root of development, but the shaping of an organism takes place through genetic instructions that prompt whole cells to take actions. You may wonder how a hand, for example, can be shaped from a seemingly formless mass of cells. The answer lies in capabilities cells have that allow for this sort of development. Three examples of these capabilities are cell movement, cell adhesion, and cell death.

Earlier, you saw examples of cell movement and cell adhesion when reviewing the process of gastrulation in the sea urchin. Recall that cells of the primitive gut were able to move up into the blastocoel, after which cells peripheral to them sent out slender extensions of themselves that adhered to selected cells that lay "above" them in the blastocoel. The first part of this process, cell movement, comes about in various ways. Often cells use the tent-pole-like structures called microfilaments that grow very rapidly at one end of the cell—in the direction of movement—while decomposing at the other.

Cell adhesion is accomplished through several families of proteins, collectively called *cell adhesion molecules*, that protrude from the surface of cells, allowing them to stick selectively onto other cells. Different groups of cells have different adhesion "affinities" for each other—depending on the proteins they put on their surfaces—and this explains how the *layers* of cells that you've seen come about. Imagine two groups of cells, A and B, that are randomly mixed in with one another. Now imagine that, through genetic control, the A cells start producing a surface protein that makes them strongly adhere to other A cells. By process of random cellular movement, the A and B cells will now start to segregate into two separate groups.

Cell death may not sound like a promising means of developing an organism, but consider that a sculptor may work not by adding material, but by chipping away at an initial mass of it. Thus it is in development, where cell death works to create spaces that define shapes. An example of this is the human hand which, but for the death of large numbers of cells between future fingers, would look more like the webbed foot of a duck (**see Figure 29.9**). Cells that die in this fashion are not attacked by other cells. Instead, they commit suicide in a process known as *apoptosis* or *programmed cell death*. Apoptosis is a very orderly process, akin to a

Figure 29.9
Soon to Be Different
The webbed hand of a human embryo, 40 days after conception. The programmed death of cells in the hand will bring about the emergence of five separate fingers.

person dying in a hospital rather than a car crash. The cell undergoing it fades away in a sense; it shuts down its processes, shrinks, and then dies, after which its remains are ingested by neighboring cells.

29.5 The Promise of Stem Cells

Having reviewed a couple of examples of wings or legs being induced to grow where they normally wouldn't, you may have the impression that groups of cells are infinitely adaptable in what they can become; that given the right morphogen or transcription factor, a cell could be induced to become anything at any point. For most cells, however, this is not the case. As you'll see, most cells are fated to become a given kind of cell, and they cannot become any other kind of cell. A relatively small number of cells, however, do have the capacity to *give rise* to different kinds of cells. These cells are called stem cells, and only in recent years have scientists begun to learn how adaptable some of them can be. This is not just a matter of academic interest, however. Research into stem cells has exploded in recent years because of the medical potential they hold. So promising are stem cells that scientists now routinely express the hope that, through them, we might someday be able to completely repair the damage done by spinal-cord injuries or heart attacks, to give just two examples. To understand the importance of stem cells, let's look first at how they differ from most cells in the body.

Cell Fates: Determined and Committed

As you've seen, development goes from the general to the specific. Early in development, therefore, a given type of cell needs to be adaptable enough to go down several different developmental pathways. Mesodermal cells, for example, need to be able to give rise not only to muscle tissue, but to bone tissue. Once the body is fully formed, however, all its specialized tissues and organs are in place, meaning there is less need for cells that have this kind of flexibility. The result is that most cells in the adult human body have undergone what is known as **commitment**: a developmental process that results in cells whose roles are completely determined. Almost all your liver cells, for example, have undergone commitment in that they can be nothing but liver cells and can give rise to nothing but liver cells.

From a human perspective, the problem with this sequence of events is that the tissues of fully developed human beings can become damaged. They break down or become diseased; they are injured in car accidents or fires. And many damaged tissues will not regenerate themselves. A person whose spinal cord is severed does not generate a new spinal cord. Thus, for medicine, the question for decades has been: Could we use developmental processes to generate new tissue? One obvious way to go about this would be to harness the power of the cells that, in nature, generate new kinds of tissue—early embryonic cells. It turns out, however, that there is also another possibility. A small proportion of *adult* cells retain the ability to produce specialized cells. Both the adult and the embryonic cells that have this generative capacity are known as **stem cells**: cells with the capacity for prolonged self-renewal that can produce at least one type of specialized daughter cell. Scientists have known about both adult and embryonic stem cells for years. What's new is our ability to find and manipulate them.

The Breakthrough in Embryonic Stem Cells

Remember that the very early embryo is a fertilized egg that has begun to undergo cell division. In humans, up through the seventh day after fertilization, any one of these cells can give rise to a whole separate organism. Indeed, it is these early cells that produce identical twins. A cell that can give rise to every kind of cell in an organism—and hence to a whole new organism—is said to be a **totipotent cell**.

Now go forward in development a little to the embryonic structure you looked at earlier called the blastula—the hollowed-out ball of cells with a fluid-filled center. In mammals, the blastula is known as a **blastocyst**, but it is very similar to the blastula you looked at earlier. It turns out that some of the cells in the human blastocyst are **pluripotent cells**: they are cells capable of giving rise to almost all of the specialized cells or tissues in the body. They do not have the flexibility of totipotent cells—they can't develop into a whole new embryo—but they are very flexible indeed. The 200-cell human blastocyst fits into a particular stage of human reproduction. One section of its cells becomes the placenta that will help nurture a growing embryo, while another section of cells, called the *inner cell mass*, constitutes the embryo itself. It is these latter blastocyst cells that are pluripotent (**see Figure 29.10**).

For years scientists could not imagine doing much with human blastocyst cells, because it was thought that these cells could exist only for fleeting periods of time *in blastocysts*. Despite many efforts, no one could first retrieve or "isolate" the pluripotent cells from human blastocysts and then get them to grow and divide *in the laboratory*. In other words, scientists could not "culture" these cells, or get them to maintain themselves in laboratory petri dishes. This changed in 1998, when a research team led by James Thomson of the University of Wisconsin announced it had been able to manage this feat. These pluripotent blastocyst cells now figure regularly in news stories, but they are referred to by a different name: **embryonic stem cells**, defined as cells from the blastocyst stage of a human embryo that are capable of giving rise to all the cells or tissues in the adult body.

**Figure 29.10
Cells that Can Become Anything**
Human development starts with the fertilization of egg by sperm and then proceeds through several days of cell division, such that by day 3 the embryo has become a tiny, solid ball of cells—the morula noted earlier in the chapter. By day 5, however, the morula has developed into a hollow ball of about 200 cells called a blastocyst. One portion of the blastocyst, the inner cell mass, will develop into the baby. The cells that make up the inner cell mass are pluripotent—each one is capable of giving rise to nearly every variety of human tissue. Another name for these cells is embryonic stem cells. Pictured to the right is a human blastocyst on day 6 of development. It has recently undergone the process of "hatching" or breaking out of the protective covering that surrounds early embryos, which is why it no longer has the spherical shape of the day-5 blastocyst.

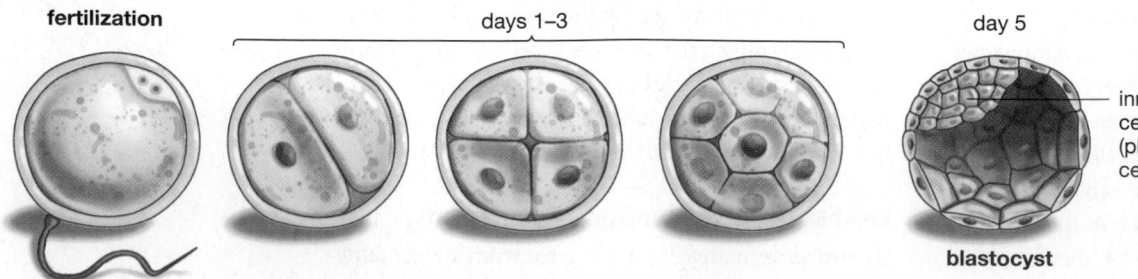

fertilization   days 1–3   day 5

inner cell mass (pluripotent cells)

blastocyst

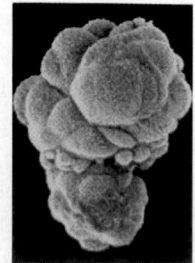

Adult Stem Cells

The breakthrough with embryonic stem cells led to a flurry of activity regarding stem cells from the other source already noted: adult tissues. Initial research seemed to indicate that, like embryonic stem cells, adult stem cells could be isolated and then give rise to many other kinds of cells. This may still turn out to be the case, but in 2002 doubts began to be raised about the potential of adult cells. Some early, promising results with them could not be reproduced when attempted by other researchers. And the possibility was raised that, at least in some instances, adult stem cells were giving a false appearance of differentiation. They only appeared to be differentiating into cells of a given tissue type, when in fact they were just fusing with existing cells of that type. At present, therefore, scientists are unclear about how much ability adult stem cells have to give rise to other kinds of cells.

The Ethical Debate over Embryonic Stem Cells

Scientists cannot generate stem cells from scratch. Investigators need a source of both adult and embryonic stem cells in order to conduct research on them. Obtaining adult stem cells can be difficult, but this is a technical issue. Human *embryonic* stem cells, meanwhile, present science with an ethical issue.

To state the obvious, human embryonic stem cells come from human embryos—from the collections of cells that have the potential to become fully formed human beings. Where do researchers get the embryos that are the source of embryonic stem cells? In most cases from fertility clinics, which each year discard thousands of excess embryos that have been produced for in vitro fertilizations. (A couple undergoing fertility treatments generally will produce many more embryos than they need to bring about a pregnancy.) With the couples' consent, excess embryos that would have been discarded are used instead in scientific research. When scientists extract stem cells from these early-stage embryos, however, the embryos are destroyed, and this is a matter of great concern to many people. For them, the destruction of an embryo is a destruction of human life.

Given such objections, you might think one alternative would be to simply stop using embryonic stem cells and instead work solely with adult stem cells. As noted, however, there are serious questions about the potential of adult cells. Meanwhile, research done in the last few years has confirmed that human embryonic stem cells can differentiate into any kind of adult tissue. Given this, there is a general consensus in the scientific community that, if stem cell research is to proceed as rapidly as possible, then research must continue on embryonic stem cells.

The practical consequence of this issue has to do with research funding. For years the federal government—the largest single source of biological research funds—did not fund any research in which embryos were destroyed. This stipulation held even if the embryos in question would be destroyed anyway, as in the case of the embryos that come from fertility clinics. Given the new interest in stem cell research, the question before President Bush in 2001 was: Should the federal government fund research that merely *involves* embryonic stem cells, even if no embryos were destroyed during this research? Could a researcher obtain embryonic stem cells from, for example, a private-sector scientist, and then receive government funding for research on the embryonic cells received?

In August 2001, the president decided that the answer is a qualified yes. Federal funding is now provided to researchers who work with cells from any of the 71 stem cell lines cultured before the date of his announcement. The effect of this decision was to allow federal funding for some research linked to the destruction of embryos, but to restrict the number of cell lines eligible for this funding. Many scientists believe that this restriction is now imposing harmful limitations on stem cell research. Two years after the president's announcement, only 11 stem cell lines actually had been developed to the point that they could be freely shared among researchers (though more are on the way). Moreover, it may be that cell lines not in existence by August 2001 may hold unique potential for combating certain kinds of human illness. As things stand, however, federal funds cannot be used for research on such cell lines.

The Future of Stem Cells

No human disease has yet been cured with stem cells; so far, these cells have demonstrated therapeutic benefits mostly in mice. Nevertheless, all parties seem agreed that stem cells hold out enormous potential. Consider just a partial list of the conditions that stem cells stand to alleviate or cure altogether: Parkinson's disease, heart disease, spinal-cord injuries, severe burn injuries, arthritis, Alzheimer's disease, multiple sclerosis, osteoporosis, and diabetes. Now consider just the last of these afflictions. People who suffer from Type I diabetes have lost the capacity to produce the hormone insulin, which moves blood sugar into cells. They have lost this capacity because the cells in their pancreas that produce insulin have been destroyed. As a result, they have to inject themselves with insulin each day. Even with this, they suffer from a host of diabetes-related afflictions. In 2001, researchers announced that embryonic stem cells they had retrieved from mice had begun secreting insulin when transplanted back into diabetic mice. Imagine a diabetic child being treated not with lifelong insulin injections, but with a similar cell transplant. Imagine scenarios like this involving *all* the conditions listed earlier, and you can see why scientists are so excited about stem cells.

On to Human Reproduction

The steps of development that you have just looked at form a kind of middle phase of the process you'll be looking at next chapter, which is reproduction—specifically human reproduction. Coming *before* the development you've reviewed are the formation of the egg and sperm that come together to create a new human being. Coming *after* it are late-stage human embryonic growth and then birth itself. With this chapter, you know something about development; in Chapter 30, you'll see how development fits into the larger scheme of human reproduction.

Chapter Review

Summary

29.1 General Processes in Development

- Development in animals begins with the formation of a zygote or fertilized egg, created when the male sperm fuses with the female egg. Once a zygote starts to divide, it is called an embryo.

- There are three phases of early embryonic development. The first is cleavage, which produces a ball of cells, called a blastula, with an interior cavity. The second is gastrulation, in which these cells rearrange themselves into three layers that give rise to specific organs and tissues. The third is organogenesis, in which organs begin to form.

- The first product of cleavage is a tightly packed ball of cells called a morula. The cells in the morula rearrange themselves into a structure composed of one or more layers of cells surrounding a liquid-filled cavity. This structure is the blastula (in mammals a blastocyst); its interior cavity is called the blastocoel.

- Gastrulation produces an embryo composed of three layers of cells, the endoderm, the mesoderm, and the ectoderm. The endoderm gives rise to interior organs and tissues, such as the liver and bladder in mammals. The mesoderm gives rise to most of the muscle and skeletal systems. The ectoderm gives rise to the epidermal (skin) cells of mammals, as well as their nervous-system tissue.

- In early organogenesis in vertebrates, a rod-shaped support organ, called a notochord, develops near the dorsal surface and induces the development of ectodermal tissue that lies above it. A neural plate develops from this tissue, folding over on itself to form a hollow neural tube that gives rise to both the brain and the spinal cord. Groups of neural crest cells break away from the top of the neural tube during its development and then migrate to different locations throughout the embryo. These groups go on to develop into different organs or tissues.

- The early stages of development represent a transition from the general to the specific. A small group of superficially similar cells gives rise to three different layers of cells, which give rise to tissues and then to specific organs.

Web Tutorial 29.1: Embryonic Development

29.2 What Factors Underlie Development?

- Induction is a process in which some embryonic cells direct the development of other embryonic cells.

- Development is fundamentally controlled by the interaction of genes and proteins. A key model organism in scientific understanding of these interactions is the fruit fly, *Drosophila melanogaster*.

- A critical early step in development is the establishment of positional information—for example, the establishment of anterior and posterior in a growing embryo. Positional information in *Drosophila* is provided in part by a protein called bicoid that exists in a concentration gradient in the fly embryo, the greatest concentration being at the anterior end of the embryo, a lesser concentration toward the center, and none at the posterior end. Bicoid helps bring about anterior structures, such as the head of the fly and center-portion structures as well.

- Bicoid is an example of a morphogen: a diffusable substance whose local concentration affects the course of local development in an organism. In general, morphogens diffuse from one set of cells to a second set of cells. Binding with these latter cells, morphogens prompt them to begin producing transcription factors: proteins that regulate DNA by binding with it, thus turning selected genes on or off. All morphogens work through the kind of concentration gradient seen with bicoid. Exposure to a greater concentration of a morphogen brings about one effect (a head in *Drosophila*), while exposure to a lesser concentration brings about another effect (center-portion structures in the *Drosophila*).

- Development works through a genetic cascade in which one set of genes regulates a subsequent set of genes. This cascade explains how development proceeds from the general to the specific. A first level of genetic instruction specifies broad positional patterns in an embryo (for example, the head and center-section portions of *Drosophila*). Subsequent levels of genetic instruction specify development within these body sections. Finally, control is exercised over the development of specific structures, such as organs.

29.3 Unity in Development: Homeobox Genes

- Within many of the developmental genes of animals as different as flies, mice, and human beings, there exists an identical sequence of about 180 DNA bases. Called a homeobox, this sequence has been highly conserved—it has remained largely unchanged over hundreds of millions of years of evolution in all animal species studied. As a result of this conservation, similar basic developmental processes are at work in all animals, and possibly in fungi and plants as well. Scientists are now looking at the differences in homeobox genes and their proteins as a means of learning more about both animal development and animal evolution.

29.4 Developmental Tools: Sculpting the Body

- Three cell capabilities help shape the animal body in development. The first is cell movement. The second is cell adhesion, in which cells produce proteins, which protrude from their surface, that selectively adhere to other cells. The third is programmed cell death, or apoptosis, in which spaces in tissues are created by means of cells dying.

29.5 The Promise of Stem Cells

- Most cells in the adult body have undergone commitment: a developmental process that results in cells whose roles are completely determined. Almost all cells in the body are committed in that they will not change type, and they will give rise only to cells of their own type.

- Cells in the early embryo have not yet undergone commitment and can give rise to various kinds of cells. A relatively small number of cells in the adult body have this same capability. Both the embryonic and adult cells that have this capability are called stem cells. Stem cells can be defined as any cell with the capacity for prolonged self-renewal that can produce at least one type of specialized daughter cell. Stem cells are the subject of intense research interest today because of their potential to alleviate or cure conditions such as spinal-cord injuries and heart attacks.

- One source of human stem cells is the early embryonic structure known as the blastocyst. Cells from the blastocyst's inner cell mass are pluripotent, meaning they can give rise to nearly all the different cells or tissues in the human body. A research breakthrough came in 1998 when a team of researchers announced they had been able to "culture" human blastocyst cells—isolate them and get them to keep dividing in the laboratory. Blastocyst cells are commonly referred to as embryonic stem cells. The advance in embryonic stem cells sparked advances in the culturing of adult stem cells, whose ability to differentiate into other kinds of cells is uncertain.

- An ethical controversy exists over the use of embryonic stem cells in scientific research, because embryos must be destroyed for the embryonic stem cells to be retrieved. Most researchers obtain embryonic stem cells from fertility clinics, which each year discard thousands of excess embryos that have been produced for in vitro fertilizations. In August 2001, President Bush decided to allow federal funding of research on a tightly restricted number of embryonic stem cell lines.

Key Terms

Understanding the Basics

Multiple-Choice Questions (answers in the back of the book)

1. In what order do the following developmental steps occur?
   a. organogenesis
   b. fertilization
   c. blastula formation
   d. morula formation
   e. gastrulation

2. The process of gastrulation involves
   a. massive cell death
   b. little or no growth of the embryo
   c. cell reorganization and movement
   d. cell enlargement
   e. organogenesis

3. In early embryonic development of the frog, the pieces of tissue that will form the backs of the eyes bulge from the growing brain. If one of these bits of tissue is removed and transplanted into the area that should become the frog's stomach, an eye develops there. This shows the importance of _____ in embryonic development.
   a. organogenesis
   b. cleavage
   c. differentiation
   d. induction
   e. gastrulation

4. The cells that migrate from the developing neural tube and eventually form different organs and tissues throughout the body are
   a. neural crest cells
   b. archenteron cells
   c. mesenchyme cells
   d. stem cells
   e. endoderm cells

5. Substances called _____ affect development by diffusing from one group of cells to another, thereby prompting the production of transcription factors in the latter cells.
   a. nurse cells
   b. mRNAs
   c. morphogens
   d. receptor proteins
   e. enzymes

6. An individual is born missing parts of the epidermal layer as well as portions of the nervous system. The problem began during development with which of these germ layers?
   a. mesoderm
   b. ectoderm
   c. neural crest cells
   d. endoderm
   e. none of the above

7. A DNA sequence such as the homeobox is said to be _____ because _____ .
   a. an induction sequence, it controls general development
   b. highly unusual, it exists in only a few animals
   c. a diversifying influence, it brings about differences in animals
   d. fast-evolving, it changes every few generations
   e. highly conserved, it has changed little over evolutionary time

8. A stem cell is valuable because it has not yet undergone _____ and can _____.
   a. gastrulation; move through the embryo
   b. commitment; give rise to specialized cells
   c. programmed cell death; still function
   d. division; produce morphogens
   e. organogenesis; stop dividing

9. A breakthrough occurred with human embryonic stem cells in 1998 when scientists
   a. learned of their existence
   b. got them to fuse with each other
   c. cultured them in a laboratory setting
   d. followed them through organogenesis
   e. transplanted them from mice to humans

10. The ethical controversy over embryonic stem cells exists because
   a. These cells are derived from human embryos, which are destroyed in the research process.
   b. These cells result from a mixing of genes between different kinds of animals.
   c. It is impossible to tell how these cells will function in actual patients.
   d. The money spent on obtaining these cells could arguably be better used for other kinds of research.
   e. These cells are pluripotent, rather than totipotent.

Brief Review

1. Briefly describe the order of events that occur after fertilization to produce an embryo with three layers of cells.

2. Outline the steps involved in the production of the chick wing.

3. How do cell adhesion molecules influence early events during development?

4. What is a morphogen concentration gradient, and how does it affect early development of the fruit fly, *Drosophila*?

5. Describe the role cell death plays during the development of an organism.

6. Why have scientists become so enthusiastic about stem cells?

Applying Your Knowledge

1. The text listed numerous examples of medical conditions that stand to be cured or alleviated through the use of stem cells. But is the potential of stem cells broader than even this list would indicate? Can you name a single medical condition that would *not* benefit from the addition of new, functional cells as replacements for malfunctioning, diseased, or missing cells?

2. Explain how the bicoid protein acts as a morphogen. What would happen to the developing *Drosophila* embryo if bicoid mRNA was introduced into the posterior region of the egg prior to fertilization?

3. It is sometimes said that the most important event in a human life is gastrulation. Why should gastrulation be thought of in this way?

30 *Human Reproduction*

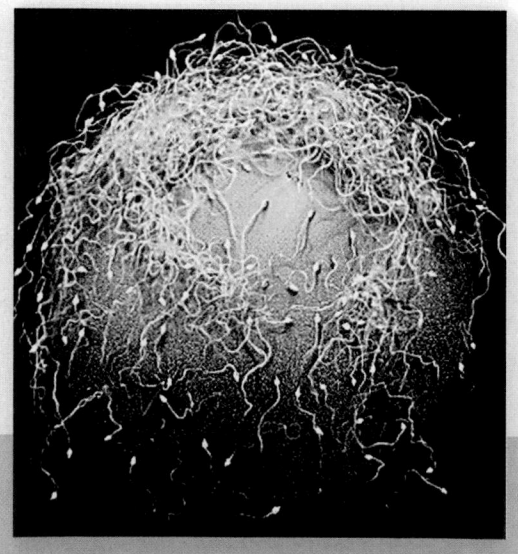

Near the moment of conception.
(Section 30.1, page 653)

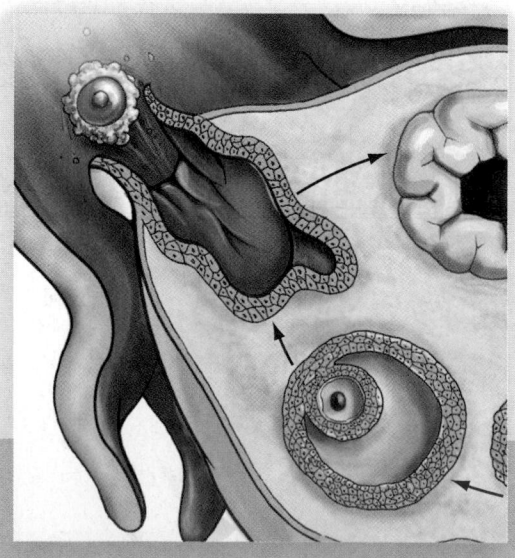

An egg's journey begins.
(Section 30.2, page 654)

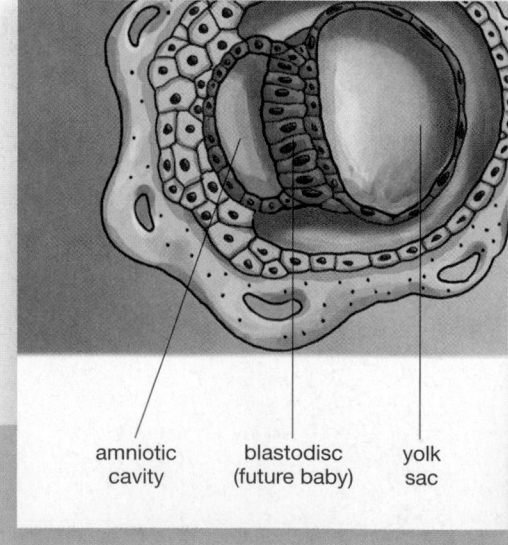

amniotic cavity   blastodisc (future baby)   yolk sac

Implantation.
(Section 30.5, page 665)

To produce a child, human males and females must first produce sperm and eggs, which come together in an act of fusion known as conception. The fertilized egg that results will, over the next 38 weeks, develop into a fully formed baby.

Memorable events mark every human life, but for parents, one event that is sure to be indelibly etched into memory is the birth of a child. The mother's labor, the final "pushing" that brings the baby forth, the first real look at the infant and the infant's first look at the world. These are moments that, once experienced, are never forgotten.

The birth of a child is a beginning, of course, and yet it is also a culmination. Human beings must grow to a certain level of biological maturity before being capable of reproduction. After this, finding a partner may be difficult, and getting pregnant more difficult yet. Eventually, however, two very special "seeds"—*this* egg and *this* sperm, out of all the millions a man and a woman produce in a lifetime, fuse to create this child.

In this chapter you'll trace the biology of human reproduction, which might be defined as all the biological steps that must fall into place before a child can be born. The process of development you studied in Chapter 29 represents part of what you'll be looking at, but other elements are involved as well.

30.1 Overview of Human Reproduction and Development

Taking this story from the beginning means picking up a narrative that was begun in Chapter 10, when you went over the formation of the reproductive cells called gametes—eggs in females, sperm in males. In this chapter the focus widens, taking into account the physical *setting* in which this formation takes place and the steps that bring egg and sperm together. Finally, you will look at human development from conception to birth. For information on some of the methods humans use to *prevent* conception, see "Methods of Contraception" on page 661.

The human male and female reproductive systems are functionally alike up to a certain point, in that they first develop their respective gametes and then deliver them to a location where they can fuse in the act known as fertilization or conception. However, the female reproductive system is called on to do all that the male system does *and more* in that, once fertilization takes place, the female system must then provide the

What's a placenta?
(Section 30.5, page 666)

10.5 inches

Lungs develop, eyelids open.
(Section 30.5, page 667)

(b) Movement through birth canal

Ready for delivery.
(Section 30.6, page 669)

environment for the embryo to develop, after which it must deliver the baby into the world. This process takes place over a period of 38 weeks, on average.

Reproduction in Outline

The first part of reproduction, the formation and delivery of egg and sperm, is a straightforward story in outline. All the eggs a woman possesses exist in her from birth in a precursor form, called oocytes, that lie within two walnut-shaped structures called ovaries. These exist just right and left of center within the female pelvic area (**see Figure 30.1**). Each oocyte sits in the ovaries within a nurturing complex of cells and fluids called a **follicle**. On average, once every 28 days one follicle-oocyte complex is brought to a state of maturity such that the oocyte and some accessory cells that surround it rupture from their ovary and begin a slow journey to the uterus. This trip takes place inside the structure called the **uterine tube** (or *Fallopian tube*). The release of the oocyte is called **ovulation**. If, during this trip, the oocyte encounters a male sperm, the two may fuse, in which case conception has occurred.

Sperm in men are produced, in unfinished form, in sets of tubules in the two male testes (**see Figure 30.2**). They then are transported to a structure called the epididymis (one for each testis) for further development. Then, with sexual excitation, sperm are transported in a loop: up and over the urinary bladder through two ducts,

each called a vas deferens. The contents of these ducts then empty into a single duct, called the urethra, from which they are ejaculated into the female vagina. Along the way, materials secreted by several glands join the sperm in a process that can be likened to tributaries feeding into a common stream. The resulting mixture of sperm and glandular materials is called **semen**.

Whereas the female releases an average of one oocyte per month, the male releases an average of 200 million sperm per ejaculation. Upon entering the vagina, the sperm and the female reproductive tract work together to propel the sperm up into the uterine tubes. Of the millions of sperm that begin the journey, a few dozen may encounter the female oocyte as it continues its journey from ovary to uterus (**Figure 30.3**). The first sperm to breach the coating that surrounds the oocyte fuses with it, while the rest are shut out through a kind of gate-slamming mechanism. When this one sperm has joined with an oocyte, conception has occurred. The now-fertilized egg still floats free in the uterine tube, where it begins to develop in the ways described in Chapter 29: one cell becomes two, two become four, and so on. Four days after fertilization, the developing embryo enters the uterus; three days more and it implants itself in the uterine wall and continues to develop.

Both the male and female reproductive systems are greatly influenced by the actions of hormones—chemical signaling molecules that move

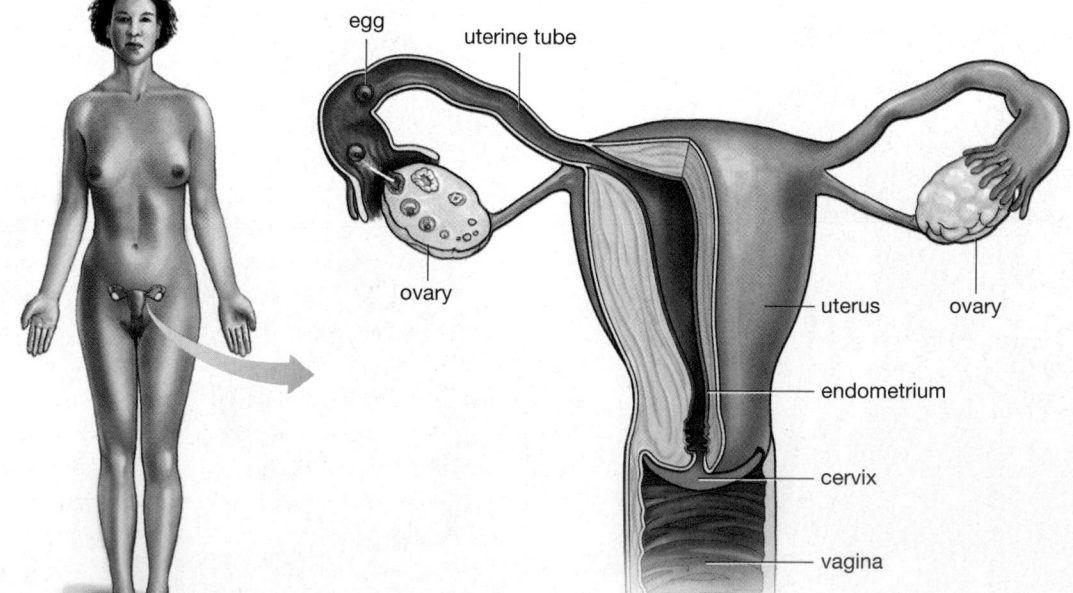

Figure 30.1
Reproductive Anatomy of the Human Female
Eggs develop in the ovaries within nurturing complexes called follicles. Once every 28 days, on average, an egg is expelled from one ovary or the other and journeys through the uterine tube to the uterus. If the egg encounters sperm on the way, pregnancy will result when egg and sperm fuse. The fertilized egg then continues traveling through the uterine tube and implants in the lining of the uterus, the endometrium.

Figure 30.2
Reproductive Anatomy of the Human Male
Sperm are produced in the testes and transported to the epididymis, where they mature and are stored. With orgasm, the sperm are transported through the vas deferens and then the urethra, from which they are ejaculated. Along the way, they are joined by materials secreted by several accessory glands.

through the bloodstream. Indeed, the reproductive organs are primary sites of production for some of the most important of these hormones, testosterone in men and estrogen and progesterone in women.

Figure 30.3
Oocyte and Sperm
Numerous sperm surround a single oocyte.

30.2 The Female Reproductive System

The Female Reproductive Cycle

Although hormones operate in both sexes, in females they bring about a reproductive *cycle* that repeats itself about once every 28 days (though it can range from 21 to 42 days). In males, conversely, there is no cycle, but instead a steady production of sperm and a destruction or removal of the sperm that are not ejaculated. Why a cycle for females and not for males? The answer lies partly in the two roles the female reproductive system must fulfill. It must form an egg *and* create an environment in the uterus in which a fertilized egg can develop. An important part of this uterine environment is essentially built up and then dismantled once every 28 days—except in those rare instances in which an oocyte is fertilized. The end result of the dismantling of the uterine environment is **menstruation**: a cyclical release of blood and the inner portion of a specialized uterine tissue, the **endometrium**, from the female reproductive tract. The endometrium is tissue that lines the interior of the uterus; it is tissue that *would have* housed an embryo, had one been implanted there (see Figure 30.1).

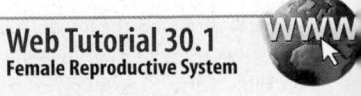

Web Tutorial 30.1
Female Reproductive System

Why Does Menstruation Exist?

From this, it's reasonable to ask: Why do women have this monthly cycle of buildup and destruction, rather than just a permanent environment for an embryo? After all, menstruation has some obvious costs attached to it; apart from discomfort, there is a loss of blood and other tissue. (On average women lose about 40 milliliters—or about 1.4 fluid ounces—of blood in a menstrual cycle, and about that much other tissue as well.) So, in the face of these costs, why has menstruation been preserved throughout human evolution? Scientists have no firm answers here, but they do have a couple of favored hypotheses. One is that, costly as menstruation may be, in terms of expended energy it is not *as* costly as the alternative of maintaining a permanent embryonic environment in the uterus. The other is that, as the time approaches each month in which an oocyte might get fertilized and then implanted in the endometrium, the inner endometrium changes form. It goes from a tissue whose primary activity is growing (in its "proliferative" phase) to one whose primary activity is secreting a nutrient-rich mucus (in its "secretory" phase). The assumption is that a fertilized egg can implant itself only in a secretory-phase endometrium, but a secretory-phase endometrium cannot perpetuate itself; it has a short life span and must develop from a proliferative-phase endometrium. Given this, it makes sense that the endometrium washes a part of itself out every 28 days and starts its growth anew.

How Does an Egg Develop?

As noted earlier, eggs develop from precursor cells called **oocytes**. If you look at **Figure 30.4**, you can see where oocytes develop in the outer portion of each ovary. Each oocyte is surrounded by a sphere of accessory cells, called *follicle cells*, that eventually provide the oocyte with nutrients. The complex of oocyte and follicle cells is called an **ovarian follicle**; it is the basic unit of oocyte development.

Follicle Development and Ovulation

Every oocyte that matures into an egg must go through the developmental steps you see in Figure 30.4. This is a monthly process of selection, running

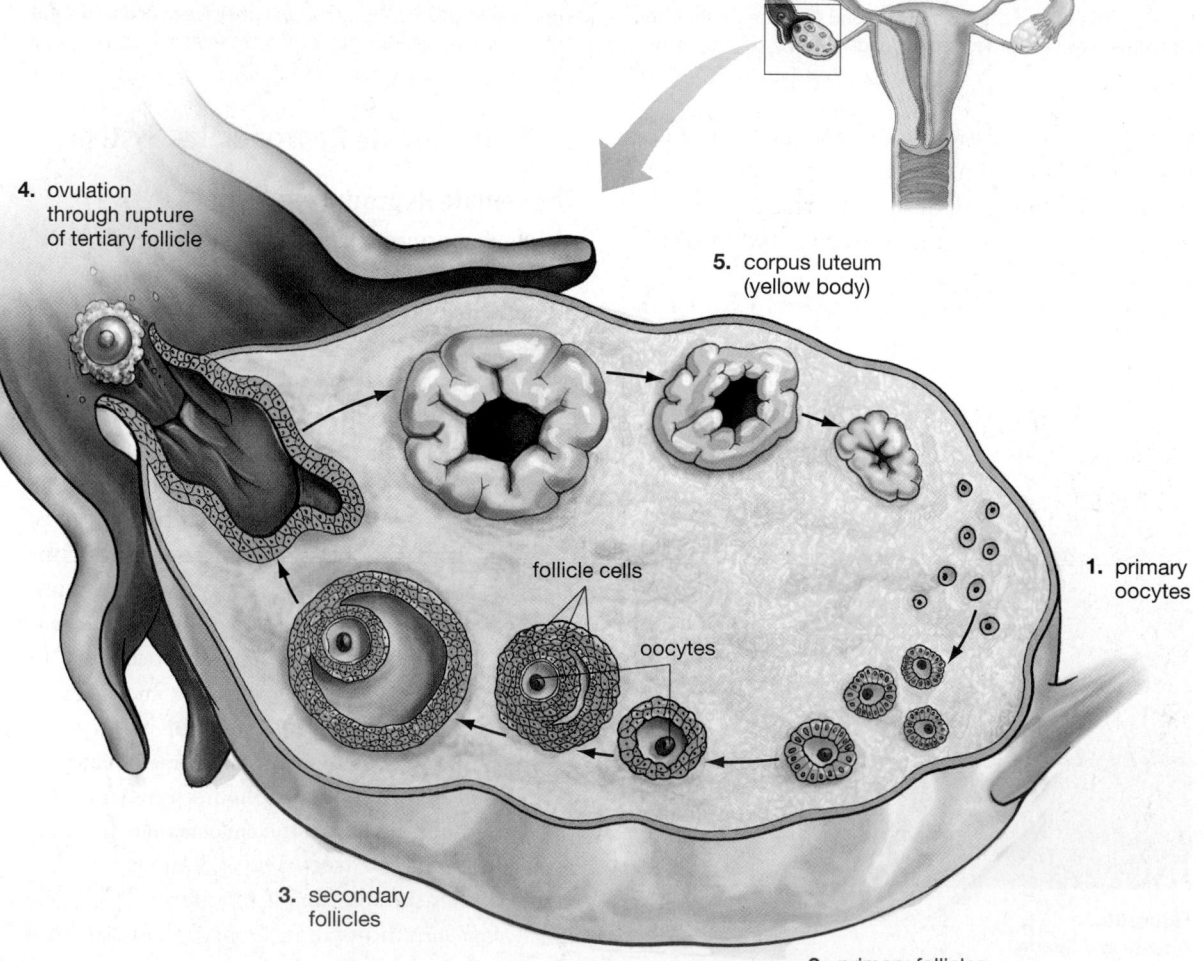

4. ovulation through rupture of tertiary follicle

5. corpus luteum (yellow body)

follicle cells

oocytes

1. primary oocytes

3. secondary follicles

2. primary follicles

Figure 30.4
Steps Leading to an Egg
An egg develops from precursor cells called oocytes that exist near the surface of the ovary. Oocytes join with nurturing complexes of cells to form ovarian follicles. On average, only one of these follicles matures—once every 28 days—through the stages of primary, secondary, and tertiary follicle. The oocyte contained in the tertiary follicle is expelled at the end of the process and then begins a journey through the uterine tube. With the oocyte's expulsion, the tertiary follicle is transformed into the corpus luteum, which for a time produces hormones that facilitate pregnancy.

from a large starting set of follicles, through fewer *primary follicles* that develop from them, to a greatly reduced number of *secondary follicles* that continue development, and finally to a single *tertiary follicle* that nurtures an oocyte through its time in the ovary. Responding to hormonal influence midway through the menstrual cycle, the tertiary follicle is squeezed until it ruptures, thus expelling the oocyte and its surrounding accessory cells not only from the follicle but from the ovary as well. With this event, ovulation has occurred. It takes place in this way in one ovary each month, with one ovary or the other selected through an unknown process.

Movement through the Uterine Tube

Freed from its ovarian housing, but still surrounded by accessory cells, the oocyte—technically not yet an egg—is now swept into the uterine tube through the actions of the finger-like *fimbriae* lying at the tube's funnel-shaped end (**see Figure 30.5**). Propelled by liquid currents and the uterine tube's whip-like cilia, the oocyte makes a journey of about 10 centimeters (4 inches) through the uterine tube over the next four days. While within the tube, the oocyte may encounter sperm and become fertilized prior to entering the uterus.

Meanwhile the ruptured tertiary follicle now takes on a new role: It develops into a body called the **corpus luteum** ("yellow body"), a structure that se-cretes hormones that help prepare the female reproductive tract for pregnancy and then maintain it during pregnancy. If pregnancy does not occur, the corpus luteum begins degenerating after about 12 days. With the corpus luteum, you can see again the part that hormones play in the monthly female reproductive cycle. For details on this hormonal regulation, see "Hormones and the Female Reproductive Cycle," on the next page.

Changes through the Female Life Span

In between the creation of oocytes and the journey of one oocyte down the uterine tube lies a multistep process that could be characterized by the phrase: "Many are called, but few are chosen." Recall from Chapter 10 that all the oocytes a woman will ever possess are produced in her prior to birth; these oocytes in turn become associated with the nurturing follicle complexes. A 6-month-old female fetus has in its ovaries about 7 million follicles that are capable of yielding eggs. At birth, this number has been reduced to about 1 million, primarily because of the process of *atresia*, or the natural degeneration of follicles. By puberty, the number has declined to about 250,000. An unknown number of these follicles are "recruited" monthly for further growth through hormonal action, but only *one* of these will, each month, go on to develop into the oocyte that bursts forth from the ovary. The only exception

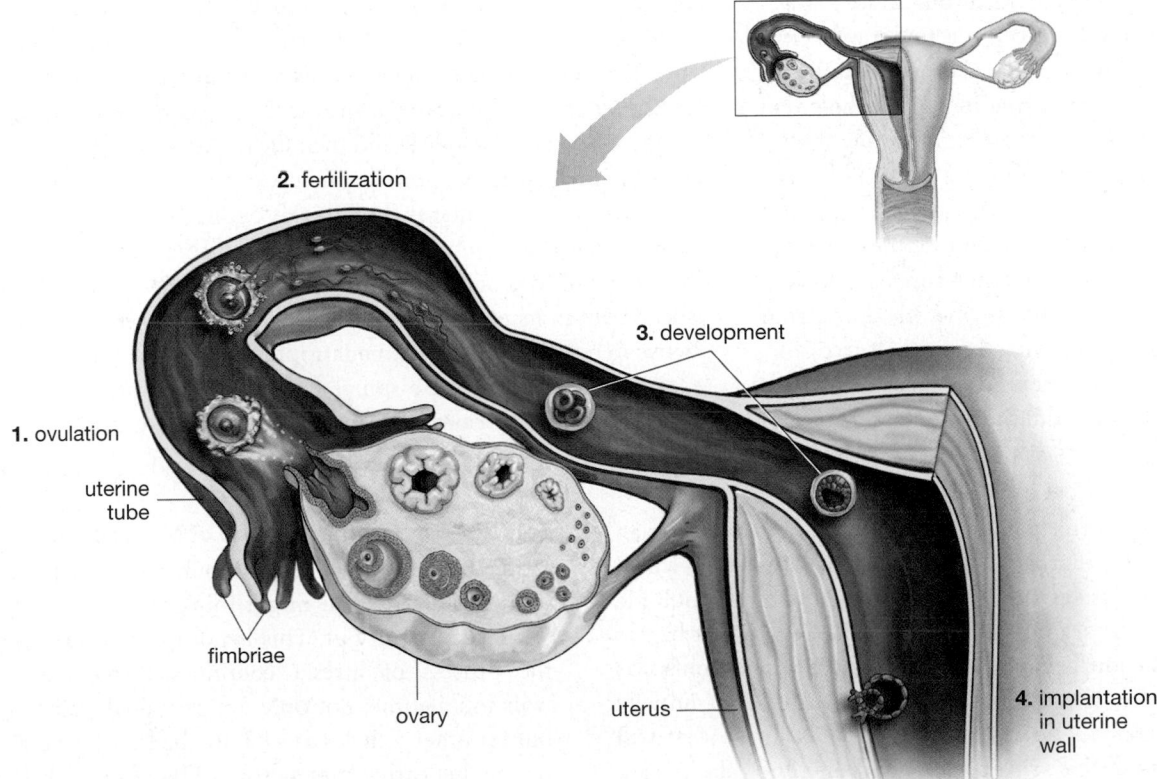

2. fertilization

3. development

1. ovulation

uterine tube

fimbriae

ovary

uterus

4. implantation in uterine wall

Figure 30.5
Journey to Pregnancy
Surrounded by accessory cells, an oocyte is expelled from the ovary into the uterine tube, where it encounters sperm and is fertilized by one of them. Now a fertilized egg (or zygote), it begins the process of development and completes its journey with implantation in the endometrium of the uterine wall.

Hormones and the Female Reproductive Cycle

In females, reproduction is carried out through a *cycle*, which is to say a series of events that repeat themselves regularly—on average, once every 28 days. But how can the female reproductive system "keep time" like this? What is the clock that governs the cycle?

A real clock is actually a good analogy for what happens. If you look at an old-fashioned mechanical watch, what you'll see is a central spring that exerts a force through a series of gears. Given these parts, it takes 12 hours for the physical mechanism of the "small hand" on the watch to make its way through a complete cycle—to end up where it began. In women, the substances called *hormones* set in motion a group of physical processes that take about 28 days to complete. The last of these processes leaves the body right where it began, at the start of another cycle.

We actually should speak of female reproductive *cycles*, in the plural, because several are going on in reproduction, all of them interlinked. There is the ovarian cycle, which has to do with the development and release of oocytes. Then there is the menstrual or "uterine" cycle, which concerns the regular buildup and then breakdown of tissue in the inner lining of the uterus. Finally, there are several hormonal cycles, which help govern both menstruation and egg creation.

If you look at **Figure 1**, you can see a timeline for all these cycles, as tracked over a period of 28 days, which you can see marked off at the bottom. To give you a feel for the processes at work, let's follow just the menstrual cycle, whose "first day," over on the far left, is defined as the first day of menstruation. What the graph tracks is the state of the tissue (the endometrium) lining the inside of the uterus. As you can see, beginning on day 1, this tissue goes through a breakdown that lasts about 6 days, after which it begins a steady buildup that continues all the way to the end of the cycle—at which point it starts to break down again. Now look at what is going on in the ovarian cycle (the second one down from the top). This part of the graph is following the single "successful" oocyte (out of many that begin development) through its progression into the oocyte that bursts from the ovary on day 14.

The real lesson, however, is to think about the menstrual and ovarian cycles as they relate to *each other*: The endometrium is built up in the uterus as a means of creating an environment in which an egg could implant itself, should one be fertilized. If such an egg begins its journey on day 14 and then takes another 7 days or so to implant itself in the uterus, you can see what stage the *endometrium* will be in at this point: near its maximum thickness (and at a highly productive stage of synthesizing a blood-vessel system). Such an environment is just what an implanted embryo would need.

And what of the figures over on the right side of the ovarian cycle? They represent the corpus luteum, the "remains" of the follicle that the successful oocyte broke out of. The corpus luteum is much more than a spent vessel at this point, however. Hormones it secretes will promote the growth of the endometrium. Without a pregnancy occurring, the corpus luteum carries out such secretion only for about a week. After that it begins to degenerate, and *this* means the degeneration of the endometrium, which washes out, along with some of the blood that supplied it, in the process called *menstruation*.

What hormones are secreted by the corpus luteum? Look now at the ovarian hormone cycle, and you'll see a line for "progestins"—a family of hormones whose most important member is progesterone. As you can see, the level of progestins takes a sharp turn upward just as the corpus luteum is formed—no surprise, because it is the corpus luteum that is secreting them.

There is a circularity to all this hormonal control, with the hormones involved influencing each other in different ways as the cycle goes on. Let's arbitrarily take as a starting point, however, first the development of a follicle and then the release of an egg from it.

One important hormone in the cycle is produced neither in the ovaries nor the uterus, but in the brain. A brain structure called the *hypothalamus* releases vanishingly small amounts of a hormone called **gonadatropin-releasing hormone**, whose function is spelled out in its name: it controls the release of *other* hormones active in reproduction, the gonadatropins.

Two gonadatropins are spurred into production in this way, **follicle-stimulating hormone (FSH)** and **luteinizing hormone (LH)**, both of

continued

to this rule comes in the 1 percent or so of ovarian cycles that result in *multiple* ovulations, in which case fraternal twins, triplets, and other multiple births are possible. In sum, the oocyte that begins the journey down the uterine tube each month has been selected from more than 7 million initially created, and it is one of only 500 or so that will make this trip in a woman's lifetime (about 13 a year for 35 or 40 years).

Follicle Loss and the Mystery of Menopause

Given that a woman begins puberty with about 250,000 follicles, you might think that her supply would never run out. This is not the case, because the process of atresia continues throughout a woman's lifetime, not only for "recruited" follicles, but for other follicles as well. By the time a woman reaches her early fifties, perhaps a thousand follicles remain; this scarcity is the primary factor that

Figure 1
The Female Reproductive Cycle

brings about **menopause**, or the cessation of the monthly ovarian cycle. Because follicles not only nurture oocytes, but are primary sites of estrogen synthesis as well, the loss of follicular activity helps cause the physical problems associated with menopause: the loss of muscle tone, the thinning of the vaginal walls, and a loss of bone deposition, which has been associated with **osteoporosis**, or a decrease in bone mass.

This whole series of events presents science with a mystery: Why should women steadily lose follicles and become infertile in mid-life? Put another way, why should menopause exist? The living world is shaped by differential success in reproduction. Traits that help a given organism to produce relatively *more* offspring will be retained over evolutionary time. Yet the trait of menopause developed in the course of evolution, and it seemingly leads to

Hormones and the Female Reproductive Cycle

continued

which are produced in a gland located beneath the hypothalamus, the *anterior pituitary gland*. You can see both FSH and LH levels charted in the gonadatropic hormone cycle at the top of Figure 1.

After being secreted by the anterior pituitary, both FSH and LH have their primary early-cycle effects at the site of the ovarian follicles. FSH promotes the development *of* the follicles, while LH stimulates the synthesis of a hormone *by* the follicles, estrogen (which actually is a family of hormones). The more the follicles develop, the more estrogen they secrete. The result, as you can see in Figure 1, is that estrogen levels slowly rise through the first week or so of the cycle. **Estrogen** is a hormone that is doing two things in the female reproductive cycle: it is promoting the growth of the endometrium in the uterus, and it is controlling the release of both FSH and LH. Early on, the relatively low (but increasing) levels of estrogen act to *decrease* FSH—not enough to stop development of the follicles, but enough to slightly reduce FSH levels over the first 10 days or so of the cycle, as you can see in Figure 1. In the second week of the cycle, however, estrogen output is greatly increased thanks to the development of the tertiary follicle, whose oocyte will burst forth from the ovary. At this level, estrogen acts to *increase* not only FSH production but LH production as well. The result, as seen in Figure 1, is the "spike" of LH production just before day 14 of the cycle. This hormonal surge is what causes the oocyte to break out from both follicle and ovary.

Now the former tertiary follicle has a new identity, the corpus luteum. In this role it produces progesterone, which as noted acts on the uterine lining to develop it for embryo implantation. Then, in tandem with estrogen, progesterone has another effect. It acts on the hypothalamus and pituitary to *lower* FSH and LH levels. But it turns out that the corpus luteum needs LH in order to remain healthy. In the absence of pregnancy, falling LH levels spell the end for the corpus luteum. This in turn causes a decline in progesterone levels, which brings about the degeneration of the endometrium, essentially by depriving it of a blood supply. Now, in the absence of a corpus luteum or developed follicles, the levels of estrogen and progesterone are *low*. Such low levels *stimulate* FSH and LH production in the anterior pituitary, and this is where we started: The cycle begins again, as LH and FSH stimulate the growth of another set of follicles.

So what keeps this cycle from continuing when pregnancy does occur? The implantation of an embryo in the endometrium causes release of a hormone from the embryo

How can the female reproductive system "keep time"? What is the clock that governs the cycle?

(called human chorionic gonadotropin), which acts like LH in that it keeps the corpus luteum robust and generating progesterone and estrogen, which in turn maintains the endometrium.

With this knowledge, you're in a position to understand what birth control pills do. In general, they are compounds that contain both synthetic estrogen and a synthetic progestin. Women usually take them beginning five days after the start of menstruation for three weeks (and during the fourth week take a chemically functionless "spacer" or nothing). Think about what is required at the beginning of a cycle to prompt the development of follicles: *low* levels of estrogen. (Recall that this low level stimulates the hypothalamus and pituitary to secrete follicle-stimulating hormone.) The pill provides a *higher* level of estrogen than exists naturally, thus suppressing the release of FSH and the development of follicles. Second, the progestin in the pill suppresses LH release by the pituitary, which prevents the *ovulation* of any follicle that might manage to develop, because the LH surge is required for ovulation.

fewer offspring for women. Through it, contemporary women are taken out of reproduction altogether for the last 20 or 30 years of their lives, during which time they suffer from a number of menopause-related physical maladies.

As was the case with menstruation, we have no firm answers on why menopause exists, but we do have several candidate hypotheses. One is that menopause is simply a product of women living longer today than their evolutionary ancestors did. Proponents of this view point out that a number of female mammals undergo what amounts to menopause, but then live only long enough to raise one additional generation of offspring after this loss of reproductive capacity sets in. Human females may once have followed this pattern and lived to, say, 60 years old—just long enough to give birth to a final child in their late 40s and then raise that child to a self-sustaining age of 10 or so. Today, however, women don't live until 60; they live until 75 or 85 and thus have decades of life following menopause.

A very different hypothesis holds that menopause is "adaptive," as biologists say—it arose through evolution because it actively helps females perpetuate their genes. The starting point for this "grandmother hypothesis" is the observation that what counts in evolution is not just whether you have children; it is whether you have children who themselves go on to have healthy children. Now, how is a given woman most likely to achieve this? Under this hypothesis, she best achieves it not by continuing to give birth throughout life but by leaving direct reproduction behind at a certain point and becoming a grandmother who provides both for her children and her grandchildren. Proponents of this view note that giving birth is inherently dangerous (while being a grandmother is not), and they point to the substantial nurturing that grandmothers provide in a number of primitive societies.

30.3 The Male Reproductive System

Switching now to males, if you look at **Figure 30.6**, you can see another view of the male reproductive system. Here you see the large-scale structures of the

system. There is the **testis**, in which sperm begin development; the **epididymis**, the tubule in which sperm mature and are stored; and the **vas deferens**, the tube through which sperm move in the process of ejaculation. (All three of these structures exist in pairs, though the second member of each pair is not visible in the figure.) Then there is the single **urethra**, the tube each vas deferens empties into and through which sperm leave the male body. There are also several accessory glands whose contributions are added to sperm as it proceeds: the seminal vesicles, the prostate gland, and the bulbourethral glands. (The seminal vesicles and bulbourethral glands also exist in pairs.)

Structure of the Testes

The testes are surrounded by a muscle whose contraction helps regulate the temperature of the sperm inside. Sperm development requires temperatures

Web Tutorial 30.2
Male Reproductive System

Figure 30.6
Development and Delivery of Sperm

(a) After the sperm develop in the testes and mature in the epididymis, orgasm prompts them to be transported through the vas deferens and then the urethra. Secretions from accessory glands (the seminal vesicles, the prostate gland, and the bulbourethral glands) join with the sperm to form semen before ejaculation.

(b) How sperm mature. Sperm development begins within seminiferous tubules, located in the testes. Sperm start out as spermatogonia at the periphery of the tubules and end up as immature sperm in the interior cavity of the tubules. From there, they are transported to the epididymis for further development and storage. Outside the seminiferous tubules are Leydig cells, which produce testosterone.

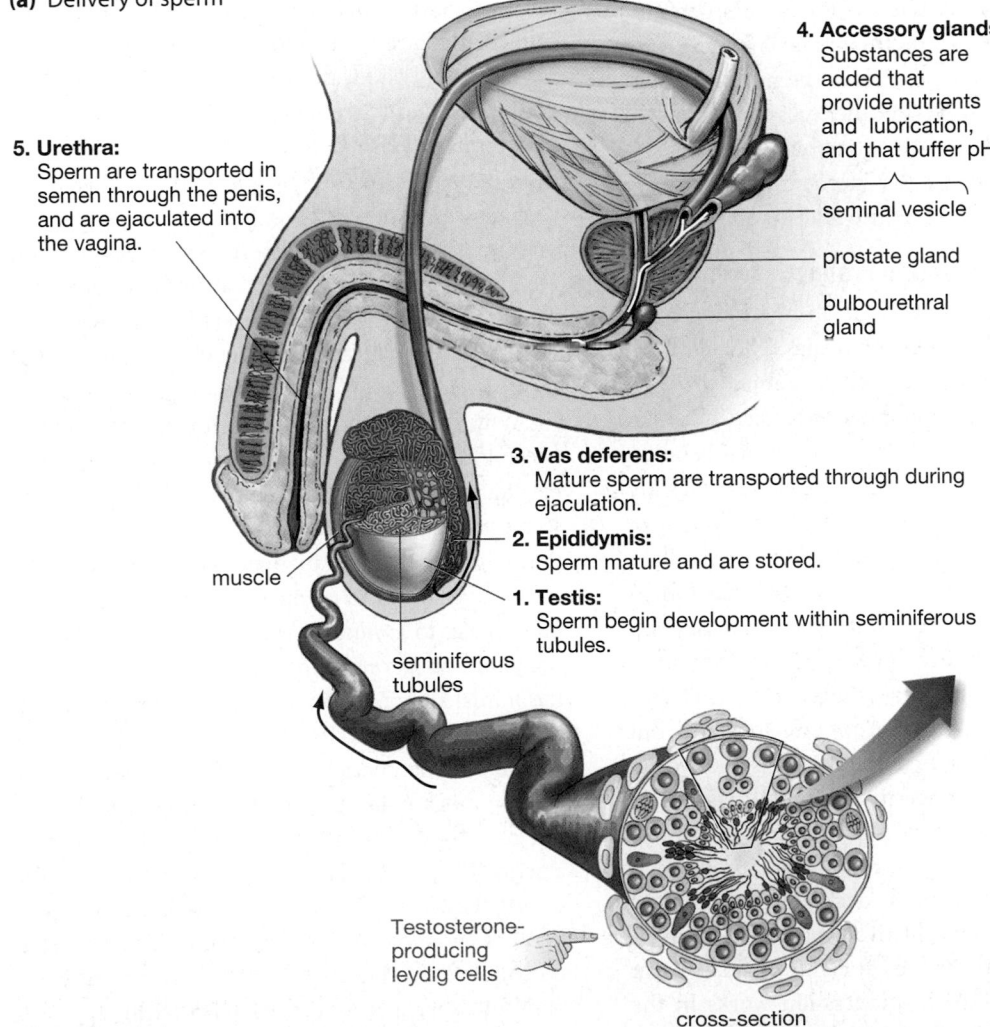

(a) Delivery of sperm

5. Urethra:
Sperm are transported in semen through the penis, and are ejaculated into the vagina.

4. Accessory glands:
Substances are added that provide nutrients and lubrication, and that buffer pH.

seminal vesicle

prostate gland

bulbourethral gland

3. Vas deferens:
Mature sperm are transported through during ejaculation.

2. Epididymis:
Sperm mature and are stored.

1. Testis:
Sperm begin development within seminiferous tubules.

muscle

seminiferous tubules

Testosterone-producing leydig cells

cross-section of seminiferous tubule

(b) Development of sperm

spermatogonia

primary spermatocyte

secondary spermatocytes

spermatids

immature sperm

somewhat cooler than those found in the rest of the body, which is why the testes are *external* to the body's torso. Sperm cannot develop in temperatures that are too cold, however. Thus, when a male steps into, say, a cold swimming pool, the muscle surrounding the testes will contract, drawing the testes up closer to the torso—and warming the sperm.

Figure 30.6a shows that the testes are divided into a small series of lobes, and that within each lobe there are a number of highly convoluted tubes, the **seminiferous tubules**: structures that are the sites of initial sperm development in men. If you now look at a single seminiferous tubule in cross section, in Figure 30.6b, you'll see how this development proceeds: from the outside of each tubule—where sperm precursors are in their *least* developed state—toward the interior cavity of each tubule, where sperm are in a more developed state. Eventually, the immature sperm are released into the interior cavity, and are transported up it, moving then to the epididymis for further processing and storage. As you can see, there is an assembly-line quality to sperm production, starting with initial development at the periphery of the tubules, continuing in the interior of the tubules, and ending with storage in the epididymis. Older sperm that are not ejaculated are destroyed (by other cells) or eliminated in the urine. Inside the testes, surrounding the seminiferous tubules, there exist numerous *Leydig cells*, which are the cells that produce testosterone.

Male and Female Gamete Production Compared

The production of sperm bears an interesting comparison with the development of eggs. The cells from which sperm develop are called **spermatocytes**. In going back to the precursors of *these* cells, however, we see a significant difference between males and females. The cells that give rise to spermatocytes are called **spermatogonia**; they exist at the periphery of the seminiferous tubules and, through normal cell division, they actually lead to two kinds of cells. One is the primary spermatocyte, which goes on to develop into a sperm; the other, however, is another spermatogonium. Thus, spermatogonia are "sperm factories," if you will, that give rise not only to sperm, but to more sperm factories as well. This is the reason males *keep* producing sperm throughout their lives while, as we've noted, females have a fixed quantity of oocytes. Although male sex hormone production lessens with age, and sperm decline in quality, it is possible for male reproductive capability to remain intact until death. If you look at Figure 30.6b, you can see how the male sperm progression works in the testes: from spermatogonium, through spermatocyte to spermatid, and finally to immature sperm.

Further Development of Sperm

As you can see in Figure 30.6a, the seminiferous tubules eventually feed into the epididymis, a single convoluted tubule (one for each testis) that is about 7 meters (about 23 feet) long. This structure serves as the site of storage and final sperm development and as a kind of materials recycling site for damaged sperm. By the time sperm arrive at the bottom portion of the epididymis, they are fairly mature, but not yet fully mature. They won't become mobile until fluid from a type of supporting gland noted earlier—the seminal vesicles—mixes with them upon ejaculation, thus supplying them with nutrients. And, as you'll see, substances in the female reproductive tract will interact with them to prompt their final maturation.

Time Sequence and Sperm Competition

How long does this whole process of sperm development take? About 2.5 months from the start of development to storage in the epididymis. About 200 million sperm are produced in this assembly line each day, which you may recall is about the number that are ejaculated in an average orgasm.

As noted, the watchword for oocyte selection could be "many are called but few are chosen." How much more extreme is the selection that goes on with sperm! The number expelled with *each ejaculation* vastly exceeds the number of oocytes a woman ever has stored in her ovaries. On average, however, only a single sperm per ejaculation will be able to fertilize an egg—assuming an egg is present in the uterine tube at the right time.

Why is there such an enormous difference between the number of sperm produced and the number that will fertilize eggs? The essential answer here seems pretty clear: Just as males often are in competition with other males to mate with females, so the sperm of males is in competition with the sperm of other males to *fertilize* female eggs. This general phenomenon of *sperm competition* goes on throughout the animal kingdom—in insects, birds, and reptiles as well as in mammals. Its root cause is that there are very few animal species in which females or males are truly monogamous. As a result, mating by itself does not guarantee offspring. If a female who is fertile over a period of several days mates with a number of males during these days, then each male's chance of fatherhood is enhanced to the degree that his sperm can outcompete the sperm of the other males. This is the basis for a sperm "arms race" that has taken place over evolutionary time. Looking at various species, we find that their sperm has gotten longer, or more "motile"

Methods of Contraception

Selected methods of contraception are presented here. The rate of effectiveness for each method refers to effectiveness with correct use during every instance of sexual intercourse. In practice, effectiveness for each method tends to be lower, because use of the method may be incorrect or inconsistent. See "Hormones and the Female Reproductive Cycle" on page 656 for information on how birth control pills work.

Table 30.1 Methods of Contraception

	Birth Control Pill	A set of pills containing a combination of hormones that suppress the female ovulatory cycle. Effectiveness: 99.9 percent.
	Condom	Made of latex, plastic, or animal tissue, condoms are put on the erect penis prior to intercourse and catch sperm after it is ejaculated. Condoms are the only method of contraception that helps protect both partners from some sexually transmitted diseases. Effectiveness: 97 percent.
	Diaphragm	A soft, circular rubber barrier inserted into the woman's vagina before sex. Covering the cervix, it prevents sperm from reaching the egg. Along with the related cervical caps, diaphragms offer females some protection against some sexually transmitted diseases, such as gonorrhea and chlamydia. Effectiveness: about 95 percent, when used with a spermicide (a chemical compound that immobilizes sperm).
	Intrauterine device (IUD)	A small device made in some instances of plastic and copper that is inserted into a woman's uterus by a physician. These IUDs can be left in place for several years. Other IUDs are made of plastic and contain a supply of a progestin hormone that is continuously released. These IUDs must be replaced once a year. Both types of IUDs help prevent fertilization of egg by sperm, in a process that may involve altering the movement of each type of gamete. Both types of IUDs also work to prevent implantation in the uterus of any embryo that might be produced. Effectiveness: copper IUD, 99.4 percent; hormone-releasing IUD, 98.5 percent.
	Tubal ligation	A surgical procedure that generally results in the sterilization of a woman, meaning permanent infertility. In it, the uterine tubes are first cut and then tied, thus blocking eggs from moving to a position in which they could be fertilized by sperm. Does not affect feminine characteristics, hormonal production, or sexual performance. Very rarely, tubes will reconnect themselves, which accounts for the (low) failure rate of the procedure. It is possible to reverse the operation in some instances. Effectiveness: 99.6 percent.
	Vasectomy	A surgical procedure that can result in the sterilization of a man, though vasectomies are sometimes reversible. In the procedure, the vas deferens are cut and tied, thus blocking the movement of sperm during ejaculation. Does not affect male hormonal production, physical capacity for erection, or ability to ejaculate. (Sperm make up a small portion of the semen that is ejaculated.) In rare instances, vas deferens will grow back together again, which accounts for the (low) failure rate of the procedure. Effectiveness: 99.9 percent.

(active), or has been produced in greater numbers—all as a means of gaining a reproductive edge. This is why men produce so many sperm. Their sperm production has followed the lottery principle: the more tickets you have, the more likely you are to win.

From Vas Deferens to Ejaculation

Maturing sperm are stored in both the epididymis and the vas deferens. With sufficient sexual stimulation, ejaculation takes place through the contractions of muscles that surround the penis at its base. This contraction pushes the sperm through the urethra and out the urethral opening at the tip of the penis—at a speed of about 10 miles an hour.

Supporting Glands

As noted, several other kinds of materials join with sperm before ejaculation to form the substance known as semen. Indeed, given the number of sperm ejaculated, it may be surprising to learn that sperm don't account for much of the volume of semen; some 95 percent of the ejaculated material comes from the accessory glands already mentioned: two seminal vesicles, the prostate gland, and two bulbourethral glands. It's helpful to think of sperm as getting "outfitted" for their travels by these glands just as they are exiting from the body. In addition to the nutrients the seminal vesicles supply, accessory glands provide alkaline and lubricating substances (which neutralize the acidic environment of the vagina and facilitate transportation).

One of these supporting glands may sound familiar. The **prostate gland** is a structure that surrounds the male urethra near the bladder and contributes a substantial amount of material to semen. Later in life, a significant percentage of men develop either enlarged prostate glands or, worse, the growth of cancerous cells in the prostate, which is to say prostate cancer. Given that the prostate encircles the urethra—and that the urethra transmits not only semen but urine as well—you can see why a warning sign of these conditions is reduced urine flow.

30.4 The Union of Sperm and Egg

To this point, you have reviewed the process by which male sperm and female egg are first created and then *positioned* so that they can come together in the process called fertilization. Now let's look at this moment of fusion in somewhat greater detail. When the oocyte is expelled from the ovaries, there still is no solitary oocyte in transit, but rather an oocyte surrounded by a group of accessory cells and connective substances.

Now consider the sperm (each one of which is known as a *spermatozoon*). As you can see in **Figure 30.7a**, each spermatozoon has a "head" that contains not only the nucleus and its vital complement of chromosomes, but an outer compartment, called an **acrosome**, which contains enzymes. These enzymes are released *externally*, so that they break down materials that surround the oocyte. To be able to do this, sperm have to undergo a final process of maturation while swimming up the female reproductive tract. Substances within the tract cause the acrosome to lose its "cap," thus allowing it to release its enzymes. Given this interaction, it's apparent that the male and female systems are working *together* to bring about fertilization. (This same kind of mutual action is required for the sperm to make it up the uterine tube in the first place. Sperm move under their own power, but they are also transported by the female reproductive tract.)

Many sperm mature fully, but only one of them completes the next step, which is to latch onto the oocyte (**Figure 30.8**). This happens by means of a sperm cell binding with receptors on the surface of the oocyte (Figure 30.7b). Once this binding has occurred, the plasma membranes of sperm and oocyte fuse; the sperm is then inside the oocyte, and sperm and egg nuclei combine. Fertilization is complete.

How Latecomers Are Kept Out

But what of the other dozens of sperm surrounding the oocyte? None of them can be allowed entry, because an embryo could not survive getting two sets of male chromosomes, but only one set of female chromosomes. To guard against this possibility, a kind of gate-slamming process is put into motion. The fusion of the first sperm with the oocyte causes the oocyte to release thousands of tiny granules into the space just outside itself. These granules release substances that harden the material immediately outside the oocyte while inactivating sperm receptors on the oocyte. The result is that, with rare exceptions, only one sperm gets in. The sexual activity that is so important to human reproduction also carries with it the risk of sexually transmitted disease, which you can read about in the essay on page 664.

30.5 Human Development Prior to Birth

Having seen how sperm and egg form and get together, you have reached a point in human reproduction that should be familiar: development, meaning the process by which a fertilized egg is transformed, step by step, into a functioning organism. As you'll see,

(a) Structure of a sperm cell

(b) How sperm fertilizes egg

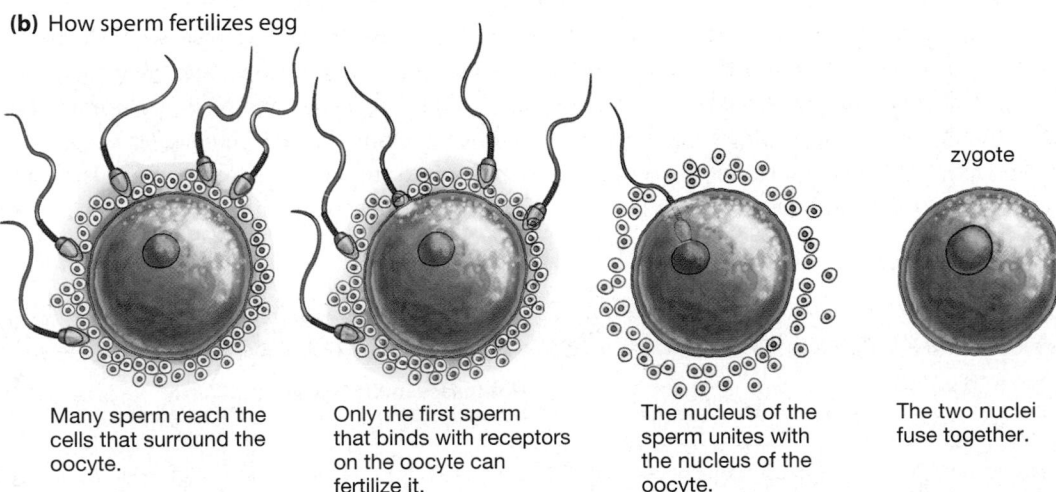

zygote

Many sperm reach the cells that surround the oocyte.

Only the first sperm that binds with receptors on the oocyte can fertilize it.

The nucleus of the sperm unites with the nucleus of the oocyte.

The two nuclei fuse together.

Figure 30.7
Anatomy of a Spermatozoon and Steps in Fertilization

(a) The "head" of each sperm includes not only its complement of chromosomes but also an acrosome, which contains enzymes that, when released externally, break down material surrounding the oocyte. (This release comes after the sperm has fully matured by coming into contact with substances in the female reproductive tract.) Behind the sperm head are the mitochondria that supply the energy for the motion of the tail that propels the sperm.

(b) The process by which a sperm fertilizes an egg.

processes you looked at in Chapter 29 in connection with frogs and flies have counterparts in human development. What may be surprising is how *early* in human development many of the critical events of development occur. Here is a list of some of the key developmental processes discussed in Chapter 29.

Figure 30.8
Near the Moment of Conception
A human sperm and oocyte at the moment the sperm binds the oocyte. Very soon after this, the sperm will enter the oocyte and its nucleus will fuse with the oocyte nucleus, producing a human zygote.

- Formation of the blastula, or hollow body of cells (called a *blastocyst* in humans and other mammals)

- Gastrulation, in which the three primary layers of cells are formed

- Formation of the neural tube (which gives rise to the brain and nervous system)

- Organogenesis, in which the organs of the body start to take shape

Now, keeping in mind that a human pregnancy lasts an average of 38 weeks, consider the timeline for these major developmental events. Blastocyst formation begins 4 or 5 days after conception; gastrulation begins 16 days after conception; neural tube formation begins in the third week after conception; and organogenesis begins in the fourth week. By the end of 12 weeks, immature versions of all the major organ systems have formed. To place some of these events in the context of what the mother experiences, organogenesis is occurring about the time the first menstrual period is missed, and formation of the immature organ systems is being completed at about the same 12-week point at which morning sickness generally ends.

Web Tutorial 30.3
Human Development

Sexually Transmitted Disease

Given the necessity of sex for the continuation of human life, it may seem surprising that so much risk can be associated with it, but such is the case. The root of the problem is that microorganisms that literally couldn't stand the light of day—that is, that couldn't exist for long in an exterior environment—are quite well adapted to life inside human tissue. More important, these microbes can be transmitted from one human being to another during the act of sex.

The risk of sexually transmitted diseases (STDs) varies in accordance with lots of things: the disease itself, the type of sexual activity a person engages in, and the precautions that are taken to avoid trouble. But one rule that holds true for all STDs and all behaviors is that as the number of partners goes up, so does risk. Here are the most common STDs, their prevalence in the United States, and the methods of treatment for them.

Table 30.2 Sexually Transmitted Disease

Disease	Caused by	Possible consequences	New cases in the United States in 2000	Treatment
Chlamydia	*Chlamydia trachomatis* organism—has features of both virus and bacteria	Spread to uterine tubes in women, causing pelvic inflammatory disease (PID), which can lead to sterility	3 million	Curable with timely use of antibiotics
Gonorrhea	Gonococcus bacterium	Arthritis, pelvic inflammatory disease	650,000	Curable with timely use of antibiotics, though antibiotic-resistant strains now exist
Syphilis	Spirochete bacterium	Heart, nervous system, bone damage if allowed to progress	70,000	Curable with timely use of antibiotics, though antibiotic-resistant strains now exist
Genital herpes	Virus	Recurrent skin lesions, eye damage, pregnancy complications	1 million	Occurence and severity of outbreaks can be lessened with treatment, but no cure exists
Genital warts	Human papilloma virus	Cervical infection in women, association with increased risk of cervical and penile cancer	5.5 million	Several treatments exist for removing warts, but virus may persist
AIDS	Human immunodeficiency virus (HIV)	Death, dementia, injury from a variety of opportunistic infections	40,000 HIV infections; 800–900,000 persons living with HIV in the U.S.	No cure; treatments to reduce symptoms exist

The embryo's development over time can be contrasted with its *growth* over time. By the end of the third week—after blastocyst formation and gastrulation—a human embryo is perhaps 2 millimeters (or less than a tenth of an inch) in diameter. Skip to the twelfth week after conception, when major portions of organogenesis are concluding, and the fetus may still be only about 13 centimeters, or a little over 5 inches in length.

The message here is that development is concentrated early in pregnancy, while the simple growth of what *has* developed comes later. So pronounced are the changes during development that biologists use different terms for the growing organism over time. The original cell—the fertilized egg—is a **zygote**. In humans, about 30 hours after the zygote is formed, it undergoes its first cell division; at this point, the developing organism is referred to as an **embryo**, a name that will be applied to it through the eighth week of development. From the ninth week of development to birth, the organism is referred to as a **fetus**. The typical 9-month pregnancy is divided into periods of roughly three months each, called **trimesters**. The first trimester ends at about the time organogenesis does.

Early Development

You saw earlier that the zygote/embryo moves from ovary to uterus during the first four days after fertilization. It arrives in the uterus on about day four as the *morula*, or tightly packed ball of cells noted in Chapter 29 (see Figure 29.1, page 636). Over the next two days the morula becomes the blastocyst, which implants itself in the endometrial lining. Actually, this "implantation" is more like an invasion. The blastocyst carves out a cavity for itself by releasing enzymes that effectively digest endometrial cells (**see Figure 30.9**). Implantation normally occurs in the dorsal wall of the uterus. Occasionally, however, a blastocyst attaches itself inside the uterine tube, or sometimes to the **cervix**, which is the lower part of the uterus that opens onto the vagina. This is an **ectopic pregnancy**: a pregnancy in which the embryo has implanted in a location other than the uterine wall. In general, embryos do not survive such an implantation.

Two Parts to the Blastocyst

Figure 30.9 shows you the arrangement of cells in the blastocyst. On one side, you can see a group of cells called the **inner cell mass**: the portion of the blastocyst that develops into the baby. The periphery of the blastocyst, however, is formed by cells called the **trophoblast**. These are the cells that etch their way into the uterine wall; with implantation, they begin extending farther into the endometrium, establishing indirect links with the maternal blood supply. In time, these cells grow into the fetal portion of a well-known structure in pregnancy, the **placenta**: a network of maternal and embryonic blood vessels and membranes that allows nutrients and oxygen to diffuse *to* the embryo (from the mother), while allowing carbon dioxide

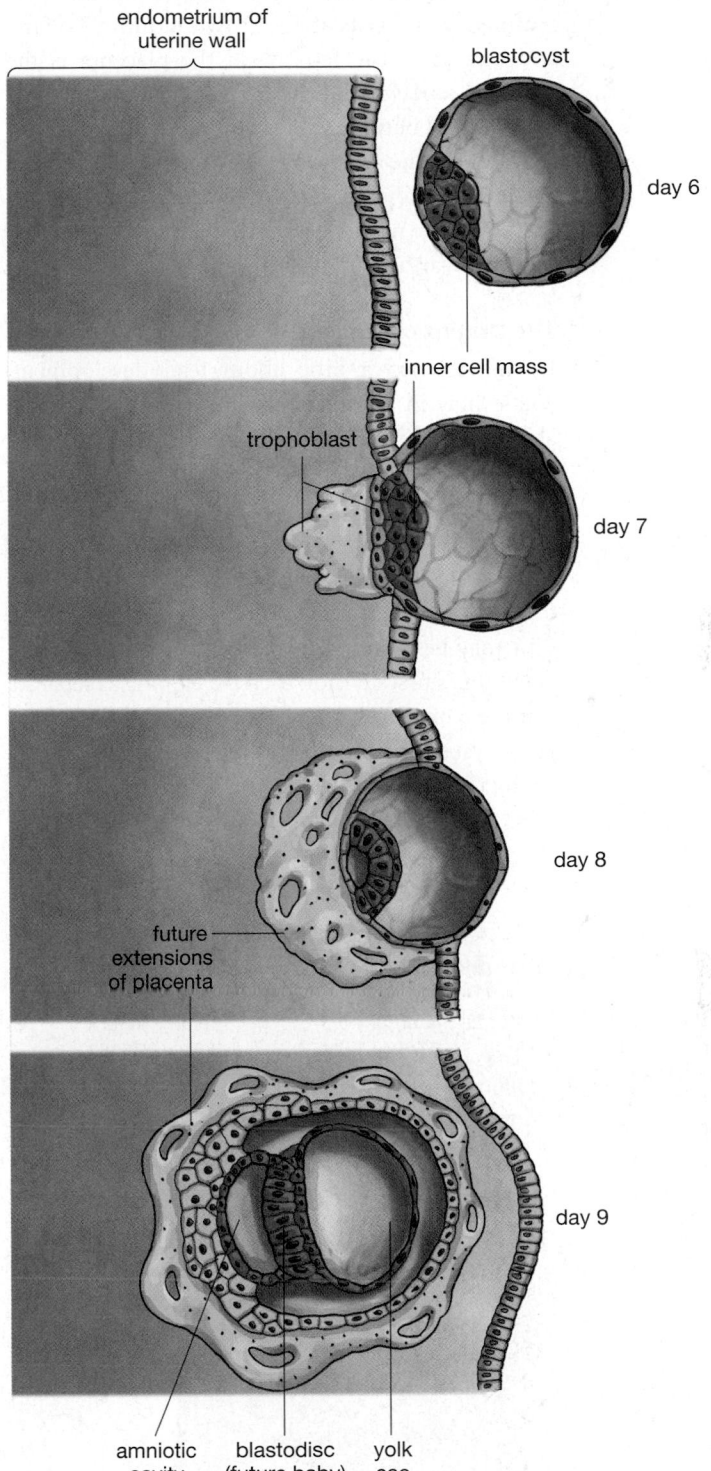

Figure 30.9
Implantation of the Embryo in the Uterus
Six days after conception, the embryo, now in the blastocyst stage of development, arrives at the uterine wall. It is composed of both an inner cell mass, which develops into the baby, and a group of cells called a trophoblast, which carve out a cavity for the embryo in the uterine wall and then begin establishing physical links with the maternal tissue. The outgrowth of this linkage is the placenta.

and waste to diffuse *from* the embryo (to the maternal blood system). See **Figure 30.10** for a look at how the placenta functions within a uterine environment as it exists at about two months. The tissue that links the fetus with the placenta is the **umbilical cord**, which houses fetal blood vessels that move blood between the fetus and the placenta. So pressing is the embryo's need for nutrients and waste removal that its circulatory system, which includes the umbilical cord, becomes functional before any other organ system.

The Origins of Twins

Having learned a little about fetal development, you're now in a position to understand something about how twins come about. Identical twins can develop at any time in the very early stages in pregnancy—from the time the zygote undergoes its first division through the seventh day after fertilization. In all cases, identical twins result from two *parts* of the embryo developing into separate human beings. This may be a matter of the two cells produced by the zygote's first division each developing as separate embryos; or it may entail the inner cell mass of the blastocyst separating into *two* masses, with each then giving rise to a different person. In contrast, **fraternal twins** (or triplets, and so on) are twins who are produced first through multiple ovulations in the mother, followed by multiple fertilizations from separate sperm of the father, and then multiple implantations of the resulting embryos in the uterus. This means that fraternal twins are like any other pair of siblings, except that they happen to develop at the *same time*. Meanwhile, **identical twins** are twins who develop from a single zygote. Strictly speaking, they are a single organism at one point in their development and as such have exactly the same genetic makeup.

Development through the Trimesters

If you look at the series of pictures and diagrams that make up **Figure 30.11**, you can see how an embryo and then fetus develops at selected points in the 38 weeks of pregnancy. Here's an overview of what happens through time.

First Trimester

As noted, blastocyst formation, gastrulation, and neural tube development all take place within the first month of conception; but much more happens during this period as well. By the 25th day, a primitive heart has formed in the human embryo and has begun pumping blood; the "somites" or repeating segments you read about in Chapter 29 have begun to take shape for muscular and skeletal formation.

Figure 30.10
Nutrient and Gas Exchange in the Placenta

(a) Oxygen- and nutrient-rich blood comes from the mother through the maternal arteries and moves, through smaller arterial vessels, into the maternal blood pools in the placenta. Oxygen-poor blood from the embryo, transported through the umbilical cord's fetal arteries, does not flow into the maternal blood pools, but instead stays within the fetal blood vessels, which project into the maternal blood pools. Oxygen and nutrients in the maternal blood pools move into the fetal blood vessels, however, through such processes as diffusion. The resulting oxygen- and nutrient-rich blood is carried back to the embryo through the umbilical cord's fetal vein. Meanwhile, carbon dioxide from the embryo moves the other way—into the maternal blood pools—to be carried away through maternal veins.

(b) Larger structure of the placenta and uterine environment at 2 months.

(a) Nutrient and gas exchange in the placenta

(b) The placenta in context

maternal vein · maternal artery · maternal blood-pools · fetal vein · fetal arteries

mother ⟵ | ⟶ fetus

placenta · 2-month fetus · yolk sac · uterus · umbilical cord · endometrium of uterine wall · cervix

(a) Embryo Development:

Vertical lines show embryo's actual size; measurements are head-to-rump lengths

3 weeks	4 weeks	5 weeks	6 weeks	7 weeks	8 weeks
0.1 inch	0.2 inch	0.3 inch	0.5 inch	0.7 inch	1.2 inch
Gastrulation and neural tube formation	Heart beats. Arm buds, tail, and gill grooves form. Somites form.	Eye development begins. Leg buds form. Brain enlarges.	Fingers and external ears form. Tail and gills disappearing.	Toes form. Bones begin to harden. Eyelids form.	Arms bend at elbows. Genitals begin to develop.

(b) Fetus Development:

3 months	5 months	7 months	9 months
3.5 inches	7.5 inches	10.5 inches	13.5 inches
Well-defined neck appears. Genital formation complete. Sucking reflex appears.	All major organs have been formed. Head and body hair appear. Movements felt by mother.	Lungs and lung circulation develop. Eyelids open. Fat deposited under skin. May be viable if born.	Fetus usually viable if born. Body hair lost, head hair well developed. Most senses are well developed.

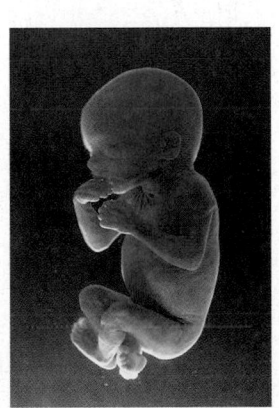

Figure 30.11
Development through the Trimesters
(a) Development of the human embryo (3 weeks to 8 weeks). **(b)** Development of the human fetus (3 months to 9 months). Photos of a human embryo at 6 weeks (left), 11 weeks (middle), and 5 months (right).

Second Trimester

The fetus lengthens considerably during this period, but most of its weight gain takes place in the third trimester. Midway through a pregnancy, a fetus has achieved about half of its birth length (which is about 50 centimeters or 20 inches on average), but only about 15 percent of its birth weight (which averages 3.5 kilograms or 7.7 pounds).

The heartbeat of a fetus can be heard through a stethoscope during the second trimester, and the mother can feel the baby begin kicking by the end of the fourth month. Kicking is only one of several movements the fetus is capable of at this point; others include facial movements and the sucking reflex.

Third Trimester

Along with the terrific growth that takes place during the third trimester, fetuses are running through a series of activities that can be thought of as practice for life outside the uterus (or womb). The fetus is surrounded by a protective and nutritive fluid in the uterus, the **amniotic fluid**, which fills its lungs. It therefore doesn't breathe, but it periodically exercises its breathing muscles by using them to move amniotic fluid in and out of the lungs.

Premature Babies and Lung Function   The end of the second trimester and the start of the third also mark the critical period for a baby being able to survive *outside* the uterus. Clinically, any baby born before 37 weeks of gestation is premature, but many babies born between 35 and 37 weeks after conception require little special care.

The *more* premature a baby is, however, the greater its risk of having difficulties with physical and cognitive development, at least for the first few years of life. In very premature babies, survival itself is called into question (**see Figure 30.12**).

A critical factor in determining whether a premature baby can live outside the uterus is lung function. As it turns out, the respiratory system is the last one to develop in a fetus. Working against the survival of very early "preemies" is the fact that, when they exhale, the air sacs in their lungs tend to close (or "collapse") and then stick together, after which they can be reopened only with great effort. Why doesn't this happen with the lungs of a full-term 38-week fetus? Because, beginning late in pregnancy, fetuses begin synthesizing a lung *surfactant*—a soap-like fatty substance that keeps lung tissue from sticking together. Babies born before the twenty-sixth week of pregnancy must undergo intensive lung therapy in order to survive because they have not produced much lung surfactant up to this point. Usually, their therapy includes the administration of a manufactured surfactant.

30.6 The Birth of the Baby

As the fetus grows, the uterus becomes an increasingly cramped place, and the fetus's movements become more restricted. In late pregnancy, the fetus's head normally will lodge near the base of the mother's spine (**see Figure 30.13**). In this "upside-down" position, the fetus is ready to make its entrance into

Figure 30.12
Tough Going Early on
A pediatric nurse attends to a premature baby in an incubator.

the world. What triggers this journey? The immediate cause is **labor**: the regular contractions of the uterine muscles that sweep over the fetus from its legs to its head. The pressure this generates opens or "dilates" the cervix (ultimately to approximately 10 centimeters or about 4 inches). This creates an opening large enough for the baby to pass through. These things must occur in stages, however. The first phase of the uterine contractions is given over to cervical dilation; then comes the expulsion of the baby and finally expulsion of the placenta (also called the *afterbirth*, for obvious reasons).

But what sets this train of events into motion in the first place? Put another way, what is the trigger that initiates labor? Despite a great deal of research on this question, we don't know. One hypothesis is that, as the fetus grows larger, it reaches the point where even the highly efficient placental system can no longer supply it with enough nutrients. As a result, it secretes hormones that break down nutrients for increased energy, and this secretion triggers a hormonal cascade that brings on labor.

What happens if 38 weeks have passed and labor still doesn't begin? After a period of watching and waiting, a physician may recommend *inducing* labor through use of a synthetic form of the hormone oxytocin. Readers of Chapter 26 will recall that, when labor begins naturally, it is accelerated by oxytocin that is released from the mother's pituitary gland. (This oxytocin brings about muscle contractions that push the fetus down into the uterus.) When a baby is overdue, synthetic oxytocin can help get labor started.

On to Ecology

In this chapter and the five that preceded it, you followed the workings of the cells and tissues that allow animals to function in their marvelously diverse ways. But animals—and for that matter all the other varieties of living things—are not self-contained units. Rather, they are constantly *interacting* with each other and with the nonliving world around them. In the next three chapters, you'll be looking at life at the level of this integrated web. What you will be studying is ecology.

(a) Baby's position prior to birth

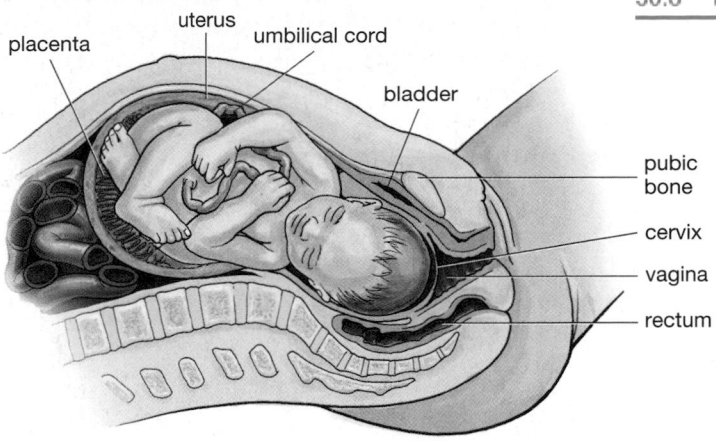

(b) Movement through birth canal

(c) Structure of "afterbirth"

Figure 30.13
Birth of the Baby
With uterine contractions, the cervix dilates, allowing room for the baby to pass through the birth canal and to the outside world. The placenta and its associated fluids and tissues are expelled shortly afterward as the "afterbirth."

Chapter Review

Summary

30.1 Overview of Human Reproduction and Development

- Both the human male and female reproductive systems must produce their respective gametes (sperm and eggs) and then deliver them to a place where they can fuse, in the moment of fertilization.

- The precursors to eggs, called oocytes, exist in the ovaries, which lie just left and right of center in the female pelvic area. Oocytes mature within nurturing complexes of cells and fluids called follicles. On average, once every 28 days, one follicle-oocyte complex is brought to a state of maturity. The egg and some of its accessory cells then rupture from the follicle and ovary and begin a journey through the uterine tube to the uterus. The release of the oocyte is called ovulation. Conception can occur if the oocyte encounters sperm on the way to the uterus.

- Sperm are produced in the male testes and then pass through two types of ducts, the vas deferens and the urethra, after which the sperm are ejaculated from the penis into the female vagina. Materials secreted by three separate sets of glands will join with the sperm before ejaculation. The resulting mixture of sperm and glandular materials is called semen. The first of the sperm to reach the oocyte moving through the uterine tube may fertilize it. Development of the fertilized egg, called a zygote, then ensues.

30.2 The Female Reproductive System

- A portion of the female reproductive system is built up and then dismantled in a reproductive cycle that takes approximately 28 days to complete. The result of the dismantling is menstruation, which is a release of blood and the specialized uterine tissue it infuses, the endometrium. The endometrium, which lines the uterus, is tissue that an embryo implants itself in when pregnancy occurs. Given the obvious costs of menstruation to the female, it is not clear why it has been preserved in evolution, though several hypotheses have been put forward to explain it.

- The basic unit of oocyte development is the ovarian follicle, a complex that includes the oocyte that develops into an egg and some surrounding accessory cells.

- On average, a single follicle each month will develop into a tertiary follicle that ruptures, expelling the egg and its accessory cells from the ovary. This complex of cells then begins a journey through the uterine tube to the uterus. The ruptured tertiary follicle develops into the corpus luteum, which secretes hormones that prepare the reproductive tract for pregnancy and maintain it during pregnancy.

- All the follicles a woman will ever possess are produced in her prior to birth. This number steadily decreases throughout her lifetime, primarily through the process of follicle degeneration called atresia. The scarcity of follicles a woman has in middle age is the primary factor that brings about menopause, the cessation of the monthly ovarian cycle. It is not clear why menopause exists, since it seems to carry a number of costs to females, but several hypotheses have been put forth to account for it.

Web Tutorial 30.1: Female Reproductive System

30.3 The Male Reproductive System

- Sperm begin development in the testes and continue development and are stored in the adjacent epididymis. Sperm move from the epididymis through the vas deferens and then the urethra in ejaculation. The accessory glands that contribute material to the sperm before ejaculation are the two seminal vesicles, the prostate gland, and the two bulbourethral glands.

- Within the testes, sperm development takes place in the seminiferous tubules. Development begins at the periphery of a given tubule, with sperm becoming more developed toward the interior of the tubule. Eventually, developing sperm are transported from the interior of a tubule to the epididymis for further development and storage.

- Sperm development in the testes begins with cells called spermatogonia, which develop into spermatocytes. These in turn give rise to spermatids and then to immature sperm. Spermatogonia give rise not only to spermatocytes, but to more spermatogonia. This self-generation of sperm precursors is the reason men keep producing sperm throughout their lifetimes.

- About 200 million sperm are produced each day—about the number of sperm ejaculated with each orgasm. Males produce such a huge number of sperm because of sperm competition: in species in which females mate with multiple partners, sperm has evolved various characteristics that serve to provide an advantage over other sperm in reaching and fertilizing eggs.

- Sperm make up only 5 percent of the semen that is ejaculated. Materials secreted by the seminal vesicles, the prostate gland, and the bulbourethral glands make up the other 95 percent of semen. These materials provide nutrients, pH neutralizers, and lubricating fluids for the sperm.

Web Tutorial 30.2: Male Reproductive System

30.4 The Union of Sperm and Egg

- Sperm release enzymes externally that break down layers of materials that surround the oocyte. To release these enzymes, the sperm must undergo a final process of maturation brought about by substances the sperm encounters while swimming up the female reproductive tract.

- The first sperm cell to reach the oocyte binds with receptors on its surface, after which the plasma membranes of the two cells fuse. Then the sperm and egg nuclei combine. Fusion of sperm and oocyte cells brings about release of substances from the oocyte that block the entry of any other sperm—an important action, since the fusion of two sperm with one egg would be fatal to the resulting embryo.

30.5 Human Development Prior to Birth

- Human development proceeds through the stages of animal development noted in Chapter 29: formation of the blastocyst, gastrulation, formation of the neural tube, and organogenesis or the formation of organs. Many of the most important stages in development are completed by the end of 12 weeks of pregnancy. The developing organism is termed a zygote at conception, an embryo from the zygote's first division through the eighth week of pregnancy, and a fetus from the ninth week of pregnancy to the birth of the baby.

- The blastocyst implants itself in the endometrial lining of the uterus during the first week of pregnancy.

- The blastocyst initially consists of an inner cell mass, which develops into the baby, and a peripheral group of cells called a trophoblast. The trophoblast is active in uterine implantation and the production of cells that extend into the endometrium, establishing links with the maternal blood supply. These trophoblast cells grow into the fetal portion of the placenta, a complex network of maternal and embryonic blood vessels and membranes. The placenta allows for the movement of nutrients, wastes, and gases between the developing embryo and the mother.

Web Tutorial 30.3: Human Development

30.6 The Birth of the Baby

- The immediate cause of birth is labor, meaning the regular contractions of uterine muscles that sweep over the fetus from its legs to its head. The pressure that results from these contractions opens or dilates the cervix, thus creating an opening large enough for the baby to fit through. It is not clear what the triggering mechanism is for the initiation of labor. When labor does not begin naturally following a full-term 38-week pregnancy, it can be induced by administering a synthetic form of the hormone oxytocin.

Key Terms

acrosome 662	menopause 657
amniotic fluid 668	menstruation 653
cervix 665	oocyte 654
corpus luteum 655	osteoporosis 657
ectopic pregnancy 665	ovarian follicle 654
embryo 665	ovulation 652
endometrium 653	placenta 665
epididymis 660	prostate gland 662
estrogen 658	semen 652
fetus 665	seminiferous tubule 660
follicle 652	spermatocyte 660
follicle-stimulating hormone (FSH) 656	spermatogonia 660
fraternal twin 666	testis 660
gonadotropin-releasing hormone 656	trimester 665
identical twin 666	trophoblast 665
inner cell mass 665	umbilical cord 666
labor 668	urethra 660
luteinizing hormone (LH) 656	uterine tube 652
	vas deferens 660
	zygote 665

Understanding the Basics

Multiple-Choice Questions (answers in the back of the book)

1. The precursors of the eggs produced by females are referred to as
   a. gametes
   b. sperm
   c. oocytes
   d. small eggs
   e. oviducts

2. The structure in which sperm are stored and complete their maturation is the
   a. epididymis
   b. oviduct
   c. penis
   d. prostate gland
   e. vas deferens

3. The tertiary follicle ruptures midway through the menstrual cycle, expelling
   a. one oocyte along with some accessory cells
   b. two oocytes along with some accessory cells
   c. the corpus luteum
   d. the endometrial lining
   e. the fourth follicle

4. The fingerlike fimbriae near the ovary act to
   a. move the incoming sperm toward the oocyte
   b. protect the oocyte from premature fertilization
   c. move the oocyte into the uterine tube
   d. force the oocyte into the uterus
   e. implant the newly fertilized egg in the uterus

5. The natural degeneration of follicles during a woman's lifetime is referred to as
   a. menopause
   b. ovulation
   c. puberty
   d. atresia
   e. apoptosis

6. Which statement is correct concerning gamete production?
   a. Sperm are produced in much higher numbers than eggs.
   b. The number of eggs a female can potentially produce is highly limited relative to the number of sperm a male can produce.
   c. Sperm cells are produced daily, whereas egg cells can be produced only at certain points in the reproductive cycle.
   d. All of the above are correct statements.

7. A fertility doctor is trying to determine why a couple is infertile. It has been determined that the woman is fertile, so the problem must be with the man. In analyzing the man's semen, the doctor notices that it seems to be lacking in proper nutrients for the sperm. The malfunctioning structure must be the:
   a. seminiferous tubules
   b. vas deferens
   c. seminal vesicles
   d. urethra
   e. epididymis

8. The portion of the sperm that contains the enzymes used to degrade materials found on the outside of the egg is the
   a. acrosome
   b. nucleus
   c. tail
   d. mitochondria
   e. chromosomes

9. The portion of the blastocyst called the trophoblast eventually helps form the
   a. head of the baby
   b. legs of the baby
   c. entire baby
   d. nervous system of the baby
   e. placenta

10. Birth of identical twins results from unusual events during
    a. egg production
    b. sperm production
    c. early cell divisions after fertilization
    d. ovulation
    e. second trimester

Brief Review

1. Describe the hormonal changes that regulate the female reproductive cycle.

2. Discuss how the testes act to protect the developing sperm.

3. Menstruation is costly to females in some ways. Why do scientists believe it occurs?

4. Compare and contrast the tertiary follicle and the corpus luteum.

5. What mechanism ensures that only one sperm will be able to fuse with a given oocyte?

6. Outline the events in human development that occur prior to the time the embryo implants in the uterine wall.

7. Define the term *premature* with respect to human development.

8. How do birth control pills work?

Applying Your Knowledge

1. When a couple is having trouble conceiving a child, the first thing fertility specialists generally will look at is the fertility of the prospective father. What do you think a specialist would be looking for?

2. Among "vertebrates," or animals with a backbone, mammals have been very successful. They are generally regarded as the most dominant modern land animals, when compared to reptiles and amphibians. Most mammals are "placental," which is to say their embryos get nourishment within the mother through the placental system of blood vessels reviewed in the text. By contrast, amphibian and reptilian embryos are nourished by substances contained in eggs the mother lays. Can you think of any advantages mammals derive from the placental means of development? Can you think of any disadvantages?

3. Forty years after birth control pills for women came into widespread use, there is still no birth control pill for men. One reason for this is the basic difference between female production of an oocyte each month and the male production of sperm. Why should it be easier to suppress fertility in women than in men?

MediaLab

Are Test Tube Babies the Solution? Understanding Reproductive Problems

Where do babies come from? This question is usually followed by parents squirming through the old-standby talk about birds and bees. Imagine, though, the difficulty some modern parents will have in describing their use of assisted reproductive technology, mechanical methods that remove the sex from sexual reproduction, like *in vitro* fertilization, egg and sperm donors, even sperm injection. These techniques seem to be the innocent product of a late-twentieth-century desire to use scientific advances to make childbirth possible for couples who could never conceive naturally. But is there a more sinister reason for the increase in reproductive technology? Are we becoming less fertile as a species? To learn more, the *Web Tutorial* will help you review normal female and male reproduction, so that in the following *Web Investigation* and *Communicate Your Results* sections, you can evaluate how these processes might be sensitive to our modern lifestyle.

This *MediaLab* can be found in Chapter 30 on your Companion Website (www.prenhall.com/krogh3).

WEB TUTORIAL

Human sexual reproduction involves multiple, highly coordinated steps. In addition to the events of meiosis to create haploid gametes, fertilization and embryonic development occur internally, so humans need accessory structures to direct sperm and egg fusion as well as structures to allow the embryo to access oxygen and food and get rid of wastes. This *Web Tutorial* leads you through the reproductive systems of males and females as well as the early internal development of a human embryo.

Activity

1. *First, you will review the female menstrual cycle: the coordinated release of an oocyte and preparation for the female body to receive and nourish a developing embryo.*

2. *Next, you will learn about the formation and maturation of sperm, and the accessory glands needed to activate sperm for their journey to fertilize the egg.*

3. *Finally, you will learn about the process of human development from blastocyst implantation in the uterine wall to full development of the fetus.*

Failure in any one of these steps can result in an inability to conceive or to carry the fetus to term; a problem for increasing numbers of couples dealing with infertility. Could factors from our environment be responsible for this problem? The following *Web Investigation* and *Communicate Your Results* sections are meant to help you evaluate that question.

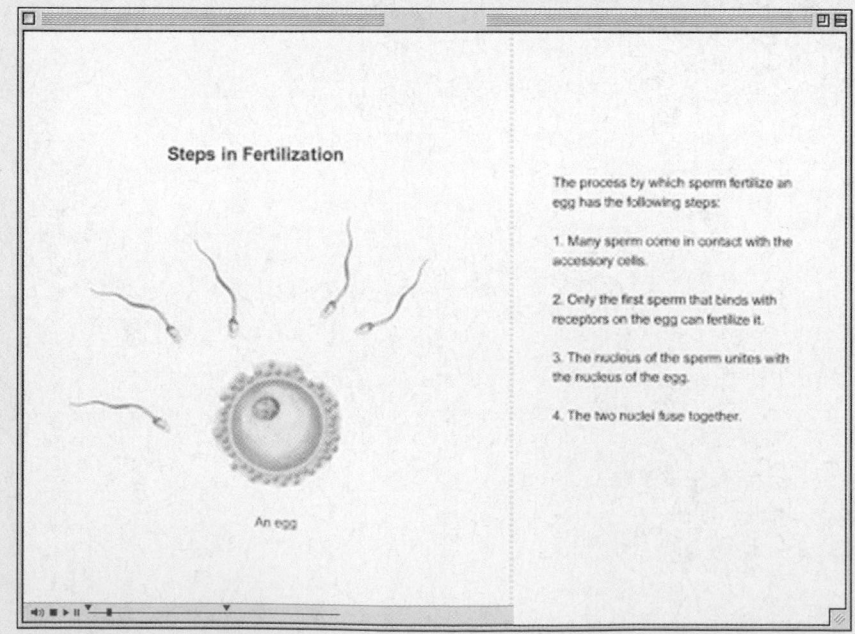

Steps in Fertilization

The process by which sperm fertilize an egg has the following steps:

1. Many sperm come in contact with the accessory cells.

2. Only the first sperm that binds with receptors on the egg can fertilize it.

3. The nucleus of the sperm unites with the nucleus of the egg.

4. The two nuclei fuse together.

An egg

674

Investigation 1
Estimated time for completion = 15 minutes

The environmental movement in the past 30 years has awakened public concern over the effects of pollution on animal health and reproduction. Now, many are questioning whether the same human-made chemicals—including pesticides, plastics, and detergents—that interfere with normal hormone function in laboratory animals are causing a decline in human sperm counts. Select the keywords **SPERM CONTROVERSY 1** or **2** on your Website for this *MediaLab* to read two contradictory articles on declining sperm counts.

Investigation 2
Estimated time for completion = 5 minutes

What have fertility specialists concluded about the major causes of infertility in most couples? Select the keyword **INFERTILITY** on your Website for this *MediaLab* to view a chart of the major causes of infertility. Then select the keyword **ART** to view a government site posting background information on couples seeking help from assisted reproductive technology (ART).

Investigation 3
Estimated time for completion = 10 minutes

Many pregnant women fear birth defects caused by environmental substances (teratogens that interfere with normal development). Although only about 5 percent of birth defects are attributed to exposure to environmental substances, these environmental agents should be clearly recognized and avoided. However, information on the identity of teratogens is often inaccurate, alarming, and not supported by scientific studies. Select the keyword **PREGNANCY** on your Website for this *MediaLab*, and list the substances that are suggested to be teratogens and are thus to be avoided during pregnancy. Then, select the keyword **TERATOGENS** to view a list of known teratogens.

Now that you have been introduced to several sources of suspicion that the environment is adversely affecting human reproduction, use the following questions to evaluate the validity of these claims.

Exercise 1
Estimated time for completion = 15 minutes

Although members of the scientific community disagree over whether sperm counts are declining worldwide, they generally agree about an increase in testicular cancer and congenital birth defects in male reproductive systems. In this exercise, form a group and propose a hypothesis to explain these observations. Your group should search the Internet to find supporting studies, and use the Message Board at the Website for your textbook to post the Internet addresses.

Exercise 2
Estimated time for completion = 15 minutes

Test-tube babies, sperm injections, frozen eggs and sperm are all commonly covered in news stories; but we often hear more about technology than about patients. Using information from the Web sites in *Web Investigation 2*, write a 250-word portrait of the average woman (or man) who is using ART. Include answers to some of these questions: What is the most common procedure? How many ART patients are not pregnant after one try or cycle? How many couples experience multiple births after one cycle? What is the average age of females receiving this treatment?

Exercise 3
Estimated time for completion = 10 minutes

Hopefully it can be said that for every inaccurate Internet site there is a well-informed, scientifically credible site. Compare the list of chemicals to avoid during pregnancy that you made for *Web Investigation 1* with the information from the site listing human teratogens. In 50 words, express your conclusions about the first article.

31 Populations and Communities in Ecology

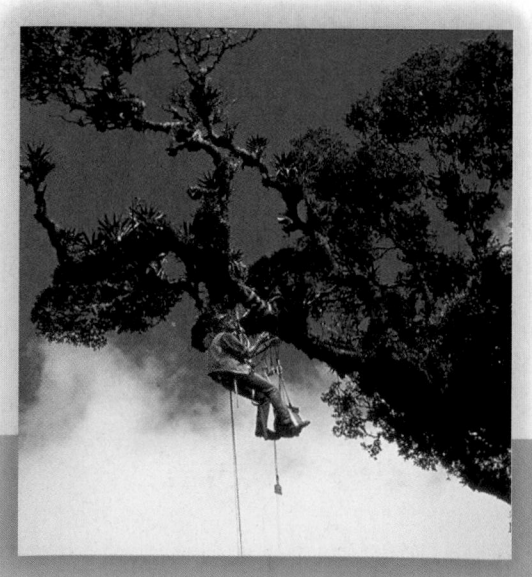

Ecologist on the job.
(Section 31.1, page 678)

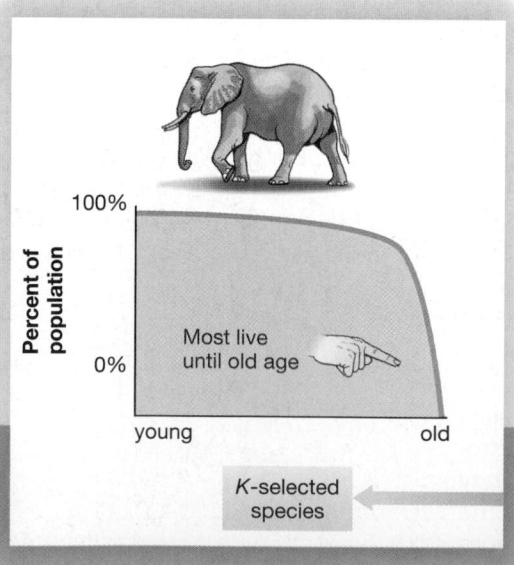

Lives lost late.
(Section 31.3, page 685)

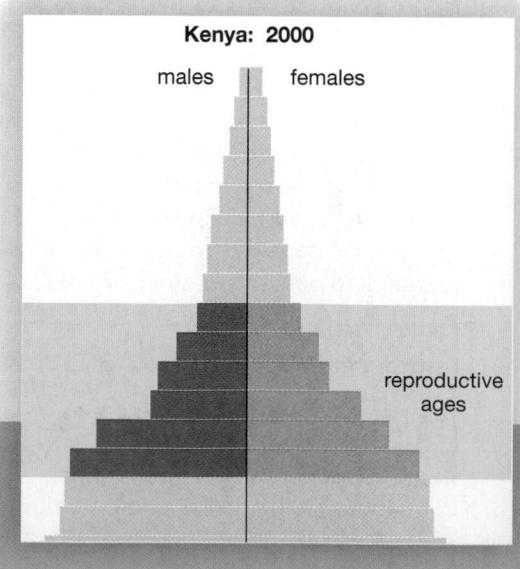

A population pyramid.
(Section 31.4, page 687)

Ecology is the study of how living things interact—with each other and with their physical environment. One way of studying these interactions is to focus on populations, meaning all the members of a single species living in one area. Another approach is to look at communities, meaning all the populations of all the species living in one area.

For those who already have been through some earlier units of this book, a word that is a favorite in the humanities by now may have come to mind in connection with biology. It is *microcosm*, which comes from the Greek *mikros* (tiny) and *kosmos* (universe): a tiny universe, which is also to say a world within a world.

What are biology's microcosms? Well, for one, in all living things, a *system* exists whereby DNA contains information that is then used for the production of proteins. Once put together, these proteins may make up some structure (your hair, for example) or get busy on some specific task (such as breaking down sugar). Critically, one of these tasks is turning on or off the very DNA that called the proteins into being in the first place. Thus it is a *self-regulating* system; it exists within a whole living being, but it has some of the characteristics of a tiny world of its own—a microcosm.

Now take a step up in scale and consider the parts of a human body. Drink some lemonade and your body will start producing insulin, which will help store away the blood sugar that is now coursing through your veins. *Stop* eating for awhile, and your body will produce a hormone called glucagon that helps bring these stored food supplies *out* of reserve. This self-regulating system is thus a kind of world of its own—one that works in concert with, and yet that is in some ways separate from, the circulatory system, the nervous system, and on and on.

By moving up another level in scale, you arrive at a whole organism—a person in the example just given, but it could be a bat or a tree. You might be tempted to think that this is the end of the line for microcosms; that here you have reached the *macro*cosm, containing all microcosms. Think again, however, because the life of, say, a tree is profoundly influenced by *other* trees around it as well as by other kinds of organisms (insects, fungi). Under this view, a living thing is a kind of microcosm that exists within the larger world of living *things*.

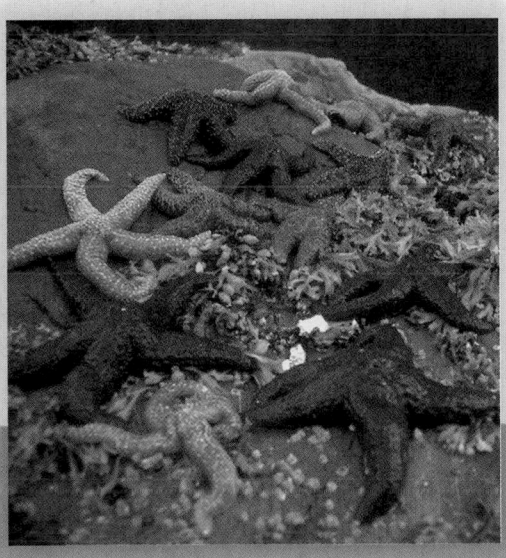

What is a keystone species?
(Section 31.5, page 691)

(a) Species diversity

many different species

(b) Geographic diversity

broad distribution of species

Biodiversity.
(Section 31.5, page 691)

Bay-breasted warbler

A sharing strategy.
(Section 31.6, page 694)

Even after taking this larger world into account, there is still one more jump to make in scale. The whole of the living world exists within the context of the *nonliving* world and universe: the Earth's climate and gases, its sea currents and volcanoes, as well as the energy from the sun. Life doesn't exist apart from these things. Instead, it is very much conditioned by them—though as you'll see, some of these things are also conditioned by life.

31.1 The Study of Ecology

In your walk through biology so far, you have made it through the molecular world (DNA, for example) and through the world of organ systems (circulation, for example) and to some extent through whole organisms, such as animals and plants. Now it is time to take the last steps up; in this chapter and the one that follows, you will consider biology's largest realm of all, **ecology**, defined as the study of the interactions that living things have with each other and with their environment. The final chapter in the book, on animal behavior, is also placed within the ecology unit because it too is concerned with interactions in the living world.

Ecology Is Not Environmentalism

In common speech the word *ecology* has become synonymous with the conservation of natural resources or with the "environmental movement" in all its political dimensions. Under this view, you might assume that the job of an ecologist is to help preserve the natural world. In fact, however, the job of an ecologist is to *describe* the natural world in its largest scale; to say what is, rather than what should be. Are ecologists environmentalists? Most are, but this shouldn't be surprising. We would no more expect ecologists to be indifferent to the environment than we would expect art historians to be indifferent to paintings. Moreover, there is a branch of biology, conservation biology, that is directly concerned with preserving natural resources. But the business of ecology per se is to tell us about the large-scale interactions that go on in the natural world. This work has an important use in that it provides the *information base* that society can use to make decisions about the environment. Does species diversity make for healthier natural communities? How many gray whales are there in the world? How important are prairie dogs to the prairie? To answer these questions, ecologists end up working in some places you might expect—in

tents near the Arctic Circle or at treetop level in tropical rain forests (**Figure 31.1**). They also work in some locations you might not expect, however, such as in offices, hunched over computers, seeing how mathematical models of the natural world work out.

Path of Study

In this chapter and the next one, you'll follow a bottom-to-top approach by moving from smaller ecological units to larger ones. What are the scales of life that concern ecology? The smallest is that of the physical functioning, or physiology, of given organisms. At this level, ecologists are examining individual living things, but at all other scales they are looking at *groups* of organisms or species. For the ecologist, life is conceptualized as being organized into:

Populations

Communities

Ecosystems

The Biosphere

Figure 31.1
An Ecologist on the Job
Ecologists spend a good deal of time going out into nature to study the conditions that exist in various ecosystems—however inaccessible those ecosystems may be. Here a researcher is studying tree branch growth in the rain-forest canopy in Costa Rica.

From Individuals to a Population

The smallest level of group organization is a **population**, defined in Chapter 17 as all the members of a single species that live together in a specified geographic region. The North American bullfrog (*Rana catesbeiana*) is a species that can be found from southern Canada to central Florida, but all the *R. catesbeiana* in a given pond constitute a single *population* of this species. Of course it's possible to define our population to be all the bullfrogs in *two* ponds, or in two states, or two countries—whatever geographic region is most useful for the question an ecologist is asking.

From Populations to a Community

Going up the scale, if you take the populations of *all* species living in a single region, you have a **community**. Often the term community is used more restrictively, to mean populations in a given area that potentially interact with one another.

From a Community to an Ecosystem

If you add to the community all the *non*living elements that interact with it—rainfall, chemical nutrients, soil—you have an ecosystem. More formally, an **ecosystem** is a community of organisms and the physical environment with which they interact. Ecosystems can be of various sizes; you'll be looking at a range that goes from fairly small (a single field, for example) up through the enormous ecosystems called *biomes* that may take up half a continent.

From Ecosystems to the Biosphere

The largest scale of life is the **biosphere**, which can be thought of as the interactive collection of all the Earth's ecosystems. Given what you've reviewed about ecosystems, this means all life on Earth and all the nonliving elements that interact with life. Sometimes, however, the term *biosphere* is used purely in a territorial sense—to mean that portion of the Earth that supports life. If you look at **Figure 31.2**, you can see a graphic representation of ecology's scales of life. We'll now begin to look at ecology through these levels of biological organization, starting small, with the population.

31.2 Populations: Size and Dynamics

So what is it ecologists want to know about a population? Well, they need to know how to count it, how and why it is distributed over its geographical area, and how and why its size *changes* over time—what its population dynamics are, to use the term employed by ecologists.

Biosphere

Ecosystem

Community

Population

Organism

Figure 31.2
The Scales of Life That Concern Ecology
In this chapter, you will consider how organisms of one species are associated in populations, and how populations of different species are associated in communities. In Chapter 32, you will look at ecosystems, which include not only living community members but the nonliving factors that interact with them (such as the rainfall in the ecosystem panel above). Chapter 32 also reviews the large-scale ecosystems called biomes and the biosphere, which is the interactive collection of all the Earth's ecosystems.

Estimating the Size of a Population

The reason ecologists want to count the members of a given population is straightforward: Without such a count, there is no way to answer a question such as how much territory a group of cheetahs must have in order to flourish, or how fast a population of finches recovers from a drought. (How would you know about the latter unless you could compare the population after the drought with the population before it?)

With large, immobile species such as trees, taking a census can sometimes be easy; just mark off an area and count. Things become more difficult when the area under consideration is so large that not all individuals in it can be counted, but rather must be estimated based on a population counted in a smaller representative area. Estimating becomes more difficult yet when the individuals are numerous and mobile, as with birds. Ecologists employ various means to estimate such populations; they count animal droppings within a defined area or survey bird populations as they migrate, for example.

Growth and Decline of Populations over Time

How is it that populations *change* size? As you begin to think about this question, it's worth going over a more general concept, which is the way a population of *anything* might increase in number. If you look at, say, the number of cars coming off the end of a production line, there might be 1,000 on Monday and then 1,000 on Tuesday, and so forth. The important thing to note is that the number of cars produced on Tuesday is not related to the number produced on Monday. The increase in the number of cars is thus an **arithmetical increase:** Over each interval of time (a day in this case), an unvarying number of new units (cars) is added to the population.

Now contrast this with what happens to living things. In most cases, each new unit (each living thing) is capable of playing a part in giving rise to *more units*, which certainly is not the case with cars. Population increases for living things are thus *proportional to* the number of organisms that already exist. Thus the increase in a population of organisms comes about through a different sort of increase, an **exponential increase**, which occurs when, over an interval of time, the number of new units added to a population is proportional to the number of units that exist. **Table 31.1** gives an example of the difference between the two kinds of growth over a period of weeks, using cars for arithmetic growth and the tiny water flea *Daphnia* for exponential growth. Let's assume we start out at the end of day 1 with the 1,000 cars produced that day and with 1,000 water fleas existing in an optimal laboratory environment. As you can see, *Daphnia* is a relatively slow starter, but its population quickly overwhelms that of the car population—not surprising, because the *Daphnia* population doubles every 3 days. If you look at **Figure 31.3**, you can see what these two kinds of growth look like when plotted on a graph.

Population Growth in the Real World

As noted, the *Daphnia* were growing in an "optimal" laboratory environment—plenty of food, habitat kept clean, no predators. Thanks to human intervention, this was a kind of paradise for water fleas, in other words. But could any population ever grow like this in the real world? In all cases the answer is "not forever," and in most cases the answer is "not for long," but some population growths can be dramatic while they last.

In 1859, Thomas Austin released 24 wild European rabbits (*Oryctolagus cuniculus*) onto his estate in southern Australia, near Melbourne, in order to provide more game for sport hunting. His was not the first attempt to introduce rabbits to Australia, but it was by far the most successful—or perhaps the most fateful. This alien species spread north and west in Australia like wildfire; within 16 years it had expanded its range through the entire latitude of the continent, a distance of almost 1,800 kilometers or 1,100 miles. And this invasion was not a matter of a rabbit here and a rabbit there; the European rabbits became a scourge that only was

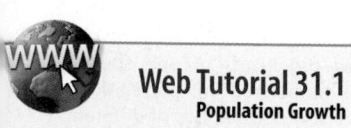

Web Tutorial 31.1
Population Growth

Table 31.1 Arithmetic Growth versus Exponential Growth									
	Day 1	Day 4	Day 7	Day 10	Day 13	Day 16	Day 19	Day 22	Day 25
Arithmetic Growth: Cars	1,000	4,000	7,000	10,000	13,000	16,000	19,000	22,000	25,000
Exponential Growth: *Daphnia*	1,000	2,000	4,000	8,000	16,000	32,000	64,000	128,000	256,000

brought under control, beginning in the mid-1990s, through use of a virus (**see Figure 31.4**). Here is Eric Rolls's description in *They All Ran Wild* of the rabbit problem east of Peterborough in South Australia in 1887:

> . . . for over a hundred miles most trees and plants had been killed. Outalpa head-station was a thousand square miles of rabbits. . . . Rabbits crawled like possums in branches several feet off the ground. They had burrowed under the beautiful granite homestead; they had taken possession of the cellar; they were in the turkeys' coop; they ran in and out of the men's huts apparently without fear; they took no notice of the dogs nor the dogs of them.

There are lots of instances of such seemingly uncontrolled growth. Charles Darwin devoted some thought to the issue as a theoretical matter. He wrote that "There is no exception to the rule that every organic being naturally increases at so high a rate, that, if not destroyed, the Earth would soon be covered by the progeny of a single pair." To put a little finer point on this, a single pair of carrion flies (which are a little larger than a housefly) could in theory give rise to enough flies in a single year to cover the state of New Jersey to a depth of 1 meter (3 feet).

The Shape of Growth Curves

If you look at **Figure 31.5a** on the next page, you can see what growth of this type, **exponential growth**, looks like when plotted on a graph. This is called the *J-shaped growth curve* because it can be so extreme that when plotted it looks like the letter J. It may look familiar, because it is the growth form you just saw with *Daphnia*. As with *Daphnia*, there is relatively slow growth at first, then faster growth, then faster yet. This is growth, in other words, in which

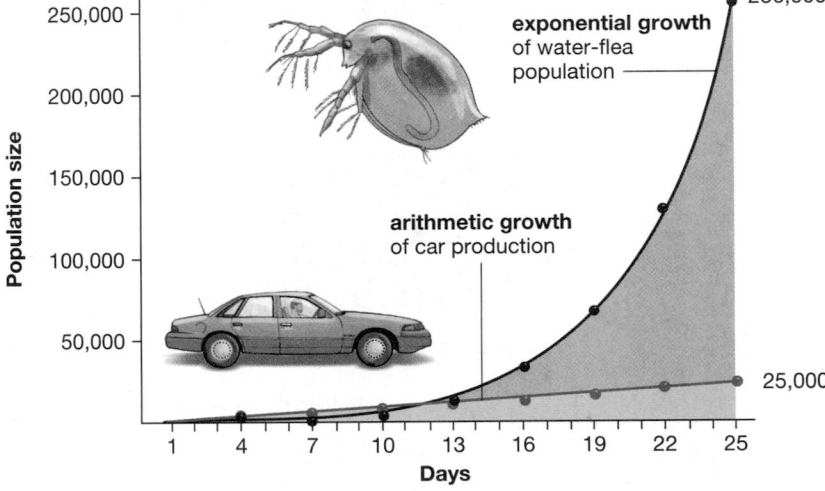

Figure 31.3
Arithmetic and Exponential Growth
When the same number of objects is produced in a given interval of time—in this case, cars from a factory each day—arithmetic growth is at work. By contrast, the populations of most organisms, such as the water flea *Daphnia*, can exhibit exponential growth, at least for a time, meaning the population grows in proportion to its own size.

Figure 31.4
Rabbit Control in Australia
Rabbits run free on one side of a "dingo fence" in Australia. Note the contrast between the barren land where the rabbits feed and the grassland, to the left, that the rabbits have been kept out of.

the *rate* of increase keeps accelerating. In the real world, the curve eventually drops off, often sharply, for reasons you'll soon go over.

Now look at **Figure 31.5b** to see a second model of growth for natural populations, the *S-shaped growth curve*, which tracks **logistic growth**. This starts like exponential growth, but eventually the rate of growth slows and finally ceases altogether, stabilizing at a certain level, denoted here as *K* (which you'll learn the significance of shortly).

What has intervened to account for the difference between the dizzying increase of the J-shaped curve and the moderate increase of the S-shaped curve? All the forces of the environment that act to limit population growth, which in ecology are known as **environmental resistance**. Organisms will run out of food or have their sunlight blocked; greater numbers of predators will discover the population; the wastes produced by the organisms will begin to be toxic to the population.

(a) Exponential growth

(b) Logistic growth

(c) More complex growth

Figure 31.5
Three Models of Growth for Natural Populations

There are populations whose dynamics over time look something like either the J- or S-shaped curve, but in the real world, population size is likely to vary in more complex patterns. In **Figure 31.5c**, you can see one example of such a pattern.

Calculating Exponential Growth in a Population

You've seen that ecologists have ways to count natural populations; but is it possible for them to *predict* the size of populations, given certain pieces of starting information? The answer is yes, as you'll now see. Let's look first at a simplified means of calculating exponential growth, meaning the J-shaped curve. For now, assume the population is isolated—that is, that no individuals are moving in or out of it.

What first needs to be done is to pick a time period to evaluate population change. This period may be 40 minutes (for bacterial populations) or 50 years (for elephants), but some unit of time needs to be chosen for the analysis. The next step is to learn the difference between the birth rate and the death rate in the population over the time period you've picked. This, of course, raises the question: What's a birth rate? It is the number of individuals born in a given time period, expressed as a proportion of the whole population. Thus, if a population of 1,000 had 100 births in a year, its birth rate would be 0.10 or 10 percent per year. Figuring the death rate is similar; if a population of 1,000 had 80 deaths per year, its death rate would be 0.08 or 8 percent per year.

The *difference* between these birth and death rates, of course, is 2 percent. This number is the population's growth rate in an optimal setting, denoted as *r*—standing for the *intrinsic rate of increase*—and it is very important. With it in hand, you can predict what the population's size will be in the future. Growing at 2 percent per year, the population of 1,000 will increase to 1,020 in the first year, and to about 1,480 in 20 years.

Growth rate (*r*) is critical because a small change in it can mean a big change in population over time. Take a population of another species, once again with 1,000 individuals in total, but this time with an *r* of 6 percent rather than 2 percent. In the first year this population would grow by 60 individuals, giving it 1,060 members as opposed to the first population's 1,020. Go 20 years out, however, and this population has about 3,200 individuals in it—it's now more than twice the size of the first population even though both were the same at the start. Meanwhile, if a population's *r* is less than zero—that is, if the number of deaths exceeds the number of births—the population is shrinking. If *r* is zero on the nose, meaning that births exactly match deaths in a given period, the population is at **zero population growth** (**see Figure 31.6**).

As noted, the *r* figure goes by another name, which is a population's **intrinsic rate of increase**: the rate at which a population would grow if there were no external limits on its growth. You could think of it as a population's potential for growth. Importantly, populations of each species have characteristic rates of increase. It won't surprise you to learn that this rate is higher for *Daphnia* populations than it is for whale populations; you can see some examples of an important factor in rate of increase, the time it takes to produce a new generation, in **Figure 31.7**.

Logistical Growth of Populations: Reality Makes an Appearance

You've now observed exponential or J-shaped growth, but you've seen that such growth never occurs for long in nature. Environmental resistance begins to assert itself. In some instances there will be a flattening out of the population increase, and in time perhaps a complex pattern with the curve moving above and below the line denoted earlier as *K*. But what is *K*? What is this point around which the population hovers? It is the maximum population density of a given species that a defined geographical area can sustain over time. The term for this measure is an area's **carrying capacity**.

A Real-Life Example of Carrying Capacity

There is an island in the San Francisco Bay called Angel Island, just a short boat ride from the Golden Gate side of the Bay, that had a small population of deer introduced to it by humans early in the twentieth century. The problem was that the island lacked any natural *predators* for the deer, with the result that the deer population proliferated way beyond what the island's vegetation could support. Had this taken place in a purely natural environment, the deer population would have shrunk in accordance with the amount of available vegetation. But there were human hikers on Angel Island and, seeing

emaciated deer, they did what you might expect: They fed the deer with what they brought along in their backpacks. Surviving through this artificial means, however, *more* deer came to live on the island and stripped it of its vegetation, thus reducing its carrying capacity.

The main lesson here is that there are limits to how many members of a given species an expanse of territory can support. Note also, however, that carrying capacity is not fixed; in the case of Angel Island, it was lowered as the deer, artificially fed by human beings, stripped the island of vegetation. In other instances carrying capacity might be raised for given

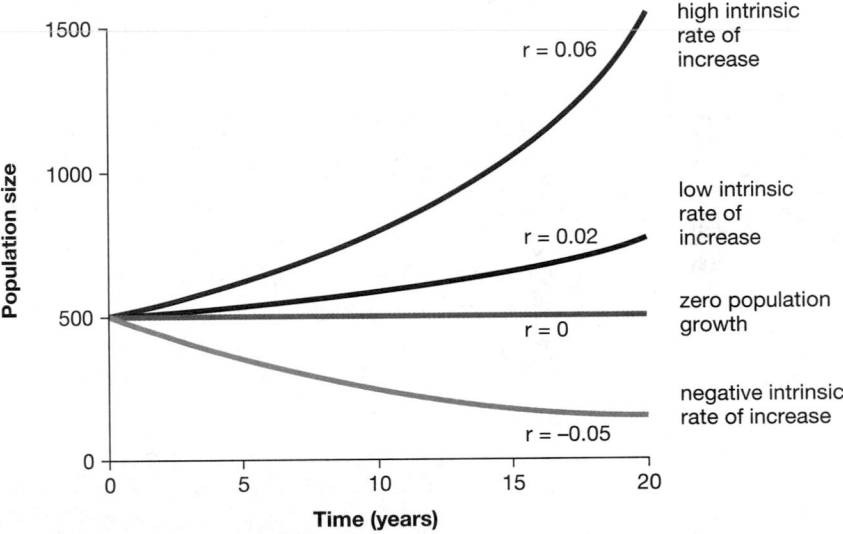

Figure 31.6
A Population's Potential for Growth: The Intrinsic Rate of Increase (*r*)
If the birth rate exceeds the death rate, then the population size will increase over time, (*r* = 0.06 in the example). If the birth rate equals the death rate, then the population size will stay constant (*r* = 0). Finally, if the birth rate is lower than the death rate, the population size will decrease over time (*r* = −0.05). Note what dramatic effects a small change in *r* can have over time, in this case on a population whose starting size is 500 individuals.

Figure 31.7
How Long between Generations?
An important factor in the population dynamics of any species is its "generation time," meaning the time that elapses between the birth of one generation and the birth of the next. Shown on the graph are the minimum generation times for a few selected species, along with a measurement of the length of each organism at the time it reproduces. The larger a species is, the longer its generation time tends to be. (Redrawn from J. T. Bonner, *Size and Cycle: An Essay on the Structure of Biology* [Princeton University Press, 1965].)

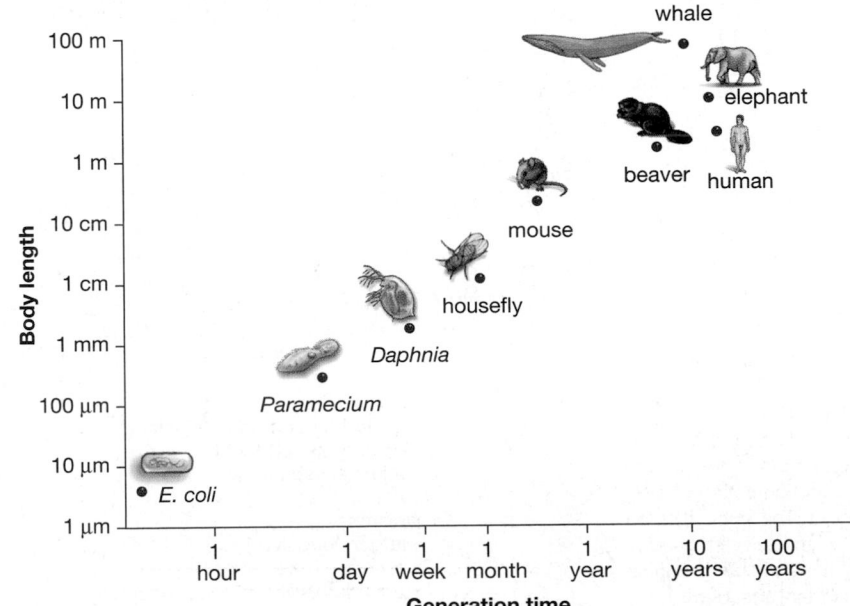

periods (perhaps through abundant rainfall). The environments that many species live in tend to be stable over time, however, meaning that their carrying capacities will tend to be stable as well.

The *K* line can generally be established for a given population by estimating its numbers over an extended period of time. For many species, their population may exceed or "overshoot" *K* at times, but this excess will be offset by periods during which the population is under *K*. Once *K* is known, it is valuable in predicting the change in a population's size, because it often serves as a *factor* that can be used in mathematical equations to calculate the limits to population growth. The higher a population is relative to *K*, the more severely its growth will be limited.

31.3 *r*-Selected and *K*-Selected Species

It's well known that for human beings, about 9 months will elapse between conception and birth; but it's less well known that for an elephant this same process takes almost 2 years. For any given human or elephant female, then, births are relatively few and far between. And once the offspring come, the amount of attention lavished on them is great indeed. It's not

unusual for an elephant calf to be nurtured by its mother and a larger kinship group for at least the first 10 years of its life. In the first year of this period, a mother might not ever let her calf wander farther than 20 meters away from her. Meanwhile, humans may lavish 18 years of constant care and concern on a child before the domestic bonds are finally broken.

By contrast, the common housefly can produce a new generation once a month, and the parental generation provides no care whatsoever to the offspring.

Houseflies and elephants lie at opposite ends of a continuum of *reproductive strategies*, by which is meant characteristics that have the effect of increasing the number of fertile offspring an organism bears. A plant or animal obviously does not consciously *decide* on a strategy for producing offspring; rather, such a strategy is handed to it by virtue of its species' evolution.

So how does the strategy of elephants differ from the strategy of houseflies? This may be apparent from what you've observed already. For elephants the strategy is to bring forth few offspring, but lavish attention on them. For houseflies it is to bring forth a multitude of offspring, but give no attention to any of them. These strategies are in turn related to other characteristics of these species, as you'll now see (**see Figure 31.8**).

K-selected equilibrium species ⟷ **r-selected opportunist species**

Population size:
- limited by carrying capacity (*K*)
- density dependent
- relatively stable

Organisms:
- larger, long lived
- produce fewer offspring
- provide greater care for offspring

Population size:
- limited by reproductive rate (*r*)
- density independent
- relatively unstable

Organisms:
- smaller, short-lived
- produce many offspring
- provide no care for offspring

Figure 31.8
K-Selected and r-Selected Species
The elephants on the left are a *K*-selected species. Here, a mother stays close to her calf, providing the kind of careful attention typical of *K*-selected species. The pond flies on the right are an *r*-selected species, bearing many young but giving no attention to them after birth.

K-Selected, or Equilibrium, Species

Elephants will not seek out a totally new environment; they experience their environment as a relatively stable entity, and compete among themselves and with other species for resources within it. Given this stability, species like elephants are known as an *equilibrium species*. In line with this, the elephant *population* stays relatively stable compared to a fly population; its numbers will fluctuate in a relatively narrow range above and below the environment's carrying capacity. This is another way of saying that the population regularly bumps up against carrying capacity (*K*), which is the density of population that a unit of living space can support. Two things follow from this. First, elephants are said to be a **K-selected species**: one whose population sizes tend to be limited by carrying capacity. The second point, which follows from this definition, is that the pressures on the elephant population are **density dependent**: As the density of the population goes up, the factors that limit the population—food supply, living space—assert themselves ever more strongly.

r-Selected, or Opportunist, Species

In contrast to elephants, houseflies are known as an *opportunist* species—a species whose population size tends to fluctuate greatly in reaction to variations in its environment. Should favorable weather suddenly arrive, or a food supply suddenly appear, the fly population in the area will skyrocket. When the food is gone, or if the temperature suddenly changes, this same population will plunge in number. In short, environment tends to be highly variable for fly populations, and the flies have a high population growth rate that allows them to take advantage of environmental opportunities. For these animals, the strategy is to produce a multitude of offspring very fast. Flies are therefore said to be an **r-selected species**, meaning one whose population sizes tend to be limited by reproductive rate.

This definition implies that fly population numbers have nothing to do with fly population *density*, at least for a time. The pressures on the population are thus said to be **density independent**. The forces at work in these populations tend to be *physical* forces—frost, temperature, rain—as opposed to the *biological* forces that operate in density-dependent control (competition for food, disease). Given this, the *r*-selected strategy of many offspring/little attention is understandable. When you exist at the whim of environmental forces, "life is a lottery and it makes sense simply to buy many tickets," as R. M. May and D. I. Rubinstein have phrased it.

The *r*- and *K*-selected groupings are categories invented by human beings and, as usual, nature refuses to fit neatly into such boxes. It is true that small, short-lived species tend to lie at the *r*-end of the continuum, and that large, long-lived species lie at the *K*-end, but sea turtles are long-lived and they give no care at all to their newborns. Meanwhile flies can be limited in a density-dependent way for at least part of their population cycle—by predators and by competition among themselves. All sorts of variations exist on this theme. You've looked at animals as examples of *r*- and *K*-selection, but the concept applies to plants as well. A plant such as ragweed is at the *r*-selected extreme in the plant world, while oak trees and cacti are at the *K*-selected extreme. The ragweed grows rapidly and has a short life span, while the oak grows slowly and lives a very long time.

Survivorship Curves: At What Point Does Death Come in the Life Span?

K- and *r*-strategies are related to the concept of "survivorship curves," which, as you can see in **Figure 31.9**, are thought of in terms of three ideal types: late loss,

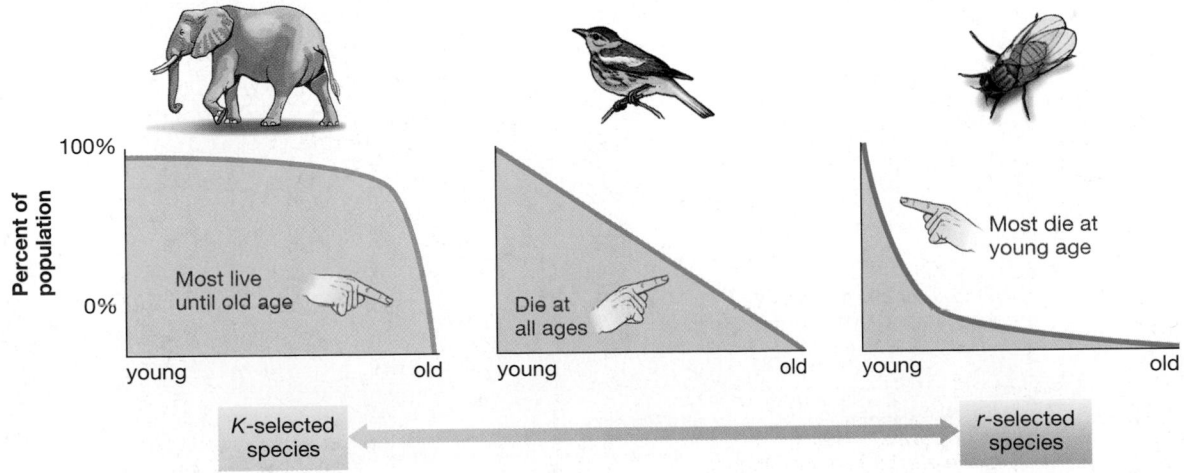

**Figure 31.9
When Is Death Likely to Come?**
An organism's chance of living a long life is related to the reproductive strategy of its species, as reflected in these survivorship curves. Elephants and humans (late-loss species) produce few young, but most survive until old age. At the other extreme, flies (early-loss species) produce many young, but most die young. In between are constant-loss species; they produce a moderate number of young, which die at a fairly constant rate during a typical life span.

constant loss, and early loss (sometimes referred to as types I, II, and III, respectively). Humans and most of our fellow *K*-selected mammals fall into type I, because we tend to survive into old age (our lives are lost late). Insects and many amphibians are type III, because their death rates are very high early in life, but level out thereafter. Other types of living things, such as birds, fall into type II, because they die off at a nearly constant rate through their life span.

31.4 Thinking about Human Populations

We'll look at the final elements in population dynamics in connection with the human population. The concepts involved could be applied to any population of living things. But here the focus is on human beings, so that you can consider population principles along with the real-world issue of human population growth, which figures so prominently in environmental issues.

Survivorship Curves Are Constructed from Life Tables

The survivorship curves you just looked at are constructed by developing what are known as **life tables** for the species in question. To create these, scientists divide the species' life span into suitable units of time—days for fruit flies, years for human beings—

and see how likely it is that an average species member will be alive after a given number of days or years. The technique for doing this was not invented by biologists who wanted to know about the survival of flies, but by a nineteenth-century British actuary—a person trained to calculate probabilities—who knew the information would be useful for life insurance companies. How likely is it that a person will be alive at 10, or 20, or 80 years of age? If you look at **Table 31.2**, you can see the answer for an average group of 100,000 persons born in the United States in the year 2000.

Population Pyramids: What Proportion of a Population Is Young?

You've seen that population growth in the natural world can be exponential (for a time) because a population of living things grows in proportion to its own size. However, all members of a population do not count equally in calculating this growth. If scientists want to peer into the future of a given population, what they want to know is: What proportion of the population is *past* the age of reproduction as opposed to the proportion that is, or will be, of reproductive age? If you look at **Figure 31.10**, you can see the answer to this question, expressed as a "population pyramid" for two countries in the year 2000. Each bar on the graph represents a 5-year

Table 31.2 A Life Table for the United States

Taking a hypothetical group of 100,000 persons born in the United States in 2000, the table shows the proportion likely to still be living at the ages indicated and the average remaining lifetime for persons at each age. Note that life expectancy does not drop 10 years for each 10 years lived. The average person surviving to age 70 can expect to live until age 84, whereas the average person at age 10 could expect to live only to about age 78.

At age	Number still living	Average remaining lifetime in years
10	99,095	67.6
20	98,654	57.8
30	97,696	48.3
40	96,349	38.9
50	93,522	30.0
60	87,498	21.6
70	74,561	14.4
80	51,037	8.6
90	18,839	4.7
100	1,781	2.6

Source: National Center for Health Statistics

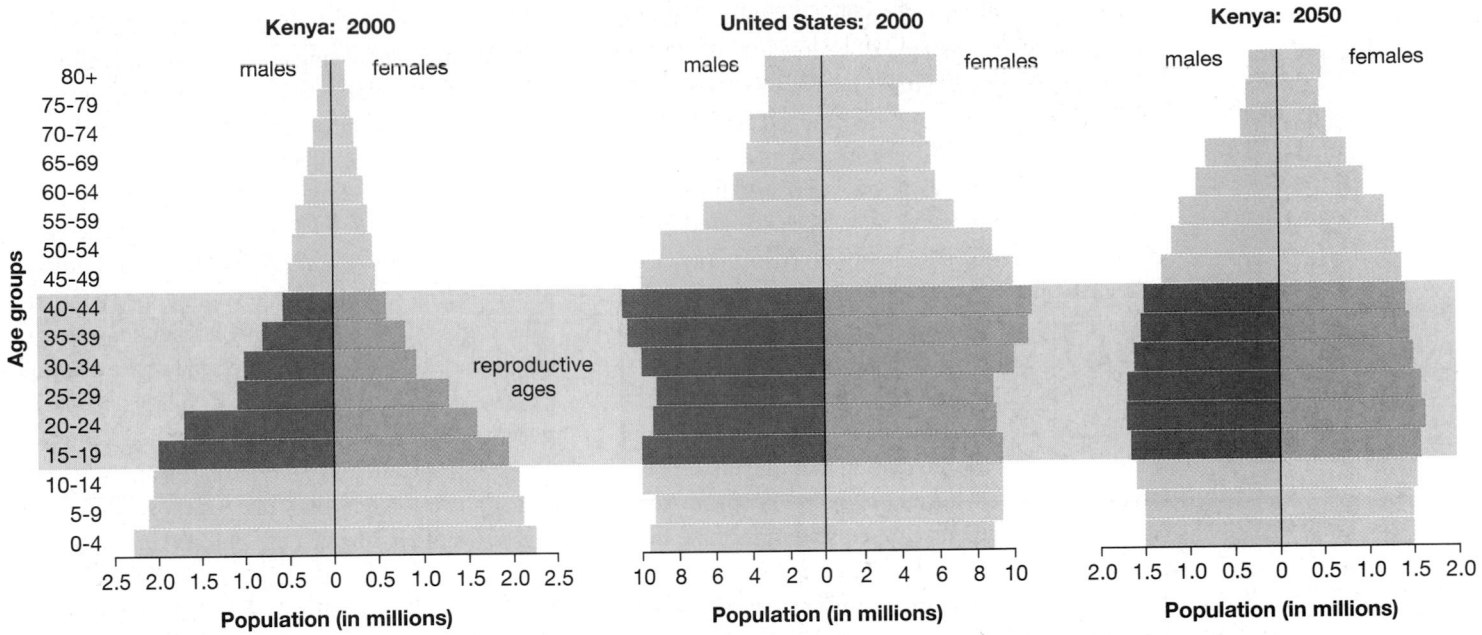

Figure 31.10 shows the top three population pyramid graphs:

Kenya: 2000 — males / females, Age groups (80+ down to 0-4), reproductive ages band highlighted, Population (in millions) axis 2.5 2.0 1.5 1.0 0.5 0 0.5 1.0 1.5 2.0 2.5

United States: 2000 — males / females, Population (in millions) axis 10 8 6 4 2 0 2 4 6 8 10

Kenya: 2050 — males / females, Population (in millions) axis 2.0 1.5 1.0 0.5 0 0.5 1.0 1.5 2.0

age grouping, or "cohort," of the population (those who are 0–4 years old, 5–9, and so on), with the length of each bar representing the size of the co-hort. The reproductive age-range for humans gen-erally is considered to be between 15 and 45. If you look at the graph for Kenya, you can see that it has many more individuals of reproductive and pre-re-productive age than of post-reproductive age. What does the future hold for Kenya? In all probability, a large growth in the population. In contrast, the age-structure diagram for the United States shows that a much greater proportion of its population is at or beyond reproductive age.

The World's Human Population: Finally Stabilizing

You probably noticed that there is a third graph in Figure 31.10, which displays Kenya's expected popu-lation pyramid for the year 2050. It's easy to see that

the projected age distribution for Kenya looks something like the current age distribution for the United States. As a result, Kenya can look forward to slower population growth in the years after 2050. This Kenyan projection actually is just one example of a momentous shift that is going on with human population around the world today. Only in the last couple of years has it become clear that, following centuries of explosive growth, the human popula-tion finally appears to be stabilizing.

To put this change into a larger context, look at **Figure 31.11**, which shows you how human popula-tion has grown during "historical time," which is to say the last 10,000 years. For centuries human numbers grew relatively little, but then began an upward climb about 1700. Improved sanitation, better medical care, and increases in the food supply came together to pro-duce the rate of growth you see. The Earth's human population didn't pass the 1-billion mark until 1804; it then took 123 years to double to 2 billion (in 1927),

Figure 31.10
Age Structure in Populations: Kenya and the United States
Each bar on the graphs represents a five-year age grouping of the population. Note the greater pro-portion of the Kenya 2000 popula-tion that is of "pre-reproductive" age—an indication of greater population increases in the future than is the case with the United States. The graph on the right shows the change expected to come about in Kenya's age struc-ture by the middle of the century. (Data from the United States Cen-sus Bureau.)

Figure 31.11
Human Population Increase through the Centuries

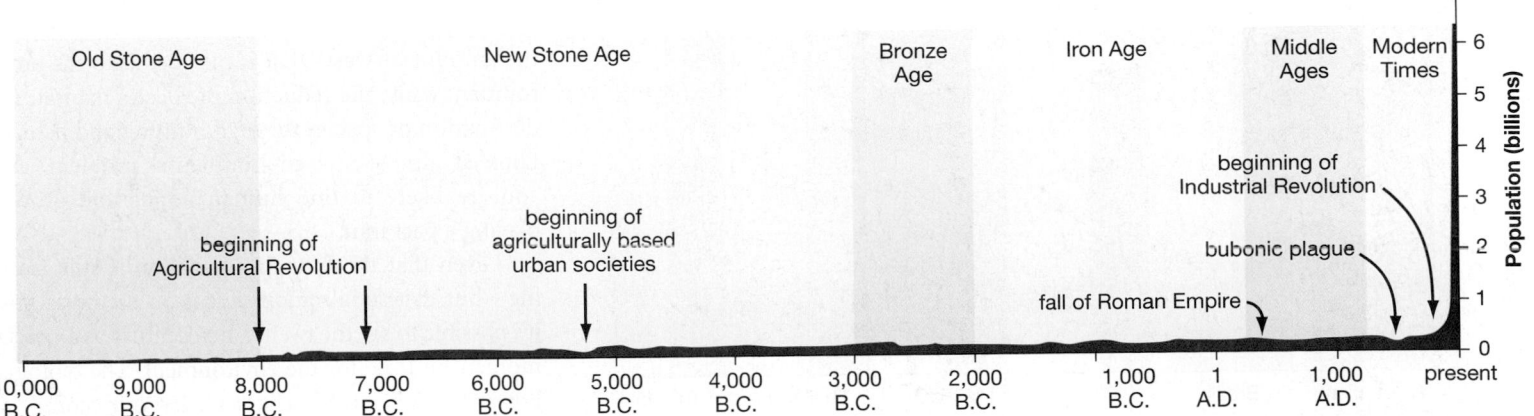

then 48 years to double to 4 billion (in 1974), and now it has exceeded 6.3 billion. The curve you see that resulted from this growth may look familiar, because it is a more extreme version of the J-shaped curve, though greatly elongated on its left side. Were we looking at any species other than our own and saw this kind of growth curve, we would predict that this kind of increase could not go on for long; that environmental resistance would assert itself and that the population might even crash in one catastrophic sense or another.

But something has changed. In 1992, demographers in the United Nations were predicting that, by 2050, the Earth would have 12 billion people on it. But by 2004, the UN was predicting that the human population will peak at about 9.2 billion people in 2075. To be sure, 8.9 billion represents a big increase from today's 6.3 billion. But the *rate* of increase is slowing. From 1990 to 1995, world population was increasing by 82 million people per year; by 2015–2020, the increase should be down to 69 million people a year. Should this trend continue, the world's human population will at least stabilize in this century—it may even decline slightly by century's end.

What has made the difference? The key measurement used by demographers to predict human population change is female fertility—the average number of children born to each woman in a population. In more developed countries, the "replacement" fertility level is 2.1. If fertility is above 2.1, the population will grow; if it's below 2.1, the population will shrink. (Why 2.1 instead of 2.0? Some children will not live to have children of their own.) With this in mind, look at **Figure 31.12**. Pictured are female fertility levels for a selected group of countries in two periods: 1960–65 and 2000–2005. The dramatic declines you can see are not being repeated in all countries. Indeed, in some countries fertility isn't dropping at all. But when all the world's countries are averaged to-

gether, it's clear there has been a major change in fertility. Women are having fewer babies, and this is why the world's population seems to be stabilizing.

The global average in fertility, however, masks some tremendous differences between more-developed and less-developed countries. Think of it this way. In 2002, the world's population was increasing by 151 people per *minute*. And of these 151 additional people, 149 were born in less-developed countries. The South Asian country of Bangladesh—which is about the size of Iowa—is expected to have a population increase of more than 100 million people between 2003 and 2050. Meanwhile, in the 15 countries of the European Union—France, Germany, Sweden, and so forth—the fertility rate is now 1.5. If this persists for another 20 years, the Union's current population of 375 million people will be reduced by 88 million people by century's end, assuming there is no change in immigration or mortality.

Where does the United States stand in this spectrum? In the coming decades, it is expected to have more population growth than any other large, developed country, both in proportional and absolute terms. The U.S. population is expected to go from 292 million people in 2003 to 422 million people in 2050—a 45 percent increase. What makes the United States different from the other developed countries? Partly the American fertility rate, which at 2.03 is not quite at replacement level, but is much higher than those of European countries. The biggest single factor driving the U.S. population increase, however, is immigration. More than 1 million people immigrate to the United States each year.

Human Population and the Environment

Almost everyone is aware of a linkage between the quality of the environment and the size of human populations. Some scientists argue that there is no greater single environmental threat than the continued growth of the human population. The basis for this conclusion is that population affects so many environmental issues: the use of natural resources, the amount of waste that is pumped into the environment daily, the reduction of species habitat, the decimation of species through hunting and fishing. Look at almost any environmental problem, and you are likely to find human population growth playing a part in it.

Given that the human population is still growing—but that stabilization of it is on the horizon—it's possible to see the twenty-first century as a crucial moment in time for the environment. The biologist Edward O. Wilson has characterized our century as

Figure 31.12
Big Changes in Fertility
Pictured are female fertility rates in six countries during two periods: first during the 1960s and then projected for the period 2000–2005. Changes such as these have brought about a remarkable decline in average female fertility worldwide. (Source: Population Reference Bureau.)

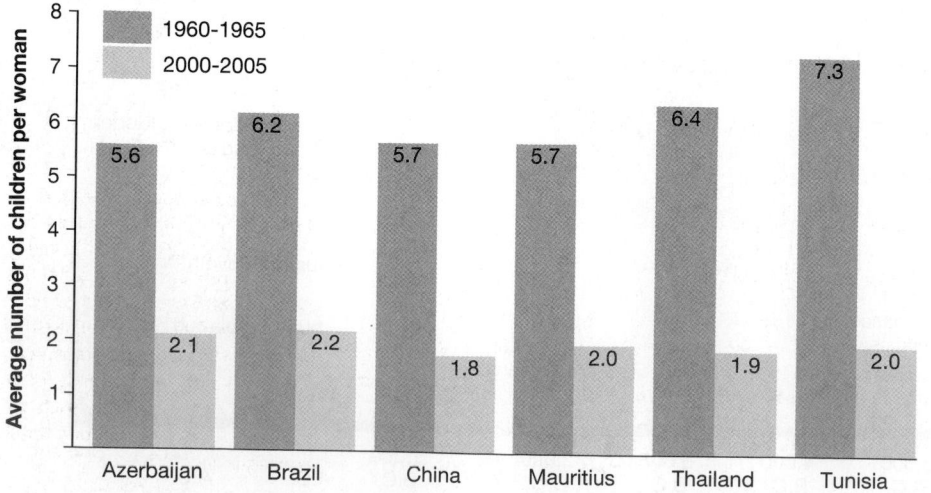

an environmental *bottleneck*: as a period in which the Earth's ecosystems will be under the greatest assault they are ever likely to face. On the other side of the bottleneck, with human population stabilized or even declining, the pressures on the environment should ease. The question is: How many species and habitats can make it *through* the bottleneck? How many primate species can be preserved? How many acres of rain forest can be kept intact? How many acres of American wetlands can remain as they are?

Some experts argue that it is not population per se, but rather the use of resources *per person* that is of most pressing concern. Consider that the United States used less water in 1995 than it did in 1980, even though the U.S. population grew by 16 percent during the period. Another perspective on this is provided by the use of resources in more-developed, as opposed to less-developed, countries. If you look at **Figure 31.13**, you can get a sense of the differences that exist. Carbon dioxide (CO_2) is a gas that is found naturally in the atmosphere, but that is also put into the atmosphere when human beings burn "fossil fuels," such as coal or gas, to power car engines or run power plants. CO_2 produced by these human activities is now regarded by most scientists as a cause of global warming—the rise in Earth's surface temperature that has occurred over the past century. Figure 31.13a shows the amount of CO_2 produced per person by human activity in five countries. Note how little CO_2 is produced per person in less-developed countries, such as India or China, compared to that produced in the more-developed countries, such as the United States. Now, in Figure 31.13b, note the effect this per-capita difference has on total CO_2 emissions. The United States put 64 percent more carbon into the atmosphere than did China in 1997, even though China had nearly five times as many people as the United States (1.3 billion compared to 265 million in the U.S.). With this, you can begin to see why environmentalists are worried about the strain that economic development will put on the Earth's environment *irrespective* of population growth. What will happen when people in China start driving cars and using air conditioners at the rate that Americans do?

31.5 Communities: Looking at the Interactions of Many Populations

In this tour of ecology, you've so far been looking at species in isolation—at one population or another as it increases or decreases in size. In nature, of course, species live together in a rich mix of combinations. How rich? To take the high end of diversity, which is the tropical rain forest, Smithsonian biologist Terry Erwin found an estimated 1,700 species of beetle in a single tree in Panama. Not 1,700 beetles, mind you; 1,700 *species* of beetle.

In beginning to think about the interactions of these diverse populations, a helpful concept is that of the community. As noted earlier, a **community** generally is defined as all the populations that inhabit a given area; all the plants, animals, fungi, bacteria, protists—every living thing, in other words. The term also is used, however, to mean a collection of populations in a given area that potentially *interact* with each other.

So what is it ecologists would like to know about any community? For starters, they'd like to know

(a) Per capita CO₂ emissions (metric tons of carbon)

U.S.	5.48
China	0.75
Russia	2.65
Japan	2.51
India	0.29

One measure of resource use is per capita carbon dioxide (CO_2) emissions: the amount of CO_2 a country releases into the atmosphere through human-caused activities, divided by the number of people that country has. The graph displays per capita CO_2 emissions for five countries in 1997, as measured in metric tons of carbon.

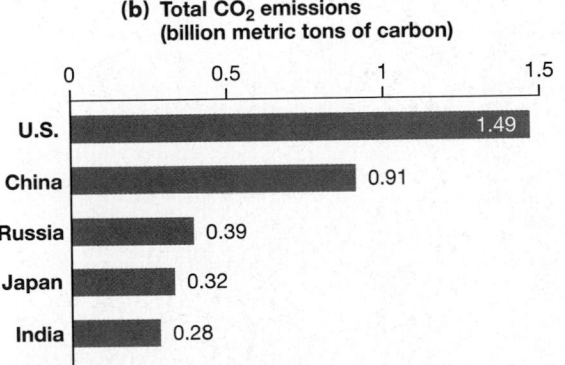

(b) Total CO₂ emissions (billion metric tons of carbon)

U.S.	1.49
China	0.91
Russia	0.39
Japan	0.32
India	0.28

The differences in per capita emissions have significant consequences for total emissions within a country. In 1997, the United States released 64 percent more CO_2 into the atmosphere than did China, even though the U.S. had only one-fifth as many people as China.

Figure 31.13
Use of Resources by Country
The use of natural resources per person (or "per capita") varies greatly from one country to the next. The average resident of a developed country, such as the United States, uses far more resources than the average resident of a less-developed country, such as India, and this has environmental consequences.

what at least some of the species are and what their relative numbers are. They'd also like to know about the importance to the community of some of its individual members.

Large Numbers of a Few Species: Ecological Dominants

There's a tremendous variability in the mix of species found in different communities, but many communities tend to be dominated by only a few species. Forests tend to be populated by certain kinds of trees, stretches of prairie by certain kinds of grasses. The few species that are abundant in a given community are called **ecological dominants** (see Figure 31.14). These generally are plants, but they can be other life-forms, as is the case with the tiny animals known as corals that are the ecological dominants in coral reefs.

Importance beyond Numbers: Keystone Species

Ecologists have long recognized that there are also species that may not be numerous in a given area, but whose *absence* would bring about significant change in the community. Each of these is a **keystone**

species: a species whose impact on the composition of a community is disproportionately large relative to its abundance within that community. The concept of the keystone species was introduced in the 1960s by marine ecologist Robert Paine, who went with his students to a shallow-water zone of the Pacific Ocean in Washington State and for six years regularly removed all sea stars in the genus *Pisaster* from a small area. Such a sea star may sound harmless enough, but *Pisaster* was, in fact, the **top predator** in the area. It preyed on other species, but no species preyed upon it (**see Figure 31.15**). The impact of the *Pisaster* removal was big: Before the change there had been 15 species in the area, and after it there were 8. One species of mussel, freed from its former predator's control, took over much of the attachment space in the area, crowding out other animals, such as barnacles.

Over time, the keystone species concept has undergone some modification. Where once scientists thought of keystones as always sitting at the top of food chains, they now recognize that organisms in other positions can take on a keystone role—beavers building dams, for example, or even lichens that are critical in getting communities going in the desert. Beyond this, it turns out that there are communities

(a) German forest dominated by single species of tree

(b) Kansas prairie dominated by tall-grass

**Figure 31.14
Ecological Dominants**

Figure 31.15
Keystone Species
When the predatory sea star *Pisaster ochraceus* was removed from a small area of rocky shore along the Pacific coast of the United States, the species composition of the community changed drastically, more so than if one of the other species had been removed. Pictured are several *Pisaster* sea stars on the Pacific Northwest coast.

without keystones; remove any one species from such a community, and its role will be taken over by another species.

Variety in Communities: What Is Biodiversity?

Apart from ecological dominants and keystones, a third element that ecologists pay attention to in any community is the *range* of species it has in it. This touches on the more general concept of **biodiversity**, which can be defined as variety among living things. In everyday speech, what biodiversity means is a diversity *of species* in a given area. This is an important measure of diversity, but it is only one among several. You can see why from an imaginary experiment that has been noted by ecologist Paul Ehrlich.

Suppose that you could get a few members of every species on Earth, but that you restricted each species to a single population housed somewhere (in a single zoo or an aquarium or botanical garden). Species *diversity* would not drop at all in such a scenario—you'd still have some of each kind of creature, after all—but the Earth quickly would become barren, because what's needed is a rich *distribution* of species in populations across the planet. This geographical distribution of populations is the second measure of biodiversity. The third measure exists *within* populations or species. It is genetic diversity, meaning a diversity of "alleles" or variants of genes in a population. Without such diversity, populations are vulnerable to disease; their members may die young or suffer from a variety of inherited mental and phys-

ical afflictions (see "Lessons from the Cocker Spaniel" in Chapter 17). In summary, biodiversity means species diversity, geographic diversity, and genetic diversity (**see Figure 31.16**).

What Are the Effects of Species Diversity?

In the last 10 years, two of the hottest questions in ecology have concerned species diversity. The first of these questions is: Do diverse communities tend to be more *productive* communities? In ecology, productivity is a measure of how much of the sun's energy plants and other photosynthesizers are able to "capture" and then turn into living material or "biomass." A really productive community is one that is rich with biomass—rich in leaves and seeds and roots and the animals that feed on them. So, does a diverse community tend to be more productive than one that is not diverse? The answer seems to be yes. The reason for this may be that, in diverse communities, each community member is able to exploit a different portion of the resources available. Some plants will bloom early while others bloom late; some plants will do well with only a little water while other plants will flourish with more. In this respect, communities may be something like Jack Sprat and his wife from the old nursery rhyme. Recall that Jack could eat no fat and that his wife could eat no lean, but that between them they licked the platter clean.

Figure 31.16
Three Types of Biodiversity

	High biodiversity	Low biodiversity
(a) Species diversity	many different species	few species
(b) Geographic diversity	broad distribution of species	narrow distribution of species
(c) Genetic diversity	high genetic diversity within population	low genetic diversity within population

A second question about species diversity has been more difficult to answer. Does species diversity lead to greater *stability*? Is a diverse community better able to recover from, say, a drought than a community that is not diverse? The preponderance of studies seem to indicate the answer is yes, but other studies indicate the answer is no. This question remains a compelling one to ecologists because it has practical ramifications. Human beings are constantly changing the environments around them—fragmenting habitats, clearing forests for farmland, and so forth. When this happens, the number of species in given area often decreases. The question is: Will a community whose diversity has been reduced retain its ability to "bounce back" from an environmental disruption? Will it remain as stable as before when confronted with a prolonged freeze or an insect invasion or a flood? If the answer is no, then societies might make different decisions about how to use land than if the answer is yes.

31.6 Types of Interaction among Community Members

Having considered some general issues regarding communities, let's now turn to the subject of how members of a community might interact with each other. Here's a short list of ways:

Competition

Predation and parasitism

Mutualism and commensalism

Before continuing with the exploration of these modes of interaction, let's go over a couple of concepts that will apply to them all.

Two Important Community Concepts: Habitat and Niche

A **habitat** is the physical surroundings in which a species can normally be found. Though two populations of a species may be widely separated, they can generally be found dwelling in similar natural surroundings. A habitat is sometimes described as a species' "address," but a more accurate metaphor might be a species' preferred type of neighborhood.

The word **niche** has been defined in several ways, but it is useful to think of it in terms of a simple metaphor: A niche is an organism's occupation. How and where does the organism make a living? What does it do to obtain resources? How does it deal with competition for these resources? The horseshoe crab

has found a niche walking on the bottom of shallow coastal waters, feeding on food items that range from algae to small invertebrates. Note that this is about more than what the horseshoe crab eats. It includes specific surroundings (shallow ocean waters), specific behaviors (ocean-floor crawling), and perhaps seasonal or daily feeding times, among other things. If you were to specify all the things that define a horseshoe crab's niche, the odds are that no other organism would exactly fit into it.

Competition among Species in a Community

With these two concepts covered, let's look at the ways organisms interact in communities, starting with a familiar type of interaction—competition.

Even though niches tend to be specific to given organisms, some species—particularly closely related species—have niches that *overlap* to some degree in a community. A large proportion of both species' diet may be made up of a given organism, or both species may occupy similar kinds of spaces on rocks or branches or pond surfaces. What arises in such instances is **interspecific competition**, meaning competition between two or more species.

What may come to mind with interspecific competition is a never-ending series of physical battles between two species, but things seldom work like this. For one thing, competition tends to be indirect. It often is a competition for *resources*, in which the winner generally triumphs not by fighting but by being more efficient at doing something, such as acquiring food. Lots of animals, including birds and many large mammals, are territorial—meaning they will attempt to keep other creatures out of a territory they have laid claim to—but this usually is a matter of them trying to repel members of their own species.

No Two Species Can Share the Same Vital Resource for Long

When the niches of two species greatly overlap, it's unlikely that you'd see *long-standing* competition among them, for the simple reason that one species or the other is likely to win such a competition in fairly short order. Because the competition is for nothing less than vital resources, the result is that the losing species will be driven to local extinction.

It was a laboratory experiment, performed by the Russian biologist G. F. Gause in the 1930s, that pointed the way on this latter principle. Gause grew two species of *Paramecium* protists, *P. caudatum* and *P. aurelia*, in culture and found that in time, *P. aurelia* was always the sole survivor. True to what was just noted, *P. aurelia* wasn't eating or wounding

(a) Competitive exclusion

When two species compete for the same limited, vital resource, one will always drive the other to local extinction—as the paramecium *P. aurelia* did to the paramecium *P. caudatum*. This is the competitive exclusion principle at work.

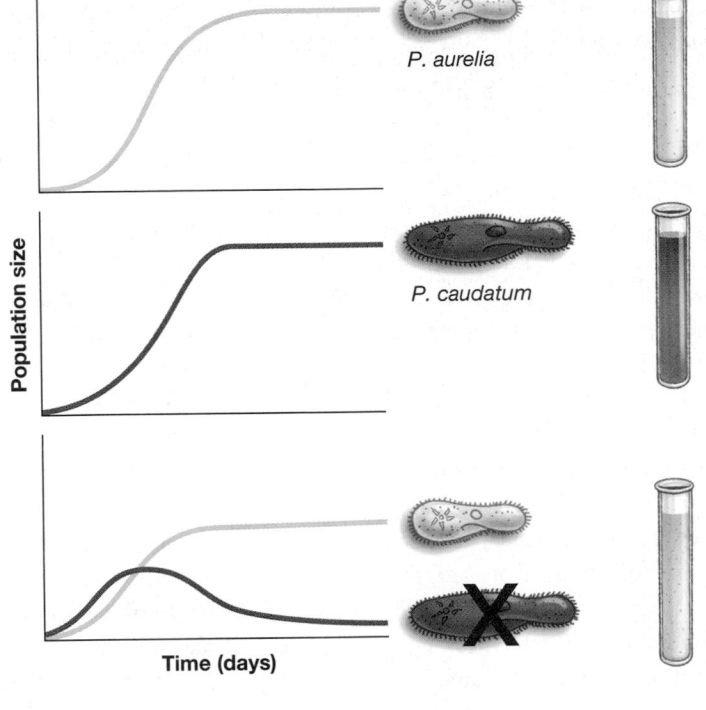

P. aurelia

P. caudatum

Time (days)

(b) Resource partitioning

Conversely, when Gause put *P. aurelia* together with another paramecium, *P. bursaria*, the two species divided up the habitat and both survived. This is a demonstration of resource partitioning.

P. aurelia

P. bursaria

Time (days)

Figure 31.17
Competition for Resources among Species
Laboratory experiments by G. F. Gause showed that competition for resources between two species can have two possible outcomes.

P. caudatum; instead, it grew faster and thus used more of the surrounding resources. Nevertheless, the outcome was always the death of all the *P. caudatum*. This led Gause to formulate what came to be called the **competitive exclusion principle:** When two populations compete for the same limited, vital resource, one will always outcompete the other and thus bring about the latter's local extinction (**see Figure 31.17a**).

Ecologists wouldn't expect to witness the competitive exclusion principle operating much in nature, however. This is because, as noted, the *Paramecium* scenario is likely to be played out quickly. Nevertheless, competitive exclusion has been observed in nature, often when humans have a hand in things. For example, humans introduced a Southeast Asian vine, the kudzu, to the American South on a large scale in the 1930s. Growing at up to 30 centimeters or 1 foot per day, kudzu has now taken over millions of acres in the South, locally eliminating many plants in its path (**see Figure 31.18**).

Figure 31.18
Kudzu Vines Run Wild
The kudzu plant was introduced in the American South in the 1930s and has since spread at a rapid rate, locally eliminating many plants in its path. This is competitive exclusion in action. Here kudzu has overgrown an abandoned house in Mississippi.

Resource Partitioning Is Common in Natural Environments

Competitive exclusion notwithstanding, there are instances in nature in which two related species will use the same kinds of resources from the same habitat over a long period of time. So, why isn't one of them eliminated? The answer is contained in another experiment conducted by Gause. He took the successful species from the earlier experiment, *P. aurelia*, and placed it in a test tube with a different paramecium, *P. bursaria*. This time, neither species was eliminated (see Figure 31.17b). Instead, the two species divided up the habitat, *P. aurelia* feeding in the upper part of the test tube and *P. bursaria* flourishing in the lower part. (*P. bursaria* had an advantage in the lower, oxygen-depleted water because it has symbiotic algae that grow with it, producing oxygen.) In a nutshell, this result describes a situation that often exists in nature: **coexistence** (meaning a sharing of habitat) through a practice called **resource partitioning**, which can be defined as a dividing up of scarce resources among species that have similar requirements. If you look at **Figure 31.19**, you can see how this works among some species that are a little more familiar—several varieties of warbler. The main message here is that species often flourish by specializing; they derive resources by feeding from different locations (or during different times) within the same habitat.

Other Modes of Interaction: Predation and Parasitism

It is one thing for two species to compete for resources; it is another for one species to *be* a resource for another—to be eaten or used by another species. Thus do ecologists distinguish the first mode of interaction in communities, competition, from the second, predation.

Predation can be defined as one organism feeding on parts or all of a second organism. Note that the prey here can be plants, protists, animals—whatever is preyed upon. Predation is generally thought of in terms of animals killing other animals, but note that the definition given includes such things as animals consuming whole plants or their seeds. **Parasitism** is a variety of predation in which the predator feeds on prey, but does not kill the prey immediately—and may not ever kill it. Parasites that come to mind tend to be animals, but there are an estimated 3,000 species of parasitic plants, one of which can be seen in **Figure 31.20**.

The Value of Predation and Parasitism

Predation and parasitism are the features of nature that many nature lovers can't stand. Why this should be so is a fascinating question, though beyond the scope of this book. If one values more complex organisms (such as ourselves), predation and parasitism have had a clear value, in that they have spurred on evolution by culling the less capable members from populations and by stimulating the

Figure 31.19
Resource Partitioning
Ecologist Robert MacArthur spent long stretches of time over several years in the 1950s observing the feeding patterns of several species of warblers. All of them ate caterpillars, but from substantially different, though overlapping, parts of the tree.

Resource Partitioning

Cape May warbler

Bay-breasted warbler

Myrtle warbler

Figure 31.20
Plants Parasitizing Plants
The orange tendrils in the picture belong to a species of dodder, *Cuscuta pentagona*, a parasitic plant that survives by tapping into the food reserves of other plants, thus feeding off them. The dodder is orange, rather than green, because it lacks the chlorophyll that is used in photosynthesis.

Purring Predators: Housecats and Their Prey

ousecats are famous for bringing home animals they've killed or captured, of course; intrigued by the carnage brought into their own homes in the 1980s, Peter Churcher and John Lawton decided to make a scientific study of the predatory behavior of the domestic cat. To do so, they enlisted the help of 172 households in the small English village of Bedfordshire, where Churcher lived. The two researchers asked the locals to "bag the remains of any animal the cat caught," and turn the evidence over to them once a week. This process went on for a year with a high degree of co-operation from the cat owners.

Some of the results were not surprising. Young cats hunt more than older cats; small mammals, such as mice, are the favored prey; and cat hunting is not based purely on hunger—all the cats were fed by their owners and yet hunting was widespread.

What was remarkable, however, was the *scale* of the killing. Concentrating on the village's house sparrow population, Churcher and Lawton found that cats were responsible for between one-third and one-half of all sparrow deaths in the village, a figure they believed no other single predator could match. When they looked at all animals killed, and projected the village figures onto the whole of Great Britain, the researchers calculated that cats were responsible for about 70 million deaths a year.

What was remarkable was the scale *of the killing.*

Given that birds account for somewhere between 30 and 50 percent of these kills, this means that cats kill at least 20 million birds a year in Britain. The "at least" here may be an important qualifier. An American biologist, the researchers note, found that cats bring home only about half of the food they catch.

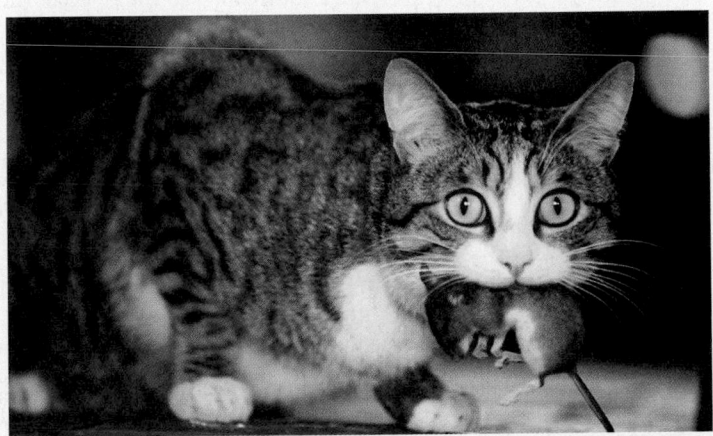

Predator on the Loose
A domestic cat carrying its prey.

"arms race" that has resulted in evolutionary adaptations such as vision and flight. (One organism's predatory adaptation spurs the development of another organism's defensive adaptation, and vice versa.) Whatever we may think of it, predation is simply a fact of nature, and it is impossible to imagine life without it. But it's also true that to admire the beauty of nature is in significant part to admire the handiwork of predation, since it has done so much to shape the living world. You can read about a very familiar predator, the house cat, in "Purring Predators: Housecats and Their Prey" above.

Predator-Prey Dynamics

It may be obvious that although predators attack prey, predators are also *dependent* on prey as a food source. An ongoing question in ecological research is how tight this linkage is. An attractive hypothesis is that when the prey population flourishes, the resulting bounty of available food makes the *predator* numbers grow; this, however, means that more

predators will hunt, which will bring the prey population's numbers down. When this happens, there may be a steep decline in the predator population, because a large part of its food supply is now gone. The end result would be a series of linked population ups and downs, or cycles. If you look at **Figure 31.21**, you can see a series that has occurred with

Figure 31.21
Predator and Prey Populations
The population dynamics of a predator species (the wolf) and its prey (the moose) in Michigan's Isle Royale National Park over several decades. (Redrawn and adapted with permission from C *Mlot*, SCIENCE 261:1115. Copyright 1993 AAAS.)

Web Tutorial 31.2
Predator-Prey Models

one linked pair of species, the moose of Michigan's Isle Royale National Park and the wolf that preys on it. At first glance, these figures seem to provide evidence for the scenario just described, because the moose and wolf numbers move generally in opposite directions. In reality, however, things are more complex than this. The huge crash in the wolf population that began in 1981 was caused in part by a canine virus that invaded the island and perhaps by a lack of genetic diversity among the wolves. Suffice it to say that population cycles generally are the result of many factors, only one of which is a given predator-prey relationship.

Parasites: Making a Living from the Living

Let's look now at the special variety of predation called *parasitism*. Some familiar parasites, such as leeches and ticks, have a straightforward strategy: Get on, hold on, and consume material from the prey, known as the **host**. But the relationship between parasites and hosts can be much more sophisticated than this. Take, for example, the barely visible roundworm *Strongyloides stercoralis*, which lives throughout the tropics and has, as one of its hosts, human beings in the southeastern United States. The worm comes into the human body from the soil in a threadlike larval form, then makes its way into the veins, which it travels through to get to the lungs. From there it moves up the trachea and then down into the digestive system, ending up in the small intestine. There it lays eggs that develop into larvae that this time move *out*, with feces, back into the Earth to start the whole life cycle over again. *Strongyloides* is not just using humans as an incubator, however; it can worm its way, you might say,

directly from the small intestines into the bloodstream, bringing about a continuous cycle of infection whose symptoms range from severe diarrhea to lung problems. (Lest all of this seem too disturbing, take heart; there is a medicine that can clear this pest from human bodies.) So, note the complexity here: *Strongyloides* not only feeds on a host, but uses the host in its reproduction cycle, something that actually is fairly common among parasitic worms and protozoans. Were you to start examining the *range* of host-parasite dynamics, you would find lots of interactions as elaborate—and chilling—as this. As you can see in "Why Do Rabid Animals Go Crazy?" on page 702, parasites often alter the *behavior* of their hosts.

The Effect of Predator-Prey Interactions on Evolution

Earlier, we noted the "arms race" spurred on by predator-prey interactions. (One organism's predatory adaptation spurs the development of another organism's defensive adaptation, and vice versa.) To see an example of predator adaptation, look at the warm-water "frogfish" in **Figure 31.22**. These fish have evolved a spine on their dorsal fins that is tipped with a piece of flesh that looks for all the world like a small worm floating free in the ocean. When a would-be predator tries to snatch up this "worm," however, it finds *itself* the prey. On the prey side, look at **Figure 31.23** to see the amazing kinds of camouflage that animals use to keep themselves hidden from the eyes of predators. Another example of prey adaptation may be as close as your own skin. Why are human beings the only primates whose bodies are not covered with a coat of hair? One hypothesis holds that, while hair warmed our evolutionary ancestors, it also provided a home for many parasites that preyed on them—lice, fleas, and ticks. The adaptation of losing our hair allowed us to lose these parasites to a great extent. Needless to say, predator-prey evolution goes on within all the kingdoms of life. Plants have developed not only spines, thorns, and other protective structures but also a vast array of chemical compounds—more than 15,000 have been characterized so far—that protect them from predators.

Mimicry Is a Theme in Predator-Prey Evolution

The ability to fool an opponent by faking is as valuable in nature as it is in sports, as you've seen with the frogfish. Another way such deception takes place in nature is through **mimicry**, a phenomenon through which one species has evolved to assume the appearance of another. One form of mimicry involves three participants: a model, a mimic, and a dupe. If you look at

Figure 31.22
Fooling Predators about Prey
The predatory frogfish uses a modified spine resembling a tasty worm to lure its prey. Here a tasseled frogfish clearly shows its lure while swimming near Edithburg, South Australia.

(a) A spanworm looking like a twig on a maple tree

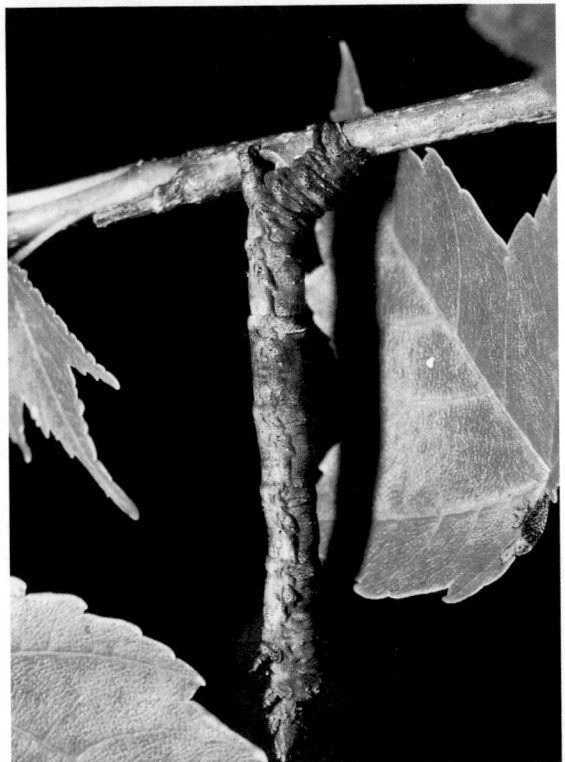

(b) A casque-head chameleon against a tree in Kenya

Figure 31.23
Avoiding Predation through Camouflage

Figure 31.24
Harmless, but Looking Dangerous
In an example of Batesian mimicry, the clearwing moth (on the right) has no sting but has evolved to look like an insect that does, the yellowjacket wasp (left). The yellowjacket is the model and the moth is the mimic.

Figure 31.24, you can see a model on the left, the yellowjacket wasp, which obviously can provide a painful lesson to any animal that tries to eat it. On the right you can see the mimic, the clearwing moth, which is harmless but *looks* a great deal like a wasp. For the dupe, you could select any predator species that sees a clearwing moth and passes it by, believing it to be a dangerous yellowjacket. This is so-called **Batesian mimicry**: the evolution of one species to resemble a species that has a superior protective capability.

In a second type of mimicry, **Müllerian mimicry**, several species that *have* protection against predators come to resemble each other (**see Figure 31.25**). This

Figure 31.25
Müllerian Mimicry
The South American butterflies *Heliconius cydno* (top) and *Heliconius sapho* are different in some ways, but they share the characteristic of tasting bad to predators. Over time, they evolved to look like each other, with their appearance serving as a warning to would-be predators. Natural selection favors this Müllerian mimicry, because predators can learn about the butterflies' unpalatable taste from both species. The result is that fewer members of either species are likely to be killed or bothered by predators.

creates a visual warning that becomes known to an array of predators. Given this, a would-be predator learns, by interacting with an individual from one species, to keep away from all individuals in any look-alike species. The result is that fewer individuals in these species will be disturbed or killed.

Beneficial Interactions: Mutualism and Commensalism

The competitive, predatory, and parasitic modes of interaction you've reviewed have an each-organism-against-all quality to them, but other kinds of relationships exist in nature as well. Consider **mutualism**, meaning an interaction between individuals of two species that is *beneficial* to both individuals. There's a great example of this in Chapter 21 (page 432), with the linkage between plant roots and the slender, belowground extensions of fungi called *hyphae*. What the fungi get from growing into the plant roots is food that comes from the photosynthesizing plant; what the plants get is minerals and water, absorbed by the network of hyphae. By some estimates, 90 percent of seed plants have this relationship with fungi. Perhaps the most famous example of mutualism,

however, is between the rhinoceros and oxpecker birds. Sitting on the back of the rhino, the oxpecker removes parasites and pests (ticks and flies), thus getting food and a safe place to perch, while the rhino gets relief from its tiny adversaries (**Figure 31.26**).

There is also **commensalism**, meaning an interaction between two species in which one benefits while the other is neither harmed nor helped. Birds can make their nests in trees, and benefit from this, but generally don't affect the trees in any way. **Table 31.3** summarizes all the kinds of interactions you've gone over in this chapter.

Coevolution: Species Driving Each Other's Evolution

Earlier you read about the effect that predator-prey interactions have had on the evolutionary arms race among species. Yet it's clear that organisms have affected each other's evolution through mutualism as well. Indeed, species that are tightly linked in any way over a long period of time are likely to shape one another's evolution. Perceiving this, scientists Paul Ehrlich and Peter Raven developed the concept of **coevolution**, meaning the interdependent evolution of two or more species. Some of the clearest examples of coevolution involve flowering plants and the animals that pollinate them. Recall from Chapter 21 that many flowers have both fragrances that attract insects and ultraviolet color patterns (invisible to us) that guide the insects to the proper spot for pollination. These features are nature's own homing signals and landing lights, communicating the messages "Food lies this way" and "Land here" (**see Figure 31.27**). Now, one of the organisms linked with flowering plants is the honeybee. Consider that the color vision of honeybees is most sensitive to the colors that exist in

Table 31.3 Community Interactions

In this type of interaction ...	One organism ...	While the other ...
Competition	Is harmed	Is harmed
Predation and parasitism	Gains	Is harmed
Mutualism	Gains	Gains
Commensalism	Gains	Is unaffected

(a) Rhinoceros and oxpecker birds

(b) Snapping shrimp and shrimp goby

**Figure 31.26
Mutually Beneficial**

Several oxpecker birds sit atop a black rhinoceros, ridding the rhino of ticks and other pests while the rhino provides a safe habitat for the birds. This is a demonstration of mutualism—an interaction between two species that is beneficial to both.

The orange–spotted shrimp goby, on the right, and the snapping shrimp at left also exhibit mutualism. Here the shrimp goby stands guard near the snapping shrimp, which digs out the burrow on the sea floor that the two creatures share.

the very flowering plants they pollinate. What seems likely is that honeybee eyesight evolved in response to plant coloration, and that plant coloration evolved to be maximally attractive to the pollinating insects. These groups of organisms coevolved, in other words.

Having considered how community members interact with one another, let's now go on to consider how communities change over time.

31.7 Succession in Communities

When Washington State's Mount St. Helens volcano erupted in May of 1980, it first collapsed inward, thus sending most of the mountain's north face sliding downhill in the largest avalanche in recorded history. Then came the actual eruption, which sent a huge volume of rock and ash hurtling not straight up but out at an angle, toward the north. Some stands of forest in the path of this blast were instantly incinerated down to bare rock; another 35,000 hectares (86,000 acres) of trees were snapped in two like so many twigs. Then came the mudslides caused by the vast expanse of snow and ice melted in the explosion; then came the fall of hundreds of millions of tons of ash, some of it landing as far away as Wyoming. After viewing the devastated area around the blast, President Jimmy Carter said that it "makes the surface of the moon look like a golf course."

(a) What we see

(b) What a bee sees

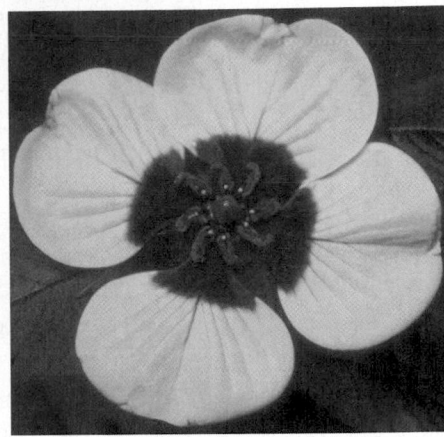

Figure 31.27
Coevolution of Plants and Their Pollinators
This flower has an ultraviolet color pattern that is not normally visible to humans, but that attracts bees. It is likely that these color patterns evolved in the flowers because they aided in attracting the bees. Meanwhile, the bees developed vision that was sensitive to the colors exhibited by these same plants.

But today? No one would claim that the Mount St. Helens area has returned to anything like its former state, but look at the pictures in **Figure 31.28** to get an idea of the transition that has occurred at one location around Mount St. Helens.

The exact form of this rejuvenation may surprise us, but don't we intuitively expect something like this? Just from our everyday experience of watching, say, an abandoned urban lot becoming progressively weed-filled, don't we expect this would generally be the case? As it turns out, our intuition is right, because almost any parcel of land or water that has been either abandoned by humans or devastated by physical forces will be "reclaimed" by nature, at least to some degree.

Figure 31.28
Rebound from Disaster
The Lang Ridge, 7 miles from Mount St. Helens crater, as it looked in August 1980, 3 months after the blast, and in 1999. This is an example of ecological succession in action.

The question is, how does this reclamation proceed? Areas that are rebounding don't just get one type of vegetation and then retain it. Instead, the vegetation changes through time—one type of growth *succeeds* another—with a general movement toward more and larger greenery as time goes by. Ecologists call this phenomenon **succession**, meaning a series of replacements of community members at a given location until a relatively stable final state is reached. Within this framework, there are two kinds of succession. The first is **primary succession**, meaning succession in which the starting state is one of little or no life and a soil that lacks nutrients. Then there is **secondary succession**, meaning succession in which the final state of a habitat has been disturbed by some force, but life remains and the soil has nutrients. The classic example of this is land that has first been cleared for farming but later abandoned by the farmer.

The relatively stable community that develops at the end of any process of succession is called a **climax community**. There will be some shifts over time in a climax community, just as there are in any other. A prolonged drought will cause some change in the mix of the community's animal and plant life, for example. But, with some exceptions, what does not happen is a shift to a *fundamentally* different mix of life-forms, barring a major change in climate. Grassland stays grassland, and forest stays forest.

Succession can be fairly predictable within small geographical areas. Two abandoned farm plots that lie close together will have very similar kinds of succession—so much so that local farmers or naturalists can sometimes tell to within a few years how long it's been since a field was abandoned. As you may be able to tell, succession generally is thought of in terms of the various *plant* communities that succeed one another, though modern ecology is attempting to bring animals into the picture as well.

An Example of Primary Succession: Alaska's Glacier Bay

One of the best examples of primary succession comes from Alaska's 65-mile-long Glacier Bay, whose lower-lying areas were covered by a glacier until about 240 years ago, when the glacier began retreating. Such withdrawal initially leaves behind a rocky terrain that is completely devoid of organic matter—no fallen leaves or branches, no decomposing animals. Indeed, what's left is "till" (not soil) that has a high pH and no available nitrogen—not a promising environment for life to establish itself. But establish itself it does. Glacier Bay's succession

particulars—what species succeeded what—are not important to us. What is important is the general process that occurred. Here's what happened in eastern arm of Glacier Bay after the glacier retreated (**see Figure 31.29**).

In the 20 years immediately following the retreat, the first "pioneer" species to come were lichens and photosynthesizing bacteria, which essentially have the ability to grow on rock. In addition, there were some primitive plants called horsetails and liverworts. Over the next 10 years, a gradual transition took place in which an Arctic dwarf shrub, called *Dryas*, took over from the pioneers, growing in a mat that was broken up only by occasional trees. *Dryas* and other early-stage plants have a capability that is critical not only to their own growth in these environments, but to the growth of plants that come after them. These plants harbor bacteria in their roots that can *fix nitrogen*—that can take nitrogen from the air and convert it into a form that plants can use. This is how the larger plant community could get started on the till in Glacier Bay, which *lacked* nitrogen.

The *Dryas* community was succeeded by a plant called the alder bush that excluded almost everything else—it was a highly successful dominant, in other words, and its success in the environment meant the end of the *Dryas*. Fifty years after the glacier's retreat, alders were growing in stands that were 10 meters, or about 33 feet tall. With their growth, the terrain got a great deal of nitrogen and, through acidic alder leaves that fell to the ground, a rapid lowering of pH.

The alder sowed the seeds of its own elimination, however. With the lowered soil pH, an extensive population of Sitka spruce trees could develop; when they did, they "shaded out" the smaller alders by blocking their sunlight. About 100 years after the glacier's retreat, a spruce forest existed—one that, within 30 more years, started becoming a combined spruce-hemlock forest.

For most of Glacier Bay, the spruce-hemlock forest appears to be the end of the line—the climax community. It's worth noting, however, that on the outer coast of the area there has been one more successional stage. Water-absorbing mosses started to grow and, with them, the forest floor became watery, the tree roots couldn't absorb the oxygen they needed, and the trees died. What eventually was left was land that was filled with ponds and watery bogs. Ecologists have speculated that all of Glacier Bay may be headed in this direction, though this transition could take thousands of years.

ponds and bogs
eventually?

spruce-hemlock

spruce

alder bush

Dryas shrub

pioneer species:
lichens, bacteria,
horsetails and
liverworts

exposed
till

**Figure 31.29
One Example of Primary
Succession: Glacier Bay, Alaska**

Common Elements in Primary Succession

In the Glacier Bay succession you can see developments that apply to many primary successions:

- An arrival of photosynthesizing pioneer species—in this case, the bacteria and lichens—that can establish themselves in the most barren environments.

- A steady increase in biomass, compared to the starting state. This increase eventually stops in all successions. In parts of Glacier Bay, it actually was reversed with the invasion of the late-stage mosses.

- A general movement toward longer-lived species. *Dryas* can live for 50 years, but alders can live for 100 years, and spruce trees can live for 700.

- A general trend toward an increase in species diversity, though not without some reversals (the alder bushes, for example).

- The facilitation of the growth of some later species (the Sitka spruce here) through the actions of earlier species (the shedding of leaves by the alders). More formally, **facilitation** is a process within ecological succession in which the qualities or actions of some early-arriving species enable the success of later-arriving species.

- The competitive driving out of some species (the alder bush) by the actions of later species (the blocking of sunlight by the spruce trees).

Lessons in Succession from Mount St. Helens

Ecologists have been studying succession for about 100 years now, but it remains a field filled with basic questions. Spirited debate has gone on for years about what factors hold true in all instances of succession, and what models of development best describe succession. (Is facilitation more important than competition?)

It turns out, however, that in just the past 25 years, Washington's Mount St. Helens has provided a treasure trove of insight into how primary succession works. If there is a silver lining behind the Mount St. Helens explosion, it is that it has given ecologists an unparalleled opportunity to understand succession.

Why Do Rabid Animals Go Crazy?

There is a tiny worm, called *Plagiorhynchus cylindraceus*, that lives its adult life as a parasite in the intestines of starlings and other songbirds. While in a starling, this worm produces eggs that pass out of the bird in its feces. After this, both eggs and feces may be eaten by pillbugs, which are the familiar little arthropods that "roll up into a ball." The worm eggs, however, are not digested by the pillbugs. As a result, a worm *hatches* inside a pillbug, which makes the bug the second "host" for this parasite. And here is where things get interesting, as researcher Janice Moore has shown.

The pillbug is dark, but once infected by a worm, it starts spending more time on light-colored surfaces. What's more, it stops sheltering itself under overhanging objects such as leaves. And the females among the bugs start moving around more and resting less. The effect of all this is that worm-infected pillbugs are more visible to their predators and thus are more likely to be eaten by them. And who are these predators? Some of them are starlings.

Now, when a starling eats a pillbug, the pillbug dies, but the worm inside the bug remains unharmed. Indeed, this is the way the worm gets back inside a starling host (where it will develop into an adult, lay eggs, and so forth). And that's just the point. It appears that the worm *engineers* this outcome by bringing about the self-destructive behavior of the pillbug. Through some unknown mechanism, this parasite prompts the pillbug to become an accomplice in its own death. When the pillbug is infected, its behaviors are such that it might as well have a sign on it saying, "please eat me." The starling is happy to oblige, but the real winner is the *P. cylindraceus* worm, which gets to move from one of its hosts to another.

It would be nice to report that such behavioral take-overs by parasites are rare, but in fact they are common. "Horsehair" worms

This is so because the Mount St. Helens succession began on a crystal-clear starting date (May 18, 1980) and proceeded from such well-defined starting states—obliteration of some habitats, and major or minor damage to others.

Figure 31.30
Important Survivor at Mount St. Helens
The pocket gopher (*Thomomys talpoides*) played a role in the restoration of the Mount St. Helens environment. The gopher's underground habitat allowed it to survive the blast, after which it continued to feed on roots, turning over soil in the process. In addition, its tunnels provided a passageway for other animals who, in the years following the explosion, were making their way to viable habitats. This gopher is in Wyoming.

So, what have we learned from Mount St. Helens? Perhaps the most important lesson is this: What is left from the past is crucial to the future. When trees were knocked over in the blast, their roots were yanked above-ground. In this moment of destruction, however, these roots literally carried the seeds of rejuvenation with them. Soil, small plants, and seeds were pulled up with the roots, and they stayed on them—above the deadening layer of ash below. Dead wood, left strewn about after the blast, provided habitat and food for wood-boring insects. These insects in turn attracted birds, which were able to build nests in "snags," meaning trees that were dead but standing. Gophers survived the blast in large numbers because they live below-ground, where they feed on roots. They actually flourished in the years following the explosion, and their activity not only turned over the soil—mixing fertile soil below with ash on top—but also provided a kind of subway system for other animals, which were migrating among patches of viable habitat (**see Figure 31.30**). So important were the gophers, snags, and surviving seeds to renewal at Mount St. Helens that a collecneed to mate in the water, but they spend most of their lives inside arthropods such as ants, whose abdomens they feed on. Just before an ant dies from this, however, it aids the worm in one final way—it makes a journey to water. Indeed, a worm-infected ant seemingly has an uncontrollable urge to get wet, as it will return repeatedly to water if blocked. Once it wades into a pool or puddle, however, things proceed quickly. In a matter of minutes, the worm inside it will emerge, ready to mate with another worm.

Now, think about all this in connection with one of the things children are taught to fear from an early age: a rabid animal. Rabies is caused by a virus that spreads through animal saliva. In the "furious" form of the disease, the virus is passed on by means of one animal biting another, thus injecting its saliva into the second animal. Not surprisingly, one of the things the virus does is affect salivary tissue in an infected animal's head and neck. This ensures that there is plenty of saliva to be transmitted. The virus also inhibits swallowing in an infected animal, which ensures more saliva. Finally, the virus affects the animal's central nervous system and this brings about the famous *behavioral* change in infected animals—frenzied, unprovoked attacks on other animals. Thus, rabid raccoons or dogs are not simply "going crazy" because of their disease.

Their behavior has a function. To be sure, it's a *perverse* function from a human perspective, but then again, aren't the behaviors of infected pillbugs or ants disturbing in a similar sort of way? The general message here is straightforward but hard to take: One living thing can succeed by manipulating the behavior of another.

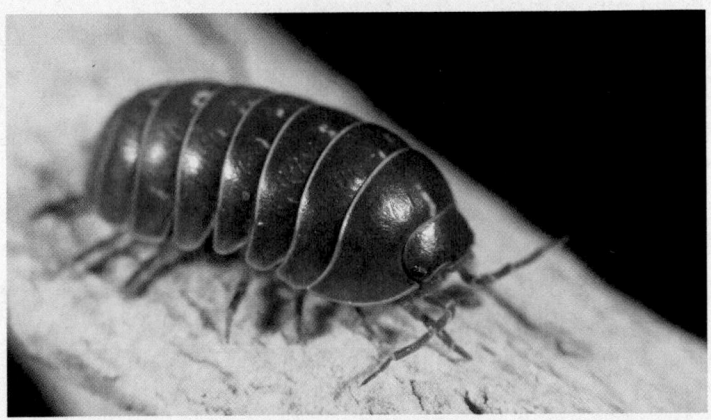

Accomplice to Its Own Death
The common pillbug *Armadillidium vulgare,* whose behavior can be manipulated by the parasitical worm *P. cylindraceus.*

tive term for them has now entered the ecological lexicon. They are examples of **biological legacies**: living things, or products of living things, that survive a major ecological disturbance.

Succession at Mount St. Helens has yielded some other surprises as well. "Classical" primary succession, as outlined in the Glacier Bay example, assumes that life will come to a devastated area from the outside. Seeds and spores will be carried in on the wind and succession will proceed, in a general way, from the periphery of the barren area to its interior. Though this happened to some degree at Mount St. Helens, in the main recovery was internal: thousands of small patches of plant habitat rejuvenated without being seeded from the outside. When organisms did come in from the outside, many were the "pioneer" species predicted by classical succession theory. However, ecologists also found solitary tree seedlings—supposedly late comers in succession—growing right out of some of the most devastated terrain in the blast area, with no pioneer species setting the stage for them. And some of the external help that did arrive took an unexpected form. In the years immediately following the

blast, insects and spiders were blown in on the wind in significant quantity. Once these creatures landed, most of them died, but they themselves went on to serve as food for indigenous ants and other species.

Given all this, another lesson from Mount St. Helens seems to be that succession is more varied and habitat-specific than our theories had predicted. Put another way, we still have a lot to learn about succession.

On to Ecosystems and Biomes

In this chapter, you have looked at populations and communities. In populations, you saw the building blocks of communities. In communities, you looked through a lens of the interactions of living things. But it's obvious that communities interact with *nonliving* forces and factors, such as weather and soil composition. When living things and nonliving factors are considered together, the resulting whole is called an ecosystem—the subject of the first part of Chapter 32. Very large-scale ecosystems are called biomes; a review of them forms the concluding portion of Chapter 32 and will bring to a close this book's coverage of ecology.

Chapter Review

Summary

31.1 The Study of Ecology

- Ecology is the study of the interactions living things have with each other and with their environment.

- Ecology is not the same thing as environmentalism. The function of ecology is to describe interactions that affect the living world, not to work on behalf of environmentalism.

- There are five scales of life that concern ecology: physiology, populations, communities, ecosystems, and the biosphere. A population is all the members of a single species that live together in a specified geographical area; a community is all the species living in a single area; an ecosystem is a community and all the nonliving elements that interact with it; the biosphere is the interactive collection of all the Earth's ecosystems.

31.2 Populations: Size and Dynamics

- Ecologists employ several means to estimate the size of populations of living things, among them counting animal droppings or surveying bird populations as they migrate.

- An arithmetical increase occurs when, over a given interval of time, an unvarying number of new units is added to a population. An exponential increase occurs when the number of new units added to a population is proportional to the number of units that exists. Populations of living things are capable of increasing exponentially, because living things are capable of giving rise to more living things.

- The rapid growth that sometimes characterizes living populations is referred to as exponential growth, or as the J-shaped growth curve. Populations that initially grow, but whose growth later levels out, have experienced logistic growth, sometimes referred to as the S-shaped growth curve.

- The size of living populations is kept in check by environmental resistance, defined as all the forces of the environment that act to limit population growth.

- Exponential growth in living populations can be calculated by subtracting a population's death rate from its birth rate, which yields the population's growth rate. Denoted as r, this rate is also known as the population's intrinsic rate of increase; it can be thought of as the population's potential for growth.

- Carrying capacity, denoted as K, is the maximum population density of a given species that can be sustained within a defined geographical area over an extended period of time.

Web Tutorial 31.1: Population Growth

31.3 r-Selected and K-Selected Species

- Different species have different reproductive strategies, meaning characteristics that have the effect of increasing the number of fertile offspring they bear.

- Some species are said to be K-selected, or equilibrium, species. These species tend to be large, to experience their environment as relatively stable, and to lavish a good deal of attention on relatively few offspring. The pressures on K-selected species tend to be density dependent, meaning that as a population's density goes up, factors that limit the population's growth assert themselves ever more strongly.

- Other species are said to be r-selected or opportunist species. These species tend to be small, to experience their environment as relatively unstable, and to give little or no attention to the numerous offspring they produce. The pressures on r-selected species tend to be density independent, meaning pressures that are unrelated to the population's density.

- Survivorship curves describe how soon species members tend to die within the species' life span. There are three idealized types of survivorship curves: late loss, constant loss, and early loss.

31.4 Thinking about Human Populations

- Survivorship curves are created from life tables, which set forth the probabilities of a member of a species being alive after given intervals of time.

- An important step in calculating the future growth of human populations is to learn what proportion of the population is at or under reproductive age. A population pyramid displays this proportion. Populations whose pyramids are heavily weighted toward younger age groups are likely to experience relatively large growth.

- Following centuries of explosive increase, the world's human population is projected to stabilize in the coming decades, going from about 6.3 billion now to a maximum of about 8.9 billion at mid-century. This stabilization is being brought about by a decrease in female fertility, defined as the number of children born, on average, to each woman in a population.

- The global reduction in female fertility masks enormous, ongoing differences between fertility in more-developed and less-developed countries. Fertility in less-developed countries tends to be much higher than that in more-developed countries. The fertility in most European nations is now so low that the continent's population stands to shrink significantly by mid-century. The population of the United States, however, is projected to grow significantly during this same period. The primary factors bringing the U.S. increase about are immigration and relatively high female fertility.

- Some scientists believe that there is no greater single threat to the environment than the continued growth of the human population. Others argue that a more important concern is the use of natural resources per person.

31.5 Communities: Looking at the Interactions of Many Populations

- An ecological community is all the populations that inhabit a given area, though the term can be used to mean a collection of populations in a given area that potentially interact with one another.

- Most communities tend to be dominated by only a few species; the few species that are abundant in a given area are called ecological dominants.

- A keystone species is a species whose impact on the composition of a community is disproportionately large relative to its abundance within that community. Some keystone species are top predators in a community, meaning species that prey upon other species but that are not preyed upon themselves. Keystone species need not be top predators, however, nor does every community have a keystone species.

- Biodiversity is variety among living things. It takes three primary forms: a diversity of species in a given area; a distribution of species across the Earth; and genetic diversity within a species.

- Recent research indicates that species diversity tends to enhance a community's productivity, defined as the amount of solar energy photosynthesizing organisms are able to capture and transform into living material or biomass. There is disagreement about whether species diversity also enhances community stability, meaning the ability of a community to retain its characteristics in the face of environmental disruption.

31.6 Types of Interaction among Community Members

- There are three primary types of interaction among community members: competition; predation and parasitism; and mutualism and commensalism.

- Habitat is the physical surroundings in which a species can normally be found. Niche can be defined metaphorically as an organism's occupation, meaning what the organism does to obtain the resources it needs to live.

- The competitive exclusion principle states that when two populations compete for the same limited, vital resource, one always outcompetes the other and thus brings about the latter's local extinction.

- There are numerous instances in nature in which two related species use the same kinds of resources from the same habitat over an extended period of time, but will divide the resources up, such that neither of the species undergoes local extinction. This phenomenon is called coexistence through resource partitioning.

- Predation is defined as one free-standing organism feeding on parts or all of a second organism. Parasitism is a variety of predation in which the predator feeds on prey, but does not kill it immediately, if ever.

- The population dynamics of a predator and its prey can be linked, but predator-prey interaction generally is only one of several factors controlling the population level of either group.

- The prey of a parasite is known as the host. A parasite can use a host not only as a food source, but as a vehicle to facilitate its reproduction.

- Mimicry is a phenomenon by which one species has evolved to assume the appearance of another. A mimic species evolves to match the appearance of a model species. In general, the value of mimicry is that the mimic species suffers less predation as a result of its resemblance to the model species. Batesian mimicry is the evolution of one species to resemble a species that has a superior protective capability. In Müllerian mimicry, several species that have protection against predators come to resemble each other.

- Mutualism is an interaction between individuals of two species that is beneficial to both individuals. Commensalism is an interaction in which an individual from one species benefits while an individual from another species is neither harmed nor helped.

- Coevolution is the interdependent evolution of two or more species. Flowers have evolved colors and fragrances that attract bees, for example, while bees have evolved vision that is most sensitive to the colors in the flowers they pollinate.
Web Tutorial 31.2: Predator Prey Models

31.7 Succession in Communities

- Parcels of land or water that have been abandoned by humans or devastated by physical forces will almost always be reclaimed by nature to some degree. The process by which this takes place is called succession: a series of replacements of community members at a given location until a relatively stable final state is reached.

- Primary succession proceeds from an original state of little or no life and soil that lacks nutrients. Secondary succession occurs when a final state of habitat is first disturbed by some outside force, but life remains and the soil has nutrients. The final community in any process of succession is known as the climax community.

- A common set of developments occurs in most instances of primary succession, including the arrival of "pioneer" photosynthesizers, facilitation of the growth of some later species through the actions of earlier species, and the competitive driving out of some species by the actions of later species.

- The rejuvenation of the Mount St. Helens area that has occurred since 1980 has provided ecologists with a wealth of information regarding both primary and secondary succession. One of the chief lessons learned concerns the importance of biological legacies, meaning living things, or products of living things, that survive a major ecological disturbance. Biological legacies have been critical to the rapid renewal of habitat at Mount St. Helens.

Key Terms

Understanding the Basics

Multiple-Choice Questions (answers in the back of the book)

1. A(n) _____ consists of members of a single species that live in a specific geographic region, while a(n) _____ consists of the populations of all species that live in a single region.
   a. ecological dominant; community
   b. ecological dominant; biosphere
   c. community; ecosystem
   d. population; community
   e. population; ecosystem

2. A community and all the nonliving elements that interact with it (sunlight, nutrients, soil, etc.) is called
   a. a population group
   b. a biosphere
   c. an ecosystem
   d. a biome
   e. a social system

3. When population growth increases in proportion to the number of members of a population, _____ growth is said to have occurred.
   a. density-dependent
   b. density-independent
   c. *K*-selected
   d. arithmetical
   e. exponential

4. The use of pesticides in many agricultural communities has led to a great reduction in many "targeted" insects. However, many other "nontarget" insects have declined as well. In particular, ecologists and fruit growers have noticed that certain species of bees that pollinate valuable plants have declined, leading to a decrease in many bee-pollinated species. In communities where great change has occurred due to the decline in this ecosystem function, bees may be
   a. ecological dominants
   b. bottleneck species
   c. keystone species
   d. top predators
   e. parasitoids

5. An interaction between two species in which one species benefits while the other is neither harmed nor helped is called
   a. parasitism
   b. mutualism
   c. mimicry
   d. commensalism
   e. cooperation

6. In the process of nitrogen fixation, plants contribute food to bacteria that are capable of fixing atmospheric nitrogen gas, and the bacteria can supply the plants with a usable form of nitrogen. This is an example of
   a. parasitism
   b. mutualism
   c. fertilization
   d. mimicry
   e. cooperation

7. The process by which one species evolves to resemble another species is called
   a. mimicry
   b. mutualism
   c. behaviorism
   d. parasitism
   e. natural deception

8. The largest scale of life, which can be thought of as the interaction of all of Earth's ecosystems, is called
   a. the biome
   b. the ecosphere
   c. the biosphere
   d. the environment zone
   e. the ionosphere

9. In communities undergoing succession (select all that apply)
   a. the general trend is toward shorter-lived species
   b. the general trend is toward longer-lived species
   c. the general trend is toward smaller species

d. the general trend is toward greater species diversity

e. the general trend is toward less species diversity

10. In primary succession, pioneer species will predominately be _____ because they _____.

a. migratory animals; can go elsewhere for their food

b. cold-weather species; can withstand harsh conditions

c. insects; can live in so many environments

d. photosynthesizing organisms; can make their own food

e. trees; can run roots deep into the soil for water

Brief Review

1. Name the four levels of group organization of living things, in order of increasing complexity.

2. Compare and contrast *r*-selected and *K*-selected species, and give an example of each. Are humans *r*-selected or *K*-selected?

3. Explain what is meant by environmental resistance and its relationship to population growth.

4. The red-spotted newt *Notophthalmus viridescens* secretes toxins from its skin that make predators avoid it. The red salamander *Pseudotriton ruber* has no such secretions but resembles the red-spotted newt and gains protection from this resemblance. What is this an example of? Which is the model, the mimic, and the dupe?

5. A volcano erupted in Hawaii, and lava covered land that had been farmed for centuries. Eventually, new lichens, and then plants, grew on the lava. Is this an example of primary or secondary succession?

Applying Your Knowledge

1. Few species can continue exponential growth for very long, because environmental resistance will assert itself. However, the human population has been growing exponentially in the last few decades. Do you think that human populations are truly without an upper bound, or do you think that carrying capacity (*K*) is just always rising? What evidence do you see that humans might eventually reach an absolute upper limit (other than that of pure physical space)? Does the emergence of disease factor into this discussion?

2. What general principle about environmental resistance can you deduce from the explosive growth of such species as the kudzu in the United States or the European rabbit in Australia?

3. Some scientists argue that no single factor poses a greater threat to the environment than the continued growth of the human population, while others believe the use of resources per person is a more critical factor. What arguments can you think of for or against either proposition?

MediaLab

Can Earth Support All of Us? Population Growth Patterns

Nineteenth-century economist Thomas Malthus noted that populations increase geometrically until they encounter a factor that limits continued population growth. We know some populations grow rapidly, others slowly. Since 1800 the number of people on Earth has increased dramatically, with more yet to come. How can we ac-curately predict the effect of this continued growth? This *Web Tutorial* reviews concepts about population growth. The following *Web Investigation* lets you examine a variety of population growth situations and the problems they cause. In *Communicate Your Results*, you can apply these concepts.

This *MediaLab* can be found in Chapter 31 on your Companion Website (www.prenhall.com/krogh3).

WEB TUTORIAL

Species can differ greatly in the type of population growth they can experience. In this *Web Tutorial*, you'll investigate the factors controlling growth and how to use these factors to predict future population increases.

Activity

1. *First, you will look at the three different models of growth seen in natural populations.*

2. *Next, you will see what factors are important for achieving a negative, low, or high intrinsic growth rate or even zero growth by using an interactive program where you can enter factors like births and deaths to determine a population's growth rate.*

The following *Web Investigation* presents examples of population growth in both human and animal populations, so that you can see how the characteristics of a species' growth influence how slowly or rapidly its population increases.

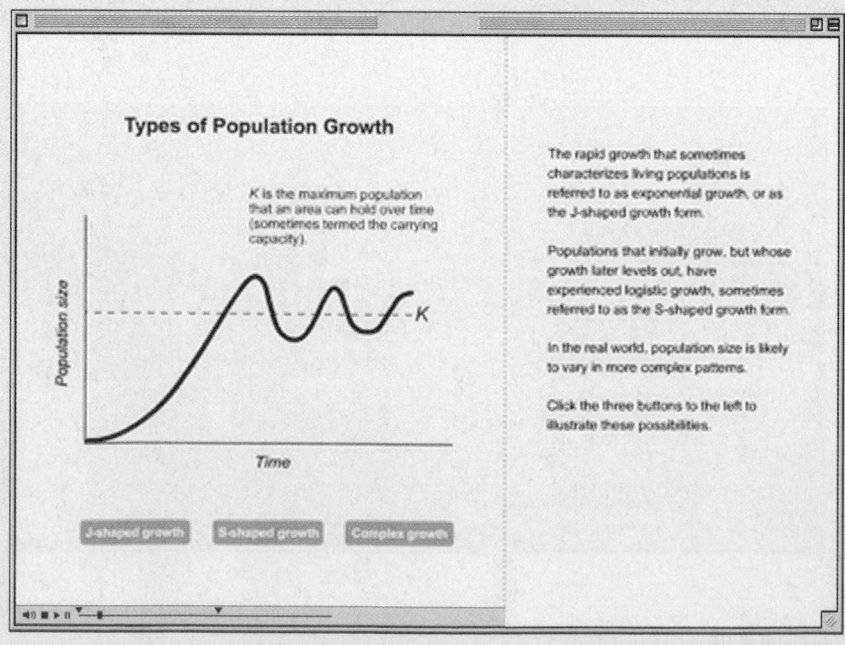

Investigation 1

Estimated time for completion = 15 minutes

Select the keyword **POP QUIZ** on your Website for this *MediaLab* and test your knowledge of human population growth. Notice how the human population has changed over time. Would you say human population is growing arithmetically (straight line) or geometrically (curved line)? What factors are increasing or slowing the rate of increase?

Investigation 2

Estimated time for completion = 10 minutes

Tour an online exhibit about population growth by selecting the keyword **BIRTH RATE** on your Website for this *MediaLab*. What factors affect the number of children a woman can have in your area of the planet? Sign in and choose another continent, and see how geography might affect the number of children a woman might have.

Investigation 3

Estimated time for completion = 20 minutes

"So what—we have more people on the planet. That doesn't concern me!" Perhaps it should. Select the keyword **OVERPOPULATION** on your Website for this *MediaLab* and read the project description. This project describes some issues that ought to concern all of us, no matter what country we are living in. Consider recent news reports. Are there any signs that population pressures, as detailed at this site, might be factors in recent aggression?

Now that you've seen how populations grow and how increasing populations might be factors in social and ecological problems, do the following exercises to determine the severity of increasing populations.

COMMUNICATE YOUR RESULTS

Exercise 1

Estimated time for completion = 5 minutes

You have seen how populations grow. Plot the following data on a sheet of graph paper (or enter it into a program).

Year	Estimated population (in millions)
8000 BC	5
1750 AD	75
1950	2,500
1975	3,700
1990	5,600

From the *Web Tutorial*, you will recall that humans are a *K*-selected species. Does the graph you produced look like a *K*-selected species? What developments and/or events might account for the shape of the human population graph?

Exercise 2

Estimated time for completion = 5 minutes

Since the 1970s, the Chinese government has promoted a policy of one child per family. Apply what you learned in the first two sections of this *MediaLab* to reconstruct the reasons why the Chinese, who traditionally valued children and family, undertook such a harsh policy. Would that policy work where you live? What measures would be needed to make such a policy work?

Exercise 3

Estimated time for completion = 5 minutes

What should be done about overpopulation? Birth rates are declining in most countries, so perhaps there is no reason to worry. Get together with some of your classmates, divide into teams, and take "sides" about human population growth, presenting evidence in a limited debate.

32 Ecosystems and the Biosphere

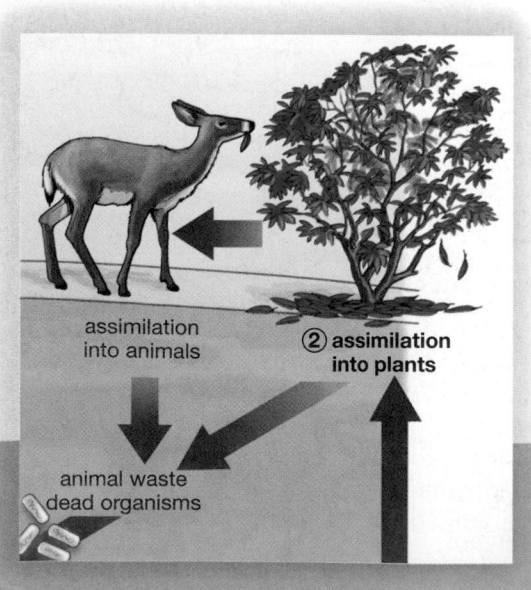

The nitrogen cycle.
(Section 32.2, page 714)

Nature's nutrients aren't enough.
(Section 32.2, page 715)

A world of difference.
(Section 32.3, page 723)

> The living world is affected by the larger physical world around it—and vice versa. The interconnected web of living things is being damaged in many ways by human activity.

The word "system" is much in use today. We hear about a given country's political system or its economic system. The term was first used in this context by academics who needed a way to refer to complex entities composed of many interacting parts. This way of looking at things is, however, as applicable to ecology as it is to economics or politics. In Chapter 31, when you went over ecological communities, you actually were studying something in isolation: the interactions of all the *living* things in a given area. It goes without saying that these living things also interact with many nonliving entities. To get a complete picture of how the living world functions, then, it's necessary to understand how living things interact not only with each other, but with these nonliving elements.

32.1 The Ecosystem Is the Fundamental Unit of Ecology

What do nonliving elements add to life? All communities need an original source of energy, generally meaning the sun; they all need a supply of water and a supply of nutrients, such as nitrogen and phosphorus; and all organisms need to exchange gases with their environment (think of your own breathing). The sun's energy is making a one-way trip through the community, ultimately being transformed into heat; but water and nutrients are being *cycled*—from the Earth into organisms and then back again into the Earth. Looking at this, we can begin to perceive the reality of ecological *systems*: of functional units that tightly link both living or **biotic** factors and nonliving or **abiotic** factors to form a whole.

What is the greenhouse effect?
(Section 32.4, page 727)

greenhouse gases

heat trapped

reflection of low-energy radiation (heat)

Here now, but not tomorrow?
(Section 32.4, page 727)

The taiga.
(Section 32.5, page 732)

Given this, the fundamental unit of ecology is the **ecosystem**, which can be defined as a community of organisms and the physical environment with which they interact. This chapter begins with a look at small-scale ecosystems and concludes with a look at the very large-scale ecosystems called biomes. In today's world, it's impossible to note the ways in which ecosystems function without also noting the ways in which human activity is damaging them.

32.2 Abiotic Factors Are a Major Component of Any Ecosystem

In Chapter 31 you learned a good deal about two of the biotic factors of the ecosystem, namely individual populations of living things and the communities that are made up of these populations. This chapter focuses on some of the abiotic factors in an ecosystem. In overview, these abiotic factors fall into two categories. First are the *resources* that exist in the ecosystem, such as water and nutrients; second are the *conditions* in which an ecosystem exists, such as average temperature. Resources will be considered first in this chapter and conditions later.

The Cycling of Ecosystem Resources

Those of you who went through Chapter 2, on chemistry, know what a chemical **element** is: a substance that is "pure" in that it cannot be broken down into any other component substances by chemical means. The 92 stable elements include such familiar substances as gold and helium, but only 30 or so of these elements are vital to life and are thus called **nutrients**. Some nutrients, such as iron or iodine, are needed only in small or "trace" quantities by living things, but others are needed in large quantities, among them carbon, oxygen, nitrogen, and phosphorus. Living things also have a great need for water, which is not an element but a molecule composed of two elements, hydrogen and oxygen. Water and nutrients move back and forth between the biotic and abiotic realms, with the term for this movement being a mouthful: **biogeochemical cycling**. Let's look now at the cycling of two elements, carbon and nitrogen, and then at the cycling of water.

Carbon as One Example of Ecosystem Cycling

A certain amount of cosmic debris makes its way to Earth's surface in the form of meteorites, but this material is pretty sparse. What else comes to Earth from space? The sun's rays, to be sure, as well as light from distant stars, and some other forms of radiation. But when we're talking about chemical ele-

ments, the Earth really is a spaceship: It carries a fixed amount of resources with it. Nothing comes to Earth *from* the outside, and relatively little leaves Earth *for* the outside. For an ecologist, this self-containment simplifies things: What we possess in terms of elements is all we'll ever possess. Thus the question becomes not so much what we have, but where we have it.

In recent years there has been considerable concern about the buildup of the heat-trapping gas carbon dioxide (CO_2) in the Earth's atmosphere, as this increase is now regarded by most scientists as a cause of global warming. Well, if Earth has this fixed quantity of elements—in this case the carbon and oxygen that make up CO_2—how could there be a buildup of carbon dioxide in the atmosphere? The answer is that carbon has been *transferred* from one place on Earth to another. It has moved from the "fossil fuels" of coal and oil, where it was stored, into the atmosphere.

Storage and transfer; these two concepts are fundamental to biogeochemical cycling. When we look a little deeper into carbon cycling, we find other players involved in carbon's storage and transfer. Plants need CO_2 to perform photosynthesis, and they take in great quantities of it for that purpose, producing their own food as a result. While the plants are alive, they use part of the carbon they take in to grow—to build up leaves and stems and roots. And as long as these structures exist, they will store carbon within them, just as coal and oil do. (Thus, one of the proposed solutions to global warming is to grow a huge number of trees, each of which could be thought of as a kind of piggy bank for carbon.) Eventually the plants die, of course, after which their decomposition by bacteria and fungi releases carbon into the soil and atmosphere, again as CO_2. With this, you can begin to see the whole of the carbon cycle in the natural world (**see Figure 32.1**).

Some plants will, of course, be eaten by *animals*, who need carbon-based molecules for tissues and energy, just as plants do. The difference is that animals get these molecules *from plants*—in the form of seeds and leaves and roots—rather than from the air. These animals will likewise lock up carbon for a time, only to return it to the soil with their death and decomposition. Note, however, the critical difference between animals and plants: Carbon comes into the living world only through plants (and their fellow photosynthesizers algae and some bacteria). An animal might take in some carbon dioxide in breathing, but nothing life-sustaining happens as a result. Conversely, a plant that takes in carbon dioxide can *incorporate* it into a life-sustaining molecule, in this case a sugar that is the initial product of photosynthesis. With this sugar as a

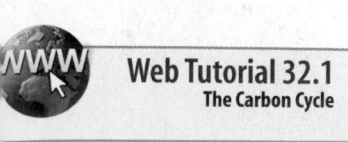

Web Tutorial 32.1
The Carbon Cycle

food source, plants grow, and this bounty ultimately feeds everything else. Look at this simplified cycle:

$$\text{atmospheric } CO_2 \rightarrow \text{plants} \rightarrow \text{animals} \rightarrow$$
$$\text{decomposers} \rightarrow \text{atmospheric } CO_2$$

What does it track, the path of carbon or the path of food? The answer is both. This is one of the reasons that biologists refer to life on Earth as "carbon-based."

How Much Atmospheric CO_2?

In following the carbon trail, it's probably apparent that, just as money is a medium of exchange in our economy, CO_2 is the living world's medium of exchange for carbon; photosynthesizers take *in* carbon as CO_2, and decomposers yield *up* carbon as CO_2. (All organisms also release CO_2 as a by-product of carrying out life's basic processes, as with your own exhalations in breathing.) Given how much **biomass** or material produced by living things there is in the world, you might think there would have to be a great deal of CO_2 in the atmosphere. But as a proportion of atmospheric gases, CO_2 is a bit player, making up about 0.035 percent of the atmosphere. But what an important player it is! It's critical in feeding us all, and it's likely that relatively small changes in its atmospheric concentration are now leading to significant changes in global temperature.

The Nitrogen Cycle

Like carbon, nitrogen is an element; and like carbon, nitrogen cycles between the biotic and abiotic domains. Nitrogen makes up only a small proportion of the tissues of living things, but it is a critical proportion because it is required for DNA, RNA, and all proteins. All living things need this element, then. The question is, how do they get it?

The source for all the nitrogen that enters the living world is atmospheric nitrogen, which exists in great abundance. You've seen that carbon dioxide makes up less than 1 percent of the atmosphere, and it turns out that oxygen makes up about 21 percent. But nitrogen makes up 78 percent of the atmosphere. So rich is the atmosphere in this element that a typical garden plot has tons hovering above it. The problem? All this nitrogen is in the form of pairs of nitrogen atoms (N_2) that have a great tendency to stay together, rather than combining with anything else. Thus, in a case of so near and yet so far, plants have no direct access to atmospheric nitrogen. So how do they take it up? In the natural world, the answer essentially is, through the actions of bacteria. It is bacteria that are carrying out the process of **nitrogen fixation**, meaning the conversion of atmospheric nitrogen into a form that can be taken up and used by living things.

Web Tutorial 32.2
The Nitrogen Cycle

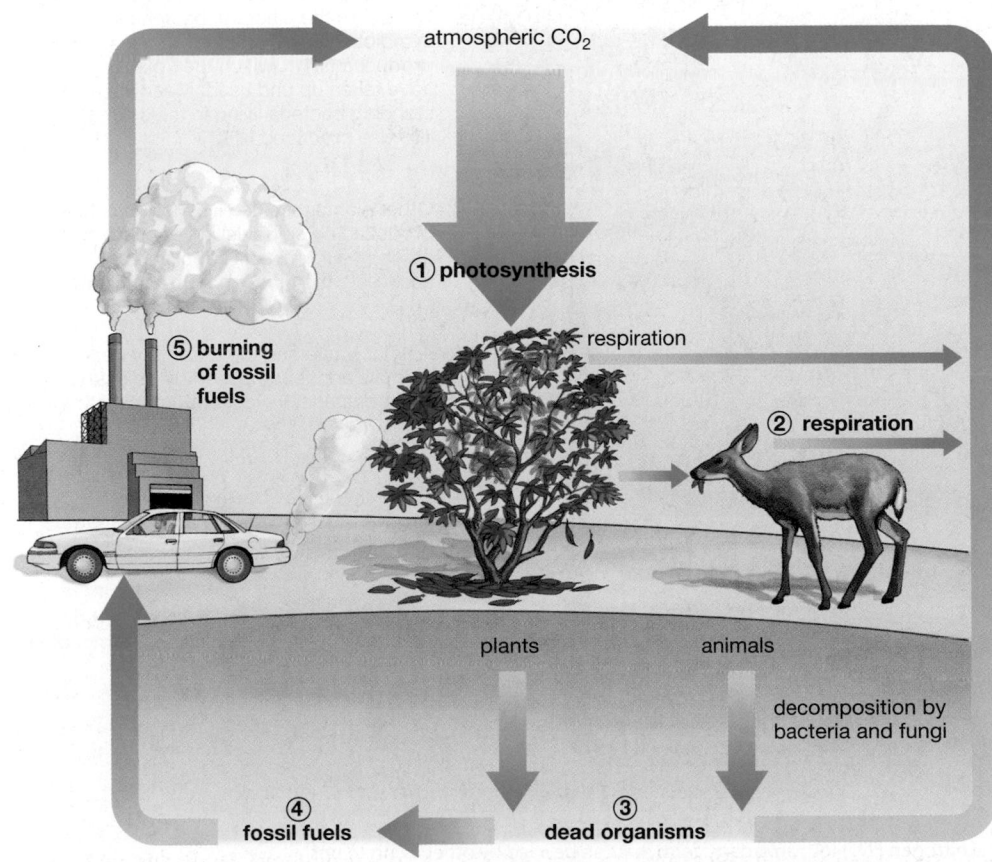

The carbon cycle

1. Plants and other photosynthesizing organisms take in atmospheric carbon dioxide (CO_2) and convert or "fix" it into molecules that become part of the plant.

2. The physical functioning or respiration of organisms converts the carbon in their tissues back into CO_2.

3. Plants and animals die and are decomposed by fungi and bacteria. Some CO_2 results, which moves back into the atmosphere.

4. Some of the carbon in the remains of dead organisms becomes locked up in carbon-based compounds such as coal or oil.

5. The burning of these fossil fuels puts this carbon into the atmosphere in the form of CO_2.

atmospheric CO_2

① **photosynthesis**

⑤ **burning of fossil fuels**

respiration

② **respiration**

plants

animals

decomposition by bacteria and fungi

④ **fossil fuels**

③ **dead organisms**

Figure 32.1
The Carbon Cycle

Bacterial Fixation of Nitrogen

You can see nitrogen fixation and the rest of the nitrogen cycle diagrammed in **Figure 32.2**. The essence of the cycle is that several types of nitrogen-fixing bacteria take in atmospheric nitrogen (N_2) and convert it into ammonia (NH_3). This ammonia then is converted (either in water or by other bacteria) into two types of nitrogen-containing compounds that plants can *assimilate*—can take up and use. And as you've seen, what comes into the plant world will come into the animal world, when animals eat plants. The two usable nitrogen compounds produced in the cycle are the ammonium ion (NH_4^+) and nitrate (NO_3^-). Some of the nitrate that results from this process is used by yet another kind of bacteria, denitrifying bacteria, which can convert nitrate back into atmospheric nitrogen, completing the cycle.

Nitrogen as a Limiting Factor in Food Production

If you were to look at the nitrogen story 100 years ago, there would be little more to it than what you've just gone over. In other words, through most of human history, nitrogen was fixed solely by bacteria (with a small assist from lightning, which can produce a usable form of nitrogen that falls to the Earth in rain). Human beings had a problem with this single route to nitrogen, however, because nitrogen is critical for all plant growth, including *agricultural* plant growth. Indeed, for centuries a lack of nitrogen was a primary limiting factor in getting more food from a given amount of land. Long before anyone knew what nitrogen was, farmers were trying to get more of it to crops in two ways. One was by applying organic fertilizer, such as rotting organic material, to their fields. (Remember how the Pilgrims were taught by the Indians to bury dead fish around their corn plants?) The second was by planting crops that carried their own nitrogen-fixing bacteria within them. This is the case with certain legumes, such as soybeans, which carry symbiotic bacteria in their root nodules. So great was the need for nitrogen that nitrogen-fixing plants were sometimes grown as "green manures"—as crops that were plowed right back into the ground to serve as fertilizers.

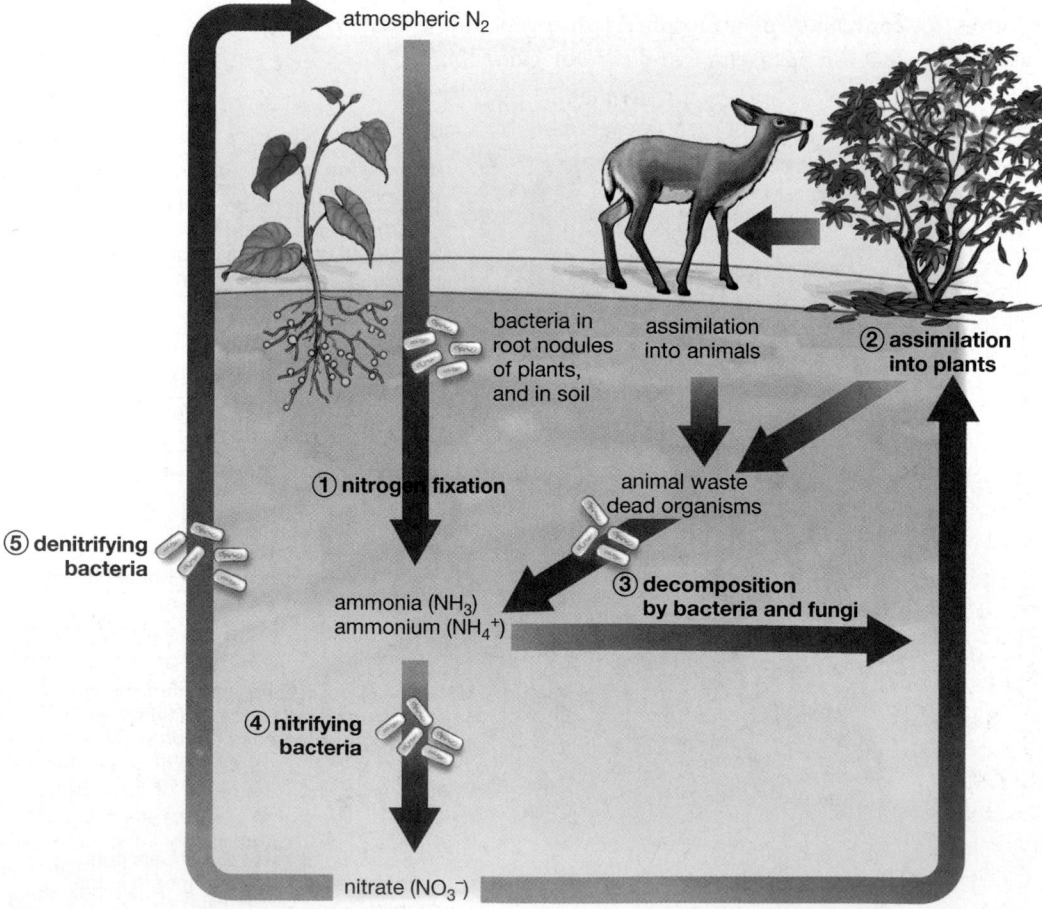

The nitrogen cycle

1. Nitrogen-fixing bacteria convert N_2 into ammonia (NH_3), which converts in water into the ammonium ion (NH_4^+). The latter is a compound that plants can assimilate into tissues. In the diagram, bacteria living symbiotically in plant root nodules have produced NH_4^+, which their plant partners have taken up and used. Meanwhile, free-standing bacteria living in the soil have likewise produced NH_4^+.

2. Other plants take up NH_4^+ that has been produced by soil-dwelling bacteria and assimilate it. Animals eat plants and assimilate the nitrogen from the plants.

3. Animal waste and the tissues of dead animals are decomposed by fungi and by other bacteria, which turn organic nitrogen back into NH_4^+.

4. Other "nitrifying" bacteria convert NH_4^+ into Nitrate (NO_3^-), which likewise can be assimilated by plants.

5. Some nitrate, however, is converted by "denitrifying" bacteria back into atmospheric nitrogen, completing the cycle.

Figure 32.2
The Nitrogen Cycle
Some bacteria "fix" nitrogen, meaning they convert atmospheric nitrogen (N_2) into an organic form that can be used by other living things.

Early in the twentieth century, however, a momentous change came about in the use of nitrogen when the German chemist Fritz Haber developed an *industrial* process for turning atmospheric nitrogen into ammonia. In essence, human beings became nitrogen fixers and, by the 1960s, they had taken up this activity on a grand scale. In 1990 about 80 million metric tons of biologically active nitrogen were manufactured for use as fertilizer; in addition, human beings planted crops that resulted in the production of another 40 million tons (**see Figure 32.3**). This human-driven production was roughly equal to the amount of active nitrogen that all of nature produced on its own.

It is hard to overstate the importance of the industrial fixation of nitrogen. Put simply, the world's human population could not be fed without such fixation. Only with synthetic nitrogen can the Earth's arable land produce enough food to feed the Earth's burgeoning human population.

This massive human intervention in the nitrogen cycle has a downside as well, however. Remember that human-manufactured nitrogen ends up being used in a very *concentrated* way—it is poured onto farmland. A good deal of this nitrogen does not end up in the crops it was intended for, however, but instead departs as runoff. The amount of runoff generated by each farm adds up, and the end result can be large amounts of nitrogen flowing into creeks, ponds, and rivers. On a regional basis, such nitrogen flows can be enormous. The Mississippi River carries an estimated 1.5 million metric tons of nitrogen into the Gulf of Mexico each year.

You might think that since nitrogen is a nutrient this would be a good thing for the Gulf waters, but the opposite is true. The nitrogen brings on a seasonal "bloom" of algae, the algae result in a huge bacterial population, and the bacteria use up most of the available oxygen at the water's lower depths. The result is a giant "dead zone" that drives away mobile fish and that kills immobile, bottom-dwelling sea creatures (**see Figure 32.4**). This problem of *nutrient pollution* is not limited to the Gulf of Mexico, however; it is played out on a smaller scale in estuaries and ponds around the world.

The Cycling of Water

Now let's turn from nutrient to water cycling. Those who went through the material on water in Chapter 3 know how important water is to life. The human body is about 66 percent water by weight, and any living thing that does not have a supply of water is doomed in the long run. As with nitrogen

or carbon, all water is either being cycled or is locked up. Carbon may be stored in coal or trees, but water can be stored in ice—in glaciers or in polar ice, for example.

Figure 32.3
Nutrients Beyond What Nature Provides
A helicopter applies fertilizer to a sugar-beet crop in California.

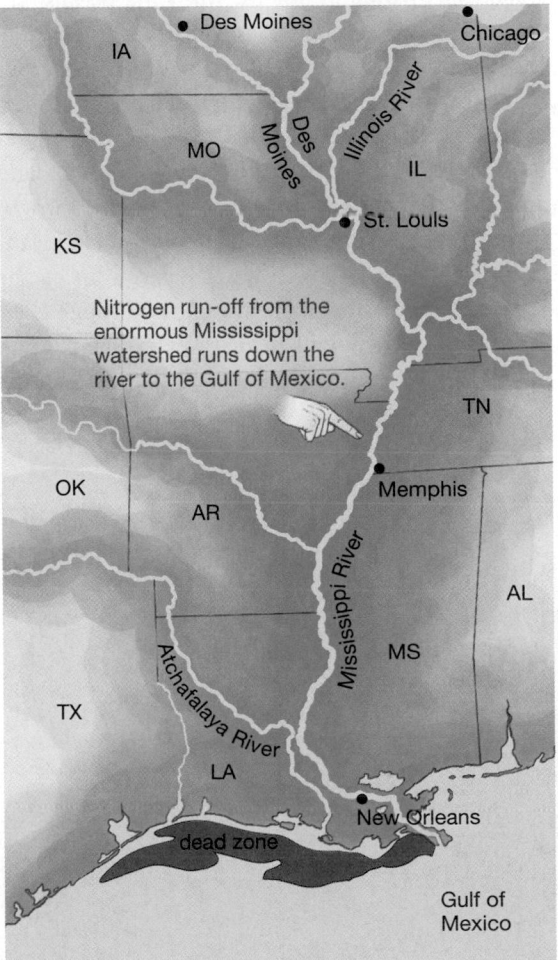

Figure 32.4
Map of the Gulf of Mexico "Dead Zone"
In 2002, the seasonal "dead zone" in the Gulf of Mexico stretched from the mouth of the Mississippi River to eastern Texas. The waters in the zone are "hypoxic," or oxygen-depleted, particularly at their lower depths. The primary cause is the tremendous amount of nitrogen carried into the Gulf from both the Mississippi and Atchafalaya Rivers. This nitrogen originates as fertilizer that is applied to farmland all the way up the Mississippi River basin.

Figure 32.5
The Hydrologic Cycle
More than 95 percent of Earth's water is stored in the oceans. When water evaporates from the ocean, 90 percent returns to the ocean directly by way of precipitation. The other 10 percent falls on land. There, the water either runs back into the ocean, is stored in such structures as glaciers, or is moved by transpiration and evaporation back into the atmosphere.

Web Tutorial 32.3
The Hydrologic Cycle

Figure 32.6
Earth's Water
Although there is a tremendous amount of water on our planet, only a small fraction of it is available to us as freshwater.

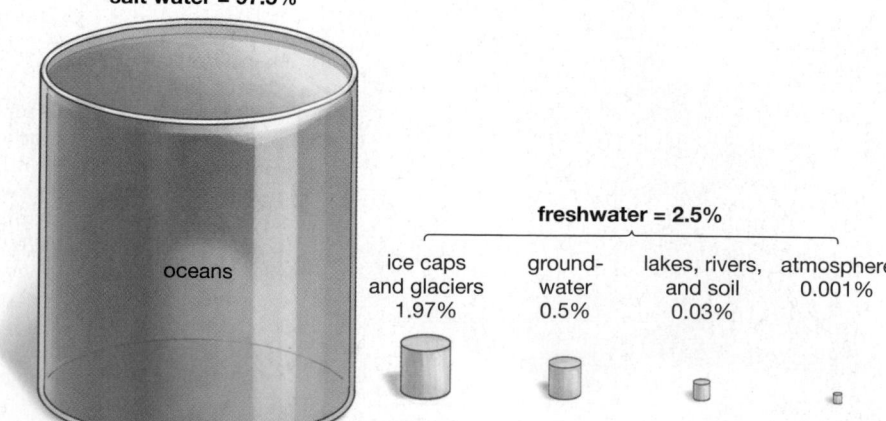

salt water = 97.5%

oceans

freshwater = 2.5%

| ice caps and glaciers 1.97% | ground-water 0.5% | lakes, rivers, and soil 0.03% | atmosphere 0.001% |

The oceans hold more than 95 percent of Earth's water, but thankfully for us, when the oceans' salt water evaporates, it falls back to Earth as freshwater. We can also be grateful that not all ocean water falls back to Earth on the oceans; instead, about 10 percent falls on land (**see Figure 32.5**). This water represents about 40 percent of the precipitation that land areas get; the other 60 percent comes from a form of cycling reviewed in Chapter 23: *transpiration*, meaning the process by which water is taken up by the roots of land plants, then moved up through their stems and out through their leaves as water vapor. After evaporating into the atmosphere, water returns to Earth as rain, fog, snow—all the forms of precipitation possible. The driving force behind the hydrologic cycle is the energy of the sun; its heat powers both evaporation and transpiration.

With more than 95 percent of Earth's water in the oceans, perhaps as little as 2.5 percent of the Earth's water is freshwater at any given time. Of this freshwater, more than 75 percent is locked up in glaciers and other forms of ice (**see Figure 32.6**). Thus any snapshot we would take of Earth would show that as little as 0.5 percent of its water is available as liquid, freshwater; but even here we have to qualify things. About 25 percent of this freshwater is **groundwater**, meaning water that moves down through the soil until it reaches porous rock that is saturated with water. In line with this, about 20 percent of the water used in the United States comes from groundwater and at least a quarter of the world's population depends on groundwater to satisfy basic needs. Groundwater is stored in porous rock called an **aquifer**, an example of which is pictured in **Figure 32.7**. Major aquifers can be enormous, as you can see from the map of the High Plains Aquifer in **Figure 32.8**. Even an aquifer of this size, however, can lose more water through pumping than it gains through replenishment from rain. In Texas, the depth of the High Plains Aquifer declined by more than a foot per year from 1940 to 1980 and then by a little less than half a foot per year between 1980 and 1998.

Global Human Use of Water

Given the sheer number of people on Earth and the importance of water to each of them, it will not surprise you to learn that human beings are laying claim to a great deal of Earth's freshwater; civilization now uses more than half the world's accessible supply. But from what you've seen so far, think of what this means. There is no less *water* than there ever was. Like nitrogen or carbon, all the water we have is either being recycled or is stored. What's changed is that the human population is using an ever-greater proportion of the water that's available. Human beings fight among themselves for water, of course, because it is a scarce commodity in locations throughout the world. Indeed, *sanitary* water is so scarce that an estimated 1 billion people worldwide lack access to it (**see Figure 32.9**). A large part of the problem is that there is a mismatch between the location of freshwater and the location of human populations. Twenty-six percent of the world's precipitation falls in South America, but only 6 percent of the world's people live there. Meanwhile, 36 percent of the world's precipitation falls in Asia, while 60 percent of the world's people live there.

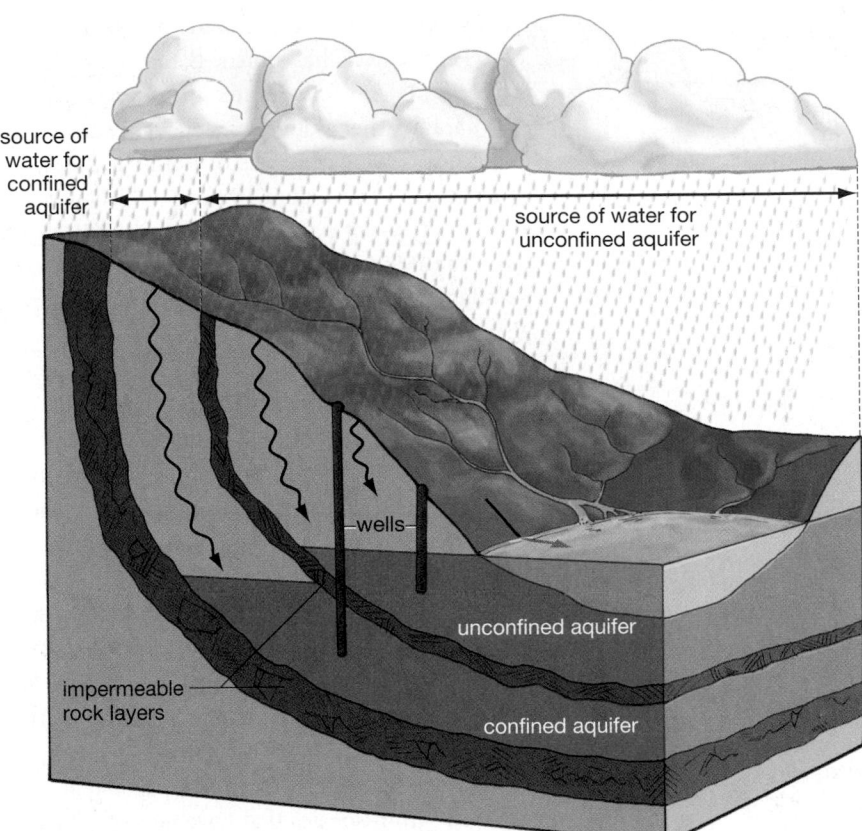

Figure 32.7
Aquifers Store Groundwater
When water seeps into the ground, it moves freely through layers of sand and porous rock but moves either extremely slowly or not at all through layers of impermeable rock. Water thus becomes trapped in different underground layers, from which humans can draw water. Unconfined aquifers receive water directly from a large surface area and therefore tend to be more vulnerable to pollution by chemicals such as fertilizers and pesticides. Confined aquifers are located between layers of impermeable rock. They are replenished more slowly but tend to contain purer water.

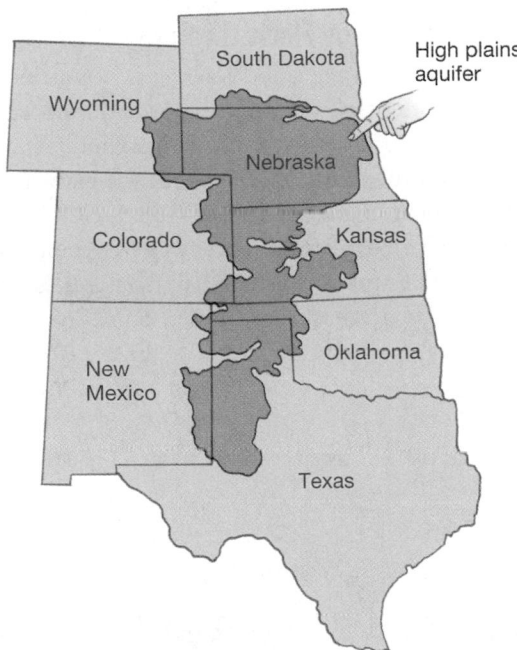

Figure 32.8
Enormous Store of Underground Water
The High Plains Aquifer, perhaps the largest aquifer in the world, underlies an expanse of land stretching across eight states. Billions of gallons of water are withdrawn from it each day, mostly for agriculture. Since the 1940s, more than 200,000 wells have been drilled into it for this purpose. (Modified from Gutentag, E. D., Heimes, F. J., Krothe, N. C., Luckey, R. R., and Weeks, J. B., 1984. Geohydrology of the High Plains Aquifer in Part of Colorado, Kansas, Nebraska, New Mexico, Oklahoma, South Dakota, Texas, and Wyoming. U.S. Geological Survey Professional Paper 1400-B.)

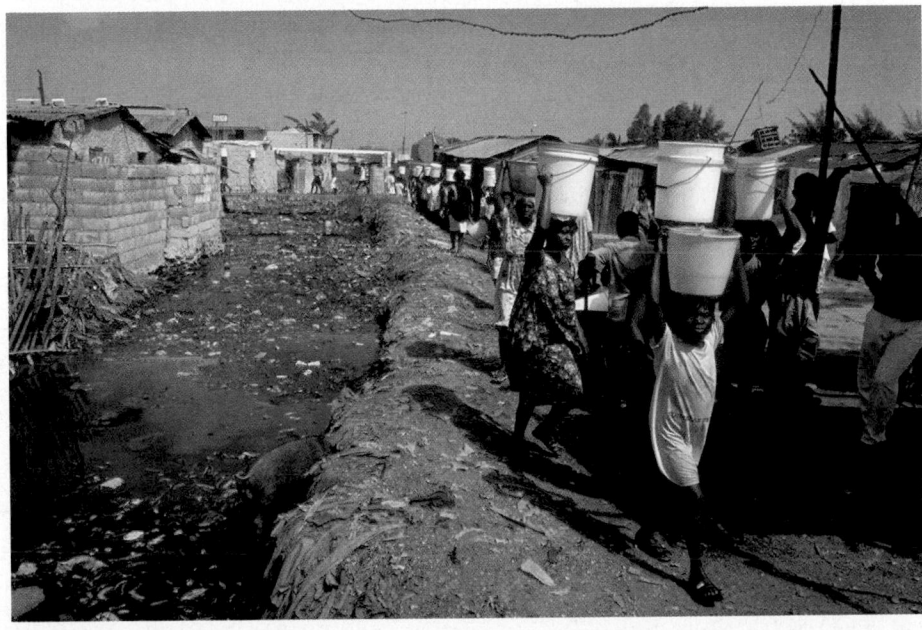

Figure 32.9
Freshwater Is a Limited Resource
Women carry drinking water through a polluted slum in Port-au-Prince, Haiti.

One part of the human water problem, water expert Peter Glieck has noted, is that humans make such poor use of the water they capture. Mexico City's leaky water system *loses* enough water to meet the needs of a city the size of Rome. If the toilet in your house is more than 10 years old, chances are it uses six gallons of water with each flush. If it was built since the 1990s, following imposition of new federal standards for low-flow toilets, it probably uses less than a third of that—a mere 1.6 gallons.

When we think of societal use of water, however, household use actually is relatively small. About 70 percent of the water we humans withdraw from rivers, lakes, and groundwater goes to agricultural irrigation. People need food, of course, but the *way* irrigation is carried out in much of the world is extremely wasteful: water moves from, say, a river to crops by means of an open channel. En route, much of this water either evaporates or is taken up by land that isn't being irrigated. An efficient alternative is "micro-irrigation" in which water gets piped to crops.

Human beings are, of course, capable of diverting water from species that have no say in this division of resources. More than 20 percent of all freshwater fish species are estimated to be threatened or endangered precisely because their water has been dammed or diverted for human use. California's natural populations of coho salmon have been reduced by some 94 percent since the 1940s, in significant part through diversions of the freshwater streams that the salmon swim up in order to spawn. If you look at **Figure 32.10**, you can get a quick idea of humanity's impact on the three resources just reviewed—carbon, nitrogen, and water.

Human Beings Are Not Separate from the Earth on Which They Live

One final thing about nutrient and water cycling. The average person, who has no knowledge of these cycling processes, may regard human beings as a kind of independent line that stretches back in time. Under this view, water and food may pass through us, but they are as separate from us as gasoline is from a car engine.

From your reading of this section, however, it may now be apparent to you that this is not true. Some of the carbon in the bread you ate this morning could have been contained in a tree that decomposed in China 100 years ago. After many cycles, carbon from this tree was taken up by a wheat plant in America whose seeds were ground up, yielding flour that ended in the bread on your shelf. This carbon may be burned by your body to supply the energy it needs, it's true, but it may also become part of your bones or your nerves. Then, when you die, the material you are made of will go *back* to the Earth to be recycled in the ways you've been reading about, perhaps to be part of a tree or a person in a future generation. We are intertwined with the Earth in some basic, physical ways.

32.3 How Energy Flows through Ecosystems

Having looked at the abiotic elements of nutrients and water, let's now turn to another important component of any ecosystem, energy. Those of you who read through Chapter 6, on energy, know that one of energy's inflexible laws—the first law of thermodynamics—is that energy is never gained or lost, but only transformed. The sun's energy is not used up by green plants; rather, some of it is

Figure 32.10
Human Impact on Resources

(a) Nearly a quarter of the current atmospheric carbon dioxide concentration is produced by human activity, primarily through the burning of fossil fuels.

(b) Over half of terrestrial nitrogen fixation comes about because of human activity, including the manufacture of fertilizer for agriculture.

(c) Over half of the Earth's accessible surface water is now diverted for use by humans, mostly for agriculture. Percentages are approximate.

converted by plants into chemical form—initially into the chemical bonds of the sugar that plants make in photosynthesis.

The second law of thermodynamics is that energy spontaneously flows in only one direction: from more ordered to less ordered. The carbohydrate molecules in bread are very ordered things—so many atoms of carbon, oxygen, and hydrogen in a precise spatial relationship to one another. Contrast this with another form of energy, heat, which is the *random* motion of molecules—clearly a disordered form of energy compared to a carbohydrate. Indeed, heat is the last stop on the energy line, because it is the least-ordered form of energy. And, because all energy spontaneously moves toward less order, heat is the ultimate *fate* of all energy. Energy relentlessly ratchets down toward the form of heat because, like a casino that must get a "cut" of each bet laid down, heat gets a cut of each energy transaction. The chemical bonds in gasoline can be broken through combustion and thus be used to power a car engine, but not all the energy released from the combustion drives the engine. Some dissipates as heat, and this happens *every* time energy is used, whether we're talking about a piston firing or a cell dividing.

All of this provides a framework to conceptualize an important part of ecosystems, which is how energy flows through them. Think of the sun's energy, with the energetic rays that leave it as a starting point; now think of the ultimate destiny of all this energy, which is heat, randomly dispersed in the universe. Looked at one way, life on Earth *intervenes* in this flow. Life is an enormous energy collection and storage enterprise, gathering some of the sun's energy and locking it up for a time in the form of chemical bonds. These bonds can then be broken—think of digesting a muffin—which *releases* this stored energy so that an organism can grow and reproduce. Life does not stop the march of the sun's energy into heat, but it does intervene in it by transforming it into chemical bonds that have order and stability.

Once we see life in these terms, we can begin to think of the *flow* of energy through it. That's what you'll be looking at in the sections that follow.

Producers, Consumers, and Trophic Levels

One way to look at food and energy is in terms of production and consumption. Plants and other photosynthesizers (algae, some bacteria) are an ecosystem's **producers**, while the organisms that eat plants are one kind of **consumer**: an organism that eats other organisms, rather than producing its own food. But as you know, there are consumers *of* consumers—grass is eaten by zebras, but zebras are eaten by lions. Thus do we get to the concept of feeding *levels* or, as ecologists put it, trophic levels. More formally, a **trophic level** is a position in an ecosystem's food chain or web, with each level defined by a transfer of energy between one kind of organism and another. Producers are one level, and then there are several levels of consumers. Here's a list of trophic levels through four stages.

First trophic level:	**Producers**— (photosynthesizers)
Second trophic level:	**Primary consumers**— plant predators (herbivores)
Third trophic level:	**Secondary consumers**— herbivore predators (carnivores)
Fourth trophic level:	**Tertiary consumers**— organisms that feed on secondary consumers (carnivores)

It is the sun's energy that is locked up in leaves and stems, and it is this energy that is being passed along through these trophic levels. Note that the levels are not just categories that could be put in any order. We must have primary consumers to have secondary consumers; sharks cannot exist on algae (**see Figure 32.11**). You may remember that an animal that eats only plants or algae is a **herbivore**; then there are **carnivores**, which eat only meat, and **omnivores**, which eat both plants and meat. Of course, many organisms cannot be assigned to just a single trophic level. Most human beings, for example, are primary, secondary, and tertiary consumers.

Figure 32.11
Trophic Levels
Plants, algae, and some bacteria are called producers because they use the sun's energy to produce their own food through photosynthesis. Organisms at all other trophic levels ultimately derive their energy from these photosynthesizers.

You have thus far thought in terms of food chains, which is to say trophic *lines* in which a single organism follows another. In reality, of course, nature is much more complex than this; what really exists are feeding patterns called *food webs*, one example of which you can see in **Figure 32.12**.

A Special Class of Consumers: Detritivores

To this scheme of trophic levels, ecologists add a special class of consumers, the **detritivores**. These are consumers that feed on *detritus*, which in normal usage simply means a collection of debris. In ecology, however, detritus is the remains of dead organisms or cast-off material from living organisms (a fallen branch from a living tree, for example). A worm or a dung beetle feeding on such material would fit this description of a detritivore.

Of particular interest, however, is a special kind of detritivore: A **decomposer**, which is an organism that, in feeding on dead or cast-off organic material, breaks it down into its inorganic components, which then can be recycled through the ecosystem. *Inorganic* here can

be thought of as building blocks; more technically, it means an element or compound that does not contain carbon bound covalently to hydrogen. The most important decomposers are fungi and bacteria. A number of detritivores usually are responsible for breaking up organic material, first into pieces and then into its inorganic components (**see Figure 32.13**).

Stepping back from this, it's worth noting that if a factory made such complete use of its materials as nature does, that factory would be considered a wonder of the world. Think of it this way: What is thrown away in the feeding and decomposing chain you've been looking at? Nothing, which is all to the good, because if there were any natural garbage of this sort, spaceship Earth would sooner or later be filled up with this useless material. This very thought ought to give us some pause about the compounds human beings currently are putting into the environment that are not **biodegradable**, meaning capable of being decomposed by living organisms. Of particular concern here are plastics, many of which will remain intact for hundreds of years following their production.

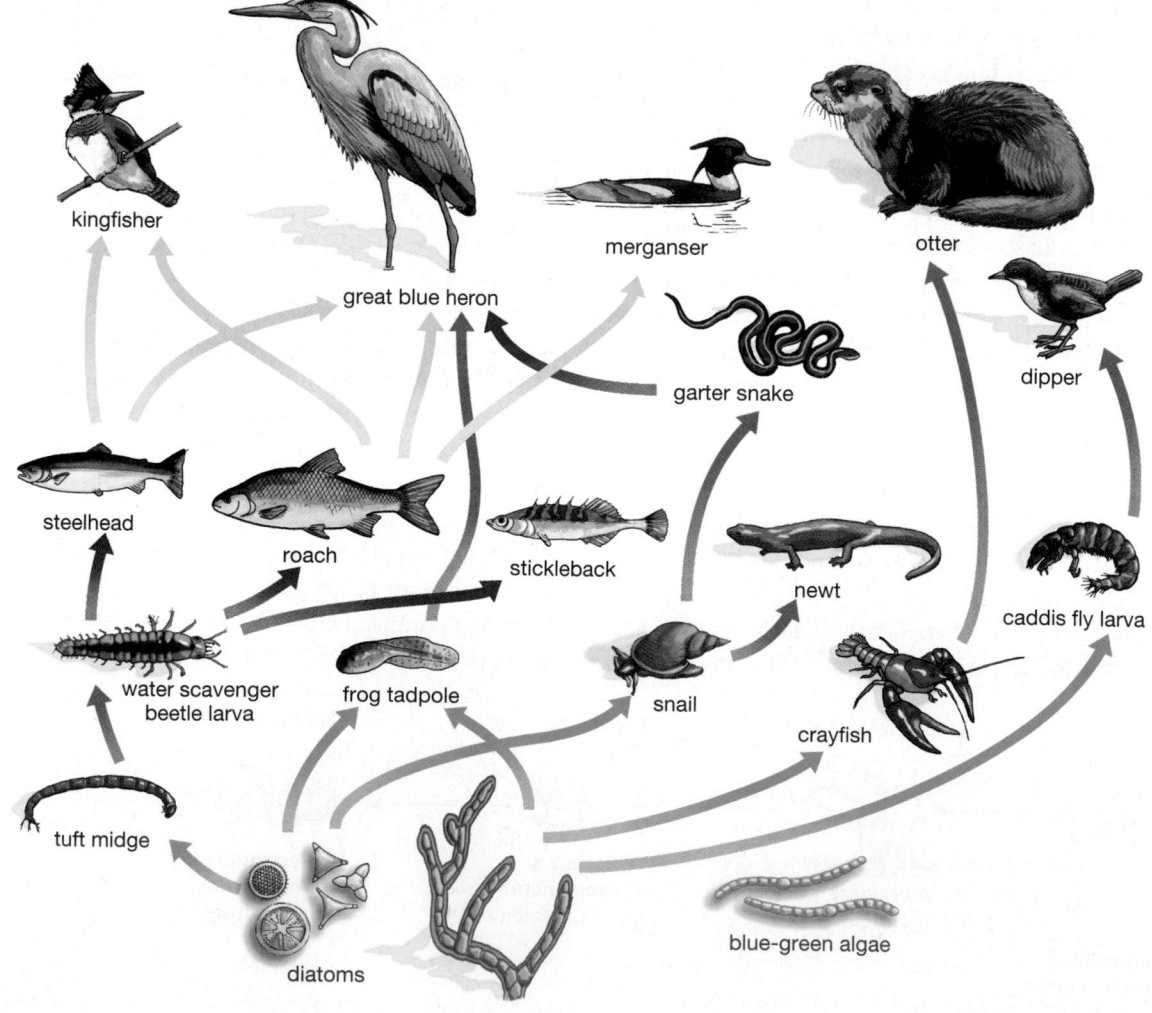

Figure 32.12
A River Food Web
The diagram indicates who eats whom along a portion of the Eel River in Northern California. The arrows have been color-coded by trophic level. Note that there are up to five trophic levels in the web. (Adapted with permission from an original drawing by Mary E. Power, University of California, Berkeley.)

kingfisher

great blue heron

merganser

otter

garter snake

dipper

steelhead

roach

stickleback

newt

caddis fly larva

water scavenger beetle larva

frog tadpole

snail

crayfish

tuft midge

diatoms

green algae

blue-green algae

Chain of Detritivores

Figure 32.13
How Organic Material Is Broken Down
Different kinds of detritivores consume the organic material in a branch that has fallen from a tree. Most of these animals are consuming pieces of the log, but the detritivore called a decomposer (a fungus in the figure) is breaking organic materials into their inorganic components, thus returning nutrients to the soil.

Accounting for Energy Flow through the Trophic Levels

All natural substances eventually are recycled in ecosystems, but this is not true of energy, which is just passing through, on its way to heat. Two interesting questions arise from this: How *much* of the sun's energy does the living world collect in the first place, and then how much of the collected energy makes it through to each successive trophic level?

This may seem like a routine set of questions, but the first ecologists who thought in these terms brought about a revolution in ecology. Working in the 1940s at Minnesota's Cedar Bog Lake, ecologist Raymond Lindeman was the first to conceptualize ecosystems as units in which energy is first captured by given organisms and then transferred on to others. This conceptualization is today known as the **energy-flow model** of ecosystems. Part of the impetus for Lindeman's research was to answer a very down-to-earth question, succinctly expressed by ecologist Paul Colinvaux: Why are big, fierce animals rare? (If you doubt that they are, think of this. It's utterly routine to see plants, insects, or small birds, but it's often the experience of a lifetime to see a bear or a shark.) The energy-flow model explained the small numbers of fierce animals, as you'll see, but it then went on to shed light on all kinds of ecological relationships. Why? Because energy is a kind of currency in the natural world; all organisms use it, and it is transferred among them. Moreover, it can be *measured*, usually in units called **kilocalories** (the amount of heat it takes to raise 1 kilogram of water one degree Celsius). If we know that a field mouse must use 68 percent of the kilocalories it consumes just to stay alive—to move, to keep a constant body temperature—but that a weasel must use 93 percent of its kilocalories for this purpose, that gives us a meaningful basis for comparison between these two animals. Beyond this, weasels *eat* field mice, and with the energy-flow model we have some basis for *tracking* this important commodity as it moves through an ecosystem.

The Capture of Energy by Plants

So, what has energy-flow research told us? To take things from the beginning, how much of the sun's energy do plants capture? As you can see in **Figure 32.14**, very little; only about 2 percent of the sun's energy that falls around plants is taken in for photosynthesis. This raises an important point, which is noting the difference between the energy that *comes to* an organism and what the organism *does with* that energy.

Figure 32.14
Absorption and Use of Solar Energy by Plants
Only 2 percent of the solar energy reaching the Earth's surface is taken in by plants for photosynthesis. Of this energy, only a fraction ends up being contained in plant material, such as tissues. It is this material (the plant's net primary production) that is available to the next trophic level in a food chain. The remaining energy is either dissipated as heat or used by photosynthesizers to power their own physical processes.

The amount of material that a plant produces as a result of photosynthesis is known as its **gross primary production**. Those of you who have been through Chapter 8 know that the initial product of photosynthesis is a sugar that serves as a starting "building block" for all the material in the plant. Every time a molecule of this sugar is produced in photosynthesis, the plant has added to its gross primary production. But plants don't get to retain all the material they produce in this way. Why? Because plants incur energy *costs* in just staying alive. It takes energy to perform photosynthesis, to move sap from one end of the plant to the other, and so forth. Such costs are subsumed under the heading of "cellular respiration," but you could also think of them as the plant's overhead; they are the price of doing business. Apart from this, we know that, in every energy transaction, some of the energy is lost as heat. After subtracting these various costs, the plant is left with its **net primary production**: the amount of material a plant accumulates as a result of photosynthesis. This is the material that serves to build the plant up—its stems and leaves and roots.

One question that arises from this framework is: What fraction of the energy a plant receives from the sun ends up as net primary production? How efficient are plants, in other words, at turning solar energy into stems and leaves and roots? Of the solar energy that plants receive, somewhere between 30 and 85 percent is transferred into net primary production. In other words, at the low end of this range, only 30 percent of the solar energy a plant assimilates is transferred into material that is even potentially available to consumers.

Up a Level, to Primary Consumers

Now, what happens when you jump up one trophic level, to those primary consumers? Well, in the first place, they can't *get to* a lot of the tissue that's been produced—it's in roots that are buried or in leaves that are too high to reach. A good deal of the material is inedible in any event, except by detritivores. Critically, most of the energy these scavengers take in is making an *exit*

from the trophic chain; it won't be available to primary consumers, which means it won't be available to secondary or tertiary consumers either. Adding all this up, you can begin to see that of the energy locked up by plants, very little is assimilated by organisms at the next step up—the primary consumers.

This pattern of energy reduction is then repeated in the successive trophic levels. But the reductions tend to get more severe because animals have higher energy costs than plants. They excrete a lot of the material they consume, and the warm-blooded or "endothermic" animals we're most familiar with spend a great deal of energy keeping a constant body temperature—producing heat, which obviously is energy lost to the food chain. So, while a plant may transfer 50 percent of the energy it receives into new material, for endothermic animals the figure is about 2 percent, meaning they use up 98 percent of the energy they assimilate just to stay alive, rather than to produce tissue with energy locked up inside it.

All of this leads to what you see in **Figure 32.15**: a reduction in available energy, and, in most cases, a reduction in the number of organisms at each trophic level. The gist of this is that each succeeding trophic level has a great deal less energy available to it than did the level before it. The amount that is passed on varies by community, but there is a rule of thumb in ecology that for each jump up in trophic level, the amount of available energy drops by 90 percent. Take all the energy converted into tissue by, say, a second trophic level herbivore, and of this, only 10 percent ends up being converted into tissue in a third trophic level carnivore. There is a great variability in conversion rates, however, and 10 percent probably is more like a maximum passed on.

The Effects of Energy Loss through Trophic Levels

So, what are the consequences of this energy reduction at trophic levels? First, *this* is the reason that big, fierce animals are rare. If you had a field that could feed 100 field mice, how many weasels could the field support, if those weasels were existing solely on the mice? Remembering that, at most, only 10 percent of a trophic level's energy is likely to be passed along to the next level, you might guess that 10 weasels could make a living in the field, but even this number would be too high. For 10 predators to make a living from 100 mice, these predators would have to be no *bigger* than the mice, which is certainly not true of weasels. Extending this further, not even a single hawk could survive on the available weasels in the field. Why are big, fierce animals rare? Because of the loss of available energy at each step in the trophic chain. Because weasels are not about to start eating the same things as

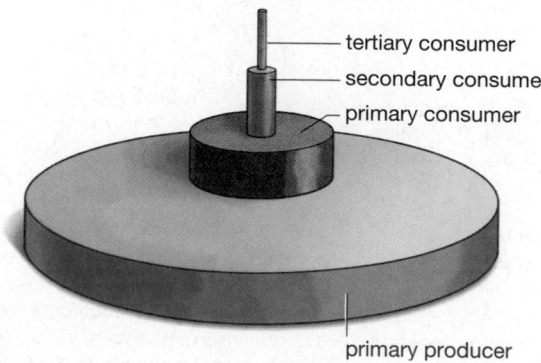

tertiary consumer
secondary consumer
primary consumer

primary producer

Figure 32.15
Energy Pyramid
Only a small fraction (10 percent or less) of energy at each trophic level is available to the next higher trophic level.

mice, weasels are locked into a trophic level with a more limited energy supply. When there's only so much energy, there can be only so many weasels.

Beyond this, the energy-flow model allows us to see the *limits* to top predators. Why couldn't we have a land carnivore bigger and fiercer than a grizzly bear? Well, imagine that you found some awesome creature that fit this bill somewhere on Earth, and that you plopped it down in Alaska. What would happen? If it could feed only on grizzly bears, it would starve to death. There simply is not enough energy locked up in grizzly bears for there to be a trophic level above them. This is why, in most food webs, there are so few trophic levels above primary producers; the energy simply runs out. This question of energy loss with each trophic level has relevance for a human issue, which is eating meat that comes from grain-fed cattle, as you can see in "A Cut for the Middleman," on page 724.

Primary Productivity Varies across the Earth by Region

Primary productivity concerns *biomass* or material produced by living things, as measured by weight. It will come as no surprise that some areas of the Earth are more productive than others. If you look at **Figure 32.16**, you can get an idea of the differences around the globe. The reasons for these differences will be explored in this chapter's section on the large ecosystems called biomes. For now, suffice it to say that much of what you see in Figure 32.16 is intuitive. Productivity is very low in such desert areas as North Africa and very high in such tropical rain-forest areas as equatorial Africa. Yet why should one part of the Earth be a rain forest and another part a desert? The answer has to do with Earth's large-scale physical environment.

32.4 Earth's Physical Environment

Earth's Atmosphere

Earth itself exists within an environment, called the **atmosphere**, which is the layer of gases surrounding the Earth. One of the main things to realize about Earth's atmosphere is how it differs from outer space. There's something *to* Earth's atmosphere (a mix of gases), while outer space really is *space*; there's almost nothing in it.

The atmosphere is divided into several layers, but here you need be concerned with only two of them, which you can see in **Figure 32.17**. The lowest layer of the atmosphere, called the **troposphere**, starts at sea level and extends upward about 12 kilometers (or 7.4 miles), and it contains the bulk of the gases in the atmosphere. Nitrogen and oxygen make up 99 percent of the troposphere, but carbon dioxide exists there in

Figure 32.16
Primary Productivity by Geographic Region
Primary productivity around the globe. This composite satellite image shows how the concentration of plant life varies on both land and sea. On land, the areas of lowest productivity are tan-colored, as with the enormous swath of land that begins with the eastern Sahara Desert in North Africa. More productive land areas are yellow, more productive yet are light green, and the most productive of all are dark green. On the oceans, the gradient runs from dark blue (the least productive), though lighter blue, green, yellow, and orange-red (the most productive). The ocean measurements are of concentrations of phytoplankton—the tiny, photosynthesizing organisms that drift on the water and form the base of the marine food web. Note the high productivity of the oceans in both the far northern and southern latitudes. Antarctica itself is gray because the imaging technique did not work well for it.

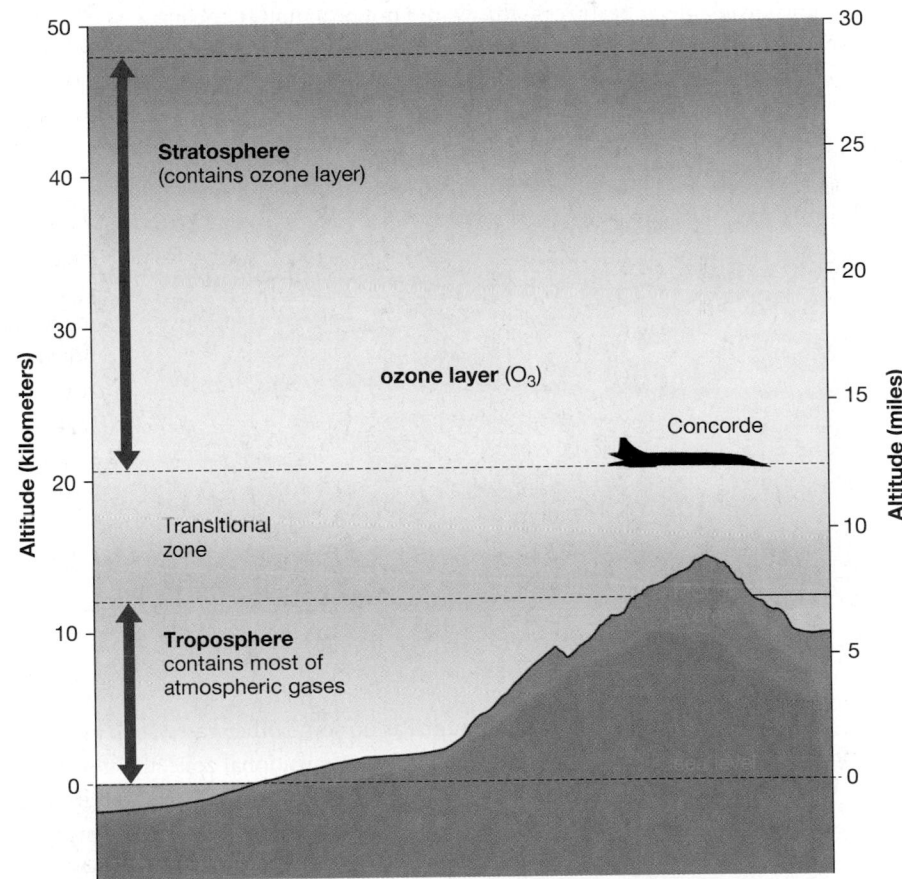

Figure 32.17
Earth's Atmosphere
The two lowest layers of the atmosphere are shown, with Mount Everest (the tallest mountain) and the Concorde (the highest-flying passenger airplane) included for vertical scale. The troposphere contains most of the atmosphere's gases—mostly nitrogen and oxygen, with some carbon dioxide, methane, and other gases. The stratosphere contains the ozone layer, which blocks 99 percent of the sun's harmful ultraviolet radiation.

A Cut for the Middleman: Livestock and Food

It may be difficult to think of cows in a field as occupants of one of the trophic levels you've been looking at, but that's just what they are, with some provocative consequences for human beings and food. People can't survive on grass the way cows and sheep can, and it follows that these animals are turning food that is useless to human beings into products that are use*ful* to human beings—meat, wool, and milk. In this sense, then, these animals are a boon to the efficiency of worldwide agriculture in that they allow us to get more human food and other products from the same amount of land.

There is another side to this story, however, having to do with the *loss* of food that occurs as we move up through the trophic levels. Recall that as a rough rule of thumb, 90 percent of the energy that is locked up in one trophic level is lost to the organisms in the next trophic level. If cattle and other domesticated animals were doing nothing but *foraging*—if they were being fed solely on the grass available in pastures—this would not be a matter of concern, because the grass is not useful to humans as a food source anyway. But in developed countries such as the United States,

much of the diet of domesticated animals comes from *grain* that is grown on farms. A large portion of this animal feed could go directly to human beings, but it instead passes through the trophic level of animals, with a predictable result: It takes 9 pounds of feed to produce 1 pound of beef ready for human consumption. What does this mean in practice? A harvest of 2,000 pounds of grain will feed five people for a year. Take roughly this same harvest, feed it to livestock, and then feed the *livestock* products to people, and you will feed only *one* person for a year.

It takes 9 pounds of feed to produce 1 pound of beef ready for human consumption.

This calculation takes on added importance when considering the scale of the grain-fed operation. In the feedlot, while being fattened for slaughter, an average steer consumes up to 2,700 pounds of grain. It may be apparent that such consumption adds up quickly; some 70 percent of the grain produced in the United States is fed to livestock. There are about 70 million cattle in the United States and Canada alone.

But does this mean that human hunger would be reduced if domestic animals were eliminated as a "middleman"? Not necessarily. In a simple calculation of calories-produced versus calories-needed, the world *already* produces enough food to feed all its people. The current problem, then, is one of food distribution, not food production. As an often-used phrase has it, "Hunger is real, scarcity is not." The burden that grain-fed animals pose may have to do with the future. As countries get richer, their human populations will eat more meat, which would mean less total food available for humans worldwide.

Fattening at the Feedlot
About 40,000 head of cattle are fed for meat production at this commercial feedlot in Imperial Valley, California.

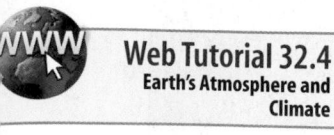

Web Tutorial 32.4
Earth's Atmosphere and Climate

small amounts, as do some other gases, such as argon and methane. After a transitional zone, the next layer above the troposphere is the **stratosphere**. Of greatest concern in it is a gas that reaches its greatest density at about 20 to 35 kilometers (13 to 21 miles) above sea level. The oxygen we breathe comes in the form of two oxygen molecules bonded together (O_2). When ultraviolet sunlight strikes O_2 in the stratosphere, however, it can put it in a form of three oxygen molecules bonded together (O_3). This is the gas known as **ozone**. Cre-

ated initially as a *product* of life—since atmospheric oxygen came from photosynthesis—this ozone layer ultimately came to protect life by blocking some 99 percent of the ultraviolet (UV) radiation the sun showers on the Earth. It was this blockage that allowed life to come onto land some 460 million years ago, and it is this blockage that protects life now. The UV radiation that pours from the sun can wreak havoc on living tissue, bringing about cancer and immune-system problems in people, and damaging vegetation as well.

The Worrisome Issue of Ozone Depletion

Given the importance of the ozone layer, it is sobering to contemplate how fragile it is. Some human-made chemical compounds have the effect of destroying stratospheric ozone, and such destruction went on unchecked for years until atmospheric chemists Sherwood Rowland and Mario Molina revealed, in 1974, that compounds called chlorofluorocarbons posed a direct threat to the ozone layer. Chlorofluorocarbons or **CFCs**—found at one time in spray cans, refrigerators, and plastic foams—are undoubtedly the most famous of the ozone-depleting compounds, but they are by no means the only chemicals that have this effect. Other harmful compounds include methyl bromide, which is used as a pesticide, notably on tomato and strawberry crops; and bromine, which is found in a group of fire-extinguishing chemicals.

The damage that these compounds have done to stratospheric ozone has brought about the spectacle of annual reports on how big the "ozone hole" is over the South Pole, along with a concern about a general thinning of the ozone layer. In 2000, the spring ozone hole grew to a record 11 million square miles—an area three times the size of the United States. So large was this hole that, for the first time, it extended over a center of human population, the city of Punta Arenas in southern Chile. The residents of this city thus joined life-forms in the Antarctic in being seasonally exposed to potentially harmful levels of ultraviolet radiation.

Despite the ominous nature of this news, the long-term outlook on ozone depletion actually is good. In an agreement signed in Montreal in 1987, many of the world's nations pledged to phase out production of ozone-depleting chemicals, and this agreement is working. Production of CFCs was banned in the United States even before the Montreal agreement was signed and has dropped dramatically throughout the world in recent years. Meanwhile, methyl bromide may be phased out in the United States by 2005, though this is not certain.

Critically, the reduction in the use of these compounds has brought about a reduction in the levels of ozone-depleting compounds in the atmosphere. As a consequence, while the ozone layer is still getting thinner, the *rate* of its thinning is slowing. Should this trend continue, it seems likely that the ozone layer will be restored, though this process may take decades.

The Worrisome Issue of Global Warming

A second environmental issue involving the atmosphere is that of global warming, which we've touched on a little already. The essential questions regarding this issue are straightforward: Is the Earth getting warmer? If so, to what degree is human activity responsible for this warming? And, if the Earth is warming, what consequences will this have? Put another way, what will a warmer Earth be like?

Is the Earth Getting Warmer?

At one time, all of these questions were contentious within the scientific community. In the last few years, however, near-unanimity seems to have been reached regarding one of them—*whether* the Earth is warming. Almost all parties are now agreed that Earth's surface temperature is indeed rising. It probably has increased by about 0.6° Celsius (or about a degree Fahrenheit) in the past century, with much of this increase coming in just the past 20 years. It's likely that, globally, the 1990s was the warmest decade since the middle of the nineteenth century. For the Northern Hemisphere, at least, the 1990s appear to have been the warmest decade in the last thousand years.

Is Human Activity Responsible?

This leads to the second question, which is whether human activity has caused this increase. Here, while there is still disagreement, a consensus seems to have emerged that the answer is yes: Human activity is at least partly to blame for global warming. In 2001, the United Nations Intergovernmental Panel on Climate Change (IPCC)—which received input from hundreds of scientists around the globe—issued a report stating "there is new and stronger evidence that most of the warming observed over the past 50 years is attributable to human activities." What activities are these? The burning of fossil fuels, such as coal and oil, and the deforestation of the Earth. Both activities put more carbon dioxide and other "greenhouse" gases into the atmosphere. Warming has resulted from this increase because greenhouse gases trap heat, as you'll see.

It's important to note that there are respected scientists who disagree with this view of global warming. From their perspective, such warming as has taken place may represent nothing more than the random temperature variations that occur on Earth over very long time scales. Under this view, society should not rush to reduce greenhouse gas emissions because it doesn't yet know whether these emissions have anything to do with global warming.

While conceding that this view is supported by some valid arguments, most experts have become persuaded that human activity is indeed playing a part in global warming. What makes them think so? If you look at **Figure 32.18**, you can see that a strong correlation exists between increasing temperatures and rising atmospheric carbon dioxide (CO_2) levels over the last 150 years. If you then look at **Figure 32.19**, you can see temperature trends in the Northern Hemisphere for a much longer period, the last thousand years. Note the strong uptick in temperature that took place begin-

ning after 1900, as civilization was becoming more industrialized, and the even more prominent upturn in the past few decades. This longer-term temperature trend is likewise consistent with longer-term CO_2 trends. The IPCC report notes that atmospheric concentration of CO_2 has increased by 31 percent since 1750 and that the Earth's current CO_2 concentration "has not been exceeded during the past 420,000 years and likely not during the past 20 million years."

A firm rule in science is that correlation is not causation; the fact that two trends are correlated does not mean that one caused the other—that rising CO_2 levels caused global warming, in this case. But by constructing theoretical models of what might be at play, IPCC scientists concluded that the most plausible explanation for the rise in Earth's temperature is that human activity has combined with natural forces, such as solar variation and volcanic activity, to produce the warming we have experienced.

What Is the Greenhouse Effect?

Why should the concentration of gases such as CO_2 have anything to do with a warmer planet? Sunlight that is not filtered out by ozone comes to Earth in the form of very energetic, short waves that can easily pass through the atmosphere (**see Figure 32.20**). Once this energy reaches the land and ocean, most of it is quickly transformed into heat that does all the things you've just read about: warms the planet, drives the water cycle, and so forth. This heat ultimately is radiated back toward space. But heat is not short-wave radiation; it is *long*-wave radiation, and it can be *trapped* by certain compounds, among them carbon dioxide and methane.

What Are the Likely Consequences of Global Warming?

All of this leads to the third question that frames the issue of global warming: What will its consequences be? The 1-degree rise recorded so far in Earth's temperature may seem tiny, but consider the effects that *already* appear to have been caused by this small increase. Arctic sea-ice has shrunk by about 6 percent since 1978; ice cover on lakes and rivers in some northern latitudes now lasts about two weeks less than it did 150 years ago; in the European Alps, some plant species have been migrating to higher altitudes at the rate of 4 meters per decade; in Europe and North America migratory birds are now arriving earlier in the spring and leaving later in the fall; and general snow coverage in the Northern Hemisphere appears to have shrunk by 10 percent since 1972. Glaciers around the world, from the Himalayas to the Andes, are shrinking because of

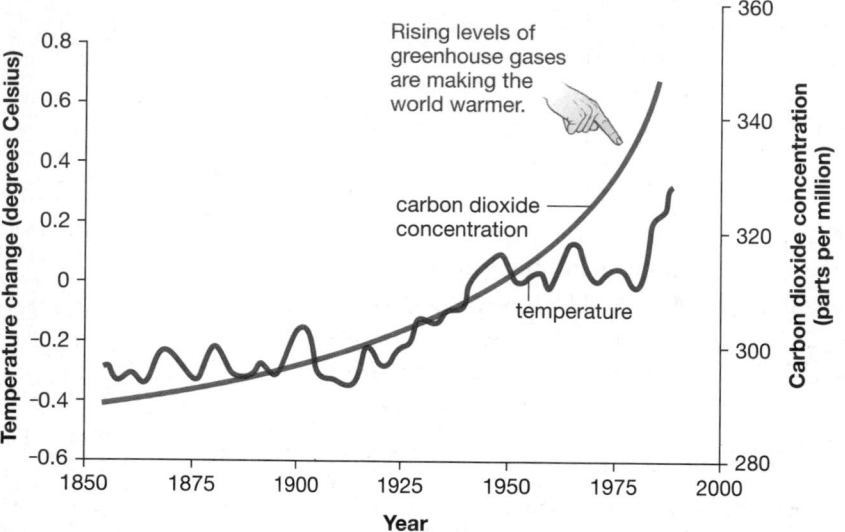

Figure 32.18
Global Warming
Atmospheric carbon dioxide concentration is increasing, and global temperature appears to be as well. It is difficult to be certain that the CO_2 increase is driving the increase in temperature because, over long periods of time, there are great natural fluctuations in global temperature. Most experts have now concluded, however, that rising levels of greenhouse gases such as CO_2 are making the world warmer.

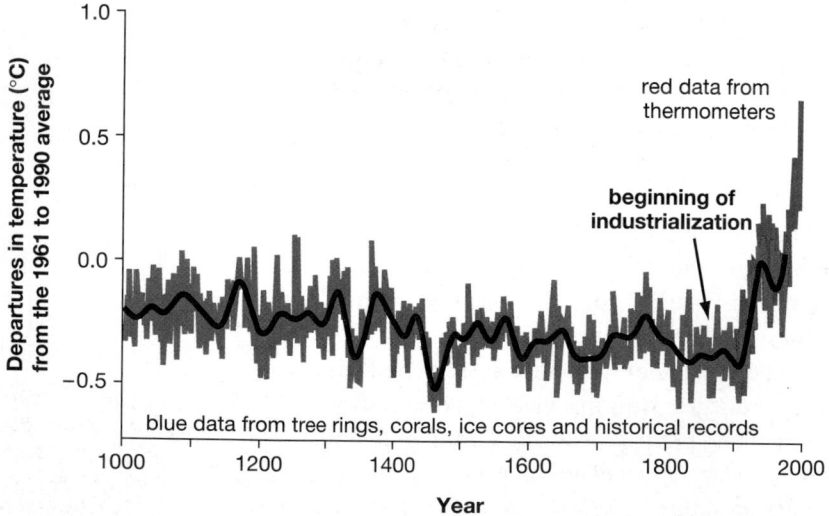

Figure 32.19
Earth's Temperature during the Past 1,000 Years
Using data from such sources as tree rings and ice cores, scientists have estimated average temperatures in the Northern Hemisphere over the last 1,000 years. They concluded that the increase in Earth's temperature in the twentieth century seems to have been greater than the increase that occurred in any other century during the last 1,000 years. Further, the 1990s appear to have been the warmest decade—and 1998 the warmest single year—over the past 1,000 years. (Adapted from *The Third Assessment Report of Working Group I of the Intergovernmental Panel on Climate Change* (IPCC) 2001, *Summary for Policymakers*, Figure 1b.)

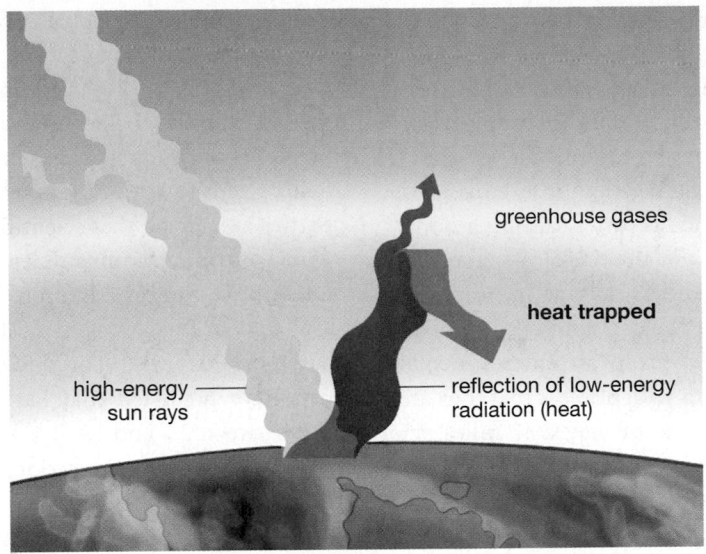

Figure 32.20
The Greenhouse Effect
The high-energy rays of the sun can easily penetrate the layer of gases in the troposphere. However, the lower-energy radiation (heat) that reflects from Earth's surface cannot penetrate the layer of gases as easily. Carbon dioxide and methane thus take on the role of glass panes in a greenhouse: They let solar energy in, but they retain a good deal of heat.

higher temperatures (**see Figure 32.21**). Meanwhile, the ice cap on top of Africa's Mount Kilimanjaro is melting at such a rapid rate that it is expected to disappear in the next 15 to 20 years.

Given such changes, if the temperature increase of the past hundred years were merely repeated in the *next* hundred years, we might worry about what is in store for the Earth. But IPCC research has predicted an increase not of 1 degree Fahrenheit for the coming century, but of 2.7 to 10 degrees. What would such a change mean? A picture of total calamity might come to mind, but the effects actually stand to be mixed. A second IPCC report notes that crop yields in some mid-latitude regions probably will increase because of the greater warmth, as would timber yields in

some areas. More water might become available in areas, such as parts of Southeast Asia, where water is scarce now. On the other hand, low-lying parts of the globe may see entirely too *much* water, since melting polar ice is likely to cause a rise in sea levels that stands to displace tens of millions of coastal residents. Insect-borne diseases, such as malaria, can be expected to move both north and south from equatorial regions into formerly temperate areas. Australia and New Zealand are expected to experience a drying trend. Crop yields in current warm-weather regions can be expected to fall. In general, it is the warmer-weather regions of the Earth—and the mostly underdeveloped countries in them—that stand to lose the most from a warmer Earth.

(a) The Qori Kalis glacier 1978

(b) The Qori Kalis glacier 2000

Figure 32.21
Warming Planet, Disappearing Glaciers
Global warming is melting glaciers around the world. Peru's Quelccaya ice cap, in the southern Andes, has shrunk by at least 20 percent since 1963. One of the main glaciers flowing from the cap, Qori Kalis, is shown here as it existed in 1978 and then in 2000. A 10-acre lake now exists where the glacier once extended. Its rate of retreat has reached 155 meters or 509 feet per year. This is three times greater than its rate of shrinkage from 1995 to 1998.

Global Warming and Societal Choices

One obvious way to combat global warming is to cut back on emissions of greenhouse gases. Any worldwide effort to do this would have to involve the United States, since it is responsible for about 20 percent of the world's greenhouse emissions. Reducing such emissions is easier said than done, however. To get an idea of the trade-offs involved, consider the question of gas mileage in American cars. More than half of the cars sold in the United States today are SUVs. From an environmental perspective, the problem with SUVs is that they are required to get an average of only 20.7 miles per gallon, as opposed to 27.7 mpg for passenger cars. This makes a huge difference in greenhouse emissions. The U.S. Environmental Protection Agency calculates that a vehicle getting 20 mpg will, over its lifetime, bring about the emission of an additional 15 *tons* of greenhouse gases compared to a vehicle that gets 25 mpg. If the answer to global warming is to impose a "carbon tax" on vehicles that fail to achieve a certain level of fuel efficiency, which politician is going to tell half the car owners in America that they need to start paying more for their cars? Alternatively, what about simply requiring better fuel efficiency from the cars that are produced? Well, to grasp the sensitivities involved, consider what has actually happened with SUVs. In 2002, the Department of Transportation mandated that SUVs *will* have to get better mileage—1.5 more miles per gallon, starting in the 2007 model year.

As another measure of the tension between global warming and economics, the United States was a party to a 1997 treaty, the Kyoto Protocol, under which 38 developed nations committed themselves to reducing their greenhouse gas emissions. But such dire economic predictions followed the signing of the treaty that the U.S. Senate never ratified it and, in 2001, President Bush decided to withdraw from it altogether. More recently, the Bush administration's primary response to global warming has been to call for additional study of it.

But is this the right approach? Many environmental scientists believe that the current evidence on global warming is strong enough that the United States needs to act on the issue, not just study it. All parties are agreed that scientific information about global warming is incomplete. Given this, society must make choices based on the best information available. In effect, society must make a series of *bets* based on this information. Recall that IPCC scientists have predicted that Earth's temperature will rise between 2.7 and 10 degrees in the coming century, barring corrective action. So, as a society, how do we bet—that scientists know *enough* that it is prudent to assume this will happen? Or do we bet that the uncertainties are so great we can just wait and see? Do we bet that, even if human-caused global warming is taking place, its consequences won't be particularly harmful? Or do we bet that the consequences may be so extreme that the only wise course is to curb production of greenhouse gases? There are no easy choices in this issue, but neither is there a way to avoid making decisions. Choosing not to act is itself a decision.

Earth's Climate: Why Are Some Areas Wet and Some Dry, Some Hot and Some Cold?

Did you ever look at a globe of the Earth and wonder why it is tilted? Earth exists in space, after all, so what could it be tilted against? When we say that a rod stuck in the ground is tilted, we mean that it is not *perpendicular* to the ground. Here, of course, we're thinking of the ground as a flat surface—a plane. Earth, too, can be viewed as existing on a plane, in this case the plane of its orbit around the sun. (We generally think of this orbit as looking like a large hula hoop with the sun as a yellow ball in the middle.) Now think of the spherical Earth on this plane as having a rod sticking through it in the form of its north-south axis—the imaginary line that runs from the North Pole straight through to the South Pole. The critical thing is that this rod does not stick straight up and down with respect to the plane of the Earth's orbit; it is *tilted*, at an angle of 23.5°. This tilt dictates a good deal about Earth's climate, and Earth's climate dictates a great deal about life on Earth. Once again, in other words, the sun determines the basic conditions for life.

You can see the effects of Earth's tilt in **Figure 32.22**: In June, our Northern Hemisphere tilts toward the sun, while in January it tilts away from it. Thus the sun's rays strike us more directly in June, and the days are warmer (and longer)

Figure 32.22
Earth's Tilt and the Seasons
The Northern Hemisphere gets more sunlight in June and less in January, while the reverse is true for the Southern Hemisphere. This is the reason for seasonal climate variations over large portions of the globe.

23.5°

vernal equinox
(March 21–22)

Northern
Hemisphere

Southern
Hemisphere

sun

summer solstice
(June 21–22)

winter solstice
(December 21–22)

autumnal equinox
(September 22–23)

than days in January. The angle at which the sun's rays strike a given portion of the Earth is very important. Relative to, say, Brazil, sunlight strikes the Arctic at an indirect or "oblique" angle. Thus, the far north gets less of the solar energy that powers photosynthesis.

The Circulation of the Atmosphere and Its Relation to Rain

The variation in temperature caused by these sunlight differences is the most important factor in the *circulation* of Earth's atmosphere. Near the equator Earth simply gets more warmth and, critically, warm air *rises*. Warm air also can retain more moisture than cold air. You've seen an example of this whenever you've looked at the beads of "sweat" that form on the outside of a cold glass in summer. Moisture-laden warm air comes into contact with the cooler air immediately around the glass; thus cooled, the air cannot hold as much moisture and releases it onto the glass.

This same thing happens with the warm air that rises on both sides of the equator. Because of the heat of the tropics, air is rising in quantity from the tropical oceans; because this air is warm, it is carrying with it a great deal of moisture. The air cools as it rises, however, and then drops much of its moisture on the tropics, which is why they're so wet.

Following this a step further, this volume of air is now cooler, drier, and moving toward the poles in both directions from the equator (**see Figure 32.23**). At about 30° north and south of the equator, it descends, warming as it drops and actually absorbing moisture *from* the land. The land will be dry at these latitudes because this is where the dry, hot air descends.

The air that has descended now flows in two directions from the 30° point. In the Northern Hemisphere this means north toward the North Pole and south toward the equator. Traveling at a fairly low alti-

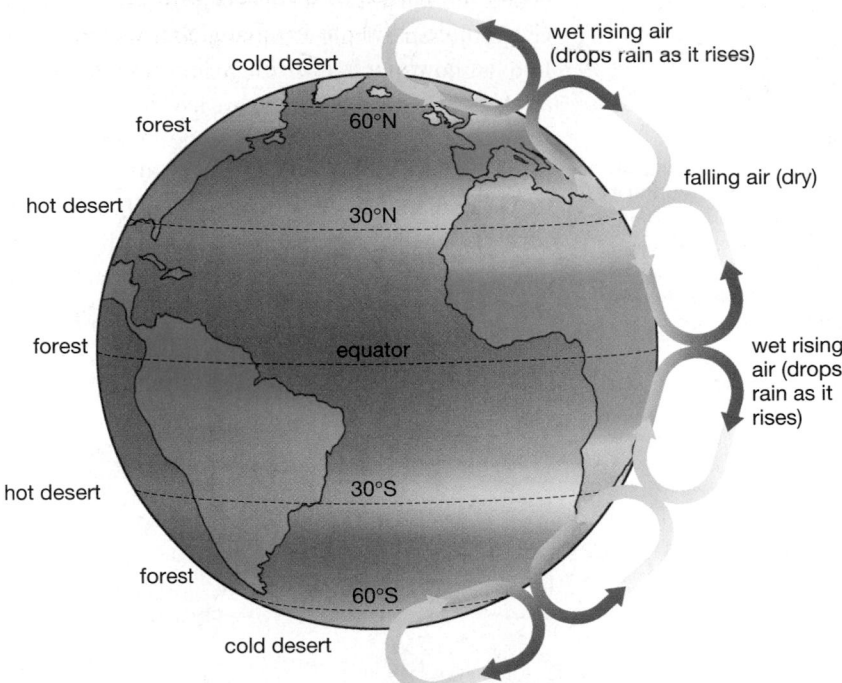

tude, this air eventually picks up moisture, rises, and deposits its moisture, this time at about 60° north and near the equator, with the same events happening at the same locations in the Southern Hemisphere.

What you get from this rising and falling is what you see in Figure 32.23: A set of interrelated "circulation cells" of moving air, each existing all the way around the globe at its latitude, and each acting like a conveyor belt that is dropping rain on the Earth where it rises but drying the Earth where it descends.

The Impact of Earth's Circulation Cells

The full meaning of this becomes obvious only when you look at a map such as the one in **Figure 32.24** (or better yet, a globe). Draw your finger across the equatorial latitude on the map and look at how much green there is—Southeast Asia, equatorial Africa, the Amazon. This is no surprise, because we

Figure 32.23
Earth's Atmospheric Circulation Cells
Because the Earth receives its most direct sunlight at the equator, this region is warm—and warm air holds moisture and rises. This air moves north and south from the equator, cooling as it rises, and then loses its moisture as rain, with the result that the land and ocean immediately north and south of the equator get lots of rain. As the now-dry air moves farther north and south, it cools and sinks again at about 30° in both hemispheres. Thus, the land at these latitudes tends to be dry. Two other bands of circulation cells exist at higher latitudes, operating under the same principles.

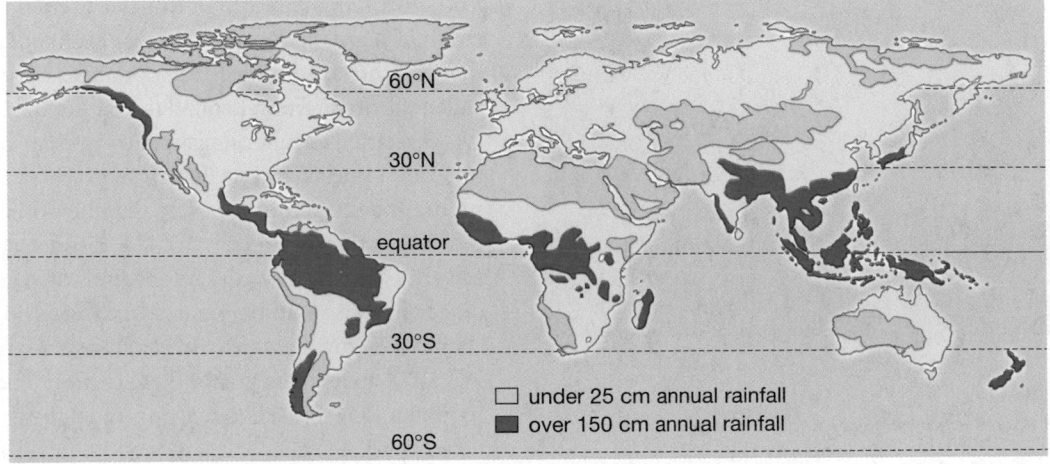

Figure 32.24
Earth's Atmospheric Circulation Cells and Precipitation
The wettest regions of the Earth lie along the equator, while the driest regions lie along the latitudes 30° N and S. Compare these regions to the circulation cells shown in Figure 32.23. The variations of rainfall patterns within cells are explained by factors such as the presence of mountain ranges.

expect the equator to be wet and green. Now, howev-er, do the same thing at the dry 30° north latitude. Look at how much desert there is at this latitude all around the globe—it's where we find the Sahara, the Arabian, and the Sonoran deserts, among others. And there's more desert territory at 30° south, with the Australian desert and Africa's Namib. From this you can see that the climatic fate of Earth's various regions is largely written in our globe's large-scale wind patterns.

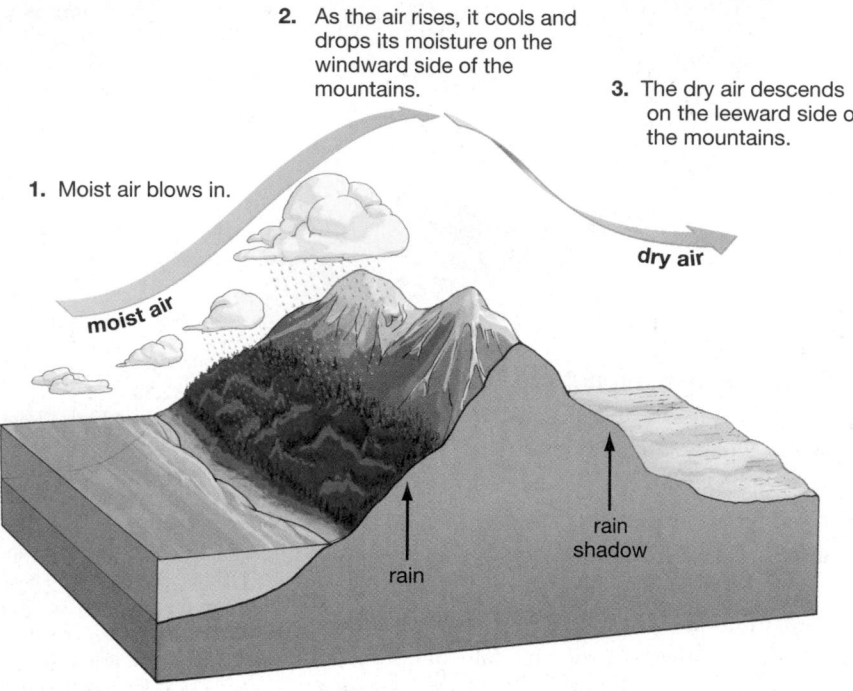

2. As the air rises, it cools and drops its moisture on the windward side of the mountains.

3. The dry air descends on the leeward side of the mountains.

1. Moist air blows in.

dry air

moist air

rain

rain shadow

Figure 32.26
Line of Transition
In Alaska's Denali National Park, a region of forested taiga vegetation gives way to a region of grassy tun-dra vegetation in a fairly abrupt way.

Mountain Chains Affect Precipitation Patterns

Latitude doesn't tell the whole story about precipi-tation on Earth, however. Mountain ranges force air upward and it too cools as it rises, dropping its moisture on the windward side of the range. Then the air descends on the opposite (leeward) side of the range, only this time it is dry air and is thus *picking up* moisture from the ground, rather than depositing it (**see Figure 32.25**). A dramatic exam-ple of this "rain shadow" effect can be seen on the Pacific Coast of the United States in southern Ore-gon, where the western side of the Cascade Moun-tains is lush with greenery all year round, while the basin below the eastern slopes is a desert.

Beyond this, we know that it's possible to be in a warm latitude, such as that of Ecuador in South America, and still be very cold—if you go to the top of the Ecuadorian Andes. As altitude increases, tem-perature drops, in other words. The changes in cli-mate that occur as you move from flatland to mountain peak are similar to the changes that occur as you move from the equator to one of the poles.

The Importance of Climate to Life

The factors you have just reviewed are among the most important in shaping the large-scale **climates** or average weather conditions we find on Earth. It's obvious that climate has a great deal of influence on life, since we never see polar bears in Panama or monkeys in Montana, but this influence is even greater than you might think. Looking over the globe, you see different forms of dominant vegeta-tion in different areas—grassland in America's Great Plains, rain forest in northern Brazil. So strongly does climate affect this pattern that Earth's vegetation regions essentially are defined by Earth's climate regions. Far in Canada's north, there is a fairly distinct boundary at which Canada's vast coniferous forest gives way to the mat-like vegeta-tion called *tundra*. North of this line there is tundra; south of it are the forests. What is this line? In sum-mer it is the far southern reach of a mass of cold air called the arctic frontal zone (**see Figure 32.26**).

Vegetative formations generally overlap one an-other to a greater extent than is seen with Canada's tundra and coniferous forest, so that the closer we get to a vegetation boundary the less distinct it looks. Nevertheless, there are discrete regions of vegetation on Earth whose boundaries are largely determined by climate—particularly by temperature and rainfall. Vegetative exceptions *within* these regions tend to be mountains, whose climates can vary greatly from base to peak.

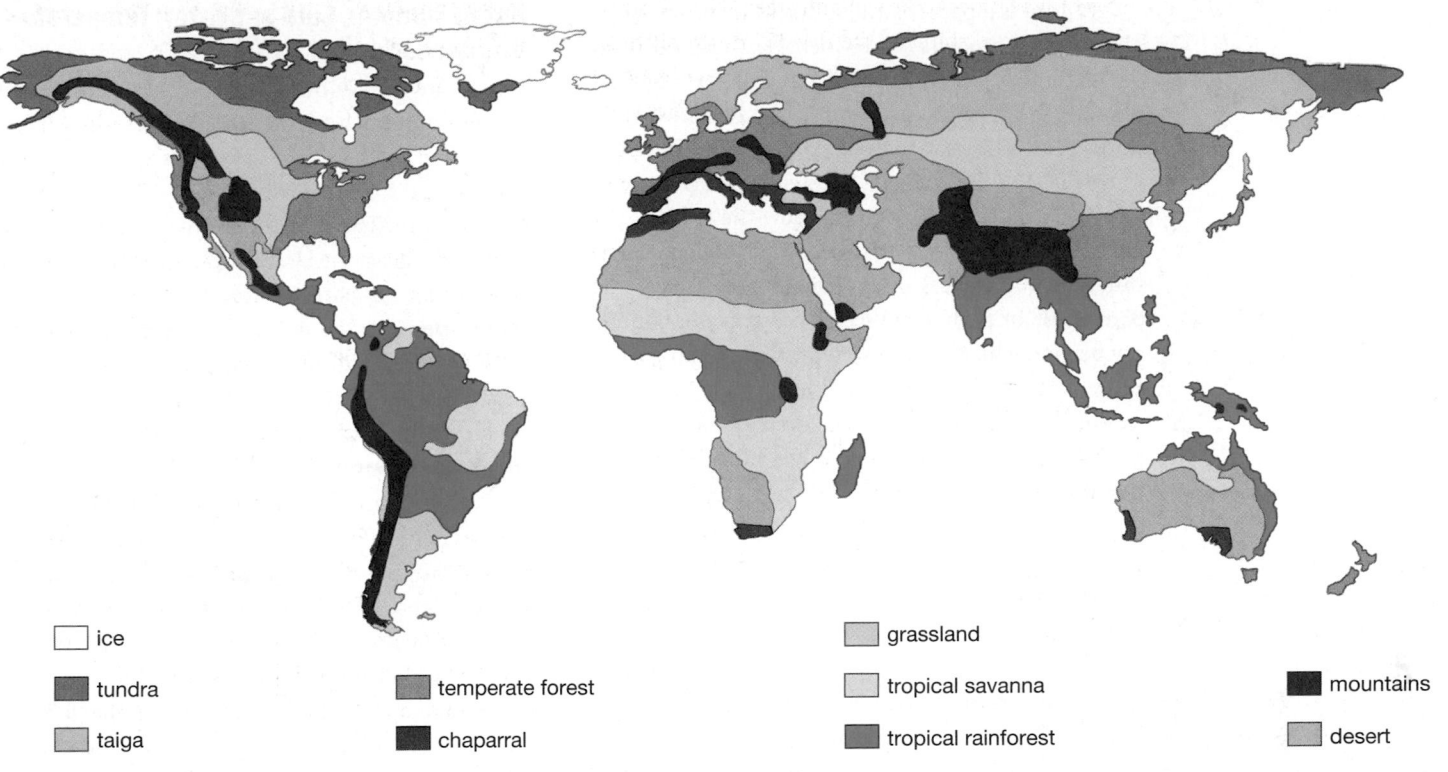

☐ ice		☐ grassland
■ tundra	■ temperate forest	☐ tropical savanna
☐ taiga	■ chaparral	■ tropical rainforest

■ mountains

☐ desert

32.5 Earth's Biomes

When these large, land vegetation formations are looked at as *ecosystems*, complete with animals, fungi, nutrient cycling, and all the rest, they go by the name **biomes**. Grasslands, whether found in Russia or in the American Midwest, are ecologically very similar to one another and thus constitute one type of biome. The tropical rain forests found in Africa, South America, and Asia constitute another. The world can be divided into any number of different biome types—this is a human classification system overlaid on nature—but six are recognized as the minimum: tundra, taiga, temperate deciduous forest, temperate grassland, desert, and tropical rain forest. Polar ice and mountains often are recognized as separate biomes as well, as is another grassland variation, the savanna, found most famously in equatorial Africa. There is also chaparral, a shrub-dominated vegetation formation found in "Mediterranean" climates such as those on California's coast. See **Figure 32.27** for an overview of locations of these biome types throughout the globe.

The fact that two biomes are of the same type does not mean that they are identical. Two areas that are broadly the same in climate can end up with some significant differences in life-forms. Let's look briefly now at each of Earth's major biome types and then at its aquatic ecosystems.

Cold and Lying Low: Tundra

Along with polar ice, **tundra** is the biome of the far north, stretching in a vast, mostly frozen ring around the northern rim of the world. So inaccessible is tundra that the average person may never have heard of it, yet it occupies about a fourth of Earth's land surface. The word *tundra* comes from a Finnish word that means "treeless plain," and the description is apt. Its flat terrain stretches out for mile after mile with little change in the vegetational pattern of low shrubs, mosses, lichens, grasses, and the grass-like sedges (**see Figure 32.28**).

Figure 32.27
Distribution of Biomes across the Earth

Figure 32.28
Tundra
Grizzly bears forage for fall berries in Alaska in the shrub-and-grass biome known as the tundra.

Tundra is a paradoxical biome in that it averages about 25 centimeters (or 10 inches) of rain per year, which almost puts it in the desert category. Yet it is marshy in summer, with numerous shallow lakes dotting its surface. How can both things be true? Once the summer rain falls, it essentially has no place to go. No more than a meter below the surface, the ground is permanently frozen down to a depth of as much as 500 meters or a quarter-mile. This is the **permafrost**, or permanent ice, which acts as a boundary beyond which neither water nor roots can go. Because water cannot drain far into the soil, it sits on top of the tundra in summer, which makes for the bogs and small lakes. The low-lying tundra vegetation makes the most of a short growing season—lasting as little as 50 days—by producing a year's worth of food through photosynthesis in only a few weeks.

The tundra has a good deal of animal life, particularly in the summer when migrating animals move north to feed on the vegetation. Large mammals such as caribou and musk oxen live there. Arctic hares and foxes are year-round residents, as are arctic lemmings—herbivores that are key to much of the tundra's animal food web. (Contrary to popular belief, these lemmings do not commit suicide by jumping off cliffs. They merely *migrate* in great numbers at certain times.)

Northern Forests: Taiga

The **taiga** or boreal (northern) forest includes the enormous expanse of coniferous trees mentioned earlier that juts up against the tundra. Conditions are still fairly dry and cold, and the growing season is short in this northern biome, but in all three respects the taiga is less severe than the tundra. Note in Figure 32.27 that, as with tundra, taiga is found almost solely in the Northern Hemisphere. This is so because there is little land in the Southern Hemisphere at the extreme latitudes of these biomes. This in turn is related to a more general point, which is that most of Earth's landmass is in the Northern Hemisphere. There are 100 million square kilometers of land north of the equator, but only 47 million square kilometers south of it.

The taiga is a model of species uniformity as only a few types of trees—spruce, fir, and pine—are the ecological dominants, but they are present in great numbers. The taiga's vegetation supports lots of animals, including large mammals such as moose, bear, and caribou (**see Figure 32.29**). When thinking of the fur trade, you might have in mind some freezing, coniferous territory in the far north. The taiga turns out to be it. Sables, minks, beavers, arctic hares, wolverines; this harsh biome has an abundance of these furred creatures.

Hot in Summer, Cold in Winter: Temperate Deciduous Forest

Temperate deciduous forest is a biome familiar throughout much of the United States, since it exists roughly from the Great Lakes nearly to the Gulf of Mexico and from the western Great Lakes to the Atlantic Ocean. The pine forests that cover large parts of the southeastern United States generally are considered to be part of the temperate deciduous biome because the pines are a successional stage *leading to* deciduous forest. (Remember, from Chapter 31, the concept of ecological succession, under which species in a community are replaced by other species over time until a final, stable state is reached.) Meanwhile, the warm Gulf Coast is not temperate deciduous forest per se, but a variant on it called *temperate evergreen forest*. Much of Europe and eastern China fit within the temperate deciduous classification, though large parts of Europe have few forests left, and China has very little.

Temperate deciduous forests are the forests of maple and beech and oak and hickory (**Figure 32.30**). The "deciduous" in the name refers to trees that exhibit a pattern of loss of leaves in the fall and regrowth of them in the spring. Trees do not dominate these

Figure 32.29
Taiga
Alaskan caribou in winter in the northern-forest biome known as taiga.

forests to the extent they do the taiga, however. Making use of the good soil, a robust "understory" of woody and herbaceous plants will spring up on the floor of the deciduous forest. Some of this activity occurs early in the growing season, before the trees have "leafed out" and blocked the sunlight. Temperate forests grow where there is plenty of water—between 75 and 200 centimeters (or 30 to 78 inches) per year, with the lower amount being three times what the tundra gets. It's worth noting that while the tundra has no reptiles or amphibians and the taiga has only a few, the temperate deciduous forest has an environment that is wet and warm enough to support a variety of both animal forms.

When Europeans first came to North America in significant numbers, in the seventeenth century, there probably were more than a billion acres of forest in what would become the United States. By 1907, about 250 million acres of this forest had been cleared, primarily for agricultural use. The temperate deciduous forest cover in the Eastern United States reached its lowest level about 1860 after which it began to rebound, because of the westward movement of farming into the Midwest. Between 1950 and 1980, forested land in the United States as a whole actually increased by about 7.5 million acres.

Dry but Sometimes Very Fertile: Grassland

There is an irregular line in western Indiana that forms the boundary between deciduous forest and prairie. What is "prairie" in the United States is known as "steppes" in Russia, "pampas" in Argentina, and "veldt" in South Africa. These are all names for the biome that ecologists call *temperate grassland* (**Figure 32.31**).

Looked at one way, grasslands are what often literally lie between forests and deserts. Whereas the precipitation range for deciduous forests is from 75 to 200 centimeters per year (30 to 78 inches), for grassland the range is from 25 to 100 centimeters per year (10 to 39 inches). The North American grassland has its own internal division based on the amount of rainfall. It ranges from tall-grass prairie in Illinois to a drier mixed-grass prairie that begins at about the middle of Kansas and Nebraska—this is where the Great Plains begin—to a short-grass prairie that lies in the rain shadow of the Rocky Mountains. (This same tall-grass/short-grass gradient exists in the

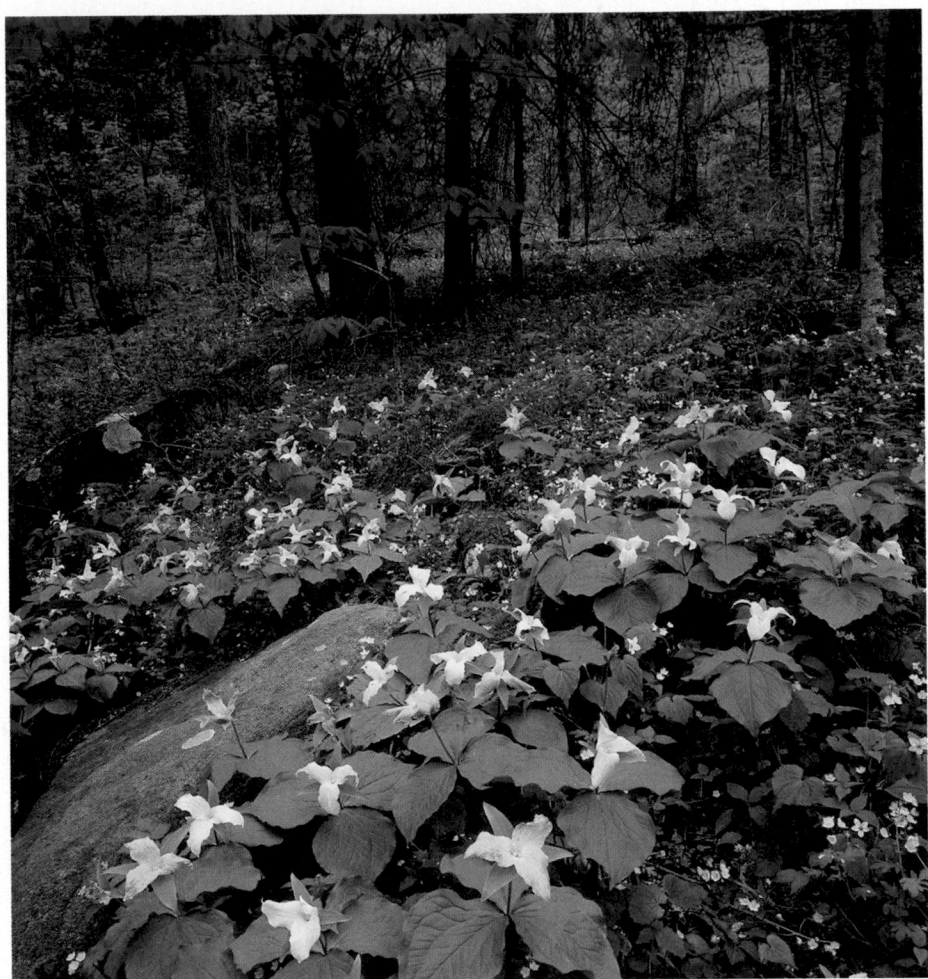

Figure 32.30
Temperate Deciduous Forest
Plenty of water and seasonally warm temperatures lead to abundant plant and animal life in the biome known as temperate deciduous forest. This forest is in the Great Smoky Mountains National Park, which straddles Tennessee and North Carolina.

Figure 32.31
Temperate Grassland
A white-tailed deer fawn stands among the grass and flowers in a tall-grass prairie in Missouri. Tall-grass is one kind of vegetation found in the biome known as temperate grassland.

steppes of Asia, only there the gradient runs from North to South.) Other American grassland areas can be found in California's Central Valley and eastern Washington and Oregon.

A type of *tropical* grassland, the **tropical savanna**, exists in Australia, Africa, and South America. Tropical savanna is characterized by seasonal drought, small changes in the generally warm temperatures throughout the year, and stands of naturally occurring trees that punctuate the grassland. This is the homeland of many of the great mammals we associate with Africa, such as lions and zebras.

When Europeans first beheld the American grasslands, they could scarcely believe what they saw, A territory that had essentially no trees, but instead a sea of grasses that could grow up to 3 meters or 10 feet tall in the wetter tall-grass prairie. Prairie soil turned out to be some of the most fertile on Earth, however, and that fact eventually spelled the end of natural prairie in the United States and most of the rest of the world. Almost all the tall-grass and mixed-grass prairie in the United States eventually was plowed under for cultivation, while the short-grass prairie is now used for crops and cattle grazing. Prior to the coming of Europeans, 22 million acres of Illinois was prairie; today that figure stands at slightly more than 2,000 acres. From the former prairie, however, the United States feeds itself and some of world

outside its borders. Illinois and Kansas and Nebraska are still grasslands, but the grasses that grow there now are not the native big bluestem or needlegrass; they are corn and wheat.

Chaparral: Rainy Winters, Dry Summers

Chaparral is not grassland, but instead is a biome dominated by evergreen shrub vegetation that is dotted with pine and scrub oak trees. Chaparral is found in areas that have a so-called Mediterranean climate. There are five of these areas in the world, all them very similar in appearance. One of them is the Mediterranean basin itself; then there is southwestern Australia, central Chile, a small part of western South Africa, and parts of coastal California. What these areas have in common is that they are on the west coast of a landmass. Thus they lie in the path of ocean winds that bring wet, mild winters and very dry summers.

The Challenge of Water: Deserts

Deserts are defined in various ways, one of them being: an area in which rainfall is less than 25 centimeters or 10 inches per year. Note that temperature has nothing to do with this definition. Thus, there can be temperate deserts (the Mojave in Southern California), cold deserts (the Gobi in China) and hot-weather deserts, like the one in **Figure 32.32**. There are areas in some deserts, such as Death Valley in California, that achieve the dubious distinction of having very little life in them, but this is rare. Most deserts harbor a variety of lifeforms, and what we think of as desert can shade imperceptibly into dry grassland.

Precipitation is not only low in the desert, it is sporadic; that is, most of the moisture a desert gets will come in just a few days during the year. Given this, desert life has relentlessly been shaped by one overriding requirement: Collect water and then conserve it. The flowering plant grouping called bromeliads have a species, *Tillandsia straminea*, that is blown around on the deserts of coastal Peru much like a dead tumbleweed; only this is a living plant, nearly rootless, that gets all its moisture from *fog* that it is able to absorb.

Desert animals are no less remarkable in this respect. The kangaroo rat (genus *Dipodomys*) can be found in many parts of the American Southwest. It comes out of its underground burrow only at night when temperatures fall, it has no sweat glands, and it generally does not drink standing water (there being almost none available). Instead, the kangaroo rat gets by on the water produced by metabolizing the seeds it eats.

Figure 32.32
Desert
When water gets sparse, life does too. Shown is a desert biome in Monument Valley, Arizona.

Lush Life, Now Threatened: Tropical Rain Forests

Many people have an idea that the Earth's **tropical rain forests** are important, but they're not quite sure why. There are two main reasons. First, along with coral reefs and algal beds, they are the most productive biome type in the world, meaning they produce more biomass per square meter of territory than any other. Second, no other ecosystem can touch them in terms of species diversity. As noted earlier, for mile after mile in the taiga, trees might be limited to one or two species. In the tropical forests of the Amazon, more than *three hundred* species of trees have been identified in a single hectare of land, which is about 2.5 acres. In Chapter 31, you read about a researcher who found an estimated 1,700 species of beetle in one tree in the Peruvian rain forest. Indeed, half of all the identified plant and animal species on Earth reside in tropical rain forests. This despite the fact that, compared to the other biomes you've looked at, they don't occupy a lot of territory: about 7 percent of the Earth's surface.

The problem, as most people know, is that the rain forests are disappearing—significant portions of them are either being burned down or cut down. The period of great temperate forest loss came before the twentieth century, but we are living in the period of great tropical forest loss. How significant is the reduction? Satellite imaging of humid tropical forests indicates that, between 1990 and 1997, about 14 million acres were lost each year—an area that is about twice the size of Maryland. South America has what is by far the world's largest tropical rain forest, the Amazon Basin Forest that runs from Colombia through Bolivia and at one point nearly from the Atlantic to the Pacific Ocean. Significant rain forests also can be found in Central America, equatorial Africa, and regions of Southeast Asia near the equator. In recent years, the greatest rain-forest losses have occurred in Asia, but in 2002, an estimated 6.4 million forest acres were burned or cut in the Brazilian Amazon. (For a different perspective on these kinds of environmental issues, see "Good News about the Environment" on the next page.)

Poor Soil, Bountiful Covering

The rain forests are lands of rain and stable, warm temperatures (**see Figure 32.33**). The norm for rainfall is between 200 to 450 centimeters or about 78 to 175 inches a year, but some areas get up to 1,000 centimeters annually, which is 390 inches.

You've seen that much of the richness of the temperate grasslands can be found in their soil. In the tropical rain forest, almost all the richness is on display above ground (much of it 20 to 40 meters above ground in the extensive forest "canopy"). The rain

Figure 32.33
Tropical Rain Forest
Abundant rain and warm weather mean abundant growth and a great diversity in life-forms in the biome known as the tropical rain forest. Shown is a lowland rain forest on the Segama River in Borneo.

forest has such a large and efficient group of detritivores that organic material dropping to the forest floor is decomposed by them and absorbed almost immediately by plant roots rather than by the surrounding soil. This means the soil never gets built up; it is nutrient-poor and often acidic.

How can this be squared with this biome's fantastic productivity? Note what is going on in the example: The nutrients are simply bypassing the soil, going from plant to detritivore and back to plant. Some rain-forest trees have roots that grow *up*, onto tree trunks, rather than down into the soil, giving them the ability to absorb nutrients from the water that washes down the trunks. Farmers on the Illinois prairie could plow under the natural vegetation and grow crops there because perhaps 90 percent of the prairie's nutrients are held in the soil. What happens, though, when a rain forest is cleared for agriculture? The nutrient-poor land will support a year or two of crops and then that's it: No more rain forest, no more crops. (The new crops don't build up the soil, because nutrients are leached out by the heavy rains.) With the loss of rain forest comes the loss of habitat for its animals, resulting in a greatly elevated rate of extinction in this biome.

32.6 Life in the Water: Aquatic Ecosystems

Marine Ecosystems

We turn now from life on land to life in the water. Because we humans are land creatures, it might be good to get our bearings by thinking about how one

Good News about the Environment

A sense of gloom about the environment may arise from between the lines of these pages as the list of current or potential environmental problems piles up: global warming, nitrogen buildup, overuse of water resources, tropical rain-forest destruction. These are real problems, but their existence should not blind us to the fact that there has been a great deal of good news about the environment in the last 30 years, much of it showing how effective government can be when prodded into action by its citizens.

If there was a time for unrestrained gloom about the environment in the United States, it probably would have been in the late 1960s, when the country had plenty of endangered species but no Endangered Species Act; when levels of smog in Los Angeles were almost twice what they are now; when there was plenty of household trash to be recycled, but almost no recycling going on; when only a third of the bodies of water in the country were safe for fishing and swimming, whereas today two-thirds are.

As a symbol of change, consider Cleveland, Ohio, whose Cuyahoga River was so polluted in 1969 that it *caught fire*, while southwestern Lake Erie, into which the Cuyahoga flows, was essentially a dead zone for fish during the late summer. The lake came to this low state in part because of the nearly 80 metric tons of phosphorus—then regularly added to washing detergents—that were dumped into it each day. That figure has now been reduced by perhaps 85 percent, and Lake Erie is biologically very active and a major freshwater fishery. Meanwhile the Cuyahoga River has been cleaned up enough that an area near the river's mouth has been transformed

Environmentalism has entered not only our lawbooks but, more important, our consciousness.

into an entertainment district complete with restaurant tables near the water's edge—not bad for a small river running through a big city. This does not mean that the Cuyahoga now looks as it did when Europeans first saw it; toxic sediment from the river, mostly the legacy of the past, still flows into Lake Erie. But if we look at the *trend*, there is no doubt that things have gotten better in Cleveland, not worse.

This same thing could be said of most of the United States. Simply put, there has been a profound change with respect to the environment over the past 35 years. From pollution controls to species protection to personal recycling, environmentalism has entered not only our lawbooks but, more important, our consciousness. When populations of Atlantic swordfish were observed to be declining in the late 1990s, a campaign titled "Give Swordfish a Break" was organized that quickly enlisted 27 top New York chefs. What could chefs do about swordfish populations? They pledged to take swordfish off their restaurants' menus. It was government action that brought the Atlantic swordfish population back to healthy levels, but initial public awareness of the swordfish campaign came about because of *personal* sensitivity to the environment—in this case, the sensitivity of a group of American chefs. And sensitivity to the environment has grown not just in America but in most developed countries. The cleanup of Lake Erie required the cooperation of the United States and Canada; the heartening trend in preservation of the Earth's ozone layer is the product of an international agreement.

None of this is to say that mechanisms are in place such that we need not worry about the environment. Far from it; largely because of the growth in human population and the greater per-capita use of natural resources, the environment is threatened on thousands of fronts and will remain so as far out as we can see into the future. But the record of the last 30 years is not just one of environmental loss; it is one of great environmental accomplishment as well. Perhaps the period's most important lesson is that there is nothing inevitable about environmental degradation. Concerned, hard-working people have made a great deal of difference in this issue.

Back to Healthy Numbers
Populations of Atlantic swordfish (*Xiaphas gladius*) were severely depleted by the late 1990s. A campaign spearheaded by environmentalists spurred governmental action that brought the swordfish numbers back to healthy levels by 2002—just three years after an international conservation program was put in place.

kind of aquatic environment, the ocean, can be divided up in terms of the life in it. The ocean's **coastal zone** extends from the point on the shore where the ocean's waves reach at high tide to a point out at sea where an ocean-floor formation called the continental shelf drops off (**see Figure 32.34**). Beyond this point there is the *open sea*. Within the coastal zone, there is an area bordered on one side by the ocean's low-tide mark and on the other by its high-tide mark. This is the **intertidal zone**.

If you look next at the ocean strictly in its vertical dimension, all of the water from the ocean's surface to its floor is called the *pelagic zone*, while the ocean floor itself is called the *benthic zone*. Within the pelagic zone, from sea level down to a depth of at least 100 meters (about 330 feet), the sun's rays can penetrate strongly enough to drive photosynthesis. This zone of photosynthesis is known as the *photic zone*.

More Productive Near the Coasts, Less Productive on the Open Sea

Each of these zones marks off an area that is meaningful in relation to life. Start first at the intertidal zone. This is a world *in between*, we might say, because the creatures in it live part of the time submerged in the ocean and part of the time exposed to the air. It turns out that the intertidal zone is extremely productive for a reason that you might think would make it *unproductive*: the ocean waves, which bring in nutrients, carry away wastes, and expose more of the surface area of photosynthesizers to sunlight.

Ocean life continues to be abundant out past the intertidal zone and in general remains so all the way to the end of the coastal zone. In short, ocean life is most productive in its shallower depths (**see Figure 32.35** on the next page). Once past the continental shelf and into the open ocean, productivity can drop off to levels that are less than those of a desert. Why should this be so? Remember that sunlight strong enough to power photosynthesis penetrates ocean waters only to a depth of 100 meters or so. Meanwhile, the average depth of the ocean is about 3,000 meters or 1.8 miles. Thus there is a vast depth of open ocean that simply isn't very productive. Indeed, life at greater ocean depths essentially depends on organic particles, referred to as "marine snow," that rain down from above. One measure of the coastal zone's importance is that it is the location of all the world's great fisheries. Fish do exist in the open ocean as well, however, and concern is increasingly being raised about the health of fish populations in both kinds of areas, as you can see in "Our Overfished Oceans" on page 739.

More Productive Near the Poles, Less Productive Away from Them

Apart from the shallow-to-deep transition, the ocean also has one other gradient with respect to the amount of life it harbors. In the pelagic zone, there is relatively more ocean life toward the poles, with this concentration decreasing with movement toward the equator—the exact opposite of what we find with land life. The oceans that surround Antarctica are filled with life. **Phytoplankton**, meaning floating, microscopic photosynthesizers such as algae and cyanobacteria, are the base producers for it all. These are consumed by the tiny floating animals known as **zooplankton**. Shrimp-like crustaceans called krill feed mostly on the phytoplankton and serve as the principal source of food for the whales and seals we associate with this area.

Cities of Productivity: Coral Reefs

Despite the richness of the colder oceans, the tropical oceans do boast marine communities that are as productive as any in the ocean—indeed, as any on Earth. These are the **coral reefs**, which lie in shallow waters at the edge of continents or islands at tropical latitudes. Coral reefs actually are the piled-up remains of many generations of coral animals, with each individual animal, known as a polyp, being a tiny relative of the more familiar sea anemones. Coral polyps secrete calcium carbonate, better known as limestone, a practice they share with a type of red algae with whom they share their habitat. The limestone forms an external skeleton for the corals and, when each coral dies, its limestone skeleton remains. Thus, coral reefs are composed largely of the stacked-up remains of countless generations of coral polyps, along with the remains of their

**Figure 32.34
Ocean Zones**

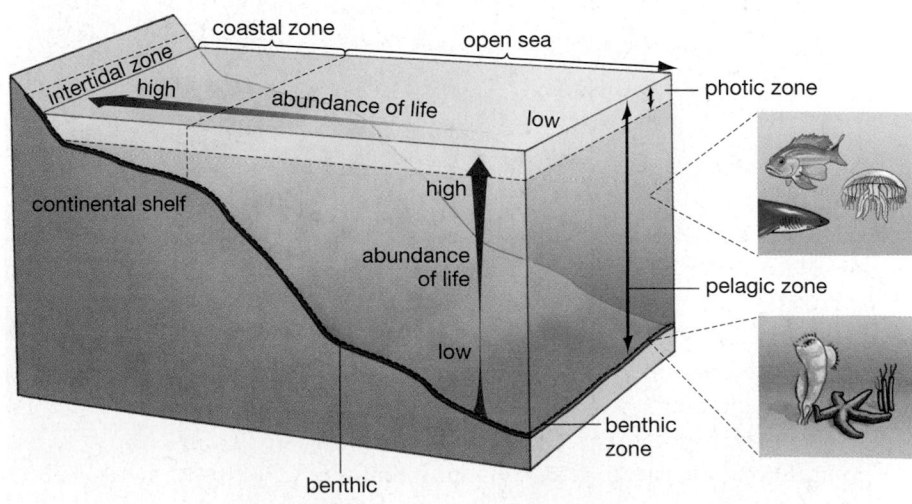

(a) A man and two children investigate tidepools

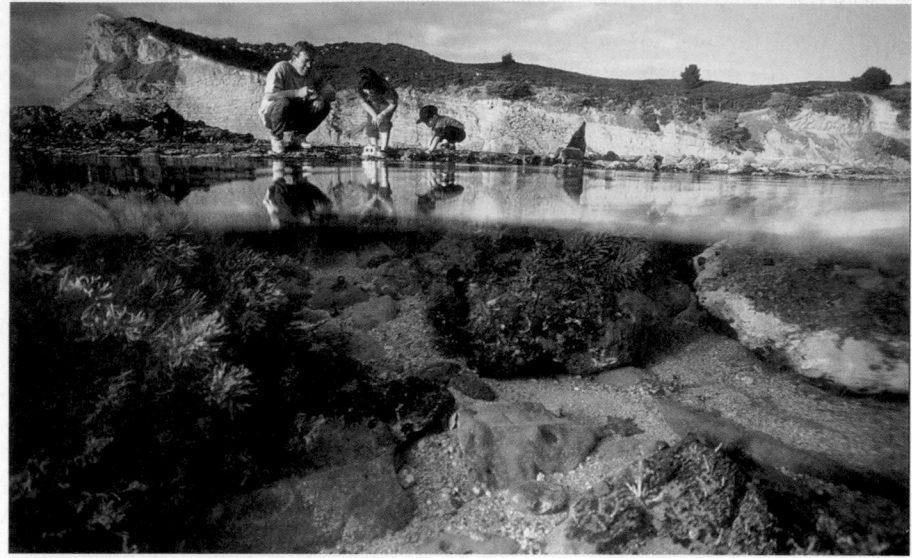

(b) King penguins swim underwater

(c) Sweepers and fairy basslets feed in currents

neighboring red algae. But the thin outer veneer of each reef is composed of *living* algae and the latest generation of pinhead-sized corals.

You can get an idea of how many generations of coral are piled up by considering that most reefs are between 5,000 and 8,000 years old—and some are millions of years old. What the reef as a whole creates is *habitat*: nooks and crannies and tunnels and surfaces that are home to an amazing array of living things. So rich is this habitat that it covers only 2 percent of the ocean's floor, but is home to perhaps 25 percent of the ocean's species. One coral reef, Australia's Great Barrier Reef, also is one of the largest structures created by any living thing, including humans. It measures some 2,000 kilometers or 1,200 miles in length.

Sadly, coral reefs are now imperiled cities of biological productivity. By one estimate, 27 percent of the world's coral reefs have now been lost as functioning ecosystems, though with coral reefs, loss of activity is not always permanent. The greatest single source of this destruction was the El Niño-caused ocean warming of 1997–1998, which brought about a phenomenon known as *coral bleaching*, meaning a discoloration of the reefs due to the death of symbiotic algae that live within the coral animals. Temporary weather events aside, the longer-term threat to coral reefs is human activity. Oil is dumped into the ocean, sewage and runoff from cities harms the reefs, divers may trample on them. Perhaps most disturbing, thousands of pounds of the poison sodium cyanide are dumped each year on coral reefs in the Philippines and other parts of Asia as a means of capturing colorful aquarium fish. (The cyanide stuns the fish, but kills the coral animals.) Global warming has now been tied to the threat to coral reefs as well; both ocean warming and increased ocean CO_2 concentrations are harmful to the reefs.

Figure 32.35
Diversity in Ocean Life
(**a**) A man and two children investigate tide pools, a part of the ocean's intertidal zone. The deeper water beyond them can be seen both above and below the surface.
(**b**) King penguins swim underwater near a breeding colony in the fertile waters off the coast of Antarctica.
(**c**) Fish called sweepers and fairy basslets feed in the currents above a coral plate covered with animals called crinoids. The structure is off the coast of Papua New Guinea.

Our Overfished Oceans

At one time, it was thought that the bounty of fish in the world's oceans was so immense it could never be exhausted. But that idea began to be challenged in the late 1980s and by the mid-1990s it was effectively dead, as it became clear that the numbers of certain kinds of fish had not just dwindled, but had dropped to alarmingly low levels. The news has not gotten better since then. In 2003, researchers reported that the global ocean has lost 90 percent of its big predatory species—bluefin tuna, blue marlin, Antarctic cod, and sharks among them (**see Figure 1**). One of the ways the researchers arrived at this conclusion was to count the number of fish caught per baited hook on the "longlines" that stretch out for miles behind oceangoing fishing vessels. Just after World War II, Japanese fishermen commonly caught 10 fish per hundred longline hooks; now that figure is often down to 1 fish per hundred hooks.

About the time this study came out, the Canadian government banned the fishing of all Atlantic cod in three large regions off the Canadian coast. The move came after an independent research group declared Canadian cod an endangered species. Meanwhile, across the ocean in Britain's North Sea, cod populations have dropped to 15 percent of their 1970s levels, with the result that scientists are calling for similar reductions in fishing there. To be sure, not all populations of commercial fish have dropped by this amount; but in many commercial species, the trend is toward depletion, if not endangerment.

How did this happen? In essence, world fishing fleets got more efficient at scouring the Earth for large populations of fish. By using ever-more sophisticated technology, the fleets have managed to find fish no matter what kind of terrain they are hidden in. But in some instances—as with Canada's Atlantic cod—there are no large populations left to find.

Fisheries scientist Daniel Pauly and his colleagues have pointed out that this turn of events actually should not be surprising. We would not expect industrialized *hunting*—of, say, deer or buffalo—to be sustainable over the long run if left unregulated. Why should we expect anything different with industrialized fishing? Many scientists believe that a three-pronged approach has to be taken if global fish populations are to bounce back. First, global fishing must be reduced in general. Second, countries need to restrict the use of "bottom trawling" techniques in which nets and accompanying gear—sometimes weighing thousands of pounds—are dragged across the ocean floor, destroying habitat as well as fish. Third, "no take" zones need to be created so that specific fish populations can have a chance to establish themselves.

Figure 1
One of a Dwindling Number
A blue marlin (*Makaira nigricans*), one of the large predatory fishes whose numbers have been reduced by 90 percent in recent decades, according to a global assessment.

Freshwater Systems

Whereas the oceans cover almost three-quarters of Earth's surface, freshwater ecosystems—inland lakes, rivers, and other running water—together cover only about 2.1 percent of Earth's surface. Like the ocean, lakes can be divided into biological zones. The most productive zone in a lake is the shallow-water area along its edge, the *littoral zone*, whose outer boundary is defined as the point at which the water is so deep that rooted plants can no longer grow. Then there is the *photic zone*, which starts at the surface of the lake and extends down to the point at which sunlight no longer penetrates strongly enough to drive photosynthesis. Finally, there is the area beneath the photic zone, the *profundal zone*, in which photosynthesis can't be performed (**Figure 32.36**).

Nutrients in Lakes

Lakes can be naturally *eutrophic*, meaning nutrient-rich, or *oligotrophic*, meaning nutrient-poor. A lake that has few nutrients will have relatively few photosynthesizers, and this in turn means few animals. Oligotrophic lakes generally are clear (and deep), while eutrophic lakes often have an abundant algal cover.

Nutrient enrichment can happen naturally over time, or it can take place because of human intervention. The latter variety is known as *artificial eutrophication*, a process that sometimes is undertaken intentionally just to increase the yield of fish from a lake or pond. There is such a thing as having too *many* human-added nutrients in a body of water, however. We touched on this earlier in connection with the Gulf of Mexico's "dead zone," which results from the tons of nitrogen that flow into it. But smaller bodies of water can undergo eutrophication as well. An overabundance of such nutrients as phosphorus or nitrogen brings on an overabundance of algae—a so-called **algal bloom**—and this eventually means an overabundance of dead algae falling to the bottom of the lake (**see Figure 32.37**). When this

Figure 32.36
Zones in a Lake
The littoral zone starts at water's edge and extends out to the point at which rooted plants can no longer grow. The photic zone starts at the lake's surface and extends down to the point at which sunlight no longer drives photosynthesis. The profundal zone is the area beneath the photic zone in which photosynthesis cannot be performed.

photic zone

profundal zone

littoral zone

Figure 32.37
Too Many Nutrients
A pond with an overabundance of nutrients has experienced an overgrowth of algae—an algal bloom—that may be detrimental to other life-forms in the pond.

happens, decomposing bacteria flourish, and they are using *oxygen*—so much of it that the fish in a lake can suffocate. How do these harmful levels of phosphorus or nitrogen get into freshwater aquatic ecosystems? Fertilizers from lawns or agriculture, construction that disturbs bedrock, sewage, and detergents are some of the sources (though in many states, phosphate-containing detergents have been banned for decades). This is one form of human environmental impact that can be reversible in a straightforward way: Reduce the nutrients that are flowing into the ecosystem.

Estuaries and Wetlands: Two Very Productive Bodies of Water

There is one important type of aquatic water system that always straddles the line between a freshwater and saltwater habitat. This is the **estuary**, an area where a stream or river flows into the ocean.

Estuaries rank with tropical forests and coral reefs in being the most productive ecosystems on Earth. The cause of this productivity is the constant movement of water—the same force at work in the ocean's intertidal zone. Ocean tides and river flow are constantly stirring up estuary silt that is rich in nutrients. Plants and algae thus get an abundance of these substances, grow in abundance, and pass their bounty up the food chain. In **Figure 32.38** you can see an image of an important estuary in the United States, the Chesapeake Bay.

Another important type of aquatic ecosystem is **wetlands**, which are just what they sound like—lands that are wet for at least part of the year. "Wet" here covers a variety of conditions, from soil that is merely temporarily waterlogged—a prairie "pothole" in Minnesota, for example—to a cover of permanent water that may be several feet in depth (the bayous of Louisiana). Wetlands go by such specific names as

Figure 32.38
Where Salt Water and Freshwater Meet
The Chesapeake Bay is one of the largest and most productive estuaries in the world. In it, the freshwater of 19 principal rivers meets the salt water of the ocean, forming zones of different degrees of saltiness. Each zone supports specific communities of organisms. (Redrawn from A. J. Lippson and R. L. Lippson, *Life in the Chesapeake Bay* [Baltimore: Johns Hopkins University Press, 1984].)

swamps, bogs, marshes, and tidal marshes; the overwhelming majority of them are freshwater *inland wetlands*, rather than the ocean-abutting *coastal wetlands*, which can be freshwater or salt water (**see Figure 32.39**). Wetlands are sites of great biological productivity, and they serve as vital habitat for migratory birds. It's been estimated that the amount of wetlands in the United States has been reduced by 55 percent since the arrival of Europeans—120 million

of the 215 million acres that were originally wetlands have been drained or paved over. Currently, the state of Florida and the federal government are working on one of the most far-reaching and expensive habitat restoration efforts in history, as they try to bring the largest expanse of wetlands in the nation, the Florida Everglades, to a healthier condition over the next 20 years.

Life's Largest Scale: The Biosphere

You've been reviewing life on a very large scale, which is to say the aquatic ecosystems and biomes of the Earth. But there is one larger scale of life yet, which is the collection of *all* the world's ecosystems, the **biosphere**, which is also thought of as that portion of the Earth that supports life. Much could be said about the biosphere, but here's just one observation about life on this global scale. The Earth is about 24,000 miles in circumference, with life existing along any line you could draw all around the globe. If we look at life in its *vertical* dimension, however, it has been found to exist only about 1.8 miles below Earth's surface and about 5.2 miles above sea level (in the upper Himalayas). This means that all of life on Earth exists in a band that is at most about 7 miles thick, with the vast bulk existing in an even narrower span. Actually, this is all the life that we know of in the *universe*, so that if we could imagine ourselves traveling by cosmic elevator, we could potentially come up from the molten center of Earth, pass through the bacteria lodged between underground rocks, and then move through a tissue-thin layer of a green living world, after which we might never see anything like it again, no matter how far out into the universe we traveled. Taking this perspective, the really remarkable thing is not how much life there is, but how little.

(a) A bird's nest in prairie wetland in the United States

(b) An overhead view of the sawgrass prairie in Florida's Everglades National Park

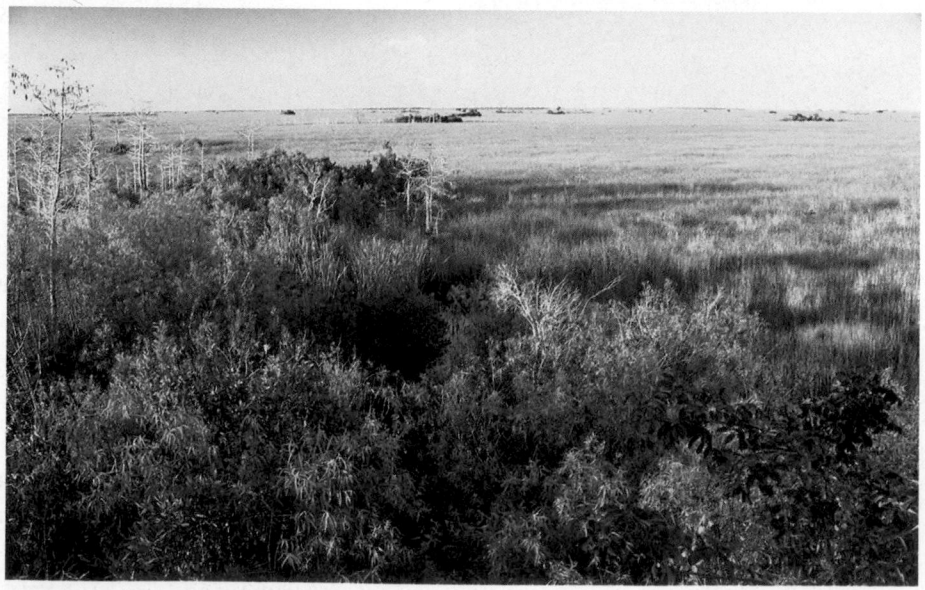

Figure 32.39
Inland Wetland and Coastal Wetland

On to Animal Behavior

Animals have figured prominently in the ecology you've been reading about in the last two chapters. The chapter coming up, however, will put a magnifying glass to one aspect of animal life, animal behavior. In the living world, only animals possess the communications networks known as nervous systems. The internal instant-messaging that comes with these systems has given animals an unrivaled ability to move, sense, seek, and react. In addition, more than any other living things, animals seemingly are able to *choose* from among an array of different possible actions. So, why do animals behave as they do? That is the subject of Chapter 33.

Chapter Review

Summary

32.1 The Ecosystem Is the Fundamental Unit of Ecology

- An ecosystem is a community of organisms and the physical environment with which these organisms interact. Very large-scale ecosystems are known as biomes, which are defined by the types of vegetation within them.

32.2 Abiotic Factors Are a Major Component of Any Ecosystem

- The approximately 30 chemical elements that are vital to life are known as nutrients. Along with water, nutrients move back and forth between abiotic (nonliving) and biotic (living) domains on Earth in a process called biogeochemical cycling.

- Elements can be stored in living things, transferred between them, or transferred between them and the abiotic domain.

- Carbon comes into the living world through the plants, algae, and bacteria that take in atmospheric carbon dioxide to perform photosynthesis. Animals obtain their carbon from these photosynthesizing organisms. Carbon moves back into the atmosphere in the form of carbon dioxide, which plants and animals give off as a product of their respiration, and as a product of their decomposition after death.
Web Tutorial 32.1: The Carbon Cycle

- Carbon dioxide makes up a small but critical proportion of the Earth's atmosphere. It is vital to life and may greatly affect global temperature.

- Prior to this century, nitrogen entered the biotic domain mostly through the action of certain bacteria that have the ability to convert atmospheric nitrogen into forms that can be used by living things. Other bacteria have the ability to convert this organic nitrogen back into atmospheric nitrogen, completing the cycle. Human beings now use industrial processes to convert nitrogen into a biologically usable form, thus greatly expanding agricultural productivity. Nitrogen runoff from agriculture can be a form of nutrient pollution that can harm both small and large aquatic ecosystems.
Web Tutorial 32.2: The Nitrogen Cycle

- As with carbon or nitrogen, all of Earth's water is either being cycled or is being stored—in such forms as glaciers or polar ice. As little as 0.5 percent of Earth's water is available as fresh, liquid water, with about 25 percent of this being groundwater, which generally is stored in geological formations called aquifers.

- Fresh, sanitary water is a scarce commodity even for human beings, despite the fact that civilization now uses more than half the world's accessible water. The scarcity of water can be traced in significant part to the inefficient ways in which humans use it.

Human diversion of water from natural environments is having harmful impacts on species such as fish.
Web Tutorial 32.3: The Hydrologic Cycle

32.3 How Energy Flows through Ecosystems

- Plants and other photosynthesizers are an ecosystem's producers, while the organisms that eat plants are its consumers. Every ecosystem has a number of feeding or trophic levels, with producers forming the first trophic level and consumers forming several additional levels.

- A detritivore is a class of consumer that feeds on the remains of dead organisms or cast-off material from living organisms. A decomposer is a special kind of detritivore that breaks down dead or cast-off organic material into its inorganic components, which can then be recycled through an ecosystem.

- The energy-flow model of ecosystems provides ecologists with a powerful analytical tool; it measures energy as it is used by and transferred among different members of an ecosystem.

- Very little of the energy that a given trophic level receives is passed along to the next trophic level. A rule of thumb in ecology is that for each jump up in trophic level, the amount of available energy drops by 90 percent. This explains why large, predatory animals are rare: Very little of the solar energy assimilated by plants is available to the higher trophic levels the predators occupy.

32.4 Earth's Physical Environment

- The atmosphere is the layer of gases surrounding the Earth. The lowest layer of the atmosphere, the troposphere, contains the bulk of the atmosphere's gases. Nitrogen and oxygen make up 99 percent of the troposphere, with carbon dioxide and small amounts of such gases as argon and methane making up the rest.

- The gas called ozone screens out 99 percent of the sun's potentially harmful ultraviolet radiation. Human-made compounds such as chlorofluorocarbons (CFCs), used in various consumer and industrial products, can destroy ozone. International action taken on this issue in the 1980s seems to be bringing the ozone back to health.

- There is near-unanimity among scientists that global warming is taking place, and a consensus has emerged that human activity is at least partly responsible for this warming. The greenhouse effect is one mechanism that underlies global warming. In it, higher atmospheric concentrations of gases such as carbon dioxide—released through fossil-fuel burning—trap additional quantities of the heat that comes to the Earth from the sun. Deforestation is also thought to be a cause of global warming, since trees serve as storage sites for carbon.

- The Earth appears to have warmed by 1° Fahrenheit in the past century. The effects of this warming can be seen in such phenomena as the shrinkage of Arctic sea-ice and the migration of mountain plant species to higher altitudes. Scientists are now predicting an increase of between 2.7 and 10° Fahrenheit in the coming century, with the consequences of this warming ranging from beneficial in some areas to catastrophic in others. Society faces some difficult choices regarding action on global warming.

- Earth is tilted at an angle of 23.5° relative to the plane of its orbit around the sun, a fact that dictates much about climate on Earth, which in turn dictates much about life on Earth.

- Sunlight strikes the equatorial region of the Earth more directly than the polar regions. The differential warming that results produces a set of enormous interrelated circulation cells of moving air, each existing all the way around the globe at its latitude. Each of these cells drops rain on the Earth where it rises, but dries the Earth where it descends. This is why some regions of the Earth get so much more rainfall than others.

- More rain will be deposited on the windward side of a mountain range than on the opposite leeward side. This rain-shadow effect can cause opposite sides of a mountain range to have dramatically different vegetation patterns.

- A climate is an average weather condition in a given area. Large vegetative formations essentially are defined by climate regions.

Web Tutorial 32.4: Earth's Atmosphere and Climate

32.5 Earth's Biomes

- A biome is an ecosystem defined by a large-scale vegetation formation.

- Six types of biomes are recognized at a minimum: tundra, taiga, temperate deciduous forest, temperate grassland, desert, and tropical rain forest. Polar ice and mountains often are recognized as separate biomes, as are the tropical grasslands called tropical savannas, and the dry, shrub-dominated formations called chaparral.

- Tundra is the biome of the far north, frozen much of the year, but with a seasonal vegetation formation of low shrubs, mosses, lichens, grasses, and the grass-like sedges.

- Taiga is another biome of the north; it includes the enormous expanse of coniferous trees that lies south of the tundra at northern latitudes. The taiga exhibits a great deal of species uniformity because only a few types of trees—spruce, fir, and pine—are the ecological dominants. The region supports large populations of fur-bearing animals.

- Temperate deciduous forests grow in regions of greater warmth and rainfall than is the case with tundra or taiga. These forests, existing over much of the eastern United States, are composed of an abundance of trees such as maple and oak, complemented by a robust understory of woody and herbaceous plants.

- Temperate grassland goes by several names around the world, including prairie and steppes. This biome is characterized by less rainfall than that of temperate forest and by grasses as the dominant vegetation formation. Such regions can be very fertile agricultural land.

- Chaparral is a biome dominated by evergreen shrub vegetation. It is found in a few, relatively small regions of the world that have a Mediterranean climate. These regions have mild, rainy winters and very dry summers.

- Deserts are characterized by rainfall that is low and sporadic. Deserts may be hot, cold, or temperate, but all desert life is shaped by the need to collect and conserve water.

- The tropical rain-forest biome is characterized by warm, stable temperature, abundant moisture, great biological productivity, and great species diversity. Rain-forest productivity is concentrated above the forest floor, often in the canopy high aboveground. Found in Earth's equatorial region, tropical rain forests are being greatly reduced in size through cutting and burning.

32.6 Life in the Water: Aquatic Ecosystems

- Ocean or marine ecosystems are most biologically productive near the coasts, with the deep open oceans having a productivity that can be less than that of deserts. Coastal areas benefit from wave actions that bring in nutrients, carry away wastes, and expose more of the surface area of photosynthesizers to sunlight.

- Modern fishing techniques have seriously depleted many once-abundant commercial fish species.

- There is relatively more ocean life toward the poles, with this concentration decreasing as one moves toward the equator. The food webs in the oceans surrounding Antarctica are based on photosynthesizing phytoplankton, meaning floating microscopic organisms such as algae and cyanobacteria.

- Coral reefs are warm-water marine structures composed of the piled-up remains of generations of coral animals. Coral reefs provide a habitat that results in a rich species diversity.

- Freshwater ecosystems, which include inland lakes, rivers, and other running water, cover only about 2.1 percent of Earth's surface. Freshwater lakes are most productive near their shores and near their surface. Lakes can be naturally eutrophic, meaning nutrient-rich, or oligotrophic, meaning nutrient-poor. The human activity known as artificial eutrophication can sometimes introduce too many nutrients into a lake, which can cause some species to flourish (algae, bacteria) while harming other species (some fish).

- Estuaries are areas where streams or rivers flow into the ocean. They are characterized by high biological productivity because of the constant movement of water within them.

- Wetlands, also known as swamps or marshes, are lands that are wet for at least part of the year. Wetland soil may merely be waterlogged for part of the year or under a permanent, relatively deep cover of water. Wetlands are very productive and are important habitats for migratory birds. The amount of wetlands in the United States is estimated to have been reduced by 55 percent since the arrival of the Europeans.

Key Terms

abiotic   711

algal bloom   740

aquifer   716

atmosphere   723

biodegradable   720

biogeochemical cycling   712

biomass   713

biome   731

biosphere   742

biotic   711

carnivore   719

CFCs   725

climate   730

coastal zone   737

consumer   719

coral reef   737

decomposer   720

detritivore   720

ecosystem   712

element   712

energy-flow model   721

estuary   741

gross primary production   722

groundwater   716

herbivore   719

intertidal zone   737

kilocalorie   721

net primary production   722

nitrogen fixation   713

nutrients   712

omnivore   719

ozone   724

permafrost   732

phytoplankton   737

primary consumer   719

producer   719

secondary consumer   719

stratosphere   724

taiga   732

tertiary consumer   719

trophic level   719

tropical rain forest   735

tropical savanna   734

troposphere   723

tundra   731

wetlands   741

zooplankton   737

Understanding the Basics

Multiple-Choice Questions (answers in the back of the book)

1. In nature, it is _____ that are primarily responsible for converting atmospheric nitrogen into a form that living things can use.
   a. plants
   b. algae
   c. bacteria
   d. animals
   e. fungi

2. In recent years there has been substantial concern about global warming, which is caused to a great extent by the build-up of the heat-trapping gas
   a. oxygen
   b. nitrogen dioxide
   c. sulfur dioxide
   d. carbon dioxide
   e. neon

3. You walk in on the middle of a nature program on television and see aerial shots of huge expanses of one or two types of coniferous trees. The type of biome you are looking at probably is
   a. chaparral
   b. taiga
   c. tundra
   d. savanna
   e. temperate forest

4. There is a simple food chain in an eastern Oregon desert grassland: Mice are consumed by several species of snakes, which themselves are consumed by hawks. The hawk is a _____ and occupies the _____ trophic level in this ecosystem.
   a. tertiary consumer; fourth
   b. secondary consumer; fourth
   c. tertiary consumer; third
   d. secondary consumer; third
   e. primary consumer; third

5. A dung beetle (can you guess what it eats?) is an example of a
   a. detritivore
   b. omnivore
   c. carnivore
   d. autotroph
   e. homeotherm

6. The greenhouse effect is caused by
   a. incoming long-wave radiation that is trapped as short-wave radiation by the atmosphere
   b. short-wavelength light that is re-radiated as long-wave radiation and is trapped by certain gases
   c. heat that is stored as short-wave radiation by rough surfaces of the Earth and then re-radiated as long-wavelength light
   d. cold air masses that mix with the warm gases and produce warm atmospheric gases
   e. reactions in the stratosphere between these greenhouses gases and ozone, producing long-wavelength heat

7. Donna is measuring rainfall over a large elevation gradient in the Cascade Mountains of Oregon. As she walks up the west side, she notices that rainfall increases, and that when she reaches the top and walks down the east side, it is much drier. This is because
   a. Dry air from the equator flows east at this latitude, dropping moisture on the west side.
   b. Wet air from the tropical equator flows east at this latitude, dropping moisture on the west, and then becomes dry by the time it reaches the eastern side.
   c. Air is flowing from the west and drops moisture as it rises and cools, then absorbs moisture from the land as it descends and warms.
   d. Warm air from 30° latitudes picks up moisture as it travels to 60° north, then drops this moisture as it cools.
   e. The rain-shadow effect means that cool, moist air drops rainfall as it warms with a rise in elevation.

8. Microscopic floating photosynthesizers such as algae that are the base producers in the oceans are known as
   a. pelagic producers
   b. secondary producers
   c. littoral consumers
   d. zooplankton
   e. phytoplankton

9. A lake affected by high levels of artificial eutrophication will have
   a. high nutrient levels, large phytoplankton populations, and low oxygen levels at depth
   b. high levels of nutrients, low phytoplankton levels, high oxygen levels in surface waters
   c. low nutrient levels, large phytoplankton populations, and low oxygen levels at depth
   d. low nutrient levels, low phytoplankton populations, and high oxygen levels at depth
   e. low nutrient levels, large zooplankton populations, and low phytoplankton levels

Brief Review

1. In a large reserve in Idaho, Forest Service wildlife scientists measured wolf populations as well as elk populations, and found that the wolf population was much lower than that of the elk population. If wolves feed on elk, why aren't the population sizes similar?

2. Explain why most deserts across the globe occur at about 30° north and south of the equator.

3. What relationship does climate have to the large-scale vegetation patterns that are seen on Earth?

4. A great many dead fish are found floating on the surface of a pond. What might be the cause of such a fish kill?

5. Name several ways in which the tundra and taiga biomes differ.

Applying Your Knowledge

1. Bacteria and fungi are to the living world as a foundation is to a house: not often thought of, but vitally important. If all bacteria and fungi were somehow instantly eliminated, almost no life-forms would survive for long. This is so because of the role bacteria and fungi play in ecological processes. Can you name two of these processes?

2. Increasing levels of carbon dioxide in Earth's atmosphere are likely to increase the rate of a basic, critically important biological process. Can you think of what that process is?

3. Tundra and desert are in some ways more fragile biomes than are grasslands or forests. Why should this be so?

MediaLab

El Niño and the Greenhouse Effect: How Climate Affects Our Weather, Food, and Water Supplies

It is almost impossible for us to imagine what the world will be like 50 or 100 years from now. Yet that is exactly the challenge facing government agencies and scientists who are planning for world food and water supplies in the next century. Will Earth's biomes, and our food and water supplies, change with forces such as global warming and climatic fluctuation over the next hundred years? To answer this question, in this *MediaLab* you'll examine the forces that shape climate from year to year and from decade to decade, and use that information to develop projections of future conditions.

This *MediaLab* can be found in Chapter 32 on your Companion Website (www.prenhall.com/krogh3).

WEB TUTORIAL

This *Web Tutorial* reviews concepts about the physical conditions that influence Earth's weather and climate, and explores their impact on the abundance of life.

1. First, you'll investigate how carbon and other chemicals cycle through.

2. Next, you will examine the implications of geographic and geologic landforms and how they influence precipitation patterns and thus climate and weather around the globe.

3. Finally, you will investigate how the relationship between the sun and Earth cause seasonal change.

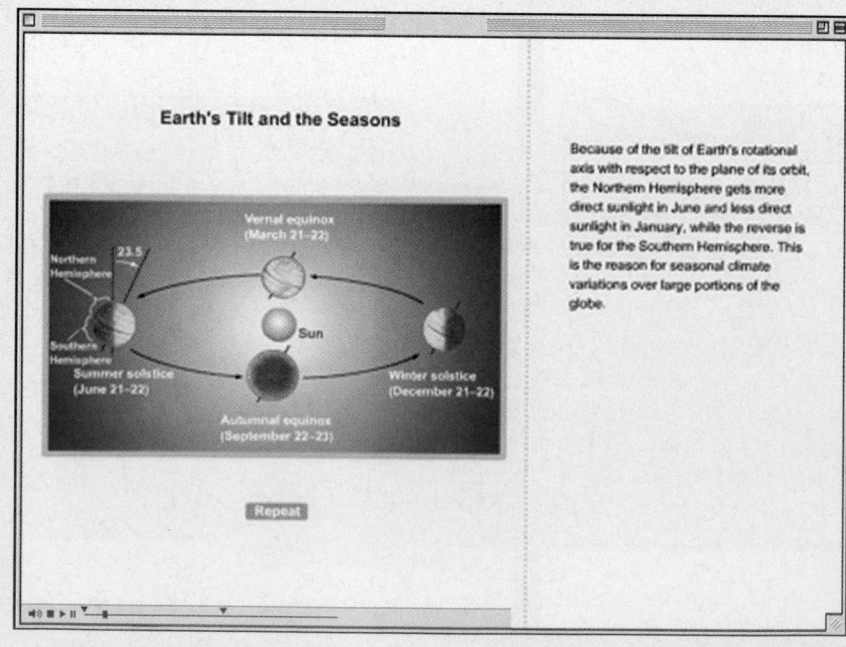

Investigation 1
Estimated time for completion = 15 minutes

What is El Niño and how does it affect our climate? To begin your investigation, select the keyword **EL NIÑO** on your Website for this *MediaLab*. Read about the history and influence of the El Niño Southern Oscillation (ENSO). Describe the warm and cold extremes of this phenomenon. How frequently does the warm phase of ENSO occur, and how does it affect different parts of the world? Then, select the keyword **CROP PROSPECTS** to view the United Nations Food and Agriculture Organization maps of current and past years' unfavorable crop prospects and food supply shortfalls in different parts of the world. How might global food supply problems be helped or worsened by ENSO phenomena?

Investigation 2
Estimated time for completion = 15 minutes

Why have El Niño events become more frequent in recent decades? The answer may lie in natural long-term climatic forces that create a "conveyor belt" of ocean water circulation that last for many years. Select the keyword **CLIMATE** on your Website for this *MediaLab* to read an article from Oregon State University on this process. Do the phenomena described in the article represent a permanent global shift or a cyclic phenomenon? What is thought to cause the "conveyor belt" of ocean circulation? Is it linked to, or separate from, global warming effects?

Investigation 3
Estimated time for completion = 10 minutes

What will Earth's natural environment look like 50 or 100 years from now? Select the keyword **PROBABILITY** on your Website for this *MediaLab* to read an article on the probability of sea-level rise. Have the climate predictions of the 1970s and 1980s been borne out by recent sampling? How large a difference exists between the low and high ends of the reported range of climate estimates? To what do you attribute these differences? Some of the world's largest cities lie at or near sea-level. Under the most pessimistic forecasts, how might low-lying areas such as these be affected? Select the keyword **MAPS** to access a wide range of map resources on the Web.

COMMUNICATE YOUR RESULTS

Exercise 1
Estimated time for completion = 15 minutes

Using the information you have gleaned about the global effects of the ENSO phenomenon, suggest some ways that an understanding of ENSO can be used to protect global food and water supplies from year to year or over longer time periods.

Exercise 2
Estimated time for completion = 15 minutes

Which of the phenomena described in the *Web Investigations* are short term? Which are reversible? Write a 250-word summary of the relative effects of ENSO, oceanic circulation, and global warming on Earth's climate. In your view, what would constitute a "worst-case" combination of these phenomena? What would be a "best-case" combination? Can you suggest a different perspective, perhaps from a different part of the world or culture?

Exercise 3
Estimated time for completion = 10 minutes

How certain are climate forecasts? Use the discussion of predictive models and uncertainty from *Web Investigation 3* to discuss the challenges of understanding and forecasting climate accurately. Does the level of certainty change if the prediction is short-term (say, one to five years) rather than long-term (say, 20 to 100 years)? Why or why not? Are models useful or misleading in planning for global water and food supply? Debate this question in your class.

Appendix

Metric-English System Conversions

Length

1 inch (in.) = 2.54 centimeters (cm)
1 centimeter (cm) = 0.3937 inch (in.)
1 foot (ft) = 0.3048 meter (m)
1 meter (m) = 3.2808 feet (ft) = 1.0936 yard (yd)
1 mile (mi) = 1.6904 kilometer
1 kilometer (km) = 0.6214 mile (mi)

Area

1 square inch (in.^{2}) = 6.45 square centimeters (cm^2)
1 square centimeter (cm^2) = 0.155 square inch (in.^{2})
1 square foot (ft^2) = 0.0929 square meter (m^2)
1 square meter (m^2) = 10.7639 square feet (ft^2) =
   1.1960 yards (yd^2)
1 square mile (mi^2) = 2.5900 square kilometers (km^2)
1 acre (a) = 0.4047 hectare (ha)
1 hectare (ha) = 2.4710 acres (a) = 10,000 square meters (m^2)

Volume

1 cubic inch (in.^{3}) = 16.39 cubic centimeters (cm^3 or cc)
1 cubic centimeter (cm^3 or cc) = 0.06 cubic inch (in.^{3})
1 cubic foot (ft^3) = 0.028 cubic meter (m^3)
1 cubic meter (m^3) = 35.30 cubic feet (ft^3) =
   1.3079 cubic yards (yd^3)
1 fluid ounce (oz) = 29.6 milliliters (mL) = 0.03 liter (L)
1 milliliter (mL) = 0.03 fluid ounce (oz) =
   1/4 teaspoon (approximate)
1 pint (pt) = 473 milliliters (mL) = 0.47 liter (L)
1 quart (qt) = 946 milliliters (mL) = 0.9463 liter (L)
1 gallon (gal) = 3.79 liters (L)
1 liter (L) = 1.0567 quarts (qt) = 0.26 gallon (gal)

Mass

1 ounce (oz) = 28.3496 grams (g)
1 gram (g) = 0.03527 ounce (oz)
1 pound (lb) = 0.4536 kilogram (kg)
1 kilogram = 2.2046 pounds (lb)
1 ton (tn), U.S. = 0.91 metric ton (t or tonne)
1 metric ton = 1.10 tons (tn), U.S.

Metric Prefixes

Prefix	Abbreviation	Meaning
giga-	G	$10^9 = 1,000,000,000$
mega-	M	$10^6 = 1,000,000$
kilo-	k	$10^3 = 1,000$
hecto-	h	$10^2 = 100$
deka-	da	$10^1 = 10$
		$10^0 = 1$
deci-	d	$10^{-1} = 0.1$
centi-	c	$10^{-2} = 0.01$
milli-	m	$10^{-3} = 0.001$
micro-	μ	$10^{-6} = 0.000001$

Answers

CHAPTER 1
Multiple Choice
1. c, 2. d, 3. d, 4. d, 5. e.
Brief Review
1. Science is a body of knowledge and a formal process for acquiring that knowledge. It is thus a collection of unified insights about the physical world, and also a way of learning about the physical world. Unlike religion, science does not acknowledge any immutable laws, nor does it acknowledge any unquestioned authority. Instead, all scientific principles are all open to modification, based on the discovery of new evidence.
2. An experiment is said to be controlled when the experimenter controls the factors in it that will change and those that will be kept constant. Suppose a scientist wanted to test the effect of the insecticide DDT on the reproductive development of lab rats. In this case, the experiment might consist of feeding DDT-laced food to one group of rats, while another similar group—called the control group—would receive the same food without DDT. It is important that the two groups of rats be as closely matched as possible in regard to all other factors. For instance, both groups must consist of the same strain of lab mice; both must be the same gender or mix of genders; they must be given the same amount of food and water, and housed in identical environments. Suppose differences were observed in, for example, the size of the offspring born to one group of rats as opposed to the other. Were the starting conditions not controlled in the experiment, there would be no way to tell whether the DDT or some other factor (such as different housing) was responsible for these differences.
3. Pasteur investigated a widely held notion of the time that living things can arise spontaneously from basic chemicals. He hypothesized that instances where life appeared to arise in medium believed to lack it could be readily explained as the result of contamination from unseen airborne microscopic organisms. He sterilized meat broth in a flask with a long, S-shaped neck, by heating both the broth and the flask. Although the mouth of the long tube remained open, any incoming dust particles laden with microscopic organisms would be trapped in the bent neck and could not gain access to the meat broth. Under these conditions, the broth remained free of any visible signs of life. In other tests, the S-shaped neck was broken off or the flask tilted so that broth made contact with the neck of the flask; in these instances, the broth came "alive" with teeming bacteria and fungi. Pasteur inferred from these experiments that the appearance of life forms depended on whether the broth was contaminated by airborne microscopic organisms or not. When the airborne organisms had no access to the broth, however, it remained sterile. There was no evidence, in other words, of life coming about through spontaneous generation.
4. All living things, as we know them on this planet, acquire, store, and use energy through metabolism; they respond to stimuli in their environment; they maintain a relatively constant internal environment (homeostasis); they reproduce, using DNA to transmit hereditary information; they exhibit cellular organization; and they show evidence of having evolved, or changed over time.
5. Atoms, molecules, organelles, cells, tissues, organs, organisms, populations, communities, the biosphere.

CHAPTER 2
Multiple Choice
1. b, d, 2. b, 3. c, 4. a, 5. d, 6. b, 7. e, 8. a.
Brief Review
1. The forms are called isotopes. Isotopes of an element differ from one another in accordance with the number of neutrons they have. A regular carbon atom has 6 neutrons in its nucleus, while a carbon-14 atom has eight neutrons.
2.
3. Free radicals exist when one of the atoms in a covalently bonded molecule has an unpaired electron. One free radical can produce many more free radicals in a chain reaction. Free radicals can do damage by irritating artery walls or by causing mutations in DNA.
4. An atom's electrons move through volumes of space outside the atom's nucleus. An entire atom is about 100,000 times larger than its nucleus. Thus, most of an atom is the space through which electrons move.
5. When the valence (outer) shell is filled, the atom is at a lower, more stable energy state.

CHAPTER 3
Multiple Choice
1. e, 2. a, 3. e, 4. e, 5. e, 6. d, 7. b, 8. d, 9. a.
Brief Review
1. Water absorbs tremendous amounts of heat from the sun, and releases this heat slowly, with the onset of night's colder temperature. The perspiration human beings throw off carries with it a great deal of heat, which has been absorbed by the water.
2. LDL is associated with deposition of cholesterol in the arteries, so you should be concerned about high levels. HDL is associated with carrying cholesterol to the liver, away from the arteries where it does damage. A high HDL count relative to LDL count is in general a good sign.
3. Table 3.2 lists several protein functions, including enzymes, transport proteins, structural proteins, contractile proteins, and so forth. Proteins can do many different kinds of jobs because they take on so many different shapes. Each shape allows the protein to do a different job.
4. The water molecules cling together so tightly that when each molecule evaporates from a plant leaf, it draws up a chain of water molecules that extends all the way down to the root.
5. Strong hydrogen bonds help explain why water is so extremely cohesive, has such a strong surface tension, and has such a high specific heat.

CHAPTER 4
Multiple Choice
1. e, 2. d, 3. a, 4. b, 5. c, 6. d, 7. b, 8. e, 9. c.
Brief Review
1. The cell would have difficulty obtaining materials from the external environment because its surface-to-volume ratio would be too low.
2. Eukaryotes have a nucleus, bound within a thin membrane, that contains almost all their DNA. The DNA of prokaryotes is localized (in a "nucleoid" region), but it is not bound within a membrane. Eukaryotes are usually much larger than prokaryotes. Eukaryotes are also quite often multicelled organisms, while prokaryotes are single-celled. Most eukaryotes need oxygen to exist, whereas many prokaryotes can survive without oxygen.
3. The DNA code is copied onto an mRNA molecule, which leaves the nucleus through the pores in the nuclear envelope. The length of mRNA then arrives at a ribosome, which reads part of it before migrating to, and embedding in, the rough endoplasmic reticulum (RER). The ribosome then continues to read the RNA chain and the resulting polypeptide chain drops into the cisternal space of the RER. There, the polypeptide chain folds up into a protein that undergoes editing. Once this editing has been completed in the RER, the protein is encased in a transport vesicle, which buds off from the RER and moves to the Golgi complex for further editing and for routing to its proper location. The finished protein then moves through the cytoplasm in a transport vesicle that fuses with the cell's outer or "plasma" membrane, thereby exporting the protein from the cell.
4. Cilia and flagella are cell extensions formed by microtubules that are either a means of propulsion or, in the case of some cilia, a means of moving material around a cell. Cilia exist as a profusion of hair-like growths extending from cells that move back and forth very rapidly, while only a few flagella sprout from a given cell—indeed, there is often just a single, tail-like flagellum. In the human body, cilia are found in the nasal passages and in the lungs. The only animal cell that has a flagellum is a sperm cell.
5. Plant cells would be isolated from each other by their thick cell walls. Because communication among cells is critical for the functioning of a plant, the result would be that the plant could not live.
6. A gap junction consists of clusters of protein assemblages that shoot through the plasma membrane of an animal cell from one side to the other, forming a tube. When these protein assemblages line up in two adjacent cells, the result is a communication channel between them. Gap junctions allow for the passage of small molecules and electrical signals between animal cells.

CHAPTER 5
Multiple Choice
1. c, 2. a, 3. c, 4. e, 5. d, 6. b, 7. b, 8. d, 9. a, 10. e.
Brief Review
1. Receptor proteins usually are specific to a single communication molecule. This is so because each receptor has a shape that severely restricts the type of communication molecule it can bind with. The receptor in question has a shape that allows it to bind with glucose, but not to insulin; thus the insulin molecules it comes into contact with simply pass it by.
2. Because steroids are lipids, they pass easily across the phospholipid bilayer by dissolving in it. Thus they can affect every single cell of the body.
3. Because the phospholipid's phosphate "heads" are charged, hydrophilic groups, they are attracted to the polar water molecules that lie on either side of the

plasma membrane, and they orient themselves accordingly. Meanwhile, the phospholipid's "tails" are hydrophobic fatty acid chains that do not bond with water and thus end up oriented away from it, toward the interior of the plasma membrane.

4. In receptor-mediated endocytosis (RME), a group of receptors extending from the surface of the plasma membrane bind with a given target substance (for example, cholesterol) and then migrate to a depression on the membrane surface, a coated pit, which invaginates, becoming a transport vesicle that carries the target substance into the cell.

5. You would not expect that communication and recognition, and possibly transport, would be as important inside the cell as on the outside. Thus the glycocalyx would be unnecessary, and the proteins in the membranes would serve different functions.

CHAPTER 6
Multiple Choice
1. a, 2. c, 3. b, 4. d, 5. e, 6. e, 7. c, 8. c, 9. e, 10. d.
Brief Review
1. Plants abide by the second law of thermodynamics in that, in building themselves up, they are contributing to the total amount of entropy in the universe; in building a leaf from carbon dioxide and water, heat is released. A plant leaf represents only a local increase in order.

2. This is a coupled reaction in that the breakdown of ATP to ADP is an exergonic or downhill reaction that powers an endergonic or uphill reaction—the movement of sodium ions against their concentration gradient to the outside of the cell.

3. In animals, the energy stored and released by ATP comes from food. ATP is an energy "currency" molecule in that it is a medium of transfer in the same way that money is. Animals eat various kinds of foods and go though different processes in digesting them, but the outcome of these efforts is production of a molecule, ATP, that acts as a medium of energy transfer. The energy it contains can be spent on any number of different processes.

4. Enzymes are involved with every aspect of cellular life. They are necessary for breaking things down, but they are also used to make larger molecules out of smaller ones.

5. Allosteric regulation of an enzyme occurs when a molecule binds with an enzyme at a site other than its active site, thereby either decreasing or increasing the rate at which the enzyme will bind with its substrate. Such binding has the effect of either decreasing or increasing the amount of product turned out by the enzyme.

CHAPTER 7
Multiple Choice
1. b, 2. d, 3. a, 4. a, 5. d, 6. b, 7. d, 8. d, 9. c.
Brief Review
1. The food that we eat contains energetic molecules, such as glucose. In cellular respiration, foods are oxidized—they have electrons removed from them—and the energy released by the "fall" of these electrons from a higher to a lower energetic state powers phosphate groups onto ADP molecules, making them ATP molecules.

2. We would expect people to have more mitochondria in their muscle cells. This is so because muscle cells use a great deal more energy than skin cells, and the organelles that supply that energy are mitochondria.

3. Hydrogen ions (H^+ ions or protons) are pumped across the mitochondrial inner membrane—against their concentration and charge gradients—and their energetic fall back through the ATP synthase in the membrane releases enough energy to move phosphate groups onto ADP.

4. The electron carriers NADH and $FADH_2$ are oxi-

dized at the ETC; the electrons that are removed from them power the movement of the H^+ ions across the membrane.

5. No. In short bursts of activity, the energy we are using comes primarily from stored ATP and from glycolysis.

CHAPTER 8
Multiple Choice
1. c, 2. e, 3. a, 4. d, 5. e, 6. c, 7. b, 8. d, 9. b.
Brief Review
1. Yes, plants are as dependent on cellular respiration as we are. Plants make food—carbohydrates—in photosynthesis. Just as we have to break down the food we eat to get the energy out and into ATP, so plants have to break down the food they make to get the energy out and into ATP.

2. The sunlight that makes it to the Earth's surface is composed of a spectrum of energetic rays (measured by their "wavelengths") that range from very short ultraviolet rays, through visible light rays, to the longer and less energetic infrared rays. The photosynthesis we are concerned with is driven by part of the visible light spectrum—mainly by blue and red light of certain wavelengths.

3. A photosystem includes, first, several hundred antenna pigments, consisting of both chlorophyll a and accessory pigments. These molecules collect solar energy and pass it along to another part of the photosystem, the reaction center. The reaction center consists of a pair of special chlorophyll a molecules and an initial electron acceptor molecule. These reaction center compounds receive both the solar energy from the antennae pigments and electrons derived from the splitting of water.

4. In a bright, moderately hot environment, the plant would grow most rapidly. But the plant would grow fastest in cloudy or shady conditions, in which the plant would be spending too much energy moving compounds around in the plant leaf. The CAM plant, which always photosynthesizes slowly, would grow most rapidly in the desert. In other words, each plant grows most rapidly in the area to which it is best adapted.

5. The ATP is used to power the steps of the Calvin cycle. ATP is used in two separate steps during the cycle: once when 3-PGA is being energized by electrons produced by the light reactions; and again when G3P is being transformed into the RuBP that begins the Calvin cycle.

CHAPTER 9
Multiple Choice
1. e, 2. d, 3. d, 4. c, 5. b, 6. a, 7. d, 8. b, 9. c, 10. c.
Brief Review
1. DNA contains information for the production of proteins. These proteins are "workers" that carry out a vast array of tasks in organisms such as ourselves. Through the work of proteins, our bodies develop and carry out everyday functions.

2. The cell is in metaphase. There are eight chromatids present in this stage, and each daughter cell will have four chromosomes.

3. Mitosis serves to equally divide a cell's genetic material, while cytokinesis is a physical separation of a parent cell into two daughter cells.

4. Prophase—Duplicated chromosomes condense and become visible, the centrosome duplicates and centrosomes migrate to the poles, the nuclear membrane breaks down, and the mitotic spindle is formed.
   Metaphase—Chromosome pairs align along the cell mid-line or metaphase plate and attach to the microtubules extending from the cellular poles.
   Anaphase—Separation of sister chromatids paired along the metaphase plate, and their migration to the separate poles of the cell.
   Telophase—The final stage of mitosis, involving

the unwinding of the condensed chromosomes at their respective poles, and the formation of new nuclear membranes. At this point, division of genetic material is complete. The cell is ready for cytokinesis.

5. Plant cells have cell walls, while animal cells do not. In plant cells, membrane-lined vesicles, filled with a complex sugar, migrate to an area near the metaphase plate and begin fusing together, eventually forming a cell plate that runs from one side of the parent cell to the other. The membrane portion of the plate fuses with the original parent-cell plasma membrane, thus dividing the parent cell in half via formation of two new plasma membranes. The material inside the cell-plate membrane then forms the foundation of the new cell walls of the daughter cells.

6. The 23 pairs of human chromosomes are matched (or homologous) in the sense that the two members of each pair contain information about similar functions, such as hair color, metabolic processes, and so forth. The one exception to the matched-pair rule comes in human males, who have 22 pairs of matched chromosomes, but then one X chromosome and one Y chromosome, which are not matched. Human females have 23 matched pairs, including two X chromosomes.

7. (a) Four different nitrogen-containing bases (adenine, thymine, guanine, and cytosine); (b) in the nucleus; (c) "messenger"; (d) mRNA is used as a cellular "messenger," copying the DNA information in the nucleus and carrying it to the cytoplasm, where the message is used by ribosomes to assemble amino acids into proteins; (e) amino acids; (f) in the cytoplasm.

CHAPTER 10
Multiple Choice
1. b, 2. a, 3. c, 4. a, 5. b, 6. b, 7. d, 8. d, 9. a, 10. d.
Brief Review
1. Chromosome reduction takes place during meiosis I.

2. No, asexual reproduction takes place in all the varieties of organisms in the world with the exception of mammals and birds. It is more common, however, among simple organisms than among more complex organisms.

3. The cells in males that go through meiosis, giving rise to immature sperm, are called primary spermatocytes and are themselves the product of cells called spermatogonia. These spermatogonia can give rise not only to primary spermatocytes but to more spermatogonia as well.

4. Meiotic cytokinesis differs from mitotic cytokinesis in the selective shunting of cytoplasm. In mitosis, cytokinesis divides the cytoplasmic contents equally; in meiotic cytokinesis, cytoplasm is preferentially shunted to the cell destined to be the ovum, and away from the polar bodies.

5. Somatic cells are diploid cells that undergo mitosis. They include every cell in the body except the reproductive cells. Gametes are haploid reproductive cells, resulting from the process of meiosis: eggs and sperm in the female and male, respectively.

6. (a) metaphase I, meiosis I; (b) anaphase II, meiosis II; (c) anaphase, mitosis; (d) metaphase II, meiosis II; (e) metaphase, mitosis.

7. Meiosis ensures genetic diversity in two ways. In the process called recombination, homologous chromosomes swap sections with one another. Then, in the process called independent assortment, homologous chromosome pairs line up in a random way, relative to one another, along the metaphase plate.

8. A sperm has 23 chromosomes and an egg has 23 chromosomes; when sperm fertilizes egg, the result is a zygote with 46 chromosomes—22 homologous pairs of chromosomes and either two X chromosomes (if the zygote is female) or an X and a Y chromosome (if the zygote is male).

CHAPTER 11

Multiple Choice
1. a, 2. a, 3. e, 4. c, 5. d, 6. b, 7. e, 8. e, 9. d, 10. e.

Brief Review
1. (a) Phenotype is the representation of visible traits in an organism (that is, yellow vs. green peas), while genotype is the genetic composition responsible for the phenotype of a trait (that is, *YY* or *Yy* = yellow peas, *yy* = green peas). (b) Dominant is used to refer to a trait that is equally expressed in either the homozygous or heterozygous genotype (i.e., *YY* or *Yy* = yellow peas). Recessive is the term used to describe a trait that will be expressed only in the homozygous condition. Recessive traits are masked in the heterozygous genotype (i.e., *Yy* = yellow peas). (c) Codominance refers to the condition in which a heterozygote simultaneously expresses the phenotype associated with each allele. This is exhibited in blood types, where an AB individual produces both A and B cell surface molecules. Incomplete dominance is displayed when the heterozygote displays a phenotype that is an intermediate between the dominant and recessive phenotypes. An example is the generation of pink flowers resulting from a parental cross of one red-flowering and one white-flowering plant.
2. True.
3. The fragile-X syndrome demonstrates the genetic principle of pleiotropy, in which one gene has more than one effect. This differs from what Mendel observed in that, in his pea plants, one gene had one effect. There was a gene for flower color, for example, that came in alleles that brought about either purple or white flowers. But that gene did not then go on to affect other characters in the plant. By contrast, the gene connected to fragile-X syndrome has multiple effects—on intelligence and various physical characteristics.
4. In Mendelian genetics, two different genotypes may represent a dominant phenotype: *YY* and *Yy*.
5. Fifty percent of the progeny will be yellow peas.
6. Mendel's "element of inheritance" is now referred to as the gene.
7. Mendel's first law (law of segregation): Members of a gene pair will segregate from each other during gamete formation such that each gamete receives one and only one of the original two genes from the gene pair. Mendel's second law (law of independent assortment): During gamete formation, gene pairs assort independently of one another.
8. (a) *Aa* × *aa*; (b) *Aa* × *Aa*; (c) *Aabb* × *aaBb*; (d) *AaBb* × *AaBb*.

Genetics Problems
1. a 2. b 3. b 4. b 5. c 6. e 7. c 8. c
9. Since the purple allele is dominant, flowers will be purple whether the allele is present in two identical copies (homozygous state) or in one copy (heterozygous state). In contrast, expression of the recessive white allele is masked if a purple allele is present in the genotype. Therefore, it must be in homozygous form for the development of white flowers.
10. b
11. (a) 3 (b) The rule of multiplication. (c) 18.75 percent of the offspring should be purple-flowered with green seeds. This answer is the product of the joint occurrence of two independent events: the probability of purple-flower color (0.75) x the probability of green seed color (0.25).
12. It is possible to unambiguously determine genotype for snapdragons because incomplete dominance governs their color; every genotype manifests as a different phenotype. In the case of flower color in peas, phenotype cannot always unambiguously tell you about genotype. For white flowers, genotype can be assigned from phenotype, but for purple flowers, there are two possible genotypes, *PP* and *Pp*.
13. d
14. c

CHAPTER 12

Multiple Choice
1. a, 2. e, 3. a, 4. d, 5. e, 6. d, 7. c, 8. e, 9. e, 10. e.

Brief Review
1. Aneuploidy goes widely unrecognized because, in most instances, it is directly affecting embryos, rather than children or adults. The most common result of aneuploidy is a miscarriage of the embryo. In many instances, prospective parents will not realize that a miscarriage has taken place and, even when a miscarriage is recognized as such, prospective parents would rarely be able to identify aneuploidy as its cause.
2. Male. Sex-linked diseases usually are associated with the X chromosome, which females have two copies of. A female can carry one faulty version (or allele) of an X-chromosome gene and still be protected by a functional allele on her second X chromosome. Males, however, have only a single copy of the X chromosome. Should an allele on it be faulty, they have no second, protective copy of it.
3. The genes for red and green color vision are very closely aligned on the X chromosome, while the gene for blue vision is on chromosome 7. It would be possible to have dysfunctional genes for red and green but a functional gene for blue.
4. Deletions—A portion of the chromosome is completely lost.
Inversions—A portion of the chromosome is broken off and rejoins the original chromosome, but in a reversed order.
Translocations—Occur when two chromosomes that are not homologous exchange pieces, leaving both with improper gene sequences.
Duplications— A portion of a chromosome is duplicated, in some instances by gaining a chromosome piece during abnormal crossing over.
5. (a) non-disjunction; (b) polyploidy.
6. Because people who have Klinefelter syndrome have a Y chromosome, which confers the male sex, but they also have two copies of the X chromosome, rather than the one copy that males normally possess. Females normally have two copies of the X chromosome. Thus it makes sense that those with Klinefelter syndrome would exhibit some female characteristics.
7. A heterozygous genotype for hemoglobin would be advantageous in areas of mosquito infestation, while neither homozygous genotype would be advantageous in such areas. Those who are homozygous for hemoglobin A would not have the increased resistance to malaria; those who are homozygous for hemoglobin S would inherit sickle-cell anemia. Those who are heterozygous would have malaria resistance and yet would not inherit sickle-cell anemia.

Genetics Problems
1. None will be affected (although half will be carriers).
2. One half of her sons will be affected. The chance that her first child is affected is $\frac{1}{4}$ since there is a $\frac{1}{2}$ chance the first child is a boy and a $\frac{1}{2}$ chance that any boy is affected (another application of the rule of multiplication).
3. d
4. Recessive. Neither of the parents shows the autosomal trait, yet one of their offspring does.
5. His genotype is *aa*.
6. Her genotype must be *Aa*. (Reasoning: if she were *AA*, none of her children would be affected, whereas one is; if she were *aa* she would manifest the trait herself, which she does not.)
7. One half will be affected.
8. d
9. Her genotype is $X^+ X^p$ (Reasoning: She is not affected, her mate is not affected, yet they have affected sons. This is possible only if she is a carrier.)
10. One quarter of children and one half of their sons will show this trait (no daughters will have the trait).

11.

The chance that the son is color blind is $\frac{1}{2}$. This is because the woman in question must be a carrier.
12. One half of sons and daughters will have hyperphosphatemia. This is in sharp contrast to what would be observed if the trait were X-linked recessive. In this case, half the sons and none of the daughters would be affected.

CHAPTER 13

Multiple Choice
1. e, 2. e, 3. d, 4. e, 5. c, 6. d, 7. d, 8. e, 9. b, 10. b.

Brief Review
1. "Something old, something new" is a shorthand means of conveying that, in DNA replication, each newly formed DNA double helix is a mixture of the old and new. Each one is made of an existing "template" strand of DNA and a new strand that is complementary to it.
2. Watson and Crick's discovery of the structure of the DNA molecule immediately suggested answers to two of the most important questions in biology. First, how can genetic information be passed on from one cell to the next or from one generation to the next? (Through base-pairing between template-strand nucleotides and complementary nucleotides.) Second, how can DNA be complex enough to contain information about the huge variety of proteins that living things produce? (Bases can be arranged in an extremely varied manner along the "rails" of the double helix.)
3. False—DNA polymerases have an editing function, moving backward to check for and correct mistakes.
4. A mutation is a permanent alteration in a DNA base sequence. A change in a DNA base sequence only becomes permanent when it goes uncorrected by a cell's DNA error-correcting mechanisms, meaning the change will be copied over and over during DNA replication. Not all mutations are harmful. Most have no effect at all and some are important in evolution.
5. The Huntington disease mutation is an abnormal number of repeats in the gene that codes for the huntingtin protein. A faulty protein results that clogs up nerve cells, eventually killing them.

CHAPTER 14

Multiple Choice
1. e, 2. d, 3. b, 4. c, 5. a, 6. e, 7. e, 8. d, 9. a, 10. a.

Brief Review
1. The replication of DNA and the production of proteins from DNA.
2. (a) mRNA (messenger RNA), which takes DNA information to ribosomes; (b) rRNA (ribosomal RNA), which helps make up the ribosomes that act at the site of protein synthesis; and (c) tRNA (transfer RNA), which brings amino acids to the ribosomes and binds with mRNA codons there.
3. Transcription is the process by which the information encoded in DNA sequences is put into the form of mobile mRNA sequences. Translation is the process by which the information encoded in mRNA sequences is put into the form of amino acid sequences; this results in the production of a protein.
4. The enzyme complex RNA polymerase both unwinds DNA that is to be transcribed and pairs DNA bases with their complementary RNA bases.
5. An intron is a portion either of a primary RNA transcript, or of the DNA that codes for it, that is removed in messenger RNA editing. An exon is a

portion of either a primary transcript, or of the DNA that codes for it, that is retained in messenger RNA editing. Introns do not code for protein, but most exons do.

6. It is inaccurate to conceptualize DNA as autonomously controlling a cell's production of proteins, for two reasons. First, while DNA contains information that is used to produce proteins, it carries out none of the actual steps of protein synthesis. All these actions are carried out by proteins. Second, some of the very proteins that are encoded in DNA sequences then feed back on DNA, binding with it to regulate its activity.

7. Three, one.

CHAPTER 15
Multiple Choice
1. c, 2. e, 3. c, 4. a, 5. e, 6. e, 7. c, 8. b, 9. b, 10. a.
Brief Review
1. It is useful because some human beings cannot turn out sufficient quantities of their own supply of needed human proteins; this is so with some diabetics and the protein insulin, for example. Meanwhile, the protein may be available only in limited quantity—or with limited purity—from other sources. Thus it can be useful for human beings to manufacture supplies of given proteins through the processes of biotechnology.

2. The key would be to locate preserved cells that contain intact DNA.

3. PCR is valuable because it allows scientists to quickly make a large quantity of a given segment of DNA from a very small starting sample.

4. The production of sticky ends is useful because this type of end allows different restriction fragments to be joined together easily to create recombinant DNA.
    #### Fragment sequences:
    ATCG   GATCCTCCG
    TAGCCTAG   GAGGC

5. Dolly looked like the sheep that donated the udder cell, rather than the sheep that donated the egg, because the udder cell was the source of Dolly's DNA, while the DNA in the egg was removed. Thus, it was the donor cell that provided the instructions for Dolly's development.

CHAPTER 16
Multiple Choice
1. b; 2. a, b, d; 3. a, c, d, e; 4. Lyell—Geological forces observable today caused changes in Earth. Wallace—Natural selection is differential survival or reproduction. Lamarck—Inheritance of acquired characters. Cuvier—Catastrophic extinction and new creations explain fossil record. 5. a, c, and d are homologous; b and e do not belong. 6. d; 7. a, b, d, e; 8. a, c, d.
Brief Review
1. The term *homology* describes structures that are similar due to common ancestry. Homology provides evidence for evolution because it shows descent with modification.

2. Figure 16.12 shows that, in a gene shared by humans, pigs, and yeast, there are fewer DNA base differences between the forms of the gene found in humans and pigs than between the forms found in humans and yeast. This is what you would expect if humans and pigs shared a common ancestor more recently than did humans and yeast.

3. Congruent lines of evidence that are consistent with the theory of evolution: (a) The placement of fossils found in geological strata is consistent with the ages of those strata as determined by radiometric dating. (b) Evidence from molecular clocks is consistent with fossil and other evidence regarding the degree of relatedness among species.

4. Darwin brought back many birds that he thought were the blackbirds, wrens, and warblers he was familiar with in Britain, but he found they were in fact all species of finches. Darwin perceived this as an example of descent with modification. Without

taking the *Beagle* voyage, Darwin would not have been exposed to such extravagant examples of branching evolution, nor would he have made various other biological observations that spurred his thinking about evolution by natural selection.

CHAPTER 17
Multiple Choice
1. c; 2. gene pool—the set of all alleles in a population; allele—a variant form of a gene; allele frequency—the relative representation of a given form of a gene in a population; genotype—the genetic makeup of an organism; gene flow—exchange of genes between populations; 3. a, c; 4. a, c, e; 5. d; 6. b, d; 7. b; 8. mutation—changes in the genetic material; gene flow—movement of alleles between populations by migration; natural selection—a process in which the fit of an organism with its environment selects those traits that will be passed on with greater frequency from one generation to the next; genetic drift—chance alterations of allele frequencies in a population, with such alterations having greatest impact on small populations; founder effect—genetic drift due to a few colonizing genotypes; 9. d; 10. c; 11. c.

Brief Review
1. An individual may be selected for survival—and hence greater reproduction—because of the qualities that individual has, such as coloration or height. But this individual's characteristics do not change because it possesses these qualities. An individual does not evolve, in other words. An individual can pass on more of its genes relative to other individuals in a population, however; this causes the population's allele frequencies to change, meaning the population has evolved.

2. A gene pool is the sum total of alleles that exist in a population. The inheritable characteristics of living things are based on the alleles they possess. Thus, for a population to change in a way that is passed on from one generation to the next—for the population to evolve—the mixture of alleles in that population must change. Thus the evolution of a population is based at root on changes in that population's gene pool.

3. The five causes of microevolution are (1) Mutation—Changes in the form of the genetic material that result in new alleles. (2) Gene flow—Brings alleles from other populations into the target population. (3) Nonrandom mating—Mating in which a given member of a population is not equally likely to mate with any other given member. Can change the genetic contribution individuals make to a succeeding generation. (4) Genetic drift—The chance alteration of allele frequencies in a population. May occur if a new population is founded by only a few individuals (founder effect), or if the size of a population is decreased suddenly (the bottleneck effect). (5) Natural selection—Differential survival and hence reproduction of individuals based on their fit with a particular environment. If the phenotypic variation is inherited, the population will evolve to be like the individuals that survive longest and reproduce most.

4. An individual in a population has to have greater reproductive success relative to other members of the population in order to contribute more to the gene pool of the succeeding generation.

5. Mutation and genetic drift alter allele frequencies in random directions, and hence have nothing necessarily to do with adaptation. Gene flow doesn't necessarily bring in alleles that will be suited to the new environment, and nonrandom mating concerns mate choice, rather than an organism's fit with its environment. Through natural selection, however, phenotypes of individuals that survive and reproduce best in a given environment spread through the population.

6. Evolutionary fitness—the relative success in contributing genes to the next generation—depends crucially on the environment. It is the fit between environment and organism that

determines which organisms will have the greatest success in survival and reproduction. Thus, the evolutionary fitness of an individual could be expected to vary greatly from one environment to another. In the Grants' study of the Galápagos finches, a deeper bill was favored after the drought, but this situation later reversed.

CHAPTER 18
Multiple Choice
1. b; 2. b, c, d; 3. b, c, d; 4. a, c, d; 5. temporal isolation—mating occurs at different times of day or year; ecological isolation—populations live in different environments; geographical isolation—populations are separated by physical barriers; gametic isolation—egg and sperm do not fuse; hybrid sterility—progeny of a cross are unable to reproduce; 6. b, c, e; 7. species, genus, family, class, phylum; 8. b, d, e; 9. a.
Brief Review
1. Convergent evolution is the evolution of a very similar character in two unrelated organisms, caused when the organisms experience similar types of natural selection in their environments. For example, many unrelated species of desert plants have succulent leaves that store water. But these similar characters are not homologous (they are analogous), so they cannot be used to determine relationships in a phylogenetic study.

2. In the gradualistic model, evolutionary changes are steady and gradual over time. In the punctuated equilibria model, organisms go through long periods of stasis (remaining the same) and then enter into relatively brief periods of rapid evolutionary change. Some of the evidence for punctuated equilibria is that bacteria, which can be observed over tens of thousands of generations in a laboratory, do seem to evolve in spurts. Secondly, it appears that, in some species at least, changes in reproductively important traits can come about as a result of a small number of genetic changes.

3. A first requirement of allopatric speciation is that two populations of the same species must become separated geographically, such that gene flow between them is restricted. This allows the forces operating in microevolution—natural selection, genetic drift, mutation, and so forth—to work separately on the two populations. Eventually, the populations may develop intrinsic reproductive isolating mechanisms, such that, should they be reunited, they would no longer interbreed. In sympatric speciation, intrinsic isolating mechanisms evolve in the absence of geographical separation. The quality that both sympatric and allopatric speciation have in common is the development of intrinsic reproductive isolating mechanisms.

4. In the biological species concept, two organisms are in the same species if they actually or potentially interbreed successfully in nature.

5. Without the evolution of intrinsic isolating mechanisms, two populations that have become geographically separated would simply resume interbreeding, remaining one species, if any physical barriers to interbreeding were removed. Thus, they can't be called separate species unless they possess intrinsic reproductive isolating mechanisms.

CHAPTER 19
Multiple Choice
1. b, e, f, c, a, g d; 2. d; 3. b, e; 4. b, c, e; 5. b, a, d, c, e; 6. False; 7. b, c, d; 8. a, b, d; 9. b, e, f; 10. e.
Brief Review
1. The organisms in Domain Eukarya can be single-celled or multi-celled, but in all cases, their cells have nuclei. Bacteria are always single-celled, with these cells not having nuclei.

2. The amniotic egg evolved in the Reptilia. It is an egg in which the embryo lives in a watery environment (albumin, the "white") while being enclosed in a protective leathery or hard shell. Special mem-

branes facilitate gas exchange while protecting the embryo from drying out. This was a huge breakthrough for terrestrial animals, because it allowed them to lay eggs outside an aquatic environment without risking drying out.

3. Primates have forward-looking eyes and an opposable thumb. This facilitates depth perception and the ability to pick up and manipulate objects, paving the way for the use of tools.
4. Humans and chimps.
5. No.
6. Life is thought to have begun by about 3.8 billion years ago; the first terrestrial plant-fungi fossils date from 460 Mya, but molecular work indicates these organisms were on land 1.3 billion years ago; if so, 2.5 billion years elapsed between the origin of bacterial cells and the colonization of land. During this period, bacteria and archaea constituted the only life on land.
7. Mammals have hair, which helps in heat retention. Most have internal development of young in the uterus, and they have mammary glands that enable them to feed their offspring with milk.

CHAPTER 20
Multiple Choice
1. e; 2. d; 3. e; 4. e; 5. c; 6. e; 7. a; 8. e; 9. d; 10. c.
Brief Review
1. Extremophiles are bacteria or archaea that live in environments that are too harsh for ordinary organisms. Such environments can exhibit extremes of heat, cold, pH, salt, or other factors.
2. Viruses cannot replicate themselves without being in a host cell. The ability to self-replicate is generally considered to be a fundamental, defining feature of life.
3. Because phytoplankton perform much of the world's photosynthesis, they produce much of the world's oxygen. Because they make their own food (through photosynthesis), they lie at the base of most aquatic food chains—larger organisms that live in the water are ultimately dependent on them for food.
4. They must kill microorganisms while leaving human cells unharmed.
5. An amoeba is a protist that moves through use of pseudopodia or "false feet," meaning an extension of one part of the cell and a flowing of the rest of the cell into that extension. Many amoebae are parasites and some of these are human parasites that cause the class of diseases known as amoebic dysentery.
6. The probable cause of Mad Cow disease is a "rogue" protein called a prion, which becomes deformed and then goes on to deform other proteins of its type. It is unusual among infectious agents because most such agents usually are living things—bacteria, fungi, or protists—or are viruses, which use living cells to replicate. Prions are only a component part of a living thing.
7. Animals, fungi, and plants all evolved from protists.
8. In nature, plants get their nitrogen from certain bacteria that are able to take in atmospheric nitrogen and turn it into a form plants can use.

CHAPTER 21
Multiple Choice
1. d; 2. e; 3. e; 4. c; 5. b, d, e; 6. a, c, e; 7. a; 8. a, c, d; 9. b, d; 10. a, d, e.
Brief Review
1. Only a tiny fraction of the spores that fungi release will be able to germinate, or grow into a new mycelium. The fungi's solution to this problem is to "buy many tickets"—to create a huge number of spores, which scatter to diverse environments strictly because of their numbers.
2. A spore is a reproductive cell that can give rise to a complete organism without fusing with another reproductive cell. A gamete (an egg or sperm) is a reproductive cell that must fuse with another reproductive cell for a complete organism to be produced—egg must fuse with sperm.

3. Fungi grow toward their food sources, through growth of their hyphae.
4. The pollen of most angiosperms is carried from one plant to another by animals. The seeds of some angiosperms are dispersed by animals who ingest these seeds or by means of fruits sticking to animals' bodies (in the form of "burrs").
5. One fungal association takes the form of mycorrhizae, which is an association of fungal hyphae with plant roots. In this association, plants provide the fungi with food (made in photosynthesis) while the fungi supply plants with water and minerals (absorbed by the fungal hyphae). A second association is lichens, which are composite organisms made of upper and lower layers of fungi and a middle layer of algae (or sometimes bacteria) interspersed with fungi. The algae or bacteria supply the fungi with food (made in photosynthesis) and the fungi may keep the algae or bacteria from drying out, though it may be that the fungi are simply parasites.

CHAPTER 22
Multiple Choice
1. e; 2. d; 3. a; 4. e; 5. c; 6. a, b, c, d; 7. c; 8. b; 9. c, e; 10. d.
Brief Review
1. A coelom provides an animal with flexibility, allows for the expansion and contraction of organs such as the heart and stomach, and helps protect an animal's organs from being damaged by external blows.
2. All animals are thought to have evolved from a single, common ancestor, probably a protist called a choanoflagellate. The evidence for this is that all animals share several physical features. All go through a blastula stage in development—whereas no other life-forms do—and all are composed of cells that lack cell walls. It would be difficult to imagine a feature as specific as a blastula stage of development arising more than once in evolution.
3. The benefit of endothermy is that animals that possess it are fully functional in a wider range of temperatures than are ectotherms, as endotherms do not have to rely on their external environment to control their internal temperature. Endothermic animals also are able to live in colder climates than ectothermic animals. The cost of endothermy is higher energy expenditure; to obtain the energy they need, endothermic animals have to eat more, per unit of body weight, than do ectothermic animals. Only mammals and birds are truly endothermic.
4. Sponges have no brains or organs of any sort, no tissues, and each of their cells functions with a great deal of independence. Thus, the cells in a sponge have a lower level of specialization and integration with one another than is the case in more advanced animals.
5. Coral reefs are the skeletal remains of many generations of a variety of cnidarian—the reef-building coral—along with the remains of an associated type of algae.
6. The mollusc's unitary foot evolved over time into the arms and tentacles of the squid.
7. A dust mite; both the spider and mite are part of the arthropod subphylum Chelicerata, while the grasshopper is part of the arthropod subphylum Uniramia.
8. The mother must be a monotreme mammal, because only mammals provide milk for their young, and only monotreme mammals are hatched from eggs.

CHAPTER 23
Multiple Choice
1. a; 2. e; 3. b, c; 4. b; 5. e; 6. c, e; 7. a; 8. d; 9. b; 10. e.
Brief Review
1. The stomata allow the movement of carbon diox-

ide into the plant and oxygen out. These same openings also allow water to escape from the plant as water vapor. The plant solves the resulting problem of water loss by moving large quantities of water up through the roots and stem and out through the stomata.
2. Roots serve to anchor the plant (usually in soil), and they are the main absorptive organs of the plant. They absorb water and minerals from their surroundings and make them available to the above ground parts of the plant. In some species, roots also store substantial reserves of food. Taproots and fibrous roots are the two main types of roots produced by flowering plants.
3. Parts of a flower and main functions of each:

Flower Part Function

pedicel	Flower stalk; lifts flower up to make it noticeable to pollinators.
sepals	Leaf-like structures that protect flower buds before they open; commonly, also augment food supplies because they are usually green and photosynthetic.
petals	Generally most conspicuous part of the flower; often brightly colored; sometimes fragrant; attract pollinators.
stamens	Male reproductive structures; consist of a stalk called a filament, which holds aloft the pollen-producing sacs called anthers.
pollen	The male gametophyte; the vehicle that conducts male sperm to the female reproductive structures.
carpel	Female reproductive structure; consists of the ovary, style, and stigma—the ovary produces and protects the egg-containing female gametophyte, and after fertilization turns into the fruit; the stigma is the receptive surface that captures pollen and promotes germination of the right kind of pollen; the slender style raises the stigma to make it accessible to pollinators.

4. While people and other animals grow over their whole body, plants confine their vertical growth to distinct zones at the tips of their roots and shoots. Because these zones can be active throughout the life span of a plant, plants continue to grow all through their lives. Animals, in contrast, typically cease growth upon reaching maturity.
5. Plants enter into cooperative arrangements with members of nearly all the kingdoms of life. The roots of some plants—those of legumes such as beans and peas, for example—harbor nitrogen-fixing bacteria; the plant supplies carbohydrate to the bacteria, which in return manufactures hard-to-obtain nitrogen-containing compounds that the plant can use. In nature, the roots of most plants are colonized by certain types of fungi (mycorrhizal fungi) whose hyphae increase the plant's ability to absorb water and minerals. In return, these fungi receive carbohydrates produced by the plant.
6. The gametophyte is the multicellular haploid phase of a plant; that is, each cell in the gametophyte has just one set of chromosomes. The gametophyte produces gametes (egg and sperm). The sporophyte is the multicellular diploid phase of the plant; the sporophyte produces the spore that gives rise to the gametophyte.

CHAPTER 24
Multiple Choice
1. a; 2. b; 3. c; 4. c; 5. b; 6. a; 7. e; 8. b; 9. c, d; 10. c.
Brief Review
1. Differences between monocots and dicots:

	Monocots	Dicots
number of cotyledons (food-storing parts of the embryo)	one	two

arrangement of flower parts	sets of three	sets of four or five
leaf vein pattern	parallel veins	net-like veins
arrangement of vascular bundles	scattered	in a discrete ring
type of root system	fibrous root	taproot

2. The three main cell types in a plant and the functions performed by each:

Cell Type	Function
parenchyma	Living cells; perform a wide variety of metabolic functions such as photosynthesis, food storage, wound repair.
collenchyma	Living cells with irregularly thickened walls; perform some metabolic functions such as photosynthesis, but also impart mechanical strength to tissues experiencing active growth.
sclerenchyma	Usually dead at maturity; main role is structural support for the plant body, and water conduction in some cases.

3. Meristematic tissue gives rise to all other tissue types in the plant. Meristematic cells remain perpetually embryonic: they are able to keep giving rise to cells that differentiate into various tissue types. Apical meristems are located at the tips of shoots and roots and contribute to the length of the plant. Lateral meristems contribute to the girth of a plant and are of two main kinds—the vascular cambium, which gives rise to secondary xylem and phloem; and the cork cambium, which creates a protective layer of cells known as bark.

4. The water-conducting xylem cells come in two types: tracheids and vessel elements. Both are thick-walled and both die at maturity, after which their contents are cleared out. Because they are stacked on top of one another, lines of these cells become water-conducting tubes. Tracheids are tapered at their ends and any two pairs of tracheid cells have matched pairs of perforations that line up with one another, allowing water to move from one cell to another. Vessel elements may lose part or all of the barriers between one cell and the next, allowing for a greater capacity to transport water than is the case with the tracheids. The food-conducting phloem cells, called sieve elements, are alive at maturity, but lack nuclei. Their housekeeping needs are taken care of by one or more adjacent companion cells. A collection of sieve element cells makes up a sieve tube, which transports sucrose, along with hormones and other compounds.

5. The line that we see as a growth ring represents a collection of narrower, darker cells that grew in the tree in late summer, when water was relatively scarce. These cells are juxtaposed with wider, lighter-colored cells that grew in the spring, when water was more plentiful. We can count a tree's age by its rings because each ring of summer cells is laid down only once each year.

6. When the two sperm cells from a pollen grain enter the embryo sac of a plant, two fertilization events take place. In the first of these, a sperm cell fuses with the embryo sac's egg cell, thus setting in motion development of a new plant embryo. In the second fertilization event, the second sperm cell fuses with the two nuclei of the embryo sac's central cell. This event sets in motion the development of endosperm—food for the growing embryo.

CHAPTER 25
Multiple Choice
1. d; 2. a; 3. b; 4. b; 5. c; 6. d; 7. d; 8. c; 9. a; 10. d; 11. b.

Brief Review
1. Cell, tissue, organ, organ system.
2. Lymphatic organs such as the spleen have high concentrations of immune cells within them that monitor passing lymphatic fluid for signs of invading microorganisms.
3. Our skin is water-resistant because the surface epidermal layer of the skin is formed of tightly interlocking cells made almost entirely of the protein keratin, which is water-resistant.
4. Three functions of the skeletal system are support, storage of minerals and fats, and blood-cell production.
5. Hair follicles can shrink later in life, meaning a shorter growing phase for each hair, thus yielding hair that is either short and fine or non-existent.
6. The sample is from the end (epiphysis) of a long bone.
7. Ligaments hold bones together in stable arrangements. The anterior cruciate ligament (ACL) links the back of the femur (thigh bone) to the front of the tibia (shin bone). If the ACL were damaged, the two bones would not be held in place properly.
8. Skeletal muscle appears striated or striped under a microscope because its alternating bands of thick and thin protein filaments line up in a parallel orientation with each other.

CHAPTER 26
Multiple Choice
1. c; 2. c; 3. e; 4. e; 5. b; 6. a; 7. b; 8. a; 9. e; 10. c.

Brief Review
1. The sensory neuron receives input about conditions inside and outside the body and conveys this received information to the central nervous system (CNS). The motor neuron exists in the peripheral nervous system (PNS) and sends instructions from the CNS to such structures as muscles or glands. The interneuron exists solely in the CNS and serves to interconnect neurons and integrate signals from them.
2. Neurons have special extensions of themselves, called axons and dendrites, that respectively carry nervous system signals away from and towards the neuron cell body. In addition, the outer or plasma membrane of each neuron has a charge difference, from one side to the other, that can change rapidly with the proper stimulation, going from negative on the membrane's interior to briefly positive, then back to negative. This change in membrane potential can be propagated down the length of the neuron's axon, after which stimulation of an adjacent neuron can take place through release of neurotransmitters that diffuse from the sending neuron across a synaptic cleft.
3. A simple reflex arc works by means of a sensory neuron sending an afferent message about some stimulation to the spinal cord. There, the sensory neuron will synapse with a motor neuron (or perhaps an interneuron), after which the motor neuron sends a signal that brings about some action at an effector such as a muscle. The brain is not involved in such an arc.
4. In the senses of hearing, touch, taste, and vision, various types of sensory receptors responded to their respective forms of stimulation and then acted as transducers, transforming the stimulation they received into the electrical impulses of the nervous system. They did the latter by releasing neurotransmitters to receiving neurons (or by not releasing neurotransmitters, in the case of vision). In each case, the resulting nerve signal went first to the brain's thalamus and then to different areas of its cerebral cortex for processing.
5. The hormones of the endocrine system take at least several seconds to have any effect. This time-frame is fine for maintaining fluid levels, but of no use in carrying out the rapid, complex movements required to shoot a basketball—the nervous system handles those.
6. A given hormone does not actually target individual cells. Rather, a "target cell" is any cell that has on it, or in it, the receptors necessary to bind with a given hormone.
7. Amino-acid-based hormones are derived from a chemical modification of a single amino acid. Peptide hormones are built from chains of amino acids, in a range running from short polypeptide chains to longer chains constituting proteins. The building block of all steroid hormones is the cholesterol molecule. Amino-acid-based and peptide hormones generally bind with receptors that are on the surface of target cells. Steroid hormones can do this, but they also can pass through the outer membrane of a target cell and bind with a receptor inside the cell.

CHAPTER 27
Multiple Choice
1. b; 2. b; 3. e; 4. d; 5. d; 6. d; 7. b; 8. e; 9. b; 10. c.

Brief Review
1. The immune system increases blood flow near the site of injury and increases the permeability of capillaries near the site (so that more substances can be transported out); it delivers cells and proteins to the site that kill the invaders; and it releases substances that help seal off the site of injury, thus limiting the area of the infection.
2. A dendritic cell is one of three classes of antigen-presenting cells (APCs). These cells destroy cells infected by an invader and then display antigens from the invader on their surface. They then migrate to a lymph node or to the spleen and present the invader's antigens to helper T cells, a small fraction of which will have receptors specific to both the APC and the antigens. The interaction between the APC and the helper T cell activates the helper T cell, thus spurring the creation of a clone of helper T cells specific to the invader. There is some evidence that dendritic cells are the only APCs that can initiate the process of T-cell activation.
3. HIV has so many effects because the disease it causes, AIDS, weakens the immune system, which normally fights off so many kind of invaders. As an example of what's at work, the cancers mentioned in the question are linked to viruses that would be taken care of by a healthy immune system.
4. The immune system regards any transplanted organ as "non-self" and thus will initiate an attack against it.
5. HIV's rapid mutation has the effect of altering the recognition proteins on the surface of the virus. Immune system antibodies work by binding with such surface proteins. With HIV, there is no fixed set of surface proteins to bind to.

CHAPTER 28
Multiple Choice
1. e; 2. e; 3. c, e; 4. c; 5. d; 6. e; 7. a; 8. c; 9. c; 10. e.

Brief Review
1. Red blood cells transport oxygen and carbon dioxide; white blood cells are central to the body's immune system function; and platelets are active in the process of blood clotting.
2. The left and right atrial chambers of the heart pump blood only into their respective ventricles, while the ventricles pump blood to locations outside the heart—the right ventricle to the lungs, the left ventricle to all the tissues of the body.
3. Capillaries are the only blood vessels whose walls are thin enough to permit diffusion of substances in and out; they are composed of but a single layer of cells, whereas arteries and veins have a three-layered structure.

4. The pulmonary arteries carry deoxygenated blood; they are carrying blood to the lungs to be oxygenated.

5. Eating animal fats raises the levels of the low-density lipoproteins (LDLs) that lodge within the coronary artery tissue; smoking may damage LDLs in a way that triggers the immune response against them; exercise lowers LDL levels while raising the levels of high-density lipoproteins or HDLs, which help clear or neutralize LDLs.

6. Oxygen enters the bloodstream at a capillary that covers an alveolus in the lungs. Oxygen is inhaled into the sac-like alveolus and then diffuses across the alveolar tissue into an adjacent capillary.

7. Food has not been broken down in the stomach to an extent that it can pass out of the digestive system to adjacent capillaries (or lymphatic vessels in the case of lipids.) Partway through the small intestine, foods have been broken down to this extent, thanks in large part to the digestive enzymes and bile that move into the small intestine from the pancreas, liver, and gallbladder.

8. Apart from waste storage and compaction, the large intestine conserves water by moving it back into circulation, and it absorbs vitamins produced by resident bacteria.

9. Blood cells and most proteins are too large to pass out of the glomerulus capillaries and into the filtrate; they remain in the circulatory system.

10. The urination signal we are aware of is an involuntary contraction of the urinary bladder. This increases the fluid pressure inside the bladder, which can be uncomfortable.

CHAPTER 29
Multiple Choice
1. b, d, c, e, a; 2. c; 3. d; 4. a; 5. c; 6. b; 7. e; 8. b; 9. c; 10. a.
Brief Review

1. After fertilization, the cleavage stage of development begins. This results in the formation of a hollow ball of cells. The embryo does not change in size during cleavage. Next, these cells undergo rearrangement and movement, in the process called gastrulation. Now the embryo has a body cavity and three layers of cells—the endoderm, ectoderm, and mesoderm.

2. After gastrulation in the chick embryo, a small group of cells is induced to form the wing of the chick. This group of cells forms a structure called the wing bud, which eventually develops into the wing. A group of the cells in the wing bud are called the zone of polarizing activity (ZPA). The ZPA sends out a morphogen that directs the proper order of digit production in the chick's wing.

3. Cell adhesion molecules allow different varieties of cells to selectively adhere to one another. This allows for all kinds of cell organization, including the organization of the embryo into different layers of cells.

4. The concentration of a given morphogen will decrease as distance increases from the cells that secrete the morphogen. Such a concentration gradient exists for all morphogens. In the fruit fly *Drosophila*, a concentration gradient of the morphogen bicoid affects the development of anterior and center-section structures of the fly. Bicoid concentrations are highest at the anterior end of the *Drosophila* embryo and this high concentration has the effect of bringing about anterior structures of the fly, such as its head. Lower bicoid concentrations at the center of the embryo help bring about center-section structures.

5. Cell death works to create spaces that define shapes in a developing organism. Without this death, the human hand would not have separate fingers, but would have a webbed structure similar to that of a duck.

6. Scientists are enthusiastic about stem cells because these cells hold the potential to produce tissues that could cure or help alleviate many kinds of human illnesses, such as heart disease and diabetes.

CHAPTER 30
Multiple Choice
1. c; 2. a; 3. a; 4. c; 5. d; 6. d; 7. c; 8. a; 9. e; 10. c.
Brief Review

1. Gonadotropin-releasing hormone, which is released by the hypothalamus, stimulates the release of follicle-stimulating hormone (FSH) and lutenizing hormone (LH). Both of these hormones are released by the anterior pituitary gland. FSH promotes the development of the follicles, and LH stimulates the production of estrogen. As estrogen levels increase, FSH levels at first begin to decrease, but as estrogen levels begin to peak due to the development of the tertiary follicle, both FSH and LH levels spike. This results in ovulation. The corpus luteum then begins to synthesize progesterone, which acts on the hypothalamus to reduce FSH and LH to original levels, resulting in degeneration of the endometrium and menstruation.

2. Sperm development is dependent on temperature. If things get too hot, then sperm production is impaired. Similarly, cold temperatures also prevent sperm development. The structure of the testes acts to keep sperm production at the correct temperature. The sperm are protected from the high body temperatures because of the location of the testes outside the body. In addition, a muscle that surrounds the testes contracts when temperatures drop, so that the testes are pulled in closer to the warm body.

3. Two hypotheses currently are favored to explain the existence of menstruation. One is that the cycle of tissue build-up and breakdown that underlies it is less costly, in terms of energy expenditure, than the alternative of keeping the endometrium in a permanent state of readiness for embryo implantation. The second hypothesis is that, when it is ready for embryo implantation, the endometrium is in a form that cannot be maintained permanently and that must arise from an earlier form. Thus, it makes sense that the inner endometrium would wash away every 28 days and then enter a new cycle of growth and development.

4. Once ovulation occurs and the tertiary follicle releases the oocyte, the tertiary follicle becomes the corpus luteum. Both structures release hormones that move the female reproductive cycle forward.

5. Fusion of a sperm with an oocyte prompts the oocyte to release granules whose secretions harden the material surrounding the oocyte and inactivate sperm receptors on the surface of the oocyte.

6. Prior to implantation, the fertilized egg divides to form a morula. This tightly packed ball of cells continues to divide, forming a hollow ball of cells called the blastocyst. The blastocyst will then implant in the uterine wall.

7. Any baby born before 37 weeks of gestation is regarded as premature.

8. Birth control pills work using a combination of synthetic estrogen and progestin. Normally, low estrogen levels trigger the beginning of follicle development. The pill creates high estrogen levels that suppress the release of FSH from the hypothalamus. The progestin in the pill suppresses the release of LH in order to prevent ovulation of any follicle that might develop in the presence of high estrogen levels.

CHAPTER 31
Multiple Choice
1. d; 2. c; 3. e; 4. c; 5. d; 6. b; 7. a; 8. c; 9. b, d; 10. d.

Brief Review
1. Population, community, ecosystem, biosphere.

2. *K*-selected species experience their environment as relatively stable, spend most of their lives in populations that are close to carrying capacity (*K*), and provide a relatively large amount of care to a relatively small number of offspring. In contrast, *r*-selected species experience their environment as relatively unstable, have populations whose numbers are limited largely by reproductive rate, and provide little or no parental care to a relatively large number of offspring. Humans and elephants are *K*-selected species; flies and ragweed are *r*-selected species.

3. *Environmental resistance* is the term used to describe all the environmental forces that act to limit population growth. Organisms will run out of food or have their sunlight blocked; temperatures will plunge or rain will cease; greater numbers of predators will discover the population; the wastes produced by the organisms will begin to be toxic to the population.

4. This is an example of Batesian mimicry, in which one species (the red salamander) has evolved to acquire the appearance of a species with superior protective capabilities (the red newt). The red newt is the model, the red salamander is the mimic, and the dupe is any predator species that would avoid the red salamander, believing it to be a red newt.

5. Because this succession begins from a state of little or no life and no soil, it is an example of primary succession.

CHAPTER 32
Multiple Choice
1. c; 2. d; 3. b; 4. a; 5. a; 6. b; 7. c; 8. e; 9. a.
Brief Review

1. According to the energy-flow model of ecosystems (and the second law of thermodynamics), the energy contained in each trophic level is much less than the energy contained in the trophic level below it, because much of the energy in each trophic level is used for metabolic processes (running, staying warm) and much energy from these processes is lost from the system as heat. In addition, not all of the prey is eaten by the predators.

2. Warm air (a) rises and (b) can carry more moisture than cold air. Near the equator, the Earth gets warm due to the direct rays coming from the Sun. As this warm air rises, it cools and drops moisture. This cooler air moves toward the poles in both directions, and descends at about 30° north and south, warming as it goes, thus absorbing moisture from the land, which is dry as a result.

3. Climate essentially defines the large-scale vegetation patterns that are seen on Earth. Variations within large-scale climate regions tend to be mountains, whose climates can vary greatly from base to peak.

4. It is likely that eutrophication has occurred in the pond. If so, large algal blooms can result from the excess nutrients. As this dead organic matter falls to the lower depths, decomposers consume the organic matter but deplete the water of oxygen, thus killing fish.

5. Permafrost makes the tundra wet during summer months, even with low rainfall, and it is too cold for trees to grow. Taiga has a less severe climate and a longer growing season, and no permafrost; coniferous trees grow slowly there and support a larger animal community.

Glossary

1n Haploid; having one chromosome of each type per cell instead of a pair of chromosomes of each type.
2n Diploid; having two chromosomes of each type per cell.

A

abiotic Pertaining to nonliving things.
acid Any substance that yields hydrogen ions when in solution. An acid has a number lower than 7 on the pH scale.
acrosome A structure located on the front end of the head of a vertebrate sperm cell; contains enzymes that help the sperm penetrate the accessory cells surrounding the oocyte.
action potential A temporary reversal of neuronal cell membrane potential at one location that results in a conducted nerve impulse down an axon.
activation energy The energy required to initiate a chemical reaction. Enzymes lower the activation energy of a reaction, thereby greatly speeding up the rate of the reaction.
active site The area of an enzyme, usually a groove or pocket, that binds the substrate and changes its shape to affect its reactivity.
active transport Transport of materials across the plasma membrane in which energy must be expended. Through active transport, solutes can be moved against their concentration gradient. The sodium-potassium pump is an example of active transport.
actively acquired immunity Immunity developed as a result of accidental or deliberate exposure to an antigen. Accidental exposure: coming into contact with someone who has a transmissible disease. Deliberate exposure: being vaccinated.
adaptation An evolutionary modification in the structure or behavior of organisms over generations that makes them better suited to their environment.
adaptive radiation The rapid emergence of many species from a single species that has been introduced to a new environment. The different species specialize to fill available niches in the new environment.
adenosine triphosphate (ATP) A nucleotide that serves as the most important energy-transfer molecule in living things. ATP powers a broad range of chemical reactions by donating one of its three phosphate groups to these reactions. In the process, it becomes adenosine diphosphate (ADP), which reverts to being ATP when a third phosphate is added to it.
adrenocorticotropic hormone (ACTH) A hormone, secreted by the anterior pituitary, that stimulates release of steroid hormones from the outer cells of the adrenal gland.
adult stem cell A cell from a tissue of an adult that is capable of giving rise to many other types of cells or tissues.
afferent division The division of the peripheral nervous system that carries sensory information toward the central nervous system, having gathered information about the body or environment.
albumins With globulins and fibrinogen, one of the three primary classes of proteins suspended in the fluid or plasma portion of the blood. Albumins function in the transport of hormones and fatty acids.
alcoholic fermentation The process by which yeasts produce alcohol as a byproduct of glycolysis they perform in oxygenless environments.
algae Protists that perform photosynthesis.
algal bloom An overabundance of algae in a body of water, resulting from an excess of nutrients. The many dead algae that fall to the bottom allow decomposing bacteria to flourish, using up so much oxygen that fish can suffocate.
alimentary canal Another term for the digestive tract, the muscular tube that runs through the body from mouth to anus and through which food passes.

alkaline Basic, as in solutions. Alkaline (basic) solutions have numbers above 7 on the pH scale.
allele One of the alternative forms of a single gene. In pea plants, a single gene codes for seed color, and it comes in two alleles—one codes for yellow seeds, the other for green seeds.
allergen A foreign substance that triggers an allergic reaction. These substances are usually derived from living things, including pollen, dust mites, foods, and fur.
allergies Immune system overreactions to antigens.
allopatric speciation Speciation that involves the geographic separation of populations. Most speciation involves geographic separation, followed by the development of intrinsic isolating mechanisms in the separated populations.
allosteric regulation The regulation of an enzyme's activity by means of a molecule binding to a site on the enzyme other than its active site.
alpha helix A common secondary structure of proteins that resembles a corkscrew or spiral staircase. Hair, nails, and horns are proteins made up almost entirely of alpha helices.
alternation of generations A life-cycle practiced by plants, in which successive plant generations alternate between the diploid sporophyte condition and the haploid gametophyte condition.
altruism A costly or risky behavior carried out by one animal for the benefit of another animal.
alveoli (singular, alveolus) Tiny, hollow air-exchange sacs that exist in clusters at the end of each of the air-conducting passageways in the lungs, the bronchioles.
amino-acid-based hormones Hormones that are derived from a single amino acid. One of three principal classes of hormones, the other two being peptide and steroid hormones.
amniotic egg An egg with a hard outer casing and an inner series of membranes and fluids that form a padding around the growing embryo. The evolution of the amniotic egg, in reptiles, freed them from the constraint of having to reproduce near water.
amniotic fluid A protective and nutritive fluid that surrounds the fetus of mammals, including filling the lungs.
analogy A structure found in different organisms that is similar in function and appearance, but is not the result of shared ancestry. Analogies must be distinguished from homologies to get a true picture of evolutionary relationships.
ancestral character A character that existed in the common ancestor of a group of organisms. Cladistics distinguishes ancestral from derived characters and uses these characters to determine evolutionary relationships.
aneuploidy A condition in which an individual organism has either more or fewer chromosomes than is normal for its species, so that the individual has the wrong number of chromosomes in its set. Down syndrome is the result of aneuploidy—generally three copies of chromosome 21.
angiosperm A flowering seed plant whose seeds are enclosed within the tissue called fruit. Angiosperms are the most dominant and diverse of the four principal types of plants. Examples include roses, cacti, corn, and deciduous trees.
animal behavior A subdiscipline of biology concerned with the study of the behavior of animals.
animal pole The end of a zygote with relatively less yolk and lying closer to the cell's nucleus. The location of the egg's poles defines the orientation in which the embryo develops.
annual A type of plant that goes through its entire life cycle—from germination of the seed through growth, flowering, and death—in one year or less. Many crop plants, such as tomatoes and grains, are annuals.
anterior pituitary An endocrine gland that releases two hormones that work directly on target cells and four other hormones that regulate the production of hormones by other endocrine glands.
anther The part of a flower that produces pollen grains. The anther is on top of a filament, and together they are called the stamen.
antibiotics Chemical compounds produced by one microorganism that are toxic to another microorganism.
antibody A protein of the immune system, found on the surface of a B cell or circulating free in the plasma,

that is formed in response to a particular antigen and reacts with it specifically, deactivating it.
antibody-mediated immunity An immune system capability that works through the production of proteins called antibodies.
anticodon The end of the transfer RNA molecule that can form a base pair with a particular codon on the mRNA transcript.
antidiuretic hormone (ADH) Substance that helps control how much water is either sent to the bladder (in urine) by the kidneys or retained in circulation. In a release controlled by the brain's hypothalamus, ADH increases the permeability of both the distal nephron tubule and the nephron's collecting duct to water, thus conserving it.
antigen Any foreign substance that elicits a response by the immune system. Certain proteins on the surface of an invading bacterial cell, for instance, act as antigens that trigger an immune response.
antigen-presenting cell (APC) Any immune-system cell that presents, on its surface, fragments of an antigen that it has ingested. Dendritic cells, macrophages, and B cells are the immune system's three classes of antigen-presenting cells.
aorta The enormous artery extending from the heart that receives all the blood pumped by the heart's left ventricle. Branches stemming from the aorta supply oxygenated blood to all the tissues in the body.
apical dominance Suppression of the growth of the lateral branches of a plant through the activity of apical meristems.
apical meristem The group of plant cells at the tips of the roots and shoots that are able to keep dividing, and from which all tissues ultimately develop.
appendicular skeleton The division of the skeletal system consisting of the bones of the paired appendages, including the pelvic and pectoral girdles to which they are attached.
aqueous solution A solution in which water is the solvent. Because living things contain so much water, nearly all solutions important in biological systems are aqueous solutions.
aquifer The porous underground rock in which groundwater is stored.
Archaea With Bacteria and Eukarya, one of three domains of the living world, composed solely of microscopic, single-celled organisms superficially similar to bacteria but genetically quite different. Many of the Archaea live in extreme environments such as boiling-hot vents on the ocean floor.
arithmetical increase An increase in numbers by an addition of a fixed number in each time period.
artery A blood vessel that carries blood away from the heart.
asexual reproduction Reproduction that occurs without the union of two reproductive cells (sexual reproduction). Offspring of asexual reproduction are genetically identical to their parents.
assortative mating Mating in which males and females that share a particular characteristic, such as short height, tend to mate with one another. Such mating tends to bring similar alleles together but does not directly alter allele frequencies in the population.
atmosphere The layer of gases that surrounds the Earth. The atmosphere is nonliving, but its presence enables life to exist on Earth.
atom The fundamental unit of matter; once thought to be the smallest particle in nature, but now known to be made up of many smaller units, including electrons, protons, and neutrons.
atomic number The number of protons in the nucleus of an atom. Gold has 79 protons in its nucleus and thus has the atomic number 79. All elements are ordered on the periodic table according to atomic number.
atomic weight The combined weight (mass) of protons and neutrons in an atom's nucleus.
ATP synthase An enzyme functioning in cellular respiration that brings together ADP and inorganic phosphate molecules to produce ATP.
autoimmune disorder An attack by the immune system on the body's own tissues.
autonomic nervous system That portion of the

peripheral nervous system's efferent division that provides involuntary regulation of smooth muscle, cardiac muscle, and glands.

autosomal dominant disorder A genetic disorder caused by a single faulty allele located on an autosomal (non-sex chromosome). Huntington disease is one example.

autosomal recessive disorder A recessive dysfunction caused by faulty alleles on an autosome (non-sex chromosome). Sickle-cell anemia is one example.

autotroph Any organism that manufactures its own food. Almost all plants and algae, and certain bacteria, are autotrophs.

axial skeleton The division of the skeletal system that forms the central column, including the skull, vertebral column, and rib cage.

axon A single, large extension of the cell body of a neuron that carries signals away from the cell body toward other cells.

B

Bacteria With Archaea and Eukarya, one of three domains of the living world, composed solely of single-celled, microscopic organisms that superficially resemble archaea but are genetically quite different.

ball-and-stick model A diagram showing the three-dimensional structure of a molecule, with the atoms drawn as balls and the bonds between them drawn as sticks. This type of representation clearly shows the spatial relationship of the atoms to each other.

bark Everything outside the vascular cambium in woody plants; bark consists of cork cambium, cork, phelloderm, and secondary phloem.

base Any substance that accepts hydrogen ions in solution. A base has a number higher than 7 on the pH scale.

Batesian mimicry A type of mimicry in which one species evolves to resemble a species that has superior protection against predators.

bell curve A distribution of values that is symmetrically largest around the average.

beta pleated sheet A common secondary structure of proteins that resembles the folds of an accordion. Silk is a protein made up almost entirely of beta pleated sheets lying stacked like pancakes on top of each other.

biennial A type of plant that goes through its life cycle in about two years, flowering in the second year.

bilateral symmetry A bodily symmetry in which opposite sides of a sagittal plane are mirror images of one another. Animals generally are bilaterally symmetrical.

bile Substance produced by the liver that facilitates the digestion of fats. Bile can be released either directly by the liver or by the gallbladder, which stores and concentrates this substance.

binary fission The form of reproduction carried out by prokaryotic cells in which the chromosome replicates and the cell pinches between the attachment points of the two resulting chromosomes to form two new cells. In this type of simple cell-splitting, each pair of daughter cells is an exact replica of the parental cell.

binding site An area of a protein or glycoprotein, located at the surface of the plasma membrane, with a particular conformation that recognizes only one molecule or a closely related group of molecules. Binding sites enable specificity of cell communication.

binomial nomenclature The system of naming species that uses two names (genus and species) for each species. This system helps identify groupings among living things.

biodegradable Capable of being broken down by living organisms.

biodiversity The diversity of living things. Includes species diversity, diversity of distributions, and genetic diversity.

biogeochemical cycling The movement of water and nutrients back and forth between biotic (living) and abiotic (nonliving) systems.

biological legacy A living thing, or product of a living thing, that survives a major ecological disturbance. Biological legacies proved to be crucial in the process of

succession that occurred at Washington State's Mount St. Helens following its eruption in 1980.

biological species concept A definition of species that relies on the breeding behavior of populations in nature. Accordingly, populations that actually or potentially interbreed in nature and are reproductively isolated from other such groups constitute a species.

biology The study of life.

biomass Material produced by living things, generally measured by weight.

biome An ecosystem dominated by a large vegetation formation, whose boundaries are largely determined by climate. The same biome type can occur on two different continents and have different species, but the two regions will bear striking similarities.

biosphere The interactive collection of all the world's ecosystems. Also thought of as that portion of the Earth that supports life.

biotechnology The application of technology to biological processes. In a stricter sense, biotechnology is often defined as the use of living organisms to create products or to facilitate processes.

biotic Pertaining to living things.

bivalves A class of molluscs that includes mussels, clams, and oysters, among other organisms.

blade In plants, the major, broad part of a leaf.

blastocoel The fluid-filled cavity in a blastula.

blastocyst Hollow, fluid-filled ball of cells that is formed in the early stages of the embryonic development of humans and other mammals. In non-mammalian animals, the blastocyst is known as the blastula.

blastula An early-stage embryo composed of one or more layers of cells surrounding a liquid-filled cavity known as a blastocoel. (In vertebrates, the blastula is referred to as the blastocyst.)

B-lymphocyte cells (B cells) The central cells of antibody mediated immune system function. B cells produce antibodies, called antigen receptors, that bind with specific antigens while remaining embedded in the B cell. Conversely, these antibodies may be exported from B cells as free-standing entities to fight antigens.

body segmentation A repetition of body parts in an animal. An example can be found in the vertebrae that make up the human vertebral column or backbone.

bone A connective tissue that provides support and storage capacity, and that is the site of blood-cell production.

bottleneck effect A change in allele frequencies in a population due to chance, following a sharp reduction in the population's size. One of the factors that potentiates genetic drift.

Bowman's capsule A hollow structure in the kidneys of vertebrates that receives the filtrate from the blood and passes it into the proximal tubule of the nephron. This structure is the point where wastes are transferred from the blood into the kidney.

bronchiole Tiny air-conducting passageway in the lungs that has at its end several alveoli, the hollow air-exchange sacs of the lungs.

bryophyte A plant that lacks a vascular (fluid transport) structure. Bryophytes are the most primitive of the four principal varieties of plants. Mosses are the most familiar example.

bud An undeveloped plant shoot, composed mostly of meristematic tissue.

buffering system A physiological system that functions to keep pH within normal limits in an organism. Buffering systems generally utilize weak acids or bases to neutralize any sudden infusion of acid or base.

bulbourethral gland A gland that, in human males, contributes fluids to the semen as it proceeds through the urethra in the process of ejaculation.

C

C₄ photosynthesis A form of photosynthesis in which carbon dioxide is first fixed into a four-carbon molecule and then transferred to special bundle sheath cells in which the Calvin cycle is undertaken. C_4 photosynthesis is

used primarily by plants in warm-weather environments as a means of reducing the photorespiration that undercuts carbohydrate production in C_3 plants.

Calvin cycle The set of steps in photosynthesis in which an energy-rich sugar is produced by means of two essential processes—the fixing of atmospheric carbon dioxide into a sugar, and the energizing of this sugar with the addition of electrons supplied by the light-dependent reactions of photosynthesis. Named for the biochemist Melvin Calvin, who elucidated its steps. Also known as the Calvin-Benson cycle.

Cambrian explosion A period of dramatic increase in the number of animal phyla that began about 540 million years ago, to judge by the fossil record.

CAM photosynthesis (crassulacean acid metabolism photosynthesis) A form of photosynthesis, undertaken by some plants in hot, dry climates, in which carbon fixation takes place at night and the Calvin cycle during the day. Practiced by succulent plants in particular, CAM metabolism allows plants to preserve water by opening their stomata only at night.

capillary The smallest type of blood vessel, connecting the arteries and veins in the body's tissues. Gases, nutrients, and wastes are exchanged between the blood and the tissues through the thin walls of capillaries.

capillary bed An interconnected network of capillaries that lies in the body's tissues. The network brings the capillaries close to each part of the tissues and provides lots of surface area for more efficient exchange.

capsid A protein coat that surrounds the genetic material in almost all viruses.

carbohydrate An organic molecule that always contains carbon, oxygen, and hydrogen and that, in many instances, contains nothing but carbon, oxygen, and hydrogen. Carbohydrates usually contain exactly twice as many hydrogen atoms as oxygen atoms. The building blocks or monomers of carbohydrates are monosaccharides, such as glucose, which combine to create the polymers of carbohydrates, the polysaccharides, such as starch and cellulose.

cardiac muscle The type of striated muscle tissue that forms the muscles of the heart.

cardiovascular system A fluid transport system of the body, consisting of the heart, all the blood vessels in the body, the blood that flows through these vessels, and the bone marrow tissue in which red blood cells are formed.

carnivore An animal that eats meat.

carpel The female reproductive structure of a flower, consisting of an ovary, a style, and a stigma.

carrier A person who does not suffer from a recessive genetic debilitation, but who carries an allele for the condition that can be passed along to offspring.

carrying capacity The maximum population of a species that can be sustained in a given geographical area over time. In ecology, this is often denoted as K.

cartilage A connective tissue that serves as padding in most joints, forms the human larynx (voicebox) and trachea (wind pipe), and links each rib to the breastbone.

catalyst A substance that retains its original chemical composition while bringing about a change in a substrate. Enzymes are catalysts in chemical reactions; one enzyme can carry out hundreds or thousands of chemical transformations without itself being transformed.

cell The functional unit of life. A highly organized, generally microscopic structure whose component parts always include an outer membrane, genetic material in the form of DNA, and a host of accessory molecules. All living things either are single cells or are composed of collections of cells.

cell cycle The repeating pattern of growth, genetic duplication, and division seen in most cells.

cell junction A linkage between animal cells. A gap junction is a type of cell junction that facilitates cell communication.

cell-mediated immunity An immune system capability that works through the production of cells that destroy infected cells in the body.

cell wall A relatively thick layer of material that forms the periphery of plant, bacterial, and fungal cells.

cellular respiration The three-stage, oxygen-dependent harvesting of energy that goes on in most cells. The three stages are glycolysis, the Krebs cycle, and the electron transport chain.

cellulose A complex carbohydrate that is the largest single component of plant cell walls. Cellulose is dense and rigid and provides structure for much of the natural world. Mammals cannot digest cellulose, so it serves as insoluble dietary fiber that helps move food through the digestive tract.

central cell Cell with two nuclei in the embryo sac (mature female gametophyte) in a flowering plant. Upon fertilization, this cell will develop into the endosperm, the food for the embryo.

central nervous system (CNS) The portion of the nervous system consisting of the brain and spinal cord.

central vacuole A large, watery organelle found in plants whose functions include the storage of nutrients and the retention and degradation of waste products.

centrosome A cellular structure that acts as an organizing center for the assembly of microtubules. A cell's centrosome duplicates prior to mitosis and plays an important part in the development of the cell's mitotic spindle.

cephalopods A class of molluscs that includes squid, octopus, nautilus, and cuttlefish.

cerebral cortex Thin outer covering of the region of the brain known as the cerebrum. Responsible for the highest human thinking and processing.

cerebral hemispheres The two halves (left and right) of the cerebrum of the vertebrate brain. This is the site of many functions, including conscious thought, sensations, and memory.

cerebrospinal fluid A fluid that circulates in both the brain and spinal cord, supplying nutrients, hormones, and immune system cells and providing the nervous tissue with protection against jarring injury.

cerebrum The largest region of the human brain, responsible for much of the human capacity for higher mental functioning.

cervix The lower part of the uterus, a narrow neck that opens into the vagina.

chemical bonding General term for a bond created when electrons of two atoms interact and rearrange into a new form that allows the atoms to become attached to each other. Ionic, covalent, and hydrogen bonds are all chemical bonds.

chitin A complex carbohydrate that gives shape and strength to the external skeleton of arthropods, including insects, spiders, and crustaceans.

chlorofluorocarbons (CFCs) A class of human-made chlorine compounds that destroys the atmospheric ozone that protects life on land from damaging ultraviolet radiation.

chlorophyll *a* The primary pigment of chloroplasts, found embedded in its membranes. Together with the accessory pigments, chlorophyll *a* absorbs some wavelengths of sunlight in the first step of photosynthesis.

chloroplast The organelle within plant and algae cells that is the site of photosynthesis.

cholesterol A steroid molecule that forms part of the outer membrane of all animal cells, and that acts as a precursor for many other steroids, among them the hormones testosterone and estrogen.

chromatid One of the two identical strands of chromatin (DNA plus associated proteins) that make up a chromosome in its duplicated state.

chromatin A molecular complex of DNA and its associated proteins that makes up the chromosomes of eukaryotic organisms.

chromosome Structural unit containing part or all of an organism's genome, consisting of DNA and its associated proteins (chromatin). The human genome is made up of 23 pairs of chromosomes, or 46 chromosomes in all.

chyme The soupy mixture of food and gastric juices that passes from the stomach to the small intestine.

cilia (singular, *cilium*) Hair-like extensions of a cell, composed of microtubules. Many cilia occur on the surface of a given cell, and they move rapidly back and forth to propel the cell or to move material around the cell.

circadian rhythms Biological cycles that can function independently of environmental cues and that are roughly synchronized to Earth's 24-hour rotation.

cisternae (singular, *cisterna*) Flattened sacs of the rough endoplasmic reticulum (ER) in which polypeptide chains, transferred in from ribosomes, fold into their protein conformations.

cisternal space Space in the middle of the cisternae (flattened sacs) of the rough endoplasmic reticulum. Polypeptide chains, newly synthesized on the ribosomes, enter the cisternal space and then fold into their protein conformations.

citric acid cycle Another name for the Krebs cycle, one of the three main sets of steps in cellular respiration; named for the first product of the cycle, citric acid.

cladistics The branch of systematics that uses shared derived characters to determine the order of branching events in speciation and therefore which species are most closely related. Cladistics is concerned only with evolutionary relationships, not classification.

cladogram An evolutionary tree constructed using the cladistic system.

class A taxonomic grouping subordinate to phylum and superordinate to order. Humans are in the class Mammalia.

classical conditioning A form of learning in which animals learn to respond in a customary way to a new stimulus that has been paired with an existing stimulus. In the case of Pavlov's dog, a customary response (salivation) was elicited when a new stimulus (the sound of a bell) was paired with an existing stimulus (food delivery).

cleavage The developmental process in which a zygote is repeatedly divided into smaller individual cells through cell division.

climate The average weather conditions, including temperature, precipitation, and wind, in a particular region.

climax community The relatively stable community that develops at the end of any process of ecological succession.

clone An exact genetic copy. Also, used as a verb—to make one of these copies. A single gene or a whole, complex organism can be cloned.

cloning vector A self-replicating agent that, in the cloning process, serves to transfer and replicate genetic material. Cloning vectors generally are bacterial plasmids or the viruses known as bacteriophages.

closed circulation system A type of circulatory system, found in all vertebrates and in some invertebrates, in which blood stays within vessels.

clotting factor A group of substances, found in blood platelets, that are important in the process of blood clotting.

coastal zone The region lying between the point on shore where the ocean's waves reach at high tide to the point off shore where the continental shelf drops off.

cochlea The coiled, fluid-filled, membranous portion of the inner ear in which vibrations are transformed into the nervous system signals perceived as sound.

codominance A condition in which two alleles of a given gene have different phenotypic effects, with both effects manifesting in organisms that are heterozygous for the gene.

codon An mRNA triplet that codes for a single amino acid or a start or a stop command in the translation stage of protein synthesis.

coelom A central body cavity, found in animals, that is lined with cells of mesodermal origin.

coenzyme A type of accessory molecule that is part of the active site of an enzyme and allows it to function. Many vitamins are important coenzymes.

coevolution The interdependent evolution of two or more species. Coevolution can benefit both species, as in flowering plants and their animal pollinators, or it can be an arms race between species, as in a plant and its predators.

coexistence The condition in which two species can live in the same habitat, dividing up resources in a way that allows both to survive.

collecting duct A tube in the nephron that receives urine from several nephron tubules. Some additional reabsorption, especially of water, takes place in the collecting duct, resulting in more concentrated urine.

collenchyma cell The type of plant cell that provides support to allow stretching and elongating the growing parts of the plant.

colon The longest region of the large intestine, between the cecum and the rectum.

colonial multicellularity A form of life in which individual cells form stable associations with one another but do not take on specialized roles.

commensalism An interaction between two species in which one benefits while the other is neither harmed nor helped.

commitment A developmental process that results in cells whose role is completely determined. Most cells in the adult body have undergone commitment, meaning they are fated to function as a particular kind of cell, and give rise only to more such cells.

common descent with modification The process by which species of living things undergo modification in successive generations, with such modification sometimes resulting in the formation of new, separate species. The lineage of all species traces back to a single common ancestor.

community All the populations of living things that inhabit a given area. The term also is used to mean a collection of populations in a given area that potentially interact with each other.

companion cell In plants, cells that are closely associated with sieve elements in phloem. The companion cells provide housekeeping needs of the sieve elements, which have lost their nuclei to provide room for faster conduction of phloem sap.

competitive exclusion principle When two populations compete for the same limited, vital resource, one will always outcompete the other and thus bring about the local extinction of the latter species.

complement A group of proteins in the blood that supplements the action of antibodies by enhancing phagocytosis, destroying the membranes of invading cells, and promoting inflammation.

complex carbohydrate A carbohydrate built of many monosaccharides. Also known as polysaccharides, these compounds include starch, glycogen, cellulose, and chitin.

concentration The process carried out in the kidneys under which the final solute concentration of tubule fluid is increased through removal of water from the filtrate in the loop of Henle and the collecting duct—actions that conserve water. One of four essential processes undertaken by the kidneys, the others being filtration, reabsorption, and secretion.

concentration gradient A gradient within a given medium defined by the difference between the highest and lowest concentration of a solute. The solute will have a natural tendency to move from the areas of higher concentration to lower, thus diffusing.

cones In human vision, photoreceptors that respond best to bright light and that provide color vision.

connective tissue A tissue, active in the support and protection of other tissues, whose cells are surrounded by a material that they have secreted. In humans, one of the four principal types of tissue.

consumer Any organism that eats other organisms rather than producing its own food.

continental drift The lateral movement of continental plates over the globe, allowing continents to divide and rejoin in different patterns. This process can separate populations of organisms, providing the geographic barriers that can result in speciation.

control A comparative condition in an experiment in which no variables are introduced.

convergent evolution Evolution that occurs when similar environmental influences shape two separate evolutionary lines in similar ways.

coral reef Ocean structure, found in shallow, warm waters, that consists primarily of the piled-up remains of many generations of the animals called coral polyps. Such reefs provide habitat for a rich diversity of marine organisms.

cork Cells, dead in their mature state, that form the outermost covering of woody plants. These cells are infused with a waxy substance that protects the plant from drying out and from invaders.

cork cambium Secondary meristematic tissue in woody plants that forms the outer living covering of woody plants. This cambium produces the cork cells that, in their dead, mature state, protect the outside of the trunk and branches.

cornea A curved membrane through which light first passes upon entering the eye.

coronary artery An artery that delivers oxygenated blood to the muscles of the heart. Blockage of coronary arteries causes heart attack.

corpus luteum The structure that develops in the mammalian ovary from the ruptured follicle after ovulation. The corpus luteum secretes hormones that help prepare the reproductive tract for pregnancy.

cotyledon An embryonic leaf. A major division in plants is between the monocots, which have one embryonic leaf, and the dicots, which have two embryonic leaves.

coupled reaction A chemical reaction in which an endergonic reaction is powered by an exergonic reaction. All "uphill" or endergonic reactions require an input of energy; this energy is supplied by "downhill" or exergonic reactions.

covalent bond A type of chemical bond in which two atoms are linked through a sharing of electrons.

Cretaceous extinction A mass extinction event that occurred at the boundary between the Cretaceous and Tertiary periods. This event, which included an asteroid impact, resulted in the extinction of the dinosaurs along with many other organisms.

cross-pollinate To pollinate one plant with pollen of another plant. Mendel used this technique in conducting his experiments to uncover rules of heredity.

crossing over (genetic recombination) A process, occurring during meiosis, in which homologous chromosomes exchange reciprocal portions of themselves.

cytokinesis The physical separation of one cell into two daughter cells.

cytoplasm The region of a cell inside the plasma membrane and outside the nucleus. Usually, this region is filled with the jelly-like cytosol containing the cell's extra-nuclear organelles.

cytoskeleton A network of protein filaments that functions in cell structure, cell movement, and the transport of materials within the cell. Microfilaments, intermediate filaments, and microtubules are all parts of the cytoskeleton.

cytosol The protein-rich, jelly-like fluid in which a cell's organelles that are outside the nucleus are immersed.

cytotoxic T cell (killer T cell) Type of T lymphocyte cell that binds to and kills the body's own cells when they have become infected.

D

deciduous Refers to plants that show a coordinated, seasonal loss of leaves. This strategy allows plants to conserve water during a time they could perform little photosynthesis anyway. **decomposer** A type of detritivore that, in feeding on dead or cast-off organic material, breaks it down into its inorganic components. Most decomposers are fungi or bacteria.

defecation The excretion of solid wastes through the rectal opening (anus).

deletion A chromosomal condition in which a piece of a chromosome has been lost. This occurs when a chromosomal fragment that breaks off does not rejoin any chromosome.

denatured Pertaining to a protein that has lost its shape, and therefore also its function.

dendrites Extensions of a neuron that carry signals toward the neuronal cell body.

density-dependent In ecology, effects on a population that increase or decrease in accordance with the size of that population. Density-dependent effects tend to involve biological factors.

density-independent In ecology, effects on a population that are not related to the size of that population. Density-independent effects tend to involve physical forces, such as temperature and rain.

derived character A character unique to groupings of organisms (taxa) descended from a common ancestor.

dermal tissue The epidermis, or outer layer of cells of a plant. In addition to covering the plant, dermal tissue forms trichomes such as root hairs.

dermis In certain animals, the thick layer of the skin—composed mostly of connective tissue—that underlies, nourishes, and supports the epidermis.

detritivore An organism that feeds on the remains of dead organisms or the cast-off material from living organisms.

dicotyledon A type of plant that has two embryonic leaves within the seed. More than three-quarters of all flowering plants are dicotyledons.

diffusion The movement of molecules or ions from areas of their higher concentration to areas of their lower concentration. Over time, the random movement of molecules will result in the even distribution of the material.

digestive system The organ system that transports food into the body, secretes digestive enzymes that help break down food to allow it to be absorbed by the body, and excretes waste products. This system consists of the esophagus, stomach, and large and small intestines, plus the accessory glands that produce the enzymes along the way.

digestive tract A muscular tube that is the central structure of the digestive system. The digestive tract passes through the body from the mouth to the anus, along the way receiving input from accessory organs that aid in digestion, such as the gallbladder, the liver, and the pancreas.

dihybrid cross An experimental cross in which the plants used differ in two of their characters.

dikaryotic Having two haploid nuclei in one cell. A dikaryotic phase occurs in the life cycle of many fungi because there is a delay between cytoplasm fusion and fusion of the nuclei.

diploblastic In animals, the state of developing from two layers of germ cells.

diploid Possessing two sets of chromosomes. All human cells are diploid with the exception of human gametes (eggs and sperm), which are haploid. Such haploid cells possess only a single set of chromosomes.

directional selection In evolution, the type of natural selection that moves a character toward one of its extremes. Compare to **stabilizing** and **disruptive selection.**

disruptive selection In evolution, the type of natural selection that moves a character toward both of its extremes, operating against individuals that are average for that character. This type of selection seems to be less common in nature than either stabilizing or directional selection.

distal tubule In the nephron tubule of the kidney, the convoluted portion that lies between the loop of Henle and the collecting duct. Some reabsorption of salt and water occurs here.

DNA (deoxyribonucleic acid) The primary information-bearing molecule of life, composed of two chains of nucleotides, linked together in the form of a double-helix. Proteins are put together in accordance with the information encoded in DNA.

DNA polymerase An enzyme that is active in DNA replication, separating strands of DNA, bringing bases to the parental strands, and correcting errors by removing and replacing incorrect base pairs.

domain The highest-level taxonomic grouping of organisms. There are only three domains: Archaea, Bacteria, and Eukarya.

dominance hierarchy A persistent power ranking in an animal population that gives those of higher rank the ability to control some aspect of the behavior of those of lower rank.

dominant Term used to designate an allele that is expressed in the heterozygous condition.

dominant disorder Genetic conditions in which a single faulty allele can cause damage, even when a second, functional allele exists.

dormancy A state in which growth is suspended and there is a prolonged low level of metabolic activity. Dormancy allows organisms to conserve energy during times of unfavorable environmental conditions.

dorsal nerve cord A rod-shaped dorsal structure consisting of nerve cells, running from the chordate animal's head to its tail.

dorsal root ganglion The collection of cell bodies of the sensory neurons that send their axons into the spinal cord through the dorsal root, carrying sensory information into the central nervous system.

double bond Type of covalent bond formed when two pairs of electrons are shared between atoms.

double fertilization In plants, the fusion of one sperm with the egg and another sperm with the central cell; the first of these fertilizations results in the zygote, the other in endosperm to provide food for the embryo. Double fertilization occurs almost exclusively in flowering plants.

Down syndrome A disorder in humans in which affected individuals usually have three copies of chromosome 21. Individuals with this syndrome have short stature, shortened life span, and low IQ.

E

ecological dominant A species that is abundant and obvious in a given community. In any community, a few species, usually plants, will dominate in numbers.

ecology The study of the interactions that living things have with each other and with their environment.

ecosystem A community of living things and the physical environment with which they interact.

ectopic pregnancy An abnormal pregnancy in which the blastocyst attaches inside the uterine tube or to the cervix, rather than in the normal position in the dorsal uterine wall.

ectothermic Having an internal temperature that is controlled largely by the temperature of the external environment. For example, lizards are ectothermic and often bask in the sun to warm up.

effector A muscle or gland that responds to instructions received from a motor neuron, thus effecting change in the body.

efferent division The division of the peripheral nervous system that carries motor commands from the central nervous system (CNS) toward the effectors (muscles and glands).

electron A basic constituent of an atom that has negative electrical charge. Electrons are distributed in an atom at a distance from the nucleus. Electrons interact to form chemical bonds between atoms.

electron carrier A molecule that serves to transfer electrons from one molecule to another in ATP formation. The most important electron carrier in ATP formation is NAD^+ (NADH in its reduced form). The other major carrier is FAD ($FADH_2$).

electron transport chain (ETC) The third stage of cellular respiration, occurring within the inner membrane of the mitochondria, in which most of the ATP are formed.

electronegativity The measure of the strength of attraction an atom has for electrons. An atom with higher electronegativity will tend to pull electrons away from atoms with lower electronegativity.

element A substance that cannot be reduced to any simpler set of components through chemical processes. An element is defined by the number of protons in its nucleus.

embryo A developing organism. In humans, the developing organism from the time a zygote undergoes its first division through the end of the eighth week of development.

embryo sac The mature female gametophyte plant, consisting of seven cells produced by the megaspore. These cells include the egg and the central cell, which contains two nuclei.

embryology The study of how animals develop, from fertilization to birth.

embryonic stem cell A cell from the blastocyst stage of a human embryo that is capable of giving rise to almost all of the cells or tissues in the body.

emulsification In digestion, the breaking of a large droplet of lipid material into many small droplets, greatly increasing the surface area on which digestive enzymes can act.

endergonic reaction A chemical reaction in which the ending set of molecules (the products) contains more energy than the starting set of molecules (the reactants).

endocrine gland A gland that releases its materials directly into surrounding tissues or into the bloodstream, without using ducts. Many hormones are produced by endocrine glands.

endocrine system The organ system that sends signals throughout the body using the chemical messengers called hormones.

endocytosis The process by which the plasma membrane folds inward and pinches off, bringing relatively large materials into the cell enclosed inside a vesicle.

endomembrane system An interactive group of membrane-lined organelles and transport vesicles that functions within eukaryotic cells.

endometrium The tissue lining the interior of the uterus in mammals, which thickens in response to progesterone secretion during ovulation and is shed during menstruation. If pregnancy occurs, this tissue houses the embryo.

endosperm The nutrient tissue that surrounds an angiosperm embryo in the seed. The rice and wheat grains that we eat consist mostly of endosperm.

endothelium The innermost layer of blood and lymph vessels, made up of a type of flat epithelial cells. Capillary walls consist of one layer of endothelial cells, and exchange of gases, nutrients, and wastes occurs through these cells.

endothermic Having a relatively stable internal body temperature and body heat that is generated internally, by the organism's own metabolism. Mammals are endothermic.

energy The capacity to bring about movement against an opposing force.

energy-flow model of ecosystems A conceptualization of ecosystems as units in which energy is first captured by given organisms and then transferred to other organisms.

entrain To initiate a new cycle of an organism's internal clock. Many biological rhythms are entrained by such environmental cues as sunlight and temperature.

environmental resistance All the forces in the environment that act to limit the size of a population. Limited food or sunshine, low temperature or rainfall, or predators are some components of environmental resistance.

enzyme A chemically active type of protein that speeds up, or in practical terms enables, chemical reactions in living things.

epicotyl All tissue of an embryonic or seedling plant above the cotyledons. The epicotyl gives rise to the first true leaves.

epidermis The outermost layer of skin in animals, or the outermost cell layer in plants.

epididymis The mass of tubules near the testis in which sperm complete their development and are stored.

epithelial tissue In humans, one of the four principal types of tissue. A tissue that covers exposed surfaces and also forms glands. In humans, skin is an epithelial tissue, as is the lining of the digestive tract.

erythrocyte A blood cell, also known as a red blood cell, that transports oxygen to and carries carbon dioxide from every part of the body.

esophagus The muscular tube that begins at the pharynx and ends at the stomach, forming a portion of the digestive tract.

estrogen A class of hormones, produced primarily by cells of the ovary, that supports egg development, growth of uterine lining, and development of female sex characteristics.

estuary An area where a river flows into the ocean, bringing freshwater and saltwater habitat together. Estuaries are among the most productive ecosystems on Earth.

Eukarya With Bacteria and Archaea, one of three domains of the living world, composed of four subordinate kingdoms: plantae, animalia, fungi, and protistia. All eukaryotes are composed of cells that have a nucleus.

eukaryotic cell A cell whose primary complement of DNA is contained within a membrane-lined nucleus. Eukaryotic cells have several other organelles in addition to the nucleus. All organisms except bacteria and archaea either are single eukaryotic cells or are composed of eukaryotic cells.

eusocial species A species of animal that is organized into a caste system in which there is a division of labor, such that different members of a population will consistently perform different tasks, and in which the young are raised through cooperative care, meaning care provided by many members of the group.

evolution Any genetically based phenotypic change in a population of organisms over successive generations. Evolution can also be thought of as the process by which species of living things can undergo modification over successive generations, with such modification sometimes resulting in the formation of new species.

exergonic reaction A chemical reaction in which the starting set of molecules (the reactants) contains more energy than the final set of molecules (the products).

exocrine gland A gland that secretes its materials through ducts (tubes). For example, sweat glands conduct perspiration through ducts to the skin.

exocytosis The process in which a transport vesicle fuses with the plasma membrane of a cell and the contents of the vesicle are ejected outside the cell. Exocytosis can be used to expel waste products in single-celled organisms or to export protein products in multicelled organisms.

exon That part of a primary transcript (or the DNA encoding it) that is retained in mRNA editing.

exoskeleton An external material covering the animal body, providing support and protection.

exponential growth A form of population growth in which the rate of growth increases with time. Exponential growth results in a J-shaped growth curve because, when plotted on a graph, the population's increase resembles the letter J.

exponential increase An increase in numbers that is proportional to the number already in existence. This type of increase occurs in populations of living things, and it carries the potential for enormous growth of populations.

extremophile Type of organism that flourishes in extreme conditions such as high heat, high pressure, high salt, or extreme pH.

extrinsic isolating mechanism A barrier to interbreeding of populations that is not an inherent characteristic of the organisms in the populations. Geographic barriers such as rivers are extrinsic isolating mechanisms.

F

facilitated diffusion The passage of materials through the cell's plasma membrane, aided by a concentration gradient and a transport protein.

facilitation In primary succession, the actions or qualities of earlier species that in some way assist growth of later species.

family A taxonomic grouping of related genera. This category is subordinate to order and superordinate to genus. Humans are in the family Hominidae.

fatty acid A molecule, found in many lipids, composed of a hydrocarbon chain bonded to a carboxyl group.

fertilization The fusion of two gametes to form a zygote. In humans (and most other organisms), the gametes known as sperm and egg fuse, resulting in a zygote.

fetus An organism at a later stage of development. In humans, the developing organism from the start of the ninth week of development to the moment of birth.

fever A sustained, elevated body temperature that speeds up the activities of the immune system and may therefore help to rid the body of an infection. In humans, fever is defined as a continued body temperature greater than 37.2°C (99°F).

fiber In skeletal muscle, a single elongated muscle cell, containing hundreds of long, thin myofibrils that run the length of the cell.

fibrinogen A type of protein in blood plasma that, under certain conditions, forms into long strands of fibrin, the framework molecule of a blood clot.

fibrous root system A plant root system that consists of many roots, all about the same size.

filament The part of a stamen (male reproductive part of a flower) that is shaped like and functions as a stalk, and has an anther at the top.

filtration The process carried out in the kidneys under which smaller blood plasma materials move from the glomerulus capillaries into the nephron tubule. One of four essential processes undertaken by the kidneys, the others being reabsorption, secretion, and concentration.

first filial generation The offspring of the parental generation in an experimental cross.

first law of thermodynamics Energy cannot be created or destroyed, but only transformed from one form to another. The process of transformation of energy is never totally efficient, and some energy is always converted into heat.

fitness The success of an organism, relative to other members of its population, in passing on its genes to offspring. Fitness is a relative concept only; some organisms are better than others at passing on their genes in a given environment at a given point in time.

fixation The process of a gas being incorporated into an organic molecule.

flagella (singular, *flagellum*) The relatively long, tail-like extensions of some cells, composed of microtubules, that function in cell movement. Often cells will have but a single flagellum, as with mammalian sperm cells.

fluid-mosaic model A conceptualization of the cell's outer or plasma membrane as a fluid, phospholipid bilayer that has moving laterally within it a mosaic of proteins. This is the consensus contemporary view of the makeup of the plasma membrane.

follicle In the vertebrate ovary, the complex of the oocyte (developing egg) and the cells and fluids that surround and nourish it.

follicle-stimulating hormone (FSH) A hormone, secreted by the anterior pituitary, that promotes egg development and stimulates secretion of estrogens in women, and supports sperm production and testosterone secretion in men.

formed elements Cells and cell fragments that form the non-fluid portion of blood. Formed elements include red blood cells, white blood cells, and platelets. Contrast with **plasma,** the fluid portion of blood, consisting mostly of water.

founder effect The phenomenon by which an initial gene pool for a population is established by means of that population migrating to a new and isolated area. One of the conditions that potentiates genetic drift.

fraternal twins Twins who are produced first through multiple ovulations in the mother, followed by multiple fertilizations from separate sperm of the father, and then multiple implantations of the resulting embryos in the uterus.

free radical A molecule with an unpaired electron, usually existing for only a very brief time. Although free radicals are natural products of biological processes, these molecules can be destructive in living tissues.

free ribosome A type of ribosome that is located in the cytosol of a cell, not attached to the endoplasmic reticulum. Generally, proteins that will reside in the cell's membranes and proteins that will be exported out of the cell are synthesized on the free ribosomes.

fruit The mature ovary of any flowering plant. Many fruits protect the underlying seeds, and many attract animals that will eat the fruit and disperse the seeds.

functional group A group of atoms that confers a special property on a carbon-based molecule. Functional groups usually are transferred as a unit among carbon-based molecules and often confer an electrical charge or polarity on the molecules they are part of.

G

gallbladder Organ of the body that stores and concentrates the digestive material bile, which is produced by the liver. Bile facilitates the breakdown fats by digestive enzymes.

gamete A haploid reproductive cell, either egg or sperm.

gametophyte generation The generation in a plant's life cycle that produces gametes (sperm or egg). This generation is microscopic in angiosperms. Contrast with sporophyte generation.

ganglion Any collection of nerve-cell bodies in the peripheral nervous system.

gap junction A protein assemblage that forms a communication channel between adjacent animal cells. Gap junctions open only as necessary, thus allowing small molecules and electrical signals to move between cells.

gastrointestinal (GI) tract Generally refers to the lower portion of the digestive tract (the stomach and intestines).

gastropods A class of molluscs that includes snails and slugs, among other organisms.

gastrulation The process in early animal development in which an embryo's cells migrate to form three layers of tissue: the endoderm, the mesoderm, and the ectoderm. Each of these layers then goes on to give rise to differing tissues and organs in the organism.

gene A segment of DNA that brings about the transcription of a segment of RNA. A gene may contain regulatory chemical sequences, information for the synthesis of one or more proteins, or sequences that bring about the production of RNA used at such sites as the ribosomes.

gene flow The movement of genes from one population to another.

gene pool The entire collection of alleles in a population.

genetic code The inventory that specifies which nucleotide triplets code for which particular amino acids, or for start or stop commands in protein synthesis. With few exceptions, the genetic code is universal in living things.

genetic drift The chance alteration of allele frequencies in a population, with such alterations having greatest impact on small populations.

genetics The study of heredity.

genome The complete haploid set of an organism's chromosomes.

genotype The genetic makeup of an organism, including all the genes that lie along its chromosomes.

genus A taxonomic grouping of related species. This category is subordinate to family and superordinate to species. Humans are in the genus *Homo*.

germ-line cell A cell that becomes an egg or a sperm cell.

gland An organ or group of cells that secretes one or more substances.

globulins With albumins and fibrinogen, one of the three primary classes of proteins suspended in the fluid or plasma portion of the blood. Globulins include antibodies, which attack foreign invaders; and transport proteins, such as the lipoproteins that transport lipids.

glomerulus Knotted network of capillaries in each of the kidneys' nephrons that receives blood and lets some smaller blood-borne materials pass out of it (and into the surrounding Bowman's capsule) while retaining larger materials.

glyceride A type of lipid, consisting of a head made of an alcohol (usually glycerol) attached to fatty-acid subunits.

glycerol A particular kind of alcohol, frequently found in the "head" of glyceride.

glycocalyx An outer layer of the plasma membrane, composed of short carbohydrate chains that attach to membrane proteins and phospholipid molecules. Such chains serve as the actual binding sites on many membrane proteins, act to lubricate the cell, and can form an adhesion layer that allows one cell to stick to another.

glycogen A complex carbohydrate that serves as the primary form in which carbohydrates are stored in animals.

glycolysis The first stage of cellular respiration, occurring in the cytosol. For some organisms, glycolysis is the sole means of extracting energy from food. In most organisms, it is a means of extracting some energy and a necessary precursor to the other two stages of cellular respiration, the Krebs cycle and the electron transport chain.

glycoprotein A molecule that combines protein and carbohydrate. Glycoproteins play important roles as cell receptors and some types of hormones, among other functions.

Golgi complex A network of membranes, found in the cytoplasm of eukaryotic cells, that processes and distributes proteins that come to it from the rough endoplasmic reticulum.

gonadotropin-releasing hormone A hormone released in tiny amounts from the brain's hypothalamus that stimulates the anterior pituitary to release two other hormones (follicle-stimulating hormone and luteinizing hormone) important in reproduction.

gravitropism The bending of a plant's roots or shoots in response to gravity. This capability helps a plant orient roots and shoots properly—roots toward the center of the Earth, shoots away from it.

gray matter The tissue within the central nervous system that appears gray and consists largely of cell bodies plus neuroglia.

gross primary production The amount of material that a plant produces as a result of photosynthesis.

groundwater Water that is found underground in porous rock saturated with water.

growth hormone In humans, this hormone stimulates overall body growth through cell growth. Also known as somatotropin.

gymnosperm A seed plant whose seeds do not develop within a fruit or carpel. One of the four principal varieties of plants, gymnosperms reproduce through wind-aided pollination. Coniferous trees, such as pine and fir, are the most familiar examples.

H

habitat The surroundings in which individuals of a species are normally found. **habituation** A simple form of learning, consisting of a reduction in a response, based on repeated exposure to a stimulus that has no positive or negative consequences.

hair follicle A tiny complex organ, formed from epidermis, from which hair grows.

hair papilla A peg-like structure of connective tissue, containing capillaries and nerves, at the base of a hair follicle.

half-life The time needed for one-half of a given amount of a radioactive element to decay into another isotope or element. This time differs among elements but is uniform for each element. Half-life can be used, along with measured proportions of elements, to radiometrically date a substance.

haploid Possessing a single set of chromosomes. Human gametes (eggs and sperm) are haploid cells, because they have only a single set of chromosomes. All other cells in the human body are diploid, meaning they possess two sets of chromosomes. Some organisms are strictly haploid. Bacteria, for example, have only a single chromosome, making them haploid.

HDL High-density lipoprotein. A type of protein that transports fat or lipid molecules (usually cholesterol) from various tissues in the body to the liver. Sometimes known as the "good cholesterol," HDLs help remove, and possibly neutralize, the LDLs or low-density lipoproteins that can harmfully reside in coronary arteries.

heart attack A complete blockage of one of the heart's coronary arteries, resulting in the death of groups of heart cells from lack of a blood supply.

helper T cell Type of T lymphocyte cell that stimulates both T-cell and B-cell immunity. Referred to in AIDS therapy as a CD-4 cell.

hemoglobin The iron-containing protein in red blood cells that binds to both oxygen and carbon dioxide, thus assisting in their transportation.

herbaceous plant A plant that never develops wood (secondary xylem), and therefore has relatively thin and weak shoots. Herbaceous plants do not undergo secondary growth (thickening).

herbivore An animal that eats only plants.

hermaphroditic A state in which one animal possesses both male and female sex organs.

heterotroph A type of organism that cannot manufacture its own food, but must instead get food from elsewhere. Animals are heterotrophs.

heterozygous Possessing two different alleles of a gene for a given character.

histamine A compound that, in the immune-system's inflammatory response, brings about blood-vessel dilation and increased blood-vessel permeability.

HIV Human Immunodeficiency Virus, the cause of the disease AIDS.

homeostasis The maintenance of a relatively stable internal environment in living things.

hominid Any member of the family *Hominidae*, the family of human-like primates. Today, all hominids are extinct with the exception of human beings.

homologous In anatomy, having the same structure owing to inheritance from a common ancestor. Forelimb structures in whales, bats, cats, and gorillas are homologous.

homologous chromosomes Chromosomes that are the same in size and function. Species that are diploid (have two sets of chromosomes) have matching pairs of homologous chromosomes; one member of each homologous pair is inherited from the male, the second member of each homologous pair is inherited from the female.

homology A structure that is shared in different organisms owing to inheritance from a common ancestor. Homologies are used to help decipher evolutionary relationships.

homozygous Having two identical alleles of a gene for a given character.

hormone A substance that, when released in one part of an organism, goes on to prompt physiological activity in another part of the organism. Both plants and animals have hormones.

host The prey in a parasitic relationship.

hydrocarbon A compound made of hydrogen and carbon. Hydrocarbons are nonpolar covalent molecules and therefore are not easily dissolved in water.

hydrochloric acid The acid, secreted in the vertebrate stomach, that lowers the pH of the gastric juice, kills microorganisms, and breaks down cell walls and connective tissues in food.

hydrogen bond A chemical bond that links an already covalently bonded hydrogen atom with a second, relatively electronegative atom.

hydrolysis The splitting of bonds in a molecule by reaction with water.

hydrophilic Property of a compound indicating that it will interact with water. Table salt (NaCl), which dissolves readily in water, is hydrophilic.

hydrophobic Property of a compound indicating that it will not interact with water. Oil is hydrophobic and will not readily dissolve in water.

hydroxide ion The ion. Compounds that yield hydroxide ions are strongly basic, so they can be used to counteract acids and shift solutions toward neutral or basic on the pH scale.

hypertonic solution A solution that has a higher concentration of solutes than another.

hyphae (singular, *hypha*) The slender filaments that make up the bulk of most fungi.

hypocotyl All tissue of an embryonic or seedling plant below the cotyledons. The hypocotyl includes the plant's radicle, or early root structure, and is first to emerge from a seed when it starts to sprout.

hypothalamus Portion of the brain important in drives, and in the maintenance of homeostasis, the latter capacity coming about because of the hypothalamus' control over a good deal of body's hormonal release.

hypothesis A tentative, testable explanation of an observed phenomenon.

hypotonic solution A solution that has a lower concentration of solutes than another.

I

identical twins Twins who develop from a single zygote; strictly speaking, identical twins are a single organism at one point in their development and as such have exactly the same genetic makeup.

imitation A sophisticated form of learning in which one animal copies behavior it observes in another animal.

immunity A state of long-lasting protection that the immune system develops against specific microorganisms.

imprinting A process of learning that results in one animal preferentially associating with another.

inclusive fitness An individual's relative genetic contribution to a succeeding generation, made both through itself and through relatives who have reproduced because of assistance the individual has provided.

incomplete dominance A genetic condition in which the heterozygote phenotype is intermediate between either of the homozygous phenotypes.

independent assortment The random distribution of homologous chromosome pairs during meiosis.

induction The capacity of some embryonic cells to direct the development of other embryonic cells. For example, the notochord induces the tissue above it to form the neural tube. Induction helps organize development. **inflammation** A localized tissue response to injury. Inflammation interferes with the spread of pathogens and initiates a wide range of defenses to overcome the pathogens and repair damaged tissues.

inner cell mass In mammalian development, the group of cells in the embryo that will develop into the baby, rather than into the placenta.

insight learning A sophisticated form of learning in which an animal makes associations between objects or events that it has previously regarded as unrelated. In short, the ability to reason.

integral protein A protein of the plasma membrane that is attached to the membrane's hydrophobic interior.

integumentary system The organ system that protects the body from the external environment and assists in regulation of body temperature. This system consists of the skin and associated structures, such as glands, hair, and nails.

intercalary meristem Meristematic tissue found at the base of each growing node in grasses. These multiple growing regions permit fast growth, and also allow grasses to keep growing even when their tops are removed by grazing or mowing.

intermediate filament Filaments of the cytoskeleton, intermediate in diameter between microfilaments and microtubules, which help stabilize the positions of the nucleus and other organelles within the cell.

interneuron A type of neuron, located only within the brain or spinal cord, that connects other neurons. These neurons are responsible for the analysis of sensory inputs and the coordination of motor commands.

interphase That portion of the cell cycle in which the cell simultaneously carries out its work and—in preparation for division—duplicates its chromosomes. The other primary phase of the cell cycle is mitotic phase (or M phase), which includes both mitosis (in somatic cells) and cytokinesis.

interspecific competition Competitive interaction between individuals of two different species.

interstitial fluid Fluid between cells in the bodily tissues of animals.

intertidal zone The region within the coastal zone of the ocean that extends from the ocean's low-tide mark to its high-tide mark.

intraspecific competition Competitive interaction between individuals of the same species.

intrinsic isolating mechanism A difference in anatomy, physiology, or behavior that prevents interbreeding between individuals of the same species or of closely related species. One or more intrinsic isolating mechanisms must exist for two populations of the same species to begin the process of evolving into separate species.

intrinsic rate of increase The rate at which a population would grow if there were no external limits to its growth. In ecology, this is often denoted as *r*.

intron That part of a primary transcript (or the DNA encoding it) that is removed in mRNA editing.

inversion A chromosomal abnormality that comes about when a chromosomal fragment that rejoins a chromosome does so with an inverted orientation.

invertebrate An animal without a vertebral column.

ion An atom that has positive or negative charge because it has fewer or more electrons than protons. Ions will be attracted to other ions with the opposite charge, thus forming ionic compounds.

ionic bonding A linkage in which two or more ions are bonded to each other by virtue of their opposite charge.

ionic compound A substance in which two or more atoms are held together through ionic bonding. Table salt (NaCl) is a familiar example.

iris A colored structure of the eye, composed largely of smooth muscle and capable of contracting and relaxing, thus controlling the amount of light that passes into the eye through the iris' central opening, the pupil.

isomer A form of a molecule that has the same chemical formula but a different spatial arrangement than another molecule. Because of their different shapes, different isomers can have different properties.

isotonic solution A solution that has the same concentration of solutes as another.

isotope A form of an element as defined by the number of neutrons contained in its nucleus. Different isotopes of an element have varying numbers of neutrons but the same number of protons.

K

karyotype A pictorial arrangement of a full set of an organism's chromosomes.

keratin A flexible, water-resistant protein, abundant in the outer layers of skin, that also makes up hair and fingernails.

keystone species A species whose impact on the composition of a community is large, relative to its abundance within that community.

kidneys The filtering organs of the urinary system, which produce urine while conserving useful blood-borne materials.

kilocalorie The amount of energy it takes to raise one kilogram of water one degree Celsius. Food consumption is measured in kilocalories, usually written as Calories.

kinetic energy The energy of motion. A rolling rock has kinetic energy.

kingdom A taxonomic grouping superordinate to every other grouping except domain. There are four kingdoms in domain Eukarya: protista, fungi, animalia, and plantae.

Krebs cycle The second stage of cellular respiration, occurring in the inner compartment of mitochondria. The Krebs cycle is the major source of electrons for the third stage of respiration, the electron transport chain.

***K*-selected species** A species that tends to be relatively long-lived, that tends to have relatively few offspring for whom it provides a good deal of care, and whose population size tends to be relatively stable, remaining at or near its environment's carrying capacity (*K*). Also known as an equilibrium species.

L

labor The regular contractions of the uterine muscles that sweep over the fetus, creating pressure that opens the cervix and expels the baby and the placenta.

lactate fermentation The process in animal cells by which pyruvic acid, the product of glycolysis, accepts electrons from NADH to form lactic acid.

lactic acid A product formed in animal cells when pyruvic acid, the product of glycolysis, accepts electrons from NADH. Lactic acid buildup causes muscle burn when a person's exertions outstrip that person's capacity to transfer energy through aerobic respiration.

large intestine That portion of the digestive tract that begins at the small intestine and ends at the anus. The large intestine serves largely to compact and store material left over from the digestion of food, turning this material into the solid waste known as feces.

lateral bud An undeveloped plant shoot, located between the stem and a leaf, that may give rise to a branch, a flower, or even take over the role of shoot apex if the apical meristem becomes damaged.

law of conservation of mass In a chemical reaction, matter can neither be created nor destroyed.

law of independent assortment During gamete formation, gene pairs assort independently of one another. Also known as Mendel's Second Law, this is one of the principles of inheritance formulated by Gregor Mendel.

law of segregation Differing characters in organisms result from two genetic elements (alleles) that separate in gamete formation, such that each gamete gets only one of the two alleles. Also known as Mendel's First Law, this is one of the principles of inheritance formulated by Gregor Mendel.

LDL Low-density lipoprotein. A type of protein that transports fat or lipid molecules (usually cholesterol) from the liver and small intestine to various tissues throughout the body. Sometimes known as the "bad cholesterol," LDLs can initiate heart disease by coming to reside within coronary arteries.

learning The acquisition of knowledge through experience.

lens A transparent structure of the eye, lying behind the iris, that serves to focus incoming light.

leukocyte Another term for white blood cell. This class of blood cells is critical to immune function.

lichen A composite organism composed of a fungus and either algae or photosynthesizing bacteria.

life cycle The repeating series of steps that occur in the reproduction of an organism.

life sciences a set of disciplines that focus on various aspects of the living world. The life sciences include biology and related disciplines such as medicine and forestry.

life table A table showing how likely it is for an average species member to survive a given unit of time.

lignin A polymer that is often a major component of the cell walls of plants. Lignin provides stiffening by binding and supporting cellulose fibers.

lipids A class of biological molecules whose defining characteristic is their relative insolubility in water. Examples include triglycerides, cholesterol, steroids, and phospholipids.

lipoprotein A molecule that combines lipid and protein. Lipoproteins transport fat molecules through the bloodstream to all parts of the body.

liver Organ that is central to the body's metabolism of nutrients and that serves as a major storage site for blood.

logistic growth A form of population growth in which exponential growth slows and then stops in response to environmental resistance. Also known as S-shaped growth because, when plotted on a graph, changes in the population's size resemble the letter S.

luteinizing hormone (LH) A hormone secreted by the anterior pituitary; in women, LH induces ovulation and stimulates the ovary to secrete estrogens and progestins to prepare the body for possible pregnancy. In men, LH stimulates the testes to produce androgens such as testosterone.

lymphatic Vessel of the lymphatic system, through which lymph flows.

lymphatic system The organ system that collects interstitial fluid, transports it as lymph through lymphatic vessels, checks the fluid for infection, and delivers the fluid to blood vessels.

lysosome An organelle found in animal cells that digests worn-out cellular materials and foreign materials that enter the cell.

M

macroevolution Evolution that results in the formation of new species or other groupings of living things.

macrophage A large type of phagocyte (a type of white blood cell) that can be found in most tissues of the body, capable of engulfing infected cells and cell fragments.

mammary glands A set of glands that, in female mammals, provide milk for the young.

marrow A loose connective tissue, found in the internal cavities of bones, that comes in two forms: red marrow, which is blood-forming tissue; and yellow marrow, which is made up of fat.

marsupial A type of mammal in which the young develop within the mother to a limited extent, inside an egg having a membranous shell. Early in development the egg's membrane disappears, after which the mother delivers a developmentally immature but active marsupial. Kangaroos are one example of a marsupial. **mass** A measure of the resistance of an object to being moved, taking into account the object's density and volume. For most biological purposes, mass is equivalent to weight.

mast cell An immune-system cell that releases histamine, which in the inflammatory response brings about blood vessel dilation and increased blood vessel permeability.

megaspore A haploid cell that results from meiosis inside the ovary of a flowering plant. The megaspore then gives rise to several types of cells, including the egg.

megaspore mother cell A single diploid cell in the ovary of a flowering plant that undergoes meiosis, producing four megaspores, one of which develops into the embryo sac containing the egg.

meiosis A process in which a single diploid cell divides to produce four haploid reproductive cells. Meiosis produces the gametes for sexual reproduction.

membrane potential The electrical charge difference that exists from one side of a neuron's plasma membrane to the other.

memory B cell One of two types of cells that the B-lymphocyte or B cell develops into (the other type being a plasma cell). Memory B cells remain in the system long after a first infection by an organism has ended and serve to produce more plasma B cells quickly, should the organism ever invade again.

menopause The cessation of the monthly ovarian cycle that occurs when women reach about 50 years of age.

menstruation The release of blood and the specialized uterine lining, the endometrium; occurs about once every 28 days in human females, except when the oocyte is fertilized.

messenger RNA (mRNA) A type of RNA that encodes, and carries to ribosomes, information for the synthesis of proteins.

metabolic pathway A sequential set of enzymatically controlled reactions in which the product of one reaction serves as the substrate for the next.

metabolism The sum of all chemical reactions carried out by a cell or larger organism.

metaphase plate A plane located midway between the poles of a dividing cell.

microevolution A change of allele frequencies in a population over a short period of time. The basis for all large-scale or macroevolution.

microfilaments The most slender of the eukaryotic cell's cytoskeletal fibers, made of the protein actin and functioning in both cell movement and support.

micrograph A picture taken with a microscope.

micrometer (μm) A millionth of a meter.

microphage A small type of phagocyte (a type of white blood cell) that generally circulates in the blood but leaves the bloodstream to enter injured or infected tissues. Neutrophils and eosinophils are the two types of microphages.

microspore A haploid cell that results from meiosis in the anthers of flowering plants. Microspores develop into pollen grains, the male gametophyte plant.

microspore mother cell A diploid cell type, found within the anthers of flowering plants, that undergoes meiosis to produce the haploid microspores that develop into pollen grains.

microtubule The largest of the cytoskeletal filaments, microtubules take the form of hollow tubes composed of the protein tubulin. They help give structure to the cell, serve as the "rails" on which transport vesicles move, and form the cellular extensions known as cilia and flagella.

migration A regular movement of animals from one location to a distant location. Also, the movement of individuals from one population into the territory of another population. Migration is the basis of gene flow among populations.

mimicry A phenomenon in which one species evolves to resemble another species.

mitochondria (singular, *mitochondrion*) Organelles that are the primary sites of energy conversion within eukaryotic cells.

mitosis The separation of a somatic cell's duplicated chromosomes prior to cytokinesis.

mitotic phase (M phase) That portion of the cell cycle that includes both mitosis and cytokinesis. Mitosis is the separation of a somatic cell's duplicated chromosomes; cytokinesis is the physical separation of one cell into two daughter cells.

mitotic spindle The microtubules active in cell division, including those that align and move the chromosomes.

modern synthesis The unified evolutionary theory that resulted from the convergence of several lines of biological research between 1937 and 1950.

molecular biology The investigation of life at the level of its individual molecules.

molecular formula A notation specifying the elements in a molecule, with the number of each shown as a subscript. This notation reveals the constituent elements of a molecule, but not the spatial arrangement of those elements.

molecule A structure with a defined number of atoms in a particular spatial arrangement. The atoms and their arrangement determine how the molecule interacts with other molecules.

molting A periodic shedding of an old skeleton.

monocotyledon A type of plant that has one embryonic leaf within the seed. Although comprising only one-quarter of all flowering plants, most important food plants are monocotyledons.

monohybrid cross An experimental cross in which the organisms used differ in only one of their characters.

monomer A small molecule that can be combined with other similar or identical molecules to make a larger polymer.

monosaccharide A building block or monomer of carbohydrates. Monosaccharides combine to form complex carbohydrates, or polysaccharides. Glucose is an example of a monosaccharide.

monotremes Egg-laying mammals, represented by the duck-billed platypus and spiny anteaters found in Australia.

monounsaturated fatty acid A fatty acid with one double bond between the carbon atoms of its hydrocarbon chain.

morphogen A diffusible substance whose concentration in a region of an embryo affects development in that region.

morphology The physical form of an organism.

morula A tightly packed ball of early embryonic cells.

motor neuron A neuron that carries instructions from the central nervous system to an effector (muscle or gland) in the body.

Müllerian mimicry A type of mimicry in which several species that have protection against predators evolve to look alike.

multiple alleles Three or more alleles—alternative forms of a gene—occurring in a population.

muscle tissue A tissue that has the ability to contract. In humans, one of the four principal types of tissue.

muscular system The organ system that produces movement and maintains posture of the body. This system consists of all the skeletal muscles of the body that are under voluntary control.

mutation A permanent alteration in a DNA base sequence.

mutualism A form of relationship between two organisms in which both organisms benefit.

mycelium A web of fungal hyphae that makes up the major part of a fungus.

mycorrhizae Associations of plant roots and fungal hyphae. The fungal hyphae absorb minerals, growth hormones, and water that are then available to the plant, and the fungus gets carbohydrates from the photosynthesizing plant.

myelin Membranous covering of some neuronal axons, provided by glial cells, that allows faster nerve signal transmission through these axons.

myofibril The contractile structure of a skeletal muscle cell, containing alternating thick and thin filaments arranged in sarcomeres.

N

nanometer (nm) A billionth of a meter.

natural killer (NK) cell Type of immune-system cell that kills foreign cells.

natural selection A process in which the differential adaptation of organisms to their environment selects those traits that will be passed on with greater frequency from one generation to the next.

navigation The use of various cues to enable movement toward a desired location.

negative feedback A system of control in which the product of a process reduces the activity that led to the product.

nephron Functional unit of the kidneys, composed of a nephron tubule, its associated blood vessels, and the interstitial fluid in which both are immersed.

nephron tubule A convoluted tubule in the kidney of birds and mammals. Filtrate passes through the tubule, where reabsorption and secretion occur during the formation of urine.

nerve A bundle of axons in the peripheral nervous system that transmits information to or from the central nervous system.

nerve cord A rod-shaped structure consisting of nerve cells, running from an animal's head to its tail.

nervous system The organ system that monitors an animal's internal and external environment, integrates the sensory information received, and coordinates the animal's responses. This system consists of all the body's neurons, plus the supporting neuroglia cells, plus the sensory organs.

nervous tissue A tissue specialized for the rapid conduction of electrical impulses. In humans, one of the four principal tissue types.

net primary production The amount of material a plant (or other photosynthesizing organism) accumulates through photosynthesis. Net primary production is gross primary production minus energy lost to heat and the plant's energy expenditures on its own maintenance.

neural crest cells Cells that break away from the top of the vertebrate neural tube as it folds together and then migrate to varying parts of the embryo, giving rise to various tissues and organs.

neural tube A dorsal, ectodermic structure that gives rise in vertebrates to both the brain and spinal cord.

neuroglia Associated helper cells of neurons, providing physical support, nourishment, insulation, and defense from infection.

neuron A nerve cell, typically possessing a cell body with a nucleus, a long extension called an axon that transmits information from the neuron, and many dendrites that transmit information to the neuron.

neurotransmitter A chemical, secreted into a synaptic cleft by a neuron, that affects another neuron or an effector by binding with receptors on it.

neutron A basic constituent of an atom, possessing no electrical charge and found in the atom's nucleus. Isotopes are defined by the number of neutrons in an atom.

niche A characterization of an organism's way of making a living that includes its habitat, food, and behavior.

nicotinamide adenine dinucleotide (NAD) The most important intermediate electron carrier in cellular respiration.

nitrogen fixation The conversion of atmospheric nitrogen into a form that can be taken up by living things. Bacteria fix nitrogen, which is essential to life.

nondisjunction The failure of homologous chromosomes or sister chromatids to separate during meiosis, resulting in unequal numbers of chromosomes in the daughter cells. Nondisjunction results in aneuploidy.

nonpolar covalent bond A type of covalent bond in which electrons are shared equally between atoms.

nonrandom mating A type of mating in which a given member of a population is not equally likely to mate with any other given member.

nonspecific defenses Immune-system defenses that do not discriminate between one invader and the next.

notochord A dorsal, rod-shaped support organ that exists in embryonic development in all vertebrates and in the adults of some vertebrates.

nuclear envelope The double membrane that lines the nucleus in eukaryotic cells.

nuclear pore A channel through the nuclear envelope surrounding the cell's nucleus. Materials pass in and out of the nucleus through the thousands of pores in the nuclear envelope.

nucleolus The area within the nucleus of a cell devoted to the production of ribosomal RNA. **nucleotide** The building block of nucleic acids, including DNA and RNA, consisting of a phosphate group, a sugar, and a nitrogen-containing base.

nucleus of atom The central core of an atom, containing its protons and neutrons. Nearly all of the mass of the atom resides in its nucleus.

nucleus of cell The membrane-lined compartment that encloses the primary complement of DNA in eukaryotic cells.

nutrient A chemical element that is used by living things to sustain life.

O

oil Fat in liquid form.

olfaction The sense of smell.

omnivore An animal that eats both plants and animals.

oocyte The precursor cell of eggs in the vertebrate ovary. Diploid primary oocytes develop from oogonia and in turn give rise to haploid secondary oocytes in the process of meiosis.

oogonia (singular, *oogonium*) The diploid cells that are the starting female cells in gamete (egg) production. Diploid oogonia develop into diploid primary oocytes, which give rise to haploid secondary oocytes.

open circulation system A type of circulation, found

in many invertebrates, in which arteries carry blood into open spaces called sinuses. The blood then bathes surrounding tissues and is channeled into veins, through which it flows back to the heart.

operant conditioning   A complex form of learning that occurs when experience teaches animals to associate one of their own actions with a particular outcome. Such learning occurs when an animal's own behavior brings about a response that has either negative or positive consequences.

order   A taxonomic grouping subordinate to class and superordinate to family. Humans are in the order Primates.

organ   A highly organized unit within an organism, performing one or more functions, that is formed of several kinds of tissue. Kidneys, heart, lungs, and liver are all familiar examples of organs in humans.

organelle   A highly organized structure within a cell that carries out specific cellular functions. Almost all organelles (meaning "tiny organs") are bound by membranes. The lone exception is the ribosome, which has no membrane and is the single organelle possessed by prokaryote cells (bacteria and archaea). Organelles in eukaryotic cells include the cell nucleus, mitochondria, lysosomes, chloroplasts, and ribosomes.

organic chemistry   A branch of chemistry concerned with compounds that have carbon as their central element.

organism   A living being. An organism can be one-celled, like a bacterium, or can contain many cells, like a dog or a rose bush.

organismal biology   The study of whole organisms.

organ system   A group of interrelated organs and tissues that serve a particular set of functions in the body. For example, the digestive system consists of mouth, stomach, and intestines, and functions in digesting food and eliminating waste.

osmosis   The net movement of water across a semipermeable membrane from an area of lower solute concentration to an area of higher solute concentration.

osteoblast   An immature bone cell that secretes organic material that becomes bone matrix, thus producing new bone.

osteoclast   A type of bone cell that dissolves bone matrix, thus liberating the minerals stored in it.

osteocyte   Mature bone cell that maintains the structure and density of bone by continually recycling calcium compounds around itself.

osteon   The functional unit of compact bone, consisting of osteoblasts and the concentric layers of bone produced by them, forming a cylinder of bone with a hole in the center, and paralleling the long axis of the bone.

osteoporosis   A medical condition stemming from a decrease in bone mass that occurs when old bone is broken down faster than new bone is produced.

ovarian follicle   The complex of the oocyte (developing egg) and a set of accessory cells that surrounds it.

ovary   In flowering plants, the area, located at the base of the carpel, where fertilization of the egg and early development of the embryo occur. In animals, the female reproductive organ in which eggs develop.

oviparous   A condition, seen in all birds and many reptiles, in which fertilized eggs are laid outside the mother's body and then develop there.

ovulation   The release of an oocyte from the ovary in animals.

oxidation   Loss of one or more electrons by an atom or a molecule. Important in energy transfer in living things as part of redox reactions, in which one substance undergoes reduction (a gain in electrons) by oxidizing another.

oxytocin   A hormone secreted by the posterior pituitary; stimulates smooth-muscle contractions in the uterus and special cells of the mammary glands in women, and in the walls of the prostate gland in men.

ozone   A gas in the Earth's atmosphere consisting of three oxygen atoms bonded together that serves to protect living things from the sun's ultraviolet radiation.

P

paired, jointed appendages   Appendages, such as legs, that come in pairs and have joints. Such appendages are characteristic of arthropods.

pancreas   In digestion, a gland that secretes, into the small intestine, digestive enzymes, along with buffers that raise the pH of chyme. In nutrient metabolism, a gland that secretes the hormones insulin and glucagon.

parasites   Organisms that feed off their prey but do not kill them, at least not immediately.

parasitism   A type of predation in which the predator gets nutrients from the prey, but does not kill the prey immediately and may never kill it.

parasympathetic division   The division of the autonomic nervous system that generally has relaxing effects on the body.

parenchyma cell   The most abundant type of cell in plants. These cells have thin cell walls, are usually alive at maturity, and serve numerous functions within the plant, including giving rise to the other plant-cell types.

parental generation   The generation that begins an experimental cross between organisms. Such a cross is used to study genetics and heredity of traits.

parthenogenesis   A type of reproduction in which offspring develop from an egg that has not been fertilized by sperm.

passively acquired immunity   Immunity gained by the administration of antibodies produced by another individual, e.g, the administration of a gamma globulin shot.

passive transport   Transport of materials across the cell's plasma membrane that involves no expenditure of energy. Simple and facilitated diffusion are examples of passive transport.

pathogen   A disease-causing organism.

pathogenic   Disease-causing. Viruses, bacteria, protists, and fungi are spoken of as being pathogenic or non-pathogenic.

pedigree   A familial history. Pedigrees can be created, generally in the form of diagrams, that trace the history of inheritable diseases through a family.

peptide hormones   Hormones composed of chains amino acids, with these chains ranging from small polypeptides to proteins composed of hundreds of amino acids. One of three principal classes of hormones, the other two being amino-acid-based and steroid hormones.

perennial   A type of plant that lives for many years, such as trees, woody shrubs, and many grasses.

peripheral nervous system (PNS)   The part of the nervous system that includes all of the neural tissue outside the central nervous system (brain and spinal cord). The PNS brings information to and carries it from the central nervous system; it also provides voluntary control of the skeletal muscles, and involuntary control of the smooth muscles, cardiac muscles, and glands.

peripheral protein   A protein of the plasma membrane that lies on the inside or outside of the membrane but is not attached to the membrane's hydrophobic interior.

peristalsis   Waves of contraction carried out by two sets of muscles in the digestive tract that push material through the tract.

permafrost   The permanently frozen ground that begins about a meter below the ground in the tundra biome of the far north. Neither roots nor water can penetrate this layer.

Permian Extinction   The greatest mass-extinction event in Earth's history. This event, in which up to 96 percent of all species on Earth were wiped out, occurred about 245 million years ago.

petal   The colorful, leaflike structure of a flower; petals attract pollinators.

petiole   The stem of a leaf, attaching it to a branch or trunk.

phagocyte   An immune-system cell capable of ingesting another cell, parts of cells, or other materials. Phagocytes ingest both invading microorganisms and tissue fragments or the body's own cells when they have become damaged.

phagocytosis   A process of bringing relatively large materials into a cell by means of wrapping extensions of the plasma membrane around the materials to be brought in and fusing the extensions together.

pharyngeal slits   In animals, openings to the pharyngeal cavity. All chordates possess pharyngeal slits at some point in their development.

pharynx   In humans, the passageway at the back of the mouth that links the mouth with both the food-trans-

porting esophagus and the air-transporting trachea. In some animals, the pharynx can be everted, or turned inside-out, and used to obtain nutrients.

phenotype   A physical function, bodily characteristic, or action of an organism.

phloem   The tissue through which the food produced in photosynthesis, along with some hormones and other compounds, is conducted in vascular plants.

phosphate group   A phosphorus atom surrounded by four oxygen atoms.

phospholipid   A charged lipid molecule composed of two fatty acids, glycerol, and a phosphate group. The phospholipid's phosphate group is hydrophilic, while its fatty acid chains are hydrophobic. Phospholipids are a major constituent of cell membranes.

phospholipid bilayer   One of the chief components of the plasma membrane, composed of two layers of phospholipids, arranged with their fatty acid chains pointing toward each other.

photoheterotrophy   The nutritional mode in which an organism gets its carbon from organic material and its energy to make food from the sun's rays. A few bacteria and archaea are photoheterotrophs.

photoperiodism   The ability of a plant to respond to changes it experiences in the daily duration of darkness, relative to light.

photoreceptor   Sensory receptor cell for vision, located in the eye's retina, that transforms light into nervous system signals. Photoreceptors come in two varieties: rods, which function in low-light situations but provide only black-and-white vision; and cones, which respond best to bright light and provide color vision.

photorespiration   A process in which the enzyme rubisco undercuts carbon fixation in photosynthesis by binding with oxygen instead of with carbon dioxide. This wasteful reaction takes place most frequently in C_3 plants. The warm-weather C_4 plants have evolved a means of reducing photorespiration.

photosynthesis   The process by which certain groups of organisms capture energy from sunlight and convert this solar energy into chemical energy that is initially stored in a carbohydrate.

photosystem   An organized complex of molecules within a thylakoid membrane that, in photosynthesis, collects solar energy and transforms it into chemical energy.

phototropism   The bending of a plant's shoots in response to light. Generally, this capability helps a plant grow toward the Sun to get the most available sunlight.

pH scale   A scale utilized in measuring the relative acidity or alkalinity of a solution. The scale, ranging from 0 to 14, quantifies the concentration of hydrogen ions in a solution. The lower the pH number, the more acidic the solution; the higher the number, the more basic the solution.

phylogeny   A hypothesis about the evolutionary relationships of a group of organisms.

phylum   A category of living things, directly subordinate to the category of kingdom, whose members share traits as a result of shared ancestry.

physical science   The natural sciences not concerned with life.

physiology   The study of the physical functioning of animals and plants.

phytoplankton   Small photosynthesizing organisms that drift in the upper layers of oceans or bodies of freshwater, often forming the base of aquatic food webs.

pinocytosis   A form of endocytosis that brings into the cell a small volume of extracellular fluid and the solutes suspended in it.

placenta   A complex network of maternal and embryonic blood vessels and membranes that develops in mammals in pregnancy. The placenta allows nutrients and oxygen to flow to the embryo from the mother, while allowing carbon dioxide and waste to flow from the embryo to the mother.

placental mammal   A type of mammal that is nurtured before birth by the placenta, a network of maternal and embryonic blood vessels and membranes. Embryonic placental mammals derive their nutrition not from food stored in an egg, but directly from the mother's circulation.

plasma The fluid portion of blood, consisting mostly of water but also containing proteins and other molecules. Contrast with **formed elements**—the cells and cell fragments that form the non-fluid portion of blood.

plasma cell One of two types of cells the B-lymphocyte develops into (the other type being a memory B cell). Plasma cells are specialized to produce the free-standing antibodies that fight invaders.

plasma membrane A membrane forming the outer boundary of many cells, composed of a phospholipid bilayer interspersed with proteins and cholesterol molecules and coated, on its exterior face, with short carbohydrate chains associated with proteins and lipids.

plasmid A ring of DNA that lies outside the chromosome in bacteria. Plasmids can move into bacterial cells in the process called transformation, thus making them a valuable tool in biotechnology.

plasmodesmata Channels in the plant cell wall that make possible communication between plant cells. The structure of these channels is such that the cytoplasm of one plant cell is continuous with that of another.

platelet One of the three varieties of formed elements within blood, platelets are small fragments of cells that facilitate blood clotting by means of releasing clotting enzymes and clumping together at the site of an injury.

pleiotropy The phenomenon by which one gene has many effects.

pluripotent cell An animal cell that is capable of giving rise to almost all of the different kinds of cells or tissues in the body.

point mutation A mutation of a single base-pair in a genome.

polar body Nonfunctional cell produced during meiosis in females.

polar covalent bond A type of covalent bond in which electrons are shared unequally between atoms, so that one end of the molecule has a slight negative charge and the other end a slight positive charge.

polarity A difference in electrical charge at one end of a molecule, as compared to the other.

pollen tube A tube-like structure that sprouts from a pollen grain that has landed on the stigma of a plant. The pollen tube grows down toward the egg, and sperm cells then move down through the pollen tube.

pollination The transfer of pollen—by wind, animal, or other means—to a plant's female reproductive structure.

polygenic Having multiple genes affecting a given character, such as height in humans.

polygenic inheritance Inheritance of a genetic character that is determined by the interaction of multiple genes, with each gene having a small additive effect on the character.

polymer A large molecule made up of many similar or identical subunits, called monomers.

polymerase chain reaction (PCR) A technique for generating many copies of a DNA sequence.

polypeptide A series of amino acids linked in linear fashion. Polypeptide chains fold up to become proteins.

polyploidy A process by which one or more sets of chromosomes are added to the genome of an organism. Human beings cannot survive in a polyploid state, but many plants flourish in it. Polyploidy is a means by which speciation can occur (most often in plants) in a single generation.

polysaccharides The polymers of carbohydrates, composed of many monosaccharides. Examples are starch and cellulose.

polyunsaturated fatty acid A fatty acid with two or more double bonds between the carbon atoms of its hydrocarbon chain.

population All the members of a species that live in a defined geographic region at a given time.

positive feedback A system of control in which the product of a process stimulates the activity that produced the product. Uncommon in living things because it promotes instability.

post-anal tail A tail, existing at some point in the development of all chordates, that is located posterior to the anus.

posterior pituitary An endocrine gland that re-

ceives its hormones directly from the hypothalamus, then stores these hormones and later releases them.

potential energy Stored energy. A rock perched at the top of a hill has potential energy.

predation One organism feeding on parts or all of a second organism.

pressure-flow model The hypothesis that the force behind the movement of phloem sap comes from water that moves into the phloem by means of osmosis, following the energetic pumping of solutes into the phloem.

primary consumer Any organism that eats producers (organisms that make their own food).

primary growth The type of growth in plants that occurs at the tips of their roots and shoots and mainly increases their length.

primary oocyte A diploid cell produced in the female embryo that may mature into an egg, initially by giving rise to haploid secondary oocytes. After the female reaches puberty, an average of one oocyte per month is selected to continue the process of maturation in the ovary.

primary spermatocyte A diploid cell in a male that will undergo meiosis to produce haploid secondary spermatocytes, which ultimately give rise to mature sperm cells.

primary structure The sequence of amino acids in a protein. This sequence dictates the final shape of the protein because electrochemical bonding and repulsion forces act on the structure to create the folded-up protein.

primary succession In ecology, succession in which the starting state is one of little or no life and a soil that lacks nutrients.

primary visual cortex An area at the back of the brain that is the primary site of visual processing in human beings.

producer Any organism that manufactures its own food. Plants, algae, and certain bacteria are producers. By converting the sun's energy into biomass, producers capture energy that is then passed along in food webs.

product A substance formed in a chemical reaction. The products are written on the right side of a chemical equation.

progestin A class of hormones, produced by the ovaries, that prepares the body for possible pregnancy.

prokaryote A single-celled organism whose complement of DNA is not contained within a nucleus.

prokaryotic cell A cell whose DNA is not located in the membrane-bound organelle known as a nucleus. Prokaryotes are microscopic forms of life, and all are either bacteria or archaea.

prolactin A hormone, secreted by the anterior pituitary, that stimulates the development of the mammary glands and their production of milk in female mammals.

promoter sequence The site on a segment of DNA to which RNA polymerase attaches prior to beginning transcription.

prostate gland In human males, a gland surrounding the urethra near the urinary bladder that contributes fluids to the semen.

protein A large polymer of amino acids, composed of one or more polypeptide chains. Proteins come in many forms, including enzymes, structural proteins, and hormones.

protein conformation The three-dimensional shape of a protein, determined by its order of amino acids and their resulting interactions. This shape is critical in allowing a protein to interact properly with other molecules to perform its function.

proton A basic constituent of an atom, found in the nucleus of the atom and having positive electrical charge. Elements are defined by the number of protons in their nucleus.

proximal tubule In the nephron tubule of the kidney, the convoluted portion that is closest to Bowman's capsule. Some reabsorption of salt and water occurs here.

pulmonary circulation The system that circulates blood between the heart and the lungs. This system brings oxygen into and takes carbon dioxide away from the body.

pupil In the eye, a central opening in the iris, which grows smaller or larger in response to contractions or relaxations of the iris muscles.

pyloric sphincter The circular muscle that regulates the flow of chyme (food mixed with gastric juices) between the stomach and small intestine.

Q

quaternary structure The way in which two or more polypeptide chains come together to form a protein.

R

radial symmetry A type of animal symmetry in which body parts are distributed evenly about a central axis. Sea stars are radially symmetrical.

radiometric dating A technique for determining the age of objects by measuring the decay of the radioactive elements within them. The age of fossils can be determined with this technique.

reabsorption The process carried out in the kidneys under which filtered materials move from the nephron tubule back into the blood vessels, while waste is retained within the tubule. One of four essential processes undertaken by the kidneys, the others being filtration, secretion, and concentration.

reactant A substance (atoms, molecules, or compounds) that goes into a chemical reaction. The reactants interact to form the product(s). The reactants are written on the left side of a chemical equation.

reaction center A molecular complex in a chloroplast that, in photosynthesis, transforms solar energy into chemical energy.

receptor-mediated endocytosis (RME) A form of endocytosis in which receptors on the surface of a cell bind to a substance and then move laterally through the plasma membrane to join other receptors of their type that have bound to the same substance. These bound receptors congregate in a cell pit that deepens and pinches off, creating a vesicle that moves into the cell.

receptor protein A protein with a binding site, located at the surface of the plasma membrane of a cell. The binding of a receptor protein with a specific molecule causes a change in the cell's activity.

recessive Term used to designate an allele that is not expressed in the heterozygous condition.

recessive disorder A condition that will not occur when an organism possesses a single functional allele for a given trait. Red-green color blindness is an example of a recessive disorder, because only one set of functional alleles need be present for normal color vision.

reciprocal altruism An exchange of altruistic acts by individual animals over time.

recombinant DNA Two or more segments of DNA that have been combined by humans into a sequence that does not exist in nature.

recombination The exchange of reciprocal pieces of chromosomes that occurs when homologous chromosome pairs intertwine during prophase I of meiosis. Also called crossing over.

rectum The terminal portion of the large intestine, and therefore the end of the digestive tract. In defecation, feces pass from the colon through the rectum and out the anus.

red blood cell (RBC) The blood cells, also known as erythrocytes, that transport oxygen to and carry carbon dioxide from every part of the body.

redox reaction A combination of a reduction and an oxidation reaction in which the electrons lost from one substance in oxidation are gained by another in reduction.

reduction Gain of one or more electrons by an atom or a molecule. Important in energy transfer in living things as part of redox reactions, in which one substance is reduced by oxidizing (or removing electrons from) another substance.

reflex Automatic nervous-system response that helps an organism avoid danger or preserve a stable physical state. The knee-jerk response is a well-known reflex.

releaser The critical element in an action or object that triggers an action pattern in animals. A releaser can be visual, such as a color; but odors, touch sensations, tastes, and sounds can also trigger behavior.

renal pelvis The chamber inside the kidney of birds and mammals that receives urine from the collecting ducts and channels it into the ureter.

replication The process by which DNA is duplicated.

reproductive cloning The cloning of whole, complex living things.

reproductive isolating mechanism Any factor that, in nature, prevents interbreeding between individuals of the same or closely related species. These factors keep species separate.

reproductive system The organ system that develops gametes and delivers them to a location where they can fuse with other gametes to produce a new individual.

resource partitioning The dividing of scarce resources among species that have similar requirements. Such partitioning allows species to coexist in the same habitat.

respiratory system The organ system that brings oxygen into the body and expels carbon dioxide from the body. In humans, this system includes the lungs and passageways that carry air to the lungs.

restriction enzyme A type of enzyme, occurring naturally in bacteria, that recognizes a specific series of DNA bases and cuts the DNA strand at that site. Restriction enzymes are used in biotechnology to cut DNA in specific places. **retina** An inner layer of tissue in the eye, containing cells that convert light signals into neural signals.

reversible reaction A chemical reaction that can go in both directions.

ribosomal RNA (rRNA) A type of RNA that, along with proteins, forms ribosomes.

ribosome An organelle, located in the cell's cytoplasm, that is the site of protein synthesis. The translation phase of protein synthesis takes place within ribosomes.

ribozyme Molecule composed of RNA that can both encode information and act as an enzyme. Molecules similar to these would have been necessary early in the evolution of life.

RNA (ribonucleic acid) A nucleic acid that is active in the synthesis of proteins and that forms part of the structure of ribosomes. Varieties include messenger RNA (mRNA), transfer RNA (tRNA), and ribosomal RNA (rRNA).

RNA polymerase The enzyme that unwinds the DNA double helix and puts together a chain of RNA nucleotides complementary to the exposed DNA nucleotides.

rods Photoreceptors that function in low-light situations, but that do not provide color vision.

root cap A collection of cells at the very tip of a root that protects the adjacent meristematic cells; the root cap secretes a lubricant to help the root move through its growing medium.

root hair In plants, a threadlike extension of a root cell. Root hairs greatly increase the surface area of roots, thus allowing greater absorption of water and nutrients.

rough endoplasmic reticulum (rough ER or RER) A network of membranes, found in the cytoplasm of eukaryotic cells, that aids in the processing of proteins.

r-selected species A species that tends to be relatively short lived, that tends to produce relatively many offspring for whom it provides little or no care, and whose population size tends to fluctuate widely in reaction to an environment that it experiences as highly variable. Also known as an opportunist species.

rubisco The large enzyme that brings the sugar RuBP together in the first step of the Calvin cycle of photosynthesis.

rule of addition In probability theory, the principle that, when an outcome can occur in two or more different ways, the probability of that outcome is the sum of the respective probabilities.

rule of multiplication In probability theory, the principle that the probability of any two events happening is the product of their respective probabilities.

S

saprobe An organism that obtains its nutrition from dead organic matter. Some bacteria, fungi, and several varieties of protists are saprobes.

sarcomere The functional unit of a striated muscle, which contracts when thin filaments slide past thick filaments. The sarcomeres shorten, thus contracting the whole muscle. **saturated fatty acid** A fatty acid with no double bonds between the carbon atoms of its hydrocarbon chain.

science A process of learning about nature by observation and experiment, as well as a collection of knowledge and insights about nature.

scientific method The process by which scientists investigate the natural world. The scientific method involves the testing of hypotheses through observation and experiment, as aided by the tools of statistics.

sclerenchyma cell A type of plant cell that is dead at maturity, has thick cell walls containing cellulose, and helps the plant return to its original shape after it has been deformed. These cells provide strong support for the plant.

sebaceous gland A type of gland in the skin that produces a waxy, oily secretion (sebum) that lubricates the hair shaft and inhibits bacterial growth in the surrounding area.

secondary consumer Any organism that eats a primary consumer.

secondary growth The type of lateral growth in plants that thickens the plant. Secondary growth occurs in woody plants such as trees, and thickens their trunks and branches.

secondary phloem Phloem tissue produced to the outside of the vascular cambium in woody plants as part of secondary growth, or thickening.

secondary structure The structure proteins assume after having folded up.

secondary succession In ecology, succession in which the final state of a habitat has been disturbed by some force, but life remains and the soil has nutrients. A farmer's field that has been abandoned is a site of secondary succession.

secondary xylem Xylem tissue produced to the inside of the vascular cambium in woody plants. This tissue, also called wood, is responsible for much of the thickening of woody plants.

second law of thermodynamics Energy transfer always results in a greater amount of disorder (entropy) in the universe.

secretion The process carried out in the kidneys under which hydrogen ions and various compounds (for example, toxins) move from capillaries into the kidney's tubules. One of four essential processes undertaken by the kidneys, the others being filtration, reabsorption, concentration.

secretory protein A protein that is exported out of a cell. These proteins are generally synthesized on the ribosomes of the rough ER.

seed A reproductive structure in plants that includes a plant embryo, its food supply, and a tough protective casing.

seed coat The tough outer layer of a seed, derived from the integuments of the ovule, which protect the embryo from mechanical damage and water loss.

seedless vascular plant A plant that has a vascular (fluid transport) structure but does not reproduce through use of seeds. One of the four principal varieties of plants. Ferns are the most familiar example.

semen The mixture of sperm and glandular materials that is ejaculated from the human male through the urethra.

seminal vesicle A gland that, in human males, contributes fluids to the semen as the semen moves down the urethra in the process of ejaculation.

seminiferous tubule A convoluted tubule inside the testes where sperm development begins. Immature sperm are eventually released into the interior cavity and travel to the epididymis, where sperm maturation is completed.

sensitive period The time interval during which an animal can learn to respond to a given stimulus.

sensory neuron A neuron that senses conditions both inside and outside the body and conveys that information to neurons in the central nervous system.

sepal The leaflike structure that, with other sepals, protects the flower before it opens.

sessile Fixed in location; organisms such as mushrooms and sponges are sessile.

sex chromosome The chromosomes that determine the sex of an organism. The X or Y chromosomes in humans.

sexual selection A form of nonrandom mating that produces differential reproductive success, based on differential success in obtaining mating partners.

shoot apical meristem The growing tip of plant shoots that produces the cells responsible for vertical growth of the plant.

sieve element In plants, a type of cell in phloem tissue that conducts nutrients.

sieve tube A tube, formed by a stack of sieve elements, that conducts nutrients in phloem.

simple diffusion Diffusion through the plasma membrane that requires only concentration gradients, as opposed to concentration gradients and special protein channels. Water, oxygen, carbon dioxide, and steroid hormones can all cross the plasma membrane through simple diffusion.

simple sugar The building block of carbohydrates. Also known as a monosaccharide; glucose and fructose are familiar examples.

single bond A type of covalent bond in which a single pair of electrons is shared between two atoms.

skeletal muscle tissue The muscle tissue responsible for movement of the body.

skeletal system The animal organ system that forms an internal supporting framework for the body and protects delicate tissues and organs. This system consists of all the bones and cartilages in the body, and the connective tissues and ligaments that connect the bones at the joints.

skin An organ consisting of two layers, epidermis and dermis, and covering the outside of an animal. The skin protects the body and receives signals from the environment.

small intestine That portion of the digestive tract that runs between the stomach and large intestine.

smooth endoplasmic reticulum (smooth ER or SER) A network of membranes within the cell that is the site of the synthesis of various lipids, and site at which potentially harmful substances are detoxified.

smooth muscle tissue Made of nonstriated muscle tissue, this tissue is responsible for contraction of blood vessels, air passages, and hollow organs such as the uterus, and is not under voluntary control.

solute The ingredient being dissolved in a solvent to form a solution. For example, sugar is the solute in the sugar-water nectar you put in your hummingbird feeder.

solution A homogeneous mixture of two or more substances in the same phase (gas, liquid, or solid). Frequently, solutions consist of a solute dissolved in water, and these are called aqueous solutions.

solvent The substance in which a solute is dissolved to form a solution. In an aqueous solution, the solvent is water.

somatic cell Any cell that is not and will not become an egg or sperm cell.

somatic nervous system That portion of the peripheral nervous system's efferent division that provides voluntary control over skeletal muscle.

somite One of the blocks of mesodermal tissue in the vertebrate embryo that lies on both sides of the notochord and gives rise to muscles and the vertebrae that enclose the spinal cord.

space-filling model A picture of a molecule showing the three-dimensional structure, particularly showing how big atoms are in relation to each other and the overall shape of the molecule.

speciation The development of new species through evolution.

species A group of actually or potentially interbreeding natural populations which are reproductively isolated from other such populations.

specific defenses Immune system defenses that provide protection against particular invaders.

specific heat The amount of energy needed to raise the temperature of 1 gram of a substance by 1 degree Celsius.

spermatocyte An immature sperm cell. Spermatocytes develop from spermatogonia; they develop into spermatids and eventually into mature sperm.

spermatogonia Diploid cells that are the starting cells in sperm production in males. Some spermatogonia will produce more spermatogonia, while others will develop into sperm. **sperm cell** In flowering plants, either of two cells in a pollen grain, one of which fertilizes an egg, the other of which fertilizes the central cell in an embryo sac. In animals, the male gamete, which fertilizes the female gamete (the egg).

spinal nerve Paired nerves that connect the spinal cord to different parts of the body. In humans, there are 31 pairs of spinal nerves.

spongy bone Type of bone that is porous and less dense than compact bone. Spongy bone fills the expanded ends of long bones.

spore A reproductive cell that can develop into a new organism without fusing with another reproductive cell. (The term spore also refers to a dormant, stress-resistant form of a bacterial or fungal cell.)

sporophyte generation The spore-producing plant generation. This generation is the dominant, visible generation in flowering plants. Contrast with **gametophyte generation**.

stabilizing selection In evolution, the type of natural selection in which intermediate forms of a given character are favored over either extreme. This process tends to maintain the average for the character. Compare to **directional** and **disruptive selection**.

stamen The male reproductive structure in a flower; consists of a filament (stalk) with an anther, bearing pollen, at the top.

starch A complex carbohydrate that serves as the major form of carbohydrate storage in plants. Starches—found in such forms as potatoes, rice, carrots, and corn—are important sources of food for animals.

stem cell Any cell with the capacity for prolonged self-renewal that can produce at least one type of differentiated daughter cell.

stereotyped Performed precisely the same way each time by individual animals of the same species.

steroids A class of lipid molecules that have, as a central element in their structure, four carbon rings. One steroid differs from another in accordance with the varying side chains that can be attached to these rings. Examples include cholesterol, testosterone, and estrogen.

steroid hormones Hormones constructed around the chemical framework of the cholesterol molecule. One of three principal classes of hormones, the other two being peptide and amino-acid-based hormones.

stigma The tip end of the carpel of a flower, where pollen grains are deposited before fertilization occurs.

stimulus Any signal that influences the activity of an organism or a part of the organism.

stomach An organ that performs digestion and that serves as a temporary, expandable storage site for food.

stomata Microscopic pores in the epidermal cells of plants, found mostly on the underside of leaves. Carbon dioxide enters and water vapor leaves through these openings.

stratosphere The layer of the Earth's atmosphere situated above the troposphere, at about 20 to 35 kilometers (13 to 21 miles) above sea level. The ozone layer lies in this level.

stroma The liquid material of chloroplasts.

structural formula A two-dimensional representation of a molecule that shows how the atoms are arranged and the types of bonds between them.

style The slender tube structure in the carpel of a flower, connecting the stigma and the ovary.

substrate The substance that is worked on by an enzyme.

succession In ecology, a series of replacements of community members at a given location until a stable final state is reached.

surface tension The cohesive strength of water at its interface with air, provided by the number and direction of hydrogen bonds.

sweat gland In the skin of animals, a type of duct-containing (exocrine) gland that produces perspiration.

swim bladder An inflatable organ in a fish that the fish can fill with gas to maintain neutral buoyancy—to float in place without expending energy.

symmetry An equivalence of size, shape, and relative position of parts across a dividing line or around a central point.

sympathetic division The division of the autonomic nervous system that generally has stimulatory effects on the body.

sympatric speciation A type of speciation that occurs without geographic separation of populations. Polyploidy is one form of sympatric speciation.

synapse An area in the nervous system in which one neuron communicates either with another neuron or with an effector, such as a muscle cell. The synapse consists of the sending neuron, the receiving cell, and a tiny gap between them called the synaptic cleft.

synaptic cleft Tiny gap that exists between a neuron sending a nervous system signal and a neuron (or effector cell) that is receiving this signal.

synaptic terminal The structure at the end of an axon or branch of the axon that helps form a synapse with another neuron or effector cells. Neurotransmitter molecules are released from the synaptic terminal and bind to receptors on the receiving cell, bringing about communication between the cells.

systematics The field of biology dealing with the diversity and relatedness of organisms. Systematists study the evolutionary history of groups of organisms.

systemic circulation One of the body's two general networks of blood vessels, the systemic circulation transports blood between the heart and the rest of the body, following oxygenation of this blood in the body's pulmonary circulation.

T

taiga The biome consisting of boreal (northern) forest, characterized by cold, dry conditions, a relatively short growing season, and large expanses of coniferous trees.

taproot system The type of plant root system that consists of a large central root and many smaller lateral roots.

target cell A cell, bearing specific receptor molecules, that will be affected by a specific hormone.

taxis In animals, a genetically predisposed movement toward or away from a stimulus. A positive taxis is a movement toward the stimulus; a negative taxis is a movement away from the stimulus.

taxon A group of organisms in a category of the taxonomic system. In order of increasing inclusiveness, these categories are species, genus, family, order, class, phylum, kingdom, and domain.

tendon The connective tissue that attaches a skeletal muscle to a bone.

terminal bud Another term for the shoot apex, or the main apical meristem of a plant; used especially when it is dormant. **territoriality** A phenomenon in which animals try to keep other animals out of a given area. In general, territoriality refers to efforts to keep members of an animal's own species from entering an area.

tertiary consumer Any organism that eats secondary consumers.

tertiary structure The large-scale twists and turns in a protein conformation.

testis The organ in the male reproductive system in which sperm begin development and testosterone is produced.

tetrad The grouping formed by two homologous chromosomes pairing up in crossing over in prophase I of meiosis. The four chromatids in this grouping give it the name tetrad.

tetrapod A four-limbed vertebrate.

thalamus Portion of the brain through which most sensory perceptions are channeled before being relayed to the cerebral cortex.

theory A general set of principles, supported by evidence, that explains some aspect of nature.

theory of punctuated equilibrium The idea that evolution takes place in rapid bursts after long periods of stasis.

thermodynamics The study of energy.

thigmotropism The growth of a plant in response to touch. This capability allows tendrils wrap around other objects, thus helping a plant climb upward toward light.

thylakoid A flattened, membrane-bound sac in the interior of a chloroplast. The light-dependent reactions of photosynthesis occur in the thylakoids.

thylakoid compartment In plants, the interior watery space of thylakoids.

thyroid-stimulating hormone (TSH) A hormone, secreted by the anterior pituitary, that acts on the thyroid gland to trigger the release of thyroid hormones.

tissue An organized assemblage of similar cells that serves a common function. Nervous, epithelial, and muscle tissue are some familiar examples.

T-lymphocyte (T cell) A class of lymphocytes that plays a central role in cell-mediated immunity. T cells come in several varieties that play specific roles in recognizing and killing infected cells in the body.

top predator A species that preys on other species but is not preyed upon by any species.

totipotent cell A cell capable of giving rise to every kind of cell in an organism, and hence to a whole new organism.

tracheid In plants, a slender, tapered cell of the xylem that has perforations (bordered pits) that match up with adjacent cells to allow water to move between them.

transcription The process in which DNA's information is copied onto mRNA. This process, the first stage in protein synthesis, occurs in the cell nucleus.

transcription factor A protein that binds to a regulatory DNA sequence, thus controlling the production of one or more other proteins.

transfer RNA (tRNA) A form of RNA that, in protein synthesis, bonds with amino acids, transfers them to ribosomes, and then bonds with messenger RNA.

transformation A cell's incorporation of genetic material from outside its boundary. Some bacteria readily undergo this process, and others can be induced to for uses in biotechnology.

transgenic organism An organism whose genome has stably incorporated one or more genes from another species.

translation The process in which a polypeptide chain is produced within a ribosome, based on the information encoded in messenger RNA. This process, the second major stage in protein synthesis (after transcription), occurs in the cytoplasm.

translocation The swapping of fragments by nonhomologous chromosomes, resulting in gene sequences that are out of order on both chromosomes.

transpiration The process by which plants lose water when water vapor leaves the plant through open stomata. More than 90 percent of the water that enters a plant evaporates into the atmosphere via transpiration.

transport protein Proteins form hydrophilic channels through the hydrophobic interior of the cell's plasma membrane, allowing hydrophilic materials to pass through the membrane.

transport vesicle A membrane-lined sphere that moves within the cell's endomembrane system, carrying within it proteins or other molecules.

triglyceride A lipid molecule formed from three fatty-acids bonded to glycerol.

trimester A period lasting about 3 months during

a human pregnancy. There are three trimesters during the 9-month pregnancy.

triple bond A covalent bond in which three pairs of electrons are shared between atoms.

triploblastic In animals, the state of developing from three germ layers of cells.

trophic level A position in an ecosystem's food chain or web, with each level defined by a transfer of energy from one kind of organism to another. Plants and other photosynthesizers are producers of food and thus occupy the first trophic level. Organisms that consume producers are primary consumers, and occupy the second trophic level, and so on.

trophoblast The cells at the periphery of the developing mammalian embryo that establish physical links with the mother's uterine wall and eventually develop into the fetal portion of the placenta.

tropical savanna A type of tropical grassland that is characterized by seasonal drought, small seasonal changes in the generally warm temperatures, and stands of trees that punctuate the grassland.

troposphere The lowest layer of the Earth's atmosphere, extending from sea level to about 12 kilometers (7.4 miles) above sea level. This layer contains most of the gases in the atmosphere.

true multicellularity A form of life in which individual cells exist in stable groups, with different cells in a group specializing in different functions.

tube cell A cell in a pollen grain that, following arrival of the pollen grain on a stigma, germinates and forms a pollen tube that conducts sperm cells to the embryo sac.

U

umbilical cord The tissue linking the fetus with the placenta in mammals and containing the fetal blood vessels that carry blood between the fetus and the placenta.

urea An organic waste product produced in the liver of vertebrates and excreted in the urine.

ureters Two tubes within which urine is transported from the kidneys to the urinary bladder.

urethra Tube in which urine flows from the bladder to the outside of the body in both males and females. In males, the urethra also transmits semen.

urinary bladder Hollow, muscular organ that serves as a temporary, expandable storage site for the waste product urine.

urinary system The organ system that eliminates waste products from the blood through formation of urine. In mammals, this system consists of the kidneys where the urine is formed; and the ureters, urinary bladder, and urethra, which transport the urine outside the body.

uterine tube (Fallopian tube) The tube that transports an ovulated egg from the ovary to the uterus in mammals. Fertilization occurs inside this tube. Also called the fallopian tube.

V

variable An element of an experiment that is changed compared to an initial condition.

vascular cambium The thin layer of tissue in woody plants between the primary xylem and phloem cylinders that generates the secondary xylem and phloem tissues. This meristematic tissue brings about secondary growth in woody plants.

vas deferens In human males, the tube that carries the sperm from the epididymis on top of the testis to the urethra for ejaculation.

vasoconstriction The decrease in diameter of a blood vessel caused by contraction of the smooth muscles in the wall of the vessel. Together with vasodilation, this process helps regulate blood pressure.

vasodilation The increase in diameter of a blood vessel caused by relaxation of the smooth muscles in the wall of the vessel. Together with vasoconstriction, this process helps regulate blood pressure.

vegetal pole The end of the zygote with relatively more yolk and lying farther from the cell's nucleus. The location of the egg's poles defines the orientation in which the embryo develops.

vein A blood vessel that carries blood to the heart.

ventilation The physical movement of air into and out of the lungs, brought about by contractions and relaxations of muscles in the chest.

vertebral column A flexible column of bones extending from the anterior to posterior end of an animal. Also known as a backbone, the vertebral column distinguishes vertebrates from other chordates.

vertebrate An animal that has a flexible series of linked bones called a vertebral column (or backbone).

vessel element One of two types of cells that make up xylem tissue, which transports water and dissolved minerals through plants. At maturity, vessel elements are dead and empty of cellular contents, thus facilitating the rapid conduction of water.

villi (singular, *villus*) In vertebrates, the many fingerlike projections of the lining of the small intestine that greatly increase the surface area for absorption.

virus A non-cellular replicating entity that is an obligate intracellular parasite, meaning an entity that must invade a living cell to replicate itself.

vitamin An organic compound required in a very small quantity for critical chemical reactions in the body.

viviparous A condition in animals in which fertilized eggs develop inside a mother's body.

W

wetlands Lands that are wet for at least part of the year. Wetlands are sites of great biological productivity, and they provide vital habitat for migrating birds.

white blood cell (WBC) The central cells of the immune system. Types of white blood cells include T cells, B cells, neutrophils, eosinophils, and macrophages, each playing a specific role in immune responses.

white matter The tissue within the central nervous system that has a white appearance from the myelin sheaths surrounding the axons that run through it.

wood Secondary xylem in a plant. This material in woody plants is responsible for most of their thickening.

woody plant A plant that has wood, or secondary xylem.

X

xylem The tissue through which water and dissolved minerals flow in vascular plants.

xylem sap The water and dissolved minerals that are conducted through xylem in plants.

Z

zero population growth State of a population in which births exactly equal deaths in a given period.

zone of cell division In plants, the area just behind the apical meristem where more cells are produced. Cells then move on to the zones of elongation and differentiation.

zone of differentiation In plants, the area just behind the zone of elongation, near the apical meristem, where primary tissue types finish taking shape.

zone of elongation In plants, the area between the zones of cell division and differentiation, near the apical meristem, where most primary plant growth occurs through the elongation of cells.

zoologist A biologist who studies animals.

zygote A fertilized egg. In humans, the developing organism from the time of fertilization through the time of the first cell division (about 30 hours after fertilization).

Photo Credits

Index

Accelerator CD
Biology: A Guide to the Natural World, 3e
CD License Agreement
© 2005 Pearson Education, Inc.
Pearson Prentice Hall
Pearson Education
Upper Saddle River, NJ

YOU SHOULD CAREFULLY READ THE TERMS AND CONDITIONS BEFORE USING THE CD-ROM PACKAGE. USING THIS CD-ROM PACKAGE INDICATES YOUR ACCEPTANCE OF THESE TERMS AND CONDITIONS.

Pearson Education, Inc. provides this program and licenses its use. You assume responsibility for the selection of the program to achieve your intended results, and for the installation, use, and results obtained from the program. This license extends only to use of the program in the United States or countries in which the program is marketed by authorized distributors.

LICENSE GRANT - You hereby accept a nonexclusive, nontransferable, permanent license to install and use the program ON A SINGLE COMPUTER at any given time. You may copy the program solely for backup or archival purposes in support of your use of the program on the single computer. You may not modify, translate, disassemble, decompile, or reverse engineer the program, in whole or in part.

TERM - The License is effective until terminated. Pearson Education, Inc. reserves the right to terminate this License automatically if any provision of the License is violated. You may terminate the License at any time. To terminate this License, you must return the program, including documentation, along with a written warranty stating that all copies in your possession have been returned or destroyed.

LIMITED WARRANTY - THE PROGRAM IS PROVIDED "AS IS" WITHOUT WARRANTY OF ANY KIND, EITHER EXPRESSED OR IMPLIED, INCLUDING, BUT NOT LIMITED TO, THE IMPLIED WARRANTIES OR MERCHANTABILITY AND FITNESS FOR A PARTICULAR PURPOSE. THE ENTIRE RISK AS TO THE QUALITY AND PERFORMANCE OF THE PROGRAM IS WITH YOU. SHOULD THE PROGRAM PROVE DEFECTIVE, YOU (AND NOT PEARSON EDUCATION, INC. OR ANY AUTHORIZED DEALER) ASSUME THE ENTIRE COST OF ALL NECESSARY SERVICING, REPAIR, OR CORRECTION. NO ORAL OR WRITTEN INFORMATION OR ADVICE GIVEN BY PEARSON EDUCATION, INC., ITS DEALERS, DISTRIBUTORS, OR AGENTS SHALL CREATE A WARRANTY OR INCREASE THE SCOPE OF THIS WARRANTY.

SOME STATES DO NOT ALLOW THE EXCLUSION OF IMPLIED WARRANTIES, SO THE ABOVE EXCLUSION MAY NOT APPLY TO YOU. THIS WARRANTY GIVES YOU SPECIFIC LEGAL RIGHTS AND YOU MAY ALSO HAVE OTHER LEGAL RIGHTS THAT VARY FROM STATE TO STATE.

Pearson Education, Inc. does not warrant that the functions contained in the program will meet your requirements or that the operation of the program will be uninterrupted or error-free.

However, Pearson Education, Inc. warrants the CD-ROM(s) on which the program is furnished to be free from defects in material and workmanship under normal use for a period of ninety (90) days from the date of delivery to you as evidenced by a copy of your receipt.

The program should not be relied on as the sole basis to solve a problem whose incorrect solution could result in injury to person or property. If the program is employed in such a manner, it is at the user's own risk and Pearson Education, Inc. explicitly disclaims all liability for such misuse.

LIMITATION OF REMEDIES - Pearson Education, Inc.'s entire liability and your exclusive remedy shall be:

1. the replacement of any CD-ROM not meeting Pearson Education, Inc.'s "LIMITED WARRANTY" and that is returned to Pearson Education, or

2. if Pearson Education is unable to deliver a replacement CD-ROM that is free of defects in materials or workmanship, you may terminate this agreement by returning the program.

IN NO EVENT WILL PEARSON EDUCATION, INC. BE LIABLE TO YOU FOR ANY DAMAGES, INCLUDING ANY LOST PROFITS, LOST SAVINGS, OR OTHER INCIDENTAL OR CONSEQUENTIAL DAMAGES ARISING OUT OF THE USE OR INABILITY TO USE SUCH PROGRAM EVEN IF PEARSON EDUCATION, INC. OR AN AUTHORIZED DISTRIBUTOR HAS BEEN ADVISED OF THE POSSIBILITY OF SUCH DAMAGES, OR FOR ANY CLAIM BY ANY OTHER PARTY. SOME STATES DO NOT ALLOW FOR THE LIMITATION OR EXCLUSION OF LIABILITY FOR INCIDENTAL OR CONSEQUENTIAL DAMAGES, SO THE ABOVE LIMITATION OR EXCLUSION MAY NOT APPLY TO YOU.

GENERAL - You may not sublicense, assign, or transfer the license of the program. Any attempt to sublicense, assign or transfer any of the rights, duties, or obligations hereunder is void.

This Agreement will be governed by the laws of the State of New York.

Should you have any questions concerning this Agreement, you may contact Pearson Education, Inc. by writing to:

ESM Media Development
Higher Education Division
Pearson Education, Inc.
1 Lake Street, Upper Saddle River, NJ 07458

Should you have any questions concerning technical support, you may write to:

New Media Production
Higher Education Division
Pearson Education, Inc.
1 Lake Street, Upper Saddle River, NJ 07458

YOU ACKNOWLEDGE THAT YOU HAVE READ THIS AGREEMENT, UNDERSTAND IT, AND AGREE TO BE BOUND BY ITS TERMS AND CONDITIONS. YOU FURTHER AGREE THAT IT IS THE COMPLETE AND EXCLUSIVE STATEMENT OF THE AGREEMENT BETWEEN US THAT SUPERSEDES ANY PROPOSAL OR PRIOR AGREEMENT, ORAL OR WRITTEN, AND ANY OTHER COMMUNICATIONS BETWEEN US RELATING TO THE SUBJECT MATTER OF THIS AGREEMENT.